JOURNAL OF APPLIED POLYMER SIENCE   VOL. 21, 2297–3303 (1977)

Fully Ordered Copolyhydrazides Based Upon Bisacid A2

R. S. LENK,* *Department of Chemical and Metallurgical Engineering, The University of Tennessee, Knoxville, Tennessee 37916*

Synopsis

The preparation of copolyhydrazides containing equimolar quantities of "bisacetyl A2" and terephthaloyl or isophthaloyl groups is described. The resulting copolymers were found to form clear colorless films which, when immersed in concentrated formic acid, softened but rehardened and turned white after subsequent immersion in water. The formic acid treatment did not bring about a morphological change from the amorphous to the crystalline state, but caused changes in the differential scanning calorimetry (DSC) traces which suggest that an α/β transformation had taken place. The possible nature of this transition is discussed. The results of tensile tests on cast film are given.

INTRODUCTION

The preparation of ordered, thermally stable polyamides, poly(amide/hydrazides), and copolyhydrazides has been reported by Preston and Black and their colleagues Culbertson, Murphy, DeWinter, Hofferbert, Holsten, and Lilyquist,[1-7] as well as by Frazer, Reed, and Fitzgerald.[8,9,13] Three earlier papers in the present bisacid A2 polymer series dealt with the *p*-phenylenediamine polyamide,[10] its *m*-analogue as well as with ring-substituted *p*- and *m*-phenylenediamine polyamides, with aliphatic polyamides[11] and with the homopolyhydrazide.[12] These were designated "bisparamid A2," "bismetamid A2," "nylons nA2," and "bishydrazid A2," respectively. All these polymers (except the aliphatic polyamide polymer) were made by the low-temperature solution method which had been developed by workers at du Pont, Monsanto, and elsewhere and which was acknowledged in the lists of references of Lenk and White.[10,11] The aliphatic polyamides of the "nylon nA2" type are more suitably made by interfacial polymerization.

The reaction scheme given in Figure 1 resulted in the production of a polymer which is of considerable interest for three reasons: (i) It affords a direct comparison with the homopolymer "bishydrazide A2" described in reference 12; (ii) it is a fully ordered copolymer and also opens up possibilities of tailoring copolyhydrazides with a variable number of ether linkages per unit length of polymer chain; (iii) the introduction of the terephthaloyl and/or isophthaloyl group would be expected to raise the softening point of the homopolyhydrazide described in reference 12.

* On leave from the Polytechnic of the South Bank, London, SE1 0AA, England.

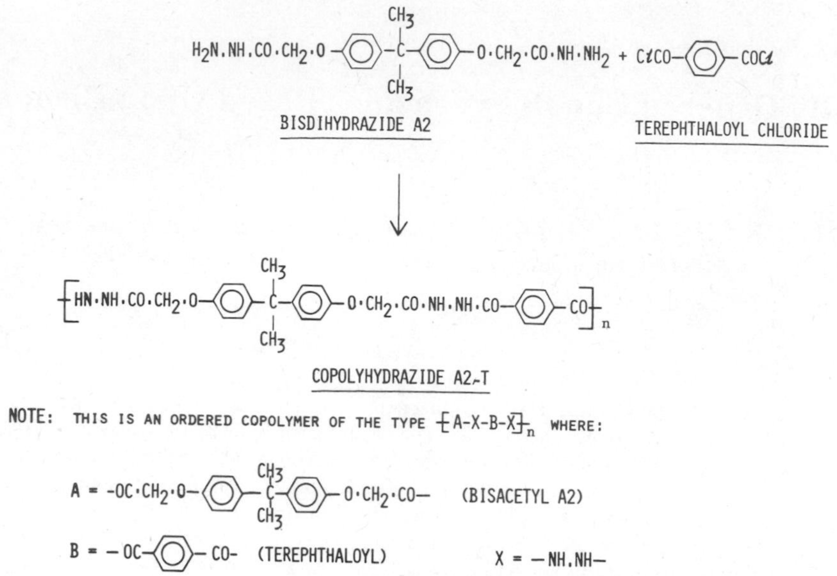

$$H_2N \cdot NH \cdot CO \cdot CH_2 \cdot O - \bigcirc - \overset{CH_3}{\underset{CH_3}{C}} - \bigcirc - O \cdot CH_2 \cdot CO \cdot NH \cdot NH_2 \ + \ ClCO - \bigcirc - COCl$$

BISDIHYDRAZIDE A2   TEREPHTHALOYL CHLORIDE

$$\left[HN \cdot NH \cdot CO \cdot CH_2 \cdot O - \bigcirc - \overset{CH_3}{\underset{CH_3}{C}} - \bigcirc - O \cdot CH_2 \cdot CO \cdot NH \cdot NH \cdot CO - \bigcirc - CO \right]_n$$

COPOLYHYDRAZIDE A2-T

NOTE: THIS IS AN ORDERED COPOLYMER OF THE TYPE $\left[A-X-B-X \right]_n$ WHERE:

$$A = -OC \cdot CH_2 \cdot O - \bigcirc - \overset{CH_3}{\underset{CH_3}{C}} - \bigcirc - O \cdot CH_2 \cdot CO - \quad (BISACETYL \ A2)$$

$$B = -OC - \bigcirc - CO - \quad (TEREPHTHALOYL) \qquad X = -NH \cdot NH-$$

Fig. 1. Preparation of copolyhydrazide A2/T by low-temperature solution polymerization.

EXPERIMENTAL

Figure 1 shows the scheme of reaction for the preparation of a fully ordered copolyhydrazide of the type $\left[A—X—B—X \right]_n$. The polymer which results from the specific reaction given in Figure 1 is the terephthalic copolyhydrazide ("copolyhydrazide A2/T"). The isophthalic copolyhydrazide ("copolyhydrazide A2/I") is made in exactly analogous fashion. The preparative details are given below.

"Copolyhydrazide A2/T"

An 8.3366-g (0.02239 mole) portion of bisdihydrazide A2 was dissolved in 50 ml N-methylpyrrolidone (NMP) and cooled to −40°C, whereupon 4.544 g (0.02239 mole) solid terephthaloyl chloride (recrystallized twice from n-hexane) was added all at once while dry nitrogen was passed through the reaction flask which was also fitted with a drying tube. After 10 min, another 5 ml NMP was used to rinse into the reaction zone any solid material from the neck through which the terephthaloyl chloride had been added. The cooling bath was removed after 20 min and the mixture was allowed to regain room temperature. The mixture was then an almost colorless viscous liquid which did not appear to wet glass readily. It was precipitated without neutralization or dilution by dropping it from a funnel into a large volume of water with agitation, giving snow white pearls, left to wash for 24 hr, similarly washed by suspension in methanol for 24 hr, and finally dried in vacuo at 50°C. It was also seen that the reaction mixture could be readily wet spun into fiber. The concentration during reaction was 18.4%, and the final concentration was 17.0%. The yield was 11.0 g (theory: 11.2 g) and the inherent viscosity (0.5% solution in dimethylacetamide containing 5% LiCl) was 0.58.

TABLE I
Inherent Viscosities of Copolyhydrazides A2/T and A2/I in 5%
LiCl/DMA and pure DMA

	η_{inh}	
	In 5% LiCl/DMA	In pure DMA
Terephthalic copolyhydrazide (A2/T)	0.63	0.45
Isophthalic copolyhydrazide (A2/I)	0.38	0.29

TABLE II
Tensile Tests on Copolyhydrazide A2/T[a]

	A2/T	A2/T(X)	A2/T	A2/T(X)	A2/T	A2/T(X)
Strain rate, cm/min	2.54	2.54	1.27	1.27	0.508	0.508
Maximum stress, (dynes/cm^2) $\times$ 10^{-8}						
Mean	6.93	1.46	9.13	1.55	8.21	1.31
S.D.	- - -	- - -	- - -	- - -	1.07	0.25
% Strain of break						
Mean	1.50	6.17	2.10	8.70	2.90	6.53
S.D.	- - -	- - -	- - -	- - -	0.37	1.26
Initial modulus, (dynes/cm^2) $\times$ 10^{-10}						
Mean	5.15	0.66	10.68	0.63	4.15	0.66
S.D.	- - -	- - -	- - -	- - -	0.33	0.07
No. of specimens	3	3	3	2	8	7

[a] All samples failed after reaching a yield point (tough failure); X denotes formic acid-treated film

"Copolyhydrazide A2/I"

A 10.4693-g (0.02814 mole) portion of bisdihydrazide A2 was dissolved in 50 ml NMP and chilled to −40°C, whereupon 5.7131 g (0.02814 mole) solid iso-phthaloyl chloride (freshly opened jar of reagent grade but not recrystallized) was added, followed by 5 ml additional NMP in order to flush any solid material down the neck into the reaction zone. The viscosity increased quickly, and the slightly straw-yellow solution was left to stir for 2 hr during which time the bath temperature rose to ambient. The resulting solution (20.6% polymer) was pre-.cipitated into water and washed and dried as in the previous preparation. The pure-white pearls obtained represented a yield of 13.4 g (theory: 14.1 g), and the inherent viscosity (solvent and concentration as before) was 0.38.

It was noted that neither of the two copolyhydrazides dissolved readily in di-methylacetamide (DMA) containing 5% LiCl at room temperature even at the low concentration of 0.5%, but that gentle warming quickly produced a clear solution. In contrast, solutions of high concentration (10–20%) would be readily obtained at room temperature with DMA in the *absence* of LiCl. Inherent viscosity measurements in pure DMA gave lower results for both copolyhydra-zides than did DMA containing 5% LiCl, as shown in Table I.

Both copolyhydrazides were made into film by casting from solution in DMA. The terephthalic copolyhydrazide film was tested in tension at three different

TABLE III
Tensile Tests on Copolyhydrazide A2/I

	A2/I(X)
Strain rate, cm/min	0.508
Maximum stress, (dynes/cm²) $\times 10^{-8}$	
Mean	0.65
S.D.	0.10
% Strain	
Tough failure (4 specimens)	3.4
Brittle failure (3 specimens)	1.5
Initial modulus, (dynes/cm²) $\times 10^{-10}$	
Mean	0.43
S.D.	0.12
No. of specimens	7

strain rates both before and after treatment with concentrated formic acid, washing, and drawing. The isophthalic copolyhydrazide film was weak and brittle as cast, but formic acid treatment gave a film which was suitable for tensile testing. This was done at one strain rate only. The results of the tests which were done at 23°C/65% R.H. are given in Tables II and III.

It was observed that the appearance of the cast film following exposure to concentrated formic acid was different in the copolyhydrazides from that shown by the bispolyaramides and bishydrazide A2: The last-mentioned films opacified instantaneously,[10–12] while the copolyhydrazides softened but remained clear until they were taken out of the formic acid and immersed in water, when they developed opacity and turned pure white instantaneously.

X-ray scattering (WAXS) patterns showed no sharp concentric rings. The copolyhydrazides are thus amorphous both as-cast and after formic acid treatment (Fig. 4).

Differential Scanning Calorimetry (DSC)

The DSC traces for both copolyhydrazides (as virgin polymer and as formic acid-treated film) are given in Figures 2 and 3.

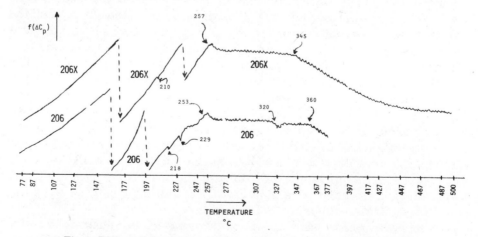

Fig. 2. Differential scanning calorimetry (DSC) traces of copolyhydrazide

DISCUSSION

It is clear that the reaction scheme as given in Figure 1 affords an excellent method for preparing fully ordered copolyhydrazides. The lower inherent viscosity of the isophthalic copolyhydrazide compared to its terephthalic analogue may have been due to the fact that the isophthaloyl chloride was used as received (although from a fresh bottle of good reagent grade), while the terephthaloyl chloride was recrystallized twice from n-hexane. It was significant to note that tough film was obtained from the terephthalic copolyhydrazide film (both as-cast and formic acid treated) at all three strain rates, while three out of seven specimens of even the formic acid-treated isophthalic copolyhydrazide film failed in brittle manner at the lowest strain rate. (It should be remembered that formic acid treatment always tends to toughen as-cast film.) The implication is that an inherent viscosity of around 0.60 is suitable for making good copolyhydrazide film (both clear and opaque, i.e., formic acid treated), but that a value of about 0.40 is too low to ensure toughness even after formic acid treatment which reduces the probability of brittle failure. Moreover, those specimens of the low inherent viscosity formic acid-treated isophthalic copolyhydrazide film which failed after first yielding (and which were, therefore, tough) had only a rather lower elongation at failure than is common after formic acid treatment of bisacid A2 polyamides and polyhydrazides.

The presence of *two* blips in the DSC trace of the virgin polymers and the appearance of one (*and only one*) of these after formic acid treatment is interesting. The bisacid A2 polyaramides and the homopolyhydrazide have only one blip, which disappears on formic acid treatment. It is taken to signify that such treatment has caused an α/β transition.[10–12] Evidently, the same transformation occurs in the copolyhydrazide, and the second blip is presumably associated with the second acyl group. The one which disappears on formic acid treatment is evidently the one associated with the bisacetyl group.

The precise nature of the α/β transformation has not yet been established, but there is good circumstantial evidence which points to a reasonable interpretation.

Sweeny,[14] in a du Pont patent dealing with the preparation, properties, and structure of polyaramides, specifically poly(m-phenyleneisophthalamide), suggested that the essentially helical and *intra*molecularly hydrogen-bonded

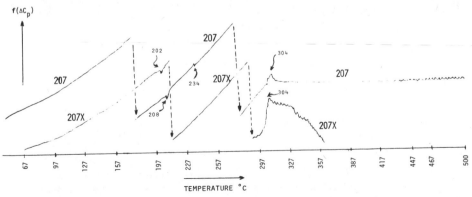

Fig. 3. Differential scanning calorimetry (DSC) traces of copolyhydrazide A2/I film: 206, as cast; 206X, formic acid treated.

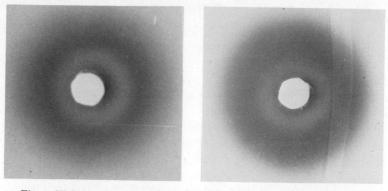

Fig. 4. Wide-angle x-ray scattering (WAXS) of formic acid-treated films of bisacid A2 ordered copolyhydrazides.

polymer presumably transforms to a pseudocrosslinked *inter*molecularly hydrogen-bonded structure and that the conditions under which this would tend to be favored include: the action of acids, notably strong formic acid; heat; and high-shearing stresses.

In our earlier work on bisacid A2 polyaramides,[10,11] we have observed: (i) That treatment of the clear as-cast polymer film caused instantaneous opacification which we consider to be not merely a surface etching phenomenon, but a more fundamental chemical or morphological change; (ii) that the blip in the DSC trace found in both virgin polymer granules and in specimens of clear (i.e., untreated) as-cast film is not found when the transition region is retraversed in the reverse direction or when the same specimen is rerun on the DSC; the transition is not, therefore, spontaneously reversible; (iii) that during the primary reaction of bischloride A2 and aromatic diamines (carried out at low temperature in an anhydrous acid-acceptor solvent with vigorous stirring), the polyaramides form a gel-like mass as they are formed. This is quite likely due to the influence of the HCl which is simultaneously produced and which, even in the presence of the acid acceptor, causes formation of the β species even as the latter is formed from the α species under the action of formic acid upon as-cast film. This may well be further favored by the fast stirring during the initial reaction which produces a high-shear field, all the more so because the oxymethylene units present in the structure of bisacid A2 polyaramides make these chains quite flexible and so facilitate interchain hydrogen bonding. The gel-like mass is not readily broken up by dilution, but neutralization (or even partial neutralization) of the HCl with lithium hydroxide does break up the gel after a few hours, especially when a little more solvent is added; a still viscous (but definitely free flowing) liquid characteristic of a solution of a high polymer results. It is not thought that *short-term* exposure of the solution to lithium hydroxide causes extensive hydrolysis, although prolonged exposure (a week or more) *does* cause loss of viscosity and reduction in molecular weight as indicated by a determination of inherent viscosity.

It is thus reasonable to assume that the observed α/β transition of polyhydrazides and copolyhydrazides of bisacid A2 is analogous to that observed with phthalic polyaramides[14] and with bisacid A2 polyaramides[10,11] which Sweeny[14] attributes to the existence of *intra*molecularly and *inter*molecularly hydrogen bonded α and β forms, respectively.

Since the β form (heat-treated or formic acid-treated material) does not spontaneously revert to the α form, we can account for the fact that the α form (virgin granules or as-cast clear film material) shows a transition blip on the DSC trace, while the β form, having already undergone the transition, does not.

It is worth noting additionally that the solubility characteristics of poly(m-phenyleneisophthalamide) may also be profoundly affected by heat treatment. Thus, Sweeny[14] reports that heat-treated film of this material—as distinct from untreated film—was no longer soluble in amide solvents and that heat treatment of a polymer solution in amide solvents even caused the polymer to precipitate. In the case of bisacid A2 polyaramides and polyhydrazides, we did *not* find any significant solubility differences between the α and β forms, but this is scarcely surprising in view of the much greater flexibility of these polymers compared with the phthalic polyaramides.

Comparing the terephthalic copolymer with the homopolymer "bishydrazid A2," [12] it is seen that decomposition with evolution of volatile matter starts in the range of 320° to 360°C for both, but that the process is more gradual in the copolymer. The fusion peak is around 290°C in the homopolymer and some 30°C lower in the copolymer. On the other hand, the α/β transition in the homopolymer was at about 170°C (rather lower than in the bisacid A2 polyamides), around 220°C in the copolymer (terephthalic: first blip at 218°C, second blip at 229°C; isophthalic: first blip at 208°C, second blip at 234°C). The DSC traces of the terephthalic and the isophthalic polymers have many similarities. But the fact that the blips indicate a much higher α/β transformation temperature than that of the bisacid A2 polyaramides and of bishydrazid A2 presumably reflects the very much smaller number of oxymethylene groups per unit chain length in the copolymers compared to the number present in the others.

The author would like to express thanks to the following bodies and individuals: (1) The Polytechnic of the South Bank London for granting sabbatical leave and their support during that period; (2) Professor J. L. White and his colleagues for making available the research facilities of the Department of Chemical Engineering of the University of Tennessee, Knoxville; (3) The Department of State for the award of a Fulbright-Hays travel grant; (4) The National Science Foundation for Research Grant GH-37248 in furtherance of research on aromatic polyamides of which this work forms a part; and (5) Shell Chemicals (U.K.) Ltd. and Ciba-Geigy (U.K.) Ltd. for supplying quantities of pure bisphenol A which were used in the synthesis of bisacid A2 and all its derivatives.

References

1. J. Preston and B. W. Black, *Polym. Lett., J. Polym. Sci.*, **B-4**, 267 (1966).
2. B. M. Culbertson and R. Murphy, *Polym. Lett., J. Polym. Sci.*, **5**, 807 (1967).
3. J. Preston and B. W. Black, *J. Polym. Sci.*, **C-19**, 17 (1967).
4. J. Preston and B. W. Black, *J. Polym. Sci.*, **C-23**, 441 (1968).
5. J. Preston, W. DeWinter, W. B. Black, and W. L. Hofferbert, Jr., *J. Polym. Sci.*, **A-1**(7), 3027 (1970).
6. J. Preston, W. DeWinter, and W. B. Black, *J. Polym. Sci.*, **A-1**(10), 1377 (1972).
7. J. R. Holsten and M. R. Lilyquist, *J. Polym. Sci.*, **A-3**, 3905 (1965).
8. A. H. Frazer and T. A. Reed, *J. Polym. Sci.*, **C-19**, 89 (1967).
9. A. H. Frazer and W. P. Fitzgerald, Jr., *J. Polym. Sci.*, **C-19**, 95 (1967).
10. R. S. Lenk and J. L. White, *J. Appl. Polym. Sci.*, to appear.
11. R. S. Lenk and J. L. White, *J. Appl. Polym. Sci.*, to appear.
12. R. S. Lenk and J. F. Kinstle, *J. Appl. Polym. Sci.*, **21**, 1469 (1977).
13. A. H. Frazer and T. H. Reed, *Macromol. Syn.*, **3**, 87 (1969).
14. W. Sweeny, U.S. Pat. 3,287,324 (1966).

Received April 28, 1976

JOURNAL OF APPLIED POLYMER SCIENCE   VOL. 21, 2305–2309 (1977)

Thermo-optical Analysis of Poly(2,6-dimethyl-1,4-phenylene Oxide)/Triblock Styrene–Butadiene–Styrene Copolymer Blends

A. R. SHULTZ and B. M. BEACH, *General Electric Company, Research and Development Center, Schenectady, New York 12301*

Synopsis

Blending of poly(2,6-dimethyl-1,4-phenylene oxide) (PPO resin) with a triblock butadiene–styrene–butadiene copolymer (Kraton 101) monotonically increases the softening temperature of the latter as measured by TOA. The TOA transition temperatures of the styrene/PPO resin phases closely approximate those of polystyrene/PPO resin blends having the same styrene/aromatic ether unit compositions. Uniform mixtures of the styrene blocks with the poly(2,6-dimethyl-1,4-phenylene oxide) molecules is inferred.

INTRODUCTION

Kambour[1] found that the blending of poly(2,6-dimethyl-1,4-phenylene oxide) (PPO resin, registered trademark of the General Electric Company) with a styrene–butadiene–styrene triblock thermoplastic elastomer (Kraton 101, registered trademark of the Shell Chemical Company) markedly elevated the elastomer's use temperature. The introduction of rather small amounts of PPO resin to the thermoplastic elastomer raised the yield temperature of its "network"-stabilizing styrene unit domains to technologically advantageous levels. The enhancement of mechanical properties actually exceeded that based solely on T_g elevation expectation. We have reported thermo-optical and differential scanning-calorimetric measurements on polystyrene/PPO resin blends.[2] The present study was initiated to determine the degree of correspondence between the thermo-optical transition temperatures T_{TOA} in the Kraton 101/PPO resin blends and the T_{TOA} of polystyrene/PPO resin blends having the same polystyrene/polyether composition ratios.

EXPERIMENTAL

The thermoplastic elastomer Kraton 101 has been rather extensively analyzed for structure.[3-5] From the various data we conclude that it is satisfactorily approximated by $M_n = 96,500$ and an average triblock copolymer structure S_{140}—B_{1250}—S_{140}, with S and B representing styrene and butadiene units, respectively. The terminal styrene blocks each have molar masses of 14,500, and the interior butadiene block has a molar mass of 67,500 on the average. The

TABLE I

Blends of PPO Resin and Kraton 101 Thermoplastic Elastomer:
Compositions and Thermo-optical Transitions T_{TOA}

| | | | T_{TOA}, °C | | | |
| | | | Annealed | | Unannealed | |
Sample	Wt. fraction PPO resin	Molding temp., °C	Run 1	Run 2	Run 1	Run 2
A	0.05		123[a]			
B	0.10		131[b]			
C	0.20		148[c]			
D	0.30		165[c]			
E	0.40	180	170[d]	163	176	163
F	0.50	190	179	171	189	173
G	0.60	200	193	187	198	181
H	0.70	220	193	190	208	201
I	0.80	230	200	193	214	217

[a] Annealed 5 min at 250°C.

[b] Drawn at 150°C.

[c] Annealed 3 min at 180°C, then 3 min at 230°C.

[d] Samples E–I annealed 3 min at 220°C.

molding-grade PPO resin has an intrinsic viscosity in chloroform of 0.51 d/g. Therefore, its M_n is approximately 20,000, and its M_w is approximately twice this value. Five-gram mixtures of Kraton 101 and PPO resin were dissolved in 45 ml chloroform with 0.025 g acetylphenylhydrazine (APH) and 0.025 g tricetyl borate (TCB). The solutions were precipitated into 250 ml methanol. The precipitates were filtered, slurried with 250 ml fresh methanol, refiltered, and dried in a 60°C vacuum oven for 16 hr. The dry blends were then compression molded into films for study. The blends, their weight fraction of PPO resin based on total polymer, and their molding temperatures are shown in Table I.

The thermo-optical analysis procedure has been previously described.[2] Birefringence is introduced into the blend samples by scratching them at room temperature with a steel stylus. They are then placed in a programmed hot stage of a polarizing microscope between a crossed (90°) polarizer/analyzer combination. Transmitted light intensity is monitored by a photocell with readout on a stripchart driven at 1 in./3 min. A heating rate of 10°/min from 60°C (or 90°C) to 250°C is used yielding a 30°/in. scale on the time axis of the chart. The thermo-optical transition temperature T_{TOA} is the temperature at which the birefringence of the scratches disappears as indicated by a near zero intensity of light transmitted through the polarizing microscope.

RESULTS AND DISCUSSION

Table I lists the blends, their compositions, molding temperatures, and their observed thermo-optical transition temperatures T_{TOA}. Figure 1 illustrates the light intensity (arbitrary scale and vertical displacement)-versus- temperature curves for the first runs on the annealed samples. The T_{TOA} are the intersections of the limiting tangents with the tangents through the curve inflections. Figure 2 displays the T_{TOA} observed in the first and second runs on the annealed and unannealed samples. The composition variable is the weight

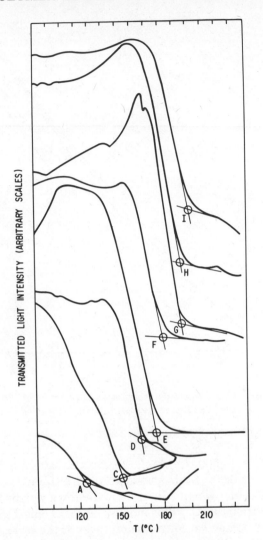

Fig. 1. Thermo-optical analysis curves of light transmission vs temperature for annealed blends. Blend compositions are given in Table I; 10°/min heating rate.

fraction PPO resin based upon the sum of the PPO resin and polystyrene segment weights. Thus, on the basis of the simplest two-phase model of the triblock copolymer, it is the weight fraction of PPO resin in the styrene + PPO resin domains.

The data in Table I and their representation in Figure 2 show that the addition of PPO resin increases the temperature of birefringence loss in the scratched Kraton K-101 in a smooth, systematic fashion. The T_{TOA} of pure Kraton 101 was not obtained because scratching did not produce sufficient birefringence for satisfactory transmitted light intensity measurements. The data indicate that its T_{TOA} should be approximately 110°C. The T_{TOA} of pure PPO resin is 222°C. The upper broken line curve shown in Figure 2 is the T_{TOA}-versus-weight fraction PPO resin relation determined for polystyrene–PPO resin blends in which the polystyrene had $M = 97,200$. The lower broken line curve is drawn to represent the expected T_{TOA}-versus-w_{PPO} relation for blends in which the

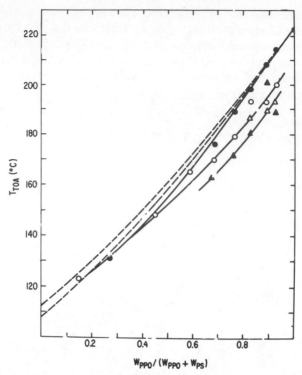

Fig. 2. Thermo-optical transition temperatures vs weight fraction of PPO resin in PPO + PS domains. Unannealed blends: (●) first run; (▲) second run. Annealed blends: (○) first run; (△) second run.

polystyrene has $M = 14,500$ for which the glass transition is 5° lower than for polystyrene of $M = 97,200$. In the present Kraton 101/PPO resin blend system, the PPO resin molecular weights lie principally (on a weight fraction basis) in the $M = 15,000-60,000$ range. This makes the chain lengths of the PPO resin comparable to, but somewhat longer than, those of the styrene blocks. Their uniform incorporation into the styrene domains of the triblock polymer appears to be quite feasible. The T_{TOA}-versus-$w_{PPO}/(w_{PPO} + w_{PS})$ relation for the unannealed, high PPO resin content blends (cf. Fig. 2) lie quite close to the curve for polystyrene/PPO resin blends. The T_{TOA} data for the annealed Kraton 101/PPO resin blends show birefringence loss at temperatures somewhat below (at most 14°) those for polystyrene/PPO resin blends of the same $w_{PPO}/(w_{PPO} + w_{PS})$ compositions. However, up to $w_{PPO}/(w_{PPO} + w_{PS}) = 0.6$, they correspond quite closely. Second runs on the annealed and unannealed samples indicate a further lowering of the T_{TOA} suggesting that some thermal degradation with production of plasticizing low molecular weight species may be occurring during pressing, annealing, and scanned temperature runs.

The blending of PPO resin to Kraton 101 $S_{140}—B_{1250}—S_{140}$ thermoplastic rubber appears to yield complete incorporation of the PPO resin into the styrene domain regions. The styrene chain/PPO resin domains exhibit birefringence loss at temperatures nearly equal to those observed in polystyrene homopolymer/PPO resin blends of the same weight fraction composition. Enhancement of elevated temperature tensile modulus retention and creep resistance under load above and beyond that expected from glass transition elevation as paralleled by T_{TOA} is quite likely due to two effects. First, the longer-chain, less flexible PPO resin molecules provide much improved chain entanglement and resistance to slippage in the styrene chain domains. Second, there exists the increased glassy filler effect of the added resin. Of the two effects, the domain stabilization should be overriding in importance.

The authors wish to thank G.A. Bernier and R. Beers for the compounded, coagulated, compression-molded blends. Also, the consultation of R.P. Kambour during the course of the study was much appreciated.

References

1. R. P. Kambour (to General Electric Company), U.S. Pat. 3,639,508, Feb. 1, 1972.
2. A. R. Shultz and B. M. Gendron, *J. Appl. Polym. Sci.,* **16,** 461 (1972).
3. L. J. Fetters, *J. Polym. Sci. C,* **26,** 1 (1969).
4. J. F. Beecher, L. Marker, R. D. Bradford, and S. L. Aggarwal, *J. Polym. Sci. C,* **26,** 117 (1969).
5. T. L. Smith and R. A. Dickie, *J. Polym. Sci. C,* **26,** 163 (1969).

Received May 21, 1976

JOURNAL OF APPLIED POLYMER SCIENCE   VOL. 21, 2311–2318 (1977)

Thermal Analysis of Thermosetting Phenolic Compounds for Injection Molding

A. SIEGMANN and M. NARKIS,* *Center for Industrial Research (CIR) Ltd., Technion City, Haifa, Israel*

Synopsis

The differential scanning calorimetry technique has been applied to investigate the curing of injection molding phenolic compounds. The data obtained include degree of cure, rate of curing, and heats and temperatures of curing as function of various heating rates, rate constants, energy of activation, and glass transition temperature. The curing temperature and heating rate were found to affect both the curing reaction kinetics and the final structure of the crosslinked network. The glass transition temperature changes continuously with the extent of curing, approaching the cure temperature.

INTRODUCTION

The recent progress in the area of thermosetting materials, namely, the development of injection molding compounds, has expanded their use and thus their production and processing. The injection molding of thermosetting materials is in certain aspects more complex than the injection molding of thermoplastics. During their path through the injection molding machine, the thermosettings undergo, in addition to rheological changes, also exothermic chemical reactions. The two simultaneous processes strongly affect each other; and, therefore, a delicate balance between material flow and heat flux has to be maintained. Because of the process complexity, prior to their molding, the thermosetting compounds have to be thoroughly characterized with respect to their behavior under shear flow and temperature programming.

Most recent reports deal with the rheological aspects of the molding process taking in consideration the time effect, namely, the chemical and structural changes taking place during the measurements. The reactivity and the exothermic nature of the thermosetting materials call for basic study of their curing reactions. The curing characteristics include the degree of cure, temperature, and duration of the curing reaction and the magnitude and variability of the heat of reaction as a function of time and temperature. These should be followed for isothermal and nonisothermal reactions. Differential scanning calorimetry (DSC) has been applied to obtain the above-mentioned information for thermosetting materials, other than phenolics, such as diallyl phthalate,[1] various epoxy resins,[2,3] and polyesters.[4]

* Present address: Department of Chemical Engineering, Technion, Haifa, Israel.

2311

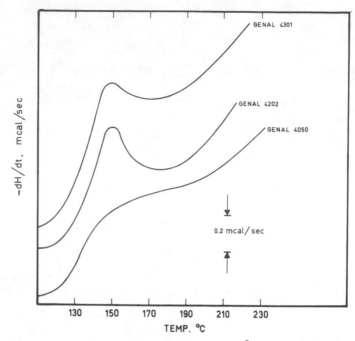

Fig. 1. DSC thermograms of three grades of Genal (heating rate of 10°C/min; the minus sign of *dH/dt* is to conform with the standard nomenclature for DSC, namely, negative *dH/dt* for "exotherm").

The purpose of the present work is the characterization of the curing reaction of injection molding phenolic compounds by the DSC technique.

EXPERIMENTAL

The injection molding phenolic compounds used in the present study were General Electric Genal 4050 (General Purpose), 4202 (Impact) and 4301 (Heat Resistant). Since these materials are commercial compounds, they are not pure phenolic resins but include also high contents of additives, mainly fillers. Thus, their composition will probably affect the experimental results. The as-received granular material was ground to powder prior to its thermal analysis.

A du Pont 990 thermal analyzer equipped with a DSC cell was employed to obtain the exothermic curing reactions data and to determine the glass transition temperature (T_g) of partially cured samples. The scanning conditions will be specified later in the text. The DSC cell was calibrated at the running conditions for temperature and heat of fusion using standard materials which melt in the temperature range of interest. The sample weight used in the DSC cell was in the range of 9 to 11 mg. Since Manley[5] has reported the strong dependence of the area under the exothermic peak per unit weight obtained in curing various sizes of epoxy resin samples, the sample size was carefully kept in the 9- to 11-mg range.

RESULTS AND DISCUSSION

The curing of various grades of the injection molding phenolic compounds was found to be different in respect to the total heat of reaction and the temperatures

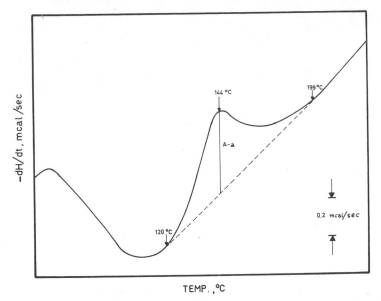

Fig. 2. Typical DSC exotherm of Genal 4050 compound (heating rate of 10°C/min).

at which the reactions were initiated, peaked, and terminated (see Fig. 1). It has been already suggested[6] that the clear differences between thermograms of various grades enable the use of the DSC technique to characterize and differentiate between these materials. In the present work, general-purpose grade (Genal 4050) was thoroughly studied as a representative of the injection molding phenolic compounds.

An unsuccessful attempt has been made to study the curing reaction isothermally. At temperatures up to about 150°C, the curing reaction proceeds very slowly and the resulting exotherm is too slight to obtain accurate and meaningful data. At temperatures higher than 150°C, the curing rate is too high to enable recording the initial stage of the reaction. (The DSC technique requires a finite time to heat up to the desired isothermal temperature.) As a result of the described behavior, this work had to be limited to the dynamic, nonisothermal technique and isothermal data were obtained indirectly.

Figure 2 shows a typical DSC thermogram for Genal 4050 resin, using a heating rate of 10°C/min. The reaction started at 120°C (departure from the baseline), reached a maximum at 144°C, and completed (return to the baseline) at 199°C. The area under the exotherm (A) is assumed to be proportional to the heat of reaction (H^0). It is also assumed[7] that the amount of reacted material is given by the area (a) to the left of an ordinate (dotted line) at any particular time and temperature. For first-order reactions, the reaction constant k, will be[7]

$$k = \frac{dH/dt}{A - a}$$

The reaction rate constants for a series of temperatures can be obtained from a single DSC thermogram by measuring the heights of the ordinate at given temperatures and the areas to the right of these ordinates under the curves. Kinetic data for Genal 4050 resin, as measured and calculated from Figure 2, are

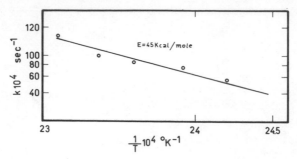

Fig. 3. Arrhenius plot for curing at a heating rate of 10°C/min of Genal 4050 compound.

given in Table I. The Arrhenius plot for these data is shown in Figure 3 over the reaction temperature range. Since the linearity of the data is good (was checked by linear regression analysis), it can be assumed that the curing reaction is indeed of first order. The calculated activation energy is 45 kcal/mole.

The Dynamic DSC method can also be employed to obtain reaction rate curves, by scanning at various rates. The Genal 4050 resin was analyzed at various heating rates in the range of 1° to 50°C/min; the thermograms are shown in Figure 4. It has been observed that the peak temperature shifts to higher value with increasing the heating rate. As shown in Table II, the peak temperature increases from 135° to 174°C in the studied range of heating rates, a shift of about 40°C. In addition, the total heat of curing was found to be dependent on the heating rate, increasing with heating rate up to a maximum followed by a decrease. This phenomenon has been observed also by Fava[3] for other thermosetting materials. The shift in peak temperature, caused by the time and temperature dependence of cure and the variation in total heat of cure, may be due to a change in the cure mechanism as suggested by Fava. There is probably an optimal temperature, at which the cure mechanism is most efficient, where the heat of curing attains a maximum.

From the above-mentioned set of thermograms, it is possible to calculate and draw isothermal reaction rate curves at various temperatures.[3] These temperatures are, however, limited to the temperature range common to all thermograms. The extent of cure as a function of time was calculated as the ratio of the reaction heat up to a certain temperature (H) to the total heat of reaction

TABLE I
Kinetic Data[a] for Genal 4050 Compound

T, °C	$10^4/T$, °K^{-1}	dH/dt,[b] mcal/sec	$A - a$,[c] mcal	$10^4 k$[d] sec^{-1}
140	24.21	0.38	69.50	55
145	23.92	0.43	57.95	74
150	23.62	0.34	40.08	85
155	23.36	0.27	28.71	94
160	23.08	0.20	17.20	116

[a] Heating rate of 10°C/min.
[b] dH/dt = Rate of heat evolution.
[c] A = Total area under DSC exotherm; a = area under DSC exotherm to time t.
[d] k = First-order reaction rate constant.

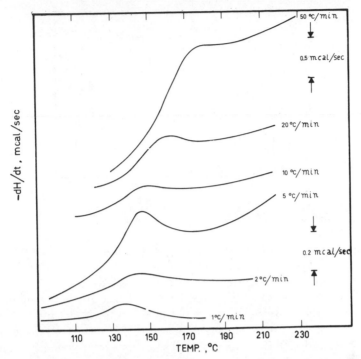

Fig. 4. DSC thermograms of Genal 4050 compound, obtained at various heating rates.

(H^0). The rate curves obtained (see Fig. 5) have a typical "S" shape. At higher isothermal cure temperatures, the initial parts of the curves are steeper, and after leveling off, they approach faster completion.

The effect of heating rate, as shown above, is very significant and thus important for the processors of thermosetting materials. As mentioned in the introduction, the main problem in processing these materials is to keep a delicate heat balance which affects both the rheology and the curing process. The heating rate of these materials during their processing is controlled by the heat supplied externally, the heat formed due to internal friction, and the exothermic curing reaction, which mutually affect each other.

The DSC dynamic method can be also employed to estimate the degree of cure by measuring the residual heat of reaction, namely, the heat evolved during the curing of the residual uncured component of the material.

TABLE II
Dynamic DSC Data of Genal 4050 Compound at Various Heating Rates

Heating rate, °C/min	Heat of reaction, mcal/mg	Exotherm peak temperature, °C
1	7.1	135
2	8.1	140
5	11.3	142
10	7.6	146
20	6.7	156
50	8.1	174

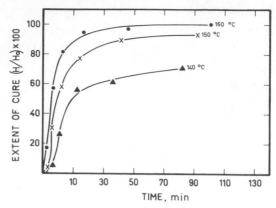

Fig. 5. Rate curves of Genal 4050 compound cured at various temperatures.

This method was used to study the effect of processing in an injection molding machine on curing of thermosetting phenolic compounds as follows: One set of samples was prepared by isothermal curing in the DSC cell for 15 min at three temperatures (180°, 190°, 220°C).   Another set of samples was prepared by injection molding the material into a mold at three temperatures (170°, 190°, 210°C).   The temperatures in the machine were 65°C in the feeding zone, 110°C in the cylinder, and 100°C in the die.   All samples were thermally analyzed at the same heating rate of 20°C/min, and their degrees of cure were calculated from the measured residual heats of reaction.   As can be seen in Table III, the injection-molded samples reached higher degrees of cure; this inspite their much shorter residence time at the given temperature (in the order of seconds).   The higher degree of cure in the molded samples compared to the isothermally cured samples is a result of the precuring process taking place in the machine.

Second-order transitions of crosslinked networks have been investigated by Gordon[8] and Fava,[3] and the temperature of the transition was shown to increase with the extent of cure.   It has been suggested[3,5,9] that for resins that show a glass transition, the T_g provides an index of degree of cure.   This might be useful in analyzing samples with high degree of cure, thus showing a small residual exotherm.   Barton reports[9] that during the final stages of the curing reaction of an epoxy resin, there is a large increase in T_g where measurements of the residual heats of reaction are least sensitive.

Genal 4050 samples were cured isothermally at two temperatures, 170° and

TABLE III
Degree of Cure as a Function of Curing Conditions

Isothermally cured		Injection molded	
Curing temperature,[a] °C	Degree of cure,[b] %	Mold temperature,[c] °C	Degree of cure,[b] %
180	74	170	90
190	88	190	97
200	100	210	100

[a] Cured for 15 min in the DSC cell.
[b] Determined at heating of 20°C/min.
[c] Residence time in mold was 8 sec.

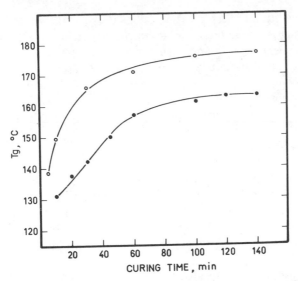

Fig. 6. T_g of Genal compound after curing at 170°C (●) and 180°C (○).

180°C, in the DSC cell for various desired lengths of time up to 140 min. Following cooling of these samples to ambient temperature, their T_g was determined at a heating rate of 20°C/min. T_g was defined as the point of intersection of the extrapolated baseline at the low temperature end and the tangent to the curve at the inflection point. The T_g was found to increase with extent of cure, approaching a limiting value which is lower than the cure temperature in agreement with Fava's results on epoxy resins.[3] As can be seen in Figure 6, there is a change of about 35°C in the T_g of samples cured at the studied temperatures.

The change in T_g for phenolic compounds is not as large as for the epoxies mentioned above.[5,9] Most of the change in the T_g of Genal takes place during the first 60 min of the curing reaction and then levels off where the degree of cure did not reach yet very high values. For example, after 60 min at 180°C, the measured degree of cure was only 75% and the corresponding T_g was already 171°C. It is important to mention that the T_g determination of highly cured compounds is inaccurate as a result of the thermogram geometry in the T_g range.

It is interesting to note that the T_g-versus-curing time curves (Fig. 6) are almost parallel in their upper part. This means that the T_g of highly cured samples cured at 170°C is always lower than that of highly cured samples cured at 180°C. It is also important to note that the T_g never exceeds the cure temperature. Hence, the final three-dimensional structure of the crosslinked material depends on the curing temperature. Curing at the lower temperature results in a structure enabling more segmental motion than in samples cured at the higher temperature. The curing temperature, at least for this particular material, affects not only the rate of curing, but in addition it affects the structure of the final product and hence it should affect its properties.

Since all samples used for studying the effect of curing on T_g where only partially cured, each of their thermograms included also an exothermic peak resulting from the completion of the residual curing. It has been observed that with increasing the initial degree of cure (larger initial curing time) the exotherms and thus the curing reactions shift to high temperatures, which are always above

T_g, and the area under these exotherms has decreased. In addition, as the T_g of the partially cured resin increases, it approaches the residual cure temperature but never exceeds it. As T_g and cure temperature get closer, the cure reaction kinetics and the final structure become probably dependent on processes controlled by segmental motion. As has been observed in the case of an epoxy resin,[3] the curing reaction is very limited at temperatures under T_g; hence, the glassy state provides a large barrier to the curing reaction. This should lead to the conclusion that curing should be carried above the resin-limiting T_g to obtain better physical properties.

In the present work, it has been shown that DSC is a very powerful technique for the characterization of various injection molding phenolic compounds. The dynamic DSC method has been employed to obtain kinetic data and reaction rate constants. It was found that the curing reaction, in the range studied, obeys first-order kinetics. The results indicate an optimal temperature, at which the cure mechanism is most efficient, where the heat of curing attains a maximum.

The T_g was found to be closely related to the extent of cure, increasing with the latter and approaching a limiting value characterized by the cure temperature. Since the curing reaction is very limited at temperatures under T_g, curing should be carried above the resin-limiting T_g to obtain better physical properties.

This study program was initiated and partially financed by the Armament Development Authority. The authors extend their thanks to Mrs. A. Dagan for technical assistance and to Messrs. A. Gilat, Dr. S. Kenig, and I. Segev for helpful discussions throughout the work.

References

1. P. E. Willard, *Polym. Eng. Sci.*, **12**, 120 (1972).
2. R. B. Prime, *Analytical Calorimetry*, Vol. 12, Plenum Press, New York, 1970.
3. R. A. Fava, *Polymer*, **9**, 137 (1968).
4. M. R. Kamal and S. Sourour, *Polym. Eng. Sci.*, **13**, 59 (1973).
5. T. R. Manley, *Polymer Characterization by Thermal Methods of Analysis*, Marcel Dekker, New York, 1974.
6. R. Slysh, A. C. Hettinger, and K. E. Gyler, *Polym. Eng. Sci.*, **14**, 264 (1974).
7. K. E. J. Barrett, *J. Appl. Polym. Sci.*, **11**, 1617 (1967).
8. M. Gordon and W. Simpson, *Polymer*, **2**, 383 (1961).
9. J. M. Barton, *Polymer Characterization by Thermal Methods of Analysis*, Marcel Dekker, New York, 1974.

Received June 15, 1976

JOURNAL OF APPLIED POLYMER SCIENCE   VOL. 21, 2319–2340 (1977)

Environmental Stress Cracking of Polyethylene

C. J. SINGLETON, E. ROCHE, and P. H. GEIL, *Department of Macromolecular Science, Case Western Reserve University, Cleveland, Ohio 44106*

Synopsis

Deformation of polyethylene in environmental stress cracking (ESC) agents results in changes in both the mechanism of deformation and structure of the resulting drawn material. Stress-cracked failure surfaces are highly fibrillar, the fibrils having less elastic recovery than those in samples drawn in air. In thin films drawn in ESC agents, small blocks of the lamellae remain undrawn and attached to the fibrils drawn across micronecks. The ESC agents are suggested to weaken the cohesion between the fibrils in samples drawn beyond yield as well as the cohesion between mosaic blocks or similar structural elements in the original lamellae as they are being reoriented to form the fibrils. The stress is thus supported by a number of independent, nonuniform fibrils rather than a coherent structure; the weakest of these fibrils fail in turn as the crack propagates through the sample.

INTRODUCTION

Environmental stress cracking (ESC) is a condition of failure exhibited by polyethylene when subjected to polyaxial stresses while in contact with a non-solvent, surface-active medium. If identical stresses are applied to the polymer in the absence of the stress crack-inducing medium, failure does not occur.

During the late 1950's and early 1960's, there was an intense amount of interest in the problem of ESC of polyethylene, largely because it was being widely used as an insulation and coating for telephone cable and underground pipework.[1] It was also used in flexble containers for soaps and detergents, which are active stress cracking agents.

The test most frequently used for ESC characterization in the United States is the bent strip test,[2] which is presumed to be representative of the stresses and strains encountered in use. In this test, ten polymer bars ($1\frac{1}{2}$ in. × $\frac{1}{2}$ in. × $\frac{1}{8}$ in.) are bent 180 degrees and immersed in a surface-active liquid (e.g., Igepal CO-530, General Aniline & Film Company, at 50°C). Each bar contains a longitudinal slit $\frac{3}{4}$ in. long × $\frac{2}{100}$ in. deep down the center of the upper face. Stress crack resistance is defined as the length of time required for five of the ten samples to show visible signs of cracking perpendicular to the slit. A photograph of several samples, in various stages of failure, is shown in Figure 1. As the samples subjected to the bent strip test progress toward failure, the original razor slit tends to deepen and widen, presumably as a result of strain-induced orientation. Following the opening of the slit, cracks (which are usually located near the base of the slit) begin to grow in a transverse direction. Figure 2 shows the

2319

Fig. 1. Branched polyethylene samples at various stages of failure in the bent-strip test. The original razor slits have deepened and widened. Transverse cracks have started to form in the samples at left and center. Complete failure has occurred in the sample on the right.

inside of a test specimen just prior to failure. This specimen was sliced parallel to the original razor slit. The dotted line indicates the outline of the original razor slit. Following initiation, the transverse cracks grow slowly until they break through to the surface of the sample. Note that crack initiation occurs in the region where the polymer is stressed approximately to its yield point and not in the region of maximum stress.

The failure surface of the regions originally in tension appears quite smooth, whereas that of regions originally under compression seems extremely rough (Fig. 1). Most probably, total failure occurred very rapidly after the region in tension "cracked," yielding this result. However, when the smooth failure surface, which was originally under tension, is viewed by optical microscopy, it has a drawn, fibrous appearance (Fig. 3). This fibrous appearance we found to be common to all environmentally stress-cracked polyethylenes examined, to varying degrees, regardless of resin or cracking agent involved. This evidence indicates that ESC failure is not brittle.

In recent years, although practical means of improving the ESC resistance (such as molecular weight control) have been developed, little scientific interest has been reported in the process. Detailed knowledge of the mechanism should not only lead to improved materials, but should also contribute to an understanding of the general mechanism of tensile deformation of crystalline polymers. In particular, the origin of the fibrous texture of the deformed matter is of concern. In this paper we discuss the effect of the presence of an ESC agent on the tensile properties of notched and unnotched polyethylene bars and on the morphology of the resulting failure surfaces. In addition, the effect of the presence of an ESC agent on the ultrastructural deformation characteristics of thin films and single crystals is described. Commercial grades of polyethylene

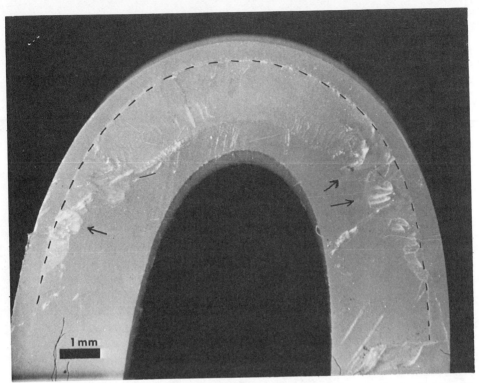

Fig. 2. Partially stress-cracked sample. The sample was cut along the razor slit after the slit had deepened and transverse cracks had just started to form. Cracks are appearing in the region marked with arrows.

with varying molecular weights and densities were used. The results of this study suggest that there is considerable potential for the techniques utilized, not only for understanding the mechanism of ESC, but also the mechanism of tensile deformation in general.

EXPERIMENTAL

Resins

The resins used for most of this research were Marlex (trademark of Phillips Petroleum Company for its polyethylene resins) 6002, 6015, 6050, 5040, and 5065 and Alathon (trademark of E. I. du Pont de Nemours and Company, Inc., for its polyethylene resins) 3B, 2020, and 4275. Marlex 6002, 6015, and 6050 are high-density (0.960 g/cc) resins having melt indices of 0.2, 1.5, and 5.0, respectively, as described by the sales literature for each resin. The ESC resistance determined by ASTM D1693-59T (bent strip test) is 60, 10, and 1 degrees F_{50}hr, respectively. Marlex 5040 and 5065 are intermediate-density (0.950) ethylene–butene copolymer resins with melt indices of 4.0 and 6.5. The ESC resistance is 20 and 10 degrees F_{50}hr, respectively. Alathon 3B, 2020, and 4275 are low-density (0.92 g/cc), free radical-polymerized polyethylene resins. The melt indices are 0.25, 1.1, and 3.7, respectively. The ESC resistance of Alathon 3B

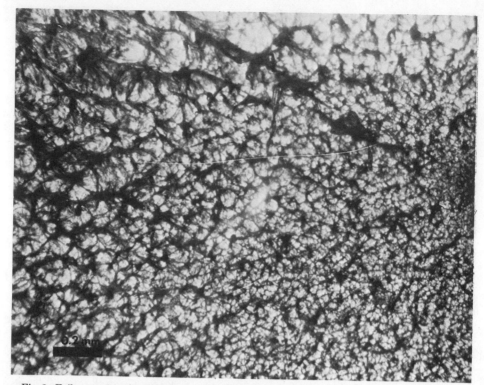

Fig. 3. Failure surface of a low-density polyethylene sample with good stress crack resistance from the bent-strip test. Scale represents 0.01 in.

is given as greater than 500 hr in the sales literature. Although not listed, the ESC resistance of Alathon 2020 is also very long, whereas that of Alathon 4275 is quite short. Some of the initial research was done using Alathon 3, 20, and 10. The corresponding values for the resins used were M.I. = 0.24, 2.2, and 2.0 and ESC resistance >1000 hr, 7 hr, and 10 min, respectively. As suggested by the ESC resistance and M.I., the two sets of resins cannot be directly compared.

Mechanical Properties

Tensile bars, 3 in. × ½ in. × ⅛ in. were cut out of sheets of various polyethylene resins which had been compression molded at 150°C and 40,000 pounds force for 5 min and quenched in ice water. A 0.020-in.-deep razor slit was made across the middle of each bar transverse to the tensile direction. These slits acted as stress risers. Sample bars of each resin were immersed in either methanol, isopropanol, or Igepal and drawn at rates of 5 cm/min and 0.5 cm/min in an Instron tensile testing machine. The failure surfaces of these samples were then compared to those of samples of the same resins drawn in air and water under the same conditions. Stress–strain curves were also measured, at a 5 cm/min strain rate, on microtensile specimens (1 in. gauge length, 0.25 in. width, 0.016–0.020 in. thick) while immersed in various liquids.

Measurements of stress relaxation in flexure and tension were made at room

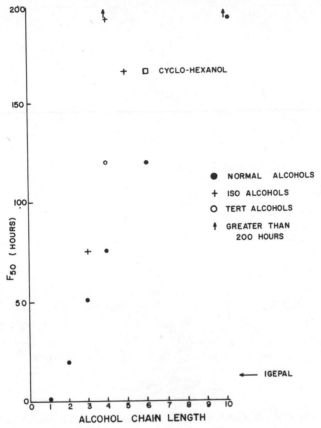

Fig. 4. Stress-crack resistance of samples of Alathon 20, as measured in the bent-strip test at room temperature, as a function of alcohol chain length. The ESC resistance in Igepal is also shown.

temperature in various cracking agents. For the flexure measurements, samples similar in size to those for the bent strip test for low-density polyethylene (1 in. gauge length, 0.125 in. thick, with and without a slit) were bent 0.2 in. at the center while immersed. The tension measurements were made on microtensile samples 0.009 in. thick, which were strained 0.05 in. and immersed in the liquid 1 min after the stress was applied.

Photographs, using a single-lens reflex camera, were made of the failure surfaces. These surfaces were also examined by scanning electron microscopy (SEM) and optical microscopy.

Thin Film Observations

Thin films were prepared from 1% solutions of various polyethylene resins in xylene. The solutions were cast hot onto strips of Mylar (trademark of E. I. du Pont de Nemours & Company for its polyester film) film fastened into stretch racks. After the xylene evaporated, the thin film specimens were remelted at 135°C or 150°C (depending on the resin used), recrystallized, and cooled to room temperature. These specimens were then deformed in air or in stress cracking environments and replicated with platinum and carbon for observation by transmission electron microscopy (TEM).

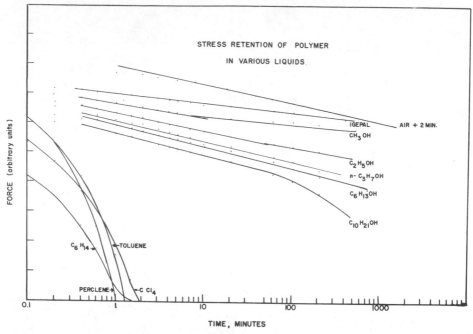

Fig. 5. Residual force of microtensile specimens strained 0.05 in. and immersed in the liquid listed 1 min after the stress was applied, plotted as a function of time of immersion.

Single Crystal Studies

Single crystals of the linear polyethylene resins (Marlex 6002, 6015, and 6050) were prepared by the self-seeding technique,[3] deposited on strips of Mylar film fastened into stretch racks, and subjected to deformation in various environments. The single crystals were shadowed with Pt–C after deformation. The resulting samples were examined by transmission electron microscopy.

Scanning Electron Microscopy (SEM)

The failure surfaces of the tensile bars were rotary coated with Au–Pd prior to insertion in a Cambridge S4-10 Stereoscan microscope. Micrographs were obtained in the secondary emission mode.

RESULTS AND DISCUSSION

Cracking Agent

Although one might expect such properties as surface tension or cohesive energy density of the ESC agent to affect the stress crack resistance in a readily interpretable manner, this does not seem to be the case. Figure 4 shows the bent strip test stress crack resistance of samples of Alathon 20 as a function of alcohol chain length; a regular progression is seen, the resistance increasing with chain length. For Alathon 3 and 10, however, a minimum in ESC resistance was found for chain lengths between 2 and 7. It is also noted that ESC failure in Igepal, which has a surface tension higher than that of any of the alcohols used, occurs just as rapidly as that in methyl and ethyl alcohol.

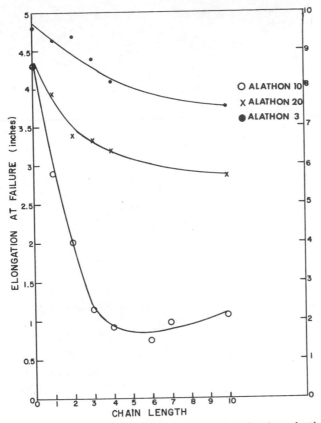

Fig. 6. Elongation at failure in various alcohols of three low-density polyethylene resins as a function of alcohol chain length.

Stress Relaxation

The stress relaxation measurements in flexure of the unslit bars of Alathon 10 were essentially the same whether in an air, water, or methyl alcohol environment. However, for slit samples (as in the bent strip test), the specimens, in the methyl alcohol environment cracked near the yield point. This observation is in agreement with the suggestion above that ESC failure occurs most readily in a polymer that is stressed close to its yield point.

Figure 5 shows a plot of residual stress versus time (measured from time of immersion) for samples immersed in various liquids. In general, it is seen that the rate of relaxation increased with increasing alcohol chain length. With decyl alcohol, curvature of the line indicates the start of solvation or swelling. In solvents such as toluene, the samples relaxed rapidly and then swelled. The linear nature of the data for some of the more active ESC agents indicate that they do not penetrate the sample and weaken it at these stresses; i.e., diffusion of the ESC agent into the stressed samples well ahead of any possible microcracks does not appear to be significant.

Tensile Tests

The elongation at failure of the microtensile specimens drawn at 5 cm/min in various alcohols is shown in Figure 6. In all cases it is seen that the elongation

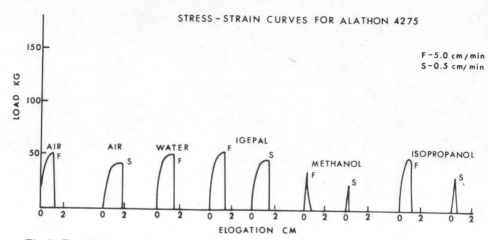

Fig. 7. Tensile force vs elongation curves for notched bars of Alathon 4275 drawn in various media.

decreases with increasing chain length; however, the failure occurs after yielding and neck formation even in the relatively low molecular weight samples of Alathon 10, which is the resin most susceptible to ESC.

Stress–strain curves for the notched samples of Alathon 4275 deformed in various media, at a strain rate of 0.5 and 5 cm/min, are shown in Figure 7. For identical strain rates, the curves are essentially the same whether the specimens were deformed in air, water (used to reduce any possible heating effect during

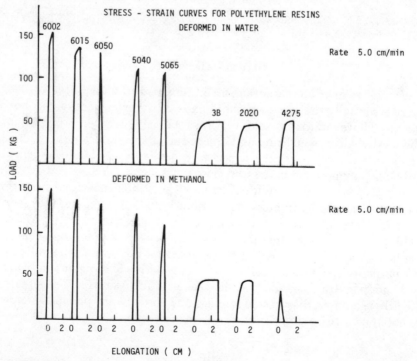

Fig. 8. Tensile force vs elongation curves for notched bars of various polyethylene resins drawn in water or methanol at 5 cm/min.

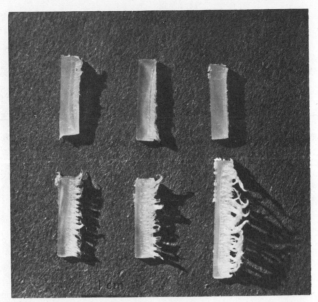

Fig. 9. Failure surfaces of Alathon 3B, 2020, and 4275 drawn in tension. The upper samples were drawn in air and the lower in isopropyl alcohol at a rate of 5 cm/min. The 0.020-in. razor slit is seen on the left-hand side of each specimen.

extension), or Igepal. Only in alcohol environment is an effect seen. Failure occurs more rapidly, with the samples failing more rapidly in methyl than in isopropyl alcohol. Note that this is opposite to the effect seen for the unnotched samples, in which the elongation at failure was less in isopropyl alcohol than in methyl alcohol. Also, failure occurs at somewhat lower elongations when the sample is drawn slowly in the alcohol than when it is drawn more rapidly.

For the other two low-density polyethylene samples, Alathon 3B and 2020, the curves for each sample, whether drawn in air, water, or any of the ESC agents used, are essentially the same and very similar to those of Alathon 4275 drawn in air, water, or Igepal, varying only with strain rate. In all of the notched samples, the total elongation was less than 3 cm. For the branched polyethylene resins, in general, higher elongations were attained for samples of higher molecular weight. As a result of the presence of the notch, deformation is localized to the vicinity of the notch. The measured elongation attained at failure corresponds to, or is less than, the extension of the resultant fibers (refer to Figs. 8 and 9) across the notch as observed after failure.

For the high- and intermediate-density polymers, the stress–strain curves for each samples were essentially the same, independent of the environment. Failure appears to have occurred at, or just prior to, the yield conditions. Typical curves for the various samples, drawn at 5 cm/min in water and methanol, are shown in Figure 8. Just as for Alathon 4275, notched tensile bars of all of the high-density samples failed at lower elongations, when drawn at the lower strain rate. Also, at this rate, the specimens exhibited considerable whitening, due to void formation, and nonrecoverable deformation. Stress–strain curves for the low-density polyethylene samples are also included for comparison purposes.

Despite the apparent similarity in most of the stress–strain curves for a given

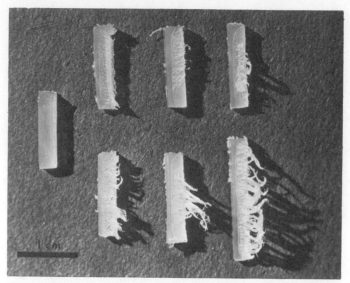

Fig. 10. Failure surfaces of notched bars of Alathon 4275 drawn in tension. From left to right, the samples were deformed in air, Igepal, methanol, and isopropyl alcohol. The samples on the top were drawn at a rate of 0.5 cm/min, whereas the air-drawn sample and those on the bottom were deformed at a rate of 5.0 cm/min.

resin, visual observation of the samples showed considerable differences in the failure process. The failure surfaces of the low-density resins drawn in air and isopropyl alcohol at 5.0 cm/min are shown in Figure 9. The failure surfaces of the samples drawn in air consist of a ridge of "collapsed" material, whereas those drawn in the ESC agent are highly fibrillar. Whether the samples were stressed in air or in isopropyl alcohol (or water or methyl alcohol), the total elongation, as measured on the stress–strain curve, was essentially the same for a given resin (except for Alathon 4275). This fact suggests that the ridge of material seen on the samples drawn in air (or water) has retracted. Contrary to the results of the stress–strain curves, which show an increase in elongation with molecular weight, the length of the fibers in the samples subjected to ESC conditions decreases with increasing molecular weight.

Figure 10 shows failure surfaces of samples of Alathon 4275 drawn in air, Igepal, methanol, and isopropyl alcohol, the samples being similar to those used for the stress–strain curves in Figure 7. As above, all samples drawn in the ESC agents have fibrous failure surfaces. The lengths of the fibers are considerably longer at the faster rate of draw. The sample drawn in air contains a ridge of "collapsed" drawn material. It is noted, in particular, that the longest fibers are observed on the failure surfaces of the samples which were drawn in methanol or isopropyl alcohol, even though the elongation at failure was smallest for these samples. The length of fibers observed, in fact, is approximately the same as the total measured elongation on the stress–strain curve, whereas the length of ridge of material on the air drawn sample is less than the measured strain value.

These observations suggest that an elastic recovery occurs in the material drawn in air, a recovery that does not occur, at least to the same extent, for the samples drawn in ESC agents. Two similar samples, drawn in isopropyl alcohol and observed from the surface opposite the slit, are shown in Figure 11. The splitting of the fibers is seen to extend all the way to the plane containing the slit,

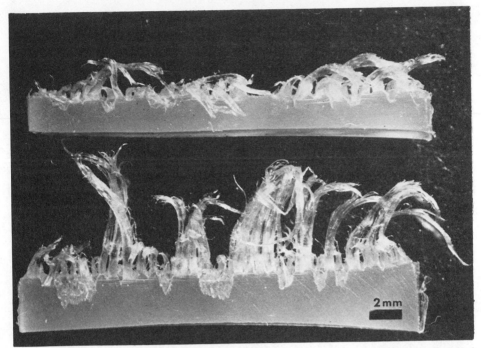

Fig. 11. Failure regions of an Alathon 10 sample drawn in isopropyl alcohol and photographed from the side opposite the slit.

with some material being drawn off the surface from a considerable distance beyond the slit plane in the regions in which the resulting long fibers are attached to the opposite failure surface.

On the basis of the above observations, the mechanism of deformation and the structure of the resulting fibrous material must differ between the samples drawn in ESC agents and for those drawn in air. In particular, it is evident that the cohesion of the fibers formed during elongation is considerably less for the samples drawn in the ESC agents. In conjunction with the observations of the site of ESC in the bent strip test, this suggests that one cause of ESC is this lack of cohesion; the small amount of transverse stress present is enough to cause the fibers to split apart. In the portions of the samples which have been stressed to yield, such that micronecking has occurred and fibers have formed, the fibers will act as independent entities in the presence of an ESC agent, whereas they will act as a more or less coherent structure in non-ESC environments. In the presence of ESC agents, the weakest and/or most highly stressed fibers fail. The load is then transferred to other fibers which fail in turn. That this is not the entire explanation, however, is shown by the observation that initial failure does not occur in the regions stressed beyond yield, regions in which a higher degree of fibrousness would be expected. The observations described below of thin films and single crystals drawn in ESC agents indicate that the mechanism of deformation, the process of forming the fibers, and the structure of the resultant fibers are also affected by the presence of the ESC agent.

Failure Surfaces

The failure surfaces of the bulk tensile samples were too rough to facilitate replication for TEM. However, SEM micrographs were obtainable and amply

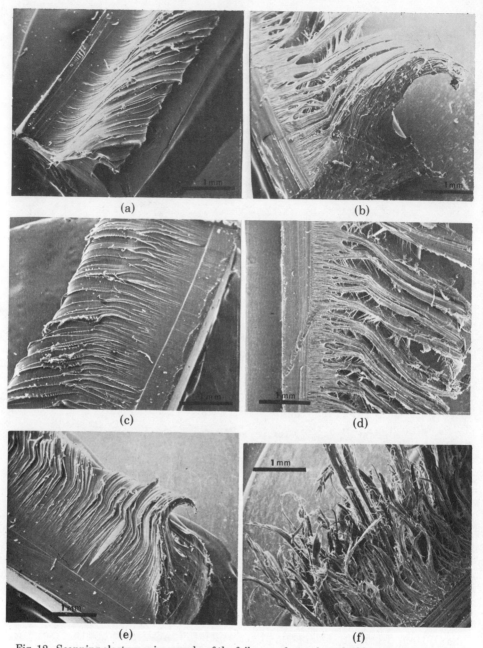

Fig. 12. Scanning electron micrographs of the failure surfaces of notched bars drawn at a rate of 5.0 cm/min. Alathon 3B drawn in (a) air and (b) isopropyl alcohol, Alathon 2020 drawn in (c) air and (d) isopropyl alcohol, and Alathon 4275 drawn in (e) air and (f) isopropyl alcohol.

confirmed the previous observations of a difference in character of the ESC and non-ESC deformed materials. Low-magnification SEM micrographs of the three low-density polyethylene resins, drawn at 5 cm/min in air and isopropyl alcohol, are shown in Figure 12. All surfaces are clearly fibrillar, but there is a significant difference in the cohesion of the fibrils. In the air-drawn samples, the ridge of collapsed material is seen to consist of a drawn fibrillar film that has curved back

(a)   (b)

Fig. 13. Scanning electron micrographs of the failure surfaces of notched bars of Alathon 4275, deformed in (a) air and (b) isopropyl alcohol at a rate of 5.0 cm/min.

on itself. A smaller value of elongation at failure is attained for the sample of Alathon 4275 drawn in isopropyl alcohol than for that drawn in air (Fig. 6). However, the length of the drawn material is larger for the ESC agent-drawn samples, although the ratio does not appear as large as suggested in the photographs in Figures 9–11. Thus, the suggestions concerning a difference in mechanism of fiber formation would still seem to apply. The decrease in cohesion of the fibers is also seen at the fiber tips (see Fig. 13). The specimen drawn in air thinned down gradually, whereas that drawn in isopropyl alcohol tended to splay apart, with each individual fiber having a gradually thinning tip.

The fact that the air-drawn samples are fibrous, the fibers being more coherent, is shown in Figure 14. It is a higher-magnification picture of a portion of the drawn material in the samples of Alathon 4275 already shown in Figure 12. The

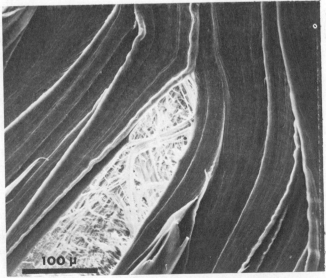

Fig. 14. Scanning electron micrograph of a fibrous region in the deformed material of the air-drawn Alathon 4275 sample.

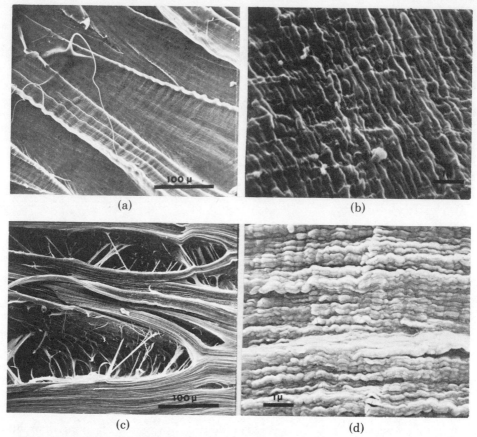

Fig. 15. Scanning electron micrographs of the failure material in a notched bar of (a, b) Alathon 2020 deformed in air and (c, d) Alathon 2020 deformed in isopropyl alcohol.

material split after shadowing but before or during insertion in the electron beam. Although it appears that the fibers along the edges of the cracks were originally present, it is not clear if they were originally present as basic structural elements or if they were formed by essentially a statistically random splitting of the drawn material.

In Figure 15 are shown several higher-magnification micrographs of the sample of Alathon 2020 deformed in air and isopropyl alcohol; 15(b) and 15(d) are higher magnifications of regions in 15(a) and 15(c). At these higher magnifications, both types of drawn material are seen to be corrugated. The corrugations run perpendicular to the draw direction. These corrugations presumably are a result of the retraction or recovery of the fibers after they were drawn out. The mechanism for such corrugating is unknown. However, it seems to indicate that the central portion of each fiber shrinks more than the outer portion. The degree of corrugation appears larger on the sample drawn in isopropyl alcohol. Despite the fact that the remaining fibers are longer in the samples drawn in isopropyl alcohol, this feature is also seen in the other two low-density resins.

The failure surfaces of the high-density samples all appear relatively smooth visually. By SEM, however, a fibrous texture, to varying degrees, is seen on all of the surfaces. Low-magnification micrographs of various surfaces (including

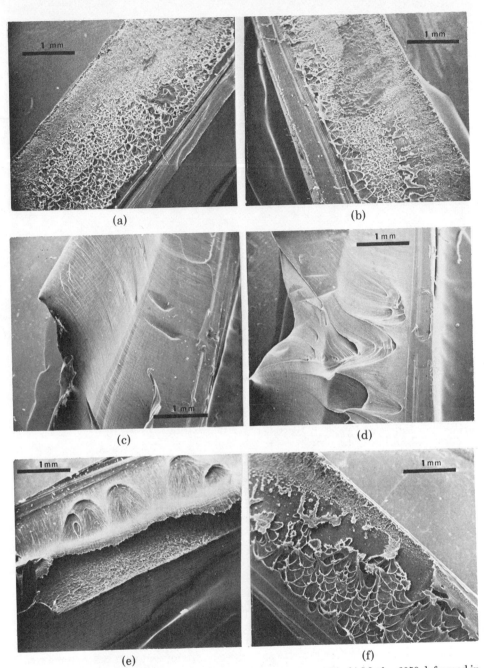

Fig. 16. Scanning electron micrographs of the failure surfaces of (a, b) Marlex 6050 deformed in air and isopropyl alcohol and (c, d) Marlex 6002 deformed in air and isopropyl alcohol, (e) Marlex 6015, and (f) Marlex 5040 deformed in isopropyl alcohol.

one micrograph of an intermediate-density Marlex 5040 sample) are shown in Figure 16. The failure surfaces for each of the resins shown in Figure 16, whether drawn in air or isopropyl alcohol, appear nearly identical even at higher magnifications. Only for the highest molecular weight material (Marlex 6002) is there possibly somewhat less cohesion, as indicated by a more fibrous texture, in the

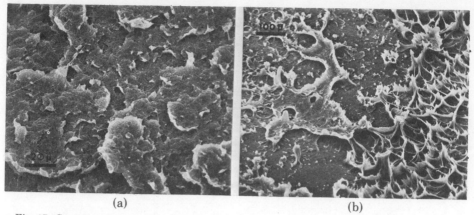

(a)   (b)

Fig. 17. Scanning electron micrographs of the failure material of Marlex 6050 deformed in (a) air and (b) isopropyl alcohol.

sample drawn in isopropyl alcohol than in that drawn in air.   Relaxation corrugations are seen in both Marlex 6002 samples.

In the low molecular weight (Marlex 6050) linear samples, both surfaces show a fibrous texture but on a much smaller scale.   In addition, in both of these samples there is a band parallel to the surface opposite the razor slit in which a more brittle-type fracture has occurred.   Figure 17 shows micrographs of these areas, with Figure 17(b) showing the transition to the fibrous surface also.   It is believed that an interlamellar-type fracture has occurred.   TEM replicas of these surfaces presumably would be similar to those obtained by fracture at liquid nitrogen temperatures, showing evidence of local deformation in which fibrils are formed and melt back to form mounds on the fracture surface.[4]

The micrographs of the intermediate molecular weight (Marlex 6015) sample drawn in isopropyl alcohol show some of both features [see Fig. 16(e)].   About half of the fracture surface consists of coherent drawn fibrillar material, while the other half is relatively smooth.   At higher magnification, as shown in Figure 18, local deformation is seen to have occurred even in the relatively smooth area.   However, on this surface also, in contrast to fibers observed on liquid nitrogen fracture surfaces, the fibers have remained extended.

Fracture surfaces of the intermediate-density resins also contain similar regions.   In comparison with the higher-density samples, the "smooth" areas that are seen in the sample drawn in isopropyl alcohol are much smoother (see Fig. 19).   The smoothness of these regions, interspersed among regions showing local deformation, may be due to a much smaller spherulite size inherent to these samples than in the higher-density samples.   A somewhat rougher region in the samples drawn both in isopropyl alcohol and air, similar to that seen in the Marlex 6015 sample, is seen along the failure surface on the side opposite the razor slit [see Fig. 16(e)].

In summary, in agreement with the stress–strain curves, there appears relatively little difference between the failure surfaces of the high-density samples drawn in air and in isopropyl alcohol; it is certainly much less dramatic than the effects seen for the low-density resin samples.   Practically, it is also known that linear polymers are less susceptible than branched polymers to ESC, although one of the advantages of the Marlex 5040 samples (with its low branch content)

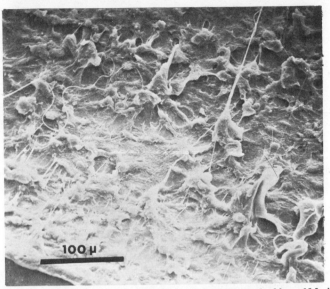

Fig. 18. Scanning electron micrograph of the failure surface of a notched bar of Marlex 6015 drawn in isoopyl alcohol.

is that it has better ESC resistance than the more linear samples. Another difference between the high- and low-density samples is their molecular weight distribution. This is known to affect ESC resistance. A narrow molecular weight distribution material has better ESC resistance than a broad molecular weight distribution polymer of the same average molecular weight.[5]

Thin Films

In as much as the primary difference in deformation behavior under ESC and non-ESC conditions was seen for the low-density samples, the deformation

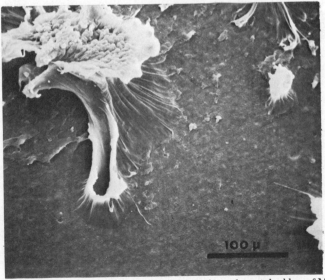

Fig. 19. Scanning electron micrograph of the failure surface of a notched bar of Marlex 5040 deformed in isopropyl alcohol.

Fig. 20. Transmission electron micrograph of a thin film of melt-crystallized Alathon 4275 deformed 100% in air on a Mylar strip.

characteristics of thin films of Alathon 4275 were examined. Figure 20 shows such a film drawn 100% in air on a Mylar film. Only uniform, plastic deformation has occurred. The lamellae, in agreement with early work of Peck and Kaye,[6] seem to have twisted more or less as units into the draw direction. Presumably twinning, phase change, lamellar slip, etc., have occurred. No fibrils were seen in any of these samples, indicating that even incipient micronecking has not yet occurred although these samples have been drawn well beyond the yield elongation.

In order to characterize the structure of the fibrils in this resin, it was necessary to draw the thin films across cracks in a carbon substrate. By this method, high local deformations can be obtained. The resulting fibrils (Fig. 21) are smooth (similar to those observed previously for thick samples, thin films, and single crystals of linear polyethylene and other polymers drawn in air), with interfibrillar links of somewhat smaller diameters connecting adjacent fibers.

Figure 22 shows two micrographs representative of the results of drawing the thin films of Alathon 4275 (67% deformation) in methanol. Although plastic deformation similar to that observed in air still occurred, numerous regions were also observed in which micronecking has occurred.

It is noted that the fibrils formed remain coherent. This possibly is an artifact of the deformation process. The substrate shrinks laterally as it is being stretched, therefore compressing rather than separating the fibrils. The unique feature of these fibrils, however, is their roughness, as noted both by the bumpy surface and the uneven shadows. It is suggested that this roughness is due to mosaic blocks, as described by Peterlin,[7] or larger crystalline units having been torn off the edge of the crystalline lamellae and yet not having been completely incorporated into a fibril structure. On the larger pieces of material drawn along the fibrils, well-defined edges of the original lamellae can be seen. That is, not only is the cohesion of the fibrils themselves reduced by the presence of an ESC agent, but the deformation mechanism itself is changed. Possibly, the ESC agent also weakens the cohesion between the mosaic blocks in Peterlin's model. These

Fig. 21. Transmission electron micrograph of a thin film of melt-crystallized Alathon 4275 deposited on a carbon substrate on a Mylar strip. The Mylar was drawn 30%.

blocks then act as individual elements, many of which are only carried along as the fiber is formed rather than acting cooperatively. The tendency for elastic recovery of the fibers is reduced, as seen in the thick samples. According to Peterlin's model,[7] recovery during annealing is due to extended tie molecules connecting nonadjacent mosaic blocks.

Single Crystals

Although no essential difference was observed in the deformation characteristics of the thick, notched samples of the high-density polyethylenes, in the presence and absence of ESC agents, apparent differences were observed for single crystals of Marlex 6002 drawn on Mylar (see Fig. 23). (Single crystals grown from the low-density polyethylene are too small to permit significant observations.) As shown previously[8], linear polyethylene single crystals can be drawn on Mylar up to 100% elongation with only plastic deformation occurring. Cracks spanned by ca. 100-Å-diameter fibrils are seen occasionally. Usually, though, the presence of these cracks is restricted to regions of multiple superimposed lamellae. When drawn on carbon-coated Mylar film, smooth fibrils, often with interfibrillar links, are observed spanning the cracks.

In contrast, when the Marlex 6002 crystals were drawn on Mylar film while immersed in methanol (as shown in Fig. 23) or isopropyl alcohol, numerous cracks spanned by fibrils were observed. The fibrils, however, are smooth, showing no signs of the roughness observed in the fibers of low-density resins subjected to ESC conditions. We suggest that this tendency for the formation of numerous micronecks in the crystals drawn in ESC agents is again a result of weakened cohesion of the structural elements, presumably mosaic blocks, within the crystals. It is also possible, however, that the cracks resulted from weakened cohesion between the crystal and the substrate of Mylar films. An intermediate number of cracks were observed in crystals deformed while immersed in water, the cracks being present predominantly at the edges of the crystals.

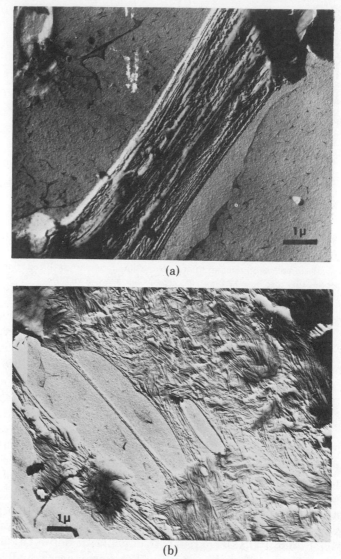

(a)

(b)

Fig. 22. Two transmission electron micrographs of a thin film of melt-crystallized Alathon 4275 deformed in methanol on a Mylar strip. The Mylar was drawn 67%.

CONCLUSIONS

It is obvious from the various micrographs that ESC of polyethylene does not result in brittle fracture, but rather is ductile in nature. Cracks are initiated in the regions where the material is strained near its yield point. Presumably, imperfections serve as stress risers and aid in the process. In particular, they introduce triaxial stresses that have a tendency to separate the fibers as they are formed. The normal drawing process in air involves a reorientation of lamellar structure (i.e., lamellar shear) and intralamellar deformation (molecular slip, tilt, twinning, etc.). In the presence of an ESC agent, the breakdown of the lamellae into mosaic blocks or larger units occurs more readily. These structures are reorganized as rigid entities in the fibers. Fewer extended tie molecules exist

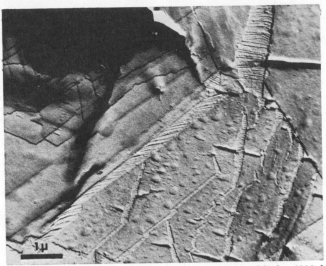

Fig. 23. Transmission electron micrograph of a single crystal of Marlex 6002 deformed 75% in the presence of methanol on a Mylar strip.

between nonadjacent mosaic blocks or crystallites, resulting in less recovery of the fibers when the tension is released by failure. It is suggested that the ESC agents, all of which are low surface-tension liquids, weaken both the cohesion between the fibers as well as the cohesion between the mosaic blocks or similar structural elements in the lamellae as they are reorienting for incorporation into fibers. On the macroscopic scale, the stress, in the bent strip test, for instance, is supported by a number of independent, nonuniform strands of drawn material. As the most highly stressed fibers break, the remaining fibers become more highly stressed and, in turn, fail. A crack propagates through the sample unless the stress is relieved. This occurrence also seems to be the case for the fibrils formed in single crystals and thin films.

The effect of the cracking agent in the stress–strain curve was seen to differ with and without a stress riser being present, the elongation at failure for the lowest molecular weight Alathon increasing with deformation speed and increasing alcohol chain length for the notched samples, while the opposite effect is seen for the effect of alcohol chain length for the unnotched samples (only one strain rate was used). This is presumably due to the difference in strain pattern in the sample; the razor slit is sufficiently deep that the region in its vicinity is drawn to failure without having the deformation progress into neighboring portions of the sample. We suggest that in the notched sample, as in the bent strip test and the thin films, the cracking agent affects both the mechanism of deformation and the cohesion between the drawn fibrils, whereas in the uniformly drawn thick samples, it primarily affects the cohesion between the fibrils after they are drawn. At this time, no conclusions can be drawn concerning the effect of type of cracking agent; the effect of surface tension or cohesive energy density was found to vary with the different resins.

Appreciation is expressed to the du Pont Company for permission to publish some results obtained while one of the authors (P.H.G.) was employed by them and to Phillips and du Pont for furnishing some of the resins used. The National Science Foundation is gratefully acknowledged for financial support of the recent research.

References

1. G. P. Marshall, N. H. Jenkins, L. E. Culver, and J. G. Williams, *SPE J.*, **28,** 26 (September 1972).
2. *Annual Book of ASTM Standards,* Designation: D1693-70.
3. D. J. Blundell, A. Keller, and A. Kovacs, *J. Polym. Sci.*, **B4,** 481 (1966).
4. P. H. Geil, *Polymer Single Crystals,* Wiley–Interscience, New York, 1963, Chap. 4.
5. J. B. Howard, *Engineering Design for Plastics,* E. Baer, Ed., Reinhold, New York, 1964, Chap. 11.
6. V. Peck and W. Kaye, *J. Appl. Phys.*, **25,** 1465 (1954).
7. A. Peterlin, *J. Mater. Sci.*, **6,** 490 (1971).
8. P. H. Geil, *Polymer Single Crystals,* op. cit., Chap. 4.

Received October 23, 1975
Revised July 23, 1976

JOURNAL OF APPLIED POLYMER SCIENCE   VOL. 21 2341–2358 (1977)

Melt Spinning of Nylon 6:   Structure Development and Mechanical Properties of As-Spun Filaments

VILAS G. BANKAR, JOSEPH E. SPRUIELL, and JAMES L. WHITE,
Department of Chemical and Metallurgical Engineering, The University of Tennessee, Knoxville, Tennessee 37916

Synopsis

The structure of melt-spun nylon 6 filaments was studied using on-line x-ray diffraction and bi-refringence measurements.   Measurements were also made on as-spun and treated filaments. On-line wide-angle x-ray scattering measurements indicated that crystallization did not occur on the nylon 6 spinline at spinning rates up to 1000 m/min when spinning was done into either ambient air of 60% relative humidity or into wet saturated air.   The filaments did crystallize gradually on the bobbin to a paracrystalline pseudohexagonal (γ) form.   The rate of crystallization was dependent on the molecular orientation developed in the spun filaments.   Crystalline orientation factors based on hexagonal symmetry were computed as a function of take-up velocity for fibers which were conditioned 24 hr in air at 65% relative humidity.   Annealing in air or treatment in water or 20% formic acid solution causes a transformation from the pseudohexagonal form to the α monoclinic form.   The tangent modulus of elasticity and tensile strength of spun and conditioned filaments increase with increasing take-up velocity and spinline stress, while elongation to break decreases with these variables.

INTRODUCTION

Nylon 6 is one of the most important of commercial synthetic fibers.[1]   While originally synthesized by Carothers and Berchet[2] and studied by du Pont[2,3] about 1930 as part of their pioneering development of melt spinning, nylon 6 was not successfully developed until the end of the decade by I. G. Farbenindustrie.[1,4] In this paper, we will present a study of structure development during the melt spinning of nylon 6 fiber, structural changes occurring in posttreatments of melt-spun fibers, and mechanical properties of these fibers.

The crystalline structure of nylon 6 was first investigated by Brill[5] who found the unit cell of drawn fibers to be monoclinic in character and determined the cell dimensions.   The problem was later reinvestigated by Holmes, Bunn, and Smith[6] who confirmed Brill's results and gave improved values for the unit cell dimensions and angles.   These authors also pointed to the existence of small amounts of a second crystallographic form in drawn nylon 6 fibers.   This point was subsequently investigated by later researchers.[7-11]   Wide-angle x-ray (WAXS) patterns of quenched nylon 6 film were made by Sandeman and Keller[12] who noted that their results were very different from those of Holmes et al. Ziabicki and Kedzierska[13] studied melt-spun (but undrawn) nylon 6 filament.

2341

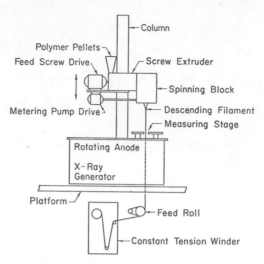

Fig. 1. Melt spinning apparatus.

They found a similar poorly formed crystalline structure represented by a broad equatorial reflection corresponding to an interplanar spacing of 4.2 Å and a meridional reflection at 8.3 Å. Cold drawing or hot-water treatment yielded the Holmes-Bunn-Smith monoclinic structure, which is generally referred to as the α form. The crystalline form of melt-spun fibers was subsequently identified by Vogelsong[10] as being the same as the second phase observed in drawn fibers. Roldan and Kaufman[14] and later Parker and Lindenmeyer[15] have attempted to rationalize all of these observations. The former authors distinguish between various classifications of amorphous, monoclinic α (Holmes et al.), paracrystalline monoclinic (Brill), hexagonal β, and a nematic pseudohexagonal γ (Ziabicki-Kedzierska).

As mentioned above, the basic studies of structure development during the melt spinning of nylon 6 are due to Ziabicki and Kedzierska[13,16] who studied both WAXS patterns and birefringence of spun fibers. The birefringence Δn was correlated as an increasing function of spinline stress. More recently, Hamana, Matsui, and Kato[17] and Ishibashi, Aoki, and Ishii[18] have made on-line measurements of birefringence and determined Δn as a function of spinline position. Ishibashi et al. note that undrawn yarns exhibit increases in birefringence if placed in a 50% relative humidity environment. Ishibashi and Ishii[19] have also investigated the effect of heating chambers placed around the spinline on the birefringence of the running filament. They have suggested that the increased birefringence observed is due to crystallization of the running filament. Further studies of melt-spun nylon 6 fibers are reported by Pasika, West, and Thurston,[20] Sakaoku, Morosoff, and Peterlin,[21] and Wasiak and Ziabicki.[22] Considerations of the mechanical properties of melt-spun fibers as related to drawing have been published by Yumoto,[23,24] Hattori, Takagi, and Kawaguchi,[25,26] Sakaoku et al.,[21] and Kitao, Kobayoshi, Ikegami, and Ohya.[27,28] Structure development in the wet spinning of nylon 6 has been described by Kiyotosukuri, Hasegawa, and Imamura[29] and by Hancock, Spruiell, and White.[30] They found that in most cases the wet-spun fibers exhibited the α monoclinic form.

While there has been substantial research on structure development in melt spinning of nylon 6, many of the most basic questions remain unanswered. It

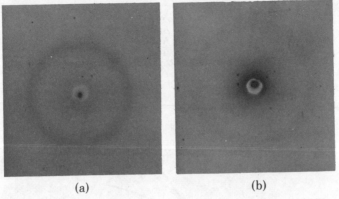

(a)   (b)

Fig. 2. Typical WAXS patterns measured on-line for a nylon 6 spinline: (a) 100 m/min, take-up velocity 160 cm below the spinneret, $T = 95°C$, 60% relative humidity; (b) 556 m/min, take-up velocity 120 cm below the spinneret, $T = 96°C$, 100% relative humidity.

is not known under what conditions this polymer crystallizes in the spinline and when it crystallizes on the bobbin. There have been no quantitative studies of the relationship of the crystalline orientation of spun fibers with spinning conditions. In this paper, we turn our attention to these problems. We will examine a running threadline using on-line WAXS and birefringence measurements. On-line WAXS measurements were first carried out on a fiber spinline by Chappell, Culpin, Gosden, and Tranter[31] and later more quantitatively by Katayama, Amano, and Nakamura,[32] Dees and Spruiell,[33] and Henson and Spruiell[34] (see Spruiell and White[35]). Recently, Spruiell and White[36] have reviewed studies of structure development during melt spinning. This paper represents a continuation of research on this topic by the authors and their colleagues at the University of Tennessee.[33-38] It also represents a contribution to our ongoing studies of nylon 6.[30,39,40] In a recent paper, we have considered the dynamic and rheological aspects of melt spinning of nylon 6.[39]

EXPERIMENTAL

Material

Nylon 6 chips were supplied by the American Enka Company (Lowland, Tennessee). Before use for any experiments, the polymer was dried at a pressure of 0.5 in. of mercury at 110°C. The sample was held under these conditions for 16 hr and then allowed to cool for 4 hr. Under these conditions, the polymer had a number-average molecular weight of 22,500 and a ratio of weight-average to number-average molecular weight of 2.08 as measured in the American Enka laboratories. The moisture content was measured using a MEECO electrolytic moisture analyzer, Model W Type LBY. The moisture content of the dried sample was 0.03–0.04%. This is the same polymer considered in our earlier paper[39]

Melt Spinning

The melt spinning operation and the measurement of forces on the spinline were discussed in some detail in our earlier paper.[39] The spinning apparatus

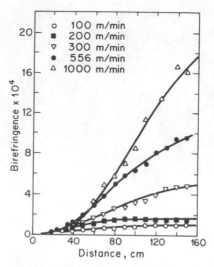

Fig. 3. On-line birefringence measurements show Δn as a function of position for several take-up velocities.

used is shown schematically in Figure 1. The fiber was melt spun through a Fourné screw extruder with a 1.3-cm-diameter screw. The extruder has a 7-liter N_2-purged hopper through which dry pellets were fed. The melt was fed from the screw through a Zenith metering pump to the spinneret block and extruded through a capillary of diameter 0.0762 cm and L/D ratio of 5. The fiber spinline was passed through a rotating-anode x-ray generator, presently to be discussed, and was taken up with a Leesona constant-tension winder. The entire extruder assembly was mounted on a vertical steel column; it could be moved up and down the column at will. Fiber diameters were measured by taking photographs, and temperatures were measured with a Hastings-Raydist null-balance contact thermocouple. These techniques and resulting diameter, velocity, and temperature profiles are discussed in our earlier paper.[39] More information is available in the Ph.D. dissertation of Bankar.[40]

Environmental Chamber

An environmental chamber in which the humidity could be controlled at any desired level surrounded a portion of the spinline. This enclosure was mounted between the spinneret and the rotating-anode generator. It consisted of a flexible canvas duct, 16 in. in diameter, connected at one end to the spinning block and at the other end to a wooden box with dimensions 18 × 17 × 22 in. Provisions were made to insert the x-ray collimator and film cassette into the box. The chamber was humidified with a nitrogen gas–steam mixture. The flow of steam was controlled by means of a Honeywell H93A humidity controller.

On-Line Structure Detection

WAXS. Wide angle x-ray diffraction patterns were made on-line using a Rigaku RU3V rotating anode x-ray generator. Nickel-filtered CuK_α radiation was used. Exposure times varied from 3 to 5 hours depending on the filament size.

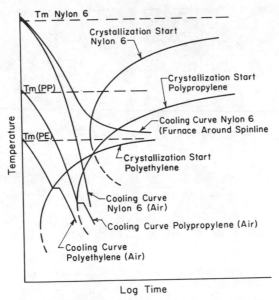

Fig. 4. Continuous cooling transformation diagram representation of structure development in nylon 6 and comparison with polyolefins.

On-Line Birefringence. The birefringence was determined using an Olympus polarizing microscope Model POS with a Berek compensator. The birefringence was computed by dividing the measured retardation by the fiber diameter. The microscope was placed on the x-ray table and the extruder was moved up and down so birefringence could be determined as a function of position along the spin path.

Characterization of Spun Filaments

SAXS. Small-angle x-ray diffraction (SAXS) patterns were determined using a Kiessig camera with pinhole collimation. The camera was mounted on the Rigaku rotating-anode x-ray generator; it was evacuated by a mechanical vacuum pump to reduce air scattering. An exposure time of 10 hr was used.

WAXS. This type of x-ray pattern was obtained using the same Kiessig camera but eliminating the extension tube used in the SAXS studies.

An XRD-5 General Electric x-ray diffractometer was also used to scan the x-rays scattered by the filaments. This instrument was used to determine Hermans-Stein-Wilchinsky[41-43] orientation factors for the pseudohexagonal unit cell of the melt-spun fiber. This approach to analysis of crystalline orientation of fibers as a function of spinning conditions was introduced by Kitao et al.[27,44] and by the Tennessee group.[33-38] The orientation factor for the j-crystallographic axis is

$$f_j = \frac{3 \overline{\cos^2 \Phi_{j,z}} - 1}{2} \tag{1}$$

where $\Phi_{j,z}$ is the angle between the fiber axis and the j-crystallographic axis. Assuming rotational symmetry about the fiber axis,

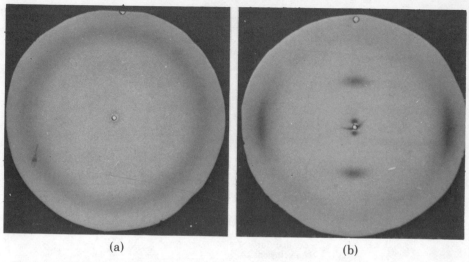

(a)   (b)

Fig. 5. WAXS patterns for as-spun filaments taken in a vacuum camera immediately after spinning: (a) 200 m/min; (b) 1000 m/min.

$$\overline{\cos^2 \Phi_{j,z}} = \frac{\int_0^{\pi/2} I_{hkl}(\Phi_{j,z}) \cos^2 \Phi_{j,z} \sin \Phi_{j,z} d\Phi_{j,z}}{\int_0^{\pi/2} I_{hkl}(\Phi_{j,z}) \sin \Phi_{j,z} d\Phi_{j,z}} \tag{2}$$

where $I_{hkl}(\Phi_{j,z})$ represents the intensity diffracted from (hkl) planes which are normal to the j-crystallographic axis as a function of the azimuthal angle $\Phi_{j,z}$. For the pseudohexagonal unit cell of melt-spun nylon 6 filaments, there are no convenient reflections from planes perpendicular to either the a- or c-axis. The most suitable reflection for intensity measurements is the 100 corresponding to a d-spacing of 4.3 Å. Using intensity measurements for this reflection in eq. (2) allows computation of an orientation factor for a crystallographic direction, henceforth called a', which is normal to the (100) planes and also the c-axis. Using Wilchinsky's analysis,[43] it is readily shown that the c-axis orientation factor, f_c (chain axis), is given by $f_c = -2f_{a'}$.

Posttreatment of Spun Fibers

The as-spun fibers were subjected to various treatments and then retested using SAXS, WAXS, and birefringence measurements. The samples were (1) treated with water at 25°, 60°, and 100°C for 2 hr, (2) treated with a 20% formic acid solution at 25°, 75°, and 102°C for 2 hr, and (3) annealed in a vacuum oven at 70°, 100° and 150°C for 2 hr.

Mechanical Properties

A table model Instron tensile tester was used to obtain force elongation curves on the melt-spun fibers. The fibers were tested only after conditioning at 65% relative humidity and 20°C for 24 hr. The tests were carried out using initial fiber lengths of 1 in. and a cross-head speed of 1 in./min.

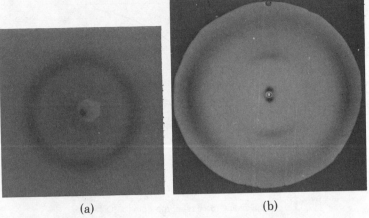

(a)   (b)

Fig. 6. WAXS patterns of spun filaments conditioned for 24 hr at 65% relative humidity and 24°C:
(a) 100 m/min; (b) 556 m/min.

ON-LINE STRUCTURE DEVELOPMENT

Results

Typical examples of on-line WAXS patterns are presented in Figure 2. In all cases, similar results were obtained whether spinning was carried out in air at 65% relative humidity or at 100% relative humidity. Also, there appeared to be little effect of take-up velocity in the range up to 1000 m/min which was investigated. As shown in Figure 2, a single diffuse halo was obtained in all cases. This corresponds to a Bragg's law d-spacing of 4.2 to 4.3 Å.

The birefringence Δn of the running filaments measured at various positions along the spinline, up to 160 cm below the spinneret, is shown in Figure 3 for take-up velocities from 100 to 1000 m/min. Birefringence increases gradually with distance from the spinneret. At any particular position below the spinneret, the birefringence increases monotonically with take-up velocity or take-up stress.

Interpretation

The WAXS patterns for the fibers spun through air and through the humid chamber show a single diffuse halo. The patterns correspond to those of the amorphous quenched nylon 6 samples described by Roldan and Kaufman[14] and not to Ziabicki and Kedzierska's[13] patterns for as-spun fibers.

In order to properly interpret these patterns, we need to explore the variation of crystallization rates with respect to temperature. Studies of the crystallization kinetics of nylon 6 under quiescent conditions have been reported by Burnett and McDevit[45] and Magill,[46] among others. Magill finds a maximum in his rate data at 138°C, which is well above the temperatures (80–99°C) of the present fibers at the position of the WAXS measurements. These results indicate that any crystallization that would occur during the actual spinning process should already have taken place by the position of our measurements.

The reason for the failure of nylon 6 to crystallize in the spinline is certainly

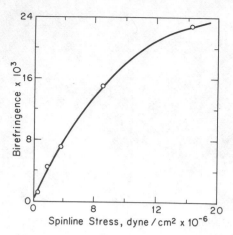

Fig. 7. Variation of fiber birefringence with spinline stress.

the slowness of the crystallization kinetics relative to the period which the melt spends in this temperature environment. As we have noted, studies of the crystallization kinetics of nylon 6 under quiescent conditions have been reported by Burnett and McDevit[45] and Magill.[46] If these are compared with similar experimental results on polyethylene[47] and polypropylene,[48] it is found that at equivalent amounts of supercooling below the melting piont, i.e., $T_m - T$, the crystallization rates are approximately an order of magnitude smaller for the nylon 6. The enhancement of the crystallization kinetics in the spinline by the presence of tension is not sufficient for nylon 6 to allow crystallization to occur under the spinning conditions for which we have performed on-line measurements (take-up velocities up to 1000 m/min and take-up stresses up to 38×10^6 dynes/cm², see our earlier paper[39]).

The relative behavior of nylon 6 and polyolefins in the spinline can be expressed in terms of the continuous cooling curves of our earlier papers.[35,36] This is shown in Figure 4. It must be realized that the curves in Figure 4 are schematic rather than actual in the present instance and are intended only to describe the situation qualitatively. In principle, we would expect different crystallization start curves for different spinning stresses. With increasing spinning stress, these curves would move to the left on the time axis to shorter times as a result of the increased crystallization kinetics. For nylon 6 spun under normal spinning conditions, the crystallization start curve lies at sufficiently large times and the rate of cooling of the filament from above the melting point is sufficiently rapid to prevent the cooling curve from intersecting the crystallization start curve and no crystallization is observed.

As indicated in Figure 4, this is not true for polyethylene and polypropylene, and these filaments crystallize during spnning. It is conceivable that spinning at higher take-up velocities (e.g., several thousand meters per minute) might increase the crystallization rates sufficiently to offset increases in cooling rates and allow nylon 6 to crystallize during spinning. Some indication that this may be the case is evidenced by the birefringence measurements as discussed below. Because of limitations in the operating speed of our take-up equipment and in the sensitivity of the x-ray technique for small-diameter filaments, we were unable to investigate this possibility fully.

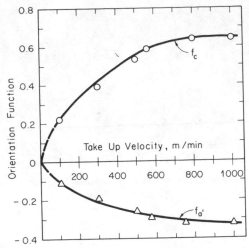

Fig. 8. Orientation factors for nylon 6 fiber as a function of take-up velocity.

Placing an isothermal column below the spinneret in which the temperature is equal to that at the maximum of the crystallization rate–temperature curve may well allow crystallization in the spinline. Such a procedure has been carried out by Ishibashi, Aoki, and Ishii[19] who report increases in fiber birefringence induced by the presence of such a chamber. This point is also illustrated in Figure 4.

The increase in birefringence with distance from the spinneret, Figure 3, can be interpreted as indicating increased molecular orientation with increased draw-down in the spinning filament. Increasing the take-up velocity at constant mass flow rate and spinneret dimensions causes an increase in the melt draw-down and cooling rate of the filament. This then results in greater molecular orientation and birefringence at a given distance from the spinneret.

At high take-up velocities, the birefringence continues to increase after the filament has reached its final diameter and velocity. This effect can be seen by comparing the birefringence profiles of Figure 3 with the velocity profiles presented as Figure 5 of our previous paper.[39] These data show, for example, that a volume element in the filament has reached the take-up velocity of 556 m/min at a point 100 cm from the spinneret. The data of Figure 3 clearly show the birefringence continuing to increase beyond this position. In this part of the spinline, the filament temperature is still above the glass transition temperature and molecular rearrangement in response to the high spinline stresses is possible. It is also possible that the increase in birefringence is due to incipient crystallization or paracrystalline order. However, the size of any such crystallite or ordered regions is too small to obtain any detectable crystalline interference effects on the on-line WAXS patterns.

AS-SPUN FIBERS

Results

Figure 5 shows WAXS patterns of spun fiber taken in a vacuum camera immediately after spinning. The time required to take the sample from the bobbin

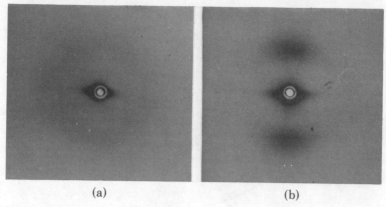

(a)   (b)

Fig. 9. SAXS patterns for the equilibrated as-spun filaments: (a) 100 m/min; (b) 1000 m/min.

and put it in the vacuum camera was less than 5 min. It is seen that the sample spun at 200 m/min shows the same single diffuse ring as the on-line patterns. The sample spun at 1000 m/min shows a pattern with two readily observable but broadened reflections at d-spacings of 8.2 and 4.13 Å. The 8.2-Å spacing is meridional, and the 4.13-Å spacing is most intense at the equator though a complete faint ring may be observed.

After conditioning for 24 hr at 65% relative humidity and 24°C, the x-ray patterns of all the samples, including those spun at low take-up velocities, exhibited weak, broadened reflections at 8.2 and 4.13 Å spacings (Fig. 6).

The level of orientation of melt-spun fibers, either before or after conditioning, increased with take-up velocity and take-up stress (see Figs. 5, 6, and 7). Figure 7 shows the variation of conditioned fiber birefringence with spinline stress. In addition to the obvious increase of birefringence with spinline stress, it should be noted that the birefringence of the conditioned fibers is much greater than the maximum birefringence observed on the running spinline; compare Figure 6 with Figure 3.

The crystalline orientation of the spun and conditioned fibers was determined using an x-ray diffractometer as described in the experimental section. The values of orientation factors are shown in Figure 8 plotted as a function of the take-up velocity.

Typical SAXS patterns for conditioned filaments are shown in Figure 9. At low take-up velocities, a diffuse ring is observed. At higher take-up velocities, a "two-point" pattern develops. This again indicates an increase in orientation with take-up velocity. The long period spacing computed from the SAXS pattern did not vary appreciably with take-up velocity; it had a value of 64 ± 2 Å for take-up velocities from 100 to 2400 m/min.

Discussion

The WAXS patterns of Figure 5(b) and Figure 6 are similar to those of Ziabicki and Kedzierska.[13] They may be interpreted to mean that these samples have partially crystallized in a form having a pseudohexagonal unit cell. We will call this the γ form. We believe that it is similar to the pseudohexagonal, paracrystalline γ form described by Roldan and Kaufman[14] and consists of a poorly

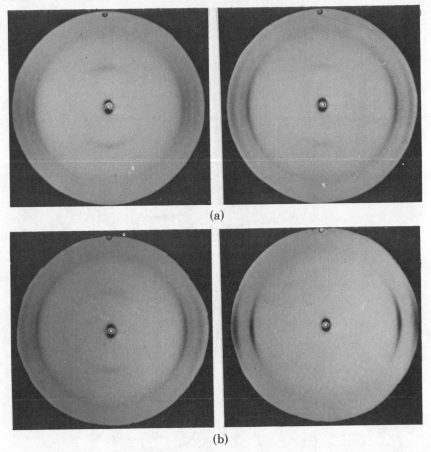

(a)

(b)

Fig. 10. WAXS patterns for nylon 6 fibers annealed in (a) water and (b) 20% formic acid at different temperatures.

developed version of their β form (hexagonal). This latter phase has also been called the γ form by several investigators.[8–11,15]

It is interesting that Figure 5(a) exhibits a diffuse halo which is essentially identical to that observed in the on-line x-ray patterns ($d = 4.2$ Å). Evidently, this sample, spun at a take-up velocity of only 200 m/min, did not crystallize into the γ form during the time required to put the sample in the vacuum camera and obtain the diffraction pattern. Under similar conditions, the sample spun at 1000 m/min exhibits a pattern [Fig. 5(b)] which is characteristic of a well-oriented γ form. This difference appears to be due to the higher rate of nucleation caused by higher molecular orientation in the latter sample. This higher molecular orientation was generated as a result of the higher spinline stress developed by the high take-up rate. Thus, although nylon 6 does not crystallize on the spinline, it does so on the bobbin, and the rate of this process depends on the molecular orientation developed by the spinning conditions.

After conditioning in a humid atmosphere, all of the spun filaments partially crystallized into the γ form. This increase in crystallinity has been observed by other investigators also and is attributed to the plasticizing action of water molecules which increase the chain mobility.

The process of conditioning also causes an increase in the molecular orientation

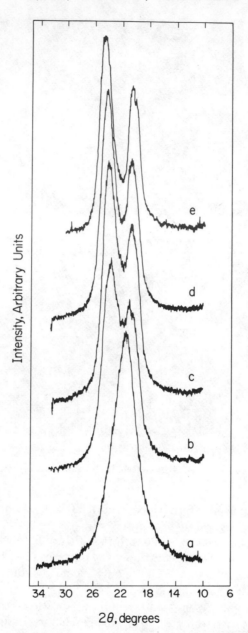

Fig. 11. Typical equatorial diffractometer scans for nylon 6 filaments. Samples spun at 556 m/min take-up velocity. The curves have been displaced along the ordinate for clarity: (a) as-spun and conditioned; (b) annealed 2 hr in water at 60°C; (c) annealed 2 hr in air (65% relative humidity) at 150°C; (d) annealed 2 hr in water at 100°C; (e) annealed 2 hr in 20% formic acid at 102°C.

of nylon 6 filaments. This is clear from a comparison of the birefringence after conditioning (Fig. 7) with the on-line values (Fig. 3). The birefringence of the conditioned filaments is of order 10 to 15 times greater than the maximum values measured on the spinline. The bulk of this change is evidently due to orientation induced by crystallization.

As shown in Figure 8, the c-axis crystalline orientation factor, f_c, increases with take-up velocity and spinline stress while $f_{a'}$ decreases. This, of course, indicates

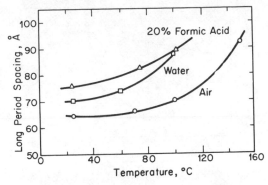

Fig. 12. Variation of long-period spacing with annealing treatment.

that the c axis or polymer chain direction tends to become more aligned with the fiber axis while the a'-direction becomes more nearly perpendicular to the fiber axis. This general behavior is very similar to that exhibited by several other polymers, including those that crystallize on the spinline such as polyethylene, polypropylene, and polyoxymethylene.[33,35,36]

In previous work on polyethylene,[33] orientation factors for each of the three crystallographic axes, f_a, f_b, and f_c, could be uniquely determined as a result of the orthorhombic symmetry of the polyethylene unit cell. This information, together with supporting information from SAXS and electron microscopy, prompted Dees and Spruiell[33] to suggest a detailed morphologic model for melt-spun polyethylene filaments based on the "row structure" models of Keller and Machin[49] (see also Spruiell and White[35,36]). According to this model, the morphology of polyethylene filaments changes from "spherulitic" at very low take-up velocities and spinline stresses to a "row nucleated" or "cylindritic" morphology at high take-up velocities and spinline stresses. In the latter case, ribbon-like lamellar crystals are assumed to grow radially outward in a direction perpendicular to the fiber axis. This results in an alternating texture of crystalline lamellae and interlamellar (disordered) regions along the fiber axis. This latter feature accounts for the observed two-point SAXS patterns of filaments spun at high take-up rates.

In the case of spun and conditioned nylon 6 filaments, the orientation data do not generally provide as much information as in the case of polyethylene. Because of the pseudohexagonal symmetry of the nylon 6 unit cell, we cannot distinguish between two axes in the plane perpendicular to the c-axis. The available data, including the SAXS patterns, are consistent with the general trend described above for the polyethylene filaments. The SAXS patterns of nylon 6 spun at low take-up velocity ($\sim$100 m/min) show a diffuse ring. This can be interpreted as indicative of an unoriented lamellar structure, probably a spherulitic morphology. The SAXS patterns of nylon 6 spun at high take-up velocities show a broadened, two-point diagram. This suggests lamellae growing perpendicular to the fiber axis and consisting of alternate crystalline and intercrystalline (amorphous) regions. In support of this suggestion, it may be noted that chain-folded lamellar crystals of nylon 6 have been produced by crystallization from solution.[50,51] Infrared studies on bulk-crystallized aliphatic polyamides also suggest the existence of a chain-folded structure.[52] Evidence for chain folding in nylon 66 has been discussed by Dismore and Statton.[53] A model

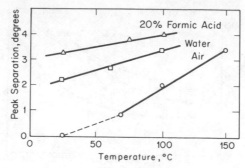

Fig. 13. Apparent angular separation between 200 and 002,202 reflections as a function of annealing treatment.

of chain-folded lamellar structure in the melt-spun and conditioned nylon 6 fibers thus seems reasonable.

The fact that the long periods of fibers spun over a wide range of take-up velocities were equal is not surprising in view of the fact that all the samples crystallized at a similar low temperature on the bobbin. The value of 64 Å may be compared with a value of 60 Å obtained by Geil[50] for single crystals of nylon 6. The observed long period corresponds to about four monomeric units. This value is very similar to that found by Dreyfuss and Keller[54] for nylons 66, 610, and 612 in lath-shaped products crystallized from solution.

ANNEALING TREATMENTS

Results

Annealing treatments were carried out in air, water, and 20% formic acid solution. The effects on the WAXS patterns of annealing spun filaments are illustrated in Figures 10 and 11. Annealing causes the intensity of the meridional reflection at 8.2 Å to decrease and the equatorial peak corresponding to 4.13 Å to divide into two reflections. This behavior is best shown using equatorial diffractometer scans as illustrated in Figure 11.

Annealing also produces changes in the long-period spacings obtained from SAXS. The long periods are shown as a function of annealing temperature in Figure 12 for samples annealed 2 hr in air, water, or 20% formic acid.

Interpretation

The WAXS patterns of Figures 10 and 11 indicate a transformation from the pseudohexagonal form to a monoclinic structure. The equatorial 100 reflection of the pseudohexagonal structure appears to split into two peaks which can be indexed as 200 and the doublet 002,202 of the monoclinic γ form. The peak positions and thus the d-spacings and unit cell constants of this form appear to vary with the annealing treatment. The most completely transformed samples, those annealed 2 hr in 20% formic at 102°C, have d-spacings which correspond closely to the monoclinic α form of Holmes, Bunn, and Smith.[6] The less completely transformed samples appear to correspond to what Roldan and Kaufman[14] called "paracrystalline α form."

The apparent angular separation of the 200 and 022,202 doublet was determined from diffractometer traces and is plotted in Figure 13 as a function of

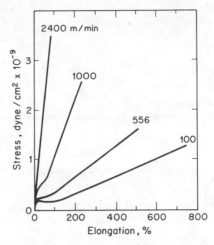

Fig. 14. Stress vs strain curves for as-spun nylon 6 fibers taken up at varying velocities.

annealing temperature and environment. This can be used as an indicator of the degree of transformation resulting from the annealing treatment. Clearly, the 20% formic acid solution is most effective in producing the transformation from the pseudohexagonal to the monoclinic α form. Of the three media investigated, the rate of transformation is slowest in air. For any of the three media, the rate of transformation increases with annealing temperature.

The reason for the difference in transformation rates in air, water, and 20% formic acid must involve the role of the medium in helping to temporarily break up hydrogen bonding; this presumably accommodates chain rearrangement, and the structure proceeds toward equilibrium more rapidly. Of the three media investigated, 20% formic acid is most effective in this regard, a point made clear by the fact that nylon 6 fibers dissolve in 90% formic acid, and this fluid may be used as a solvent for wet spinning.[30]

The long-period spacings were effected by both annealing temperature and environment. In general, samples which exhibited the greatest transformation to the α form also seemed to have the greatest long-period spacings. On annealing in air, the long-period spacing increased gradually with temperature. This behavior is similar to that observed for other polymer fibers such as polyethylene[55,56] and polypropylene,[57] but it seems to differ from the behavior of crystalline mats of aliphatic polyamides such as nylons 66, 610, and 612 grown from solution.[54]

MECHANICAL PROPERTIES

Results

Plots of engineering stress (force/initial cross-sectional area) as a function of elongation are shown in Figure 14 for fibers spun at different take-up velocities. The shapes of the "stress–strain" curves vary qualitatively as the take-up velocity or spinline stress changes. Increasing take-up rate results in an increasing tangent modulus, yield stress, and tensile strength, and decreasing elongation to break and natural draw ratio. The yield point seems even to disappear at high take-up velocities. In Figure 15, we plot the variation in tangent modulus, tensile strength, and elongation to break with take-up velocity.

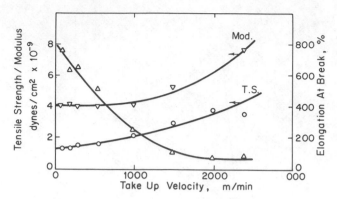

Fig. 15. Tangent modulus, tensile strength, and elongation to break as a function of take-up velocity.

Discussion

The variation of mechanical properties with spinning conditions results from variations in the morphology of the spun fibers. One of the major aspects of this morphology is the molecular orientation developed in the filament. In Figure 16, we plot the variations in the properties of Figure 15 with birefringence and with the c-axis crystalline (Hermans) orientation factor. Modulus and tensile strength increase with orientation and elongation to break decreases. The properties vary in a nonlinear way with either birefringence, which measures the average orientation in the sample, or with c-axis crystalline orientation factor. It is interesting that there is little change in modulus and tensile strength in the low orientation range, but these properties rise significantly at higher orientation levels. The behavior of the elongation to break appears just the opposite; its value seems more sensitive to orientation in the low orientation range. Either birefringence or c-axis crystalline orientation factor seems to give reasonable correlations of the mechanical properties. Similar correlations have been used by Abbott and White[37] and others[33-36,38] from our laboratories for polyethylene[33,36-38] and polypropylene.[34-36]

CONCLUSIONS

1. Nylon 6 filaments melt spun through ordinary air or air saturated with moisture do not crystallize in the spinline at take-up rates below 1500 m/min. The present experiments were inconclusive for filaments spun at higher rates.

2. Nylon 6 filaments "crystallize" on the take-up bobbin into a paracrystalline pseudohexagonal structure. The rate of "crystallization" and the orientation in the filaments increase with take-up velocity and take-up stress. Orientation factors may be defined and measured to interpret this latter behavior.

3. The oriented, conditioned fibers exhibit a broadened two-point SAXS pattern which suggests the existence of a poorly developed row structure.

4. Annealing treatment with hot water or formic acid solutions transforms the pseudohexagonal structure to monoclinic. The rate of transformation increases with temperature and is greatest in acid solutions.

5. The stress–strain curves for as-spun fibers show increasing modulus and tensile strength and decreasing elongation to break with increasing take-up velocity and stress.

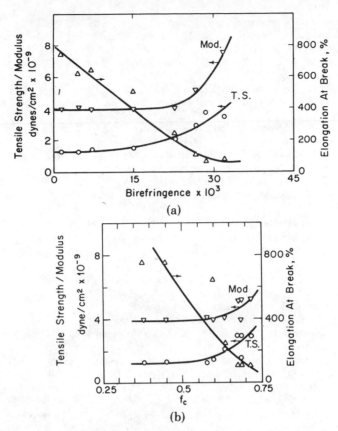

Fig. 16. Tangent modulus, tensile strength, and elongation to break as a function of (a) birefringence and (b) c-axis crystalline orientation factor f_c.

The authors would like to thank E. S. Clark, T. Ishibashi, M. Matsui, J. Parker, D. Prevorsek, and A. Rickards for helpful discussions on aspects of this research. This research was supported in part by the National Science Foundation.

References

1. W. Sbroli, in *Man-Made Fibers,* Vol. 2, H. Mark, S. Atlas, and E. Cernia, Eds., Wiley, New York, 1967.

2. W. H. Carothers and G. J. Berchet, *J. Amer. Chem. Soc.,* **52,** 5289 (1930).

3. W. H. Carothers and J. W. Hill, *J. Amer. Chem. Soc.,* **54,** 1566, 1579 (1932).

4. P. Schlack, Germ. Pat. 748,253 (1938); U.S. Pat. 2,241,321 (1941).

5. R. Brill, *Z. Phys. Chem.,* **B53,** 61 (1942).

6. D. R. Holmes, C. W. Bunn, and D. J. Smith, *J. Polym. Sci.,* **17,** 159 (1955).

7. S. Ueda and T. Kimura, *Chem. High Polym. Jpn.,* **15,** 243 (1958).

8. M. Tsuruda, H. Arimoto, and M. Ishibashi, *Chem. High Polym. Jpn.,* **15,** 619 (1958).

9. Y. Kinoshita, *Makromol. Chem.,* **33,** 1 (1959).

10. D. C. Vogelsong, *J. Polym. Sci.,* **1,** 1655 (1963).

11. K. Miyasaka and K. Ishikawa, *J. Polym. Sci. A-2,* **6,** 1317 (1968).

12. I. Sandeman and A. Keller, *J. Polym. Sci.,* **19,** 401 (1956).

13. A. Ziabicki and K. Kedzierska, *J. Appl. Polym. Sci.,* **2,** 14 (1959).

14. L. G. Roldan and H. S. Kaufman, *J. Polym. Sci., Polym. Lett. Ed.,* **B1** 603 (1963); L. G. Roldan, F. Rahl, and A. R. Patterson, *J. Polym. Sci.,* **C8,** 145 (1965).

15. J. Parker and P. H. Lindenmeyer, paper presented at the Fiber Society Meeting, Williamsburgh, Virginia, May 1974.

16. A. Ziabicki and K. Kedzierska, *J. Appl. Polym. Sci.,* **6,** 111 (1962).

17. I. Hamana, M. Matsui, and S. Kato, *Melliand Textilber.*, **4**, 382 (1969).

18. T. Ishibashi, K. Aoki, and T. Ishii, *J. Appl. Polym. Sci.*, **14**, 1597 (1970).

19. T. Ishibashi and T. Ishii, *J. Appl. Polym. Sci.*, **20**, 335 (1976).

20. W. M. Pasika, A. C. West, and E. L. Thurston, *J. Polym. Sci., Polym. Phys.*, **10**, 2313 (1972).

21. K. Sakaoku, N. Morosoff, and A. Peterlin, *J. Polym. Sci., Polym. Phys.*, **11**, 31 (1973).

22. A. Wasiak and A. Ziabicki, in *Fiber and Yarn Processing*, J. L. White, Ed., *Appl. Polym. Symp.*, **27**, 111 (1975).

23. H. Yumoto, *Bull. Chem. Soc. Jpn.*, **29**, 45 (1956).

24. H. Yumoto, *Bull. Chem. Soc. Jpn.*, **29**, 141 (1956).

25. H. Hattori, Y. Takagi, and T. Kawaguchi, *Bull. Chem. Soc. Jpn.*, **35**, 1163 (1962).

26. H. Hattori and Y. Takagi, *Bull. Chem. Soc. Jpn.*, **36**, 675 (1963).

27. T. Kitao, Ph.D. Dissertation, Kyoto University, 1975.

28. T. Kitao, H. Kobayoshi, S. Ikejami, and S. Ohya, *J. Polym. Sci., Polym. Chem.*, **11**, 2633 (1973).

29. T. Kiyotosukuri, H. Hasegawa, and R. Imamura, *Sen-i-Gakkaishi*, **26**, 399 (1970).

30. T. Hancock, J. E. Spruiell, and J. L. White, *J. Appl. Polym. Sci.*, **21**, 1227 (1977).

31. F. P. Chapell, M. F. Culpin, R. G. Gosden, and T. C. Tranter, *J. Appl. Chem.*, **14**, 12 (1964).

32. K. Katayama, T. Amano, and K. Nakamura, *Kolloid Z.-Z. Polym.*, **226**, 125 (1968).

33. J. R. Dees and J. E. Spruiell, *J. Appl. Polym. Sci.*, **18**, 1053 (1974).

34. H. Henson and J. E. Spruiell, unpublished research.

35. J. E. Spruiell and J. L. White, *Polym. Eng. Sci.*, **15**, 660 (1975).

36. J. E. Spruiell and J. L. White, in *Fiber and Yarn Processing*, J. L. White, Ed., *Appl. Poly. Symp.*, **27**, 121 (1975).

37. L. E. Abbott and J. L. White, in *U.S.–Japan Seminar on Polymer Processing and Rheology*, D. C. Bogue, M. Yamamoto, and J. L. White, Eds., *Appl. Polym. Symp.*, **20**, 247 (1973).

38. J. L. White, K. C. Dharod, and J. L. White, *J. Appl. Polym. Sci.*, **18**, 2539 (1974).

39. V. Bankar, J. E. Spruiell, and J. L. White, *J. Appl. Poly. Sci.*, **21**, 2135 (1977).

40. V. Bankar, Ph.D. Dissertation in Chemical Engineering, The University of Tennessee, Knoxville, 1976.

41. J. J. Hermans, P. H. Hermans, D. Vermaas, and A. Weidinger, *Rec. Trav. Chim.*, **65**, 427 (1946).

42. R. S. Stein, *J. Polym. Sci.*, **31**, 327 (1958).

43. Z. W. Wilchinsky, *J. Appl. Phys.*, **30**, 792 (1959); *ibid.*, **31**, 1969 (1960); *Advan. X-Ray Anal.*, **6**, 231 (1962).

44. T. Kitao, S. Ohya, J. Furukawa, and S. Yamashita, *J. Polym. Sci., Poly. Phys.*, **11**, 1091 (1973).

45. B. B. Burnett and W. F. McDevit, *J. Appl. Phys.*, **28**, 1101 (1957).

46. J. H. Magill, *Polymer*, **3**, 655 (1962).

47. L. Mandelkern, in *Growth and Perfection of Crystals*, R. H. Doremus, B. W. Roberts, and D. Turnbull, Eds., Wiley, New York, 1958, p. 478.

48. J. H. Griffith and B. G. Ranby, *J. Polym. Sci.*, **38**, 107 (1959).

49. A. Keller, and M. Machin, *J. Macromol. Sci.-Phys.*, **81**, 41 (1967).

50. P. H. Geil, *J. Polym. Sci.*, **44**, 449 (1960).

51. M. Ogawa, T. Ota, O. Yoshizaki, and E. Nagai, *Polym. Lett.*, **1**, 57 (1963).

52. J. L. Koenig and M. C. Agboatwala, *J. Macromol. Sci.*, **B2**, 391 (1968).

53. P. F. Dismore and W. O. Statton, *J. Polym. Sci.*, **C13**, 133 (1966).

54. P. Dreyfuss and A. Keller, *J. Macromol. Sci.*, **B4**(4), 811 (1970).

55. W. O. Statton and P. H. Geil, *J. Appl. Polym. Sci.*, **3**, 357 (1960).

56. R. Corneliussen and A. Peterlin, *Makromol. Chem.*, **105**, 193 (1967).

57. H. D. Noether and W. Whitney, *Kolloid Z.-Z. Polym.*, **251**, 991 (1973).

Received July 16, 1976

Kinetics of Epoxy Resin Polymerization Using Differential Scanning Calorimetry

P. PEYSER and W. D. BASCOM, *Naval Research Laboratory, Surface Chemistry Branch, Code 6170 Chemistry Division, Washington, D.C. 20375*

Synopsis

The kinetic parameters of the polymerization of diglycidyl ether of bisphenol A with hexahydrophthalic anhydride and benzyldimethylamine as catalyst were determined using differential scanning calorimetry. The reaction was found to be first order with some variation with temperature, and the activation energy and natural log of the frequency factor were 25 kcal/mole and ~25 sec^{-1}, respectively. These results are discussed with respect to a steady-state mechanism of the polymerization and compared with results reported for other epoxide–anhydride reactions.

INTRODUCTION

An earlier paper[1] reported a differential scanning calorimetry (DSC) determination of the kinetics of polymerization of diglycidyl ether bisphenol A (DGEBA) with "nadic" methyl anhydride (NMA) and benzyldimethylamine (BDMA) as catalyst. Data analyses for the activation energy, reaction order, and frequency factor were carried out using four computational methods. The results indicated a two-stage polymerization process: an initial relatively slow reaction which after about 12% completion was followed by a sharp increase in both rate and activation energy.

In this report, a study of the DGEBA–hexahydrophthalic anhydride (HHPA) polymerization kinetics with BDMA as catalyst is described. The two anhydrides, NMA and HHPA, are chemically similar except that HHPA is a solid at room temperature. Also the effect of amine concentration and exploratory work on the effect of a silica filler on the kinetics are reported.

Data analyses of the DSC results indicate that the kinetics of the DGEBA–HHPA system differs significantly from those of the NMA–DGEBA reaction despite the similarities of the two anhydrides. The analyses were performed using the previously described methods.[1] In addition, new methods are presented for data analysis of the effect of variation in frequency factor and for determining the reaction order from isothermal DSC experiments.

EXPERIMENTAL

The procedures used in this study were essentially the same as those previously described.[1] The DGEBA (diglycidylether bisphenol A, DER 332, Dow Chemical Co., epoxy equiv. = 175) and HHPA (hexahydrophthalic anhydride, Matheson,

2359

Coleman and Bell, mp 35–36°C) were used as received. Prior to mixing, the reactants were melted at ~50°C. A white, insoluble precipitate of unknown composition settled out of the liquid HHPA and was separated by decantation. Test DSC samples were prepared by mixing equivalents of epoxide and anhydride and stirring at slightly above ambient (~25°C) temperature for 10 min to give a clear, slightly yellowish solution. The BDMA (benzyldimethylamine, 98%, Eastman Organic Chemicals) was then added from a microsyringe to the solution and stirring was continued for another 15 min. At this point, the solution became yellow-brown in color. Ten to 40 mg was transferred to aluminum micropans, covered, and placed in a Perkin-Elmer DSC-2. The instrument had been preset at 315°K. After 10 min at 315°K, the sample was either heated to 500°K at 0.3125°K/min or 1.25°K/min (dynamic tests) or rapidly heated (320°K/min) up to a predetermined temperature (isothermal tests). Difficulties encountered earlier[1] with condensate forming on the pan covers were not evident here. The DSC output (change in heat content per unit time, dH/dt) was digitally recorded along with the temperature and time elapsed using a Digitem Model DAS-1A data logger. The experimental output was corrected for instrumental baseline shift by a point-by-point subtraction of the output for two empty pans run against each other. A computer program was used to smooth the data, to connect the initial and final baselines by an iterative process (in which it was assumed the baseline changed in proportion to the fraction reacted), and to analyze the data according to the various DSC kinetic equations described in the next section. The baseline for the isothermal data was established by back extrapolating the final data points which after the reaction was completed were essentially constant with time.

The silica filler (Cabosil, Cabot Corp.) had a nominal surface area (BET) of 150–200 m^2/g. The powder was heated overnight in a muffle oven at 500–720°C to remove physically (H-bonded) adsorbed water and probably some chemically absorbed water as well.[2] After cooling, weighed portions of the silica were added to the epoxy–anhydride–catalyst mixture. To assure realistic comparison, DSC runs were conducted on unfilled samples of the same epoxy mixture used to prepare the silica filled samples.

DATA ANALYSIS

The mathematical methods of obtaining kinetic information from thermogravimatric analysis (TGA) are applicable to DSC data. Except when noted, the methods described here are discussed in the review on TGA analysis by Flynn and Wall.[3] In using these analyses, it is assumed that the reactions can be described by a simple nth order, Arrhenius-type temperature dependence. Such an assumption is not usually justified for complex plymerizations, especially in the latter stages of reaction. However, in the system studied here, the reaction appears to follow simple Arrhenius kinetics through at least 75% completion (see Fig. 1).

Dynamic Studies

The assumption is made that the extent of reaction is proportional to the heat evolved, so that the Arrhenius equation becomes

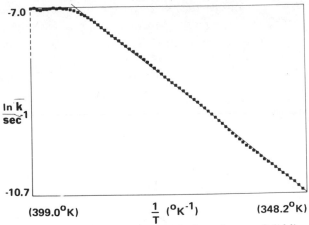

$$\frac{\ln k}{\sec^{-1}}$$

(399.0°K) $\frac{1}{T}$ (°K⁻¹)   (348.2°K)

Fig. 1.   Equation (1b) plot of DSC data for a single dynamic run.   Solid line is least-squares fit.

$$\frac{1}{H_T}\frac{dH}{dt} = Ae^{-E_a/RT}f\left(\frac{H}{H_T}\right) = Ae^{-E_a/RT}\left(\frac{H_T - H}{H_T}\right)^n \qquad (1a)$$

or, in the more useful logarithmic form,

$$\ln\frac{dH}{dt}\frac{1}{H_T} - n\ln\frac{H_r}{H_T} = -\frac{E_a}{RT} + \ln A \equiv \ln k \qquad (1b)$$

where H_T = total heat of reaction (cal/g) $\sim$ area under DSC curve; $H_r = H_T - H$; H = heat of reaction at a given time and temperature $\sim$ partial area under curve; E_a = Arrhenius activation energy (kcal/mole); A = Arrhenius equation frequency factor; n = order of reaction; R = gas constant; T = temperature (°K); and $f(H/H_T)$ = a function of H_T which is assumed here to be $(H_r/H_T)^n$. If the reaction order n is either known or assumed, then a plot of $\ln k$, i.e., LHS of eq. (1b), against $1/T$ gives a straight line of slope E_a and intercept $\ln A$.

DSC data can be treated using alternate forms of eq. (1) evaluated at variable heating rate but under conditions of constant temperature or constant fraction reacted. In so doing, expressions are obtained which can be used to establish the uniqueness of the kinetic parameters which were obtained from applying eq. (1) to data for a single heating rate. In the remainder of this section, various of these relationships are described, but a more complete discussion can be found in references 1 and 3.

The maximum point of a DSC curve, dH/dt versus T, can be used to obtain the ratio E_a/n from the expression

$$\frac{E_a}{n} = \left[\left(\frac{RT^2}{(H_T - H)\beta}\right)\frac{dH}{dt}\right]_{(dH/dt)\text{max}} \qquad (2)$$

where β is the heating rate. The reaction order n can be obtained independently using

$$(1 - \alpha)_{\text{max}} = e^{-r_2} \qquad n = 1 \qquad (3a)$$

$$(1 - \alpha)_{\text{max}} = \left[\left(\frac{1 - n}{n}\right)r_2 + 1\right]^{1/(n-1)} \qquad n \neq 1 \qquad (3b)$$

where $\alpha = H/H_T$ (fraction reacted) and r_2 is a second-order correction derived from a series solution of the integral form of the rate equation. The term r_2 approaches 1 as E_a/RT approaches infinity. Values of r_2 as a function of E_a/RT can be obtained from Table I of reference 3.

The Freeman-Carroll (FC) methods of analysis[3,4] permit the simultaneous determination of both activation energy and reaction order, and the form of the FC equation used here was

$$\frac{\Delta \ln dH/dt}{\Delta \ln H_r} = \frac{(E_a/R) \, \Delta \, 1/T}{\Delta \ln H_r} + n. \tag{4}$$

The activation energy can be obtained by comparison at equal fraction reacted of two DSC scans at different heating rates, i.e.,

$$\left(\frac{\Delta \ln \dfrac{dH}{dt} \dfrac{1}{H_T}}{\Delta \, 1/T} \right)_\alpha = -\frac{E}{R} \tag{5a}$$

Assuming that the fraction reacted is the same at the maximum point of DSC curves regardless of the heating rate, then, from (2) and (5a),

$$\left(\frac{\Delta \ln (\beta/T^2)}{\Delta \, 1/T} \right) = -\frac{E_a}{R} \tag{5b}$$

Equations (5a) and (5b) are valid only if the frequency factor A is constant for the different DSC runs. (In the study of reference 1, it was incorrectly assumed that (5b) is valid even if A changed between runs. This error did not affect the conclusions reported.) A more general form of (5a) is

$$\left(\frac{\Delta \ln \dfrac{dH}{dt} \dfrac{1}{H_T}}{\Delta \, 1/T} \right)_\alpha = -\frac{E_a}{R} + \frac{\Delta \ln A}{\Delta \, 1/T} \tag{6a}$$

and, if evaluated at the maximum point,

$$\left(\frac{\Delta \ln (\beta/T^2)}{\Delta \, 1/T} \right) = -\frac{E_a}{R} + \frac{\Delta \ln A}{\Delta \, 1/T} \tag{6b}$$

A similar formalism can be derived for two runs of different heating rates compared at the same temperature. In general form,

$$n_a \equiv \left(\frac{\Delta \ln d\alpha/dt}{\Delta \ln (1 - \alpha)} \right)_T = n + \left(\frac{\Delta \ln A}{\Delta \ln (1 - \alpha)} \right)_T \tag{7}$$

where n_a is the apparent reaction order. All of these expressions, (6a), (6b), and (7), can be derived from (1b) by subtracting one run from another at constant α or T. A plot of the LHS of (7) against $1/\Delta \ln (1 - \alpha)$ gives a straight line of slope $\Delta \ln A$ and intercept n. Use of eq. (7) gives more accurate results than (6a) or (6b) since the variable in the latter, $\Delta(1/T)$, is nearly constant at constant α. However, if $\Delta \ln A$ is known independently, then (6b) is a convenient means for computing the activation energy.

Isothermal Studies

Difficulties in analysis of isothermal DSC runs arise because of uncertainties in the initial 10% of the scan as the sample is rapidly heated to the test temperature. Consequently, the total heat evolution, H_T, is not known with sufficient accuracy. On the other hand, H_r, the heat evolution from any time after the initial equilibration to the end of the reaction $(H_T - H)$, can be determined accurately. Equation (1b) can be transformed to

$$\ln \left(\frac{1}{H_T}\frac{dH}{dt}\right) = n \ln \left(\frac{H_T - H}{H_T}\right) + \ln k \qquad (8)$$

so that a linear plot of $\ln (dH/dt)$ versus $\ln H_r$ will have a slope of n and an intercept of $\ln k + (1 - n) \ln H_T$. Note that H_T need not be known to determine n. On the other hand, if H_T is known or can be reasonably estimated and $\ln A$ does not change between runs, then a plot of $\ln k$ versus $1/T$ for runs at different isothermal temperatures gives the activation energy. The linearity of the plot of eq. (8) provides a test of whether the reaction is following simple, eq. (1), isothermal kinetics.

RESULTS

The reaction conditions for the DSC experiments are given in Table I along with the heats of reaction. The values of the latter were reasonably constant despite the variation in sample size, heating rate, amine concentration, etc.

Data analysis using eq. (1b) is illustrated by the plot in Figure 1 for experiment A. The solid line represents the least-squares fit to that portion of the data used for analysis. This plot is typical of the results obtained and indicates the accu-

TABLE I
Sample Parameters

Experi- ment	Heating rate, °K/min	BDMA, ml/g[a]	Sample weight, mg	Weight fraction of Cabosil	Heat of reaction, cal/g
		Dynamic experiments			
A	0.3125	0.00338	47.33	—	83.7
B	0.3125	0.00338	31.91	—	77.3
C	1.25	0.00338	15.04	—	82.5
D[b]	1.25	0.00338	17.01	—	~71.2
E[b]	1.25	0.00338	32.76	0.05	~87.1
F[b]	1.25	0.00338	21.64	—	80.5
G[b]	1.25	0.00338	28.09	0.06	85.2
H	0.3125	0.00166	29.01	—	87.4
I	0.3125	0.00076	19.66	—	85.7
	Temp., °K	Isothermal experiments			
J	400	0.00338	33.05	—	~78.2
K	415	0.00338	26.57	—	~84.1
L	430	0.00338	33.49	—	~75.9

[a] ml BDMA/g of (DER + HHPA).
[b] D and E are pairs and F and E are pairs. Pairs were from the same sample and were scanned in close proximity, timewise.

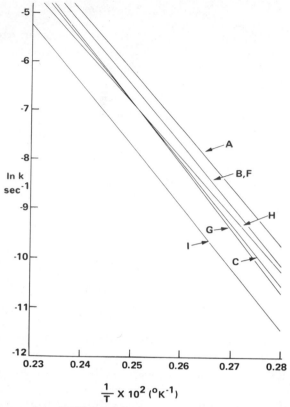

Fig. 2. Least-squares plots of DSC dynamic run data. See Table I for sample composition and Table II for kinetic parameters derived from these plots.

racy of the least-squares fit. In this plot and all other computations using eq. (1b), it was assumed that n was unity.

The effects of amine concentration and heating rate on the reaction rate are shown in Figure 2 by least-squares plots of eq. (1b). Note that the lines are reasonably parallel indicating that the activation energy was more or less constant. However, the lines did not superimpose on each other, even when the amine contents and the heating rates of the experiments were the same, e.g., experiments A and B. Inspection of eq. (1b) suggests that differences in the frequency factor could cause the plots to be parallel but shifted along the ln k axis.

The values of E_a and ln A obtained from the least-squares plots of the data fitted to eq. (1b) are listed in Table II along with the least-squares regression coefficient, and the range of fraction reacted over which the data were linear for each experiment. The ln A values obtained by extrapolation to $1/T = 0$ are only approximate since slight variations in line slope well within experimental precision would severely affect the long extrapolation. For example, compare experiments A and I which gave the same values of ln A, yet in Figure 2 are considerably displaced from each other.

The results of data analysis from the maximum points of the DSC curves are listed in Table III. The E_a/n values were obtained using eq. (2) and the n values in the fifth column from eqs. (3a) and (3b). These latter results are probably inaccurate since the maxima of the DSC curves were rather broad as evidenced (Table III) by the range in temperature and fraction reacted near the maximum points. A somewhat more accurate estimate of n was made using the values for E_a in Table II and E_a/n in Table III, and the results are listed in column six of Table III.

The reaction order was determined directly using eq. (7) which compares the fraction reacted for two DSC scans at fixed temperature. The equation is simplified if the frequency factor is constant between the two runs. This appears to be the case for experiments B and F, since their least-squares plots in Figure 1 are quite close. In Table IV, the values of n calculated for this pair of experiments are given along with the temperatures at which they were compared and the corresponding fraction reacted. The results indicate first-order kinetics in agreement with the other analyses (Table III).

Comparison of other pairs of DSC scans required the use of the full form of eq. (7) since $\Delta \ln A$ could not be assumed to be zero. In Figures 3 and 4, linear plots of eq. (7) for various pairs of experiments are seen to intercept the axis at $n = 1$. The slope of these plots gives $\Delta \ln A$ for each pair of experiments and the values obtained were equal to the separation along the ordinate axis of the parallel lines of Figure 3. The $\Delta \ln A$ values did not correlate with the $\ln A$ values of Table II because of the large extrapolation error mentioned earlier. Not all experimental pairs gave linear plots of eq. (7), e.g., experiments I and H in Figure 3. These two runs had a greater difference in slope in the eq. (1b) plots of Figure 3 than the other pairs, indicating an experimental difference in E_a, and the derivation of eq. (7) assumes that the E_a values of the two experiments are not significantly different.

The value of $\Delta \ln A$ obtained in comparing experiments A and C (Fig. 4) was used to compute E_a from eq. (6b), and the results listed in Table V agree with. the results in Tables II and III.

The Freeman-Carroll, eq. (4), results for E_a and n are given in Table VI and are essentially identical to those obtained by the other analysis methods. Note in Table VI that the ratio E_a/n is more nearly constant for the different experiments than either of the parameters alone. This difference arises because errors in the slope of these plots tend to change E_a and n in the same direction.

Usually, the dynamic runs gave no indication of a change in reaction rate at

TABLE II
Data Analysis Using Equation (1b)[a]

Experiment	Activation energy, kcal/mole	$\ln A$, sec^{-1}	Range of linearity (fraction reacted)	Regression coefficient
A	23.8	23.8	0.004–0.86	0.9999
B	24.3	24.1	0.010–0.92	0.9997
C	25.0	24.6	0.030–0.98	0.9990
D	~27.1	~27.4	0.015–0.75	0.9990
E	~25.8	~25.8	0.12–0.72	0.9992
F	24.5	24.3	0.12–0.80	0.9997
G	25.9	25.8	0.018–0.75	0.9980
H	22.8	21.9	0.080–0.94	0.9992
I	24.9	23.6	0.045–0.79	0.9996
Average	24.9 ± 1.26			

[a] Assume $n = 1$.

the start of the reaction. However, for experiment I (Fig. 5), where the amine concentration was the lowest and the reaction rate was the slowest, a slight indication of a change in reaction rate at very low values of α was found. Clear indications of an increase in reaction rate at the start of the reactions was found for the isothermal runs, as can be seen from Figure 6 in which the reaction rate is plotted versus $\ln H_r$, eq. (8). (Note that time increases from right to left in Figure 6.)

The isothermal data can be used to compute $\ln k$ from eq. (8) if it can be assumed that H_T can be determined accurately and $\ln A$ is constant. Since the range of isothermal temperatures was chosen not to be so high that the beginning of the reaction was obscured nor so low that the reaction could not go to completion, it is likely that the total heat of reaction, H_T, can be reasonably estimated from the isothermal scan results. As for $\ln A$, the samples used for the isothermal runs were taken from a single batch of reactant mixture. This procedure differs from that of the dynamic scan experiments where a new batch was mixed each time to avoid any possible aging effects. This problem was less severe for the isothermal experiments since the runs took much less time than the dynamic scans. It is judged that the variation in $\ln A$ in the dynamic experiments was due to using different reactant batches; and, if so, $\ln A$ may have been relatively constant for the three isothermal runs.

The values of $\ln k$ obtained using eq. (8) were plotted against $1/T$ as in Figure 7. Initially, the reaction order n in eq. (8) was assumed to be 1, but the slope E_a obtained from the Arrhenius plot gave an anomalously low value of ~14 kcal/mole, significantly less than the 25 kcal/mole from the dynamic experiments. On the other hand, when the experimental values of n (Fig. 6) were used to compute $\ln k$, the Arrhenius plot (Fig. 7) gave $E_a = 21$ kcal/mole, quite consistent with the dynamic results.

TABLE III
Data Analysis Using Equations (2), (3a), and (3b)

Experiment	Maximum temp., °K	Fraction reacted at max.	E_a/n, kcal/mole[a]	n (3a + 3b)	n[b]
A	378.5–381.0	0.56–0.64	23.1	1.28–0.85	1.03
B	383.3–386.0	0.58–0.67	25.4	1.16–0.73	0.96
C	402.0–404.0	0.56–0.62	23.4	1.28–0.95	1.07
I	386.6–389.7	0.59–0.68	24.1	1.10–0.69	0.95
J	398.0–401.0	0.59–0.68	25.4	1.10–0.69	0.98

[a] Calculated from the midpoint of the maximum temperature range.
[b] Calculated from E_a/n (column 4) and E_a of Table II.

TABLE IV
Equation (7) Applied to Experiments B and F ($\Delta \ln A = 0$)

$(1-\alpha)_F$	$(1-\alpha)_B$	T, °K	n
0.798	0.406	383.5	1.04
0.704	0.247	388.5	0.99
0.584	0.117	383.4	1.00
0.407	0.033	399.6	1.12

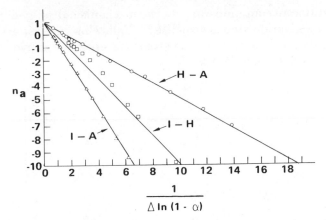

Fig. 3.   Comparison of pairs of DSC dynamic runs at constant temperature using eq. (7).

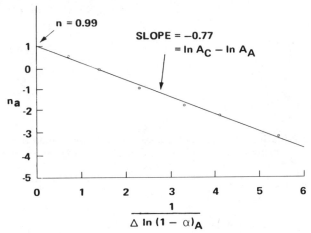

Fig. 4.   Comparison of DSC dynamic runs A and C at constant temperature using eq. (7).

There was no discernible effect of adding silica filler to the reaction mixture (compare experiments D with E and F with G in Tables II and VI), and the matter was not pursued further.

DISCUSSION

The mechanisms of epoxy–anhydride polymerizations in the presence of a tertiary amine catalyst are unquestionably complex and by no means fully understood. However, there is more-or-less general agreement that a cocatalyst is involved such as water, alcohols, phenols, or other H-bonding agents present as contaminants in the reactants. Thus, Tanaka et al.[5,6] propose a catalyst activation step

$$R_3N + HA \underset{k_2}{\overset{k_1}{\rightleftharpoons}} [R_3N \ldots HA] \tag{a}$$
$$C_A \qquad C_{HA} \qquad \qquad C_E$$

to form an initiator. Tanaka and Kakiuchi[6] suggest the formation of α,β-unsaturated alcohols as cocatalysts by the action of the tertiary amine on the epoxide, in addition to contaminants. In the mechanism proposed by Feltzin et al.,[7] a similar activation step is visualized. Following catalyst activation, the complex is believed to associate with either the epoxy or anhydride as in the mechanism of Tanaka and Kakiuchi:[8]

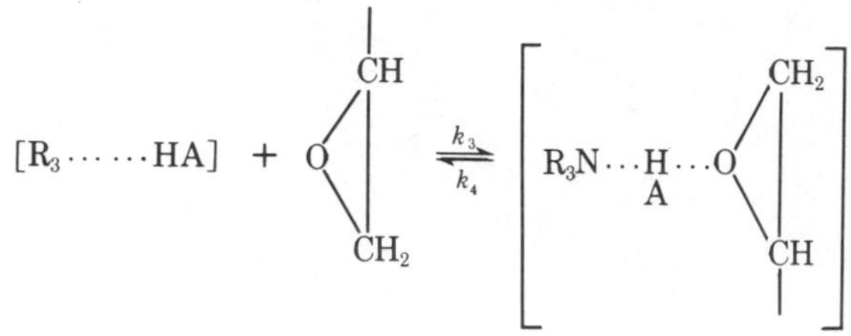

(b)

$$C_E \qquad C_B \qquad C_C$$

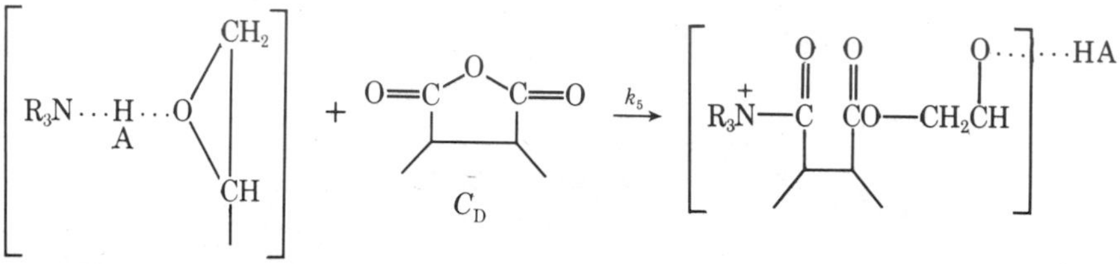

(c)

$$C_C \qquad\qquad C_D$$

TABLE V
Determination of Activation Energy from Experiments A and C
using Equation (6b) and $\Delta \ln A$ from Figure 5

α	E_a/R uncorrected	E_a/R corrected	E_a, kcal/mole
0.1	7.36×10^3	12.35×10^3	24.5
0.2	7.84×10^3	12.71×10^3	25.3
0.3	8.20×10^3	13.08×10^3	26.0
0.4	8.31×10^3	13.25×10^3	26.3
0.5	8.33×10^3	13.29×10^3	26.4
0.6	8.41×10^3	13.40×10^3	26.6
0.7	8.39×10^3	13.40×10^3	26.6
0.8	8.43×10^3	13.45×10^3	26.7
		Average	26.0 ± 0.77

TABLE VI
Freeman-Carroll Method

Experiment	Activation energy E_a, kcal/mole	n	E_a/n	Range of α	Regression coefficient
A	26.2	1.18	22.2	0.10–0.86	0.997
B	25.4	1.18	21.5	0.04–0.97	0.954
C	25.3	1.20	21.1	0.03–0.98	0.954
F	25.0	1.09	23.0	0.12–0.83	0.999
G	26.3	1.11	23.8	0.13–0.75	0.997
H	21.9	0.96	22.8	0.13–0.94	0.981
I	27.2	1.29	21.0	0.07–0.57	0.979
	Average	1.14 ± 0.10	22.2 ± 2.2		

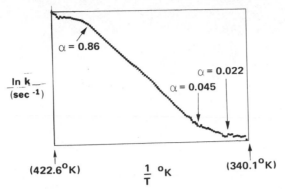

Fig. 5. DSC dynamic data plot of eq. (1b) for a sample with low amine concentration (experiment I).

which is modified here to meet the more recent conclusion[5,6] that the attack of the activated complex is on the epoxide rather than the anhydride. They assume a steady-state condition such that $dC_E/dT = dC_C/dT = 0$ and obtained the rate equation

$$\nu = \frac{dC_B}{dt} - \frac{k_1k_3k_5C_AC_BC_DC_{HA}}{k_2k_4 + k_2k_5C_D + k_3k_5C_BC_D}$$

Depending upon which of the reaction steps is rate determining, a variety of kinetics are possible. If the formation of activated complex is slow (k_5 and $k_3 \gg k_2, k_4$), then

$$\nu = k_1C_AC_{HA}$$

and the reaction rate is dependent only on the catalyst (and cocatalyst) concentration. Feltzin et al.[7] found this to be the case in their study of the DGEBA/NMA/BDMA system. On the other hand, if reactions of type b are controlling ($k_3, k_4 \ll k_2$), then

$$\nu = -\frac{k_1k_3}{k_2} C_AC_{HA}C_D$$

and the rate is first order with respect to epoxy concentration, as was found here and for the initial stages of the DGEBA/NMA/BDMA system. Tanaka and Kakiuchi found second-order kinetics[8] for a variety of epoxy–anhydride systems and suggested that reactions of type C were rate controlling ($k_1 > k_2, k_3, k_4 > k_5$) so that

$$\nu = -\frac{k_1k_3k_5}{k_2k_4} C_AC_BC_DC_{HA}$$

The monomer–time consumption curves for epoxy/anhydride/amine reactions have been generally found to be sigmoidal in shape, indicating an accelerating reaction over as much as 50% of the reaction time.[8] The curves of Feltzin et al.[7] for the DGEBA/NMA/BDMA indicate an initial accelerating stage, as do those of Fava[9] for the DGEBA/HHPA system catalyzed with tris-2,4,6-dimethylaminomethylphenol. An early accelerating stage was observed here in the first 5–10 min of the isothermal experiments (Fig. 7) and in the dynamic scan at low amine

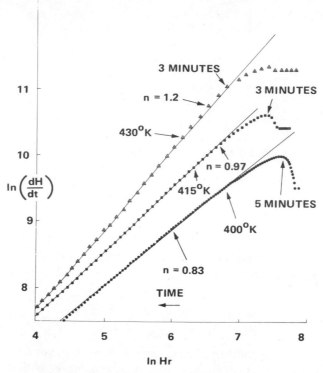

Fig. 6.   DSC isothermal data plots of eq. (8).

concentration.   Quite possibly, this initial stage represents an induction period in which the reaction is reaching the steady-state condition.   Evidently, the induction period for the DGEBA/HHPA/BDMA system is so short as to be undetectable in dynamic DSC experiments if the catalyst concentration is sufficiently high.   In support of this argument, the consumption–time curves given by Tanaka and Kakiuchi[8] for epoxy–anhydride reactions catalyzed by BDMA indicate that the induction periods were much shorter than for reactions with most other catalysts.

In view of the complexity of the epoxy–anhydride polymerization, it is not surprising that studies of the reaction kinetics have such a diversity in the observed kinetic parameters.   Some of the results to be found in the literature are listed in Table VII.   The reaction orders of 0, 1, and 2 predicted by the steady-state kinetics are reported along with activation energies of 12–38 kcal/mole.   In two instances, the rate-controlling step was found to change during the course of the reaction.   Tanaka and Kakiuchi[8] found that the reactions in nonaqueous media of substituted phenyldiglycidyl ethers with HHPA catalyzed by t-butylamine were initially controlled by reaction step b and that the rate increased (autocatalysis) with the buildup of such specie as C_C until the formation of the activated complex, reaction a, became rate controlling.   Peyser and Bascom[1] found the kinetics of the DGEBA/NMA/BDMA system to be initially first order and persumably controlled by type b reactions, but then to exhibit second-order kinetics indicating control by type c reactions.   Actually, the process probably becomes diffusion controlled since a large increase in activation energy accompanied the change in reaction order.   This change to diffusion control did not

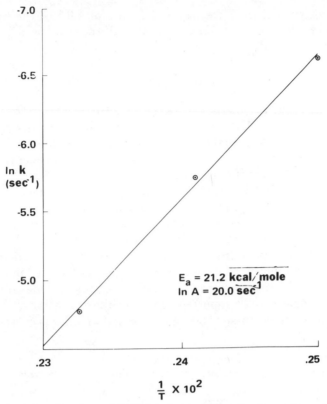

E_a = 21.2 kcal/mole
ln A = 20.0 sec⁻¹

Fig. 7. Arrhenius plot of isothermal DSC data but including the change in reaction order with temperature.

occur for the HHPA-cured system possibly because of the smaller molecular size compared to NMA. Measurements of molecular models indicate the rotational volume swept by the NMA to be 75% greater than for the HHPA.

In view of the important role of cocatalysts in the reaction mechanism, it is quite likely that contaminants such as water or low molecular weight acids and bases can decisively affect the reaction kinetics. This problem is especially acute when studying industrial-grade materials which are difficult to impossible to adequately purify. A case in point is the NMA curing agent which is available only as a technical-grade material, and this may explain the very different results obtained by Feltzin et al.[7] compared to Peyser and Bascom[1] in their studies of the DGEBA/NMA/BDMA polymerization (Table VII).

Part of the discrepancy in the activation energies of Table VII may lie in the indiscriminate use of Arrhenius plots. As was previously mentioned in connection with the isothermal experiments, a small systematic change in the reaction order with temperature has a large effect on the slope of $\ln k$-versus-$1/T$ plots. Also, the dynamic experiment results are affected by a change in n with T although to a lesser degree than the isothermal results. The computations listed in Table VIII show that a change of n in the range of 1.0 to 1.5 does not detectably affect the linearity of the dynamic $\ln k$-versus-$1/T$ plots or the ratio E_a/n. There is, however, a variation in E_a due to the $n(\ln H_r)$, i.e., $(1 - \alpha)^n$, term in eq. (1b). This term has a relatively small effect in the early stages of the reaction ($\alpha < 0.5$); and for this reason, the variation in n has a less severe effect on the dynamic results than on the isothermal results. Ideally, the variation of n with T could be determined from the isothermal study and used as a correction for the dynamic scan data.

SUMMARY

The kinetics of the polymerization of the DGEBA/HMPA/NMA system were determined using DSC. The results of both dynamic and isothermal scans were subject to extensive data analysis. The dynamic experiments indicated the reaction to be approximately first order and the activation energy and natural log of the frequency factor found to be 25 kcal/mole and $\sim$25 sec^{-1}, respectively. The isothermal results indicated first-order kinetics with some variation with temperature and an activation energy of 22 kcal/mole.

These results are consistent with the generally accepted steady-state mechanism of the epoxide–anhydride polymerization reaction. Actually, this reaction mechanism predicts zero-, first-, and second-order kinetics depending on the experimental conditions; and inspection of the results reported in the literature indicates that all three have been observed for various epoxide–anhydride systems. Discrepancies in the reported values for the activation energies may be partly due to incorrectly assuming that the reaction order is constant.

TABLE VII

Kinetic Parameters Obtained for Various Epoxy Resin Polymerizations

Anhydride	Epoxide	Catalyst	Reaction order n	E_a, kcal/mole	ln A, sec^{-1}	Reference
HHPA	DGEBA	BDMA	$\sim$1	25	27	this work
HHPA	cyclo-aliphatic	BDMA–ethylene glycol	—	12.2	—	9
HHPA	DGEBA	DMAMP[a]	—	17.8	—	8
HHPA	PGE[b]	t-butylamine	1 (initial)[c]	13.6–14.8	9.1–9.9	5
			0 (maximum)[c]	17.6–12.9	9.1–9.5	
NMA	DGEBA	BDMA	0[d]	13.2	16.5	6
NMA	DGEBA	BDMA	1 (initial)	15	10.5–11.1	1
			2 (final)	38	38.0–46.1	

[a] Tris-2,4,6-dimethylaminemethylphenol.

[b] Substituted phenyldiglycidyl ethers.

[c] Initial stage, second order with respect to epoxide and amine catalyst; at maximum rate, first order with respect to catalyst.

[d] First order with respect to catalyst.

TABLE VIII

Effect of Varying n on E_a and ln A Calculated from Equation (1b)[a]

Assumed n	E_a, kcal/mole	E_a/n	ln A	Regression coefficient
2	39.6	19.8	46.0	0.972
1.5	30.7	20.5	33.5	0.994
1.4	28.9	20.6	31.0	0.996
1.3	27.1	20.9	28.4	0.997
1.25	26.2	21.0	27.2	0.998 (max)
1.2	25.3	21.1	25.9	0.997
1.1	23.5	21.4	23.4	0.993
1.0	21.8	21.8	20.9	0.985

[a] Data taken from experiment A in the α = 0.03 to 0.97 range.

References

1. P. Peyser and W. D. Bascom, in *Analytical Chemistry,* Vol. 3, R. S. Porter and J. F. Johnson, Eds., Plenum Press, New York, 1974, p. 537.

2. W. D. Bascom, *J. Phys. Chem.,* **76,** 3188 (1972).

3. J. H. Flynn and L. A. Wall, *J. Res. Natl. Bur. Stand.,* **70A,** 487 (1966).

4. E. S. Freeman and B. Carroll, *J. Phys. Chem.,* **62,** 394 (1958).

5. Y. Tanaka and T. F. Mika, in *Epoxy Resins,* C. A. May and Y. Tanaka, Eds., Marcel Dekker, New York, 1973, Chap. 3, p. 135.

6. Y. Tanaka and J. Kakiuchi, *J. Macromol. Chem.,* **1,** 307 (1966).

7. A. Feltzin, M. K. Barsh, E. J. Peer, and I. Petker, *Macromol. Sci.,* **A3,** 261 (1969).

8. Y. Tanaka and H. Kakiuchi, *J. Polym. Sci.,* **A2,** 3405 (1964).

9. R. A. Fava, *Polymer* (London), **9,** 137 (1968).

10. P. G. Babayevsky and J. K. Gillham, *J. Appl. Polym. Sci.,* **17,** 6067 (1973).

Received May 21, 1976
Revised July 30, 1976

JOURNAL OF APPLIED POLYMER SCIENCE   VOL. 21, 2375–2392 (1977)

Use of Auger and X-Ray Photoelectron Spectroscopy to Study the Locus of Failure of Structural Adhesive Joints

M. GETTINGS, *Materials Development Division, AERE Harwell, Oxfordshire, England,* and F. S. BAKER and A. J. KINLOCH, *Ministry of Defence, ERDE, Waltham Abbey, Essex, England*

Synopsis

The techniques of Auger electron spectroscopy (AES) and x-ray photoelectron spectroscopy (XPS) have been used to study the locus of failure of epoxy resin joints. The effects of a long water immersion and the application of a silane-based primer have also been studied. Results indicated that for dry joints fracture occurred near an epoxy resin/metal interface while with water-soaked unprimed joints, fracture occurred interfacially between the adhesive and iron oxide. The application of the primer to the metal surface prior to bonding prevented the formation of a water-formed oxide although fracture was then found to occur through the primer.

INTRODUCTION

Epoxide resin-based structural adhesives cure to form thermosetting rigid polymers and are extensively used for joining metals, plastics, carbon- and glass-reinforced composites, etc., in many diverse industries. However, a serious limitation frequently encountered in the use of structural adhesives is the deleterious effect which moisture has upon the strength of a bonded component, especially when the component is also subjected to conditions of relatively high stress and temperature.[1,2] Unfortunately, the fundamental mechanisms leading to this loss of strength have not, as yet, been completely elucidated; correlations between accelerated and outdoor weathering tests are poor, and predictions of the stability of joints exposed to hostile environments are correspondingly unreliable. Consequently, the logical selection of materials and techniques to avoid joint failure has been severely restricted.

A major consideration in identifying the mechanics and kinetics of adhesive joint failure is the locus of fracture, i.e., whether the joint failed by cohesive fracture of the adhesive or the substrate, interfacially between the adhesive–substrate interface (it has been argued that true interfacial failure can never occur[3]), or a complex mixture of these possible failure paths. The poor durability of adhesive joints has been ascribed to (a) stress hydrolysis of covalent bonds in a boundary layer of adhesive close to the interface,[4] (b) hydration of the oxide surface, invariably present on most metallic substrates, which then is mechanically weak and causes premature joint failure,[5] or (c) the displacement of the

2375

adhesive on the substrate surface by water resulting in interfacial failure.[6,7]

In spite of the lack of fundamental knowledge concerning the mechanisms of environmental failure, it has been established empirically that the use of silane-based primers at the adhesive–substrate interface may lead to considerable increases in joint durability. It is sufficient to note here that the most common type of silane primers employed have the general structure $X_3Si(CH_2)_n Y$, where $n = 0$ to 3, X is a hydrolyzable group on silicon, and Y is an organofunctional group selected for compatibility with a given adhesive. The generally, but not universally, accepted mechanism by which the durability of the joint is increased is the formation of strong, covalent interfacial bonds. For the substrate–silane interface, this arises from the formation of $\equiv$Si—0—substrate bonds; and for the adhesive–silane interface, from the reaction of the Y group on the silane with reactive groups in the adhesive. However, other features, such as wetting[8] and the possible formation of a boundary layer in the adhesive, differing in chemical and physical properties to that of the bulk resin, must be considered.[9] Experimentally, silane primer films have been found[10] to be polymeric, composed of a strongly held polysiloxane network along with some hydrolyzed or partially hydrolyzed silane and small polysiloxane molecules.

The aim of the present study is to use Auger electron spectroscopy (AES)[11,12] and x-ray photoelectron spectroscopy (XPS)[13] to identify the modes of failure for joints consisting of mild steel substrates bonded with an epoxide adhesive. The effects of water immersion and the use of a silane-based primer on the joints will be described.

AES and XPS are particularly suited for examining fractured adhesive joints as both are surface techniques sampling to a depth not With XPS, chemical information can be derived by studying the shift in binding energy of an atom bound near the surface from that expected for a neutral atom. The far more complex nature of the Auger process does not, in general, lend itself so easily to such interpretation.

The two techniques are, in many ways, complementary. In Auger electron spectroscopy, Auger electrons are excited from surface atoms with a small-diameter electron beam ($1–50\ \mu$), thereby giving good spatial resolution. In this work, a $30–\mu m$ diameter beam is used, but useful spectra have been obtained with probes 0.3 μm in diameter.[13] Since XPS depends on x-ray photons to excite photoelectrons, spatial resolution comparable to AES cannot as yet be obtained. The advantage of XPS is, however, that charging effects are minimized and surfaces of insulators can be analyzed. In the work described, both conducting (using AES and XPS) and insulating surfaces (using XPS) were examined.

EXPERIMENTAL

The Analysis System

The AES/XPS techniques are housed in a vacuum chamber capable of being pumped to 3×10^{-11} torr using a combination of turbomolecular and sublimation pumps. In the experiments reported here, pressures were in the region of 5×10^{-10} torr before and after fracture. On fracture, released gases could be monitored with a residual gas analyzer.

Auger electrons and photoelectrons emitted from a solid surface are detected using a double-pass cylindrical mirror analyzer (CMA) supplied by Physical Electronics Inc. (PHI) and whose principles of operation have been described by Palmberg.[14] In the AES mode, Auger electrons are generated from a $30 \mu m$ diameter spot during bombardment by electrons from a coaxial 0–5-keV electron gun. During transmission through the analyzer, electrons pass through 1-mm-diameter apertures which effectively define the resolution measured as 0.7% at 2 keV and enter a channel electron multiplier for amplification. Operating conditions are conventional in that the swept potential on the outer cylinder is modulated and the multiplier signal detected using a lock-in amplifier.

In the XPS mode, two spherical retarding grids between the specimen and the first aperture are used as electron velocity filters; in the AES mode, these grids are grounded. On passing through the grids, photoelectrons are retarded from their initial kinetic energy to a fixed band-pass energy which can be pre-selected in the range of 5–200 eV. To obtain greater sensitivity, the apertures are changed from 1 mm to 3.75 mm in diameter by means of a rotatable feed-through. The specimen is flooded with Al K_α x rays of characteristic energy 1486.6 eV, and the photoelectrons ejected are accepted into the analyzer from an approximately circular area of about 7 mm^2. The x-ray source (600 W max) is some 10 cm from the analysis point, and surfaces are irradiated at 60 degrees to the normal.

The mild steel specimens bonded with epoxy resin were mounted (up to five at a time) on a carrousel which was fitted to a manipulator in such a way that each specimen could be maneuvered individually into the jaws of a fracture attachment (PHI Model 10–520). Fracture was achieved inside the vacuum system by striking the side of the sample with a small hammer, following which the section attached to the carrousel was moved until the fracture surface was in the optimum position for analysis.

Since the same analyzer is used for both AES and XPS, and optimum specimen positions for the two techniques are coincident. At this position, the surface under analysis can be eroded by sputtering with a 2-keV Ar ion gun (PHI Model 04-167) having a maximum current density of 80 $\mu A/cm^2$; in this study, the gun was used to profile through epoxy or oxide films on the fractured surfaces.

After AES and XPS analyses, the fractured joints were transferred to a scanning electron microscope and both low- and high-magnification photographs were obtained from the fractured surfaces.

Specimen Preparation

Two mild steel (BS 970, EN3B) stubs, 3.7 mm in diameter and of respective lengths 19.5 and 8 mm, were bonded together to form a fracture sample using a standard adhesive and curing agent. The surfaces to be bonded were first immersed in a degreasing bath of trichloroethylene, then grit blasted with 180–220 mesh alumina, then degreased again, and finally air dried. The adhesive used was a diglycidyl ether of bisphenol A (Epikote "828" epoxy resin Shell Chemicals Ltd) mixed with 9.4 wt-% of a curing agent (HY 959 Ciba-Geigy U.K. Ltd).

Of the three series of samples (five specimens per series), two were bonded with only the above-mentioned adhesive, while for the remaining series, the steel was coated with a primer Union Carbide A187 (1% γ-glycidoxylpropyltrimethoxy-

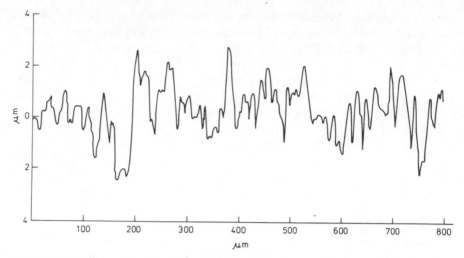

Fig. 1. Typical Talysurf profile of an abraded mild steel surface prior to coating with epoxy resin.

silane aqueous solution) prior to bonding with the 828/959 adhesive/curing agent. All bonds were established by curing at 23°C for 96 hr, followed by 100°C for 1¼ hr, and finally 180°C for 2¼ hr. After the cure the specimens were allowed to cool slowly.

TABLE I

Mild Steel Reference Sample. Variation in Surface Concentration of Elements Detected by XPS[a]

Element	Surface concn., atomic % as received	Surface concn. after indicated amount of material removed		
		50 Å	150 Å	400 Å
Fe	18.8	32.4	60.6	70.7
O	56.3	43.5	27.7	20.8
C	19.7	8.5	4.2	1.8
Al	trace	15.6	7.5	6.7
Mn	2.7	—	—	—
Zn	2.5	—	—	—
Cu	—	—	—	—

[a] Estimated error ± 15%.

TABLE II

Mild Steel Reference Sample. Variation of Binding Energy of Iron, Carbon, and Oxygen Detected at surface[a]

Element	Binding energy eV, as received	Binding energy after indicated amount of material removed		
		50 Å	150 Å	400 Å
Fe	710.2	706.6 710.0 (Sh)	706.0	705.9
O	529.8	530.5	530.2	530.5
C	285.0	284.8	284.5	284.7

[a] Sh = Shoulder on main peak. Error on peak position ± 0.4 eV.

Two of the three series (one unprimed joint and one primed joint) were soaked for one calendar month in distilled water at 60°C prior to analysis to investigate the influence of a water environment on bonding.

RESULTS

The Cleaned Steel Surface

Scanning electron micrographs and Talysurf measurements of the abraded mild steel surface established that the surface was rough, with peak-to-valley readings being several microns. A typical Talysurf profile is shown in Figure 1. The resolution of the instrument is not sufficient, however, to show the deep fissures and microcracks which were almost certainly present.

XPS and AES analyses of the cleaned mild steel surface were performed for the as-cleaned condition and as a function of depth into the surface. The latter was achieved by analyzing the surface after it had been eroded away by argon ion bombardment. The amount of material calculated to have been removed by this process is estimated to be in error by ±20%. The results of the XPS analyses are presented in Tables and I and II. It should be noted that throughout this work, the photoelectron yields from which atom concentrations are obtained have been corrected for the variation in sensitivity of each element to the XPS

TABLE III

Dry Unprimed Joint. "Metal" Surface: Variation in Surface Concentration of Elements Detected by XPS[a]

Element	Surface concn., atomic % freshly fractured surface	Surface concn after indicated amount of material removed	
		50 Å	130 Å
Fe	19.3	47.3	50.2
O	53.2	27.9	25.0
C	26.3	20.0	20.1
N	0.5	—	—
Cl	0.7	—	—
Al	trace	4.8	4.7

[a] Estimated error ± 15%.

TABLE IV

Dry Unprimed Joint. "Metal" Surface: Variation of Binding Energy of Iron, Oxygen, and Carbon

Element	Binding energy, eV freshly fractured surface	Binding energy after indicated amount of material removed	
		50 Å	130 Å
Fe	709.7	706.5	706.7
	706.5 (Sh)[a]	710.0 (Sh)	710.0 (Sh)
O	534.5	530.7	530.6
	530.5 (d)[a]		
C	286.4	284.0	284.3

[a] Sh = Shoulder on main peak; d = doublet. Error ±0.4 eV.

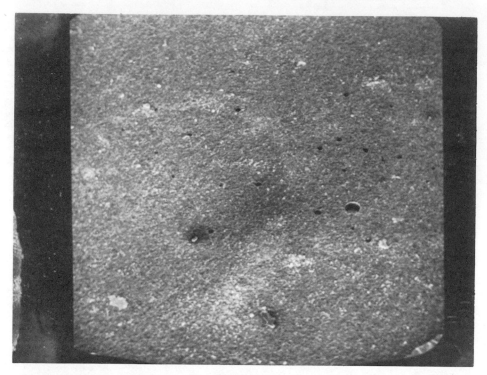

Fig. 2. Auger electron spectroscopy "line scans" of iron, carbon, and oxygen taken across a fracture surface immediately after fracture and at a depth of about 50 Å.

technique. Earlier work[15] on pure elements indicated that variations in reported sensitivities could lead to errors of ±15% in atomic concentration calculations. Binding energies (BE) are quoted to an accuracy of ±0.4 eV and are related to the position of the gold $4f_{7/2}$ photoelectron peak.

Comparison of the binding energies quoted by Hirokawa et al.[16] for iron and its oxides with those found on the mild steel specimen shows that the surface was covered with an iron oxide, probably Fe_2O_3. It is also evident that on ion bombardment, the oxide was progressively removed until, at a depth of 150 Å, only pure iron $(BE\ 706.0\ eV)$ was detected suggesting that the oxide layer was between 50 Å to 150 Å thick.

The position of the oxygen peak is the same as that found for oxygen in metal oxides,[16–19] and the concentration of the element on the surface can be assigned to the oxides of the metals found. After removal of 400 Å of the surface an appreciable quantity (~20%) of oxygen was still present. Two metals were detected at this depth, aluminum and iron; and since the iron was in the metallic state, only the Al could have been associated with this oxygen. The aluminum must have originated from alumina particles embedded in the metal surface during the grit blasting process. At first inspection, the aluminum–oxygen ratio does not appear correct, but Coad[20] has found that prolonged ion bombardment of alumina reduces the aluminum–oxygen ratio to a value close to that measured here.

The 1s carbon photoelectron peak at 285.0 eV can be associated with elemental carbon or hydrocarbon.[21,22] On ion bombardment, the carbon concentration decreased such that, at 400 Å, it constituted only 2% of the total atom concentration. Since the particular steel used in these experiments contained only 0.25% of carbon, the excess carbon probably existed as contamination residing within deep fissures or as carbides formed as a result of the ion bombardment.

In addition to the elements detected by XPS, AES revealed the presence of nitrogen, chlorine, sulfur, and sodium, all common surface contaminants which were easily removed by a light ion bombardment.

Dry Unprimed Joints

On fracture, each joint released a small quantity of gas which raised the system pressure momentarily from 5×10^{-10} torr to 5×10^{-9} torr. To the eye, the fracture appeared purely interfacial, leaving two faces, one of which was covered with adhesive while the other was apparently bare metal. One of the five samples broke in such a way that the surface covered with adhesive (here called the "epoxide" surface) could be analyzed while the other four broke, offering an apparently clean metal surface (here called the "metal" surface) for analysis.

The XPS data from the metal surface listed in Tables III and IV show that the iron detected was in both the metallic (BE 706.5 eV) and oxidized (BE 709.7 eV) states. The oxygen peak at 530.5 eV can readily be ascribed to oxygen in the iron oxide, while the oxygen species with a binding energy of 534.5 eV may

TABLE V

Dry Unprimed Joint. Epoxide Surface: Variation in Surface Concentration of Elements Detected by XPS[a]

Element	Surface concn., atomic %, freshly fractured surface	Surface concn. after indicated amount of material removed		
		50 Å	130 Å	1150 Å
Fe	6.6	14.5	20.1	11.6
O	33.2	9.7	10.9	13.9
C	42.7	63.7	52.1	70.8
N	5.1	2.4	4.0	—
Cl	12.4	9.7	12.9	3.7
Al	trace	trace	trace	trace

[a] Estimated error ±15%.

TABLE VI

Dry Unprimed Joint. Epoxide Surface: Variation of Binding Energy of Iron, Oxygen, and Carbon[a]

Element	Binding energy, eV, freshly fractured surface	Binding energy after indicated amount of material removed		
		50 Å	130 Å	1150 Å
Fe	713.4	712.5	710.2 707.5 (Sh)	708.8
O	535.4	533.7	532.2	531.5
C	288.0 289.5 (Sh)	286.2 289.2 (Sh)	284.7	284.2

[a] Sh = Shoulder on main peak. Error ±0.4 eV.

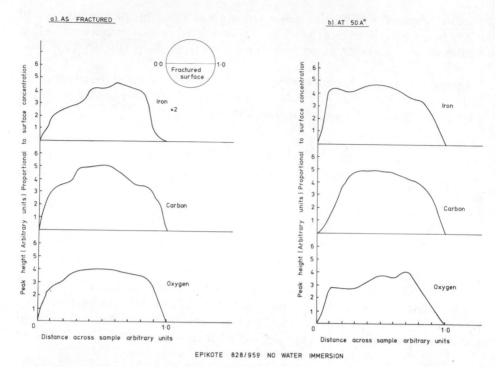

EPIKOTE 828/959 NO WATER IMMERSION

Fig. 3. Scanning electron micrograph (SEM) of an epoxy-covered surface—note the appearance of holes as black spots distributed over the surface. Magnification is ×50.

be associated with the carbon $1s$ peak at 286.4 eV, as both peaks disappear after a small amount of iron bombardment.

Significant changes in the concentrations of the elements occurred when 50 Å of the surface were removed. The amount of iron increased, with the majority of the element existing in the metallic form; the oxygen peak at 534.5 eV disappeared, and the carbon photoelectron peak shifted to 284.0 eV. This carbon peak shift could have been due either to the removal of the higher binding energy species of carbon to reveal the lower binding energy form or the reduction of the original carbonaceous material to carbon by ion bombardment.

Although further erosion of the surface to a depth of 130 Å produced no major changes in the concentrations of the elements detected, a close examination of the iron photoelectron peak shape shows that at this depth, the amount of oxidized iron present decreased from 50% to 30% of the total iron concentration.

AES analyses were performed on the "metal" surface at various points after fracture and ion bombardment. In addition, the variation in concentration of an element across a surface was achieved by monitoring a selected Auger electron peak as the sample was moved through the electron beam. The results from these "line scans" for carbon, oxygen, and iron are summarized in Figure 2 from the as-fractured surface and from a depth of 50 Å. It appears that all elements were evenly distributed across the sample, particularly after 50 Å were removed. The AES results supported the XPS analyses in that ion bombardment caused the iron concentration to increase and the oxygen concentration to decrease.

Study of the epoxide surface of the joint by XPS (Tables V and VI) revealed several interesting effects. Iron, for example, exhibited a peak at a binding energy of 713.4 eV which could not be identified with iron in dry iron oxides. This

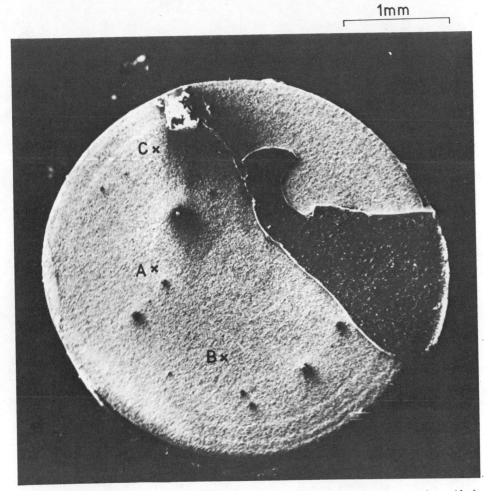

Fig. 4. Typical SEM of a fracture surface showing both metal surface and epoxy resin lump (dark area middle right). AES performed in areas A, B, and C.

high-energy species was also observed on the freshly fractured surfaces of the silane-treated joints, while one with an even higher binding energy was found on the surface of the water-soaked unprimed samples. Associated with these high-energy peaks were oxygen species ranging in binding energy from 536.2 to 535.5 eV. It has been demonstrated[19] that water condensed on aluminum, manganese, and magnesium gives oxygen signals corresponding to binding energies from 535.0 to 535.6 eV, while oxygen in the hydroxides of these metals gives rise to peaks in the range 532.6 to 533.5 eV. It is proposed, therefore, that the high binding-energy species of iron and oxygen observed in this present study are due to heavily hydrated iron oxide to which may be attached chemisorbed water.

A further intriguing feature of the epoxide fractured surface was the detection of a significant quantity (~12%) of heavily oxidized iron at a depth of 1150 Å. There is strong evidence, from scanning electron microscopy studies of the surface (see, for example, Fig. 3), that holes exist in the epoxy resin. This evidence is further supported by earlier work from a mild steel/epoxide/stainless steel joint

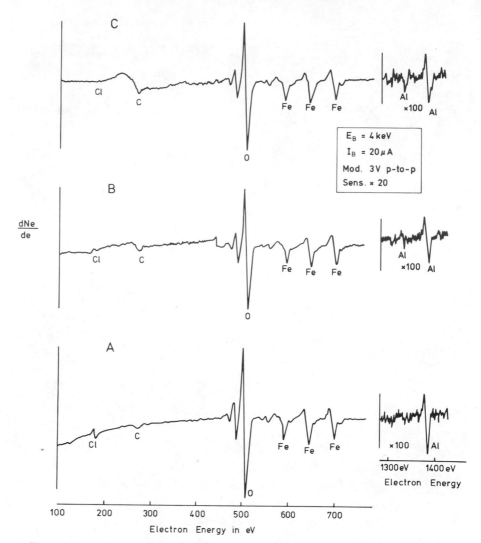

Fig. 5. AES spectra taken from points A, B, and C. Note small carbon peak at 271 eV.

where fracture occurred with epoxy covering the stainless steel. Photoelectron peaks characteristic of components of the stainless steel were detected, suggesting that epoxide coverage of the surface was not complete.

Not surprisingly, the concentration of carbon on the epoxide surface was high with the element existing in two chemical states (288.0, 289.5 eV) prior to ion bombardment. This doublet was found whenever freshly fractured epoxide was analyzed and thus can almost certainly be said to be characteristic of epoxy resin. The carbon species of BE 286.4 eV which was found after removal of 50 Å of material (and also found on metal surfaces) may be due to a polymer in intimate contact with the metal oxide surface since Wyatt et al.[23] observed a similar binding energy for C(1s) for a polyurethane adhesive in contact with an aluminum surface. After erosion of the surface to a depth of 130 Å, only one carbon peak (BE ~284.5 eV, typical of a hydrocarbon or elemental carbon) was detected. It should be emphasized that prolonged ion bombardment leads to a degradation of most organic species to carbon, resulting in a loss of chemical information.

No satisfactory explanation can be put forward for the observed concentrations of nitrogen and chlorine, except that the latter may be due to traces of trichloroethylene used in the cleaning process. Information from AES was not possible from the epoxide surfaces, as charging of the surface by the primary electron beam produced excessive spectral distortion.

Water-Soaked Unprimed Joints

On fracture, the water-soaked joints released a considerable amount of gas which raised the system pressure momentarily from 8×10^{-10} torr to 3×10^{-7} torr. Almost all the gas evolved was water vapor. All the samples broke by apparently interfacial failure, with the crack path jumping from one interface to the other and hence leaving clumps of adhesive on both fractured surfaces; a typical SEM photograph of one of the surfaces is shown in Figure 4. Auger analyses were carried out on the "metal" surface at points A, B, and C (Fig. 4), and the spectra recorded are presented in Figure 5. It is clear from these spectra that the carbon concentration over the metal fraction of the surface was low ($\leq 5\%$), suggesting that little organic material existed on the "metal" surface. From these AES results it can be concluded that virtually all the carbon de-

TABLE VII
Water-Soaked Unprimed Joints. Variation in Surface Concentration
of Elements Detected by XPS[a]

Element	Surface concn., atomic %, freshly fractured surface	Surface concn. after indicated amount of material removed		
		50 Å	130 Å	640 Å
Fe	10.5	10.5	33.7	27.1
O	65.0	55.5	50.2	59.9
C	21.0	7.8	12.6	8.3
N	—	—	—	—
Cl	—	—	2.5	0.8
Al	—	3.0	4.8	3.9
F	3.5	—	—	—

[a] Estimated error ±15%.

TABLE VIII
Water-Soaked Unprimed Joints. Variation of Binding Energy
of Iron, Oxygen, and Carbon[a]

Element	Binding energy, eV, freshly fractured surface	Binding energy after indicated amount of material removed		
		50 Å	130 Å	640 Å
Fe	715.0 710.2 (d)	710	710	709.8 706.2 (Sh)
O	536.2 531.2 (d)	530	529.9	529.9
C	288.2 290.1 (Sh)	287.5 284.7 (d)	287.5 284.8 (d)	284.9

[a] Sh = Shoulder on main peak; d = doublet. Error ±0.4 eV.

tected by XPS, ~21% (see Table VII), was associated with the epoxide, which covered some 10% of the analyzed surface. This conclusion is reinforced by the detection of the carbon doublet (see Table VIII) ascribed in the previous section to the epoxy resin. After prolonged ion bombardment, the carbonaceous material was reduced either to elemental carbon or to a hydrocarbon.

In the XPS analyses, an iron peak was found at a binding energy of 715.0 eV, that is, some 2 eV higher than that observed from either the dry or the silane-primed specimens. Since so much water was evolved on fracture and since it must have been present originally at the interface, it is tentatively suggested that the iron species of BE 715.0 eV, together with the oxygen of be 536.2 eV, derived from a heavily hydrated iron oxide onto which a considerable amount of water had been chemisorbed. Light ion bombardment to a depth of 50 Å removed both iron and oxygen peaks associated with the hydrated iron. The iron peak at 710.2 eV and the oxygen peak at 531.2 eV can be ascribed to a more stable iron oxide. Since pure iron (BE 706.5 eV) appeared only weakly at a depth of 640 Å, the oxide layer on the "metal" surface must have been over 600 Å thick, a considerably thicker layer than observed on the dry specimens.

TABLE IX
Water-Soaked Primed Joint. "Metal" Surface: Variation in Surface Concentration of Elements Detected by XPS[a]

Element	Surface concn., atomic %, freshly fractured surface	Surface concn. after indicated amount of material removed		
		50 Å	130 Å	400 Å
Fe	21.5	39.5	50.9	67.2
O	60.9	45.9	38.6	27.6
C	7.4	2.5	1.8	1.8
N	—	—	—	—
Cl	3.0	1.7	0.9	—
Al	5.8	8.4	7.8	3.4
Si	1.4	2.0	—	—
F	—	—	—	—

[a] Estimated error ±15%.

TABLE X
Water-Soaked Primed Joint. "Metal" Surface: Variation of Binding Energy of Iron, Carbon, and Oxygen[a]

Element	Binding energy, eV, freshly fractured surface	Binding energy after indicated amount of material removed		
		50 Å	130 Å	400 Å
Fe	709.5	708.7 705.7 (Sh)	708.5 705.2 (Sh)	705.8 708.5 (Sh)
O	531.2 529.2 (Sh)	530.2	530.2	530.5
C	286.8	284.2 286.2 (Sh)	284.2	unassignable

[a] Sh = Shoulder on main peak. Error ±0.4 eV.

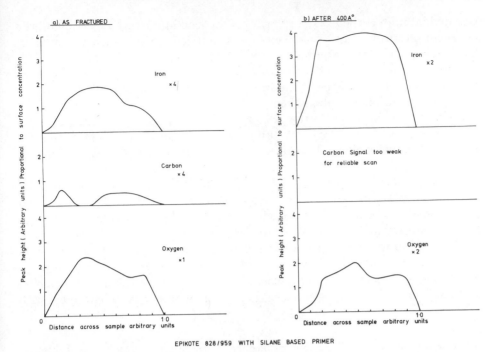

EPIKOTE 828/959 WITH SILANE BASED PRIMER

Fig. 6. AES "line scans" taken from the "metal" side of a water-soaked primed joint. Note the patchiness of the carbon over the surface and the increase of both iron and oxygen after removal of 400 Å.

Water-Soaked Primed Joints

When fractured, the silane-primed joints produced a momentary pressure rise comparable in magnitude to that observed for the dry joints. The five specimens broke such that two "metal" and three "epoxide" surfaces could be presented for analysis.

The XPS analyses of the as-fractured metal surfaces revealed (see Tables IX and X) that the iron existed in the dry iron oxide form while the carbon existed in a form ascribable to a polymer existing in contact with a metal. Erosion of surface revealed increased amounts of iron whose chemical state changed from the oxide (20%) to an almost pure metal state (80%) at a depth of 400 Å. Coupled to this increasing Fe concentration with depth was a decreasing carbon concentration. All the excess oxygen found at this depth could be ascribed to oxygen in the alumina and in traces of iron oxide.

It was found possible to perform AES on the metal surfaces, and "line scans" similar to those performed for the dry joints were taken for carbon, oxygen, and iron. Results are presented in Figure 6. Areas of high carbon concentration corresponded to areas of low iron and oxygen concentrations, suggesting a patchwork arrangement of carbonaceous polymer material existing over the metal surface. Removal of 400 Å of surface resulted in a removal of this carbonaceous material and an increase in the iron concentration, which at this depth was found (by XPS) to be almost entirely pure metal.

The XPS analyses of the epoxide surfaces (see Tables XI and XII) revealed that the carbon existed in the two forms ascribed earlier to the epoxy resin (i.e., with binding energies 288.0 eV and 289.7 eV) and that removal of the surface layer resulted in more carbon being exposed. The iron and oxygen existing on the as-fractured surface can be ascribed to hydrated iron oxide which, on ion bombardment, reduced to the normal oxide existing on the surface by dry iron. Some 12% iron was detected at a depth of 400 Å, an estimated 10% of which existed as pure metal. The presence of the iron at this depth can be explained by the previously mentioned pinhole theory.

Since 12% of the atoms in the primer were silicon, then, provided the metal surface is covered by a film of the primer greater than 10 Å thick, this concentration of the silicon should be detected. It was found, however, that the amount of silicon residing on the "epoxide" and "metal" surfaces was about the same, the total concentration being about 4.0%. To clarify this anomaly, a cleaned mild steel specimen was coated with a similar amount of primer as used for the primed joints and analyzed using XPS; no silicon was detected, suggesting that the solution volatilized on being subjected to vacuum. This volatilization was thought to be due either to a lack of polymerization or to failure of the silane to chemisorb. Addition of a 1% solution of the amine HY 959 to the primer catalyzed polymerization of the silane, following which XPS analysis (see Table XIII) revealed that 5% silicon existed at the surface. The latter value is in close agreement with

TABLE XI

• Water-Soaked Primed Joint. Epoxide Surface: Variation in Surface Concentration of Elements Detected by XPS[a]

Element	Surface concn., atomic %, freshly fractured surface	Surface concn. after indicated amount of material removed		
		50 Å	130 Å	400 Å
Fe	5.0	9.3	9.9	11.8
O	48.9	40.1	36.2	31.1
C	34.3	43.3	45.6	51.1
N	2.4	—	—	—
Cl	3.7	2.7	3.5	2.0
Al	0.9	1.8	2.4	2.0
Si	1.8	2.8	2.4	2.0
F	3.0	—	—	—

[a] Estimated error ± 15%.

TABLE XII

Water-Soaked Primed Joint. Epoxide Surface: Variation of Binding Energy of Iron, Carbon, and Oxygen[a]

Element	Binding energy, eV, freshly fractured surface	Binding energy after indicated amount of material removed		
		50 Å	130 Å	400 Å
Fe	713.7	712.5	711.7 710.2 (Sh)	709.2 706.2 (Sh)
O	536.2	533.7	532.5 535.5 (Sh)	531.2
C	288.0 289.7 (Sh)	287.7	286.0	284.2

[a] Sh = Shoulder on main peak. Error ± 0.4 eV.

the total silicon concentration detected on the two fracture surfaces (4.5%), suggesting that the silane primer does not cover the fracture surface completely after polymerization.

DISCUSSION

Dry Joints

From the XPS results it is clear that, after fracturing the joint, not only was an appreciable amount of carbon left on the "metal" surface but also that it existed in a different chemical environment from that found on the mild steel reference sample. The observed shift in binding energy to 286.4 eV has been attributed here to a polymer in intimate contact with the surface. The question of how this polymer is distributed across the sample now arises.

The fact that strong iron and oxygen signals were obtained in both XPS and AES rules out the possibility that the polymer existed as a continuous film greater than about 20 Å thick, since the mean free path of a 1000-eV electron is estimated from other work[24,25] to be of that order. Further, as metallic iron was present after ion bombardment, the polymer cannot have covered the surface completely. The Auger line profiles (Fig. 2), however, indicate that the concentrations of carbon, oxygen, and iron were evenly distributed across the sample. Since the diameter of the electron beam was 30 μm, these results would suggest that neither the iron, iron oxide, nor polymer existed in areas greater in diameter than that of the electron probe.

It is postulated that the fracture propagated very close to the epoxide/metal interface; a diagram illustrating the proposed path of failure is given in Figure 7. Some epoxide was left buried in crevices in the metal surface, and in places the fracture actually passed through the metal substrate itself. It would seem that any corrosion products came away with the epoxide surface. A consideration of the results obtained from the epoxide surface shows that holes were probably present in the adhesive and also that a certain amount of corrosion of the metal substrate had occurred.

Water-Soaked Unprimed Joints

These joints broke by interfacial failure between the oxide and adhesive, but the crack jumped from one interface to the other during fracture leaving part of the surface covered in epoxy resin and part apparently free of epoxy. The Auger analysis of the "metal" at points A, B, and C (Fig. 4) showed that very little carbon was present on that part of the surface, ssggesting a clean break between the epoxide and the metal substrate. Analysis by XPS showed that the doublet

TABLE XIII

Silane Control Experiment. Surface Concentration of Elements Detected by XPS

Element	Surface concn., atomic %
Fe	11.1%
O	45.1%
C	38.6%
Si	5.2%

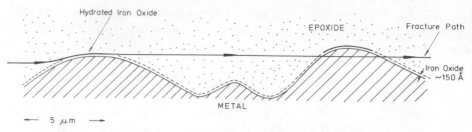

Fig. 7. Proposed model for the fracture path of a dry, unprimed epoxy resin joint. Epoxy resin exists in the deep valleys while small areas of pure metal and hydrated iron oxide are exposed.

typical of the bulk epoxide was detected (presumably coming from the visible lump of adhesive which was estimated to cover some 10% of the analyzed area), and this precludes the possibility of the crack path being solely through the oxide layer.

The XPS results also indicated that the iron oxide thickness had increased from the 100 Å observed on mild steel to at least 640 Å and that some of the iron existed in a heavily hydrated state. Using somewhat cruder analytical techniques, Kinloch and Gledhill[6] have proposed that for joints similar to those investigated here, water should initially displace the adhesive from the metal surface and that corrosion would follow subsequently. The results presented here are in general agreement with their findings, since water was certainly present at the interface and corrosion definitely had occurred. It is impossible to say, however, from the present experiments whether displacement of the adhesive by water alone caused joint failure or whether failure occurred owing to simultaneous adhesive displacement and corrosion.

Water-Soaked Primed Joints

Silicon from the silane primer was found on each of the fractured surfaces from the above joints, with the concentration on each being approximately 2.5 atomic percent. The control experiment in which a similar amount of silane solution was polymerized on a mild steel surface gave a silicon concentration of 5%, a value very close to the total amount detected on the two surfaces, thus suggesting that the fracture had proceeded within the silane layer. The Auger line profile of the "metal" surface indicated that the specimen was covered by a patchy layer of some carbonaceous material; and as a C(1s) peak at 286.8 eV was observed, the layer can be attributed to the polymerized silane. The presence of some hydrated iron oxide brought about by water corrosion of the substrate supports further the contention that the silane covering was incomplete. Nevertheless, the primer did offer a considerable amount of protection to the metal since here, the iron oxide thickness was only marginally greater than that found on the mild steel sample.

Therefore, although previous work[7,26] has demonstrated that the presence of a silane primer may increase the environmental stability of adhesive joints, the above results suggest that the silane primer is now the weakest link in the joint and fracture occurs by cohesive failure of this layer. This conclusion is in agreement with results reported from radioisotope studies[27] on debonded glass–γ-aminopropyltriethoxysilane primer–epoxy adhesive joints and in both cases may possibly arise from hydrolysis of siloxane bonds in the silane primer structure, which, as discussed previously, is essentially a polysiloxane network. The present spectroscopic studies have not revealed whether the silane primer is physisorbed or chemisorbed onto the metal oxide surface.

CONCLUSIONS

Although prior to water immersion, the unprimed mild steel–epoxy joints appeared visually to fail at the metal oxide–epoxy interface, AES and XPS analysis has clearly demonstrated that the actual failure pattern is far more complex. The crack propagated close to, but not exactly at, the interface, traveling partially through the adhesive (leaving epoxide material buried in crevices in the metal substrate surface) and in places even through the metal substrate itself. Whether this failure pattern arises from a weak boundary layer of adhesive close to the interface or stress concentration effects[28,29] has yet to be resolved.

After exposure to water, the fracture path is exactly between the adhesive–metal oxide interface, and corrosion of the iron oxide leads to a considerable increase in the oxide thickness. When a silane-based primer is employed which is known to increase joint durability, the polysiloxane–metal oxide interface appears to be resistant to water attack, and the primer itself is now the weakest part of the joint, fracture occurring by cohesive failure of this layer.

Thus, AES and XPS have proved to be invaluable analytical techniques for identifying exactly the locus of joint failure and it appears that to increase joint durability further, attention should be focused on increasing the intrinsic strength of the silane-based primers commonly employed.

The paper is published by permission of the Controller, Her Majesty's Stationery Office, holder of Crown Copyright, London 1976. The authors would like to thank Dr. John Riviere and Dr. Paul Coad for their helpful discussions during the course of this study.

References

1. W. C. Wake, in *Aspects of Adhesion*, Vol. 7, D. J. Alner, Ed., University Press, London, 1969, p. 64.

2. R. F. Wegman, *Appl. Polym. Symp.*, **19**, 385 (1972).

3. J. J. Bikerman, *The Science of Adhesive Joints*, 2nd ed., Academic Press, New York, (1968).

4. C. Kerr, N. C. Macdonald, and S. Orman, *J. Appl. Chem.*, **17**, 62 (1967).

5. G. S. Koboyashi and D. J. Donnelly, Boeing Aircraft Company Report D6-41517, 1974.

6. R. Gledhill and A. J. Kinloch, *J. Adhesion*, **6**, 315 (1974).

7. A. J. Kinloch, W. A. DuKes, and R. A. Gledhill, *Amer. Chem. Soc. Prepr.*, **35**(1), 546 (1975).

8. W. A. Zisman, *Ind. Eng. Chem., Prod. Res. Dev*, 8(2), 99 (1969).

9. W. D. Bascom and R. L. Patrick, *Adhesive Age*, **17**, 25 (1974).

10. W. D. Bascom, *Macromolecules*, **5**, 792 (1972).

11. C. R. Brundle, *Appl. Spectrosc.*, **25**, 8 (1971).

12. C. C. Chang, *Surf. Sci.*, **25**, 53 (1974).

13. N. C. Macdonald and J. R. Waldrop, *Appl. Phys. Lett.*, **19**(9), 315 (1971).

14. P. W. Palmberg, *J. Elect. Spectrosc.*, **5**, 691 (1974).

15. M. Gettings and J. P. Coad, *Surf. Sci.*, **53**, 636 (1975).

16. K. Hirokawa, F. Honda, and M. Oku, *J. Elect. Spectrosc.*, **6**, 333 (1975).

17. D. Briggs, *Disc. Faraday Soc.* (1975).

18. M. K. Bahl, *J. Phys., F.: Metal Phys.,* **4,** 497 (1974).

19. J. C. Fuggle, L. M. Watson, D. J. Fabian, and S. Affrossman, *Surf. Sci.,* **49,** 61 (1975).

20. J. P. Coad, private communication.

21. F. R. McFeeley, S. P. Kowalczyk, L. Ley, R. G. Cavell, R. A. Pollak, and D. A. Shirley, *Phys. Rev. B* **9,** 5268 (1974).

22. U. Gelius, P. F. Heden, J. Hedman, B. J. Lindberg, R. Manne, R. Nordberg, C. Nording, and K. Siegbahn, *Phys. Scripta,* **2,** 70 (1970).

23. D. M. Wyatt, R. C. Grey, J. C. Carver, D. M. Hercules, and L. Masters, *Appl. Spectrosc.,* **28,** 439 (1974).

24. C . R. Brundle, *Surf. Sci.,* **48,** 99 (1975).

25. C. J. Powell, *Surf. Sci.,* **44,** 29 (1974).

26. R. L. Patrick, J. A. Brown, and L. Dunbar, U.S. Naval Air System Command Final Report No. 0019-70-C-0184, (1970).

27. M. E. Schroder, *J. Adhesion,* **2,** 202 (1970).

28. C. W. Jennings, *J. Adhesion,* **4,** 25 (1972).

29. W. D. Bascom, C. O. Timmons, and R. L. Jones, *J. Mat. Sci.,* **10,** 1037 (1975).

Received April 16, 1976
Revised July 15, 1976

JOURNAL OF APPLIED POLYMER SCIENCE   VOL. 21, 2393–2404 (1977)

The Effluent Analysis of Several Pyrrone and Polyimide Precursors During Cyclization

GEORGE F. SYKES and PHILIP R. YOUNG, *NASA—Langley Research Center, Hampton, Virginia 23665*

Synopsis

A study was conducted to determine the degree of cyclization occurring in a series of four pyrrone and two polyimide prepolymers. These materials were heated from 25° to 400°C at 2°C/min in a helium atmosphere, and the effluent was sampled at regular intervals by a gas chromatograph/mass spectrometer technique. Quantitative analysis of this effluent indicated that the pyrrone polymers were less than 80% converted under these conditions while the polyimides were essentially fully converted. Significant amounts of carbon dioxide were found to be eliminated as the pyrrone polymers cured. This evolution was attributed to the loss of carbon dioxide from intermediate stages during cure and, in some cases, to the decarboxylation of unreacted groups. Support data obtained on model compounds are also presented.

INTRODUCTION

Stepladder and ladder polymers based on the polymerization of aromatic five-membered ring dianhydrides with bis(o-diamines) have been reported.[1–6] These polymers are commonly referred to as pyrrones. They are usually prepared in solution at room temperature, either precipitated or cast as films, and then given thermal treatment to effect cyclization. Water is eliminated during this cyclization:

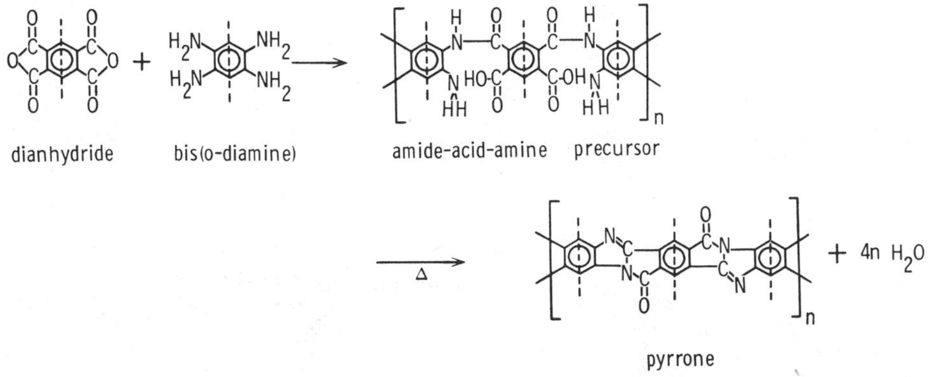

dianhydride   bis(o-diamine)   amide-acid-amine   precursor

pyrrone

Initially, pyrrones were expected to possess unusual thermal properties since two bonds in the same ring had to be broken for loss of polymer integrity compared to only one bond for most other polymer systems. Despite these expec-

2393

tations, pyrrones did not always live up to their anticipated thermo-oxidaive stability. A possible explanation to be considered was the likelihood that the amide-acid-amine was not completely cyclodehydrated to the theoretical pyrrone structure. With few exceptions,[7,8] little quantitative information was available on this cyclodehydration of the precursor through various intermediate stages en route to pyrrone. The present investigation was made to provide an insight into these cyclization reactions.

The degree of ring closure should be readily determined by measuring the amount of water eliminated as the polymer is cured. An earlier model compound study involving stepwise thermal treatment and gas-chromatographic analysis for water verified that this approach could provide meaningful information.[9] However, this earlier study also indicated that reactions other than simple cyclodehydration were occurring and that a more complete analysis of the effluents was needed. Therefore, the present study employed an improved gas-chromatographic/mass-spectrometric technique and provided a quantitative identification of all major effluents as a function of cure temperature for a series of pyrrone precursors. Two polyimide precursors were included for comparison. Model compounds were also run under identical conditions for correlation with polymer results.

EXPERIMENTAL

Model Compounds

The synthesis and characterization of model compounds used in this study have been reported elsewhere.[10,11] They were prepared by reacting phthalic anhydride (PA) or pyromellitic dianhydride (PMDA) with *o*-phenylenediamine (OPD) in aprotic solvents. Each was synthesized to represent a portion of the polymer repeat unit at various stages of cyclization. The structures of these compounds are given below:

PA-IA
I

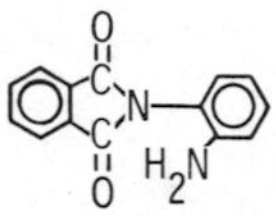

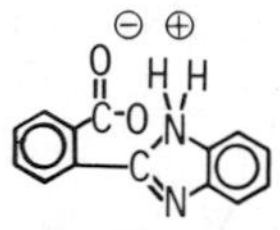

PA-BA
II

PMDA-AAA
III

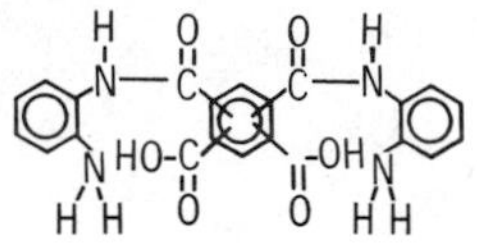

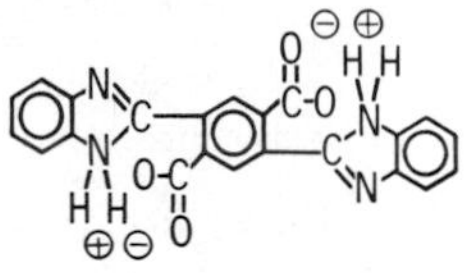

PMDA-pBA
IV

PMDA-IA
V

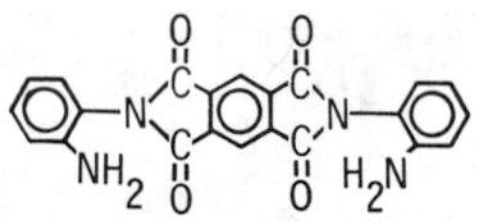

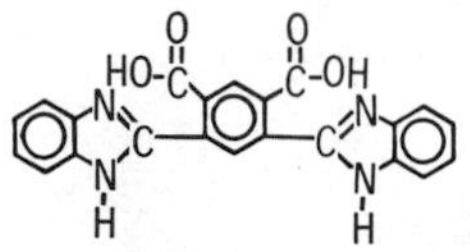

PMDA-mBA
VI

trans-pyrrone
VII

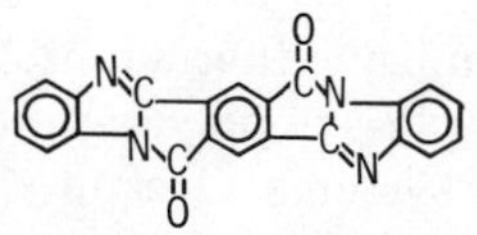

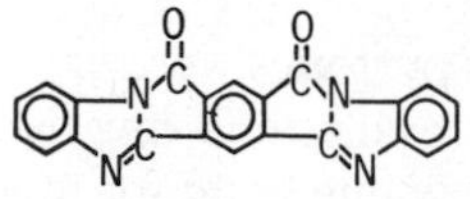

cis-pyrrone
VIII

All compounds were isomerically pure, except the PMDA-OPD amide-acid-amine III which was a mixture of meta and para isomers.

Polymers

The four pyrrone precursors were prepared by the polymerization of two dianhydrides, pyromellitic dianhydride (PMDA) and 3,3′,4,4′-benzophenonetetracarboxylic dianhydride (BTDA), with each of two tetraamines, 3,3′-diaminobenzidine (DAB) and 3,3′,4,4′-tetraaminobenzophenone (TABP). For comparison, two polyimide precursors were also prepared using PMDA and BTDA with 4,4′-diaminodiphenyl ether (DADPO). The polymerizations were conducted at room temperature in N,N-dimethylacetamide (DMAc) using procedures reported elsewhere.[12,13] Table I gives the inherent viscosity of each polymer solution. The products were precipitated into methanol and the resultant powders were vacuum dried for 18 hr at room temperature and stored in a desiccator until used. Theoretical repeat units of the six polymers are given below; each is presumed to be a mixture of isomers:

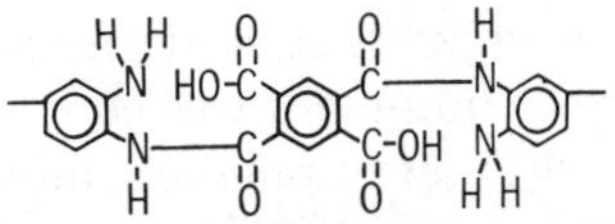

PMDA-DAB

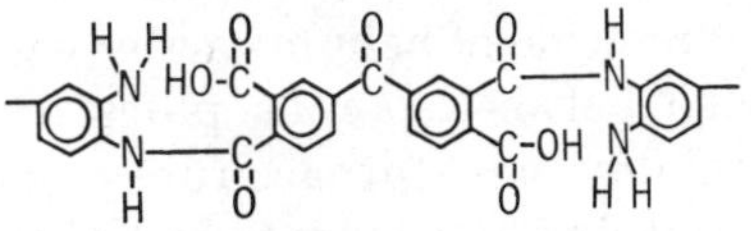

BTDA-DAB

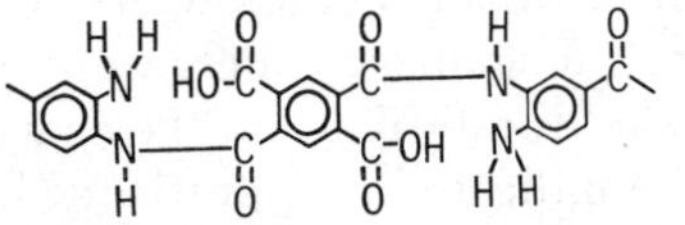

PMDA-TABP

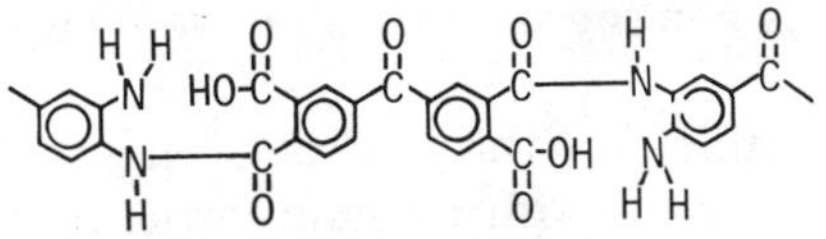

BTDA-TABP

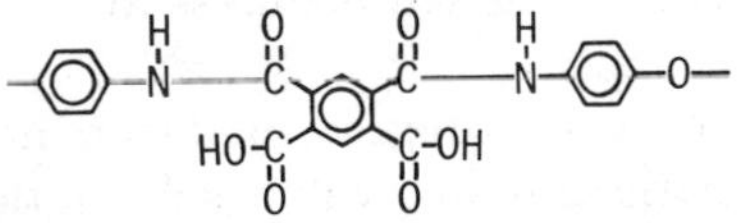

PMDA-DADPO

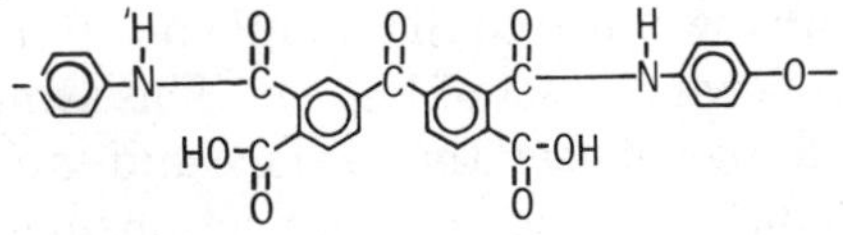

BTDA-DADPO

TABLE I
Solution Viscosity of Test Materials

Precursor polymer	Inherent viscosity 0.5% DMAc, 35°C[a]
PMDA-TABP	0.57
PMDA-DAB	0.81
BTDA-TABP	0.36
BTDA-DAB	0.56
PMDA-DADPO	1.55
BTDA-DADPO	0.95

[a] DMAc = N,N-Dimethylacetamide.

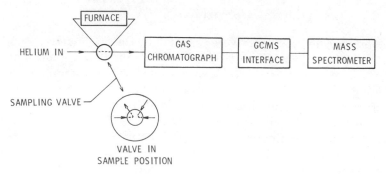

Fig. 1. Schematic of gas analysis system.

Test Procedure

A schematic of the experimental equipment used for analysis of the gaseous effluents is shown in Figure 1. The equipment was composed of a furnace assembly for heating the sample materials, an automatic sampling valve for periodic sampling of the furnace atmosphere, and a tandem gas chromatograph/mass spectrometer with interface for removal of helium carrier gas. The individual sample materials were retained between porous plugs of quartz fibers in 0.457-cm-I.D., 15.2-cm-long stainless steel furnace tubes. Each furnace tube was cleaned prior to use by heating under vacuum to 800°C and stored in a desiccator at ambient temperature. The quartz fibers were cleaned in a vacuum furnace and also stored in a desiccator until used. Tests with the system using blank sample tubes (no sample) indicated no significant background changes between ambient and 400°C when the sample tubes were cleaned in this manner.

The sample mass was determined to the nearest 0.1 mg in the furnace tube, and the tube was placed in the furnace with a helium carrier purge for a minimum of 1 hr before the test was started. The sample mass for each test was about 5 mg.

In operation, the sample furnace was programmed from ambient to 400°C at a rate of 2°C/min. The automatic sampling valve (schematic, Fig. 1), normally kept in the bypass position, was switched to the sample position for 15 sec every 8 min (valve sample position shown in inset of Fig. 1). This sample time allowed for a complete purge of all tubing between the furnace and sampling valve. In order to prevent condensation, all tubing and connections between the valve, furnace, and chromatograph were wrapped with heating tape and insulation to maintain these parts at 175°C.

A Varian Model 1800 gas chromatograph containing a thermal conductivity detector was employed for effluent detection. For all tests, the detector current was 200 mA and the helium carrier flow rate was 18 cc/min. A Waters Associates Porapak Q column, 0.238 cm I.D. by 90 cm and maintained at 80°C, was used for product separation. The column and chromatograph were calibrated for quantitative analysis of the gaseous products of interest by injecting known quantities of each identified product into the instrument and noting the detector response. Each peak observed on the chromatogram was identified from mass spectra obtained on an EAI Quad 250 B mass spectrometer connected through an interface to the gas chromatograph. The mass spectrometer had a range of 1 to 500 amu and was always operated at 10^{-6} torr.

RESULTS AND DISCUSSION

Preliminary experiments showed that water and carbon dioxide were the two major effluents given off during the curing process of both the models and polymers. The chromatographic conditions which yielded quantitative data on these were then determined and optimized.

The total amounts of water and carbon dioxide yielded by each model compound and polymer are given in Tables II and III, respectively. The results are normalized to a 10-mg test specimen. The next-to-last column in the tables, the percent conversion, is the ratio of observed water to the theoretical amount of water which should be eliminated after complete cyclization. The progress of the cyclization reactions was followed by plotting observed water versus temperature. These data are given for the model compounds in Figures 2 and 4, the four pyrrone precursors in Figure 6, and the polyimide precursors in Figure 8. Similar data for the elimination of carbon dioxide from the model compounds are given in Figures 3 and 5. Data for the elimination of carbon dioxide from the pyrrone and polyimide precursors are given in Figures 7 and 9, respectively.

Model Compounds

Except for the PMDA-mBA (VI) model, Table II shows that none of the PMDA or PA model compounds achieved essentially complete cyclodehydration

TABLE II
Results of Effluent Analysis on Model Compounds

Model compound	MW	Calculated[a] H_2O, mg	Observed H_2O, mg	Conversion,[b] %	Observed CO_2, mg
PA-IA (I)	238.25	0.76	0.67	89	0.03
PA-BA (II)	238.25	0.76	0.67	89	0.04
PMDA-AAA (III)	434.41	1.66	1.29	78	0.11
PMDA-pBA (IV)	398.38	0.90	0.68	75	0.35
PMDA-IA (V)	398.38	0.90	0.77	85	0.19
PMDA-mBA (VI)	398.38	0.90	0.87	96	0.06
trans-Pyrrone (VII)	362.30	0	0	—	0.03
cis-Pyrrone (VIII)	362.30	0	0	—	0.02

[a] Normalized to a 10-mg sample size.
[b] Based on the ratio of observed to calculated water.

TABLE III
Results of Effluent Analysis on Polymers Heated to 400°C

Precursor polymer	MW[a]	Calculated[b] H_2O, mg	Observed[b] H_2O, mg	Conversion,[c] %	Observed[b] CO_2, mg
PMDA-TABP	460.41	1.56	1.02	65	0.35
PMDA-DAB	432.40	1.66	1.13	68	0.38
BTDA-TABP	564.62	1.27	0.97	76	0.18
BTDA-DAB	536.51	1.34	1.06	79	0.22
PMDA-DADPO	418.37	0.86	0.81	94	0.07
BTDA-DADPO	522.48	0.69	0.64	92	0.05

[a] Molecular weight of the idealized repeat unit.
[b] Normalized to a 10-mg sample size.
[c] Based on the ratio of observed to calculated water.

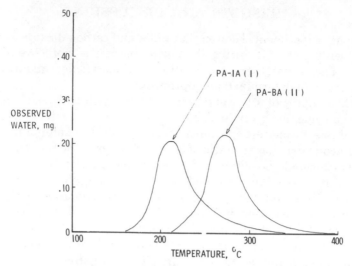

Fig. 2. Evolution of water during cure of PA model compounds.

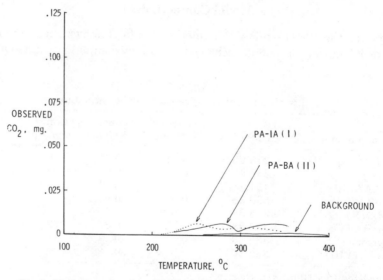

Fig. 3. Evolution of carbon dioxide during cure of PA model compounds.

under the conditions of this experiment. Substantial amounts of carbon dioxide were observed for those models which did not convert efficiently. This carbon dioxide was eliminated in two general regions, where maximum water loss occurred and at elevated temperatures. The early evolution of carbon dioxide from the amide-acid-amine model (III) as it loses water might be attributed to decarboxylation and hydrolytic cleavage of amide bonds as proposed by Bruck,[14] while the early evolution of carbon dioxide from the imide-amine models (I and V) may result from rearrangement and subsequent isoimide degradation.[15] The benzimidazole-acid models (II, IV, and VI) apparently partially decarboxylate during cyclodehydration as proposed in earlier polymer studies.[2,8,16] This is particularly evident for the PMDA model (IV). The thermal decarboxylation

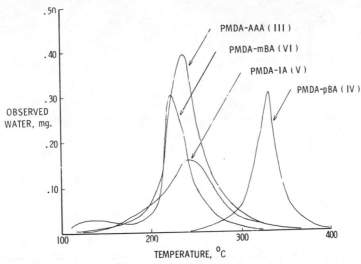

Fig. 4. Evolution of water during cure of PMDA model ompounds.

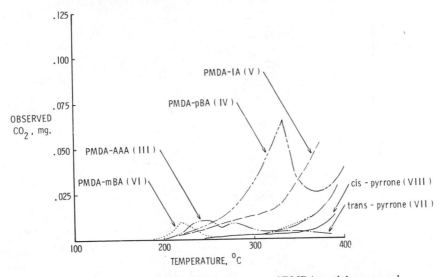

Fig. 5. Evolution of carbon dioxide during cure of PMDA model compounds.

of aromatic acids is a fairly common phenomenon and is promoted by the close proximity of electron-withdrawing groups.

Since the benzimidazole-acid model (IV) eliminated more carbon dioxide than any other model, an independent experiment was conducted to confirm that it did indeed partially decarboxylate during the thermal cyclization process. Approximately 100 mg of this compound was heated to 200° at 5°C/min in a helium atmosphere and then programmed to 350° at 3°C/min. Upon cooling, the residue was extracted with chloroform and a sample of insoluble portion was introduced directly into the ionization chamber of a mass spectrometer by a solid inlet probe. The probe was then heated to vaporize the sample. Figure 10 gives the resulting mass spectrum. In this spectrum, background has been subtracted

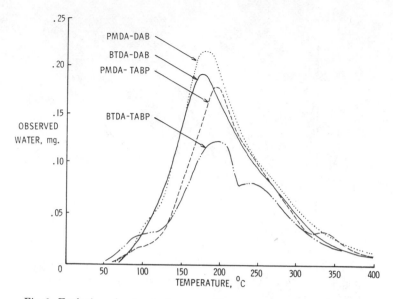

Fig. 6. Evolution of water during cure of four pyrrone precursor polymers.

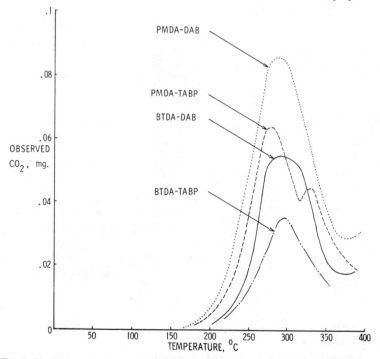

Fig. 7. Evolution of carbon dioxide during cure of four pyrrone precursor polymers.

and the data normalized to the highest peak, m/e 362. The parent ion peak at m/e 362 is assigned to *trans*-pyrrone (VII). However, the peak at m/e 336 can only occur if one side of the PMDA-pBA model (IV) decarboxylated while the other side converted to pyrrone such that a benzimidazole-pyrrone structure resulted. This helps explain the source of carbon dioxide during maximum water evolution from this model and probably confirms Thiele's earlier observations on the PA-BA model (II) as well.[17]

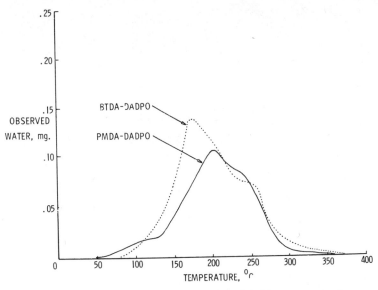

Fig. 8. Evolution of water during cure of two polyimide precursor polymers.

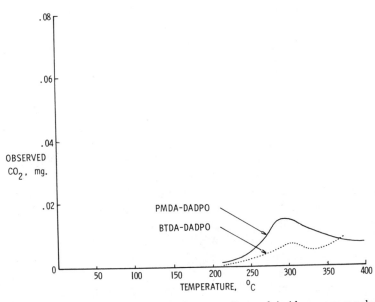

Fig. 9. Evolution of carbon dioxide during cure of two polyimide precursor polymers.

Figures 3 and 5 show that very little carbon dioxide is lost from the fully cyclized *trans*- or *cis*-pyrrone models (VII and VIII) over that coming from background. However, all of the other models exhibited carbon dioxide loss at temperatures above where cyclodehydration occurred. Since this could not have come from any pyrrone present, the initial cyclization reactions must also yield products which degrade at elevated temperatures to produce the observed carbon dioxide. These unidentified model products may be of the type which would

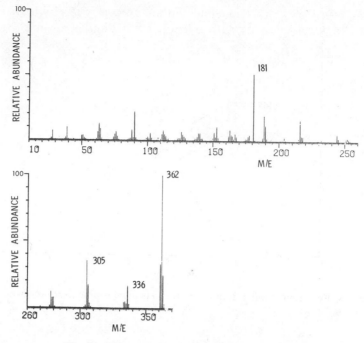

Fig. 10. Mass spectrum of PMDA-pBA (IV) model.

produce crosslinks if similar reactions occurred during the cure of pyrrone polymers.

Polymers

BTDA polymers gave better conversion to the pyrrone structure than did PMDA polymers. However, the results in Table III show that all four of the pyrrone precursors exhibited less than an 80% conversion under the conditions of this study. Inspection of Figures 6 and 7 reveals that during the cure process, significant amounts of carbon dioxide were also eliminated. A comparison of Figures 4 and 6 and Figures 5 and 7 suggests a similarity between the curing reactions occurring in the models and polymers. Thus, the incomplete conversion (Table III) can be partly explained by assuming that the carbon dioxide resulted from the same sources previously suggested for the model compounds. Whenever carbon dioxide is lost, complete cyclodehydration to the pyrrone structure cannot occur and the conversion must be less than 100%.

Incomplete conversion may also be a result of the increase in chain rigidity which is inherent in the pyrrone ladder structure.[18] As the polymer chains become more rigid, unreacted groups may find it difficult to attain the proper orientation in order to participate in cyclodehydration. Some decarboxylation of these unreacted groups also seems likely to occur under these conditions. There are several other possible reasons why complete cyclization was not observed. First, infrared spectra of the precursor polymers indicated that some cyclization during workup of the amide-acid-amine may have occurred prior to GC/MS analysis. Second, the assumption that the precursor polymer is linear may not be valid; some branching may have occurred during polymerization.[12,19]

Finally, the precursor polymers could contain an overly large number of end-groups, although the viscosity data given in Table I and solution property determinations reported earlier on PMDA-DAB polyamide-acid-amine precursors[20] tend to discount this. While these explanations might account for low yields of pyrrone, they cannot be applied to the model compounds which also exhibited low yields, although not quite as low as for the polymer. The reactions occurring in the polymers and models are probably the same, except that the polymers begin reacting at a slightly lower temperature.

The two polyimides were found to cyclize with little difficulty and, as shown in Figures 8 and 9, both were essentially converted at 350°C. Only a minor amount of CO_2 was observed up to this temperature. These results are consistent with the published results of Teleshova et al.[8] for PMDA-DADPO, and the agreement further verifies the viability of the GC/MS technique. Comparing the curves for the evolution of water and CO_2 in the imide precursors with that observed for the pyrrone precursors (Figs. 6 and 7) suggests that cyclodehydration occurs in a similar fashion for both polymer systems.

The double-stranded stepladder pyrrone structure should inherently be more thermally stable than the polyimide structure. However, in reality, no improvement in thermo-oxidative stability is afforded by pyrrones over polyimides. This is probably because polyimides largely attain their theoretical structure while pyrrones do not. This work shows that PMDA-mBA (VI) was the only model compound which achieved essentially complete cyclization. If a synthesis could be conducted which went exclusively by this route, the resulting cis polymer should have very nearly the theoretical pyrrone repeat unit. The true contribution of the complete pyrrone structural unit to the thermal stability of the polymer could then be evaluated with certainty.

CONCLUSIONS

The conclusions drawn from the study of the effluents produced during the thermal cyclization of these materials are:

1. The GC/MS technique as described herein was used effectively to characterize the cyclization of pyrrone and polyimide precursors.

2. The four pyrrone precursors studied did not achieve complete cyclization under the conditions of this experiment, while the polyimide precursors were almost completely converted.

3. The low conversion to pyrrone was due in part to the loss of carbon dioxide during thermal cyclization.

4. Based on model compound studies, a high conversion of the precursor to the pyrrone structure probably would be obtained if the precursor could be made to cyclize exclusively through the *meta*-benzimidazole-acid intermediate.

References

1. V. L. Bell and G. F. Pezdirtz, *J. Polym. Sci. B*, **3**, 977 (1965).
2. J. G. Colson, R. H. Michel, and R. M. Paufler, *J. Polym. Sci. A-1*, **4**, 59, 2349 (1966).
3. F. Dawans and C. S. Marvel, *J. Polym. Sci. A*, **3**, 3549 (1965).
4. V. L. Bell, in *Encyclopedia of Polymer Science and Technology*, Vol. 11, Interscience, New York, 1969, p. 240.
5. A. A. Berlin, B. I. Liogon'kii, and G. Shamraev, *Russ. Chem. Rev.*, **40**, 284 (1971).

6. H. D. Burks, NASA TM X-2641, December 1972.

7. L. A. Laius, M. I. Bessonov, M. M. Koton, and F. S. Florinskii, *Vysokomol. Soedin.*, **A12**, 1834 (1970).

8. A. S. Teleshova, E. N. Teleshov, and A. N. Pravednikov, *Vysokomol. Soedin.*, **A13**, 2309 (1971).

9. P. R. Young, M. S. Thesis, Virginia Polytechnic Institute and State University, May 1971.

10. P. R. Young, *J. Heterocyclic Chem.*, **9**, 371 (1972).

11. P. R. Young, *J. Heterocyclic Chem.*, **10**, 325 (1973).

12. N. J. Johnston, *J. Polym. Sci. A-1*, **10**, 2727 (1972).

13. G. M. Bower and L. W. Frost, *J. Polym. Sci., A-1*, 3135 (1963).

14. S. D. Bruck, *Polymer*, **6**, 49 (1965).

15. F. P. Gay and G. E. Berr, *J. Polym. Sci. A-1*, **6**, 1935 (1968).

16. L. W. Frost and G. M. Bower, *J. Polym. Sci. A-1*, **9**, 1045 (1971).

17. J. Thiele and K. G. Falk, *Ann.* **347**, 129 (1906).

18. A. N. Pravednikov, I. Ye. Kardash, E. N. Teleshov, and B. V. Kotov, *Vysokomol. Soedin.*, **A13**, 425 (1971); *Polym. Sci. USSR*, **13**, 483 (1971).

19. V. L. Bell and R. A. Jewell, *J. Polym. Sci. A-1*, **5**, 3043 (1967).

20. N. J. Johnston and L. B. Epps, *J. Polym. Sci. A-1*, **10**, 2751, (1972).

Received October 5, 1973
Revised June 22, 1976

JOURNAL OF APPLIED POLYMER SCIENCE   VOL. 21, 2405–2407 (1977)

Physical Properties and Structure of Silk.   III.   The Glass Transition and Conformational Changes of Tussah Silk Fibroin

JUN MAGOSHI and YOSHIKO MAGOSHI, *Sericultural Experiment Station, Wada, Suginami-ku, Tokyo, Japan,* and SHIGEO NAKAMURA, *Department of Industrial Chemistry, Faculty of Engineering, University of Tokyo, Hongo, Bunkyo-ku, Tokyo, Japan*

Synopsis

The glass transition, crystallization, and α–β transition of the Tussah silk fibroin were studied by means of DSC (differential scanning calorimetry) and infrared spectroscopy. The endothermic shift due to the glass transition was observed at 162°C. The endothermic peak at 220°C was attributed to the α–β conformational transition from the infrared spectra. The exothermic peak due to the crystallization occurred at 230°C.

INTRODUCTION

In the previous report,[1] the glass transition temperature of amorphous silk fibroin with random coil conformation has been determined by differential scanning calorimetry (DSC), and the exothermic peak at 212°C in the DSC curve has also been assigned to the crystallization of amorphous silk fibroin by recording the x-ray diffraction patterns of silk fibroin before and after heat treatment at 220°C.

The present work was intended to investigate the glass transition, conformational transition and crystallization of Tussah silk fibroin by DSC and infrared spectroscopy.

EXPERIMENTAL

Silk fibroin solution was obtained from the posterior division of the silk gland in full-grown larvae (one day before spinning) of *Antheraea pernyi*. After the aqueous solution of silk fibroin was dialyzed against deionized water and diluted to a concentration of about 0.1%, films for DSC and IR measurements were cast from the solution onto thin polyethylene films and dried at 20°C.

Differential scanning calorimetry was performed on a Perkin-Elmer DSC-II differential scanning calorimetry under nitrogen. Infrared spectra were obtained using a JASCO Model IR-G-type infrared spectrometer at 4000–400 cm^{-1}.

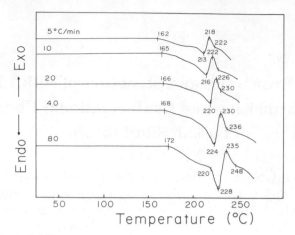

Fig. 1. DSC curves of Tussah silk fibroin at various heating rates.

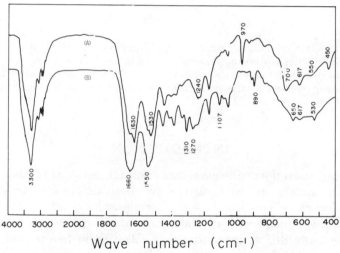

Fig. 2. Infrared spectra of Tussah silk fibroin: (a) untreated, (b) heat treated at 220°C for 30 min.

RESULTS AND DISCUSSION

Figure 1 shows DSC curves at various heating rates of Tussah silk fibroin film. The specimen was dried in a sample pan at 120°C for 10 min under nitrogen before measurement. For each curve, an exothermic and endothermic peak and an endothermic shift are observed. Both peaks shift to higher temperatures with increasing heating rate, namely, the exothermic peak shifts from 218° to 235°C and the endothermic peak, from 213° to 228°C. The endothermic shift also moves from 162°C at 5°C/min to 172°C at 80°C/min. An abrupt increase in linear thermal expansion was observed at this temperature.[2] Accordingly, the glass transition temperature of Tussah silk fibroin was determined to be 162°C from the endothermic shift at the slowest heating rate of 5°C/min.

In order to clarify the origin of the exothermic and the endothermic peaks, infrared spectra of Tussah silk fibroin were recorded before and after heat treatment at 220°C for 30 min (Fig. 2). The infrared spectrum of untreated silk fibroin film shows bands characteristic of the α-helix of silk fibroin, 1660, 1550, 1310, 1270, 1107, 890, and 617 cm^{-1}, and a band characteristic of random coil conformation at 650 cm^{-1}. After heat treatment at 220°C, the bands attributed to the extended β-form of silk fibroin are found at 1630, 1530, 1240, 970, and 700 cm^{-1}, and that of the α-helix at 617 cm^{-1} in the infrared spectrum. The band at 650 cm^{-1} due to the random coil conformation and most of the bands due to the α-helix disappear as a result of the heat treatment at 220°C.

This result indicates that the conformational transitions from random coil to β-form and from α-helix to β-form are induced by heat treatment at 220°C. Green et al.[3] reported that a α–β transition of poly(β-alkyl-L-aspartates) such as the methyl, ethyl, and benzyle esters are endothermic in character. Therefore, the endothermic peaks in the range of 213° to 228°C are attributed to the conformational transition from α-helix to extended β-form. The exothermic peaks ranging from 218° to 238°C are assigned to the crystallization of the amorphous region of Tussah silk fibroin to β-form crystals.

References

1. J. Magoshi and S. Nakamura, *J. Appl. Polym. Sci.,* **19,** 1013 (1975).
2. J. Magoshi and S. Nakamura, in preparation.
3. D. B. Green, F. Happey, and B. M. Watson, *Eur. Polym. J.,* **6,** 7 (1970).

Received July 23, 1976

JOURNAL OF APPLIED POLYMER SCIENCE   VOL. 21, 2409–2418 (1977)

Preparative Gel Permeation Chromatography.
I. Polypropylene

M. F. VAUGHAN and M. A. FRANCIS, *Division of Chemical Standards,*
National Physical Laboratory, Teddington, Middlesex TW11 OLW,
England

Synopsis

Preparative gel permeation chromatography was used to produce a number of polypropylene reference samples, within the molecular weight range of 10,000–600,000, from commercial materials. Some of these materials were degraded in a controlled manner to give base materials having suitable molecular weight characteristics. A procedure has been developed using a single preparative column packed with equal quantities of Styragel with nominal exclusion limits of 10^2, 10^3, 10^4, and 10^5 nm. The volume of solvent for recovery was minimized by use of higher loading factors than in analytical GPC (some 2–20 times more polymer was thus fractionated in each experiment). Under these conditions the fractions first eluted were sharpest having polydispersities of about 1.5. First fractions, from different base materials, were characterized by analytical GPC, and those of similar molecular weight and polydispersity were combined to give the reference samples. Refractionation was necessary with the highest molecular weight base material because the first stage fractions were not sharp enough. Some of these fractions were recovered at elution volumes where much lower molecular weight material was expected. Comparison with results from the other base materials indicates that the primary cause of the spreading is not overloading. This spreading is explained in terms of slower partitioning of the larger molecules between the interstitial fluid and the gel particles.

INTRODUCTION

Certified reference polymers having sharp molecular weight distribution (i.e., polydispersities $\overline{M}_w/\overline{M}_n$ approaching unity) are required for molecular weight studies on thermoplastics, in particular, for (i) the calibration of analytical gel permeation chromatography (GPC); (ii) the evaluation of Mark-Houwink constants for viscosity measurements; (iii) for theoretical studies on the behavior of polymer molecules in solution; and (iv), if available in sufficient quantity, for the evaluation of the variations of the physical, mechanical, and other properties of polymers with molecular weight. Polystyrene certified reference samples, covering a wide molecular weight range, have been available for some time, and more recently reference samples have also been prepared for high-density polyethylene.[1] In addition, a program has been initiated at the National Physical Laboratory to produce reference samples of other important industrial polymers such as polypropylene, poly(vinyl chloride), and poly(vinyl acetate).

Polystyrene reference materials having narrow molecular weight distributions (i.e., $\overline{M}_w/\overline{M}_n \sim 1.1$) can be prepared economically by anionic polymerization.

Individual batches of 100–1000 g are characterized in terms of molecular weight by light scattering ($\overline{M}_w$) and osmometry ($\overline{M}_n$). (Throughout this paper the term "molecular weight" replaces the more correct "relative molecular mass.") This synthetic method cannot be used with most other polymers; and with high-density polyethylene (HDPE), preparative gel permeation chromatography has been used to recover sharp fractions from commercial broad-MWD materials.[1] Each HDPE reference sample is an individual fraction (1–10 g) characterized by analytical GPC, using a calibration based on particular HDPE fractions which had been characterized in absolute terms.

Preparative GPC was used to prepare the polypropylene reference samples also. Individual small fractions were combined together to give samples of about 10 g, these combined materials being characterized by absolute determination of $\overline{M}_w$ and $\overline{M}_n$.

Preparative GPC is simply analytical GPC carried out on a larger scale. In analytical GPC, the aim is to characterize a sample as accurately as possible using the lowest amount of material, the only constraints being the operational parameters of the instrument. On the other hand, in preparative GPC, the objective is to fractionate as much polymer as possible in an efficient manner. The economics of the fractionation are usually a major consideration, and this leads to compromises over the sharpness of the fractions produced.

Two factors that have an important bearing on the economics of preparative GPC are the columns, which are expensive, and the volumes of solvent that have to be recovered in isolating the fractions. A common procedure in analytical GPC is to use four narrow columns each packed with gels of different porosities (e.g., nominal exclusion limits of 10^2, 10^3, 10^4, and 10^5 nm). In the preparation of the HDPE samples, a similar combination of four columns was used, each with a wider diameter than is customary in analytical GPC. By contrast, in the present work a single wide column was used; but, in order to preserve the ability to fractionate polymers covering an extensive range of molecular weights, it was packed in layers with equal proportions of the same combination of gels used in analytical GPC.

In analytical GPC, typically 0.004 g polymer (2 cm^3 of a 0.2% solution) is eluted through a column combination of total volume about 220 cm^3; and with a broad-MWD sample, the volume of eluant containing polymer is about 110 cm^3, which is approximately equivalent to the so-called pore volume of the column. Thus, during its passage through the column, such a polymer sample becomes considerably diluted. This dilution is important both theoretically and practically since the greater the separation of the polymer molecules, the more efficient the fractionation; and from a practical, particularly the preparative, point of view, the greater the dilution, the more solvent that has to be recovered. In analytical GPC, where conditions are usually highly standardized (i.e., similar combinations of columns of standard dimensions, eluting the same weight of polymer), the dilution is normally not of great interest. But in preparative GPC, where not only the number of columns may be different but also their dimensions and the weight of polymer fractionated can vary considerably, it is important to know this dilution for particular experiments. The volume of eluant containing polymer is approximately half the total volume of the column, and this represents the total dilution of the solid polymer during the operation. It is proposed to call the quantity (column volume/2)/polymer weight the specific

TABLE I
Fractionation of Polypropylene by Preparative GPC

Base material fractionated	Specific dilution, cm³/g	1 (1,200 / 581) %w/w	$\bar{M}_w$/10³	$\bar{M}_w$/$\bar{M}_n$	2 (1,320 / 309) %w/w	$\bar{M}_w$/10³	$\bar{M}_w$/$\bar{M}_n$	3 (1,440 / 128) %w/w	$\bar{M}_w$/10³	$\bar{M}_w$/$\bar{M}_n$	4 (1,560 / 62.2) %w/w	$\bar{M}_w$/10³	$\bar{M}_w$/$\bar{M}_n$	5 (1,680 / 27.8) %w/w	$\bar{M}_w$/10³	$\bar{M}_w$/$\bar{M}_n$	6 (1,800 / 17.7) %w/w	$\bar{M}_w$/10³	$\bar{M}_w$/$\bar{M}_n$	7 (1,920 / 11.8) %w/w	$\bar{M}_w$/10³	$\bar{M}_w$/$\bar{M}_n$	8 (2,040 / 7.43) %w/w	$\bar{M}_w$/10³	$\bar{M}_w$/$\bar{M}_n$	9 (2,160 / 6.96) %w/w	$\bar{M}_w$/10³	$\bar{M}_w$/$\bar{M}_n$	10 (2,280) %w/w	$\bar{M}_w$/10³	$\bar{M}_w$/$\bar{M}_n$
A/2[a]	10,000	4.8	581	2.13	20.1	567	2.04	28.7	385	1.78	18.1	370	1.83	11.6	369	2.39	7.2	393	1.77	4.3			3.0			2.2					
A/5[a]	4,000	2.4			6.2	309	2.09	18.5	256	1.66	24.6	160	1.75	19.4	148	2.21	14.2	136	2.29	7.9			4.2			2.6					
B	2,000	0.1			0.5			5.3	271	1.50	17.3	167	1.47	22.0	97.0	1.65	21.2	58.7	2.40	17.7	69.0	2.63	11.5			4.1					
C	2,000	0.0			1.7			15.6	128	1.41	27.0	90.2	1.57	23.6	74.4	1.80	17.9	77.5	1.82	10.4	76.5	1.95	3.7			0.1					
D	2,000	0.0			0.0			0.0			7.7	62.2	1.33	23.2	55.0	1.34	31.9	40.0	1.48	24.3	27.5	1.60	12.3			0.8					
E	2,000	0.0			0.0			0.0			6.1			24.5	43.7	1.30	34.0	37.3	1.45	25.3	21.1	1.62	10.0	25.7	1.91	0.1					
F	4,000	0.0			0.0			0.0			1.9			18.6	31.4		39.3	22.8	1.47	28.9	14.8	1.56	10.3	12.3	1.80	0.8					
G	1,000	0.0			0.0			0.0			0.0			6.1	38.4	1.25	19.8	26.8	1.32	31.0	11.8	1.40	27.3	10.9	1.53	16.2	6.96	1.66	1.8	7.01	2.20
H	1,000	0.0			0.0			0.0			0.0			3.7	27.8	1.23	17.4	17.7	1.30	32.1	11.8	1.40	26.8	7.43	1.66	16.2			3.8		

Header key: Flask number (Elution volume, cm³ / "Calibration," $\bar{M}_w \times 10^{-3}$).

[a] Refractionations of base material A: /2 from flask 2 of first fractionation; /5 from flask 5 of first fractionation.

TABLE II
Degradation of two Commercial Polypropylenes at 135°C

Time, hr	Sharp MWD		Broad MWD	
	$\overline{M}_w \times 10^{-3}$	$\overline{M}_w/\overline{M}_n$	$\overline{M}_w \times 10^{-3}$	$\overline{M}_w/\overline{M}_n$
0	611	4.24	544	7.89
3			372	7.52
17	393	2.62		
20			106	2.84
24			64.0	2.42
44			29.0	1.90
48			24.0	2.00
49	115	1.94		
100	41.9	1.79		

dilution (SD) and express it in cm³/g. Since in this work the concentrations of the polymer solutions *before* fractionation are usually 1–2% w/w, SD is always ≫1. Thus, for analytical GPC, the SD is about 27,000, and every gram of polymer fractionated in this way involves the recovery of 27.5 liters of solvent. In order to minimize the volume of solvent to be recovered, lower values of SD were used in the present work.

In general, lower values of SD lead to less efficient fractionation; but it has been found in this laboratory, and elsewhere,[2,3] that in preparative GPC the loss of resolution is not uniform over a set of fractions derived from a particular polymer. Usually, the first fractions to be eluted are sharper than the later fractions (see Table I), the differences becoming more pronounced as SD is decreased. Thus, the polydispersities of these first fractions increase comparatively slowly as SD decreases; and, in some cases even with quite low SD values, these first fractions are still quite sharp. The data in Table I from experiments G and H where SD's of 1000 were used (equivalent to fractionating over 20 times the weight of polymer eluted in analytical GPC) include first fractions which nevertheless have polydispersities as low as 1.2–1.3. By combining a number of such first fractions, a reference sample can be prepared; and by fractionating different base materials, one can prepare a series of reference samples covering a wide range of molecular weights.

Commercial polypropylenes generally have broad molecular weight distributions, and only two were found with MWD's narrow enough for the purpose of the present work, one of high molecular weight (base material A in Table III) and the other of very low molecular weight (base material H). Base materials for the intermediate molecular weight ranges were prepared by controlled thermal degradation of some of the higher molecular weight materials. When solutions of polypropylenes are heated, the chain length is reduced and the material gradually changes to a lower molecular weight product with a sharper distribution (see Table II). In this way, a number of base materials were prepared covering a wide molecular weight range (see Table III).

The greater the number of subdivisions of the eluting solution, the sharper the individual fractions. However, each extra subdivision increases the number of individual fractions required to give a combined weight of 10 g. To limit the number of fractionations, in the present work the eluant was subdivided into only 10 to 12 fractions. Even so, 50 or more fractions were required. Combination of the fractions was carried out in two stages. The same fractions from successive runs were collected in the same flask, the reproducibility of the fractionations being monitored by passing a small amount of the eluant through the differential refractometer of the analytical side of the instrument. Combined fractions were recovered daily and characterized in terms of molecular weight by analytical GPC. Fractions of the same molecular weight were subsequently combined to give the 10-g samples.

EXPERIMENTAL

Preparative GPC

A Waters Associates ANA-PREP gel permeation chromatograph was used with a column of length 1.2 m, I.D. 5.8 cm, and a volume of 3200 cm^3. It had been packed in four equal layers by the manufacturers with Styragels of different porosities expressed nominally as 10^2, 10^3, 10^4, and 10^5 nm. The apparatus was run automatically and programmed such that successive injections occurred after collection of 10 to 12 fractions, each of which had a volume of about 120 cm^3. An injection loop of 150 cm^3 was used with solutions containing 0.1% to 1.0% polymer (i.e., loads of 0.15 to 1.50 g), the lower concentrations with the higher molecular weights. Polypropylene stays in solution only at high temperatures, and these fractionations were carried out at 135°C with 1,2-dichlorobenzene as solvent. Generally, best results were obtained with a volumetric flow rate of 15 cm^3/min,* but slower rates were necessary with the highest molecular weight materials.

Preparative GPC gives reproducible results over a large number of successive runs (see Table IV), but variations can occur and it is necessary to monitor the experiments. This was done in two ways: (i) with individual experiments, by bleeding off a small amount of the eluant and passing it through the differential refractometer of the analytical side of the instrument,[4] and (ii) with the combined fractions by comparisons of the gravimetric data.

Solvent

With preparative GPC, large volumes of solvent are involved (up to 20 liters a day in this work), and this creates problems in relation to toxicity and fire. Generally, with organic solvents it is advisable to take precautions against inhalation of the vapors and absorption through the skin so that, in practice, the major hazard is that of fire. Only a limited number of solvents is available for polypropylene such as 1,2-dichlorobenzene, 1,2,4-trichlorobenzene, tetralin, decalin, etc. 1,2-Dichlorobenzene was chosen for this work, for it is less inflammable than the aromatic hydrocarbons and is more readily available than 1,2,4-trichlorobenzene.

Antioxidant

The antioxidant used in this work was Santonox R, bis(2-methyl-4-hydroxy-5-tert-butylphenyl) sulfide. In the analytical experiments, a concentration of 0.05% w/v was used in both the polymer solution and the eluting solvent. In the

---

* This corresponds to a linear flow rate of 0.56 cm/min, which is much slower than the 2.2 cm/min normally used in analytical GPC.

TABLE III
Polypropylene Base Materials

Base material	$\overline{M}_w \times 10^{-3}$	$\overline{M}_w/\overline{M}_n$
A	611	4.24
B	188	3.77
C	100	1.90
D	47.4	1.86
E	34.0	2.10
F	24.0	2.00
G	16.6	3.37
H	11.6	1.69

TABLE IV
Reproducibility of Preparative GPC Over 545 Runs.
Polymer Recovered from Flask 4 of Fractionation of Base Material A

No. of runs in combined fraction	% w/w	$\overline{M}_w \times 10^{-3}$	$\overline{M}_w/\overline{M}_n$
6	19.6		
16	26.7	231	1.94
21	18.2	300	2.47
68	19.6	267	2.04
74	19.2	277	2.92
79	21.3	212	2.02
89	20.8	284	2.39
92	19.6	256	2.51
100	17.2	228	2.47

preparative experiments, the overall concentration was 0.05%, but the Santonox R was dissolved only in the polymer solution. This different procedure had two advantages: (i) it eliminated the necessity of preparing large volumes of solvent containing Santonox R, and (ii) the presence of a high concentration (0.5%) of the antioxidant helped to prevent degradation of the polymer solution, which resided for as long as 24 hr at 135°C in the metal sample chamber before injection. As a further precaution against degradation, this solution chamber was flushed with nitrogen.

Isolation of Fractions

The polypropylene separated as a layer on top of the cold solvent; it was collected by filtration, washed with acetone, and dried at 40°C. The fractions were weighed, and from these gravimetric data, polymer concentration-versus-elution volume graphs were plotted.[4]

Analytical GPC

A Waters Associates 200 instrument was used with four columns (1.2 m × 1 cm) packed with Styragel of nominal exclusion limits 10^2, 10^3, 10^4, and 10^5 nm. The eluting solvent was 1,2-dichlorobenzene containing 0.05% Santonox R, the temperature was 135°C, and the flow rate was 1.4 cm³/min. Sample concentrations were 2–3 mg/cm^3, and the injection volume was 2 cm^3. Column calibration was carried out with narrow molecular weight distribution polystyrene standards (Pressure Chemical Co.) and values of $\overline{M}_w$ and $\overline{M}_n$ were calculated by the universal calibration method, using Mark-Houwink constants for polypropylene[5] and polystyrene.[6] No correction was made for dispersion.

Combinations of Fractions

Fractions having similar molecular weights and polydispersities were combined by dissolution in 1,2-dichlorobenzene containing 0.05% Santonox R at 135°C and recovered in the manner described above. These combined materials were characterized by analytical GPC and subsequently by light scattering $\overline{M}_w$ and osmometry $\overline{M}_n$.[7]

RESULTS AND DISCUSSION

The general method for the preparation of these polypropylene reference materials was the single fractionation of the base materials followed by combination of suitable fractions. The specific dilutions (SD's) were the lowest possible to give fractions having polydispersities of about 1.5. The results are shown in Table I, data from individual fractionations running from left to right across the table and the % figures being wt-% of all the polymer recovered in that particular fractionation.

Low Molecular Weight Samples ($\overline{M}_w < 40,000$)

Low molecular weight fractions were prepared from a commercial sample H and a degraded material G, using SD's as low as 1000. The results (see Table I) show that in both cases the first two fractions were sharp (polydispersities between 1.23 and 1.32) with molecular weights $\overline{M}_w$ ranging from 38,400 down to 17,700. With these materials, even some of the later fractions were quite sharp, those of $\overline{M}_w \sim 7000$ having polydispersities of 1.66.

The fractions from the degraded materials tended to be yellow, the problem increasing the greater the degradation. By a combination of (i) reprecipitation and (ii) treating with alumina much of the color was removed but it persisted with the very low molecular weight material.

Intermediate Molecular Weight Samples ($\overline{M}_w$ 40,000–250,000)

In the intermediate molecular weight range, the degraded materials B–E (see Table III) were used. With these base materials, it was necessary to use the higher SD of 2000 (see Table I). Initial fractions were obtained having $\overline{M}_w$'s in the range 40,000 to 270,000 with the polydispersities increasing from 1.3 to 1.5 as the molecular weight increased.

High Molecular Weight Samples ($\overline{M}_w > 250,000$)

The commercial sample A was used as base material for the high molecular weight samples. Even with the higher specific dilutions of 4000, the initial fractions from this material had polydispersities of about 1.8, some greater than

TABLE V
Polypropylene Reference Samples[7]

Reference no.	$\overline{M}_w \times 10^{-3}$	$\overline{M}_n \times 10^{-3}$	$\overline{M}_w/\overline{M}_n$
PP 10A	10.2	7.83	1.30
PP 13A	13.0	10.4	1.25
PP 21B	23.5	17.2	1.37
PP 31B	31.3	23.4	1.34
PP 46B	45.6	33.2	1.37
PP 66C	66.1	46.0	1.44
PP 93C	93.0	59.8	1.56
PP 141D	141.0	93.6	1.51
PP 200D	200.0	131	1.53
PP 241E	241	150	1.61
PP 325E	325	170	1.91
PP 628E	628	400	1.57

2.0. As the use of higher SD's would have involved working with very dilute solutions and small quantities of polymer, it was decided in this case to refractionate.

In order to obtain sufficient material for refractionation, the initial fractionation consisted of nearly 600 repetitive runs. Over this period, the polymer recovered from a particular flask was reasonably reproducible both in respect of wt-% of total polymer recovered and $\overline{M}_w$ (see Table IV).

Polymers from the same flask were combined and refractionated. Although overall the fractions recovered from these refractionations had lower polydispersities, only a few of the initial fractions were less than 1.8 (see Table I). No improvement was observed when a specific dilution of 10,000 (i.e., approaching that used in analytical GPC) was used in the refractionation of the highest molecular weight material $\overline{M}_w \sim 500,000$). A second refractionation of some of the lower molecular weight materials ($\overline{M}_w \sim 250,000$) produced initial fractions having polydispersities of about 1.5.

Combination of Fractions

Each reference sample was formed by combining ten or more daily combined fractions, each of which itself contained fractions from ten to 20 different runs. To ensure that only similar materials were being mixed, smaller batches were combined and recharacterized before the final combination.

Reference Samples

Fractions were combined to give 11 reference samples covering the molecular weight range of 10,000–600,000 (see Table V). The polydispersities of these materials, although approximately 1.5, increased with molecular weight, a reflection of the increasing difficulty of fractionating higher molecular weight materials.

Spreading of Fractions

In analytical GPC, when a range of polymers of narrow MWD are eluted through the columns, the traces produced are a series of sharp peaks which are used to calibrate the elution volume in terms of molecular weight. When an unknown polymer is eluted through the column, it is assumed that the broadening of the chromatogram reflects the wider MWD of the sample. Although this is basically true, there are other factors which cause chromatogram broadening, such as (i) diffusion effects, (ii) overloading, and (iii) viscous effects. Corrections can be made for (i) numerically and for (ii) and (iii) by eluting as small a polymer sample as possible. In analytical GPC, it is assumed that the polymer eluting at any point on a trace has a molecular weight corresponding to the calibration value. One advantage of preparative GPC is that one can study this variation of molecular weight with elution volume.

Although the preparative column was not calibrated in the conventional way can be made by using the lowest values of $\overline{M}_w$ (see Table I) for the fraction recovered from a particular flask (i.e., in general those with the lowest polydispersity). Spreading occurs when polymer of higher molecular weight appears at an elution volume (flask number) where polymer of lower molecular weight would have been expected, and thus this calibration can be used to detect it. From the other results in Table I, it would appear that some degree of spreading occurred in most of the fractionations.

In Table I are the results for base material F using a specific dilution of 4000, which is serious overloading by analytical GPC standards. Nevertheless, the fractions have values of $\overline{M}_w$ close to the calibration values and are reasonably sharp. Furthermore, when the load was increased four times (SD 1000) with base material G (very similar to F), the fractions again had $\overline{M}_w$'s close to the calibration values, although the recovered polymer appeared in a slightly larger elution volume. It would appear, therefore, that, in these experiments, the spreading due to overloading is quite small.

On the other hand, the results in Table I for base material A/2 show serious spreading, successive fractions having $\overline{M}_w$ values generally much higher than the calibration values and high polydispersities. The specific dilution in the experiment was 10,000; but if allowance is made for the possibility that only 25% of the gel (that with nominal exclusion limits of 10^5 nm) is available for these high molecular weight molecules, then in respect of fractionation efficiency the effective SD may be 2500. This is similar to the values used with the low molecular weight base materials F and G where no serious spreading was observed. So it would appear that the spreading with base material A/2 is not due to overloading but is associated with its high molecular weight.

The observation in GPC that the polymer molecules emerge in order of decreasing molecular weight is usually explained in terms of differential retardation of the smaller molecules due to the fact that they can penetrate a larger number of pores on the surfaces of the gel particles. Although this simple explanation accounts for most of the GPC phenomena, it does not involve the partitioning process as the polymer molecules enter and leave the gel. When at the same moment two polymer molecules of different size enter the gel through pores of the same diameter, there are three possibilities: (i) the two molecules emerge from the gel at the same time; (ii) the largest molecule emerges first; and (iii) the smaller molecule emerges first. In the case of (i), the rates of retardation of the two molecules will be unaffected; and if (ii) applies, the progress of the smaller molecule through the column will be delayed still further and the effect will enhance, and be indistinguishable from, the usual GPC explanation. However, if the smaller molecule partitions at a faster rate, then the larger molecule will be differentially retarded, which is the opposite of the usual explanation. Under such conditions, the larger molecules would tend to tail into elution volumes where smaller molecules would be expected, and one would expect the effect to become more pronounced with increasing molecular weight. This would explain why, in these preparative GPC experiments, the first fractions were always sharpest (the higher polydispersities of the subsequent fractions being due to delayed elution of the higher molecular weight polymer) and why the resolution with high molecular weight materials was poor.

The movement of the polymer molecules into and out of the gel is governed by the concentration differential between the interstitial fluid and the inside of the gel. Thus, while the concentration is highest outside, the polymer molecules move into the gel; and when it becomes lower outside, the molecules move out of the gel. The two molecules which enter a gel particle at the same moment are, therefore, subjected to the same forces; and although the smaller molecule will diffuse faster and further into the gel, one might expect it to return to the surface of the particle at the same time as the slower-moving larger molecule. However, on this return journey to the interstitial fluid, there is an important difference. The surface of the gel has a distribution of pore sizes, some larger than the pore through which the two molecules entered the particle, and some smaller. Thus, on the return journey, the smaller molecule has a much larger number of possible exits to the interstitial fluid than the larger molecule, and this would explain faster partitioning of the smaller molecule and thus tailing of the larger molecule.

This model would also explain why the tailing effect becomes more pronounced at higher concentrations since under these conditions the larger molecules would be pushed further into the gel, making it increasingly more difficult for them to find a way out. For example, the further a larger molecule penetrates the gel, the greater the delay through attempting to leave the gel through pores which are too narrow. On the other hand, with the dilute solutions used in analytical GPC, penetration would be minimal, partitioning taking place mainly at the surface of the gel particle.

The authors wish to thank Dr. J. H. S. Green for his continued interest in this work and for his advice in preparing this paper. The authors also wish to acknowledge gifts of materials from the following: Shell Chemicals U.K. Limited; Imperial Chemical Industries Limited (Plastics Division); Sanyo Chemical Industries Limited for commercial polypropylene samples; and Durham Raw Materials Limited for the Santonox R.

References

1. A. Peyrouset, R. Prechner, R. Panaris, and H. Benoit, *J. Appl. Polym. Sci.*, **19**, 1363 (1975).
2. P. G. Montague and F. W. Peaker, *J. Polym. Sci. Symp.*, **43**, 277 (1973).
3. A. R. Cooper, A. J. Hughes, and J. F. Johnson, *J. Appl. Polym. Sci.*, **19**, 435 (1975).
4. M. F. Vaughan, *Industrial Polymers: Characterization by Molecular Weight*, Transcripta Books, London, 1973, p. 112.
5. J. V. Dawkins, J. W. Maddock, and D. Coupe, *J. Polym. Sci. A-2*, **8**, 1803 (1970).
6. T. Ogawa, S. Taraka, and S. Hoshino, *Kobunshi Kagaku*, **29**, 6 (1972).
7. C. M. L. Atkinson and R. Dietz, *Makromol. Chem.*, **177**, 213 (1976).

Received April 28, 1976
Revised July 16, 1976

JOURNAL OF APPLIED POLYMER SCIENCE   VOL. 21, 2419–2437 (1977)

Stress–Strain Behavior, Hardness, and Thermomechanical Properties of Butadiene–Styrene Block Copolymers as a Function of Processing Technique

JEAN L. LEBLANC, *University of Liege, Belgium**

Synopsis

Stress–strain properties of star-shaped butadiene–styrene block copolymers were carried out on extruded sheet and injection molded samples. A striking "plastic-like" behavior was observed during the first extension, with a marked yield point, a drawing process, and an important hysteresis. These phenomena disappeared on the second elongation, but annealing below the polystyrene glass transition temperature gave again the initial behavior. A marked processing technique dependence was observed in the stress–strain experiments. An important variation in hardness was observed before and after stretching, and annealing experiments permitted the study of hardness recovery. A logarithmic relation between recovered hardness and the annealing time at constant temperature was deduced from the experimental data. Thermomechanical analysis curves show singular transitions between 20° and 85°C, which disappear on stretching. An important discrepancy occurs in TMA curves of extruded and injected samples. A comparison is made of thermomechanical behavior of linear and star-shaped SBS block copolymers. A modified model is proposed for a reversibly deformable structure composed of polybutadiene and polystyrene linked ends at the diffuse interfacial region between the PS domains and the PB matrix.

INTRODUCTION

A growing interest in block copolymers has emerged in the past few years, especially in the case of the new class of elastomers called "thermoplastic elastomers" or "thermolastics," which consist of ordered, triblock copolymers of the general structure P-E-P, where P is a thermoplastic block polymer and E is an elastomeric block polymer. These materials exhibit a particular mechanical behavior generally attributed to the fact that the blocks decompose into separate phases when the lengths of the block sequences are sufficiently large.

Elastomeric block copolymers, particularly butadiene–styrene, have become important materials of commerce in the past few years. Essentially, two kind of structure are recognizable in commercial thermolastics: the classical linear triblock structure S—B—S, where S denotes polystyrene sequences and B the polybutadiene sequence, and the star-shaped structure

* Present address: Monsanto Technical Center, B-1348, Louvain-La-Neuve, Belgium.

Commercial examples for the first class are Kraton of the Shell Co., and for the latter class, Solprene of the Phillips Petroleum Co. Physical properties of linear SBS copolymers have been well investigated in the literature, but little attention has been given at this time to star-shaped butadiene–styrene block copolymers. The purpose of this paper is to present some investigations on tensile properties of star-shaped SBS copolymers in relation to processing techniques. Transition temperatures will also be considered and comparison made with linear SBS copolymers.

EXPERIMENTAL

Butadiene–styrene block copolymers used in this study are Kraton 1101 (Shell Co.), a linear SBS triblock copolymer with 25% PS and a molecular weight of 102,000, and Solprene 406, 411, and 415 (Phillips Petroleum Co.) star-shaped block copolymers with 38%, 31%, and 40% PS, respectively, and molecular weights of 208,000, 258,000, and 153,000, respectively. Other characteristics of the samples have been given elsewhere.[1]

In order to test the influence of processing conditions of butadiene–styrene

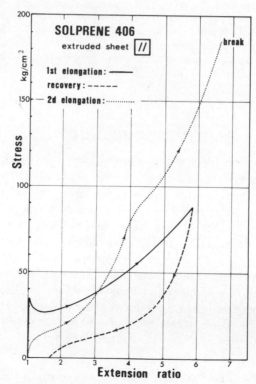

Fig. 1. Typical stress–strain experiment with Solprene 406, at extension rate of 2 cm/min, at 25°C. □ Dumbbell from extruded sheet; parallel to processing flow direction. ① Dumbbell from injected disk; perpendicular to processing flow direction.

block copolymers on their mechanical properties, Solprene samples were kindly provided by Phillips Petroleum (Technical Center at Overijse, Belgium) in the form of extruded sheets and injected discs.

Specimens for tensile experiments were cut from extruded sheets and injected disks, in such a manner that dumbbells were parallel or perpendicular to the flow direction of the processing technique. Stress–strain measurements on ASTM D638-68 dumbbell tensile specimens were made using an Instron tester at a cross-head speed of 2 cm/min and at a temperature of 25°C.

Thermomechanical measurements were carried out on extruded and injected Solprene samples, and on a compression-molded Kraton sample, before and after stretching. Measurements were made using a du Pont 900 differential thermal analyzer combined with a du Pont 941 thermomechanical analyzer (TMA).[2] The probe used for the TMA was a quartz rod, radius 0.123 cm, with a flat end. Samples approximately 0.5 × 0.5 cm were cut from the dumbbell tensile specimens and placed under the end of the probe. The probe was adjusted to just touch the surface of the sample using the probe position controller, after cooling at the starting temperature (−120°C). A load of constant weight (10 g) was applied to the probe, and the displacement of the probe was recorded as a function of the temperature. The temperature was increased from −120° to +200°C at a heating rate of 10°C/min.

With the observation that the mechanical properties of the surface of our samples varied with stretch, hardness measurements were made with a Shore A durometer (ASTM D 2240-68). A dead load of 1 kg was used to apply the durometer, and the scale was read within 5 sec after the presser foot was in firm contact with the specimen. At least five measurements at different positions were made to determine the mean value.

RESULTS AND DISCUSSION

Stress–Strain Experiments

A typical stress–strain experiment is shown in Figure 1. A first elongation is made up to a strain of 400–500%, which generally corresponds to a stress of 80–90 kg/cm². The recovery curve is then recorded in order to obtain the unrecovered strain, and the second elongation is carried out up to sample break. (Note that in the second cycle, the strain is increased to include the residual set from the first cycle.)

All the various specimens of Solprene 406, 411, and 415 exhibited generally the same shape of stress–strain curve, except for the injection-molded Solprene 411 samples which break at the first elongation.

A striking "plastic-like" behavior is clearly observed in the first extension cycle, with a marked yield point at about 13% elongation according to the tensile specimen and the material. After this yield point, specimens deform in a small region well defined by sharp boundaries which correspond to an abrupt change in thickness. Further elongation increases the size of this region until the entire specimen is again uniform. At this time, the strain reaches usually 100–150%, and during the drawing process the stress remains essentially constant, at a value slightly below yield stress. An elastic extension follows drawing, and recovery curves show a marked hysteresis with a residual unrecovered strain of at least 50%. In the second elongation, the deformation is more homogeneous, and

TABLE I

Stress–Strain Experiments with Solprene Butadiene–Styrene Block Copolymers

	Solprene 406				Solprene 411				Solprene 415			
	⊘	①	⊘	⊡	⊘	①	⊘	⊡	⊘	①	⊘	⊡
First Elongation												
Young's modulus, (kg/cm²)	1159	1702	670	1259	a	a	1129	601	397	591	336	340
Yield point												
stress, kg/cm²	36.7	37.6	34.7	39.8	—	—	33.3	34.9	26.4	29.1	22.8	26.3
strain, %	6.0	4.9	6.5	4.1	—	—	6.8	7.3	11.9	13.2	10.5	12.2
Unrecovered strain, %	57	72	64	65	—	—	61	49	64	55	62	69
Second Elongation												
Break												
stress, kg/cm²	96.4	210.2	182.7	183.5	48.3	55.6	201.4	182.9	135.5	222.2	208.5	217.0
strain, %	316	592	564	590	424	471	622	617	468	651	693	693

a Break at first elongation.

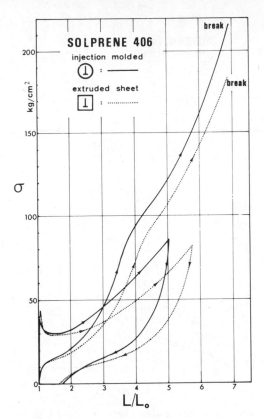

Fig. 2. Stress–strain curves for Solprene 406 at extension rate of 2 cm/min, at 25°C. Comparison between extruded sheet and injection-molded samples.

stress–strain curves resemble those of vulcanized elastomers. This tensile behavior of our Solprene samples is nearly similar to that of linear butadiene–styrene block copolymers of the same monomer ratio, as reported in the literature.[3–5]

If all the Solprene samples we used exhibit the same general tensile behavior described above, some differences appear which are dependent not only on the material characteristics (monomers ratio, molecular weight) but also on the processing technique of the specimens (injection molded or extruded) and upon the direction of the applied stress with respect to the direction of the processing flow. Mechanical properties as measured by stress–strain experiments are given in Table I. At same butadiene/styrene ratio (60/40), it is clearly seen that the initial Young's modulus and the yield stress increase with molecular weight (compare Solprene 406 and Solprene 415); inversely, yield strain and ultimate properties (stress and strain at break) decrease when the molecular weight increases. This molecular weight dependence of the mechanical properties of star shaped butadiene–styrene block copolymers is not observed for linear SBS block copolymers, for which, at constant proportion of segmental polystyrene, the mechanical properties are essentially unaffected by molecular weight changes, as reported in reference 3.

Stress–strain experiments show that the mechanical behavior is very dependent on the manner in which the tensile specimens are prepared. Figure 2

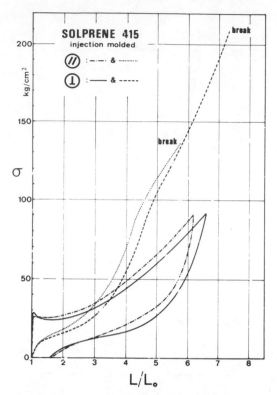

Fig. 3. Stress–strain curves for Solprene 415 (injection-molded sample) at extension rate of 2 cm/min, at 25°C; dumbbells parallel or perpendicular to the processing flow direction.

compares stress–strain curves for Solprene 406 extruded sheet and injection-molded samples, the stress being applied perpendicularly to the processing flow direction.   Young's moduli are very different, higher for the injection-molded sample.   The drawing appears more marked in the case of the extruded sheet sample, though the unrecovered strain is more important for the injection-molded sample.   After an initial common part, second elongation curves differ in that the extruded sample presents a more smooth curve than the injected sample. Stress at break is higher for injection-molded sample, but strains at break are similar.

Figure 3 shows stress–strain curves for injection-molded Solprene 415 samples, and behavior differences can be seen when stress is applied in parallel or perpendicular direction to the processing flow direction.   It is surprising that ultimate properties are higher when the stress is applied perpendicularly to the processing flow direction, because it is well known that chain orientation by processing of thermoplastics increases their mechanical properties in the melt flow direction.   This discrepancy is not observed for extruded sheet samples, as shown in Figures 4 and 5.

All these observations can be made for all the Solprene samples, and quantitatives differences in mechanical properties can be deduced from Table I. Measured Young's moduli are higher for injection-molded samples, but application of the stress perpendicularly to the processing flow direction gives ever higher moduli when compared to parallel application of the stress.   Some dif-

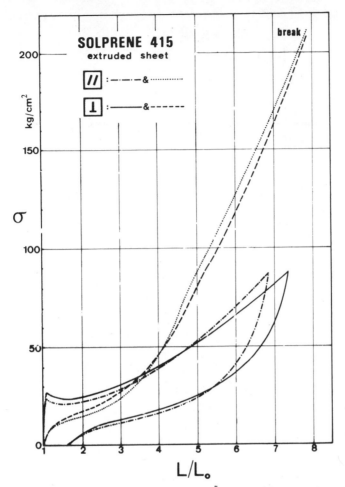

Fig. 4. Stress–strain curves for Solprene 415 (extruded sheet sample) at extension rate of 2 cm/min, at 25°C.

ferences appear in yield point values and unrecovered strains, just like for Young's moduli.

This important dependence of mechanical properties on processing techniques is very surprising and seems typical of block copolymers, according to similar observations reported by others[5] for Kraton 101 films. But compression-molded samples of Kraton 101 (a linear SBS block copolymer) do not present a yield point in their stress–strain curves. Somes differences appear thus between star-shaped and linear butadiene–styrene block copolymers, high initial Young's moduli and yield points being more processing sensitive in the case of linear copolymers.

The separated phase morphology is well established at this time for SBS block copolymers, and the mechanical behavior during the first elongation is currently attributed to a kind of "structure" which is broken during the first extension.[4,5] The high values of the Young's modulus and the process of yielding are related to the size and the shape of the polystyrene domains. The high Young's modulus indicates that, at low extensions, the polystyrene domains cannot move independently of each other. In this case, the polystyrene regions interact with each other by interparticle contacts to form a loosely bound continuous phase of

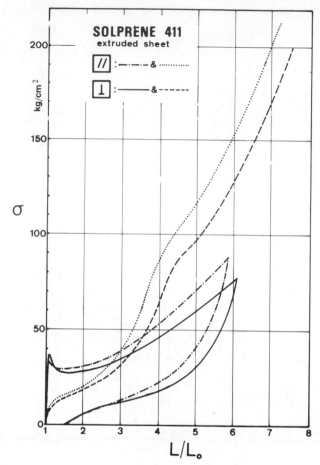

Fig. 5. Stress–strain curves for Solprene 411 (extruded sheet sample), at extension rate of 2 cm/min, at 25°C.

polystyrene, as has been assumed before.[6] With this model, yielding and stress softening could result from partial destruction of the polystyrene structure during extension.

Although some rigid structure seems to be "broken" during the drawing of butadiene–styrene block copolymers, this phenomenon appears reversible. Solprene samples stretched 100% and annealed at 60°C for different times show a progressive recovery of the original stress–strain behavior. Figures 6 and 7 show the recovery of original stress–strain response as a function of annealing time; further, we have verified that annealing of unstretched samples does not induce changes in the first extension curve. Since recovery occurs at annealing temperature below the polystyrene T_g, it is reasonable to assume, as a speculative hypothesis, that the deformation mechanism does not concern the polystyrene glassy domains themselves, but rather the diffuse interfacial regions between the polybutadiene matrix and the polystyrene domains. With this assumption, yielding and stress softening could be related to the (reversible) deformation of some structure depending of the processing technique.

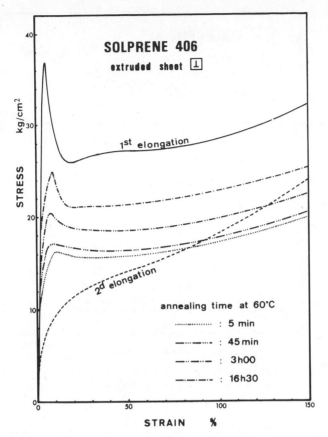

Fig. 6. Stress–strain experiments with annealing after second elongation, for Solprene 406 (extruded sheet sample).   Extension rate 2 cm/min.   All tensile tests made at $T = 25°C$.

Hardness Experiments

An important change in the mechanical properties of surface before and after stretching was fortuitously observed with our Solprene samples.   Although "hardness" is not a fundamental property, some experiments were carried out in order to observe an eventual recovery of the "hardness loss" by stretching. Table II gives Shore A values before and after stretching for Solprene samples and hardness losses in percent of the original hardness.

After stretching, the samples were annealed (in a water bath) and Shore A hardness was measured after different annealing times.   Annealing experiments were carried out at 40°, 50°, and 60°C, and an example of the obtained experimental data is given in Figure 8 for Solprene 406 extruded sheet sample. Comparison between extruded sheet sample and injection-molded sample is made in Figure 9 for Solprene 415.   The straight lines are drawn by least-squares adjustment of the experimental data, and it is clearly seen that, at constant annealing temperature, the hardness recovery can be expressed by a logarithmic law as follows:

$$h_t = h_0 + k(\ln t) \qquad T = \text{const.}$$

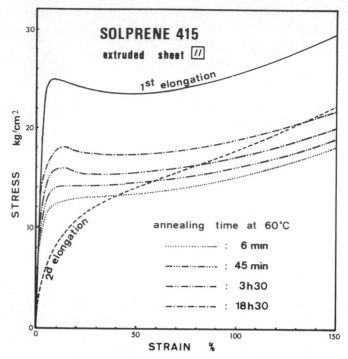

Fig. 7. Stress–strain experiments with annealing after second elongation, for Solprene 415 (extruded sheet sample). Extension rate, 2 cm/min. All tensile tests made at $T = 25°C$.

where h_0 is the hardness just after stretching ($t = 0$); k is a constant; t is the annealing time; and h_t is, naturally, the hardness measured at room temperature, after annealing for time t at temperature T and reconditioning to room temperature.

As an example, experimental values of annealing experiments on Solprene 406 extruded sheet sample are given in Table III. Values of h_0 and k, as computed by the least-squares method, are also given, and correlation coefficient r^2 values show that the adjustment is excellent. If we compare the computed values of h_0 with the experimental hardness measured just after stretching, a difference is noted which varies with annealing temperature. We can conclude that the logarithmic law described above does not apply to initial hardness recovery, the recovery rate just after the stretch being lower or higher, according to annealing temperature, than expected by the logarithmic relation.

TABLE II
Shore A Hardness

	Solprene 406		Solprene 411		Solprene 415	
	Disk	Sheet	Disk	Sheet	Disk	Sheet
Before stretch	91.6	88.4	79.9	85.7	84.0	86.9
After stretch	74.7	72.5	67.1	67.6	67.2	70.8
Hardness loss, %	18.4	18.0	16.0	21.1	20.0	18.5

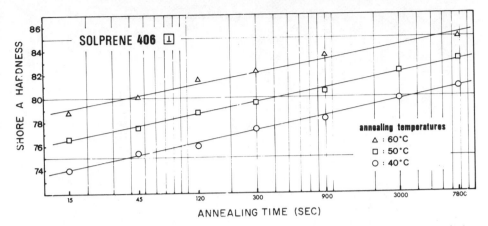

Fig. 8. Hardness recovery by annealing for Solprene 406, extruded sheet sample. Hardness before stretch, 88.4; after stretch, 72.5.

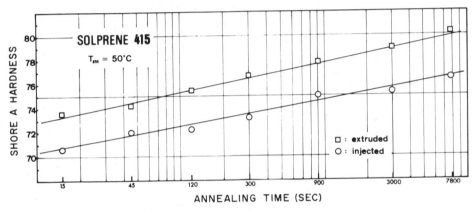

Fig. 9. Hardness recovery by annealing at $T = 50°C$ for Solprene 415. Comparison between extruded sheet and injection-molded samples.

From the logarithmic law described above, it is possible to calculate the annealing time for the complete recovery of the initial hardness (before stretching), following the relation

$$t = \exp\left(\frac{h_t - h_0}{k}\right)$$

Introducing the values of h_0 and k, we computed the annealing time t_{tr} necessary to recover the original hardness. Results show naturally that this time of total recovery t_{tr} increases when the annealing temperature T_{ann} decreases and, moreover, that a linear relation exists between log t_{tr} and T_{ann}, as shown in Figure 10 for Solprene 406 extruded sheet sample. An exponential function can be computed by the least-squares method, and the following relation between t_{tr} and T_{ann} is obtained:

$$t_{tr} \text{ (hr)} = a \cdot e^{-b \cdot T_{ann}}$$

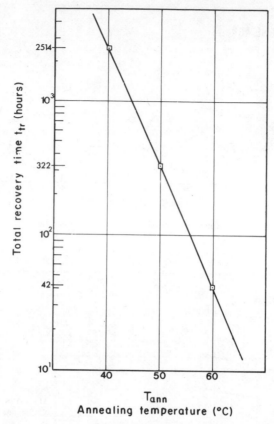

Fig. 10. Relation between time of total hardness recovery after stretch and annealing temperature.

TABLE III

Annealing Experiments on Solprene 406, Extruded Sheet Samples Computed Values of the Recovery Logarithmic Law

Annealing time, sec	T_{ann} = 40° C exp. hardness	T_{ann} = 50° C exp. hardness	T_{ann} = 60° C exp. hardness
0[a]	72.5	72.5	72.5
15	74.0	76.6	78.8
45	75.4	77.5	80.1
120	76.0	78.8	81.6
300	77.4	79.6	82.2
900	78.2	80.5	83.6
3000	79.9	82.2	—
7800	80.8	83.2	85.0
h_0	71.1	73.6	76.4
k	1.08	1.06	1.00
r^2	0.99	0.99	0.98

[a] Hardness just after the stretch.

TABLE IV

Time of Total Hardness Recovery as a Function of Annealing Temperature

Sample	$T_{ann} = 40°C$			$T_{ann} = 50°C$			$T_{ann} = 60°C$			$t_{tr} = a \cdot e^{-b \cdot T_{ann}}$		
	h_0	k	t_{tr}, hr	h_0	k	t_{tr}, hr	h_0	k	t_{tr}, hr	a	b	r^2
Solprene 406 inj.	74.0	1.08	3320	74.3	1.18	460	78.0	1.12	51	1.46×10^7	0.209	0.9991
Solprene 406 ext.	71.1	1.08	2514	73.6	1.06	322	76.4	1.00	42	8.98×10^6	0.205	1.0000
Solprene 411 inj.	65.1	0.88	5560	67.6	0.87	368	70.8	0.75	50	6.10×10^7	0.237	0.9923
Solprene 411 ext.	66.8	1.14	4404	70.2	1.08	480	72.4	1.17	25	1.55×10^8	0.259	0.9931
Solprene 415 inj.	65.3	1.20	1627	68.1	1.13	381	72.4	0.99	34	4.38×10^6	0.193	0.9801
Solprene 415 ext.	68.1	1.64	2013	70.3	1.18	275	75.0	0.88	27	1.19×10^7	0.216	0.9985

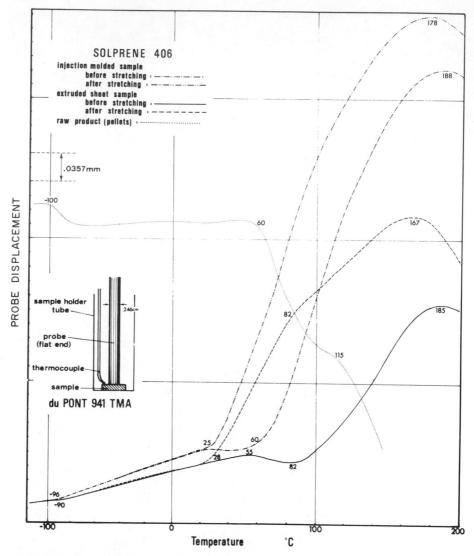

Fig. 11. Thermomechanical analysis of Solprene 406, at heating rate of 10°C/min. Load, 10 g.

Values of coefficients a and b and correlation coefficients r^2 are given in Table IV. On the basis of r^2 values obtained, the adjustment of this relation to experimental data seems be excellent. As practical check, stretched samples were annealed at 60°C for time periods equal to t_{tr}; depending on the sample, the recovery was 98.7% to 99.6% of the initial hardness value. A sample of Solprene 406 (extruded) was annealed at 60°C during 48 hr to recover all its initial hardness; stored six months at 23°C, the recovery reached 95.5%.

Hardness, a surface property, is a low-amplitude modulus measurement and can be connected with microstructure of the block copolymers in such a way that the same speculative conclusions can be drawn from these experiments as from tensile experiments, in the sense that hardness loss by stretching and annealing

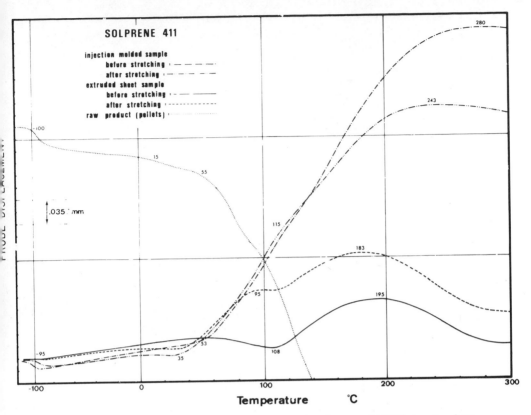

Fig. 12. Thermomechanical analysis of Solprene 411, at heating rate of 10°C/min. Load, 10 g.

recovery are attributable to a (reversible) deformation of the interfacial regions between the block domains. Particularly the annealing temperature dependence of the hardness recovery is incompatible with the *break* of a rigid structure during the first elongation.

Thermomechanical Analysis

The differences observed in the tensile behavior of samples processed by different ways made us suspect that differences would exist in their thermomechanical analysis curves. If "superstructures" exist which are deformed by stretching, they will be revealed by transitions in thermomechanical curves and important stress-induced variations.

Thermomechanical analysis (TMA) curves are drawn in Figures 11, 12, and 13 for Solprene 406, 411, and 415, respectively, in order to compare the recordings obtained before and after stretch, for injection-molded samples as well as for extruded sheet samples. (Note that the position of the curves on the probe displacement scale is quite arbitrary; only expansion variations are considered here.) Also given is the TMA curve for raw products in the form of pellets. An important behavior difference is first observed between raw products and processed samples, and it is attributed to the fact that raw products present a heterogeneous foaming nature. Under the applied weight on the probe, the mac-

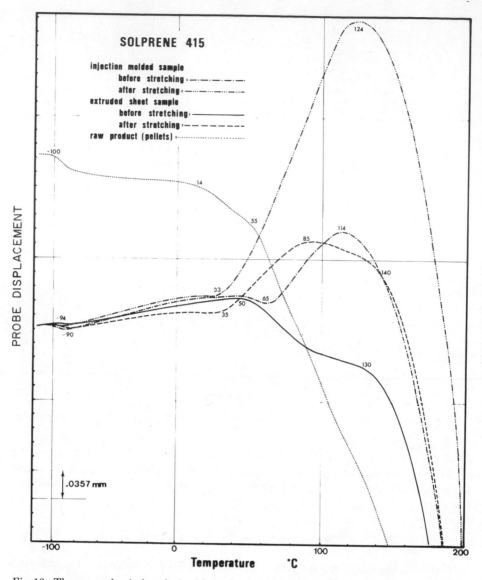

Fig. 13. Thermomechanical analysis of Solprene 415, at heating rate of 10°C/min. Load, 10 g.

roscopic cellular structure is easily destroyed by an increase in temperature, and consequently an apparent and nonsignificant melting curve results.

As expected, important thermomechanical behavior differences appear between extruded and injection-molded samples. Thermal expansion is higher for injection molded than for extruded material, and this is probably attributable to a larger stress storage during the injection molding process. Moreover, transitions appear in extruded samples which are not apparent in injected material. This is particularly clear for Solprene 406 with a transition at 82°C for extruded sheet samples (Fig. 11). Another important observation is the absence of a clear, well-defined transition point in the vicinity of the classical polystyrene T_g (100°C), and the other clear transitions observed between room temperature and 85–90°C give a first confirmation of our hypothesis that the mechanical

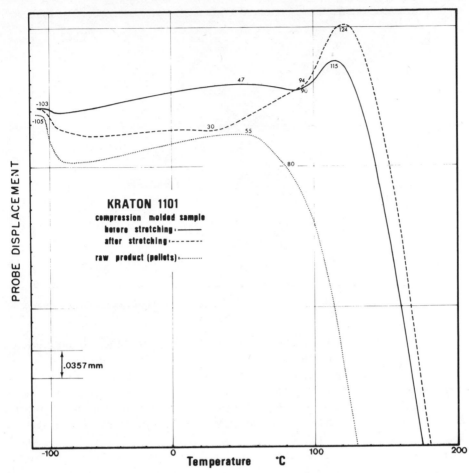

Fig. 14. Thermomechanical analysis of Kraton 1101, at heating rate of 10°C/min. Load, 10 g.

behavior is interfacial complex structure dependent rather than glassy polystyrene domain dependent.

Most interesting observations can be made when the TMA curves are compared before and after stretching for a given sample. After an initial common
part from the butadiene glass transition up to 20°C, discrepancies appear in the
curves in such a manner that transitions, well-observed for unstretched samples,
disappear after stretching. As an example, let us consider the TMA curves of
Solprene 406 injection-molded samples. The unstretched specimen exhibits
an expansion up to 25°C, followed by a horizontal plateau up to 60°C, and a rapid
increase up to 188°C. After stretching, the transition at 25°C is still observed,
but it is followed by a direct increase up to 178°C. The same kind of observation
can be made on extruded Solprene 406 sample and with Solprene 411 and
415.

For comparison, the thermomechanical analysis curves of Kraton 1101 compression-molded sample are given in Figure 14. The difference between unstretched and stretched material is not very important but appears very clearly.
With the restriction that the processing techniques are quite different, a quan-

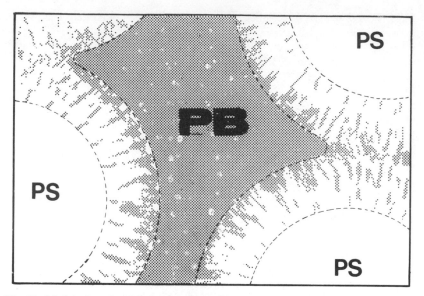

Fig. 15. Model of a reversibly deformable superstructure, at diffuse interfacial region.

titative difference is easily observed between linear SBS block copolymer, i.e., Kraton 1101, and star-shaped SBS block copolymers, i.e., Solprene.

This disappearance of TMA transitions with stretch can reasonably be attributed to some "structures" which are altered during drawing, and since those transitions do *not* correspond to the polystyrene glass transition temperature, we can conclude that the "superstructures" do not concern glassy polystyrene domains *alone*. According to tensile experiment results, with progressive recovery of initial behavior by annealing of stretched samples, and according to hardness experiments, the most reasonable model seems be a kind of reversibly deformable structure composed of interfacial diffuse regions between polystyrene glassy domains and the polybutadiene matrix, as shown in Figure 15.

CONCLUSIONS

The remarkable mechanical properties of butadiene–styrene block copolymers are attributed to the formation of a two-phase system, but some striking phenomena such as yielding and stress softening cannot be attributed to the deformation of a pure polystyrene structure. Thermomechanical analysis shows that stretch-induced structural variations correspond to thermomechanical transitions between room temperature and 65–80°C, far below the polystyrene T_g. A model is thus proposed for a reversibly deformable "superstructure" composed of polybutadiene and polystyrene linked ends, at the diffuse interfacial region between the PS domains and the PB matrix.

A very important dependence of the mechanical properties on processing technique is observed in the case of star-shaped block copolymers, and it seems that the classical macromolecular orientation process is not a satisfactory explanation. A hypothesis is that interfacial superstructures, as described above, are processing sensitive and that stress storage by these superstructures during processing can induce mechanical behavior differences.

The author would like to thank Professor H. A. Dieu for helpful discussions and Professor K. Gamski for stress–strain measurements carried out in his laboratory and constant attention brought to this work. Thanks are also due to Mr. Ledent, Director, and Mr. Saussez of the Institut National des Industries Extractives for TMA experiments. Sincere gratitude is expressed to Miss D. Degeimbre for her support in the experimental work. The author wishes to acknowledge the Phillips Petroleum Company (Technical Center at Overijse, Belgium) for providing the Solprene samples.

References

1. J. L. Leblanc, *Tribune du Cebedeau*, **28** (378), 231 (May 1975).

2. E. I. du Pont de Nemours and Co., Instrument and Equipment Division, *Instruments Instruction Manual: 900 Thermal Analyzer and Modules, TMA and Accessories*, Wilmington, Delaware, 1968.

3. G. Holden, E. T. Bishop, and N. R. Legge, *J. Polym. Sci. C.* **26**, 37 (1969).

4. E. Fischer and J. F. Henderson, *J. Polym. Sci. C.* **26**, 149 (1969).

5. J. F. Beecher, L. Marker, R. D. Bradford, and S. L. Aggarwal, *J. Polym. Sci. C*, **26**, 117 (1969).

6. D. M. Brunwin, E. Fischer, and J. F. Henderson, *J. Polym. Sci. C*, **26**, 135 (1969).

Received September 30, 1975
Revised August 4, 1976

The Effects of Flow Rate and Column Combination on the Separation Efficiency in Multicolumn Gel Permeation Chromatography

M. R. AMBLER*, L. J. FETTERS, and Y. KESTEN,[†] *Institute of Polymer Science, The University of Akron, Akron, Ohio 44325*

Synopsis

Using general-purpose multicolumn sets, it was found that separations could be increased by increasing analysis time, either by decreasing flow rate or increasing column length. Several examples are shown illustrating the influence of these system variables. The generation of linear calibration curves over extended molecular weight ranges is discussed. In particular, the desirability of using high molecular weight standards to extend the calibration curve and eliminate extrapolation of the curve is shown. Not using all available gel porosities, i.e., gapped column sets, is shown to be detrimental to the resolution of molecular species. It was found that with the use of sufficiently long column lengths and low flow rates, accurate molecular weights of both narrow and broad molecular weight distribution samples are directly calculable from the chromatogram without the need for peak spreading corrections.

INTRODUCTION

Gel permeation chromatography (GPC) has found widespread acceptance as a characterization tool because of the speed with which it can generate a visual picture of the molecular weight distribution (MWD) of a sample from which molecular weights can be calculated through the proper calibration of the columns used. Because of the attractive rapid analysis time, much of the research work done with GPC has dealt with possible ways to decrease analysis time, usually by increasing flow rate or by decreasing column legth. However, it has been our experience that more information can be obtained by increasing analysis time and, conversely, that decreasing the analysis time by the usual means produces often misleading and sometimes useless data.

It has been shown that reducing the flow rate can greatly improve resolution.[1,2] However, many of the flow rate studies reported in the literature have been done on short columns with narrow porosity ranges, usually to allow a more fundamental interpretation of the results connected to the gel porosity. As a consequence, it is difficult for the GPC user to ascertain *a priori* the extent to which general-purpose, multicolumn sets will respond to changes in the flow rate. In addition, how the multicolumn set is best assembled to perform specific sepa-

---

* Present address: Goodyear Tire and Rubber Co., Chemical Materials Development, Akron, Ohio 44316.

† Present address: Allied Chemical Co., Corporate Research and Development, Morristown, New Jersey 07960.

rations has received scant attention in the literature. One example is a study by Slagowski and co-workers[3] who found a column set which had a linear calibration of at least 10^7 g/mole for polystyrene samples of narrow molecular weight distribution.

Because of these disparities, we feel it appropriate to comment here on our approach to the use of GPC to fulfill our characterization needs. Specific examples will be shown where, although the analysis time is increased relative to that of so-called "normal" conditions, system variables such as flow rate and column combination are tailored to optimize the GPC separation.

EXPERIMENTAL

The Waters Ana-Prep, 100, 200, and 501 gel permeation chromatographs were used with up to twelve 4-ft Styragel columns. The porosities of these columns ranged from 50 to 10^7 Å. The solvent used was either tetrahydrofuran or chloroform at a temperature of 25° or 40°C. The detectors used were the Waters UV and differential refractometer instruments. Solution concentrations were 0.25% (w/v) or less. Flow rates of 0.25 and 1 ml/min were used. Full-loop (2 ml) injections were made. The Ana-Prep instrument was equipped with a 5-ml syphon, while the other instruments had 2.5-ml syphons. These syphons were covered and the syphon chambers saturated with solvent vapor in order to minimize solvent evaporation at the 0.25 ml/min flow rate.

A seven-column set with a porosity range from 2×10^3 to 5×10^6 Å was used to obtain most of the data presented in this paper. This column combination had a plate count of 750 ppf at the 1 ml/min flow rate and a value of 950 ppf for the 0.25 ml/min flow rate.[4]

Column calibrations were carried out with commercial polystyrene standards and polystyrenes synthesized and characterized in these laboratories.[5] Other polystyrenes[6] and the poly(α-methylstyrene), polybutadiene, and poly(n-butyl isocyanate) samples were synthesized and characterized in these laboratories[5,6] and at the National Bureau of Standards.[6,7] In the main, these samples were obtained from termination-free anionic polymerization systems.

The synthetic polyisoprene was the Natsyn 2200, a commercial material prepared by a Ziegler–Natta catalyst. Hence, this sample may contain some branched material. The microstructure was virtually 100% cis-1,4.

The oligomeric ($<3 \times 10^2$ g/mole) polybutadienes were separated by vacuum distillation under high vacuum from commercial, polydisperse low molecular weight polybutadienes. The molecular weights of these fractions were determined by the MC-2 mass chromatograph (Chemalytics Crp.).[8]

Polystyrene, PS-6, was synthesized using a difunctional initiator made from 2,4-hexadiene and lithium.[9] Some termination probably took place at the outset of the polymerization thus causing the development of a bimodal molecular weight distribution.

DISCUSSION

Generation of Linear Calibration Curves

Figure 1 shows a calibration curve constructed with the usual commercial polystyrene standards. For the typical four-column set used here, the familiar

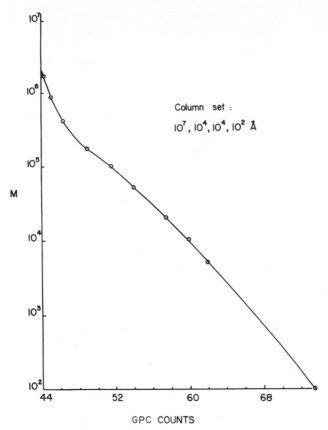

Fig. 1. S-Shaped Polystyrene Calibration Curve for a "gapped" four-column set (1 count represents 2.5 ml). Flow Rate, 1 ml/min.

S-shaped calibration is obtained where resolution is lost at both high and low molecular weights. This degree of resolution is usually sufficient if rather average samples are analyzed which elute within the region of optimum resolution between 50 and 64 counts. But if the sample elutes in the high molecular weight region of 44 to 50 counts, or in the low molecular weight region of 64 to 74 counts, resolution will be reduced, as suggested by the more vertical slopes. What can be done in these cases is to change the column set to concentrate more on the specific molecular weight range to be fractionated. That is, the idea is to flatten out the calibration curve by increasing the resolution. For example, a column set was assembled specifically for high molecular weights. In Figure 2, the column set can be seen to maintain adequate resolution clear up to 10^7 g/mole and possibly beyond.

Since the slopes above and below 10^6 g/mole are the same, this illustrates that it is possible to get as good a resolution for the high molecular weight species as is normally obtained at lower molecular weight. The asymptotic region of Figure 1 is extended to a much higher molecular weight region. However, to accomplish this, a rather cumbersome ten-column set was needed which was weighted heavily to the high-porosity packings. This increased the analysis time, but the resolution range was greatly extended. Resolution in the low molecular weight region is possible also. In Figure 3, a special twelve-column set designed to enhance

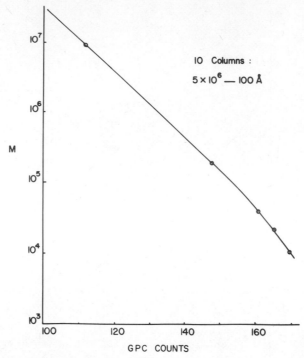

Fig. 2. Polystyrene calibration curve for a ten-column set (1 count represents 2.5 ml). Flow rate, 1 ml/min.

the oligomeric range had a linear calibration curve down to 160 g/mole. The slope of the line is the same over the entire molecular weight range, indicating a constant degree of resolution.

Use of High Molecular Weight Standards

The ability to separate high molecular weight components is demonstrated in Figure 4. A commercial high molecular weight, broad molecular weight distribution polyisoprene was fractionated on a column set similar to that of Figure 2. Inserted on the high molecular weight end of the chromatogram are the polyisoprene molecular weights at four different retention volumes. It was apparent that this sample had a large percentage of high molecular weight material. However, with the use of high molecular weight standards, much more of the chromatogram was explicitly defined than if the 2×10^6 molecular weight polystyrene standard were the highest standard used. This point deserves some further comment here. Most GPC workers do not use high molecular weight standards but rather rely on extrapolation of a calibration curve from the available low molecular weight (2.6×10^6) data points into the region of higher molecular weight (e.g., an extension of a calibration line such as in Fig. 1). Extrapolation in this region is risky, especially if the calibration curve is curving upward rapidly as it usually is. This is because extrapolation procedures are usually based on fitting data points eluting in one region to some mathematical function, even though the behavior of this function in another region outside of the data points (where resolution may be decreasing) is not necessarily related

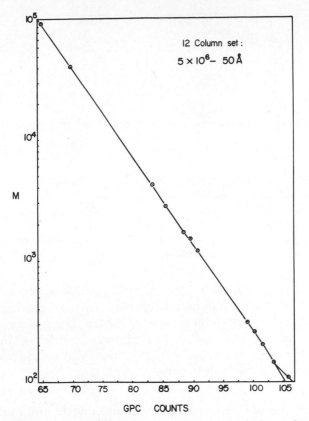

Fig 3. Polybutadiene calibration curve for a 12-column set in the low molecular weight region (1 count represents 2.5 ml). Flow rate, 1 ml/min.

to that of the interpolated function. Hence, it is relatively ineffective to eliminate the drawback of curvature in the calibration by building a linear calibration to fractionate higher molecular weights if there is no means to calibrate this high molecular weight region. It is useful to use high molecular weight standards as data points. This allows interpolation instead of extrapolation of the calibration curve. In this way, the entire chromatogram of Figure 4 is defined.

Both points, linear calibration curves *and* high molecular weight standards,

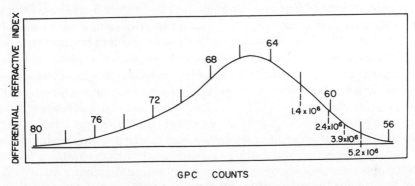

Fig. 4. Chromatogram of a high molecular weight synthetic polyisoprene (1 count represents 2.5 ml). Flow rate, 1 ml/min.

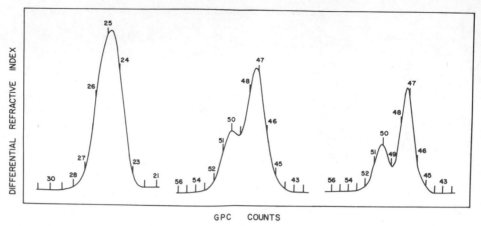

Fig. 5. Chromatograms of bimodal polystyrene, PS-6. The third chromatogram was obtained at a flow rate of 0.25 ml/min; (1 count represents 5 ml).

illustrate that column sets must be tailored to the specific separation to be done. To get the most out of the separation, long column sets are needed. Time will have to be sacrificed to achieve these types of separations, but it can be done if so desired. The accuracy of the calibration curve can be improved by developing linear calibration curves and using high molecular weight standards to extend the interpolation of the calibration curve.

Effects of Column Combination, Column Length, and Flow Rate

To obtain an adequate molecular weight separation, the molecular weights of the separated species must be properly matched to the pore size of the gel packing. High molecular weight polymers cannot be fractionated by tight-porosity packings nor can oligomers be separated by the high-porosity pack-ings . In the same context, when assembling a multicolumn set, if a continuous transition of gel packings is not achieved by linking all the available gel packings together, "gaps" are created in the column set. Using a "gapped" column set as a general-purpose column set, e.g., Figure 1, can lead to misleading results, especially when analyzing narrow molecular weight distribution samples that would have been fractionated by the missing column porosities. To illustrate what could happen, the first two chromatograms of Figure 5 are the GPC curves of the same polystyrene sample, PS-6, run on two different column sets at the same flow rate. The first column set (with the same column arrangement shown in Fig. 1) was gapped, and the chromatogram appeared at first glance to be fairly monodisperse with a slight shoulder on the low molecular weight side of the peak. When the sample was chromatographed on the second column set (seven columns with a porosity range of 5×10^6 to 2×10^3), this one not gapped, separation of two species was clearly indicated in the second chromatogram. To be sure, to some extent the improvement in separation was due to the longer column length of the second column set and to the switch from chloroform to tetrahydrofuran, but the important variable here was the influence that gapping made. What probably happened in generating the "one-peak" chromatogram was that the sample was of a molecular weight range that was above the permeation limit of

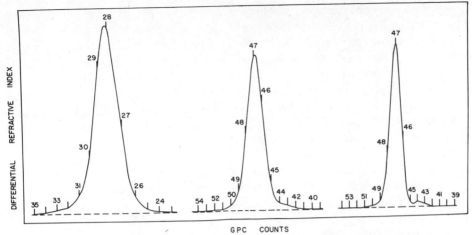

Fig. 6. Chromatograms of the NBS 705 polystyrene. The third chromatogram was obtained at a flow rate of 0.25 ml/min; (1 count represents 5 ml).

the small porosity columns and yet was capable of total permeation in the high-porosity columns. There was no column available to perform an adequate separation on this sample. This seriously inhibited the separation of this narrow MWD sample, and would be expected to influence the chromatograms of broad MWD samples as well.

Consider now the effect that the column length has on the separation. By increasing the column length, resolution usually increases. For example, Figure 6 shows three chromatograms of polystyrene standard NBS 705. The first chromatogram was obtained on a four-column set (no gaps), while the second was from a seven-column set (both at 1 cc/min). The presence of a high molecular weight component was indicated on the chromatogram from the longer column set. (The third chromatogram, obtained by lowering the flow rate of 0.25 cc/min on the seven-column set,[10] revealed a clearly resolved component of twice the molecular weight of the main peak.) Resolution was increased by increasing the column length. This effect is to be expected. The equation for the plate count of a column,

$$P = \frac{16}{f} \left(\frac{x}{d}\right)^2 \qquad (1)$$

is widely used as an indicator of the performance of a column or column set, where P is the resolution factor in plates/foot, f is the column length, x is the elution volume of the eluted peak, and d is the width of the eluted peak. When the column length f is doubled while P is held constant, the length of the interval between the void volume and total permeation volume (the width of the calibration curve) is doubled, as is x. When this happens, d increases only by $\sqrt{2}$, the net effect being that the width of the peak becomes effectively narrower and an increase in resolution is indicated. Thus, just by increasing the column length, resolution is improved. This is one way to increase the accuracy of molecular weight calculations from GPC measurements, even for narrow MWD samples. The need for resolution corrections can be minimized or even eliminated in this way.[11]

The first two chromatograms of Figures 5 and 6 were both generated at a flow rate of 1 ml/min. It is clear that the elimination of gaps in the porosity range covered markedly enhanced resolution. One other way[1,2] to increase resolution is to decrease the flow rate. In the third chromatograms of Figures 5 and 6, the flow rate was lowered to 0.25 ml/min. A further increase in resolution is indicated. The high molecular weight component (counts 42–45) seen in the chromatogram of the NBS 705 corresponds to an $\langle M_n \rangle$ of 3.3 × 10⁵ g/mole and an $\langle M_w \rangle$ of 3.5 × 10⁵ g/mole. This "dimer" of the parent material may be the result of the presence of carbon dioxide or oxygen during the termination of this anionically prepared polystyrene. These species can cause the coupling of organolithium compounds.[12,13]

It is germane to note that recently published chromatograms[14] of the NBS 705 polystyrene fail to show the coupled product present in the two chromatograms of Figure 6. This is probably due to the fact that too few columns were used in the analysis by the National Bureau of Standards.

Thus, it is apparent that multicolumn sets are sensitive to changes in flow rate. These findings are not new,[1,2] but Figures 5 and 6 serve to illustrate the importance of using not only the proper column set and the proper gel packings but also the improvement of resolution that can be achieved by a decrease in the flow rate. Hence, GPC separations can be improved by optimizing either one or both of these techniques. An increase in analysis time will result, but more information and, more importantly, more correct information will be obtained.

A general view has been established that GPC data can only be rendered accurate after suitable dispersion corrections have been performed. As a result, corrections for imperfect resolution in GPC have been developed.[15–17] An outcome of our work has been the result that accurate data can be generated on near-monodisperse and polydisperse samples without the need for dispersion corrections. This can be achieved through the proper choice of column length, porosity combination, and rate of flow.

McCrackin[11] (using polystyrene chromatograms generated on our seven-column set) has calculated the p factor (which represents the resolving power for a set of columns) to be 0.98 at a flow rate of 1 ml/min, while at the 0.25 ml/min flow rate the value of p is 0.99. For ideal resolution, p is equal to 1. Hence, McCrackin's analysis demonstrates that corrections of the molecular weight averages obtained by integrating the chromatograms obtained from the seven-column set are of a trivial nature. His conclusions are fortified by the good agreement between the values of $\langle M_n \rangle$ and $\langle M_w \rangle$ in Table I obtained from GPC and absolute measurements for a series of polystyrenes. These GPC results were obtained from chromatograms generated by the seven-column set. The samples cover a molecular weight distribution range of <1.1 to 2.1.

The synthesis of the polydisperse S-1 through S-6 polystyrenes was accomplished by the use of tert-butyllithium. We have found,[4] as has Hsieh,[22] that this initiator reacts slowly with styrene. The claim has been advanced[23] that highly purified tert-butyllithium will react rapidly with styrene. However, our work with the purified initiator consistently reveals that this organolithium reacts slowly with styrene in hydrocarbon solvents.[24]

It should be noted that the chromatograms of samples 28, 30, 31, and 31D were symmetrical. No bimodal character in the molecular weight distribution was found. The presence of a bimodal molecular weight distribution was a possibility

TABLE I
Molecular Weights of Polystyrene Samples

| Sample[a] | Absolute molecular weight measurements | | | | GPC molecular weights | | | |
| | $\langle M_n \rangle$ $\times 10^{-3}$, g/mole | $\langle M_v \rangle$ $\times 10^{-3}$ g/mole | $\langle M_w \rangle$ $\times 10^{-3}$ g/mole[b] | $\langle M_w \rangle$ $\times 10^{-3}$ g/mole[c] | 0.25 ml/min | | 1 ml/min | |
					$\langle M_n \rangle$ $\times 10^{-3}$ g/mole	$\langle M_w \rangle$ $\times 10^{-3}$ g/mole	$\langle M_n \rangle$ $\times 10^{-3}$ g/mole	$\langle M_w \rangle$ $\times 10^{-3}$ g/mole
28	149	197.7[d]	203	235	—	—	151	225
30	547.2	717.5	700	820	—	—	550	800
31	80.2	82.7	88	102	—	—	81	100
31D	88.8	82.7	89	102	—	—	85	95
S-6	27	42[e]	45	—	24	46	24	46
S-3	57	103	120	—	55	113	55	112
S-4	90	145	148	—	90	147	88	145
S-7	97	97	98	—	96	97	95	97
S-1	185	272	320	—	184	318	175	320
S-2	190	296	327	—	195	337	190	350
S-5	380	550	540	—	384	530	370	540
NBS-705	170.9	173[d]	179.3	189.8	169	179	167	179
NBS-706	<136.5	216	257.8	288.1	140	290	137	287

[a] Samples 28 to 31D were prepared by sodium naphthalene in tetrahydrofuran[6]; S-1 to S-6 by t-butyllithium in cyclohexane;[4] S-7 by s-butyllithium in cyclohexane;[4] NBS-705 by n-butyllithium in benzene;[18,19] NBS-706 by thermal polymerization in bulk.[20] The absolute molecular weights in this table are from references 4, 7, 18, 19, and 20.

[b] By light scattering.

[c] From sedimentation equilibrium.

[d] $[\eta]_{\text{cyclohexane}}^{35°C} = 8.5 \times 10^{-4} M^{0.5}$ (ref. 21).

[e] $[\eta]_{\text{benzene}}^{30°C} = 8.5 \times 10^{-5} M^{0.75}$ (ref. 21).

in view of the fact that the initiator, sodium naphthalene, will form difunctional chains. Partial termination would then lead to the creation of a contingent of active chains growing at one end only.

It was found that there is a molecular weight dependence of the change in elution volume with a change in flow rate. As can be seen in Figure 7, high molecular weight polymers will remain in the GPC longer at low flow rates than at higher flow rates; but at lower molecular weights, no change in retention volume is found. This gives some insight into the GPC separation mechanism.[25] A slower linear velocity of the polymer molecules down the column allows a longer residence time in front of each gel pore and provides a greater opportunity for the molecule to enter the gel pore only on the merits of its hydrodynamic size. At faster flow rates, molecules may be swept past a gel pore before they can enter it. Thus, the slower flow rate allows more of the molecules of the same molecular weight to follow the same paths through the column uninfluenced by extraneous effects caused by the linear velocity. This results in a narrowing of the peak due to a narrowing of the distribution of path lengths. All of these samples had $\langle M_w \rangle / \langle M_n \rangle$ of less than 1.1.

Other System Variables

There are other variables that can be utilized to improve resolution. For ex-

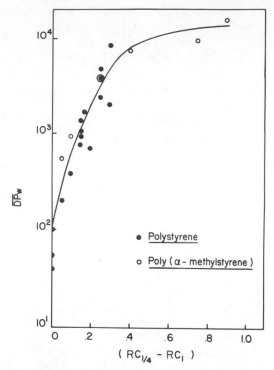

Fig. 7. Dependence of retention count (RC) on flow rate.

ample, the solvent plays a major role in the GPC separation. When all else is equal, it has been our experience that THF provides better resolution than chloroform, and toluene allows even less resolution. This has been pointed out by Cooper and co-workers.[1,2] Presumably this is related to the viscosity of the solvent (or perhaps to the solvent polarity and its influence on solute–gel packing adsorption). Resolution can also be increased by raising the temperature, thereby reducing the viscosity of the solvent. Another way of increasing resolution is by increasing the solvent power for the polymer. An increase in the Mark–Houwink coefficient a will result in a flatter molecular weight calibration curve.

Another variable influencing resolution is the posture of the polymer. For example, poly(n-butyl isocyanate)(PBIC) has the peculiar property of being a rigid rod ($a = 2.0$)[7,26] at molecular weights below 10^5; but at higher molecular weights, PBIC attains sufficient flexibility to warrant its description as a non-Gaussian, worm-like chain with $a = 0.5$. Thus, the conformation of PBIC is molecular weight dependent. For this reason, it was of interest to construct a calibration curve for this polymer in order to evaluate the effect that conformational changes can exert. Figure 8 is the PBIC calibration obtained[25] on the seven column set over a molecular weight range of 2.5×10^4 to 1.2×10^7. In Figure 8, the molecular weight calibration curve is seen to dramatically flatten for the more rigid PBIC chains, indicating an increase in resolution. For comparison, the dashed linear line represents the polystyrene calibration for this seven-column set. Parenthetically, it should be noted that the low molecular weight PBIC materials do not fit[27] the GPC universal calibration.[28] This

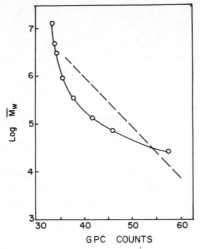

Fig. 8. Calibration curve for poly(n-butyl isocyanate) in tetrahydrofuran (1 count represents 5 ml). Flow rate, 1 ml/min.

finding[25,27] seemingly demonstrates that $M[\eta]$ can serve as a universal calibration parameter only when the molecular geometries involved are similar.

The effect of chain geometry regarding resolution in GPC can be seen in Figure 9, which contains the chromatograms of a rigid PBIC sample and a flexible polystyrene (Waters Associates 25168) possessing similar molecular weights and molecular weight distributions ($\langle M_w \rangle / \langle M_n \rangle$ less than 1.1). As can be seen, these two polymers exhibit radically different chromatograms even though both eluted in the same region. This aspect of the resolution question has not been emphasized in the past in the literature. Usually, this property is not one that can be altered or optimized, but it does contribute to the separation process.

Because of the rod-like shape of PBIC, part of this species is retained on the seven-column set for a longer time than the polystyrene. This leads to an increase in resolution and a decrease in the slope of the calibration curve (Fig. 8). However, at the same time, the PBIC shows a broad peak, relative to the polystyrene, for a sample with a narrow molecular weight distribution.[26] Obviously, increased rigidity has caused peak spreading. The elution behavior of this rigid species can be rationalized as follows. When the flow field in the columns pre-

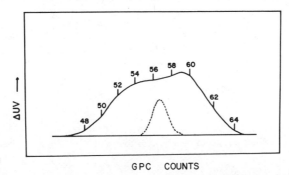

Fig. 9. Chromatograms of rod-like poly(n-butyl isocyanate) and polystyrene of the same molecular weight. Polystyrene $\overline{M}_w = 20.8 \times 10^3$; PBIC $\overline{M}_w = 25 \times 10^3$ (1 count represents 5 ml). Flow rate, 1 ml/min.

sents a rigid polymer to the entrance of a pore, the molecule can do one of three things, to wit: (a) enter the Styragel pore structure and become permanently stuck or held for a long period of time; (b) enter the pore structure and flow through; or (c) enter the pore structure, travel partly through, and then come back out. A combination of these three steps will thus place these rigid molecules at the next position in the column at different times, i.e., they will be spread out in the column. This is, in reality, the mechanism of peak spreading in all chromatographic separation processes whereby different molecules end up taking different paths through the column. Based on the chromatogram in Figure 9, it would appear that the stiffness of a chain affects the GPC separation mechanism to a significant degree. Hence, it would be expected that the more rigid the species, the greater the probability that (a) and (c) will occur; but with increasing flexibility, the probability of (b) occurring becomes much greater. This would then lead to less peak spreading. This has been observed[25,26] for PBIC chromatograms as the molecular weight and flexibility of this polyisocyanate increase.

CONCLUSIONS

All of the separate experiments presented herein contribute to the overall view that increasing the analysis time—either by increasing column length, increasing the number of pertinent columns used, or decreasing the flow rate—will increase the resolution. Multicolumn sets can be used advantageously for many types of separations by following these generalities. The use of linear calibration curves, high molecular weight standards, and long column lengths can improve the accuracy of the GPC experiments to the point that the GPC data can directly represent the polymer without the need for mathematical resolution corrections.

It should also be noted that the μ-Styragel columns afford an alternative route to enhanced resolution. Our experience with the PS-6 sample has apparently shown that a six-column μ-Styragel set with a porosity range of 10^2 to 10^6 Å and a flow rate of 1 ml/min is equal in resolving power to the seven-column set at the same rate of flow. The addition of a recycling step would doubtlessly lead to increased resolution from the μ-Styragel column set.

References

1. A. R. Cooper, J. F. Johnson, and A. R. Bruzzone, *Eur. Polym. J.*, **9**, 1381, 1393 (1973).
2. L. D. Moore, Jr., and J. I. Adcock, in *Characterization of Macromolecular Structure*, D. McIntyre, Ed., Publication 1573, National Academy of Sciences, Washington, D. C., 1968, p. 289.
3. E. Slagowski, L. J. Fetters, and D. McIntyre, *Macromolecules*, **7**, 394 (1974).
4. L. J. Fetters and M. Morton, *Macromolecules*, **7**, 552 (1974).
5. L. J. Fetters, unpublished results.
6. M. Morton, R. Milkovich, D. McIntyre, and L. J. Bradley, *J. Polym. Sci. A*, **1**, 443 (1963).
7. A. J. Bur and L. J. Fetters, *Chem. Rev.*, **76**, 727 (1976).
8. D. G. Paul and G. R. Umbreit, *Res. Dev.*, **18**, May (1970).
9. M. Morton, L. J. Fetters, J. Inomata, D. C. Rubio, and R. N. Young, *Rubber Chem. Technol.*, **49**, 303 (1976).
10. L. J. Fetters, *J. Appl. Polym. Sci.*, **20**, 3437 (1976).
11. F. L. McCrackin, *J. Appl. Polym. Sci.*, **21**, 191 (1977).
12. D. P. Wyman, V. R. Allen, and T. Altares, Jr., *J. Polym. Sci. A*, **2**, 4545 (1964).
13. H. Yasuda, M. Walczak, W. Rhine, and G. Stucky, *J. Organomet. Chem.*, **90**, 123 (1975).

14. H. L. Wagner, National Bureau of Standards Special Publication 260–33, Government Printing Office, Washington, D.C., 1972.

15. L. H. Tung, *J. Appl. Polym. Sci.*, **10**, 375 (1966).

16. W. N. Smith, *J. Appl. Polym. Sci.*, **11**, 639 (1967).

17. M. Hess and R. F. Karatz, *J. Polym. Sci. A-2*, **4**, 731 (1966).

18. National Bureau of Standards Certificate, Standard Sample 705 Polystyrene.

19. D. McIntyre, *J. Res. Nat. Bur. Stand.*, **71A**, 43 (1967).

20. National Bureau of Standards Certificate, Standard Sample 706 Polystyrene.

21. T. Altares, Jr., D. P. Wyman, and V. R. Allen, *J. Polym. Sci. A-2*, 4533 (1964).

22. H. L. Hsieh, *J. Polym. Sci. A*, **3**, 163 (1965); *J. Polym. Sci., Polym. Chem. Ed.*, **14**, 379 (1976).

23. J. E. L. Roovers and S. Bywater, *Macromolecules*, **8**, 251 (1975).

24. L. J. Fetters and J. Rupert, unpublished results.

25. M. R. Ambler, Ph.D. Thesis, The University of Akron, Akron, Ohio, 1975.

26. A. J. Bur and L. J. Fetters, *Macromolecules*, **6**, 879 (1973).

27. M. R. Ambler and D. McIntyre, *J. Polym. Sci., Polym. Lett. Ed.*, **13**, 589 (1975).

28. Z. Grubisic, P. Rempp, and H. Benoit, *J. Polym. Sci. B*, **5**, 753 (1967).

Received July 7, 1976
Revised August 15, 1976

JOURNAL OF APPLIED POLYMER SCIENCE   VOL. 21, 2453–2463 (1977)

On the Form of the Strain Energy Function for a Family of SBR Materials

R. J. ARENZ, *Propulsion and Materials Research, Jet Propulsion Laboratory, Pasadena, California 91103, and Mechanical Engineering Department, Loyola Marymount University, Los Angeles, California 90045*

Synopsis

A strain energy function of the Valanis-Landel type, $W = w(\lambda_1) + w(\lambda_2) + w(\lambda_3)$, is shown to be applicable to styrene–butadiene rubber (SBR) materials having varying crosslink densities ν_e. A previously obtained functional form of the strain energy derivative $w'(\lambda)$, normalized by dividing by ν_e, is confirmed by one of the validity check plots in which a single curve represents the whole body of large-deformation test results for all degrees of biaxiality and crosslink density.

INTRODUCTION

Recent widespread interest in the strain energy function W for rubberlike materials has focused on methods of representing in a satisfactory way the complexities of the experimental dependence of the stored energy on various strain states. These complexities are illustrated by the well-known deviations at even moderate strain levels of the observed stress–strain behavior from the predictions of Gaussian statistical theory. Representations of W as a function of the strain invariants and in terms of the extension ratios are both possibilities. As examples of the first approach, there are multiple-term series expansion of James, Green, and Simpson[1] in the usual strain invariants (I_1, I_2, I_3) and a four-parameter formula of Blatz, Sharda, and Tschoegl[2] with the strain invariant being based on a generalized measure of strain. The second approach has been taken by Valanis and Landel[3] in the form of a separable symmetric function of the principal extension ratios $(\lambda_1, \lambda_2, \lambda_3)$ and by Ogden[4] who also used a series of terms based on a generalized strain measure. (Ogden gives a good review of the methods proposed prior to his theory.) In general, isotropy and incompressibility have been assumed to apply to the elastomers under consideration in these representations.

The analytical expressions of references 1, 2, and 4 provide reasonable fits to experimental data in the examples given by the authors but require four or more constants which in several cases involve a computer approach to evaluate. Although the Valanis–Landel approach by itself does not explicitly give a mathematical expression for W, it does directly provide the complete functional form of the strain energy function. It consequently possesses the possibility of predicting the behavior of elastomers under various geometric strain states by simple

2453

mathematical calculations and readily lends itself to comparison with experiment.

These characteristics make it appropriate to consider, in a more comprehensive way than previously, the applicability of the Valanis–Landel hypothesis to the strain energy function of styrene–butadiene rubber (SBR). Results of extensive finite deformation biaxial and uniaxial tests made at the Jet Propulsion Laboratory on a family of SBR materials have been reported previously.[5] Stress relaxation tests of thin sheet specimens of five different crosslink densities were made in a universal biaxial tester arranged to provide varying amounts of biaxiality.[6]

In addition to the basic data, reference 5 included an indication of the functional form at equilibrium of the spatial derivative of the strain energy function, determined from strip biaxial (pure shear) data according to the Valanis–Landel approach. The necessity of verifying the general validity of the proposed strain energy function for all test geometries as well as subsequent refinement of the precise level of moduli for the SBR materials, which enters into the test of the hypothesis, motivate this further investigation. Since most of the original data furnishing the basis of this study appeared only in a foreign-published volume[5] of the proceedings for a conference and perhaps have not received wide distribution, it may be helpful to review the pertinent experimental aspects and some of the prior data analysis forming the background of the present study.

EXPERIMENTAL ASPECTS

A full description of the apparatus and experimental procedure is available in reference 6 and details of the material composition and specimen preparation are given in reference 5. The universal biaxial relaxometer is illustrated in Figure 1, where it is shown mounted at an angle $\alpha = 16.7$ deg to the vertical axis of the Instron test machine; this is one of the six possible mounting angles available to produce various biaxial configurations. The trolleys and hooks supporting the thin-sheet test specimen along its sides are equipped with individual strain-gauged load cells to give the force distribution throughout the sheet width.

The SBR specimens had five different crosslink concentrations, given by 1, 2, 3, 4, and 5 parts by weight of the vulcanizing agent, tetramethylthiuram disulfide (TMTD), per 100 parts of Shell 1502 SBR. (These compositions are designated herein either as 1 TMTD, 2 TMTD, etc., or more simply on the figures as $n = 1, 2$, etc.) Uniaxial tensile stress–strain tests on specimens swollen to equilibriun in toluene established the elastically effective network chain density ν_e. The values of ν_e for the SBR materials are listed in Table I. The basic biaxial test specimens of SBR were molded sheets approximately 0.13 cm thick and 6.15 $\times$ 6.15 cm square overall, with seven small reinforced holes per side to accommodate the supporting hooks.[5]

All the tests were run at room temperature (approximately 26°C), and the bulk of the data reported[5] was for a relaxation time of 10 min. Complete mechanical characterizations were given for the SBR compositions under various biaxial strain states and to the highest strain levels attainable before failure occurred in one or more of the reinforced support holes. A typical plot showing the principal stresses σ_1, σ_2 (based on unstrained area) as functions of λ_1, λ_2 for the

TABLE I
Characteristics of SBR Vulcanizates

Specimen code (n = parts TMTD)	ν_e, mole/m^3	$G(10$ min$)$, N/m$^2 \times 10^{-5}$	G_e, N/m$^2 \times 10^{-5}$
1	17.5	2.07	0.77
2	54	3.45	2.23
3	90	4.46	3.65
4	117	5.22	4.59
5	131	5.70	5.09

2 TMTD material is given in Figure 2. (Reference 5 provided plots for the 1, 3, and 5 TMTD compositions.)

Several long-time relaxation tests performed to establish the variation of stress with time indicated that the strain dependence and time dependence of stress were separable for the materials.[5] Thus the stress relaxation data for various geometries and strain levels covering periods usually up to 10 hr (but, in a few cases, to 30 hr) could be used to obtain a reliable estimate of the equilibrium

Fig. 1. Biaxial stress relaxometer, showing sample configuration, attachments with individual proof-ring load cells, and circular target used for strain measurements.

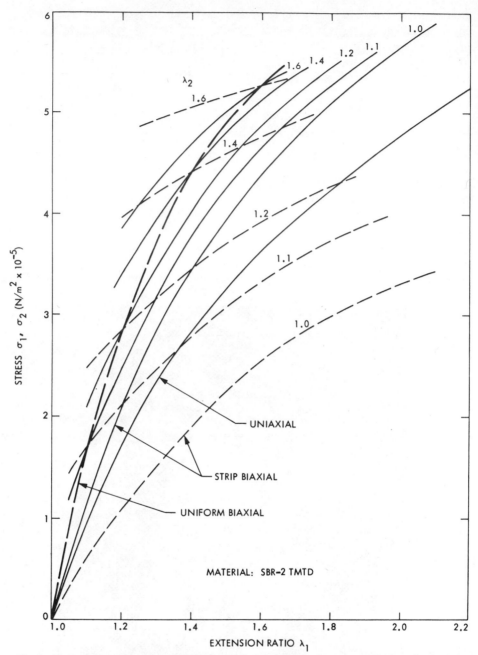

Fig. 2. Typical dependence for an SBR material of the principal stresses σ_1 (—), σ_2 (- - -) on the principal extension ratio λ_1 for various λ_2 values; relaxation time = 10 min, T = 26°C.

behavior.   For this relaxation, use was made of the power law representation which has been found to be valid for a variety of elastomers.[7]   Indeed, the accuracy of the power law extrapolation for this family of SBR materials has been verified by a reduced variable analysis[8] involving a crosslinking density–time shifting procedure that superposes the relaxation data into a single master curve covering 16 decades of log time.   The equilibrium modulus values obtained by this wide-spectrum relaxation curve agreed within a few percent of those obtained by applying the power law to each material test history over a much shorter time span. Moreover, the equilibrium moduli for the SBR materials were in generally good agreement[8] with those obtained for SBR with similar crosslinking levels by creep tests[9] that established equilibrium compliance levels.

ANALYSIS BY VALANIS-LANDEL HYPOTHESIS

With estimates of equilibrium behavior, a representation of the equilibrium strain energy function could be determined for this substantially incompressible rubber by using the Valanis-Landel hypothesis[3] of a separable symmetric function given by

$$W = w(\lambda_1) + w(\lambda_2) + w(\lambda_3) \tag{1}$$

where λ_1, λ_2, and λ_3 are the three principal extension ratios. Following the analysis given in reference 3, a functional form of $w_e'(\lambda)$, where w' denotes the deriative of w with respect to its argument and the subscript e designates the long-time equilibrium condition, was obtained for the five SBR compositions using data from strip biaxial (pure shear) tests, in which $\lambda_2 = 1$. This is the only test to explicitly determine it,[3,5] and w' was evaluated for tensile strains ($\lambda_1 >$ 1) using eq. (45) of reference 3, namely,

$$w'(\lambda_1) = \frac{t_1 - t_2}{\lambda_1} \tag{2}$$

where t_1 and t_2 are the true stresses in the principal directions in the plane of the sheet ($t_3 = 0$ for the thin-sheet specimen). It was found that the w_e' values could be normalized by dividing by the crosslinking density ν_e out to the highest strains tested. The resulting single master curve of w_e'/ν_e showed that the functional form of $W(\lambda)$ is independent of the network chain concentration. This would be expected for small strains from the Gaussian statistical theory, which predicts direct proportionality of elastic modulus to ν_e, but the inadequacy of the theory at larger deformations points to the need of approaches such as the one used here to test the applicability of scaling by ν_e.

As the emphasis in reference 5 was this correlation of strain energy function to ν_e, no thorough comparison was made there to verify that the strain energy function W derived from data corresponding to the strip biaxial (pure shear) test condition would also apply to all the biaxial strain states as well as uniaxial stress conditions. It is imperative here (as in the study of the validity of any candidate form of representation of W) to thus verify that it does, in fact, represent the behavior of the material for all loading conditions. Accordingly, it is the purpose of this paper to demonstrate that the Valanis–Landel stored energy representation is indeed a valid characterization of the family of SBR materials.

At the same time, an application of the representational method of Blatz, Sharda, and Tshoegl[2] to SBR[10] required additional combined treatment of uniaxial tension data (also obtained in the previous experimental program[5]) and uniform biaxial tension results. The latter geometry for an incompressible material has the same state of deformation as occurs in simple compression.[2] It hence furnishes simple compression behavior since $t_c(\lambda_c) = -t_t(\lambda_t)$, where the

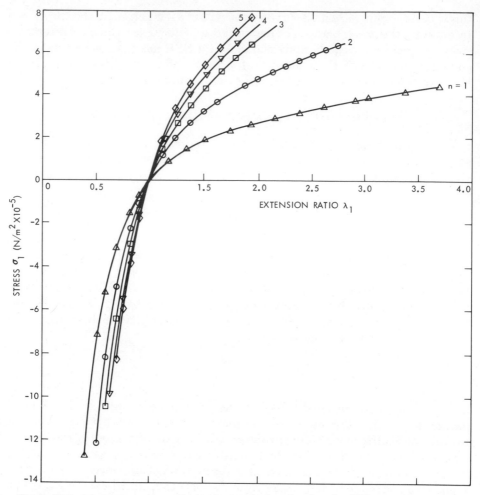

Fig. 3. Uniaxial stress–strain results at 10 min of relaxation time for SBR materials of varying crosslink density; n denotes the number of parts of TMTD crosslinking agent. Compression data derived from uniform biaxial tension tests; $T = 26°C$.

subscript c refers to simple compression, the subscript t refers to uniform biaxial tension, and $\lambda_c = \lambda_t^{-2}$. The use of this "BST" strain energy function* showed the need to determine the zero strain modulus with the maximum precision possible. This is facilitated by plotting the stress–extension ratio data for both tensile and compressive strains to provide a continuous curve through the zero-strain point, as shown in Figure 3 for SBR at 10 min of relaxation time. The moduli previously reported[5,8] for these SBR materials represented slopes of

---

* Since the SBR data exceeded $\lambda = 3$ in only one case (cf. Fig. 3), the material parameters in the second term of the Blatz–Sharda–Tschoegl equation[2] for simple extension could not be adequately established. The one-term equation, i.e., $t = (\lambda^n - \lambda^{-n/2})(2G/n)$, where t is true stress and G is the shear modulus (with the values listed in this paper) gave a value of $n = 1.32$ to very satisfactorily represent uniaxial and strip biaxial data at a relaxation time of 10 min for the five SBR compositions, indicating n to be a material parameter substantially independent of ν_e. Since $n = 2$ corresponds to statistical theory, the SBR material exhibits a λ dependence more complex than predicted by the simple theory.

stress–strain curves obtained from the tensile side only. As a result, the path through $\lambda = 1$ was not as well defined, and, in effect, the moduli approximated the average stress–strain ratio out to perhaps 5% strain. The refined values of $G(10)$, the shear relaxation modulus at 10 min, obtained by use of tangents at $\lambda = 1$ to the curves of Figure 3, are listed in Table I (where incompressibility has been used in converting Young's modulus to G). The corrected values are not significantly modified from those previously listed,[8] but the change is discernible, being approximately 5% higher for most of the SBR compositions. (These modifications in $G(10)$ are small enough that, in conjunction with the fact that the time dependence of the relaxation process remains entirely unaltered, none of the essential conclusions previously published[5,8] is changed. The equilibrium modulus levels given in the references should all be increased slightly, but this does not modify the results of superposition or shifting procedures of ref. 8 to a degree sufficient to require correcting.)

Analysis of the biaxial test results (e.g., as in Fig. 2) confirmed these values as applicable within a few percent experimental scatter to all the loading geometries tested for each material. For completeness, we also list in Table I the modified equilibrium shear moduli G_e corresponding to the corrected $G(10)$ values just given.

VERIFICATION OF THE STRAIN ENERGY FUNCTION

We now proceed to test the validity of the form of the strain energy function W derived from the strip biaxial test by checking the functional form in uniaxial and the rest of the biaxial test configurations. If it satisfies tests in all these geometries, then it can be truly said to characterize the material. Inasmuch as results and analysis of reference 5 proved separability of strain and time, the simpler approach will be chosen of using isochronal data at a relaxation time of 10 min since the bulk of the stress–strain data was obtained at that point in the relaxation process.

To use the isochronal approach, we first need to calculate the $w'(\lambda)$ function from strip biaxial data at 10 min of relaxation time. For positive strain ($\lambda > 1$), use is made of the λ_1-direction data and eq. (2). For negative strains ($\lambda < 1$), use is made of strip biaxial data in the thickness, or λ_3, direction (where $t_3 = 0$ and, since $\lambda_2 = 1$, $\lambda_3 = 1/\lambda_1$) and the applicable equation is[3]

$$w'(\lambda_3) = -t_2/\lambda_3 \tag{3}$$

The results for both tension and compression are shown in Figure 4, where the function $w'(\lambda)$ is now determined for the 1 TMTD material in the range of values $0.3 < \lambda < 3$, with lesser ranges for the stiffer materials.

Various empirical relations as functions of λ could be used to attempt to fit the SBR curves, such as the $2G \ln \lambda$ variation proposed by Valanis[3] or the $2G[(1 - (1/\lambda)]$ form suggested by Dickie and Smith,[11] with varying regions of approximate representation. However, our purpose here is rather to prove the validity of eq. (1) for SBR by applying the functional forms obtained in Figure 4 to all the uniaxial and biaxial tests. To do this, we note that in accordance with the relation of stress to the strain function derivative w' resulting from eq. (1), a straight line of unit slope should be given[3] by a plot of $(t_1 - t_2)/2G$ versus $(1/2G)$ $[\lambda_1 w'(\lambda_1) - \lambda_2 w'(\lambda_2)]$, where $w'(\lambda)$ is given by the curves of Figure 4. Figure 5

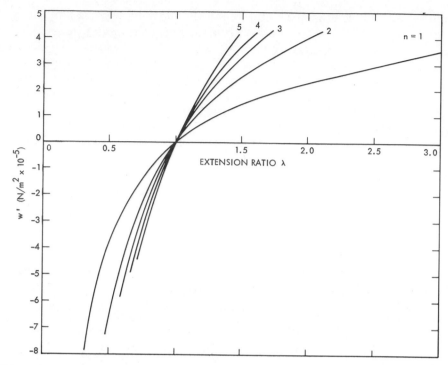

Fig. 4. Variation of $w'(\lambda)$ with λ for the materials of Figure 3 at 10 min of relaxation time; $T = 26°C$.

shows this to be the case within experimental error; of all the results, only the uniaxial data at high strains appear to deviate in a systematic manner, falling a bit below the theoretically predicted line. The reason for this is uncertain, but it may stem from the difficulty in cutting uniaxial test samples from the biaxial sheet specimens; uniform widths and smooth edges are far less likely than in the case of molded specimens.

A further test of the consistency of the form of W proposed in eq. (1) follows from additional analysis of the biaxial tests. The relations between strain function and stress become[3]

$$(1/2G)\lambda_3 w'(\lambda_3) = (1/2G)[\lambda_2 w'(\lambda_2) - t_2]$$

and   (4)

$$(1/2G)\lambda_3 w'(\lambda_3) = (1/2G)[\lambda_1 w'(\lambda_1) - t_1].$$

The right-hand sides of eq. (4) can be evaluated from test data so that the values of $\lambda_3 w'(\lambda_3)/2G$ are known and can be plotted against λ_3, as shown in Figure 6. If the proposed form of W is valid, then the general biaxial data should lie on the curve obtained from the strip biaxial test. That this is the case within experimental error is evident from Figure 6.

Particularly powerful verification from Figure 6 lies in the fact that the abscissa λ_3 is not normalized by dividing by the relaxation modulus (as occurs on both coordinates of Fig. 5), yet the plot of data shows that essentially a single curve (obtained from strip biaxial test results) represents all the data from tests ranging

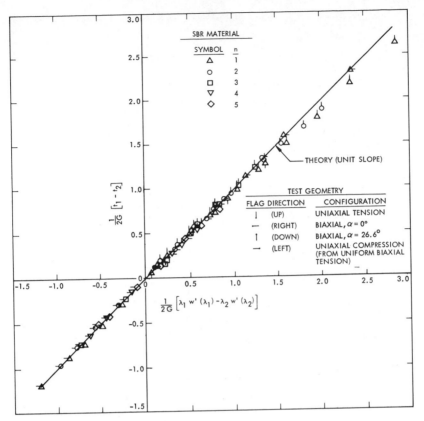

Fig. 5. Test of the basic separability hypothesis for W, showing that the stresses (or stress differences) measured in uniaxial and arbitrary biaxial conditions can be calculated from a shear modulus and the function $w'(\lambda)$ determined solely from pure shear measurements.

over various strain levels and all the possible degrees of biaxiality for all five SBR materials. Thus, the W hypothesis has been shown to be applicable not only to each individual material, but also for the whole family of materials as a system with a unified strain dependence. The latter feature confirms the previously published[5] equilibrium w_e' master curve normalized by dividing by ν_e, which demonstrated that the functional form of $W(\lambda)$ is independent of the network chain concentration. These two factors taken together show that use of the Valanis–Landel W hypothesis is potentially capable of predicting the mechanical response of whole families of elastomeric material systems once a single member of the family has been characterized.

CONCLUSIONS

The generality of applicability and ease of use of the Valanis-Landel functional representation of W shown above indicates its value as a method of representing and determining W without a strong *a priori* constraint as to mathematical form. In some cases, however, the assumption of a specific mathematical form may offer practical advantages; in this sense, the two approaches to the determination of W may be viewed as complementary.

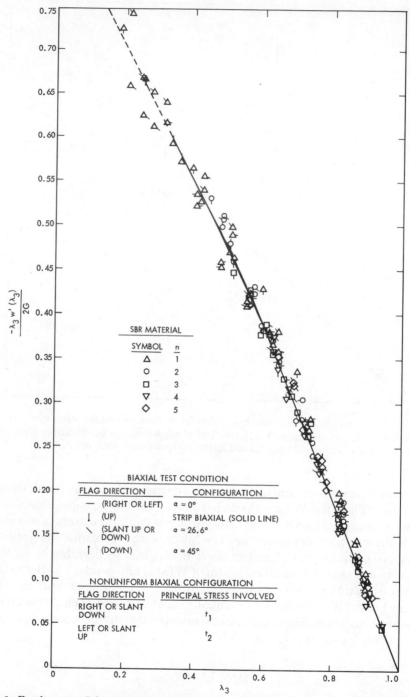

Fig. 6. Further test of the separability hypothesis for W, based on eq. (4). The strain function $\lambda_3 w'(\lambda_3)$ calculated from either λ_2 and t_2 or λ_1 and t_1, using data from a variety of biaxial test conditions, is independent of these variations within experimental error.

It is the author's pleasure to express thanks to Dr. R. F. Landel for his encouragement and discussions during the course of this study. Gratitude is also due Dr. Kenji Tsuge, who contributed greatly in conducting the test programs which provided the data for the study. This paper represents one phase of research performed by the Jet Propulsion Laboratory, California Institute of Technology, sponsored by the National Aeronautics and Space Administration, Contract NAS7-100.

REFERENCES

1. A. G. James, A. Green, and G. M. Simpson, *J. Appl. Polym. Sci.*, **19**, 2033 (1975).
2. P. J. Blatz, S. C. Sharda, and N. W. Tschoegl, *Trans. Soc. Rheol.*, **18**, 145 (1974).
3. K. C. Valanis and R. F. Landel, *J. Appl. Phys.*, **38**, 2997 (1967).
4. R. W. Ogden, *Proc. R. Soc.*, **A326**, 565 (1972).
5. K. Tsuge, R. J. Arenz, and R. F. Landel, in *Mechanical Behavior of Materials* (Proceedings of the International Conference), Vol. III, The Society of Materials Science (Japan), Kyoto, 1972, p. 443.
6. R. J. Arenz, R. F. Landel, and K. Tsuge, *Exp. Mech.*, **15**, 114 (1975).
7. J. D. Ferry, *Viscoelastic Properties of Polymers,* 2nd ed., Wiley, New York, 1970, p. 439.
8. R. J. Arenz, *J. Polym. Sci., Polym. Phys. Ed.*, **12**, 131 (1974).
9. R. G. Mancke and J. D. Ferry, *Trans. Soc. Rheol.*, **12**, 335 (1968).
10. R. J. Arenz, unpublished results.
11. R. A. Dickie and T. L. Smith, *Trans. Soc. Rheol.*, **15**, 91 (1971).

Received March 13, 1976
Revised September 15, 1976

JOURNAL OF APPLIED POLYMER SCIENCE   VOL. 21, 2465–2474 (1977)

The Dielectric Behavior of The Natural Resin Manila Copal

DIPENDRA N. GOSWAMI and PROMODE R. BHATTACHARYA,

Division of Chemistry, Indian Lac Research Institute NAMKUM, Ranchi, Bihar, India

Synopsis

The dielectric relaxation data of the natural resin Manila copal, obtained by Bhattacharya,[1] has been analyzed by the Cole–Cole method at temperatures from 30° to 150°C. Two distinct relaxation processes were found for temperatures of 70°, 80°, and 90°C as opposed to only one as observed by Bhattacharya.[1] The relaxation at 100°C and at higher temperatures could be represented by the typical Cole–Cole patterns. The variation by temperature of the static dielectric constant (ϵ_0) exhibited three distinct slopes, which indicated the different phases of the resin during thermal transformation. Two "transformation points," around 70° and 100°C, were found instead of only one at 105°C as observed by Bhattacharya.[1] The static dielectric constant, the dielectric increment, the Cole–Cole distribution parameter, and the relaxation time decreased markedly owing to the increase of temperature from 100° to 150°C. These indicated some changes in conformation of the resin molecules during transition from the solid to the liquid state.

INTRODUCTION

Dielectric behavior studies provide information about the electric polarization and the relaxation time of molecules. The former is related to the dipole moment, and the latter is essentially a function of the molecular dimensions. An analysis of the data on these two parameters provides information about the molecular structure.[2] An investigation on the variation of different dielectric parameters with the temperature and frequency of polymers offers a suitable device to detect molecular motions. This includes whole molecule rotation and motion in the backbone or of side chain movements.[3,4] The relaxations arising from different modes have been assigned α, β, γ, etc.[3,4] Dielectric behavior studies of resins have also revealed such multirelaxation processes.[5,6] The data available on the dielectric properties of natural resins are few and require more detailed study.

The dielectric dispersion of the natural resin Manila copal was studied by Bhattacharya[1] in the frequency range of 50 Hz to 500 kHz at temperatures ranging from 30° to 150°C. Both the frequency profiles of the dielectric constant and the dielectric loss exhibited single dispersion in the observed frequency range for all temperatures. The existence of one "transformation point" around 105°C was reported.[1] The dielectric dispersion of the resin was attributed to the relaxation of a rotator of radius 3.8 Å in the alternating field.

2465

The Cole–Cole[7] diagram is helpful in understanding the relaxation process of a dielectric substance in an alternating electric field. This was not applied in Bhattacharya's work. The present paper consists of a critical analysis of the dielectric dispersion data obtained by Bhattacharya[1] for the resin Manila copal in light of the Cole–Cole[7] method.

The study revealed the existence of two clear "transformation points" instead of only one as reported by Bhattacharya[1]—one in the low-temperature region and the other in the high-temperature region. The different dielectric parameters evaluated by the present method appeared to throw further light on the relaxation processes and on the conformational changes undergone by the resin molecules due to the increase in temperature from 30° to 150°C.

THEORETICAL

The Debye[8] expression for the complex dielectric constant is given by

$$\epsilon^* = \epsilon' - i\epsilon'' = \epsilon_\infty + [(\epsilon_0 - \epsilon_\infty)/(1 + i\omega\tau)] \tag{1}$$

when the real (ϵ') and imaginary (ϵ'') parts of the complex dielectric constant (ϵ^*) at any frequency ω are given by

$$\epsilon' = \epsilon_\infty + [(\epsilon_0 - \epsilon_\infty)/(1 + \omega^2\tau^2)] \tag{2}$$

$$\epsilon'' = (\epsilon_0 - \epsilon_\infty)\omega\tau/(1 + \omega^2\tau^2) \tag{3}$$

where ϵ_0 and ϵ_∞ are the low- and the high-frequency dielectric constants, respectively, and τ is the relaxation time. Equations (2) and (3) can be put in the following form:

$$[\epsilon' - (\epsilon_0 - \epsilon_\infty)/2]^2 + \epsilon''^2 = [(\epsilon_0 - \epsilon_\infty)/2]^2 \tag{4}$$

From eq. (4) it is clear that a plot of ϵ'' versus ϵ' will give a semicircle with its center on the abscissa $[0, (\epsilon_0 + \epsilon_\infty)/2]$ and radius $(\epsilon_0 - \epsilon_\infty)/2$. For some materials, Cole and Cole[7] obtained a plot of depressed arc with the center lying below the ϵ'-axis. They introduced a distribution parameter α in the original Debye eq. (1) after which the modified equation is written as follows[7]:

$$\epsilon^* = \epsilon' - i\epsilon'' = \epsilon_\infty + (\epsilon_0 - \epsilon_\infty)/[1 + (i\omega\tau)^{1-\alpha}] \tag{5}$$

The real and the imaginary parts are given by

$$\epsilon' - \epsilon_\infty = (\epsilon_0 - \epsilon_\infty)[1 + (\omega\tau)^{1-\alpha}\sin(\alpha\,\pi/2)]/$$
$$[1 + 2(\omega\tau)^{1-\alpha}\sin(\alpha\,\pi/2) + (\omega\tau)^{2(1-\alpha)}] \tag{6}$$

$$\epsilon'' = (\epsilon_0 - \epsilon_\infty)(\omega\tau)^{1-\alpha}\cos(\alpha\,\pi/2)/\ [1 + 2(\omega\tau)^{1-\alpha}\sin(\alpha\,\pi/2) + (\omega\tau)^{2(1-\alpha)}] \tag{7}$$

Thus, it is concluded that if the dielectric relaxation is characterized by a single relaxation time, the ϵ'' versus ϵ' plot will be a semicircle with its center on the abscissa. If there is a distribution of relaxation times, the center will lie below the abscissa and a depressed arc is obtained. The correct low- and high-frequency dielectric constants (ϵ_0 and ϵ_∞) are obtained from the intersections of the circle with the abscissa. The angle between the abscissa and the line joining the center with the ϵ_∞ point is expressed by $\alpha\pi/2$, α being the distribution parameter appearing in the Cole–Cole eq. (5).

In the present paper, the Cole–Cole plot has been used for the determination of ϵ_0 and ϵ_∞, and relaxation times have been calculated from the following equation:

$$(\omega\tau)^{1-\alpha} = v/u \tag{8}$$

where v and u are the distances from ϵ_0 and ϵ_∞, respectively, from a point on the semicircle corresponding to the frequency ω.[7]

RESULTS

The Cole–Cole plots (ϵ'' versus ϵ') for the resin Manila copal at different temperatures were drawn from the data of Bhattacharya[1] (Fig. 1).

The dielectric constant and the dielectric loss were reported constant throughout the observed frequency range (50 Hz to 500 kHz), and no dielectric dispersion was observed for temperatures from 30° to 60°C.[1] The ϵ''-versus-ϵ' plot at 60°C [Fig. 1(a)] also revealed the same information. The plots for temperatures 30°, 40°, and 50°C were found to be similar.

The Cole–Cole patterns for temperatures 70°, 80°, and 90°C differed from those at other temperatures. All the points in the ϵ''-versus-ϵ' plots were not contained in a single Cole–Cole arc. It appeared from the patterns that the dielectric dispersions of the copal resin for these temperatures were the result of two relaxation processes (I and II); each process could be represented by a Cole–Cole semicircle. The ϵ''-versus-ϵ' patterns for 100° to 150°C were, however, perfect semicircular Cole–Cole types.

The different dielectric parameters evaluated from the Cole–Cole diagrams at various temperatures are given in Table I. The ϵ_0 and ϵ_∞ values obtained from the same plots for 100° to 150°C are shown in columns 2 and 3, respectively. The values of ϵ_0 and ϵ_∞ determined experimentally by Bhattacharya[1] are also included for comparison. It is found that the ϵ_0 and ϵ_∞ values obtained from the Cole–Cole plots differ from the values observed experimentally.

The variation of the static dielectric constant (ϵ_0) with temperature has been illustrated in Figure 2. The ϵ_0-versus-temperature curve indicates three distinct slopes (marked 1, 2, and 3 in Fig. 2). From the same figure, it may be seen that ϵ_0 is almost constant up to 60°C; it increases sharply and reaches a maximum at 100°C. ϵ_0 then decreases with further increase in temperature. The ϵ_∞, on the other hand, increases with temperature.

The values of the dielectric increments $\Delta\epsilon(=\epsilon_0 - \epsilon_\infty)$, which are related to the dipole moments, are given in column 4 of Table I. The $\Delta\epsilon$ for temperatures 100°C to 150°C were evaluated using ϵ_0 and ϵ_∞ obtained from the Cole–Cole diagrams. The $\Delta\epsilon$ values for temperatures 70° to 90°C were obtained from the experimental values of ϵ_0 and ϵ_∞. As there was no dielectric dispersion for temperatures from 30° to 60°C, the ϵ_∞ values could not be ascertained and, therefore, $\Delta\epsilon$ values were not determined. The $\Delta\epsilon$ value increases from 0.22 at 70°C to 1.93 at 100°C (about an 8.8 times increase) and then decreases to 0.91 at 150°C (52.8% decrease).

The relaxation time for the resin molecules for temperatures 100°C to 150°C was calculated using eq. (8) and is given in column 5 of Table I. The relaxation time τ decreases markedly from a value of 1.18×10^{-4} sec at 100°C to 1.75×10^{-7} sec at 150°C (a 99.8% decrease). This suggests increased compactness of the molecules at high temperatures.

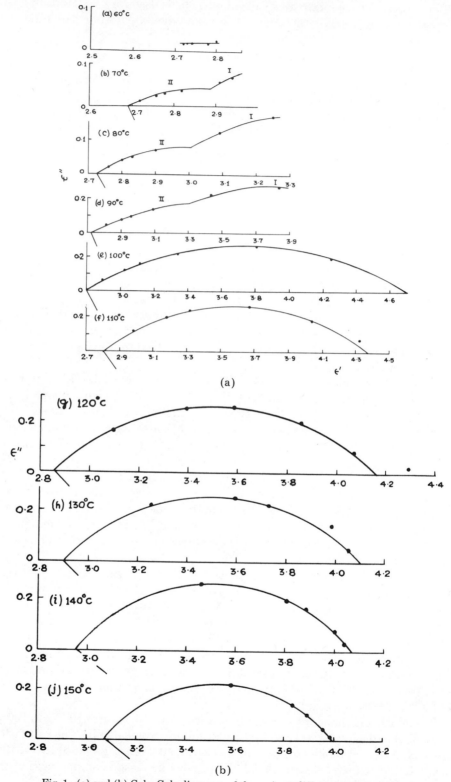

Fig. 1. (a) and (b) Cole–Cole diagrams of the resin at different temperatures.

TABLE I
Different Dielectric Parameters of Manila Copal at Different Temperatures,
Obtained from Cole-Cole Diagrams

Tempera-ture, °C	ϵ_0		ϵ_∞		Dielec-tric in-crement	τ, sec	α
	Obtained from diagram	Observed value[a]	Obtained from diagram	Observed value[a]			
30		2.70					
40		2.72					
50		2.75					
60		2.80					
70		2.94	2.69	2.72	0.22		
80		3.25	2.73	2.76	0.49		
90		3.88	2.72	2.81	1.07		
100	4.73	4.25	2.80	2.89	1.93	1.18×10^{-4}	0.66
110	4.38	4.33	2.80	2.98	1.58	1.04×10^{-4}	0.59
120	4.17	4.30	2.85	3.09	1.32	2.09×10^{-6}	0.51
130	4.10	4.22	2.90	3.26	1.20	8.09×10^{-7}	0.49
140	4.08	4.12	2.96	3.46	1.12	3.03×10^{-7}	0.44
150	3.99	4.02	3.08	3.58	0.91	1.75×10^{-7}	0.43

[a] Bhattacharya.[1]

The variation of ln $(T\tau)$ with $(1/T)$ is represented in Figure 3. The linear plot suggests no change in the state of the resin between 100° and 150°C. The activation energy calculated from the slope of Figure 3 (on the basis of the Arrhenius equation) was 30 kcal/mole. This value is in good agreement with the value earlier reported by Bhattacharya[1] from the slopes of dc conductivity, resistivity, and viscosity-versus-$1/T$ plots above the melting point.

The Cole–Cole distribution parameter α for temperatures of 100° to 150°C of the resin are given in the last column of Table I. There is a decrease in α from a value of 0.66 at 100°C to 0.43 at 150°C (a 34.8% decrease).

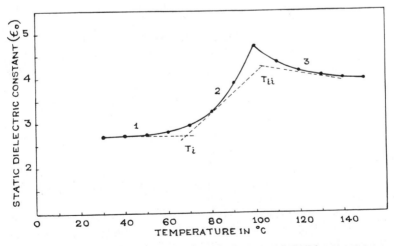

Fig. 2. Variation of the static dielectric constant (ϵ_0) with temperature.

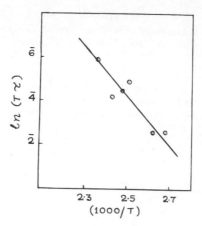

Fig. 3. Plot of ln $(T\tau)$ vs $(1/T)$.

DISCUSSION

The assembly of the electrodes for investigation of the dielectric properties was so designed that during the experiment, the physical state of the resin, changing from solid to liquid, could be maintained at any temperature between 30° and 150°C.[1,9] Thus, the dielectric behavior exhibited was a true reflection of the changes in the physical state of the resin with temperature. An inspection of the Cole–Cole diagrams of the Manila copal resin revealed that distinct variations in the relaxation processes developed with the increase in temperature. The changes in the different dielectric parameters obtained from the Cole–Cole patterns indicated that some molecular transformations had occurred as the temperature increased from 30° to 150°C.

Bhattacharya[1] reported only one relaxation process in the whole frequency region for all temperatures between 70° and 150°C. The present investigation, however, indicates the existence of two distinct relaxation processes for temperatures 70°, 80°, and 90°C (Fig. 1). For temperatures beyond 90°C, the resin molecules follow the typical Cole–Cole type of behavior. The present investigation confirms the early study:[1] below 70°C no dielectric dispersion was observed in the frequency range of 50 Hz to 500 kHz.

The different slopes in the ϵ_0-versus-temperature plot indicates three distinct phases of the resin during thermal transformation and the possibility of the existence of two "transformation points" around 70° and 100°C, respectively (marked T_i and T_{ii} in Fig. 2). The transition points T_i and T_{ii} are attributed to the glass transition temperature and the melting point of the resin, respectively. Bhattacharya[1] also had postulated the existence of such a transformation point at about the same temperature of 105–106°C, which is the melting point of the copal resin. He indicated the possible existence of another transformation point around 50°C, which actually was found in the present study (around 70°C). An inspection of the Cole–Cole diagrams (Fig. 1) at different temperatures also supports the above phenomenon.

The low values of both the dielectric constant and the loss at 60°C and below were attributed by Bhattacharya[1] to the limited orientational freedom of the dipoles due to high viscosity. According to Yano and Wada,[10] below the glass transition temperature where the segmental motion is frozen, the relaxation may arise from local motion in the form of rotation or rotational oscillation.[10,11] It may be mentioned, however, that segmental motion has been reported for poly(dimethylsiloxane) even below the temperature at which the fluid solidified.[12] In the present experiment, as the temperature of the resin reached the glass transition temperature (T_i), the viscosity decreased rapidly and the orientation of the dipoles resulted in a higher value of ϵ_0. The 8.8 times increase in the dielectic increment (and hence in the dipole moment) due to an increase in temperature from 70° to 100°C lends support to this phenomenon. A similar increase in ϵ_0 with temperature was noted in the transition phase for many polymers such as polyamides,[13] styrene–acrylonitrile copolymers,[14] and poly(vinylidene fluoride).[15]

When the temperature changed from 60° to 70°C, two dispersion regions appeared suddenly, suggesting an abrupt change in phase of the resin in this region [Figs. 1(b)–1(d)]. The reason for the occurrence of two relaxation processes is not clearly known. Between the glass transition temperature and the melting point, the different segments of the resin molecules experience various hindering forces depending on the internal viscosity. This renders different degrees of segmental orientation producing the two relaxation processes. The segmental orientation (β process) in the transition phase has been reported in polymers, viz., polymaleimide,[4] ethylene–methacrylic acid copolymers,[16] polystyrene,[10] poly(invylidene fluoride),[15] styrene–acrylonitrile copolymers.[14]

Between 100° and 150°C, only one relaxation process was observed with distribution in relaxation times. The process exhibited to some extent the characteristics of a dipole orientation polarization. In a study on the dielectric properties of phenol–formaldehyde resin in paper laminates, the relaxation process above 10^4 Hz was reported to be due to rotational movements of the hydroxyl groups present in the resin and cellulose.[6] A similar conclusion was reached from dielectric studies of natural resin shellac[9] and shellac–melamine–formaldehyde compositions.[5] For other polymers such as poly(vinylidene fluoride)[15] poly(chlorotrifluoroethylene),[17] and styrene–acrylonitrile copolymers,[14] the relaxation at high temperature was attributed to molecular motions (α process). The dielectric data were explained from the viewpoint of intermolecular interaction and molecular motions.[15,17] In the present experiment, the symmetrical Cole–Cole patterns of the resin, the 52.8% decrease in $\Delta\epsilon$, the 99.8% decrease in τ, and the 35% reduction in α due to the rise in temperature from 100° to 150°C also indicated some changes in the conformational rearrangement of the resin molecules in the liquid state. This is presumably due to the formation of crosslinks as reported in the case of natural resin shellac and its composites.[18,5]

It may be mentioned that two kinds of relaxation processes, one at high temperature and the other at low temperature, were also reported for various amorphous polymers: (i) with flexible polar side groups, viz., poly(acrylic esters)[19] and poly(vinyl esters)[20], and (ii) of molecules without flexible side groups, viz., amorphous polyesters,[21] poly(vinyl chloride)[22] and polychloroprene.[23] The molecular mechanism of high-temperature relaxation was attributed to large-scale conformational rearrangement of the main chains, while the low-temperature relaxation resulted from the local twisting modes of the main chain or from the motion of the side groups.[19–23] In semicrystalline polymers, such as polyester, polycarbonates, dry polyamides, and polyethers, two kinds of relaxation processes were also observed.[3]

TABLE II

Comparison of Calculated and Observed ϵ_M'' Values

Temperature, °C	Calculated ϵ_M''	Experimentally observed[a] ϵ_M''
100	0.263	0.26
110	0.26	0.26
120	0.266	0.27
130	0.255	0.26
140	0.26	0.26
150	0.22	0.22

[a] Bhattacharya.[1]

From an extensive study on the dielectric behavior of biopolymers of different molecular weights, Takashima[24] suggested that the distribution in the relaxation time arises either from asymmetry in the shape of the molecules or from the distribution in molecular weights. It was suggested later that changes in the shape of the molecules were the most important contributing factor,[25] and the increase in α was attributed to the increased asymmetry of the molecules.[26] The 35% decrease in the value of α observed in the present experiment indicates that the resin molecules become dielectrically more symmetrical with increase in temperature from 100° to 150°C. The Cole–Cole plots of some ethylene–carbon copolymers also revealed narrowing of distribution of relaxation times with temperature.[27] The decrease of α was attributed to chain folds and chain torsion mechanisms. A similar decrease in the distribution parameter was reported for poly(vinylidene fluoride).[28]

Bhattacharya[1] calculated the relaxation time τ from the relation

$$\omega\tau = (\epsilon_\infty' + 2)/(\epsilon_0' + 2)$$

at a temperature corresponding to the peak of the dielectric loss–temperature curve at a fixed frequency. The dielectric relaxation of the resin Manila copal is explained in the present study in light of the Cole–Cole theory, and correct values of the relaxation times are given in Table I.

The observed maximum ϵ'' value (ϵ_M'') of the resin was reported[1] to be somewhat less than one third of the value obtained from Debye's eq. (3), $\epsilon_M'' = (\epsilon_0 - \epsilon_\infty)/2$. A similar result was obtained from the dielectric study of other plastic materials.[29] The discrepancy was attributed to the existence of a distribution in the relaxation time.[1,29] In eq. (7), ϵ'' signifies the molecules obeying a Cole–Cole type of distribution. The maximum value of ϵ'', in eq. (7), is obtained by using $\omega\tau = 1$. Then

$$\epsilon_M'' = \frac{(\epsilon_0 - \epsilon_\infty)\cos(\alpha\pi/2)}{2[1 + \sin(\alpha\pi/2)]}. \tag{9}$$

The ϵ_M'' value calculated using relation (9) for temperatures 100° to 150°C are shown in Table II. The corresponding values for ϵ_M'' obtained experimentally are given in the last column for comparison. It was found that the values of ϵ_M'' obtained by calculation were in close agreement with those obtained by experient. The data in Table II, therefore, justify the application of the Cole–Cole method to understand the different processes involved in the dielectric dispersion of copal resin.

Bhattacharya[1] used the Debye equation relating relaxation time (τ), radius of the molecule (a), coefficient of viscosity (η) of the medium, Boltzmann constant (K), and temperature (T):

$$\tau = 4\pi\eta a^3/kT \tag{10}$$

and calculated a value of 3.8Å as the radius of the Manila copal rotator. The dielectric behavior of the copal resin was interpreted by him as due to the relaxation of the rotator (3.8Å) in the alternating electric field.

A comparatively larger value of the relaxation time, e.g., 1.18×10^{-4} sec at 100°C, was observed in the present case; the marked decrease in τ due to the increase in temperature from 100° to 150 °C and the transition from two relaxation processes to one with the rise in temperature cannot be explained by the relaxation of the rotator of size 3.8 Å as suggested by Bhattacharya.[1] Moreover, eq. (10) was derived on the basis of molecules of spherical shape and moving in a continuous viscous fluid having an internal coefficient of viscosity η.[30,31] The resin molecules are not spherical, and since each molecule is surrounded by other similar molecules, the molecular environment was very different from a homogeneous fluid. Later, it was shown that eq. (10) does not represent adequately the relation between the relaxation time, molecular radius, and the macroscopic viscosity.[30,31]

It appears from the present study, that below the glass transition temperature, the orientation of the polar groups was due less to high viscosity, thus yielding one relaxation time distribution. Between the glass transition and the melting point, segmental orientation occurred giving rise to two relaxation processes. For temperatures above the melting point, different degrees of molecular orientation, resulting from conformational rearrangements of the resin molecules in the liquid state, yielded the Cole–Cole-type single relaxation process.

The authors wish to acknowledge with thanks the continuous encouragement of Dr. B. B. Khanna, Head of the Chemistry Division. They are also grateful to Dr. T. P. S. Teotia, Director of this Institute, for his kind interest in this work.

References

1. G. N. Bhattacharya, *Indian J. Sci. Ind. Res.*, **4**, 713 (1946).
2. N. E. Hill, in *Dielectric Properties and Molecular Behavior*, N. E. Hill, W. E. Vaughan, A. H. Price, and M. Davies, Eds., Van Nostrand-Reinhold, London, 1969.
3. N. G. McCrum, R. E. Reed, and G. Williams, *Anelastic and Dielectric Effects in Polymeric Solid*, Willey, New York, 1967.
4. H. Block, R. Groves, and S. M. Walker, *Polymer*, **13**, 527 (1972).
5. T. R. Lakshminarayanan and M. P. Gupta, *J. Appl. Polym. Sci.*, **18**, 2047 (1974).
6. J. T. Jux, A. M. North, and R. Kay, *Polymer*, **15**, 799 (1974).
7. K. S. Cole and R. H. Cole, *J. Chem. Phys.*, **9**, 341 (1941).
8. P. Debye, *Polar Molecules*, Chemical Catalogue Co., New York, 1929.
9. G. N. Bhattacharya, *Indian J. Phys.*, **18**, 1 (1944).
10. O. Yano and Y. Wada, *J. Polym. Sci. A2*, **9**, 669 (1971).
11. M. E. Baird and E. Houston, *Polymer*, **16**, 308 (1975).
12. M. E. Baird and C. R. Sengupta, *Polymer*, **12**, 802 (1971).
13. M. E. Baird, G. T. Goldsworthy, and C. J. Creasey,*Polymer*, **12**, 159 (1971).
14. M. Cook, G. Williams, and T. T. Jones, *Polymer*, **16**, 835 (1975).
15. K. Nakagawa and Y. Ishida, *J. Polym. Sci. A2*, **11**, 1503 (1973).
16. P. J. Philips and W. J. MacKnight, *J. Polym. Sci. A2*, **8**, 72 (1970).
17. H. Sasabe, *J. Polym. Sci. A2*, **11**, 2413 (1973).

18. A. Kumar, *J. Appl. Polym. Sci.*, **8**, 1185 (1964).
19. Y. Ishida and K. Yamafuji, *Kolloid-Z.*, **177**, 97 (1961).
20. Y. Ishida, M. Matsuo, and K. Yamafuji, *Kolloid-Z.*, **180**, 108 (1962).
21. W. Reddish, *Trans. Faraday Soc.*, **46**, 459 (1950).
22. Y. Ishida, *Kolloid-Z.*, **168**, 29 (1960).
23. M. Matsuo, Y. Ishida, K. Yamafuji, M. Takayanagi, and F. Irie, *Kolloid-Z.*, **201**, 89 (1965).
24. S. Takashima, *J. Mol. Biol.*, **7**, 455 (1963).
25. D. N. Goswami and N. N. Das Gupta, *Biopolymers*, **13**, 391 (1974).
26. D. N. Goswami and N. N. das Gupta, *Biopolymers*, **13**, 1549 (1974).
27. P. J. Phillips, G. L. Wilkes, B. W. Delf, and R. S. Stein, *J. Polym. Sci. A2*, **9**, 499 (1971).
28. S. Yano, *J. Polym. Sci. A2*, **8**, 1057 (1970).
29. C. P. Smyth, *Dielectric Behavior and Structure*, McGraw Hill, New York, 1955, Chap. V, p. 188.
30. Reference 29, Chap. IV, p. 103.
31. C. P. Smyth, *Molecular Relaxation Processes*, Academic Press, New York, 1966.

Received March 12, 1976
Revised August 20, 1976

JOURNAL OF APPLIED POLYMER SCIENCE   VOL. 21, 2475–2479 (1977)

Semiconductor Properties of Polyamide-6 Containing Dispersed Copper or Zinc Additives

TADEUSZ CZEKAJ and JERZY KAPKO, *Institute of Organic Chemistry and Technology, Technical University in Kraków, 31-155 Kraków, Poland*

Synopsis

It was expected that elemental copper or zinc introduced into polycaproamide would interact with amide groups of the polymer and that the materials would be characterized by semiconductor properties. To prove this theory, resistivity at several temperatures was determined and thermal activation energies calculated. As the metal contents were relatively low, metallic conductivity was avoided. Temperature-resistivity dependence and a negative temperature coefficient of the resistivity prove that polyamide–metal compositions can be classified as semiconductors.

INTRODUCTION

Recently, an increased interest in electrical properties of some polymers has been observed. Due to these electrical properties, several polymers, among them polymers modified with metal atoms, are classified as organic semiconductors. Well known are polychelates with azoporphyrin rings, poly(phthalocyanines) and poly(tetracyanoethylene), as well as ferrocene, characterized by 0.8 − 1.0 eV activation energy and electrical resistivity less than 10^{14} ohm·cm.[1-3]

Some interest was directed as well to polymers with a straight hydrocarbon chain containing metal additives.

Polyisoprene modified with metallic iron[4] was studied and proven to have a marked semiconductivity. One can expect, thus, that even a double-bond system (π electrons) can interact with electron shells of metal atoms. In poly(methyl methacrylate) containing colloidal dispersed copper, semiconductivity was shown by means of conductivity-versus-temperatures measurements and subsequent calculations of decreased activation energy.[5]

Nonbonding electron pairs existing in amide groups of the polycaproamide chains

$$-(CH_2)_5-\overset{..}{\underset{:\ddot{O}:}{C}}-\overset{..}{N}H-$$

are suitable to form coordination bonds with electron acceptors; and this phenomenon is broadly utilized in proposing copper compounds for polyamide antioxidants or plasticizers.

In the case of polycaproamide modified with powdered iron,[6] marked changes in the electrical properties were observed. Polyamides, even in the basic state, are characterized by an interesting electrical behavior: their specific resistance

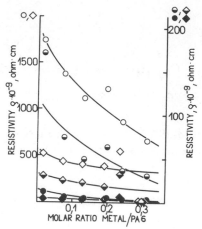

Fig. 1. Dependence of resistivity of the sinters on the molar ratio metal/PA 6: (O) copper at 25°C; (◓) copper at 54°C; (●) copper at 78°C; (◈) zinc at 26°C; (◆) zinc at 48°C; (◆) zinc at 68°C.

under direct current decreases from 10^{13} ohm·cm to 10^7 ohm·cm at room temperature and 160–180°C (433–453°K), respectively. This phenomenon is explained on the basis of proton mobility of amide groups.[7] Later works, however, proved the electron character of the polyamide conductivity at increased temperatures.[8]

These observations permit one to postulate a high possibility for added metal to interact with amide groups in the polymer and subsequently change the electrical properties of polyamides.

Copper and zinc were selected for addition to polycaproamide, PA6, because they should easily form coordination bonds. It was expected that they would influence polyamide properties even if heterogeneous systems resulted. Only electrical measurements could be taken into consideration either because of a lack of optical transmission or the necessity of powdering the samples which destroys metal–polymer interactions.

EXPERIMENTAL

Monomer-free powdered PA 6 with a degree of polymerization $P = 250$ and mp 215–217°C (488–490°K) was desiccated *in vacuo* before use.

Metal powders were strained through a 0.078-mm sieve. Copper was warmed with paraformaldehyde up to its evaporation temperature and kept in CO_2. Zinc was oxide free and did not require reduction.

Melting of polyamide with metal powders proved unsuitable due to the great differences in density, which caused metal sedimentation; therefore, sintering was employed as an alternate method. It was first stated that PA 6 could be molded 6° below its melting point under 1000 kg/cm² pressure. The structure of the resulting material could not be distinguished from the polyamide formed from the melt. An electrically heated mold was used to form six tablets simultaneously. Samples with metal additives were formed under the same conditions. Tablets 6 mm in diameter and 2.9–3.0 mm thick were obtained.

The electrical resistivity of the tablets was determined using an electrometer VA-J-5118 (Ger. Dem. Rep.) with a controlled temperature measuring chamber.

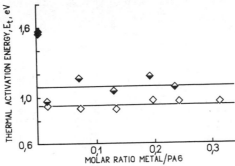

Fig. 2. Thermal activation energy E_t vs. molar ratio metal/PA 6: (♦) polycaproamide; (◊) PA–Cu sinters; (♠) PA–Zn sinters.

The face surfaces of the tablets were covered with silver paste; tension was applied by means of copper electrodes; and tests were made in a nitrogen atmosphere.

RESULTS

Experiments were made on samples containing 0.02–0.30 gram-atoms of metal per mole of polyamide (calculated on the basic unit of polycaproamide, MW = 113). This range differs substantially from the one described in reference 6, where up to 60% iron was introduced into polycaproamide, and simple metallic

TABLE I
Experimental and Calculated Data for PA–Zn Sinters

No.	Composition of sinters % of Zn in sinters	Zn/PA mole ratio	Temp., °C	$1/T \times 10^3$, $1/°K$	$\rho \times 10^{-9}$, ohm·cm	lg ρ	Thermal activation energy E_t, eV
1	1	0.0175	25	3.36	514.0	11.711	
			48	3.12	30.2	10.480	0.964
			72	2.90	3.04	9.483	
2	4	0.072	26	3.34	430.3	11.634	
			48	3.12	25.0	10.398	1.152
			69	2.93	3.18	9.503	
3	7	0.130	26	3.34	401.0	11.604	
			49	3.11	20.9	10.320	1.050
			68	2.93	3.22	9.508	
4	10	0.192	26	3.34	389.0	11.590	
			48	3.12	18.2	10.260	1.172
			68	2.93	3.07	9.487	
5	12	0.236	26	3.34	542.0	11.734	
			48	3.12	32.3	10.509	1.080
			68	2.93	4.44	9.647	
6	15	0.301	24	3.37	<2.58	9.412	
						Average	1.083
						stand. dev.	0.083
						variance s_{n-1}^2	0.0069

TABLE II
Experimental and Calculated Data for PA–Cu Sinters

No.	Composition of sinters		Temp., °C	$1/T \times 10^3$ 1/°K	$\rho \times 10^{-9}$, ohm·cm	$\lg \rho$	Thermal activation energy E_t, eV
	% of Cu in sinters	Cu/PA mole ratio					
1	1	0.018	22	3.38	1740.0	12.241	
			52	3.08	171.0	11.233	0.921
			79	2.84	12.0	10.079	
2	4	0.074	24	3.37	1370.0	12.137	
			54	3.06	73.4	10.866	0.902
			78	2.85	6.56	9.817	
3	7	0.134	24	3.37	1118.0	12.049	
			52	3.08	49.0	10.690	0.890
			79	2.84	5.08	9.706	
4	10	0.198	26	3.34	1210.0	12.083	
			52	3.08	63.2	10.801	0.964
			79	2.84	5.42	9.734	
5	12	0.243	24	3.37	864.0	11.937	
			52	3.08	35.9	10.555	0.955
			78	2.85	2.95	9.470	
6	15	0.314	25	3.36	660.0	11.820	
			53	5.07	29.8	10.474	0.952
			78	2.85	2.25	9.352	
						Average	0.930
						stand. dev.	0.031
						variance s_{n-1}^2	0.00095
7	Pure poly-(caproamide)		23	3.38	38800	13.589	
			43	3.16	5000	12.699	1.554
			63	2.98	81.5	10.911	
			82	2.81	4.19	9.622	

conductivity could not be avoided. The results and calculated activation energies E_t are given in Tables I and II.

Thermal activation energy E_t was calculated in eV according to

$$\rho = \rho_0 \cdot \exp(E_t/kT)$$

where ρ_0 = standard resistivity, ohm·cm; k = Boltzman constant, 8.617×10^{-5} eV; and T = temperature, °K.

DISCUSSION OF THE RESULTS

The decrease in the electrical resistivity of the sinters, if compared to polyamide, was greater in the case of the PA–zinc system than in the PA–copper system (Fig. 1).

It can thus be concluded that the resistivity of PA–metal sinters is of nonmetallic character and that it is not the simple sum of a nonmetallic polyamide and a metallic additive.

The changes in the E_t and the resistivity of the sinters when compared to polyamide itself prove that there exists a different interaction between the polyamide and copper or zinc (Fig. 2).

It is possible to some extent that electronegative zinc ($E_{Zn} = -0.76$ V) can substitute for acidic hydrogen atoms in amide groups at the high temperature of molding, while copper can only interact with free electron pairs of nitrogen atoms ($E_{Cu} = +0.35$ V).

The resistivity of polyamide containing dispersed zinc does not depend on the amount of zinc additive, but on the probability (degree) of the substitution of acidic hydrogen atoms by zinc atoms. Below the melting temperature, only those groups can be substituted which are not crosslinked (bounded) by the hydrogen bonds. It was observed in our case that the substitution takes place with 1% or less of zinc in the sinters. Only part of the zinc reacts with the polyamide and decreases the value of the resistivity and E_t. The other part remains as a metallic filler dispersed in the polymer matrix and cannot change the resistivity remarkably. That is the reason why the resistivity is almost constant with increasing amounts of zinc in the sinters (ρ of PA–Zn fluctuates around ca. $4.6 \times 10^{11} \pm 0.6 \times 10^{11}$ ohm·cm at 22–25°C, around $2.5 \times 10^{10} \pm 0.7 \times 10^{10}$ ohm·cm at 48–49°C, and around $3.6 \pm 0.8 \times 10^9$ ohm·cm at 68–72°C for samples 1–5 (Table I). A negative coefficient of resistivity is caused by ionic conductivity and not semiconductivity. The rapid drop of the resistivity at 15% of Zn can be attributed to a combination of metallic and ionic conductivities.

The increase of metal content in PA–Cu sinters causes a marked decrease in resistivity—as much as a fivefold-decrease at 78–79°C (Table II).

Analysis of the basic linear dependence of the resistivity logarithms on the temperature reciprocal lg $\rho = f(10^4/T)$ and negative temperature coefficient of the resistivity prove that the above-described polyamide–copper compositions can be classified as semiconductors.

References

1. A. A. Berlin and N. G. Matviejeva, *Usp. Chim.*, **29**, 277 (1960).
2. R. S. Bradley, J. D. Grace, and D. C. Munro, *Trans. Faraday Soc.*, **58**, 776 (1962).
3. C. Y. Liang, E. G. Scallo, and G. Onetal, *J. Chem. Phys.*, **37**, 459 (1962).
4. S. D. Levina and K. P. Lobanova, *Dokl. Akad. Nauk SSSR*, **132**, 1140 (1960).
5. M. G. Batsikadze and M. K. Begiashvili, *Soobshch. Akad. Nauk Gruz. SSR*, **75**(3), 617 (1974).
6. J. I. Chimitchenko, M. M. Chvorov, and I. S. Radkevitch, *Vysokomol. Soedin., Ser. B*, **15**, 895 (1973).
7. W. O. Baker and W. A. Yager, *J. Amer. Chem. Soc.*, **64**, 2171 (1942).
8. M. E. Baird, *J. Polym. Sci. A-2*, **8**, 739 (1970).

Received March 23, 1976
Revised May 24, 1976

JOURNAL OF APPLIED POLYMER SCIENCE   VOL. 21, 2481–2488 (1977)

Preparation of Crosslinked Poly(styrene–g–N-carboxyalkylated Ethylenimine) as Chelating Resin

TAKEO SAEGUSA, SHIRO KOBAYASHI, and AKIRA YAMADA,
Department of Synthetic Chemistry, Faculty of Engineering, Kyoto University, Kyoto, Japan

Synopsis

Carboxymethyl and ethyl groups were introduced into crosslinked poly(styrene–g–ethylenimine) (PSt–g–EI), consisting of a crosslinked polystyrene backbone with linear polyethylenimine branches, by the reaction of PSt–g–EI with monochloroacetic acid and β-chloropropionic acid. Carboxyethylation was also performed by reaction of the PSt–g–EI with acrylic acid. The extent of the reaction was determined by the change in the nitrogen content of the resin. The adsorption of metal ions such as Cu^{2+}, Cd^{2+}, Hg^{2+}, Ni^{2+}, and Ca^{2+} by carboxyalkylated PSt–g–EI was examined. With the introduction of carboxyalkyl groups, the adsorption capacity for metal ions (per gram of resin) decreased, whereas the affinity of the resin for these ions increased.

INTRODUCTION

Recently, we reported the preparation of poly(styrene–g–ethylenimine) (PSt–g–EI) containing the linear structure of polyethylenimine. It was prepared by the graft polymerization of 2-methyl-2-oxazoline onto chloromethylated polystyrene (noncrosslinked or crosslinked) and by the subsequent hydrolysis of the graft copolymer[1]:

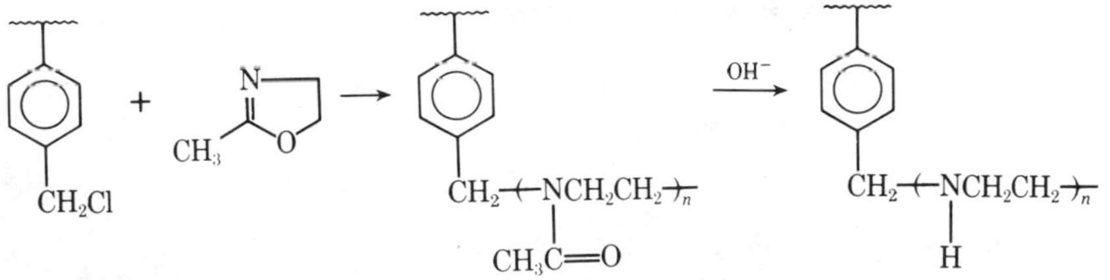

Crosslinked PSt–g–EI was quite effective for the adsorption of heavy metal ions such as Cu^{2+}, Hg^{2+}, and Cd^{2+}. However, the resin could not be used for the adsorption of metal ions which do not form stable amine complexes, because the site for coordinating metal ions in PSt–g–EI is the secondary amino group.

It is well known that the carboxymethylation of amines produces effective chelating agents such as EDTA. Indeed, prior to the present study, Amberlite IR-4B and IR-45, two polyamine-type anion exchange resins, had been carboxymethylated by condensation with monochloroacetic acid.[2] Aminated PSt prepared by the reaction of chloromethylated PSt with ethylenediamine, diethylenetriamine, or triethylenetetramine had been carboxymethylated.[3] Crosslinked poly(N-carboxyalkylethylenimines) had been prepared by the co-polymerization of 1-aziridinealkanoic acid esters and β,β'-di-(1-aziridinyl)diethylbenzene.[4] Furthermore, an iminodiacetic acid-type resin (I) had been obtained by Okawara et al.[5]:

$$\text{CH}_2\text{N} \begin{array}{c} \text{CH}_2\text{CO}_2\text{Na} \\ \\ \text{CH}_2\text{CO}_2\text{Na} \end{array}$$

I

The chelation of metal ions by resin I is analogous to their chelation by EDTA. It is claimed that resin I adsorbs metal ions more effectively than other resins because of their chelation through nitrogen and oxygen atoms. Because of this adsorption advantage, it was considered worthwhile to introduce carboxyalkyl groups into PSt–g–EI in order to explore a new type of chelating resin. The present paper describes the preparation of crosslinked poly(styrene–g–N-carboxymethylethylenimine) and poly(styrene–g–N-carboxyethylethylenimine) and their chelating properties with several metal ions.

RESULTS AND DISCUSSION

In this paper, crosslinked poly(styrene–g–ethylenimine) (PSt–g–EI) was employed as the parent polymer in all cases. Three kinds of PSt–g–EI (A, B, and C) were employed (see experimental section).

Carboxymethylation of PSt–g–EI

PSt–g–EI was carboxymethylated by condensation with monochloroacetic acid under alkaline conditions:

$$\text{PSt-}g\text{-EI} + \text{ClCH}_2\text{CO}_2\text{Na} \xrightarrow{\text{NaOH}} \qquad + \text{NaCl} \qquad (1)$$

$$\text{CH}_2\text{-}(\text{NCH}_2\text{CH}_2)_n \\ | \\ \text{CH}_2\text{CO}_2\text{Na}$$

As the reaction between PSt–g–EI and ClCH$_2$CO$_2$Na proceeded, the pH of the system gradually decreased. The system was then made alkaline with excess sodium hydroxide, and the reaction was allowed to continue until the pH of the system remained constant. The conditions employed and the results obtained are shown in Table I. Degree of substitution and the CO$_2$Na content were calculated based on the difference in the nitrogen content between the starting PSt–g–EI and the product. The determination of the CO$_2$Na content by pH titration was very difficult because the system was heterogeneous. The titration curve varied monotonously and the endpoint could not be resolved. It has been

TABLE I
Carboxymethylation and Carboxyethylation of PSt-*g*-EI

Sample[a]	Kind of PSt-*g*-EI,[b] g	Reagent	Reagent/ EI unit, molar ratio	Time at 70°, hr	Yield, g	N in the product, %	CO₂Na content, mmole/g	Degree of substitution, %
CM1	A (1.10)	ClCH₂CO₂H	10.1	33[c]	1.64	9.14	5.11	94.2
CM2	B (3.51)	ClCH₂CO₂H	23.9	70[c]	3.11	11.03	5.90	108.3
CM3	C (4.03)	ClCH₂CO₂H	1.43	30[d]	5.60	15.00	3.42	47.4
CE1	C (2.09)	ClCH₂CH₂CO₂H	1.42	30[d]	2.96	14.15	3.34	49.2
CE2	C (4.11)	CH₂=CHCO₂H	1.12	20[e]	7.06	12.46	4.22	70.4
CE3	C (3.04)	CH₂=CHCO₂H	1.12	20	—	11.16	4.88	91.0

[a] CM and CE mean carboxymethylation and carboxyethylation, respectively.

[b] (a); EI unit content = 9.17 mmole/g, degree of hydrolysis = 83.1%, $\overline{D.P.}$ of the grafted EI unit = 4.3; (b); 10.30 mmole/g, 69.1%, 15.9; and (c); 9.92 mmole/g, 67.3%, 15.9.

[c] Under weak alkaline conditions.

[d] 7 hr under acidic conditions and 23 hr under weak alkaline conditions.

[e] At 60°C.

reported that the carboxyl groups in a crosslinked polystyrene cannot be satisfactorily determined by titration.[6]

In the preparation of sample CM2, PSt–*g*–EI was treated with a 10 molar excess of monochloroacetic acid for 35 hr, followed by repeated washing with water. The procedure was repeated. The extent of reaction exceeded 100%, i.e., 108.3%. A value greater than 100% may be explained as follows: (1) the acetyl group, present in the starting PSt–*g*–EI due to incomplete hydrolysis, was further hydrolyzed and carboxymethylated under the above conditions; and/or (2) a fraction of the amino groups was quaternized. Using a slight excess of monochloroacetic acid, the degree of substitution was low because of a side reaction, i.e., hydrolysis of monochloroacetic acid (sample CM3).

The IR spectrum (KBr pellet) of the carboxymethylated PSt–*g*–EI (sample CM3) showed two new absorption bands at 1550 and 1400 cm⁻¹ due to the carboxylate anion [Fig. 1(b)]. The characteristic band at 1130 cm⁻¹ of ν_{N-C} assigned to the crystalline polyethylenimine unit[7] almost disappeared, most likely due to the decreased crystallinity introduced by the carboxymethylation.

Carboxyethylation of PSt–*g*–EI

The carboxyethylation was carried out by two methods. The first (method I) used β-chloropropionic acid as a condensation reagent in the same manner as monochloroacetic acid was used for the carboxymethylation. In the second method (method II), the carboxyethylation was accomplished under a nitrogen atmosphere by the Michael addition of the N—H to acrylic acid in ethanol containing a small amount of 2,6-di-*tert*-butyl-*p*-cresol as a radical inhibitor:
Method I

$$PSt\text{-}g\text{-}EI + ClCH_2CH_2CO_2Na \xrightarrow{NaOH} \qquad + NaCl \qquad (2)$$

$$CH_2\text{-}(NCH_2CH_2)_n$$
$$CH_2CH_2CO_2Na$$

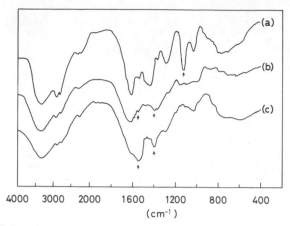

Fig. 1. Infrared spectra of polymers: (a) PSt–g–EI (C); (b) CM3; (c) CE2.

Method II

$$\text{PSt-}g\text{-EI} \xrightarrow{\text{CH}_2=\text{CHCO}_2\text{H}} \xrightarrow{\text{NaOH}}$$ (3)

The product was isolated and converted to the Na salt by washing with an aqueous NaOH solution. The results are also listed in Table I. The extent of the reaction and the CO_2Na content were calculated as described above. The second method gave better results for the carboxyethylation.

The IR spectrum (KBr pellet) of sample CE2 revealed two clear absorption bands at 1550 and 1400 cm^{-1}. These are due to the carboxylate anion group [Fig. 1(c)].

Adsorption of Metal Ions by the Resins (Batch Method)

The adsorption of Cu^{2+}, Cd^{2+}, Hg^{2+}, Ni^{2+}, and Ca^{2+} was carried out in H_2O at 30°C for 72 hr, although the adsorption actually reached saturation within about 48 hr. The effect of pH on the adsorption of these metal ions by carboxymethylated and carboxyethylated PSt–g–EI is shown in Figures 2 and 3, respectively. The extent of adsorption was $Hg^{2+} > Cu^{2+} > Cd^{2+} > Ni^{2+} > Ca^{2+}$ at pH 6 with both resins. The dependence on pH of the adsorption was larger with carboxyethylated PSt–g–EI than with carboxymethylated PSt–g–EI. This may be due to the smaller stability constant of β-carboxylamine chelate than that of α-carboxylamine chelate.[8–10]

By introducing carboxyalkyl groups into PSt–g–EI, a new type of chelating resin which adsorbs Ca^{2+} has now been prepared, whereas PSt–g–EI exhibits little adsorption capacity for Ca^{2+}. The capacity for Ca^{2+} is related to the CO_2Na content as shown in Figure 2 (samples CM2 and CM3) and Figure 3 (samples CE2 and CE1). In Figures 2 and 3, the capacity noted for Hg^{2+}, Cu^{2+}, Cd^{2+}, and Ni^{2+} includes the adsorption by secondary amino residues which have not been

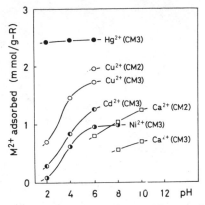

Fig. 2. Effect of pH on the adsorption of metal ions by carboxymethylated resin: resin (0.25 g) in 50 ml aqueous metal ion solution (0.025 mole/l.), 30°C for 72 hr.

carboxyalkylated. In the case of Ca^{2+}, the adsorption capacity is obviously due only to carboxyl groups. At pH 10, 1 mole Ca^{2+} is captured by 4.7 (CM2) and 3.2 (CE2) moles aminoacid groups, respectively (Figs. 2 and 3).

Adsorption and Elution of Cu^{2+} by Column Method

The adsorption and elution experiments of Cu^{2+} with CM3, CE3, and PSt–*g*–EI (C) were carried out using the column method; the results are graphically presented in Figures 4 and 5. The column experiment with PSt–*g*–EI has been described in a previous paper.[1] Copper leakage with CM3 was lowest, and that with PSt–*g*–EI was greatest. Therefore, resins having higher apparent affinities for metal ions than the PSt–*g*–EI resin can be obtained by introducing carboxyl groups, although the adsorption capacity (per gram of resin) becomes smaller; e.g., for Cu^{2+} the capacity is 3.85 and 2.88 mmole/g-R with PSt–*g*–EI (C) and

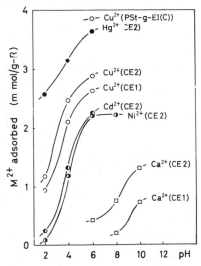

Fig. 3. Effect of pH on the adsorption of metal ions by carboxyethylated resin: resin (0.25 g) in 50 ml aqueous metal ion solution (0.025 mole/l.), 30°C for 72 hr.

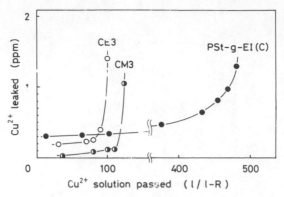

Fig. 4. Adsorption of Cu^{2+} by column method. Aqueous Cu^{2+} solution (32.0 ppm, pH 4.4) was passed through a column packed with 5 ml resin at a flow rate of SV 10.

CE2 at pH 6, respectively (Fig. 3). The pale yellow resins of CM3 or CE3 turn blue on complexation with Cu^{2+} and decolorize completely when a $1N$ HCl solution is passed through the column. Complete recovery of Cu^{2+} is achieved as shown in Figure 5. Furthermore, the adsorption–desorption procedures can be repeated.

EXPERIMENTAL

Materials

Commercial monochloroacetic and β-chloropropionic acids were used without further purification. Acrylic acid and EtOH were dried and distilled under nitrogen atmosphere.

Preparation of crosslinked PSt–g–EI was carried out according to the method described previously,[1] in which chloromethylated polystyrene (85.1% ring substitution) crosslinked with 3% divinylbenzene was used. Three graft copolymers were prepared: A (EI unit content = 9.17 mmole/g, degree of hydrolysis = 83.1%, $\overline{D}.\overline{P}$. of the grafted part = 4.3); B (10.30 mmole/g, 69.1%, 15.9); and C (9.92 mmole/g, 67.3%, 15.9).

Carboxymethylation of PSt–g–EI

A typical experiment (preparation of sample CM1) proceeded as follows: A mixture of 1.10 g PSt–g–EI (A), 9.64 g monochloroacetic acid, and 30 ml water was heated at 70°C under alkaline condition (pH 8–10) using NaOH until the pH of the system remained constant. The product was isolated by filtration and washed with water. When the effluent was neutral, the product was washed with methanol and diethyl ether, and then dried *in vacuo* at 70°C to a constant weight of 1.64 g. The detailed reaction conditions of the additional experiments may be found in Table I.

Carboxyethylation of PSt–g–EI

Method I. A mixture of 2.09 g PSt–g–EI (C), 3.19 g β-chloropropionic acid, and 15 ml water was heated at 70°C for 7 hr with gentle shaking. Further, the

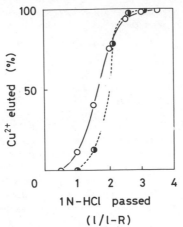

Fig. 5. Elution of the adsorbed Cu^{2+} with aqueous $1N$ HCl (flow rate = SV 2): (◑) CM3 (adsorbed Cu^{2+} = 0.33 mmole); (○) CE3 (adsorbed Cu^{2+} = 0.23 mmole).

mixture was heated at the same temperature keeping the pH of the system in the range of 8–10 by adding $6N$ NaOH into the mixture. After 23 hr, no decrease in the pH was observed. The product was treated as described above. The yield was 2.96 g.

Method II. PSt–*g*–EI (C) (4.11 g) and 2,6-di-*tert*-butyl-*p*-cresol (0.06 g) were placed in a 100-ml flask equipped with a reflux condenser and a three-way cock. After the atmosphere in the flask was replaced with nitrogen, 22 ml EtOH and 3.1 ml acrylic acid were added to the flask. The mixture was kept at room temperature for a day so that the PSt–*g*–EI could be swollen sufficiently and then heated at 60°C for 20 hr with gentle shaking. The product was isolated by filtration and washed with MeOH, treated with aq. NaOH, and then washed with water until the washings became neutral. After drying at 70°C *in vacuo,* the product weighed 7.06 g.

Adsorption of Metal Ions by the Resins (Batch Method)

As metal salts, commercial $Cu(NO_3)_2$, $HgCl_2$, $CdCl_2$, $NiCl_2$, and $CaCl_2$ were used without further purification. More details of the procedure have been described in the previous paper.[1]

Adsorption and Elution of Cu^{2+} by a Column Method

Resin of CM3, CE3, or PSt–*g*–EI (C) (5 ml in the wet state) was packed in a column with an 8-mm internal diameter. The height of the resin column was about 10 cm. An aqueous solution of Cu^{2+} (concentration of 32.0 ppm, pH 4.4) was allowed to flow through the column at a flow rate of space velocity (SV) 10. The effluent solution was sampled every 10 ml, and the Cu^{2+} concentration was determined by the method described in the previous paper.[1]

After the adsorption experiment, the column was washed with 30 ml water. An eluting agent ($1N$ HCl aq.) was passed through the column at a flow rate of SV 2. The Cu^{2+} content in every 2.5 ml of eluate was determined by chelatometry.

The authors wish to acknowledge financial support by a Scientific Research Grant (No. 011011) from the Ministry of Education, Japan.

References

1. T. Saegusa, S. Kobayashi, and A. Yamada, *Macromolecules,* **8,** 390 (1975).
2. Y. Kosaka, A. Shimizu, and T. Matsumoto, *Toso Kenkyu Hokoku,* **2,** 206 (1958).
3. E. Blasius and I. Bock, *J. Chromatogr.,* **14,** 244 (1964).
4. G. Manecke and H. Heller, *Makromol. Chem.,* **55,** 51 (1962).
5. M. Okawara, Y. Komeda, and E. Imoto, *Kobunshi Kagaku,* **17,** 30 (1960).
6. C. R. Harrison, P. Hodge, J. Kemp, and G. M. Perry, *Macromol. Chem.,* **176,** 267 (1975).
7. T. Saegusa, H. Ikeda, and H. Fujii, *Macromolecules,* **5,** 108 (1972).
8. G. Schwarzenbach, G. Gut, and G. Anderegg, *Helv. Chim. Acta,* **37,** 937 (1954).
9. G. Schwarzenbach and G. Anderegg, *Helv. Chim. Acta,* **40,** 1773 (1957).
10. R. C. Courtney, S. Chaberek, and A. E. Martell, *J. Amer. Chem Soc.,* **75,** 4814 (1953).

Received April 23, 1976
Revised July 27, 1976

JOURNAL OF APPLIED POLYMER SCIENCE   VOL. 21, 2489–2503 (1977)

Domain Structure and Time-Dependent Properties of a Crosslinked Urethane Elastomer*

R. R. LAGASSE, *Polymer Research and Development, Division 5813, Sandia Laboratories, Albuquerque, New Mexico 87115*

Synopsis

The morphology of a chemically crosslinked urethane elastomer is correlated with its time-dependent mechanical properties. Evaluation of this amorphous elastomer by electron microscopy and small-angle x-ray scattering reveals that incompatible chain segments cluster into separate microphases having a periodicity in electron density of about 90 Å. This observed domain structure is similar to that seen previously in uncrosslinked, thermoplastic urethane elastomers. As in earlier studies on such linear systems, thermal pretreatment of the crosslinked elastomer causes a time-dependent change in its room temperature modulus. However, the magnitude of this modulus change (about 20%) is generally less than observed previously with the linear systems. Another contrast with previous findings is that this time-dependent phenomenon is apparently not caused by thermally activated changes in microphase segregation. Rather, the observed time dependence in modulus is believed to be caused by molecular relaxation resulting in densification of amorphous packing within the hard-segment domains. The validity of this proposed mechanism is supported by differential scanning calorimetry experiments showing evidence of enthalpy relaxation during room-temperature aging of the elastomer. This relaxation is qualitatively similar to that observed previously during sub-T_g annealing of single-phase glassy polymers.

INTRODUCTION

Over the past ten years, considerable progress has been made in understanding the mechanical properties of the linear segmented urethane elastomers. The molecular backbone of these thermoplastic elastomers usually consists of long polyether or polyester chains, referred to as the *soft* segments, linked together by relatively short, *hard* segments consisting of aromatic diisocyanates reacted with diols or diamines. Many studies of the morphology of these hard–soft segmented systems have demonstrated that the two kinds of chain segments can preferentially cluster into separate microphases.[1-6] On the basis of these morphologic studies, it has become quite clear that the high strength and modulus of these elastomers arise from physical crosslinking or reinforcement caused by the hard-segment domains dispersed in a soft-segment matrix.[7,8]

In these segmented systems, hydrogen bonding can be established in two different ways: (1) between urethane groups in the hard segments themselves, and (2) between these urethane groups and ether or ester groups in the soft

---

* Presented to the Division of High Polymer Physics, American Physical Society Meeting, Atlanta, Georgia, April 1, 1976. Work supported by the U.S. Energy Research and Development Administration.

segments.[9]   Although hydrogen bonding probably does not directly influence mechanical properties to any great extent, the balance between hard–hard and hard–soft hydrogen bonding may exert a secondary effect by modulating the degree of microphase separation between hard and soft segments.[8,9]   In fact, a model based on changes in the perfection of microphase separation has been recently developed to explain thermal history dependence in the modulus of these materials.[10,11]

In contrast with the extensive studies that have been carried out on the linear systems, relatively little attention has been directed at the chemically crosslinked urethane elastomers.   These materials have important technological applications as liquid castable resins for encapsulation, coating, and adhesive applications. Previously, the results of creep experiments on a crosslinked casting system were interpreted to suggest the existence of domain structure.[12]   On the other hand, it is quite reasonable to expect that the presence of crosslinks in a segmented system could restrain the chains from achieving those configurations necessary for phase separation.   This hypothesis is supported by the results of Cooper and Tobolsky[13] who modified linear thermoplastic elastomers by adding various crosslinking agents.   On the basis of observed changes in thermomechanical spectra, these workers inferred that the domain structure initially present in the linear systems could be either maintained or destroyed when crosslinking was introduced, depending on the number and location of the crosslinks in the segmented copolymer chains.   In fact, in the only direct study of the morphology of a crosslinked urethane elastomer small-angle x-ray scattering measurements showed no immediate evidence of any domain structure.[2]   Thus, although the mechanical properties of urethane network polymers have suggested that microphase segregation may be present in some cases, neither characterization of the inferred domain structure nor development of correlations between this morphology and mechanical properties appears to have been carried out.

This paper reports the results of a detailed morphologic study of a chemically crosslinked urethane elastomer having polybutadiene soft segments.   Besides chemical crosslinking, another significant feature of the material studied is the restriction of hydrogen bonding to the hard segments only.   Obviously, the nonpolar nature of polybutadiene precludes hydrogen bonding between hard and soft segments.

Techniques utilized to characterize this material are small-angle and wide-angle x-ray diffraction, transmission electron microscopy, and differential scanning calorimetry.   In addition, some mechanical properties of the elastomer, including their thermal history dependence, are discussed in light of the observed morphology.   The results presented lead to new insights with regard to the origin of time-dependent phenomena in both crosslinked and linear segmented elastomers.

EXPERIMENTAL

Materials

The system chosen for study is a two-part liquid castable urethane elastomer; its composition has been described previously.[14]   (This castable elastomer is marketed by CONAP, Inc., under the trade name EN-7.)   The first component is a mixture of 2,4-toluene diisocyanate plus a multifunctional polybutadiene endcapped with the same diisocyanate, the mix having 9.0 wt-% unreacted isocyanate (NCO). The polybutadiene in this prepolymer has a number-average functionality[15] of about 2.3 and a number-average molecular weight[16] of about 2700. The second component, or curing agent, of the casting system consists of 55 wt-% 2-ethyl-1,3-hexanediol, 45 wt-% N,N-bis(2-hydroxypropyl)aniline, and 45 ppm of a catalyst.

Bulk samples of the elastomer for mechanical testing and x-ray characterization were prepared by mixing the two components in stoichiometric proportions and curing in a steel mold at 80°C for 16 hr. Specimens were stored in a desiccator at room temperature prior to testing.

Very thin electron microscopy specimens of the crosslinked elastomer were prepared by a modified solvent casting technique. Stoichiometric amounts of the two reactive components were dissolved separately in toluene to form a 3 wt-% solution. A drop of this diluted mixture of prepolymer and curative was cast onto a clean mercury surface. The solvent evaporated instantaneously to leave a film of the reactive components with estimated thickness 400 Å. Films cast in this way were cured at room temperature for time periods of up to 47 days. In order for complete reaction to occur under these conditions, it was necessary to increase the catalyst concentration in the diol curing agent. This room-temperature cure schedule and the previously described 80°C cure yield elastomers having approximately the same mechanical properties.[17] Accordingly, the solvent-cast films were assumed to be representative of the 80°C cured bulk samples. Additional evidence supporting this assumption is given in the results section.

Samples of the cured film were mounted directly from the mercury surface onto 200-mesh electron microscopy grids. Some grid-mounted specimens were stained in the vapor above a 1 wt-% aqueous solution of osmium tetroxide.

Curing of this urethane elastomer consists of the reaction of the two diols with the toluene diisocyanate to form hard segments which interconnect the polybutadiene soft segments. The chemical crosslinks in the system arise from the multifunctionality (>2) of the polybutadiene prepolymer. It can be shown that stoichiometric mixing of the two reactive components produces a crosslinked elastomer composed of about 31 wt-% of the hard segments.

Characterization Methods

X-Ray diffraction patterns were obtained at both small and wide angles by means of a Warhus camera mounted on a Norelco unit which generated nickel-filtered CuKα radiation. Sample thicknesses were 1.1 mm for small-angle exposures and 0.51 mm for wide-angle exposures. Microdensitometer scans on the diffraction patterns were performed with an Optronics S-2000 instrument. In addition, electron micrographs were taken with a Philips EM-200 operated at an accelerating voltage of 100 kV. Differential scanning calorimetry was carried out with a Perkin-Elmer DSC-2; polymer samples weighing about 14 mg were scanned at 10°C/min with a synthetic sapphire reference material.

Dynamic mechanical measurements were made at 0.1 and 3.5 Hz using a Rheometrics mechanical spectrometer in the forced torsion pendulum mode and a Rheovibron DDV-II in the tensile mode, respectively. Finally, softening

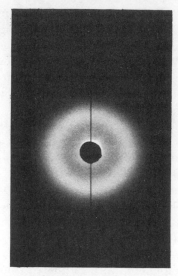

Fig. 1. Small-angle x-ray scattering pattern from the crosslinked urethane elastomer.

temperatures were determined by means of a Perkin-Elmer TMS-1 ther-momechanical analyzer operated in the penetrometer mode.

RESULTS

Morphologic Characterization

The small-angle x-ray scattering pattern obtained from the crosslinked elas-tomer is shown in Figure 1. It consists of a dark area around the beam stop and a broad, but distinct, halo at larger scattering angles. The radial microdensi-tometer scan of this x-ray exposure clearly shows the maximum in scattered in-tensity (Fig. 2). This is indicative of a quasi-periodic fluctuation in electron density within the material.[18] A semiquantitative characterization of the pe-riodicity can be given by the Bragg spacing corresponding to the scattering angle at peak intensity[19]; the computed d-spacing is 93 ± 1 Å. In polymer systems such an electron density fluctuation can be caused by microphase segregation of incompatible chain segments or by a crystal-amorphous texture.[19]

The chemical structures shown in Figure 3 suggest that crystallinity is unlikely to be present in the subject material. The polybutadiene soft segment, being a random copolymer of about 20% cis isomer, 60% trans isomer, and 20% vinyl isomer, is expected to be noncrystalline.[20] Furthermore, the presence of two different diols and the lack of symmetry in both the aliphatic diol and the di-isocyanate would seem to preclude crystallinity in the hard segment.

Wide-angle x-ray diffraction experiments on this material revealed only a single diffuse halo, rather than sharp diffraction rings (Figs. 4 and 5). These results verify that no appreciable crystallinity exists in the elastomer. Ac-cordingly, the small-angle scattering peak shown in Figure 2 is believed to be caused by clustering of the hard and soft segments into separate microphases.

The presence of domain structure in this crosslinked urethane elastomer is confirmed by transmission electron microscopy examination of solvent-cast films.

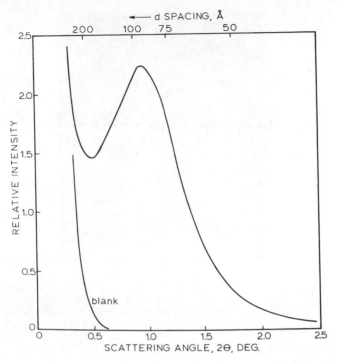

Fig. 2. Microdensitometer scan of the small-angle x-ray scattering pattern.

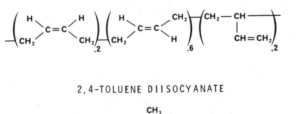

Fig. 3. Chemical structures of constituents of the urethane elastomer.

An electron micrograph of the unstained elastomer vaguely suggests a pebbly texture of high and low electron-density regions (Fig. 6a). If this texture indeed represents microphase segregation of incompatible chain segments, then treating the film with osmium tetroxide should enhance the contrast. The reason is that the high electron density stain preferentially attaches to the double bonds in the

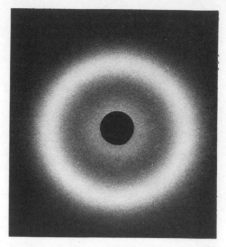

Fig. 4. Wide-angle x-ray diffraction pattern from the urethane elastomer.

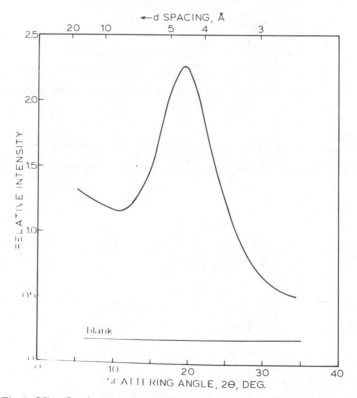

Fig. 5. Microdensitometer scan of the wide-angle x-ray diffraction pattern.

polybutadiene soft segment.[21]   The electron micrograph of stained elastomer
shows greatly enhanced contrast and therefore demonstrates the presence of
domain structure (Fig. 6b).   (The micrographs in Figure 6 were taken after 12
days of room-temperature cure, but these are representative of domain structure
observed after longer cure times, up to the maximum of 47 days.)   It should be
emphasized that the same result was obtained when the casting solvent was

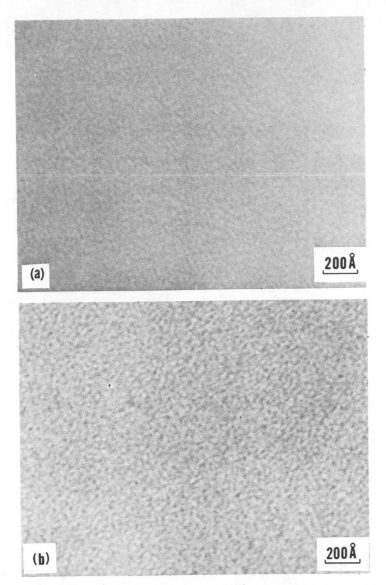

Fig. 6. Transmission electron micrographs of thin films of the urethane elastomer: (a) unstained;
(b) OsO$_4$ stained.

changed from relatively nonpolar toluene to polar tetrahydrofuran and when
the casting surface was changed from mercury to carbon.   Thus, it is believed
that the domain structure shown in Figure 6b is genuine and not an artifact of
the method used to prepare the thin films.

Mechanical Properties

A characterization of the crosslinked urethane elastomer by means of the
forced torsion pendulum is shown in Figure 7, as a plot of the in-phase shear
modulus versus temperature.   By analogy with previous work on the linear
segmented systems, the two major transitions centered at about −80° and +50°C

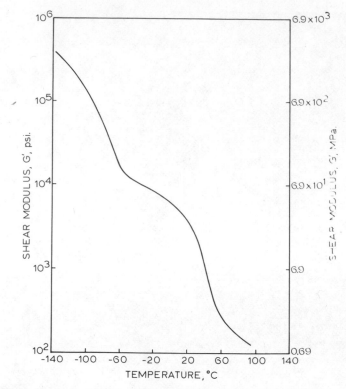

Fig. 7. Dynamic mechanical spectrum of the urethane elastomer at 0.1 Hz.

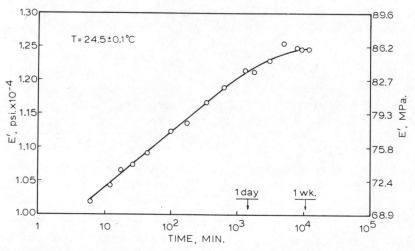

Fig. 8. Time dependence of the 3.5-Hz tensile modulus of the urethane elastomer after quenching to room temperature from 80°C.

can be assigned to the soft-segment (polybutadiene) phase and the hard-segment phase, respectively. In the range of temperatures between these two glass transitions, a region of enhanced rubbery modulus evidently arises from *physical* crosslinking by the glassy hard-segment domains. It appears that at temperatures above the hard-segment transition, the modulus asymptotically approaches

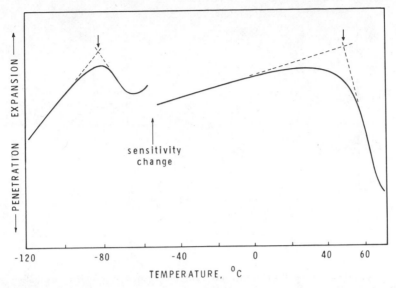

Fig. 9. Thermomechanical analyzer characterization of a well-aged sample of urethane elastomer: penetration of a weighted probe during a 5°C/min scan.

a low value, which would be dependent solely on the degree of *chemical* cross-linking in the elastomer.

Thermal history dependence in the enhanced rubbery modulus of this material was investigated by heating a well-aged sample through the upper transition to 80°C for 5 min and then quenching to room temperature between highly conductive steel blocks. Then, the in-phase tensile modulus was monitored by means of the Rheovibron during aging at room temperature to produce the results shown in Figure 8. It is seen that at 3.5 Hz frequency, the room temperature modulus gradually increased over a period of a week to an equilibrium value more than 20% above the initial value. A similar time dependence in room-temperature modulus was observed when the measurement frequency was raised to 110 Hz, except that the magnitude of the effect was smaller. That is, while the 3.5-Hz modulus increased by 21.7% during room-temperature aging, the 110-Hz modulus increased by only 13.5%. It is to be emphasized that in either case, this time dependence in room-temperature modulus was found to be a reversible phenomenon; repeating the thermal cycle on the same sample again caused the modulus to drop and then gradually recover with aging.

In order to understand the origin of this time-dependent phenomenon in the crosslinked elastomer, the effect of 80°C thermal treatment on its room-temperature morphology was studied. Small-angle x-ray scattering experiments indicated that the thermal pretreatment caused a slight reduction of less than 10–15% in scattered intensity near the interference peak (only). However, direct observation of the domain structure by electron microscopy revealed no detectable change in microphase separation between hard and soft segments due to thermal cycling.

The effect of thermal cycling on the glass transition temperatures of the crosslinked elastomer was also determined. The relatively rapid time scale of the process would have made it difficult to precisely measure true thermomechanical transition temperatures by means of the usual dynamic mechanical

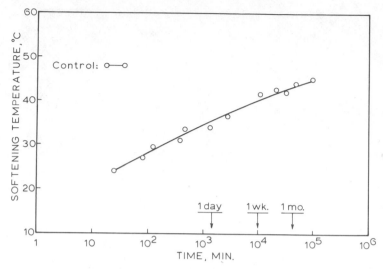

Fig. 10. Time dependence of the upper level softening temperature of the urethane elastomer after quenching to room temperature from 80°C. Control sample: aged six months at room temperature.

instruments (e.g., the Rheovibron). Thus, it was deemed necessary to settle for more qualitative softening temperatures determined by the thermomechanical analyzer.

An example of the results obtained with this instrument is given in Figure 9; this shows the displacement of a weighted penetrometer as a well-aged sample of the elastomer was heated at 5°C/min. Thermal expansion of the sample causes upward motion of the penetrometer, whereas softening of the sample causes indentation, or downward motion, of the penetrometer. The two main softening transitions, attributed to the soft- and hard-segment phases, are characterized by initial penetration temperatures of −83° and +48°C. Replicated penetrometer scans gave softening temperatures in agreement to within ±1°C.

By analogy with the time-dependent experiments described above, a well-aged elastomer sample was cycled to 80°C and then tested intermittently with the thermomechanical analyzer during aging at room temperature. Thermal cycling to 80°C caused no change whatsoever in the lower softening temperature of the elastomer. On the other hand, the upper softening temperature initially dropped by more than 20°C and then gradually recovered during room-temperature aging (Fig. 10). As with the modulus, the thermal history dependence of the upper transition was found to be completely reversible: the phenomenon could be reproduced by repeat thermal cycling on the same sample.

The thermal history dependence of the transitions in the urethane elastomer was further studied by means of differential scanning calorimetry. The thermoanalytical results revealed the presence of a second-order transition at about −70°C; this was the usual broad step change in specific heat characteristic of transitions in amorphous polymers. This lower transition, which can undoubtedly be attributed to the soft-segment phase, was found to be exactly the same in both a virgin sample of the elastomer and one which had been thermally cycled to 80°C. This lack of thermal history dependence in the glass transition

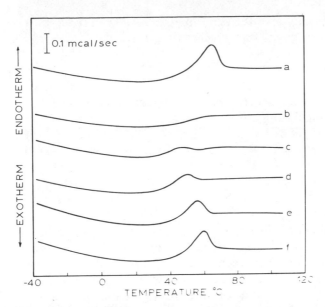

Fig. 11. Differential scanning calorimetry at 10°C/min on urethane elastomer samples: (a) aged six months at room temperature (R.T.); (b) quenched from 80°C to −50°C; (c) quenched from 80°C to R.T., then aged for 80 min; (d) quenched from 80°C to R.T., then aged for 8.5 hr; (e) quenched from 80°C to R.T., then aged for four days; (f) quenched from 80°C to R.T., then aged for 27 days. A new sample was used for each of the six thermograms, which have been vertically shifted for purposes of clarity.

of the soft matrix confirms the thermomechanical analyzer results described above.

The glass transition of the hard domains in the subject material showed considerably more complex thermal behavior. Fixing attention on the top thermogram in Figure 11, one sees that in a well-aged sample, this upper transition consisted of a distinct endothermic peak superimposed on a very broad step change in specific heat. The next thermogram (b) was obtained on a sample which had been heated to 80°C for 5 min, quenched to −50°C within 5 min, and then immediately scanned. It is seen that the upper glass transition in this quenched sample was accompanied by only the step change in specific heat. The remaining thermograms in Figure 11 show that aging a thermally cycled sample at room temperature caused the superimposed endothermic peak to gradually increase in size and move upward in temperature, thereby approaching the appearance of the peak characteristic of the well-aged sample (a).

The results in Figures 10 and 11 suggest that the reversible thermal history dependence in the mechanical properties of the urethane elastomer is related to physical changes within the hard-segment domains rather than the soft-segment matrix. The possibility that these physical changes are caused by ordering phenomena within the hard domains was checked by means of wide-angle x-ray diffraction and infrared spectroscopy. Evaluation of room-temperature samples by these two techniques revealed that pretreatment at 80°C caused no reduction in either the degree of interchain ordering or the extent of hydrogen bonding between hard segments. (Methods of detecting changes in the degree of hydrogen bonding by means of infrared spectroscopy are described in refs. 8 and

9.) Further analysis of the experimental results in the next section leads to a more plausible explanation of these time-dependent phenomena.

DISCUSSION

As stated above, the urethane elastomer studied in this investigation has two features distinguishing it from the materials that have been studied previously: (1) the absence of hydrogen bonding between hard and soft segments, and (2) the presence of chemical crosslinks. In spite of the crosslinking, microphase segregation of hard and soft segments definitely exists in this material. In fact, the periodicity in electron density estimated from the small-angle x-ray scattering peak, 94 Å, is quite similar to values observed before in linear polyether- and polyester-based segmented elastomers.[4,6,22]

Another similarity between the results of this and previous work is the detection of a reversible thermal history dependence in the room-temperature modulus. Time dependence in modulus has been previously noted for a number of thermoplastic urethane elastomers when these were thermally cycled to temperatures in the vicinity of the hard-segment transition interval.[10,11] This phenomenon has been attributed by Wilkes and co-workers to thermally activated disruption of domain structure which results in increased mixing of hard segments in the soft matrix. The time dependence in room-temperature modulus then arises from a finite rate of phase separation between hard and soft segments. Support for this hard–soft mixing model comes from the observation of parallel changes in the glass transition temperature of the soft matrix: differential scanning calorimetry experiments showed that the rise in modulus following thermal cycling is accompanied by a reduction in the lower transition temperature.[10,11] (It should be noted that these thermoanalytical experiments also demonstrated thermal history dependence in the hard-segment transition, but this phenomenon was not featured in the proposed model.)

The time-dependent change in modulus observed in the present work (~20%) is less than that observed previously with linear polyester-based elastomers, but about the same as observed with a linear polyether-based material.[11] However, the phenomenon presently observed with the polybutadiene-based system is markedly different in that it is not accompanied by any measurable change in the lower transition temperature, as described above. This difference between the linear materials studied previously and the crosslinked material with regard to the response of the soft matrix to thermal cycling has been confirmed by pulsed NMR experiments carried out in this laboratory.[23] In terms of the model discussed above, these observations mean that there may not be any significant thermally activated mixing of hard segments in the soft matrix with the present material. This behavior could be caused either by the presence of chemical crosslinks or by the absence of hydrogen bonding between hard and soft segments.

Thus, it is clear that time dependence in the mechanical properties of hard–soft segmented elastomers need not necessarily be accompanied by changes in the glass transition temperature of the soft matrix. Also, wide-angle x-ray diffraction and infrared spectroscopy experiments showed that the time-dependent effects observed with the crosslinked elastomer are not accompanied by any measurable changes in the extent of interchain ordering within the hard-segment domains.

Accordingly, it is believed that the observed phenomena are not at all related to morphologic changes, but rather to relaxation effects occurring within the hard domains at room temperature. Support for this view comes from recognizing the similarity between the phenomena observed in this work and the behavior of a single-phase amorphous polymer when it is annealed slightly below its glass transition temperature.

Recent studies have shown that when a single-phase amorphous polymer is quenched from the liquid state to a temperature 10–30°C below its glass transition, a time dependence in mechanical properties is observed during annealing at that temperature. For example, when quenched atactic polystyrene is annealed at 13°C below T_g, its dynamic, in-phase modulus (0.6 Hz) at the annealing temperature gradually rises by about 20%.[24] Furthermore, this time-dependent change in modulus during sub-T_g annealing is accompanied by a reduction in the enthalpy of the glass. This enthalpy relaxation process is made evident in scanning calorimetry experiments by the development of an endothermic peak superimposed on the usual step change in specific heat over the glass transition interval.[24,25] The peak both grows in size and shifts upward in temperature with increased annealing time at a given temperature. The magnitude of this endotherm gives a measure of the enthalpy reduction during annealing, which can become sufficiently large that the endotherm becomes the dominant feature of the thermogram in the transition interval.[26] A similar time dependence in mechanical properties accompanied by growth and upward shift of an endotherm during sub-T_g annealing has been observed by many other workers and with at least one material other than polystyrene.[27–29]

These time-dependent changes in the thermal and mechanical properties of annealed glasses are believed to be caused by structural relaxation resulting in simple densification of amorphous packing rather than by molecular ordering.[24,26,30] In fact, direct measurement of the collapse of free volume during annealing below T_g has been used to interpret thermal history dependence in the viscoelastic behavior of various polymeric glasses: poly(vinyl acetate),[31] poly(butyl methacrylate),[32] and polystyrene.[33] Furthermore, it has been concluded[33] that the magnitude of the change in mechanical properties observed during annealing of glassy polymers depends on the effective time scale of the viscoelastic experiment: for example, in a dynamic mechanical test, a lower measurement frequency results in a larger thermal history dependence. (This frequency dependence of the thermal history effect is related to the fact that viscoelastic data obtained at various annealing times can be superimposed by horizontal shifts along the frequency axis.[31,32])

It seems likely that similar sub-T_g annealing effects could take place within a separate microphase of a segmented or block copolymer. In fact, preliminary experiments have already indicated that such annealing effects can occur in styrene–butadiene block copolymers having well-defined domain structure.[34] In the subject material of this investigation, the glass transition interval of the hard-segment domains is centered about 15–25°C above room temperature (Fig. 7). Thus, time-dependent changes in its modulus observed during room-temperature aging could very well be caused by slow collapse of free volume within the amorphous, hard domains after quenching from above their T_g. This proposed mechanism is consistent with the observed reversibility of the time-dependent phenomenon, as well as the absence of any significant morphologic changes within the elastomer. Additional strong support for this model comes from observation of the same phenomena that occur during annealing of glassy polymers: first, the growth and upward shift in the superimposed endothermic peak (Fig. 11); and second, the increase in the thermal history dependence of the in-phase modulus when the measurement frequency is decreased from 110 to 3.5 Hz. (It is anticipated that additional data will be obtained to strengthen this second point.)

It should be noted that assignment of an endothermic peak in the thermogram of a segmented elastomer to enthalpy relaxation has not been proposed before. One or more endotherms have often been detected in the hard-segment transition interval of thermoplastic urethane elastomers,[10,11,35] but these have generally been attributed to thermally activated disruption of various kinds of molecular order within the hard-segment domains.[8] The presence of incipient, paracrystalline-like order[2,5,36] is quite reasonable for those cases in which the hard segment is regular in structure and therefore crystallizable.[8,35,37] However, as was pointed out earlier, the hard segment in the subject material of this investigation has a very irregular chemical structure and accordingly is considered to be noncrystallizable. On the basis of this plus the analogies with glassy systems described above, it is believed that the observed endothermic behavior of the crosslinked urethane elastomer is caused by enthalpy relaxation within the amorphous hard-segment domains rather than an ordering process. In order to further confirm the distinction between these two sources of an endothermic peak, the influence of different heating and cooling rates on the calorimetric results can be evaluated.[26,30,38]

Finally, it should be pointed out that, although this study has been directly concerned with a chemically crosslinked segmented elastomer, the results reported herein may have significance for a wider class of materials. In particular, it seems reasonable that the same sub-T_g annealing effect could contribute to the thermomechanical behavior of linear, uncrosslinked segmented copolymers if these also contained some amorphous hard segments.

SUMMARY

The morphology of a chemically crosslinked urethane elastomer was characterized in some detail. No crystalline structure could be detected in this material by means of wide-angle x-ray diffraction. On the other hand, a domain structure due to microphase separation of incompatible chain segments was detected by both small-angle x-ray scattering and transmission electron microscopy. To the author's knowledge, this work represents the first successful effort to detect and characterize such a domain structure in a chemically crosslinked urethane elastomer. It is, therefore, concluded that the presence of crosslinks in a segmented elastomer does not necessarily prevent microphase separation between the so-called hard and soft chain segments, in agreement with an earlier study of Cooper and Tobolsky.[13]

In addition, some mechanical properties of the crosslinked elastomer were correlated with the observed morphology. Of particular importance was the detection of time dependence in the room-temperature modulus after thermal treatment. In contrast with previous findings on linear systems, this time dependence in the crosslinked elastomer was not accompanied by any measurable change in the T_g of the soft-segment phase. Rather, the results of differential scanning calorimetry experiments suggested that the room-temperature aging phenomenon was caused by sub-T_g annealing effects within the glassy hard-segment phase. Accordingly, it is believed that such relaxation of amorphous packing may contribute to the thermal history sensitivity of both crosslinked and linear segmented elastomers, along with previously discussed morphologic changes in the domain structure.

The forced torsion pendulum results shown in Figure 7 were supplied by Mr. D. J. Caruthers of the Bendix Corporation (Kansas City Division). The author wishes to extend special thanks to Professor G. L. Wilkes of Princeton University for many helpful discussions.

References

1. S. B. Clough, N. S. Schneider, and A. O. King, *J. Macromol. Sci., Phys.*, **B2**, 641 (1968).
2. R. Bonart, L. Morbitzer, and G. Hentze, *J. Macromol. Sci., Phys.*, **B3**, 337 (1969).
3. S. L. Samuels and G. L. Wilkes, *J. Polym. Sci.*, **C43**, 149 (1973).
4. C. E. Wilkes and C. S. Yusek, *J. Macromol. Sci., Phys.*, **B7**, 157 (1973).
5. R. Bonart, L. Morbitzer, and E. H. Muller, *J. Macromol. Sci., Phys.*, **B9**, 447 (1974).
6. Y. P. Chang and G. L. Wilkes, *J. Polym. Sci., Polym. Phys. Ed.*, **13**, 455 (1975).
7. T. L. Smith, *J. Polym. Sci., Polym. Phys. Ed.*, **12**, 1825 (1974).
8. R. W. Seymour and S. L. Cooper, *Macromolecules*, **6**, 48 (1973).
9. R. W. Seymour, G. M. Estes, and S. L. Cooper, *Macromolecules*, **3**, 579 (1970).
10. G. L. Wilkes, S. Bagrodia, W. Humphries, and R. Wildnauer, *J. Polym. Sci., Polym. Lett.*, **13**, 321 (1975).
11. G. L. Wilkes and R. Wildnauer, *J. Appl. Phys.*, **46**, 4148 (1975).
12. T. Nishi, *J. Appl. Polym. Sci., Appl. Polym. Symp.*, **20**, 353 (1973).
13. S. L. Cooper and A. V. Tobolsky, *J. Appl. Polym. Sci.*, **11**, 1361 (1967).
14. C. A. Arnold, *Proc. 7th National SAMPE Technical Conference*, Albuquerque, N.M., October 1975.
15. S. K. Baczek, J. N. Anderson, and H. E. Adams, *J. Appl. Polym. Sci.*, **19**, 2269 (1975).
16. P. W. Ryan, *Br. Polym. J.*, **3**, 145 (1971).
17. C. A. Arnold, *J. Elast. Plast.*, **8**, 3 (1976).
18. W. O. Statton, in *Newer Methods of Polymer Characterization*, B. Ke, Ed., Wiley-Interscience, New York, 1964.
19. G. L. Wilkes, *J. Macromol. Sci., Rev. Macromol. Chem.*, **C10**, 149 (1974).
20. D. W. French, *Rubber Chem. Technol.*, **42**, 71 (1969).
21. J. F. Beecher, L. Marker, R. D. Bradford, and S. L. Aggarwal, *J. Polym. Sci.*, **C26**, 117 (1969).
22. R. Bonart, L. Morbitzer, and H. Rinke, *Kolloid-Z. Z. Polym.*, **240**, 807 (1970).
23. R. A. Assink, *J. Polym. Sci., Polym. Phys. Ed.*, to appear.
24. S. E. B. Petrie, *A.C.S. Polym. Prepr.*, **15**(2), 336 (1974).
25. A. S. Marshall and S. E. B. Petrie, *J. Appl. Phys.*, **46**, 4223 (1975).
26. S. E. B. Petrie, *J. Polym. Sci. A-2*, **10**, 1255 (1972).
27. R. M. Mininni, R. S. Moore, J. R. Flick, and S. E. B. Petrie, *J. Macromol. Sci., Phys.*, **B8**, 343 (1973).
28. A. Siegmann and E. Turi, *J. Macromol. Sci., Phys.*, **B10**, 689 (1974).
29. S. M. Ellerstein, *J. Appl. Polym. Sci., Appl. Polym. Symp.*, **2**, 111 (1966).
30. A. E. Tonelli, *Macromolecules*, **4**, 653 (1971).
31. A. J. Kovacs, R. A. Stratton, and J. D. Ferry, *J. Phys. Chem.*, **67**, 152 (1963).
32. H. H. Meyer, P. M. F. Mangin, and J. D. Ferry, *J. Polym. Sci.*, **A3**, 1785 (1965).
33. L. C. E. Struik, *Rheol. Acta*, **5**, 303 (1966).
34. R. R. Lagasse, unpublished results.
35. R. W. Seymour and S. L. Cooper, *J. Polym. Sci., Polym. Lett.*, **9**, 689 (1971).
36. R. Bonart, *J. Macromol. Sci., Phys.*, **B2**, 115 (1968).
37. D. S. Huh and S. L. Cooper, *Polym. Eng. Sci.*, **11**, 369 (1971).
38. S. M. Wolpert, A. Weitz, and B. Wunderlich, *J. Polym. Sci. A-2*, **9**, 1887 (1971).

Received May 3, 1976
Revised July 2, 1976

JOURNAL OF APPLIED POLYMER SCIENCE   VOL. 21, 2505–2514 (1977)

On the Structure of Concentrated Cellulose Acetate Solutions*

B. KUNST and Z. VAJNAHT, *Institute of Physical Chemistry,*
Technological Department, University of Zagreb, 41001 Zagreb, Yugoslavia

Synopsis

The supermolecular structure of cellulose acetate membrane casting solutions was determined by measuring their rheological behavior. The method was applied to both clear and turbid casting solutions. The resulting data on activation energy of viscous flow are shown to depend on the cellulose acetate content of the casting solution and on the nature of solvent used. The separation properties of the prepared asymmetric membranes determined by reverse osmosis testing indicate a good correlation with the data obtained by the rheological measurements of the casting solutions. The latter can, therefore, be used as a practical tool for the investigation of early stages in the asymmetric membrane formation process.

INTRODUCTION

Since Loeb and Sourirajan[1] first prepared asymmetric cellulose acetate membranes, much work has been done to elucidate their formation mechanism. A number of proposed concepts dealing with this problem have been reviewed elsewhere.[2,3] All the approaches used were based on the phenomenon of phase separation within a cast solution layer as the crucial step during membrane formation.

The solution structure–evaporation rate concept for controlling the porosity of asymmetric cellulose acetate membranes[4–10] has particularly emphasized two parameters affecting the phase change within the solution layer: the rate of solvent removal from the solution surface and the structure of casting dope, i.e., the state of polymer supermolecular aggregation in it. Whereas the first parameter has been successfully measured,[5] the second could not be easily defined. Indirect conclusions concerning its relative value were made,[5] and only recently[2] a direct, light-scattering technique was applied to indicate the extent of polymer supermolecular ordering in the membrane-casting solutions. A correlation of the data obtained by such measurements with the properties of prepared asymmetric membranes has shed more light on the early stage of membrane formation and contributed to more controllable membrane preparation.

A main drawback of the light-scattering characterization method is its inapplicability to turbid solutions which are very often used for asymmetric membrane making. Such typical turbid membrane-casting solutions are, for example,

---

* Part of this paper was presented at the International Symposium on Fresh Water from the Sea, Alghero, Italy, May 16–20, 1976.

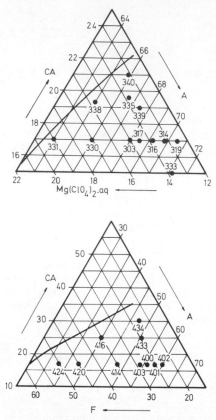

Fig. 1. Compositions of membrane casting solutions and corresponding phase separation boundaries.

Loeb-Sourirajan-type mixtures consisting of cellulose acetate, acetone, and aqueous magnesium perchlorate. The objective of this paper is, therefore, to characterize various cellulose acetate membrane casting solutions by measuring their rheological properties, viz., to use a method which is applicable to turbid solutions as well.

The viscosity coefficient of concentrated polymer solutions is known to depend on the applied shear stress. The flow of such solutions at low shear stresses is Newtonian, which means that the solution viscosity coefficient at such conditions is constant. Low shear stresses applied to the concentrated polymer solution cannot break down the strutures present in it; hence, the Newtonian viscosity measured at low shear stresses describes the solution flow without any disturbance of its structure. The viscosity measurements can thus be used[11,12] for characterizing the state of supermolecular polymer ordering in a concentrated polymer solution.

It was also found[13] more appropriate to employ the temperature dependence of solution viscosity rather than the viscosity itself, as a value related to the polymer solution structure. The temperature dependence of viscosity has been theoretically derived by Eyring[14] who treated the flow as an activation process, and the temperature–viscosity relationship was given in the form

$$\eta = A e^{E_{\mathrm{visc}}/RT}$$

where E_{visc} = energy of activation of viscous flow. This quantity depends on the same parameters as the viscosity coefficient η, i.e., on polymer concentration, temperature, and nature of solvent, and it was used here to characterize quantitatively the state of structurization of the membrane casting solutions.

The applicability of the rheological testing method was checked with various membrane casting solutions, and the results obtained were correlated to characteristic properties of the membranes made from all the employed casting solutions. Properties which supply information on average pore size on the membrane surface are the separation of solute (sodium chloride) of thermally untreated membrane and/or the membrane shrinkage temperature profile giving the temperature needed for a membrane to achieve a certain level of solute separation.

EXPERIMENTAL

Materials and Solutions

Eastman cellulose acetate E-398-3 and reagent-grade acetone, formamide, and magnesium perchlorate were employed for both the solution preparation for viscosity measurements and the membrane casting.

Two series of solutions, the first using aqueous magnesium perchlorate with magnesium perchlorate–water ratio of 1:8.5 (series 300) and the second using formamide (series 400) as the swelling agents, were prepared (Table I.). The positions of points representing the casting solution compositions in relation to the phase separation boundaries for the two systems are shown in triangular polymer–solvent–swelling agent diagrams in Figure 1.

Determination of Solution Viscosity

The viscosity of concentrated polymer solutions is usually measured by rotational viscometers. These are rather sophisticated and expensive devices and it did not seem appropriate to use them in the exploratory experiments, the more so because some practical problems with the membrane casting solutions became evident. One of them related to the casting solution composition, which usually contains a low-boiling liquid (acetone) as solvent component. Viscosity measurements should, therefore be carried out in a closed system.

The simplest approach at present was to use a rolling ball type instrument such as a Hoeppler viscometer, in which the shear stress value depends on the density difference between the ball and the investigated solution. Low shear stresses which keep the flow of a concentrated casting solution within the Newtonian region can be achieved by using a glass ball of relatively low density. Klein[12] has pointed out that the temperature dependence of the viscosity can be determined satisfactorily in the Hoeppler viscometer if the same ball is used throughout the measurements. In such a way, all the measurements are performed at constant, low shear stress, a condition rendering comparable viscosity values. Even a slight deviation from the Newtonian type of flow is allowed without any noticeable error in the finally calculated E values.

The determination of the solution viscosity in the Hoeppler viscometer consisted in measuring the rolling time of a ball between two marks in the viscometer tube. To evaluate the viscosity of a fluid, a simplified equation of the form

$$\eta = k(\rho_s - \rho_-)\theta$$

was applied, where k = the instrument constant obtained by the viscometer calibration with a liquid of known viscosity and density, ρ_s and ρ = densities of the rolling ball and the fluid, respectively; and θ = time of roll. This equation shows that, besides the rolling times at different temperatures, the solution density ρ or, more precisely, its temperature dependence should be determined. A weight dilatometer of the type described by Gibson and Loeffler,[15] used as a pycnometer, was found suitable. The dilatometer partly filled with a known amount of the solution and partly with mercury contained, at various temperatures, different quantities of mercury. The volume changes of the casting solution in the dilatometer were easily calculated from the amount of mercury, its densities at various temperatures, and the volume changes of the dilatometer. Using these data, the absolute value of the solution density at any temperature could be determined.

Membrane Preparation and Testing

Porous asymmetric membranes were cast from all the solutions listed in Table I. Temperature of the casting solutions for the formamide-based membranes was 25°C, and for the series 300 membranes, 0–2°C. The glass plates were kept at the same temperatures as the casting solutions. Temperature of the casting atmosphere was always 20–25°C, and its relative humidity was 65%. The casting was done practically without an evaporation period, i.e., the cast solution was immediately immersed into a gelation bath consisting of ice-cold water. In such a way, the variations in the membrane surface porosities could be attributed to the solution structure effects only, with changes caused by the evaporation step being negligible.

The membranes obtained by the casting procedure were tested in the standard reverse osmosis setup.[16] Reverse osmosis experiments for the membranes in the as-cast condition were carried out at 7.0 atm using a feed solution containing 200 ppm sodium chloride. The thermally treated membranes were tested at 17.4 atm using the 3500-ppm sodium chloride feed solution. Before the reverse osmosis experiment, each film was subjected to a pure-water pressure treatment for 1–2 hr at 20% higher pressure than that to be used in the reverse osmosis run. All experiments were of the short-run type and performed at laboratory temperature. A feed flow rate of 450 cc/min was used, giving a mass transfer coefficient $k = 45 \times 10^{-4}$ cm/sec on the high-pressure side of the membrane.

For all salt concentrations, a conductivity bridge was used for analysis. The fraction solute separation f was calculated from the relation

$$f = \frac{\text{solute concn. in feed (ppm)} - \text{solute concn. in product (ppm)}}{\text{solute concn. in feed (ppm)}}$$

RESULTS AND DISCUSSION

The results of rheological measurements, either in the form of viscosities or as the activation energies of viscous flow, depend on the applied shear stress, the structure of the polymer chain (its molecular mass, flexibility, etc.), the nature of the solvent, the polymer concentration, and the temperature. As the shear stress in this work was kept at a constant low value, and as the same polymer sample was used throughout the measurements, only the last three variables mentioned were operative.

The form of the log η–$1/T$ relationships presented in Figure 2 for all the cellulose acetate solutions is fairly linear. There is a very slight tendency of some of the highest viscosity values to deviate from linearity, but this can hardly be considered as systematic. The linearity of the log η–$1/T$ relationship is shown[11,12] to be typical of nonassociable fluids or fluids with unchangeable supermolecular associations. Accordingly, the results obtained here indicate that the extent of supermolecular polymer structurization in the cellulose acetate multicomponent solutions practically does not change within the investigated temperature interval. Such a conclusion is not quite in accordance with the behavior of some binary concentrated polymer solutions,[11,12] which exhibit slightly curved log η–$1/T$ dependences, pointing to some changes in the structural properties of the solutions with temperature variation. The explanation of this difference cannot be given yet, because too little is known about the interactions of components

TABLE I

Casting Solution Compositions and Their Activation Energies of Viscous Flow

| Solution type | Solution composition[a] | | | E_{exp}, cal/mole | E_{solv}, cal/mole | ΔE, cal/mole |
	CA, wt-%	Swelling agent, wt-%	SwA/S			
316	17.0	13.8	0.199	9,190	2,580	6,610
339	19.0	13.5	0.200	9,780	2,580	7,200
340	21.0	13.1	0.199	10,380	2,580	7,800
333	15.0	13.8	0.194	8,470	2,530	5,940
316	17.0	13.8	0.199	9,190	2,580	6,610
335	19.6	13.8	0.207	10,000	2,650	7,350
319	17.0	12.5	0.177	9,110	2,280	6,830
314	17.0	13.2	0.189	9,260	2,480	6,780
316	17.0	13.8	0.199	9,190	2,580	6,610
317	17.0	14.5	0.212	9,450	2,690	6,760
303	17.0	15.0	0.221	9,550	2,740	6,810
330	17.0	17.0	0.258	9,710	2,930	6,780
331	17.0	19.0	0.297	10,190	3,080	7,110
335	19.6	13.8	0.207	10,000	2,650	7,350
338	19.3	15.7	0.242	10,260	2,850	7,410
400	17.0	27.0	0.482	8,590	2,230	6,360
433	25.0	24.4	0.482	10,030	2,230	7,800
434	30.0	22.8	0.483	14,220	2,230	11,990
402	17.0	23.0	0.383	8,570	2,110	6,460
401	17.0	25.0	0.431	8,540	2,170	6,370
400	17.0	27.0	0.482	8,590	2,230	6,360
403	17.0	29.0	0.537	8,820	2,290	6,530
414	17.0	35.0	0.729	9,020	2,520	6,500
420	17.0	45.0	1.184	9,760	3,050	6,710
424	17.0	50.0	1.515	10,510	3,440	7,070
433	25.0	24.4	0.482	10,030	2,230	7,800
416	25.0	35.0	0.875	10,960	2,680	8,280

[a] CA = cellulose acetate; SwA = swelling agent; S = solvent-acetone

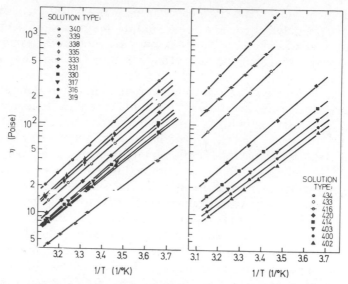

Fig. 2. Plot of log η vs $1/T$ of the membrane casting solutions.

in the process of supermolecular association of both binary and multicomponent concentrated polymer solutions.

The slopes of the log η–$1/T$ dependences for various cellulose acetate solutions differ from each other, which is best expressed by the values of the activation energy of viscous flow, E_{visc}. These are calculated from the experimental data by a least-squares analysis and tabulated in Table I (column 5) along with the compositions of the various casting solutions.

The absolute values of E_{visc} show similar trends for both the aqueous magnesium perchlorate-based and the formamide-based casting solutions (series 300 and 400, respectively). The differences appearing in the activation energies of viscous flow for the various solutions within each of the series are due to the compositional effects, more specifically to changes in the cellulose acetate concentration, and partly to the variation of the solvent nature produced by varying the solvent and swelling agent contents.

An increase in the cellulose acetate content of the casting solution systematically increases its activation energy of viscous flow. Such a trend is most correctly shown in the series of solutions with the same, constant swelling agent-to-solvent ratio, and differing only in the cellulose acetate concentrations (solutions 316, 339, and 340; and 400, 433, and 434, respectively). These results indicate the progressive enlargement of supermolecular structures caused by the increasing cellulose acetate concentration, and they are consistant with both theoretical considerations and the earlier experimental findings.[17]

The nature of the solvent appears to be the second factor which affects the structure of membrane casting solutions and their rheological behavior. Most of the results presented here in the form of E_{visc} values are lower than those reported for the corresponding binary cellulose acetate–dimethylformamide and cellulose acetate–dioxane solutions[11] amounting to 11,000–19,000 cal/mole. This indicates that the solvent power of the acetone–formamide and acetone–aqueous magnesium perchlorate combinations for the secondary cellulose acetate is su-

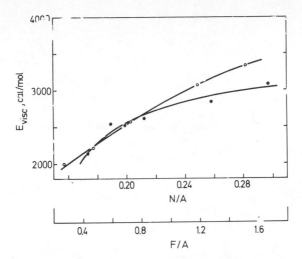

Fig. 3. Activation energies of viscous flow in relation to swelling agent-to-solvent ratio: N = magnesium perchlorate:water = 1:8.5; F = formamide; A = acetone.

perior to that of dimethylformamide and dioxane, i.e., the former mixed solvents produce less structurized cellulose acetate solutions.

The activation energies of viscous flow for the membrane casting solutions of constant (17%) cellulose acetate content consistently rise with increase in swelling agent concentration. This result would imply an ordering action of the swelling agent on the cellulose acetate solutions in acetone. In analyzing such data, one must not overlook a variation of the activation energy of flow of the solvent combination itself (solvent + swelling agent) with composition. The measured E_{visc} values of the solvent composition also happen to rise with an increase of the swelling agent-to-solvent ratio (Fig. 3). In order to get the real effect of the swelling agent content on the casting solution structure, the E_{visc} values of different cellulose acetate solutions should be corrected by subtracting the activation energies of flow of the corresponding solvent combinations. By such a procedure, ΔE_{visc} values have been obtained for all the casting solutions (last column in Table I).

Whereas the discussed effect of the cellulose acetate concentration on the corrected activation energies of viscous flow remains the same, the solvent nature dependence changes its character. This is illustrated in Figure 4, where two sets of data (E_{visc} and ΔE_{visc}) for both series of solutions are plotted against the swelling agent concentration. In contrast with the steady increase of the activation energies of flow, the ΔE_{visc} values remain practically constant over a fairly wide range of swelling agent content, indicating practically unchanged supermolecular structurization of the cellulose acetate solutions. This important conclusion is very close to earlier findings,[2] which showed that an increase in the swelling agent concentration may even slightly reduce the casting solution structurization. Small differences between these two results might be assigned to the different experimental techniques used, which still need improvement in sensitivity.

A massive increase in swelling agent concentration brings the casting solution composition very close to the phase separation boundary [solutions 331 and 424

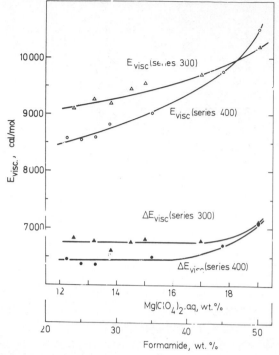

Fig. 4. Activation energies of flow and their corrected values for different membrane casting solutions.

in Fig. 1(a) and (b), respectively] and produces a definite rise in their ΔE_{visc} values, viz., better ordering of polymer structures in the solutions. This observation is consistent with the earlier one,[2] attributed to a modified role of the swelling agents close to phase separation conditions, where they act more as nonsolvents.

TABLE II
Reverse Osmosis Separation of Some Thermally Untreated Membranes

Membrane type	CA in casting solution, wt-%	Sodium chloride separation f
316	17.0	0.348
339	19.0	0.513
340	21.0	0.495
400	17.0	0.272
433	25.0	0.386
434	30.0	0.455

Membrane type	Swelling agent in casting solution, wt-%	Sodium chloride separation f
316	13.8	0.348
303	15.0	0.325
330	17.0	0.250
331	19.0	0.209
402	23.0	0.332
400	27.0	0.272
420	45.0	0.215

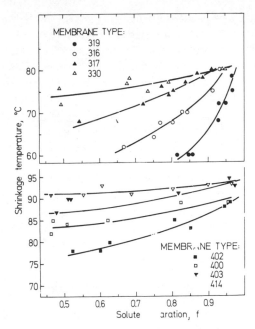

Fig. 5. Shrinkage temperature profiles of membranes prepared from some casting solutions.

All structural differences in the membrane casting solutions should be reflected in the properties of prepared asymmetric membranes. According to the improved concept of asymmetric membrane formation,[2] the phase separation process in concentrated cellulose acetate solutions takes place within a long-range dynamic polymer network. The dimensions and density of the polymer structures in a casting solution affect the size and number of droplets of the newly formed phase in the solution's upper layer, and eventually the porosity of the membrane's surface layer. The latter property may be indirectly determined from the reverse osmosis data (sodium chloride separation) of thermally untreated membranes[10] or from the relative positions of membrane shrinkage temperature profiles[5,6] obtained by the usual reverse osmosis experiment. Both types of results give a relative measure of average pore size on the membrane surface in the as-cast condition.

Table II illustrates the effect of changes in the membrane casting solution composition on the average pore size of thermally untreated membranes. An increase of the cellulose acetate content in both series of casting solutions (upper part of Table II) decreases the relative dimensions of average membrane surface pores, which is manifested in higher sodium chloride separation values. The effect is not quite equal for both series of the membrane casting solutions, presumably because of the inherent differences in their nature. When correlated to the results of the supermolecular ordering in the casting solutions obtained rheologically, these data show that more extensive structurization in a casting solution leads to membranes having smaller average pores in the surface region.

A change in solvent nature brought about by an increase in swelling agent content (lower part of Table II) produces membranes with lower separation characteristics, indicating the presence of bigger average pores in the membrane surface. The identical conclusion is obtained from the relative positions of the membrane shrinkage temperature profiles (Fig. 5). A shrinkage temperature-versus-solute separation curve located at higher temperature points to the presence of relatively big pores on the membranes surface in the as-cast condition, and membranes with smaller pores should be shrunk at lower temperatures to give the same level of solute separation. For instance, the average surface pores in membranes 319 and 402, made from solutions with low swelling agent content, are relatively small, and quite large in membranes 330 and 414. A higher concentration of swelling agent in the cast dope, making the supermolecular network in it looser and less extensive, increases, therefore, the average pore dimensions in the finally prepared membrane.

In conclusion, the results presented here point again to the usefulness of the membrane casting solution structure determination and show that the rheological measurements can be successfully applied for such purposes. They also confirm the validity of the refined membrane formation concept, which takes into account the structure of membrane casting solution and its influence on the events occurring later in the process.

This work was supported by the Office of Saline Water, U.S. Department of the Interior, under Contract 14-01-0001-1427.

References

1. S. Loeb and S. Sourirajan, Dept. of Engineering, University of California, Los Angeles, Report No. 60-60, 1961.

2. B. Kunst, D. Škevin, Gj. Deželić, and J. J. Petres, *J. Appl. Polym. Sci.*, **20**, 1339 (1976).

3. H. Strathmann, K. Kock, P. Amar and R. W. Baker, *Desalination*, **16**, 179 (1975).

4. B. Kunst and S. Sourirajan, *J. Appl. Polym. Sci.*, **14**, 723 (1970).

5. B. Kunst and S. Sourirajan, *J. Appl. Polym. Sci.*, **14**, 1983 (1970).

6. B. Kunst and S. Sourirajan, *J. Appl. Polym. Sci.*, **14**, 2559 (1970).

7. R. Pilon, B. Kunst, and S. Sourirajan, *J. Appl. Polym. Sci.*, **15**, 1317 (1971).

8. L. Pageau and S. Sourirajan, *J. Appl. Polym. Sci.*, **16**, 3185 (1972).

9. B. Kunst and B. Floreani, *Kolloid-Z. Z. Polym.*, **251**, 600 (1973).

10. B. Kunst and S. Sourirajan, *J. Appl. Polym. Sci.*, **18**, 3423 (1974).

11. A. A. Tager, V. E. Dreval, M. Kurbanaliyev, M. S. Lutskiy, N. E. Berkovits, I. M. Granovskaya, and T. A. Charikova, *Vysokomol. Soedin.*, **A10**, 2044 (1968).

12. J. Klein and R. Woernle, *Kolloid-Z. Z. Polym.*, **237**, 209 (1970).

13. V. P. Budtov, *Vysokomol. Soedin.*, **A12**, 1355 (1970).

14. H. Eyring, S. Glasstone, and J. Laidler, *The Theory of Rate Processes,* McGraw-Hill, New York, 1941, Chap. 9.

15. R. E. Gibson and O. H. Loeffler, *J. Amer. Chem. Soc.*, **61**, 2515 (1939).

16. S. Sourirajan, *Reverse Osmosis,* Logos Press, London, and Academic Press, New York, 1970, Chap. 2.

17. A. A. Tager and V. E. Dreval, *Russ. Chem. Rev.*, **36**, 361 (1967).

Received May 3, 1976

Posttreatment Effects on Pore Size Distribution of Loeb-Sourirajan-Type Modified Cellulose Acetate Ultrathin Membranes

HARUHIKO OHYA, HOZUMI KONUMA,* and YOICHI NEGISHI, *Department of Chemical Engineering, Yokohama National University, Yokohama, Japan*

Synopsis

The nitrogen gas adsorption isotherms at −195°C on modified cellulose acetate ultrathin membranes were measured, and the surface area of the pores was determined by the method employed by Cranston and Inkley. A relationship between reverse osmosis characteristics and the mean pore radius was correlated, and it was observed that any method (such as longer evaporation period, heat treatment, or reduction of swelling agent) reducing the mean pore radius to below 20–22 Å improves membrane characteristics of reverse osmosis separation significantly.

INTRODUCTION

The porous structure of Loeb-Sourirajan-type cellulose acetate membranes was examined by electron microscopy by Riley et al.[1,2] They confirmed that the membrane consists of a dense, thin surface layer on the film side exposed to air during casting, with a highly porous substructure underneath the surface layer. This dense, thin surface layer plays a significant role in reverse osmosis separation.

There have been many discussions on the structure of the surface layer. Riley et al.[1,2] reported that it was devoid of structural characteristics, showed no evidence of pores greater than 100 Å, and has a thickness of about 0.25 μm. Several workers[1,2,3] reported on its thickness: Schultz and Asunmaa[4] reported that there were pores of average radius 23 Å between cellulose acetate crystallites of size 188 Å.

Several attempts have been made to obtain an ultrathin membrane consisting of only a dense, thin cellulose acetate membrane. For example, Riley et al.[5] prepared ultrathin membranes using the Carnell-Cassidy technique,[6,7] which consists essentially of slowly withdrawing a clean glass plate from a dilute solution of a polymer in a suitable solvent. Their membrane was devoid of porous structure, and an effort was made to obtain as thin a membrane as possible to increase water flux.

Ohya et al.[8] showed that there are no pores in the ultrathin membrane cast

---

* Present address: Central Research Laboratory, Ebara Mfg. Co., LTD., Fujisawa City, Kanagawa, Japan.

TABLE I

Composition, Physical Properties, Pore Volume, Surface Area, and Reverse Osmosis Characteristics of Membranes[a]

Batch no.	Ratio of cellulose acetate to 10% $Mg(ClO_4)_2$ aqueous soln.	Weight fraction of cellulose acetate	Viscosity cp	Density, g/cm³	Superficial surface area of membrane, m²/g	Estimated membrane thickness, μm	Surface area of pores, m²/g	Mean pore radius based on cross-sectional area, Å
K-1	5:0.0	0.04843	4.10	0.8013	1.885	0.408	0.0	0.0
K-2	5:0.1	0.0482	10.61	0.8290	1.360	0.539	13.9	19.8
K-3	5:1	0.0482	16.65	0.8359	0.9385	0.941	16.4	20.4
K-4	5:5	0.0482	19.28	0.846	0.8738	1.096	19.3	21.2
K-5	5:18	0.0482	41.34	0.8988	0.5645	1.754	58.8	21.8

	Percent cross-sectional area of pore open on membrane, %	Flux, g/cm²·hr		Salt separation, %	
		Air side in contact with salt solution	Glass side in contact with salt solution	Air side in contact with salt solution	Glass side in contact with salt solution
K-1	0.0	0.067	0.060	95.5	87.5
K-2	4.68	0.62	0.37	79.5	74.4
K-3	2.88	4.22	4.31	44.4	19.4
K-4	6.72	3.85	5.53	18.4	18.4
K-5	8.68	—	—	—	—

[a] Evaporation period 4.5 min, without heat treatment.

from a solution of cellulose acetate in acetone, but that there do exist pores in the modified ultrathin membrane from a solution of cellulose acetate in acetone and a swelling agent, formamide. This modified ultrathin membrane about 1 μm thick, shows symmetric characteristics of good separation and higher permeability than the ultrathin membrane 600 Å thick by Merten et al.[5]

It is the purpose of this paper to obtain a relationship between pore size distribution and the reverse osmosis characteristics of the modified ultrathin membranes.

EXPERIMENTAL

The Modified Ultrathin Membrane

A number of the modified Loeb-Sourirajan-type ultrathin membranes were prepared, using almost the same method reported earlier,[8] from casting solutions whose compositions are shown in Table I. The temperature of the casting solution was kept at 1–2°C, the ambient temperature at 20°C, and the ambient humidity at 50%. Membrane thickness was estimated by the following equation[8] using withdrawal rate, measured physical properties of the casting solutions, and the density of the porous ultrathin membranes:

$$\bar{\delta} = 0.4 \frac{\rho_L}{\rho_S} W_S \sqrt{\frac{\mu u_0}{\rho g}} \tag{1}$$

The evaporation period was 2 to 12 min. Even a 2-min period gave a symmetric, modified, ultrathin membrane as shown in Table II. The membranes, having a 37-cm^2 area, were floated off each surface of the glass plate onto the surface of the water and stored wet. After more than 30 leaves of membranes were collected, thermal treatment was used at a designated temperature in a water bath for 20 min. After the thermal treatment, the membranes were freeze dried as reported earlier.[8]

Adsorption Isotherms

The adsorption isotherms of the freeze-dried membrane at −195°C were determined on a standard Emmett and Brunauer apparatus. The gas used was

TABLE II
Effects of Evaporation Period on Reverse Osmosis Characteristics[a]

Evaporation period, min	PWP, g/hr		Salt separation, %	
	Air side in contact with pure water	Glass side in contact with pure water	Air side in contact with salt solution	Glass side in contact with salt solution
1.0	32.97	34.41	22.2	51.4
2.0	37.65	37.71	42.9	40.0
3.0	43.95	46.43	44.8	44.8
4.5	41.78	46.12	44.4	19.4
6.0	37.59	48.52	41.7	30.6
8.0	54.4	45.38	31.6	26.3
10.0	42.61	42.06	40.5	32.4
15.0	11.30	11.35	75.68	75.68

[a] Casting solution Batch K-3, without heat treatment.

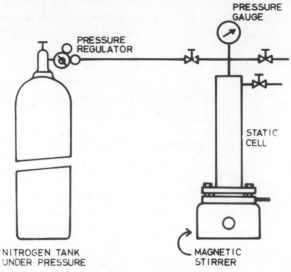

Fig. 1. Reverse osmosis cell assembly.

prepurified nitrogen dried through a cold trap and cooled to liquid nitrogen temperature.

Reverse Osmosis

The reverse osmosis experiments with the modified ultrathin membranes were carried out at laboratory temperature at a pressure of 20 kg/cm^2 g, using the reverse osmosis cell shown in Figure 1.

Other experimental procedures were conducted in the manner previously reported.[8]

RESULTS

Isotherms of Freeze-Dried Membranes

Figure 2 gives the experimental isotherms of five different kinds of freeze-dried Loeb-Sourirajan-type modified ultrathin membranes without thermal treatment at −195°C. Figure 3 gives the experimental isotherms of five kinds of freeze-dried modified ultrathin membranes with varying evaporation periods and thermal treatment temperatures. The data of batch K-2 in Figure 2, expressed as a B.E.T. plot in Figure 4, yields a pore surface of 10.2 m^2/m^2 of membrane area. The latter was estimated from the B.E.T. equation from the nitrogen isotherm, using 16.2 Å^2 as the area occupied by each adsorbed nitrogen molecule. Similar calculations were done for batch K-3 to K-5, and some of the results are shown in Table I.

The ultrathin membrane batch K-1, obtained from the cellulose acetate–acetone solution, was the only one that did not adsorb nitrogen at all.[8]

Reverse Osmosis

Results obtained in batches K-1 to K-4 of the ultrathin membranes which were used without thermal treatment are also presented in Table I. Membranes of

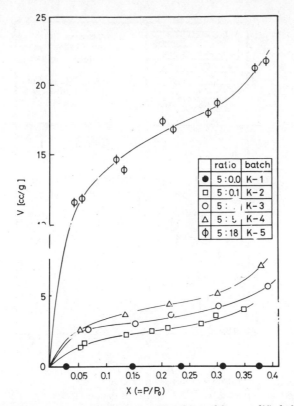

Fig. 2. Nitrogen gas adsorption isotherms for one ultrathin and four modified ultrathin membranes at −195°C. Withdrawal rate u_0 = 0.224 cm/sec, no heat treatment, evaporation period 4.5 min; the ratio in figure is that of cellulose acetate to 10% aqueous magnesium perchlorate.

composition K-5 were too fragile to be handled; therefore, reverse osmosis experiments were not carried out with these membranes. Reverse osmosis tests were carried out to verify the symmetry of the ultrathin membrane as follows: Two membranes were chosen at random from about 50 samples composed on both sides of the glass plate which was withdrawn from the casting solution. One membrane, facing air, was set in a reverse osmosis test cell in the high-pressure salt solution at 20 kg/cm^2 g, while the other facing the glass side, was set. If the membranes were asymmetric, we could not obtain the same pure-water flux rate and salt rejection.

But as shown in Tables I and II, the pure-water flux rate and the salt rejection are almost the same for the data obtained on both sides. Hence, we might say that the ultrathin membranes obtained by this procedure are symmetric membranes.

DISCUSSION

Pore Size Distribution

The pore size distribution of the freeze-dried membranes was determined by the method of Cranston and Inkley[9] using low-temperature adsorption isotherms. The volume of the pores for each pore size range was calculated. The cross-

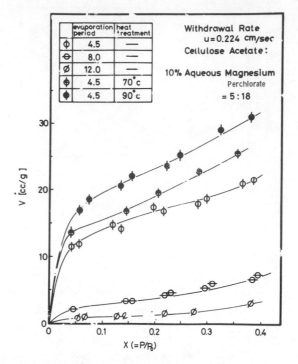

Fig. 3. Nitrogen gas adsorption isotherms for five modified ultrathin membranes at −195°C, varying three evaporation periods and heat treatment temperatures.

sectional area assigned to the pores of each radius was calculated assuming that all pores were straight cylindrical, perpendicular to the membrane surface, and that the length of each pore was the same as the thickness of the membrane calculated by eq. (1).

For batch K-2 (cellulose acetate: 10% aqueous magnesium perchlorate = 5:0.1), with evaporation period 4.5 min and no thermal treatment, the total cross-sectional area of the pores was 468 cm^2 per m^2 of membrane surface, which corresponds to 4.68% of membrane surface. For batch K-1 (cellulose acetate:10% aqueous magnesium perchlorate = 5:0), there were no pores.[8]

Effects of Composition

The increase in the amount of 10% aqueous magnesium perchlorate in the casting solution corresponds to an increase in water flux through the membrane from 0.06 g/cm^2·hr to 4–5 g/cm^2·hr up to a ratio of 5:1, but to a steady decrease in salt rejection from 95 to 18%. From the adsorption isotherm shown in Figure 2, there are no pores at all on the ultrathin membrane cast from the solution composed of cellulose acetate and acetone containing no aqueous magnesium perchlorate. Its structure is dense and might be assumed to be homogeneous judging from the identical results obtained on the reverse osmosis tests for both sides of the membrane. Batch K-2 to K-4 were obtained with the addition of 10% aqueous magnesium perchlorate to the above solution. The 10% aqueous magnesium perchlorate content of the latter solution was increased from zero

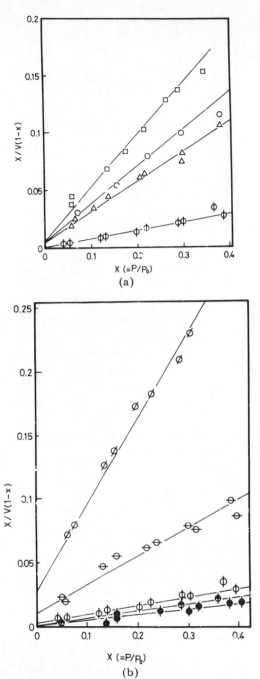

Fig. 4. (a) B.E.T. plots for the adsorption of nitrogen gas on modified ultrathin membranes shown in Fig. 2. (b) B.E.T. plots for the adsorption of nitrogen gas on modified ultrathin membranes shown in Fig. 3.

to 5 parts per part of cellulose acetate; this modification of the ultrathin membranes increased the porous structure of the membranes.

The water flux and salt separation at a pressure of 20 kg/cm² g were essentially identical with the air side and the glass side of the membrane facing the high-

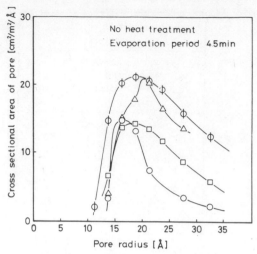

Fig. 5. Distributions of cross-sectional area of pores in ultrathin membranes. Symbols same as in Fig. 2.

pressure solution in all cases.   These results show that porous structure of the membrane used was not asymmetric.

When the 10% aqueous magnesium perchlorate content of the casting solution increased from 0.1 to 5 parts per part of cellulose acetate, the salt separation decreased greatly from 80 to 18%, with a slight increase in the mean pore radii from 19.8 to 21.2 Å, and with an increase in the percent cross-sectional area of

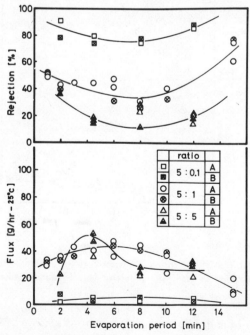

Fig. 6. Relationship between reverse osmosis characteristics and evaporation periods for batches K-2, K-3, and K-4:   (a) air side in contact with salt solution; (b) glass side in contact with salt solution; symbols same as in Fig. 2.

TABLE III
Effects of Evaporation Period and Composition of Casting Solution on Surface Area of Pores and Average Diameter[a]

Batch no.	Evaporation period, min	Surface area of pores based on B.E.T. equation, m^2/g	Average pore diameter, Å	Percent pore cross-sectional area, %
K-2	4.5	13.9	41.51	4.68
K-3	2.0	10.9	36.67	2.43
	4.5	16.4	43.05	2.88
	8.0	6.9	50.59	3.30
K-4	4.5	19.3	48.38	6.72
	8.0	8.2	45.65	2.93
K-5	4.5	58.8	48.44	8.68
	8.0	20.7	53.67	4.88
	12.0	7.0	51.47	3.29
	15.0	essentially no nitrogen absorption		

[a] Without heat treatment.

the pores open on the membrane from 4.68 to 6.72%. The water flux through the membrane increased about eightfold from 0.06 to 0.5 g/cm²·hr with addition of a small amount of 10% aqueous magnesium perchlorate by 0.1 parts of cellulose acetate and also about eightfold from 0.5 g/cm²·hr to 4.3 g/cm³·hr by 0.9 parts of cellulose acetate. But further addition of 10% aqueous magnesium perchlorate by 4 parts of cellulose acetate caused a very small increase in water flux. The total cross-sectional area of pores per unit area membrane surface passed through a minimum value of the ratio of 5:1 and then increased as shown in Table I.

The distribution of the cross-sectional area of pores for four different kinds of composition without heat treatment are shown in Figure 5. Comparing the two curves of the pore size distribution for the ratios 5:0.1 and 5:1, it can be seen that the value of the pore radius (or the cross-sectional area of pores on the membrane) at the maximum is higher and its shape narrower for the curve of ratio 5:1 than for the curve of ratio 5:0.1. These two facts indicate that there were a few larger pores, but many more smaller pores, resulting in an average pore size of smaller radius in the modified ultrathin membranes from the 5:0.1 casting solution than from the 5:1 casting solution.

Evaporation Period

Figure 6 shows a relationship between the reverse osmosis characteristics and the evaporation periods for batches K-2, K-3, and K-4. Salt separation curves pass through a minimum around 8 min in the evaporation period for the three batches. Minimum values of salt separation were 75% for batch K-2, 29% for batch K-3, and 12% for batch K-4. On the other hand, the curve of the water flux through the membrane has a maximum. Batch K-2 takes a maximum value of water flux at about 8 min of the evaporation period, batch K-3 at about 6 min, and batch K-4 at approximately 4 min. It might also be derived from Figure 6 that the membranes cast under the conditions investigated in the figure were not asymmetric.

Table III lists the variation of the surface area of the pores based on the B.E.T.

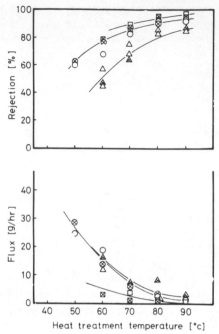

Fig. 7. Relationship between reverse osmosis characteristics and heat treatment temperatures. Symbols same as in Fig. 6.

equation and the mean pore radii against the evaporation period for batches K-2 to K-5. When increasing the evaporation period, the pore surface area showed a tendency to pass through a slight maximum around 4.5 min and then decreased. Especially for the modified ultrathin film cast from the 5:18 ratio casting solution, the pore surface area decreased to almost zero 15 min into the evaporation period.

In an early stage of evaporation, micelles of the swelling agent began to separate from the casting solution. This was caused by condensation of water vapor from the air on the membrane surface because the glass plate had been immersed in the casting solution at 1–2°C. Thus, the micelles might be much smaller and dispersed. Hence, when the mean pore radii are smaller, the micelles might coalesce to become larger, and the number of micelles might be reduced, because of the depletion of evaporated acetone. The mean pore radii then increased until 8 min as shown in Table III. Thereafter, the radii again decreased. This phenomenon of the changes of the mean pore radius explains the existence of a minimum on the curve of the reverse osmosis separation, and a maximum on the water flux in Figure 6.

Heat Treatment Effects

Figure 7 shows the relationship between reverse osmosis characteristics and temperature of thermal treatment for batches K-2, K-3, and K-4. When the temperature of thermal treatment is increased, salt separation is improved and water flux decreases for every batch. This is always observed on a typical asymmetric reverse osmosis membrane of cellulose acetate. The improvement

TABLE IV

Effects of Heat Treatment on Surface Area of Pores and Averaged Pore Diameter[a]

Batch no.	Temperature of heat treatment, °C	Surface area of pores based on B.E.T. equation m²/g	Averaged pore diameter, Å	Percent cross-sectional area of pores, %
K-2	—	13.9	41.51	4.68
	90	27.3	36.58	5.89
K-3	—	16.4	43.05	2.88
	70	22.7	34.69	2.99
	90	40.3	35.23	4.90
K-4	—	19.3	48.38	6.72
	90	31.0	41.58	5.74
K-5	—	58.8	48.44	8.68
	70	76.3	36.74	9.54
	90	96.7	28.44	10.49

[a] Evaporation period 4.5 min.

is significant in batch K-4, not very significant in batch K-2, and fairly significant in batch K-3.

Heat treatment above 70°C makes the modified ultrathin membranes of batches K-2 to K-5 adsorb more nitrogen or have smaller pores and more pore surface area, as shown in Table IV. This phenomenon may reasonably explain the tendency of reverse osmosis separation and flux shown in Figure 7. As stated by Sarbolonski,[10] cellulose acetate segments seem to move easily above 65°C, and to rearrange their position, resulting in the formation of smaller pores and increasing their numbers due to increasing surface area and decreasing average

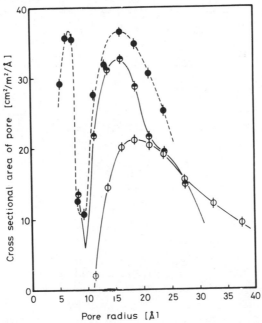

Fig. 8. Effects of heat treatment on pore size distribution for batches K-5. Symbols same as in Fig. 3.

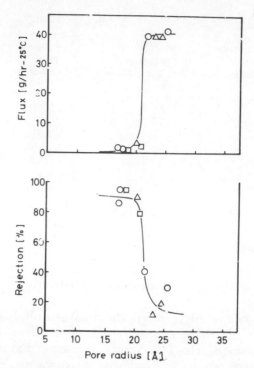

Fig. 9. Effects of pore size on reverse osmosis characteristics of modified ultrathin membranes. Symbols same as in Fig. 2.

pore diameter. Note in particular that the shape of the pore size distribution for the ultrathin membrane cast from the 5:18 casting solution shifts from a single peak in the case of no heat treatment to a twin peak by the heat treatment, as shown in Figure 8. The average pore radii corresponding to the twin peaks are 8 and 15.2 Å at 70°C, and 7 and 15.5 Å at about 90°C. The number of pores assigned to the smaller pore radius is larger at 90°C than at 70°C.

These phenomena might be reasonably explained as follows. The as-cast ultrathin membrane from the 5:18 casting solution has a broader pore size distribution and a larger average pore radius. Application of thermal treatment makes cellulose acetate segments rearrange themselves, but the larger pores might remain because the intersegmental forces are not sufficient. Then, the rather small and medium pores shift to the smaller pores and the larger pores remain unchanged, so smaller pore groups and larger pore groups appear. The pore size distribution has two peaks; and as the temperature increases, the smaller peak becomes smaller and the larger one increases.

Manjikian and Foley[11] observed an increase of iodine absorption by the cellulose acetate butyrate membrane with increasing thermal treatment temperature. They showed that heat treatment resulted in an expansion of membrane pores through shrinkage of surrounding membrane material away from the pore area and that this increase in pore size was reflected in the degree of iodine adsorption.

It may be concluded from the increase in amount of nitrogen adsorption at −195°C and the decrease of the pore size with increasing thermal treatment temperature, as shown in Table IV, that thermal treatment may result in an increase in the number of small pores through shrinkage of the membrane matrix.

Reverse Osmosis Characteristics and Average Pore Radius

A relationship between reverse osmosis characteristics of a modified ultrathin membrane and its average pore radius is shown in Figure 9. The water flux and the salt separation change abruptly at an average pore radius of 20–22 Å. Any method (longer evaporation period, heat treatment, or reduction of swelling agent) which lets the average pore radius shrink below 20–22 Å improves the reverse osmosis characteristics of the modified ultrathin membrane. This critical pore radius is identical to that reported by Ballow[12] on porous glass reverse osmosis membranes and that by Sourirajan and Agrawal[13] on freeze-dried cellulose acetate membranes.

CONCLUSIONS

The results presented in this paper show that the presence of 10% aqueous magnesium perchlorate in the casting solution leads to a porous structure in the resulting membrane and that heat treatment causes larger pores to be split into several smaller pores.

It is observed that membrane permeability and salt separation change abruptly when the average pore radius is reduced to less than 20–22 Å originally or by subsequent heat treatment.

The authors are grateful to the Ministry of Education of Japan for Grant-in-Aid 011003.

References

1. R. L. Riley, J. O. Gardner, and U. Merten, *Science,* **143,** 801 (1964).
2. R. L. Riley, J. O. Gardner, and U. Merten, *Desalination,* **1,** 30 (1966).
3. R. Nakane, S. Suzuki, and S. Ishizaka, 20th Annual Meeting of the Society of Sea Water Science of Japan, Tokyo, 1969.
4. R. Schultz and S. Asunmaa, *Rec. Progr. Surface Sci.,* **3,** 291 (1970).
5. R. L. Riley, M. K. Lonsdale, C. R. Lyons, and U. Merten, *J. Appl. Polym. Sci.,* **11,** 2143 (1967).
6. P. H. Carnell and H. G. Cassidy, *J. Polym. Sci.,* **55,** 233 (1961).
7. P. H. Carnell, *J. Appl. Polym. Sci.,* **9,** 1863 (1965).
8. H. Ohya, Y. Imura, T. Moriyama, and M. Kitaoka, *J. Appl. Polym. Sci.,* **18,** 1855 (1974).
9. R. W. Cranston and F. A. Inkley, *Adv. Catal.,* **9,** 143 (1957).
10. M. N. Sarbolonski and L. F. Miller, *Desalination,* **12,** 343 (1973).
11. S. Manjikian and M. I. Foley, O.S.W. R & D. P. Report No. 654, 1971.
12. E. V. Ballou and T. Wydever, *J. Colloid Interface Sci.,* **41,** 198 (1972).
13. J. P. Agrawal and S. Sourirajan, *J. Appl. Polym. Sci.,* **14,** 1303 (1970).

Received June 1, 1976
Revised July 6, 1976

JOURNAL OF APPLIED POLYMER SCIENCE   VOL. 21, 2529-2550 (1977)

Localized Radiation Grafting of Flame Retardants to Poly(ethylene Terephthalate). I. Bromine-Containing Monomers

R. LIEPINS, J. R. SURLES, N. MOROSOFF, and V. T. STANNETT,*

Polymer Research Laboratory, Chemistry and Life Sciences Division, Research Triangle Institute, Research Triangle Park, North Carolina 27709

Synopsis

Vinyl bromide was used as a model for bromine-containing flame retardants in developing methodology for localizing flame retardants either on the surface of the filament, uniformly throughout it, or predominantly at the core. SEM–x-ray microprobe techniques were used in the verification of the location of the flame retardant in the filament. The flame retardance efficiency of PVBr was then correlated with its location in the filament. Grafting other bromine-containing flame retardants showed a wide range of efficiencies which depended not only upon the location of the graft within the filament but also upon the structure of the compound. For the various bromine homopolymer grafts, the apparent thermal stability of the graft and its flame retardance efficiency may be simply related to the alpha aliphatic hydrogen-to-bromine ratio. The lower this ratio is, the higher the efficiency. VBr copolymers and terpolymers showed wider variation in flame retardance efficiencies. This is attributed to large variations in melt viscosity of the different grafted materials. The grafts showed only small changes in their melting points and minimal changes in tenacity and stiffness. However, grafting induced large increases in the elongation.

INTRODUCTION

In an effort to obtain basic information which could be utilized in designing flame retardant systems for cotton/polyester blends, we chose model systems which should be applicable to a broad scope of blend compositions. Thus, the two basic flame-retarding elements—bromine and phosphorus—were represented by vinyl bromide (VBr) as the model for bromine-containing flame retardants and dimethyl and diethylvinyl phosphonates as the models for phosphorus-containing flame retardants. The work described here deals with grafting of the poly(vinyl bromide) (PVBr) compositions on poly(ethylene terephthalate) (PET) and the investigation of the effects of PVBr distribution within the grafted PET filament upon its flame retardance efficiency. Grafting of other bromine-containing flame retardants showed a wide range of efficiencies which depended not only upon the location of the graft within the filament but also upon the structure of the compound. The work conducted with the phosphorus-containing monomers will be described in part II of this series.

* Present address: North Carolina State University, Raleigh, North Carolina 27607.

HISTORICAL

The first attempt at grafting a flame-retarding monomer, vinyl chloride, to PET appears to be that of Armstrong, Walsh, and Rutherford.[1] The objective of that work was to explore the modifications of fiber properties that might be possible by radiation grafting. Vapor-phase gamma-radiation grafting techniques were used, and under those conditions the general findings were that it was not possible to graft vinyl chloride to PET (best add-on reported 0.1%). The use of various radiation sensitizers did not help much; the best sensitizer found was acetic anhydride, which led to an add-on of 0.4%.

The first explicit descriptions of flame retarding of polyesters by radiation grafting techniques come from patent literature.[2-5] In the Farbwerke and Hoechst patent of 1971,[2] the use of diallyl 2,3-dibromopropyl phosphate and allyl bis(2,3-dibromopropyl) phosphate was claimed. In the Hooker Chemical Corp. patent of 1972,[3] six phosphonate acrylamides of the general structure

$$
\begin{array}{cc}
O & O \\
\parallel & \uparrow \\
CH_2\!=\!CCNCH_2P(OR'')_2 \\
\mid\ \ \mid \\
R\ \ R'
\end{array}
$$

were claimed for flame-retarding cotton, cotton/polyester blends, and wool. In the Stauffer Chemical Co. patent of 1973,[4] a combination of two compounds of the following general structures is claimed:

$$
\begin{array}{cc}
O & O \\
\uparrow & \parallel \\
(CH_2\!=\!CHCH_2O)_2PCH_2CHCNH_2 \\
\mid \\
R
\end{array}
\quad \text{and} \quad
\begin{array}{c}
O \qquad O \\
\uparrow \qquad \parallel \\
[(CH_2\!=\!CHCH_2O)_2PCH_2CHCNH\,]_2CH_2 \\
\mid \\
R
\end{array}
$$

In the Hooker Chemical Corp. patent of 1974,[5] the use of a family of compounds of the general structure

$$
\begin{array}{cc}
O & O \\
\parallel & \uparrow \\
CH_2\!=\!CCOCHP(OR'')_2 \\
\mid\ \ \mid \\
R\ \ R'
\end{array}
$$

is claimed in the flame retarding of cellulosic, proteinaceous, and analogous man-made materials (polyester mentioned).

The only other openly described work that deals with radiation flame retarding of cotton/polyester blends appears to be that at North Carolina State University.[6] The monomers studied were Fyrol 76, Fyrol BB, bis(2,3-dibromopropyl) phosphate ester of hydroxyethyl methacrylate, and N-methylolacrylamide.

BACKGROUND

Swelling Agents

It was discovered in the early 1960's that grafting to cotton took place only when the cotton was sufficiently swollen to allow the monomer to diffuse to the radical sites in the fiber. Thus, for example, effective grafting of styrene to cotton was very much dependent upon the water content in the system.[7] Subsequent studies with many different polymer–monomer grafting systems demonstrated the great importance of the swelling in radiation grafting. Diffusion in radiation grafting processes plays a dual role: (1) it controls the chain growth via diffusion of monomer to the growing chain end, and (2) it controls termination via diffusion (combination) of two polymeric species. This can lead, for example, to the well-known gel effect. Another consequence of diffusion control is that the grafting often tends to be concentrated in the surface regions, particularly in poorly swollen systems or in systems with high dose rates. Because one of the objectives of this work was the study of the effect of changing the location of the grafted flame retardant on properties, the swelling behavior of PET in different solvents was thus a very important factor.

Amorphous PET develops crystallinity after immersion in a number of different organic liquids at 25°C.[8-11] Although interaction of organic liquids with, and their diffusion into, amorphous PET have not been related quantitatively to the rate or final degree of crystallization induced in the polymer, it has been shown that liquids having a solubility parameter (δ) near the estimated δ of amorphous PET (10.7) induce appreciable crystallinity in the polymer. The use of total solubility parameter may not provide a sufficiently precise characterization of a solvent's capability to interact with PET. The work of Moore and Sheldon[8] showed that induced crystallization in unoriented amorphous PET and maxima of density changes were observed in solvents with total δ around 9.5 and 12.0. More recent work on longitudinal shrinkage and swelling volume of PET fibers evaluated in terms of the δ concept together with iodine displacement studies indicated that PET may be treated as an $(AB)_x$ alternating copolymer.[11] The A may be $-CO-\langle\bigcirc\rangle-$ with a δ value of 9.8, and B may be $-OCH_2CH_2OCO-$ with a δ value of 12.1. Thus, preferential interaction of a solvent with either of these two PET segments was demonstrated.

For our studies of a special case of the effect of swelling agents on the grafting rates, we selected solvents with a narrower range of solubility parameters, namely, 10.6 to 10.8. We wanted to use reasonably good swelling agents, but not so good (either δ 9.5 or 12.1) that they would also induce maximum crystallinity and density changes in PET which would result in reduced monomer diffusion to the active sites and, hence, decreased grafting yield. The ease of grafting, in general, is a function of the degree of crystallinity.[12,13,14]

Radiation Sensitivity of PET

Polyesters in general are very stable toward radiation and show little tendency to undergo grafting. Free radicals form by γ-irradiation of PET with a $G(R\cdot)$ value of only 0.02.[15] This compares to polystyrene with $G(R\cdot)$ 0.7 and cellulose with $G(R\cdot)$ 1 to 6. It is not entirely clear why PET should form, by more than an order of magnitude, fewer free radicals than polystyrene does. Two types of free radicals were apparently generated: one was identified by ESR as

$$-CO-\langle\bigcirc\rangle-COO\dot{C}HCH_2-;$$

TABLE I
Radiation Sensitizers Used in Grafting Acrylic Acid onto PET[16-19]

Radiation sensitizer	Add-on, %
None	2.8
Methylene chloride	36.4
Chloroform	32.3
Carbon tetrachloride	3.2
Ethylidene dichloride	33.1
Ethylene dichloride	34.1
1,1,1-Trichloroethane	4.1
1,1,2-Trichloroethane	41.8
1,1,1,2-Tetrachloroethane	20.8
1,1,2,2-Tetrachloroethane	33.8
Pentachloro ethane	29.3
cis-1,2-Dichloroethylene	31.3
trans-1,2-Dichloroethylene	32.0
Trichloroethylene	29.3
1,1,2,2-Tetrachloroethylene	38.5
n-Propyl chloride	19.4
Isopropyl chloride	33.1
n-Butyl chloride	32.2
Monochlorobenzene	41.4
o-Dichlorobenzene	37.8
Benzyl alcohol	2.0
Dimethylformamide	1.1
Dimethyl sulfoxide	0.7
Nitrobenzene	1.2
Formic acid	4.3

the other, a minor component (5–10%), was tentatively assigned the structure of

$$-CO-\bigcirc-CO-$$

The use of radiation sensitizers in the grafting of PET was extensively investigated by Okada and co-workers.[16-19] A list of the various sensitizers that they investigated is given in Table I. They found that the best sensitizers were halogenated hydrocarbons which also acted as swelling agents and increased not only the per cent graft but also the grafting efficiency and grafting rate. Presumably, this action was due to radiation-induced decomposition of the halogenated hydrocarbons into active free radicals which then participated in the chain reactions. In addition to the sensitizers listed in Table I, we found vinyl bromide and vinylidene chloride, but not vinylidene bromide, to be excellent radiation sensitizers.

Localized Grafting

The radiation process can be varied in such a way as to change the location of the grafted polymer. Diffusion of the monomer to the active sites and dose rate are the two important variables used to achieve localized grafting. Since the monomer must diffuse into the fiber from the outside, the diffusion control also leads to control of the location of the graft. Preswelling of the fiber not only

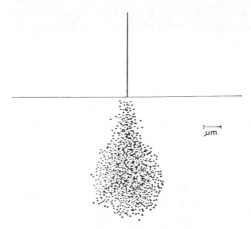

Fig. 1. Locus of scattered electrons.

increases the rate of diffusion of the monomer into the fiber but may also result in a higher initial monomer concentration in the fiber. By judicious control of the swelling conditions, the time of contact with the monomer, and the dose rate, it becomes possible to locate the graft at various depths in the fiber. In the work reported here, we have been able to concentrate the grafting of the flame retardants in three locations: surface only, uniformly throughout the fiber, and predominantly in the core of the fiber. The effect of the location of a flame retardant upon its flame retardance efficiency was then correlated.

Scanning Electron Microscopy and X-Ray Microprobe Analysis

To investigate the distribution of the grafted polymers across the section of a 13.5-μm PET filament by means of the intensity of characteristic peaks in the x-ray spectrum, a resolution of the order of about 1 μm is required. Since the intensity of characteristic x-rays given off by an element is affected by take-off angle (the angle between specimen surface and x-ray detector), it is required that the surface of a cross section be uniformly smooth if valid conclusions are to be drawn. In addition, the resolution of the scanning electron microscope, when emitted x-rays are used for imaging, is considerably worse than when secondary electrons are used. All x-rays excited by the electron beam, as it impinges on a bulk sample and is then scattered below the surface, can be equally effective in contributing to the image. The resolution is, therefore, determined by the locus of scattered electrons originating at the point of electron beam impingement on the surface. This locus turns out to be "pear shaped" with the narrow end at the surface and has a continuously increasing radius until the energy of scattered electrons becomes smaller than the excitation energy for characteristic x-rays from a given element (see Fig. 1). The maximum diameters of such pear-shaped scattering volumes may vary from about 4 to 16 μm depending on impinging electron energy, density of the matrix, and the element being imaged.[20,21] The scattering volume may have a depth of 10 μm or more. The resolution of x-rays can be increased by using 1- to 2-μm sections such that only the top of the pear-shaped volume can contribute to the image. For these two reasons—the need for a smooth surface and sections of fibers that are only 1–2

μm in thickness—the work described here was done on sections cut on an ultramicrotome from embedded fibers.

EXPERIMENTAL

Materials

Substrate Grafted. American Enka Co. polyester fiber; 150/96 S.D. polyester filament yarn; 0.35% TiO_2; ~0.2% water soluble finish. Information on the original draw ratio and crystallinity of the yarn was not available to us.

Bromine Compounds Grafted. Vinylbromide (VBr); vinylidene bromide (VBr$_2$); 2,3-dibromopropyl acrylate (DBPA); 2,3-dibromopropyl methacrylate (DBPM); 2,4,6-tribromophenyl methacrylate (TBPM); 2,4,6-tribromophenyl acrylate (TBPA); tribromoneopentyl acrylate (TNPA); 2,2,2-tribromoethyl acrylate (TBEA); 2-(2,4,6-tribromophenoxy)ethyl acrylate (TBPOEA); bisacrylate of 2-hydroxyethyl ether of tetrabromobisphenol A (BABA-50). VBr and VBr$_2$ were supplied courtesy of Ethyl Corporation; DBPA, DBPM, BABA-50, and TBPOEA were courtesy of Great Lakes Chemical Corp.; TBPM and TBPA were courtesy of Hooker Chemical Corp., and TNPA and TBEA were purchased from Polysciences, Inc., and used as received.

Techniques

Grafting Technique. Gamma Radiation. A series of initial investigations showed no discernible differences in the per cent weight gain obtained with scoured and unscoured yarns; thus, all subsequent work was carried out on unscoured samples. The samples were degassed by means of three freeze–thaw cycles to at least 10^{-5} torr. In most cases, the grafting (Co-60 source) was performed using a mutual irradiation technique in a small glass ampule at dose rates of from 0.01 to 0.1 Mrad/hr. Following irradiation, the fiber samples were extracted with solvent for the homopolymers or copolymers, first at room temperature and then at elevated temperature. The extracted fibers were vacuum dried at constant weight and stored in a desiccator for subsequent evaluation. The data for weight gain achieved during grafting was obtained following this drying procedure.

FR Localization Techniques. Surface coating. Approximately 10% solution of the compound in THF was used. After immersing the fibers in the solution, they were dried in a vacuum oven at 50°C/16 hr. **Uniform grafting.** The fibers were preswollen in ethylene dichloride at 70°C/½ hr, then placed in the flame retardant solution for about 2 hr, and then irradiated. **Surface grafting.** Fibers were placed in the flame retardant solution and immediately irradiated. **Core VBr grafting.** Fibers were preswollen in ethylene dichloride at 70°C/½ hr, then placed in vinyl bromide for about 2 hr. The excess VBr was decanted and the swollen fiber frozen to −78°C. Next, the tube was opened to the atmosphere and then placed in the γ-radiation source.

Oxygen Index. Since the samples in the initial phase of this work were in the form of individual yarns or fibers, it was necessary to develop a modified technique for measuring the oxygen index (OI) of these materials. The development of the sample holder and the procedure for measuring the OI have been

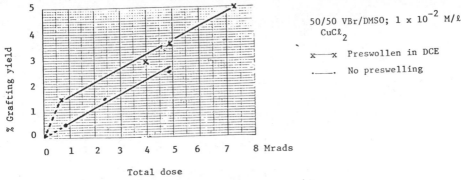

Fig. 2. Percent grafting yield vs total dose.

described.[22] The procedure permitted not only the determination of the *OI* values, but also an estimation of the char yield as the material burned in the tester. This procedure was also applied to the evaluation of the various grafted fabric samples.

Scanning Electron Microscopy and X-Ray Microprobe Analysis. Thin cross sections of the grafted PET fibers were prepared by embedding in an epoxy or poly(methyl methacrylate) resin and sectioning with a Reichert "Omu2" ultramicrotome using a glass knife. The epoxy yielded the better sections. The sections were floated off onto water during the sectioning and then transferred to a drop of water on a carbon stub using an eyelash. The water droplet on the stub was then evaporated and the section examined in the scanning electron microscope. No coating was required.

Differential Scanning Calorimetry. The DSC instrument used in this work was a Perkin-Elmer Model DSC-1. The instrument allows one to record a specific heat-versus-temperature curve in a relatively short time and convenient manner. The melting was taken as the temperature at which the specific heat-versus-temperature curve goes through the maximum of the melting peak. Typically, 5 to 10 mg of cut fiber sample was sealed in an aluminum cup, and an empty aluminum cup was used in the other sample holder. The instrument was operated at 10°C/min heating rate.

Thermogravimetric Analysis. Typically, 10-mg samples were used in a quartz pan provided with the instrument. The analyses were conducted in a nitrogen atmosphere (26 ml/min) at a programmed heating rate of 5°C/min.

RESULTS AND DISCUSSION

Polyester fiber

Vinyl Bromide Grafts

Effect of Dose. When VBr is grafted from a dimethyl sulfoxide solution at room temperature, the percent graft increases linearly with dose (time) and without any induction period (see Fig. 2). Preswelling the fibers in ethylene dichloride at 70°C/½ hr produced a parallel dependence of weight gain on total dose, but displaced 1% higher on the weight gain axis.

Effect of Dimethyl Sulfoxide (DMSO) Concentration. The effect of the concentration of DMSO (as well as that of hexamethylphosphoramide, HMPA)

TABLE II
Effect of Temperature on Grafting of VBr

Grafting temp., °C	Total dose, Mrads	Grafting yield, %
−194	2.7	2.0
−64	2.1	8.2
−44	2.5	9.9
~24 (R.T.)	2.3	9.1
+81	2.4	17.7

TABLE III
Effect of Swelling Agent on Grafting Yield

Swelling agent	δ	Grafting yield, %
—	—	9.1
Morpholine	10.8	3.6
Dimethylacetamide	10.8	4.3
Propionitrile	10.7	5.1
Dimethyl phthalate	10.7	5.8
Dimethylformamide	10.6	4.7
n-Butanol	10.6	9.1

TABLE IV
Radiation Sensitizers/Swelling Agents Studied

	Boiling point, °C	δ
Methylene chloride	40	9.7
Chloroform	61	9.3
Carbon tetrachloride	77	8.5
Ethylene dichloride	84	9.8
1,1,1-Trichloroethane	71	8.8
1,1,2,2-Tetrachloroethane	130	9.7
Chlorobenzene	132	9.5
Bromobenzene	152	9.9
Bromonaphthalene	281	10.6
Methylene bromide	97	12.4
p-Chlorotoluene	162	8.8
n-Butyl chloride	68	8.1

on the grafting of neat vinyl bromide was similar to that on the grafting of styrene on polyester.[12,13] The addition of a small amount of DMSO (or HMPA) increased the grafting yield considerably, followed by a gradual decrease with increasing concentration. Typical grafting yields (%) at room temperature for the following DMSO concentrations (moles/l.) (total dose 4.80 Mrads) were as follows: 0.5 mole/l., 9%; 1.0 mole/l., 11%; 2.0 moles/l., 8%; 4.0 moles/l., 5%; 8.1 moles/l., 2.5%.

TABLE V
Effect of Radiation Sensitizers

Radiation sensitizer	Total dose Mrads	Grafting yield, %
Methylene bromide	2.3	19.1
Bromobenzene	4.7	14.0
1,1,2,2-Tetrachloroethane	2.2	13.0

Effect of Monomer Structure on OI

Graft type	Grafting yield, %	OI	Bromine, %
TBPM	13.5	32.5	8.1
VBr$_2$	9.4	28.6	8.1
VBr	10.8	24.7	8.1

Effect of Temperature. The effect of temperature on the grafting of VBr (neat, no preswelling of the fiber) is illustrated in Table II. It can be seen that, within the temperature range explored, there is a maximum in the grafting yield at +81°C. The maximum reached in the vicinity of the glass transition temperature of PET is understandable, as it has been observed before.[12,13] Conceivably, a still higher yield may be achievable above the glass transition temperature.

Effect of Swelling Agents. A series of experiments were conducted using different swelling agents to explore their effect upon grafting yield. The swelling agents used, their δ values, and grafting yield at room temperature, at total dose of 2.3 Mrads, are illustrated in Table III. The swelling agents were used in approximately 1:100 (by weight) ratio of fiber to swelling agent. None of these swelling agents improved grafting yield above that of grafting VBr neat. We believe the decreased grafting yield with these swelling agents is due to their efficient induction of crystallinity and density changes in the amorphous regions of PET. There is at least one correlation that has been observed before, and that is pertinent here. It was found that dimethyl phthalate induced in amorphous PET an equilibrium crystallinity of 41.7%, while n-butanol induced one of only 4.2%.[8] Our grafting yields in these two solvents agree at least qualitatively with the induced crystallinity-decreased grafting yield hypothesis.

Effect of Radiation Sensitizers/Swelling Agents. A list of the various halogenated organic solvents that we investigated as radiation sensitizers/swelling agents is given in Table IV. In general, the effect of the best radiation sensitizers was that of increasing the grafting yield of PVBr. Some typical data are illustrated in Table V. The radiation sensitizers were used in approximately 1:100 (by weight) ratio of fiber to radiation sensitizer during the preswelling step. Subsequently, the excess radiation sensitizer was decanted off. However, the effect of these compounds on VBr grafting is not very pronounced because VBr itself is a radiolytically labile molecule and therefore acts as a self-sensitizer. The effect of these compounds is much more remarkable when used in formulations with monomers that are difficult to graft (e.g., certain vinyl phosphonates).

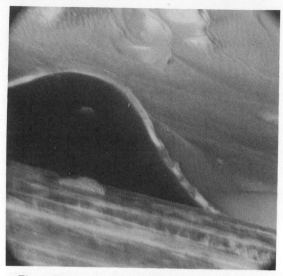

Fig. 3. Thickness of sectioned embedding medium.

Scanning Electron Microscopy and X-Ray Microprobe Analysis. The distribution of VBr grafts across the PET fiber cross section was determined in a semiquantitative fashion using an x-ray microprobe attachment to the scanning electron microscope. In Figures 5–15 are depicted the bromine distributions in the fiber cross section. Figure 3 shows the thickness (1 μm) of the embedding medium after sectioning and the fiber cross sections are seen in the top of the photograph. In some of the sections, part of some fiber would break loose from the embedding medium revealing the thickness of the fiber cross section. This is depicted in Figure 4, where the fiber cross section is shown to be 1 μm. Figure 5 is a secondary electron image of a cross section of PVBr-coated filament. The thickness of the coating is seen to be 1–2 μm. Figure 6 depicts the energy spectrum for x-rays emitted from the cross section shown in Figure 5. The L_α bro-

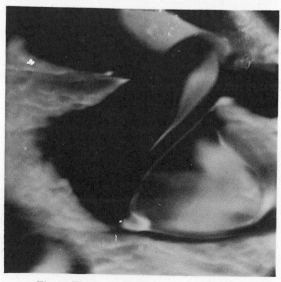

Fig. 4. Thickness of fiber cross section.

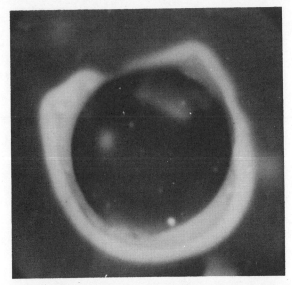

Fig. 5. Secondary electron image of a PVBr-coated filament.

mine emission line was used for mapping the bromine distribution in the cross section. Figure 7 shows the parts in the cross section from which the x rays were emitted and, hence, the location of the bromine atoms. In order to ascertain that such a map actually indicated the site of bromine atoms and not an especially favorable topography at the boundaries of the fiber for emission of all x rays, a map was obtained with a "window" corresponding to background. Such a map is depicted in Figure 8 and is featureless. The above-described procedure was routinely followed on all subsequent samples analyzed. For the purposes of this paper, we will present only the photographs of secondary electron images and the corresponding element distribution maps.

Figures 9 and 10 show the secondary electron image and the bromine L_α map for uniformly VBr-grafted samples. Figures 11 and 12 clearly show that the PVBr graft is localized at the surface of the filament. Figure 13 is the secondary electron image of a core-grafted sample. The percent grafting yield in this case

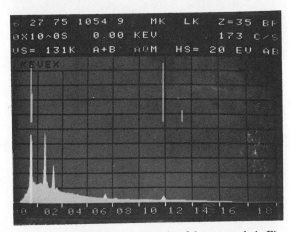

Fig. 6. Energy spectrum for x rays emitted from sample in Figure 5.

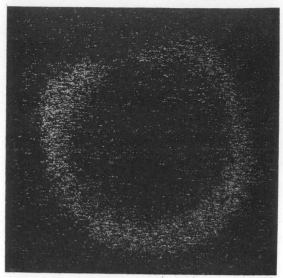

Fig. 7. Bromine distribution from sample in Figure 5.

was only 1.2%. Figure 14 dipicts the energy spectrum for x rays emitted from the cross section. Because of the low bromine concentration, mapping would require extremely long times to obtain reasonable photographs. Thus, to obtain the distribution of bromine across the fiber cross section, x-ray counts were obtained from 1-μm^2 areas at the center of the fiber and from four points 1 μm from the edge of the filament. Both L_α and K_α peaks were used and corrected for background, and the total counts under these peaks were recorded. In order to correct for possible variations in incident beam intensity, these counts were corrected for variations in the total count from 0 to 20 kV, consisting mostly of Bremsstrahlung. The results are depicted schematically in Figure 15. Four locations 1 μm from the edge of the filament yielded 73 to 85% of the bromine

Fig. 8. Background from sample in Figure 5.

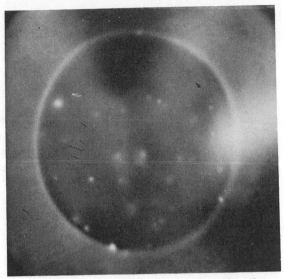

Fig. 9. Secondary image of uniformly PVBr-grafted polyester.

count at the center of the filament. Presumably, the closer the site of x-ray emission to the edge of the fiber, the lower the count would be relative to that at the center.

OI versus **PVBr Location.** *OI* -versus-PVBr location data are summarized in Figure 16. Although the per cent add-on varied greatly, the correlation seems clear. The placement of the PVBr in the interior of the fiber enhanced its flame retardance efficiency the most, followed by uniform grafting and then surface grafting. Thus, these results indicate that better flame retardance results might be obtained if penetration of the PET filament is achieved. The less thermally stable a flame retardant is (e.g., PVBr), the more efficient it becomes and the more it is incorporated in the core of the filament. Thus, in general, it would

Fig. 10. Bromine distribution from sample in Figure 9.

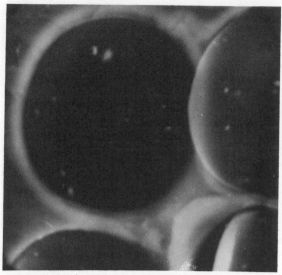

Fig. 11. Secondary electron image of surface PVBr-grafted polyester.

seem that factors which will delay the volatilization of the bromine from the flame front will increase its efficiency.

OI **versus PVBr Grafting Yield.** Data on uniformly grafted PVBr grafting yield versus *OI* is depicted in Figure 17. The initial rapid increase in *OI* with percent grafting yield starts to slow down after about 10% PVBr content. The results would seem to indicate that the maximum *OI* achievable with PVBr on PET is in the vicinity of 27. The last two points on the graph for 20.3 and 24.4% grafting yields represent PVBr grafts that also contain sulfur—0.5 and 1.8%, respectively. The sulfur must have come from the SO_2 pretreatment of the fibers for these two grafts and is probably incorporated as a SO_2–VBr copolymer. Thus, these two points are left outside the general trend of the data. However,

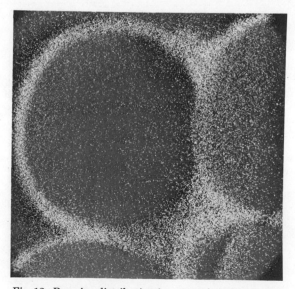

Fig. 12. Bromine distribution from sample in Figure 11.

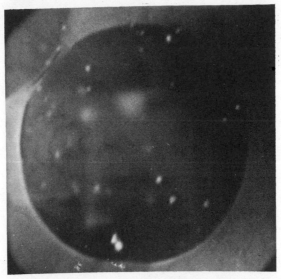

Fig. 13. Secondary electron image of core PVBr-grafted polyester.

they do perhaps indicate that incorporation of sulfur in this type of a graft leads to increased *OI* beyond that achievable by bromine.

Other Bromine-Containing Monomer Grafts

A variety of other bromine-containing monomers have been studied, both by themselves and in various combinations. In general, the acrylates grafted the easiest, and usually their rate of grafting had to be moderated. Next in the ease of grafting were the methacrylates, followed by vinyl bromide and then vinylidene bromide, which was the most difficult to graft. The bisacrylate of 2-hydroxyethyl ether of tetrabromobisphenol A was found to be a very efficient crosslinking agent in our grafting formulations. The *OI* data obtained with the uniformly grafted homopolymers showed a wide range of efficiencies; examples are shown in Table V.

From data of this type, it soon became obvious that the efficiencies of the

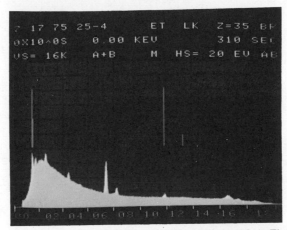

Fig. 14. Energy spectrum for x rays emitted from sample in Figure 13.

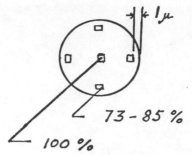

Fig. 15. X-ray count for sample in Figure 13.

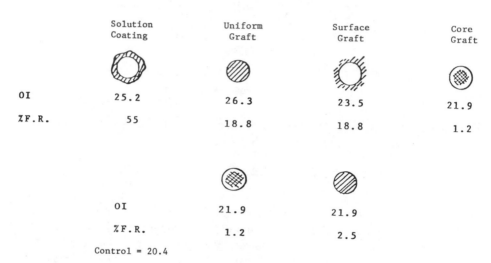

	Solution Coating	Uniform Graft	Surface Graft	Core Graft
OI	25.2	26.3	23.5	21.9
%F.R.	55	18.8	18.8	1.2

OI	21.9	21.9	
%F.R.	1.2	2.5	

Control = 20.4

Fig. 16. *OI* vs PVBr location.

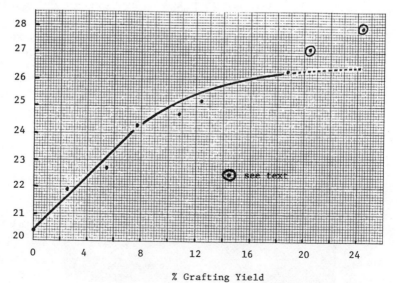

% Grafting Yield

Fig. 17. *OI* vs PVBr percent grafting yield.

TABLE VI
Alpha Aliphatic Hydrogen-to-Bromine Ratio Versus Thermal Stability Versus FR Efficiency

Compound	H/Br	Dec. pt., °C	$\Delta OI/1\%$ Br
(tribromophenyl ester)	0	303	1.5
(tribromophenoxyethyl ester)	0	—	1.2
(tris(bromomethyl) ester)	0	300	—
(dibromoneopentyl type)	2/3	220	1.1
$-CH_2-C(Br)_2-$	1	204	1.0
$-CH_2-CH(Br)-$	2	150	0.5
$-CH_2-CH(Br)-CH_2(Br)-$	2.5	132	(0.2)
$-CH_2-CH(Br)-CH(Br)-CH_2-$	3	127	—
$-CH_2-C(CH_3)(Br)-CH(Br)-CH_2-$	4	122	—

various flame retardants varied quite widely depending upon the structures of the compounds in addition to the location of the graft within the filament. A further correlation between the flame retardance efficiency and the structure of a compound and its thermal stability was noticed once a detailed analysis of the TGA data of the various grafted samples was undertaken. A summary of these data is given in Table VI. In the case of various bromine homopolymer grafts, the apparent thermal stability of the graft and its flame retardance efficiency may be simply related to the alpha aliphatic hydrogen-to-bromine ratio. The lower this ratio is, the higher the efficiency. The most efficient flame retardants appear to be those with no alpha aliphatic hydrogens to bromine. Note the large drop in thermal stability of the graft as soon as alpha aliphatic hydrogens are introduced: neopentyl acrylate versus tribromoethyl acrylate. The

TABLE VII

OI of VBr Copolymers

Copolymer	Grafting yield, %	*OI*
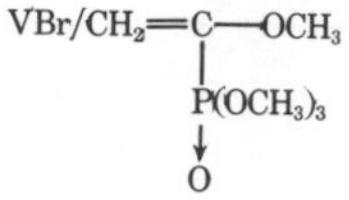 VBr/CH$_2$=C—OCH$_3$ P(OCH$_3$)$_3$ ↓ O (1:1)	3.9	>30.1
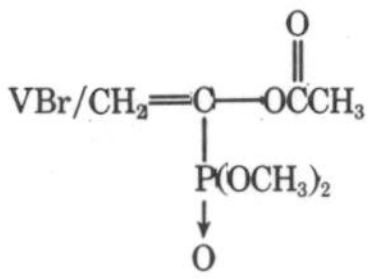 VBr/CH$_2$=C—OCCH$_3$ (O) P(OCH$_3$)$_2$ ↓ O (4:1)	2.3	28.6
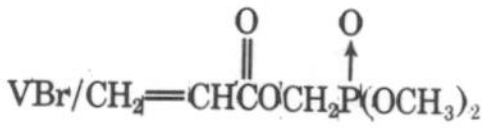 VBr/CH$_2$=CHCOCH$_2$P(OCH$_3$)$_2$ (O)(O) (7:3)	14.4	27.6
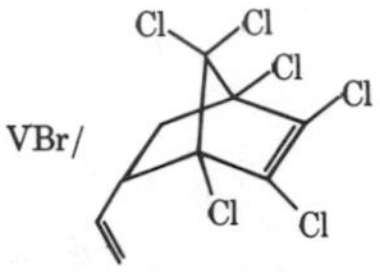 VBr/ (Cl, Cl, Cl, Cl, Cl, Cl bridged structure) (1:1)	1.8	33.5
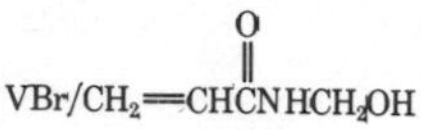 VBr/CH$_2$=CHCN HCH$_2$OH (O) (1:1)	62	22.7
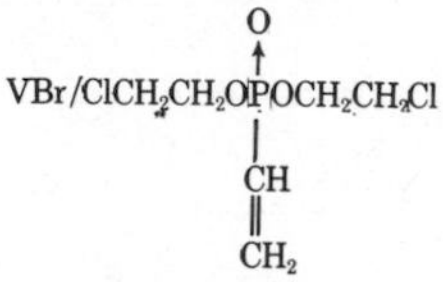 VBr/ClCH$_2$CH$_2$OPOCH$_2$CH$_2$Cl (O↑) CH CH$_2$ (1:1)	6.9	28.3
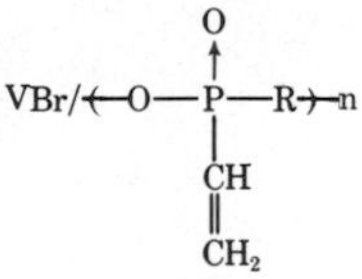 VBr/←O—P—R→n (O↑) CH CH$_2$ (2:1)	17.0	27.9

second large drop in thermal stability occurs as soon as more than one alpha hydrogen per bromine atom is introduced: vinylidene bromide versus vinyl bromide.

VBr Copolymers

Various VBr copolymers in various weight ratios have also been investigated. A set of copolymers, with the charged monomer weight ratios indicated, is given in Table VII. The flame retardance efficiencies of different copolymers range even more widely than those of the homopolymer grafts. When dealing with copolymer grafts, we believe that large variations in melt viscosity of the different grafted materials are predominantly responsible for the large variations in the apparent efficiencies. That this may be so can be easily seen in the large variations in the "viscosity" of the melt of the fiber in the *OI* determination. Grafts with high oxygen indices tend to have very low "viscosity" melts that easily run away from the flame front. This was most pronounced with the methoxyvinyl

TABLE VIII
OI of VBr Terpolymers

Terpolymer	Grafting yield, %	OI
VBr/VCl₂/CH₂=C—OCH₃ P(OCH₃)₂ ↓ O	4.2	>29.4
VBr/CH₂=C—OCCH₃ P(OCH₃)₂ ↓ O	2.8	30.6
VBr/VCl₂/CH₂=CHCOCH₂P(OCH₃)₂	25.9	27.6
VBr/ClCH₂CH₂OPOCH₂CH₂Cl/ ... (hexachlorocyclopentadiene adduct) CH=CH₂	13.8	32.8
VBr/ClCH₂CH₂OPOCH₂CH₂Cl/CH₂=CHCNHCH₂P(OCH₃)₂ CH=CH₂	3.1	25.5

and acetoxyvinyl phosphonate and the butadiene–hexachlorocyclopentadiene adduct copolymers, which therefore tended to have unusually high *OI* values.

VBr Terpolymers

A set of VBr terpolymers, all charged in a 1:1:1 weight ratio, is given in Table VIII. The same conclusions apply to these grafts as the copolymer grafts. Incorporation of vinylidene chloride did not seem to contribute to increased *OI*. In general, the terpolymer compositions that we looked at did not seem to have any advantages over the copolymer compositions.

TABLE IX
Tenacity and Elongation Versus Percent PVBr Grafting Yield

Grafting yield, %	Tenacity, g/den	Elongation at yield point, %
—	4.4	38
2.9	4.5	92
5.5	4.3	90
7.6	4.8	82
10.7	4.8	73
17.7	4.5	84
20.3	3.9	94
24.4	4.6	120

TABLE X
Tenacity and Elongation Versus Copolymer Graft

Copolymer		Grafting yield, %	Tenacity, g/den	Elongation at yield point, %
None		—	4.40	38
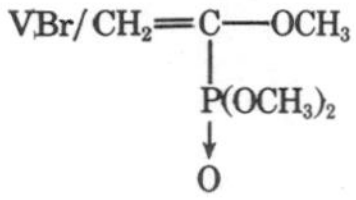	(1:1)	3.9	4.73	101
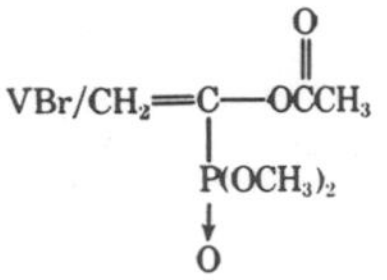	(4:1)	2.3	4.60	83
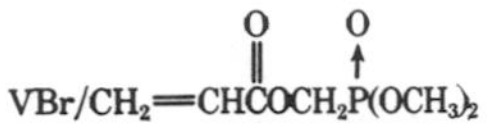	(7:3)	14.4	4.73	84
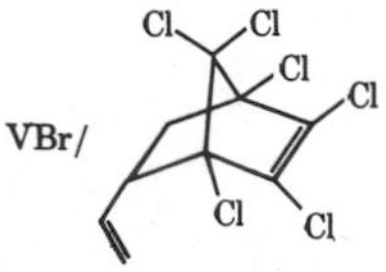	(1:1)	1.8	4.40	87
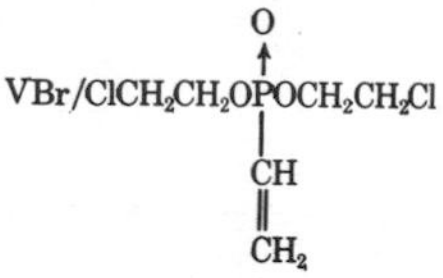	(1:1)	6.9	4.60	84
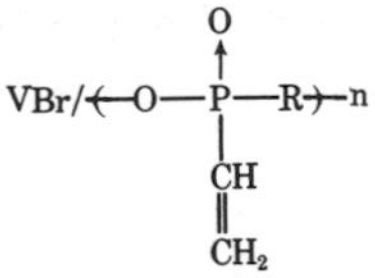	(2:1)	17.0	4.40	78

Properties

Melting Point versus Type of Graft

In general, the various grafts that we examined, regardless of the grafting yield (up to about 30%), showed only a small decrease or increase in the melting point. The one trend that was always noticed was that grafting VBr either as a homopolymer or as a copolymer always resulted in a decrease in the melting point.

Tenacity and Elongation versus Type of Graft

Selected data on tenacity and elongation versus percent grafting yield of PVBr are given in Table IX, and that versus type of copolymer grafts is given in Table X. From all of our work, two generalizations can be made: (1) grafting produced minimal changes in tenacity and stiffness, and (2) in practically all cases grafting induced large increases (up to 120% to yield point, and up to 150% total) in the elongation. These results would suggest that the main grafting occurred in the amorphous regions of the substrate, with only a few changes in the crystalline regions. In the case of PVBr grafts from 2.9% to about 20% grafting yield, the elongation varied from 73 to 94%. The 24.4% graft, which also contained 1.8% sulfur, had a jump in elongation at yield point to 120%, with a small increase in tenacity (4.60 g/den). In the case of different copolymer grafts, again the elongation at yield point varied between 78 and 101% and a small increase in tenacity in most cases. Considering the low grafting yields, the elongation values are remarkable in most cases.

These increases in elongation are difficult to explain, but have appeared consistently in all our grafting work. Presumably, the small decreases in crystallinity which inevitably must accompany grafting plus the "plasticization" of the noncrystalline regions cause the increased elongation. Further work is needed with regard to these unexpected results.

CONCLUSIONS

Vinyl bromide can be graft copolymerized either at the surface, uniformly throughout, or predominantly at the core of the polyester filament. The core location for the PVBr was the most efficient in its utilization, followed by uniform and then surface location. Grafting of other bromine-containing flame retardants showed that their flame retardance efficiencies depended not only upon the location of the graft within the filament but also upon the structure of the compound. For the various bromine homopolymer grafts, their apparent thermal stabilities and their flame retardance efficiencies could be related to the alpha aliphatic hydrogen-to-bromine ratio in the repeating unit of the graft. The lower this ratio was, the higher the thermal stability and the higher the efficiency. For VBr copolymer and terpolymer grafts, the apparent very large variations in flame retardance efficiencies were attributed to large variations in melt viscosity of the grafts.

The authors are indebted to Drs. Robert H. Barker, William Walsh, Derek Turner, and Eli M. Pearce for many stimulating discussions; and to Ms. G. Hess and Mr. J. Kearney for their assistance. This work was supported by the National Bureau of Standards, ETIP Contract No. 4-35963.

References

1. A. A. Armstrong, Jr., W. K. Walsh, and H. A. Rutherford, *Modification of Textile Fiber Properties by Radiation-Induced Graft Polymerization*, School of Textiles, North Carolina State University, Raleigh, N.C., USAEC Report NCSC-2477-11, Oct. 31, 1963.

2. W. Loeffler and M. Rieber (to Farbwerke Hoechst), Ger. Offen. 2,006,899 (Sept. 2, 1971); U.S. Pat. 3,708,328 (Jan. 2, 1973).

3. J. J. Duffy and P. Golborn (to Hooker Chemical Corp), Ger. Offen. 2,215,434 (Oct. 12, 1972).

4. E. D. Weil (to Stauffer Chemical Co.), U.S. Pat. 3,762,865 (Oct. 2, 1973).

5. P. Golborn (to Hooker Chemical Corp.), U.S. Pat. 3,817,779 (June 18, 1974).

6. Seminar on Radiation Processing of Textiles, School of Textiles, North Carolina State University, Raleigh, N.C., May 14–15, 1975.

7. R. E. Kesting and V. Stannett, *Makromol. Chem.*, **55**, 1 (1962).

8. W. R. Moore and R. P. Sheldon, *Polymer*, **2**, 315 (1961).

9. E. L. Lawton D. M. Cates, *J. Appl. Polym. Sci.*, **13**, 899 (1969).

10. A. S. Ribnick and H. D. Weigmann, *Text. Res. J.*, **43**, 316 (1973).

11. B. H. Knox, H. D. Weigmann, and M. G. Scott, *Text. Res. J.*, **45**, 203 (1975).

12. I. Vlagiu and V. Stannett, *J. Macromol. Sci.-Chem.,* **A7**(8), 1677 (1973).

13. I. Vlagiu and V. Stannett, *Rev. Roumaine Chim.,* **17**(1,2), 379 (1973).

14. F. Geleji and L. Odor, *J. Polym. Sci. C,* **4,** 1223 (1964).

15. D. Campbell, K. Araki, and D. T. Turner, *J. Polym. Sci. A-1,* **4,** 2597 (1966).

16. T. Okada, Y. Suzuki, K. Kohdera, and I. Sakurada, *JAERI* (Japanese Atomic Energy Research Institute Survey Reports and Reviews), **5018,** 5 (1968).

17. T. Okada, Y. Schimano, and I. Sakurada, *JAERI,* **5028,** 35 (1972).

18. Y. Shimano, T. Okada, and I. Sakurada, *JAERI,* **5028,** 43 (1972).

19. K. Kaji, T. Okada, and I. Sakurada, *JAERI,* **5028,** 52 (1972).

20. A. T. Marshall, in *Principles and Techniques of Scanning Electron Microscopy,* M. A. Hayat, Ed., Van Nostrand-Reinhold, New York, 1975.

21. J. C. Russ, *J. Submicrosc. Cytol.,* **6,** 55 (1974).

22. R. Liepins, *J. Fire Flammibility,* **6,** 326 (1975).

Received June 8, 1976
Revised July 7, 1976

JOURNAL OF APPLIED POLYMER SCIENCE   VOL. 21, 2551–2564 (1977)

The Ultimate Polymer Application: Resin-Bonded Cellulose Separators for Lead–Acid Batteries

JAMES R. DAFLER,* ESB Incorporated, Technology Center, Yardley, Pennsylvania 19067

Synopsis

Because it represents a polymer system routinely used in a highly corrosive environment, the resin-bonded cellulose separator is a paradigm of bad polymer application that succeeds. It succeeds because of the remarkable properties of cellulose itself, and through the formation of a highly modified structure that serves to protect both the resin and the cellulose in a reactive environment known to completely degrade both. X-ray diffraction analysis was used to determine the quality of retained cellulose in lead–acid battery separators made by impregnating thick cellulose matrixes with phenolic resins. The hydrolytic weight loss of separators stored in battery acid at 52°C was also measured and related to x-ray diffraction measurements of *intensive* degree of crystallinity *and* "qualitative perfection." The x-ray diffraction analyses and hydrolysis measurements are consistent with the formation of a copolymer between the cellulose and the impregnating resin. Treated and rewetted α-cellulose displays a capability for reorganization, indicated by increases in *intensive* crystallinity and qualitative perfection that are absent in the resin-bonded cellulose separator matrix. Rewetting of the separator matrix actually decreased the "qualitative perfection" of the cellulose present. X-ray diffraction measurements indicate that *extensive* crystallinity of acid-treated separators increases, due probably to the higher reactivity of the "so-called" amorphous fraction of the cellulose present. The degree of crystallinity, an intensive measure, does not change significantly during acid treatment, but the "qualitative perfection" of the cellulose decreases with time of hydrolysis and increases in acid strength.

INTRODUCTION

No polymer system in widespread use is required to perform well in as destructive an environment as the resin-bonded cellulose (RBC) battery separator. Cellulose is known to hydrolyze rapidly in mineral acids,[1-6] but the RBC separator must maintain its integrity in sulfuric acid media ranging from ~8% to ~40% (w/w), where it also encounters ranges in temperatures from −10°C to ~+70°C.

Despite these extremes, the RBC separator performs exceptionally well. In the most intense application, electric vehicle batteries with RBC separators frequently perform more than 250 full, 100% depth-of-discharge cycles. For automotive battery applications, where depth-of-discharge is shallow, such separators frequently cycle more than 5500 times (SAE J240a test schedule).

For separators, a good grade of α-cellulose is used to make a thick paper sheet, usually 0.50 to 0.75 mm thick. The paper is treated, while swelled, with waterborne thermosetting resin of phenolic type, then partially dried. After curing,

* Present address: Institute of Gas Technology, Chicago, Illinois 60616.

the phenolic resins provide binding for the cellulose fibers and very good resistance to nonoxidizing acids.[7] At the end of the cure (~205°C), the composite matrix is quite rigid and has a porosity of ~65–70%.

The thermal curing of the resin, however, may modify the cellulose somewhat. Ruznak and Tanczos[8] found a monotonic drop in degree of polymerization (D.P.) when cotton cellulose was thermally treated at 190°C. They also found a sharply defined rise is initial hydrolysis rate in dilute HCl as the cellulose was heated for increasing periods, indicating the formation of labile —OH groups.

In the battery industry, the stability and useful life of separators has long been a subject of study,[9,10] but only recently has the character of the matrix with respect to the effects of the acid medium been investigated. Campbell and Dafler measured stability of separators in dilute H_2SO_4 using a quantitative or *extensive* measure of retained crystalline material.[11] They compared separators stored for long periods in battery acids to raw material cellulose, using a normalized comparison technique. They showed that there was a rapid initial loss of crystalline material, after which the matrix appears very stable in battery-grade acids (H_2SO_4, 6–10N).

Ray and Bandyopadhay[12] pointed out that the index of crystallinity as defined by Hermans and Weidinger and Segal et al.[13,14] is insufficient to characterize cellulose in a hydrolytic medium, because the apparent degree of order may increase while part of the material is being irreversibly degraded.[15] They suggested that a measure of "qualitative perfection" was required to rationalize the two approaches. Viswanathan[16] used metallographic concepts to discuss fiber structures—particularly Ashmouni cotton—and we propose a measure used in the inorganic chemical industry to index the "qualitative perfection" of the retained cellulose in aged, hydrolyzed RBC separators.

In the acceptance of some inorganic oxides for use as battery-active materials or process raw materials, one of the material specifications (at ESB Inc.) is a maximum value for the ratio $I(hkl)/W(hkl)$, where $I(hkl)$ and $W(hkl)$ are the x-ray line intensity and width, respectively, of a specific x-ray diffraction line. For two samples of raw material of the same particle size distribution, that having the smallest value of the ratio is considered "to be preferred." In certain battery processes, small, average crystallite-size samples have proven most active due, undoubtedly, to a larger number of grain boundaries, dislocations, and similar heterogeneous reaction sites.

The value of $W(hkl)$ can be used in the Scherrer equation[17] to calculate an average crystallite size, and the ratio $I(hkl)/W(hkl)$ should be indicative of the distribution of crystallite sizes. The numerical determination of crystallite size distribution is a complex analytical procedure and was used by Warren and Averbach[18] to calculate the distribution of diffracting domains in strained alloys. Bienenstock[19] later generalized the procedure to calculate numerical distributions of crystallite sizes. In these methods, Fourier transform analysis is applied to the intrinsic broadening of the diffuse line. The distribution of diffracted x-ray power is seen to be proportional to the distribution of crystallite sizes. Buchanan and Miller[20] used these methods and other approximate methods to interpret the x-ray diffraction line broadening of isotactic polystyrene. The more primitive measure, $I(hkl)/W(hkl)$, is seen, therefore, as a rather simplified indicator of the distribution of crystallite sizes.

Morosoff[21] used the Scherrer equation to calculate what he called lower limits to the crystallite size of "never-dried cotton." He found significant differences

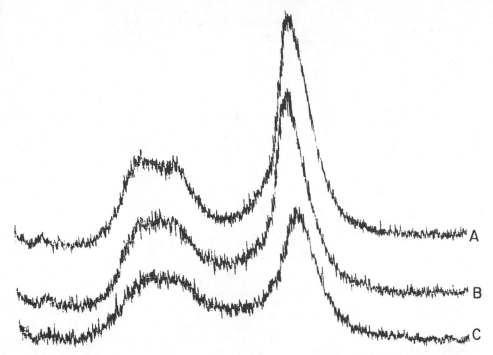

Fig. 1. X-ray diffraction profiles of α-cellulose and RCB separators: (a) α-cellulose stock before pulping; (b) RBC separator before use; (c) RBC separator after storage in 1.280 specific gravity H_2SO_4 at 52°C for 3960 hr.   This figure is reproduced from Campbell and Dafler[11] with the kind permission of The Electrochemical Society.

in line widths as function of the wetted history of the cotton fibers.   In our studies, however, we found few and slight variations in line width *but* large changes in profile shape, as seen in Figure 1.   The linewidths shown are in very close agreement, but intensities, indicative of the number of diffracting species of a given crystallite size, are quite different.   Using only linewidths would limit us to "qualitative perfection" parameters that did not change with increased hydrolysis of separators.   In the remainder of this discussion, we use the ratio $I(hkl)/W(hkl)$ as an index of "qualitative perfection," and call it CrA.   It is simple to measure experimentally and, being characteristic of the substance under study, it is not affected by variations in beam intensity or density of the sample.   For a given sample, one calculates the same CrA value for any beam power that yields an acceptable signal/noise ratio.   [If, for example, a fine nickel powder is diluted with another material, crystalline *or* amorphous, the resultant line, say, the Ni[111] line, is less intense than the line for the undiluted powder, but the ratio $I(111)/W(111)$ remains the same.]

In this study, CrA is defined as $I(002)/W(002)$, where $W(002)$ is the uncorrected line width.   The parameter has proven to correlate well with direct hydrolysis measurements.

CRYSTALLINITY

A characteristic index of crystallinity and quantitative ratio of crystallinity was measured for all acid-treated samples.   No great pains were taken to ensure random orientation of fiber, but care was taken that samples had experimentally

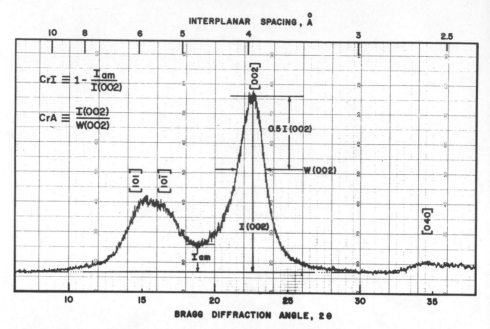

Fig. 2. Method of Segal et al.[14] for determining the *intensive* degree of crystallinity, *CrI*, and current method for determining the degree of "qualitative perfection," *CrA*.

identical access to the x-ray beam. Ordinary wide-angle, powder diffraction techniques were used,[22] and the familiar crystallinity index of Segal et al., *CrI*, was used to calculate the index of crystallinity,[14] a material characteristic. Segal's method has found wide acceptance.[22,23] The essence of Segal's method is shown in Figure 2, as is the method for calculating *CrA*.

The *extensive* crystallinity was measured by a comparative normalized x-ray technique.[11] Integrated [002]-line intensities were compared directly to the integrated [002]-line intensities of virgin RBC separators, and the ratio normalized with respect to density of the material. The value for the integrated intensity was approximated by triangulation, defining the integrated intensity as

$$A(002) = I(002) \times W(002) \tag{1}$$

where $W(002)$ is the [002]-linewidth [the operational linewidth at 0.5 $I(002)$]. Because of the nature of beam collimation, we can assume that, for any measured line of finite width,

$$A_x = A_t N_x \tag{2}$$

where N_x is the number of diffractors present, and A_t, the x-ray beam target area, is an instrumental standard. The value of N_x is proportional to the density ρ_x of the analyzed material and a constant k_x related to the crystalline nature of the sample. For the comparison standard, we also have $A_{\text{std}} = A_t k_{\text{std}} \rho_{\text{std}}$. Equating target areas and rearranging, a crystallinity ratio *CrR* is resolved:

$$CrR = (k_x/k_{\text{std}}) = (\rho_{\text{std}}/\rho_x)(A_x/A_{\text{std}}) \tag{3}$$

and since intercepted volumes are the same, this simplifies to

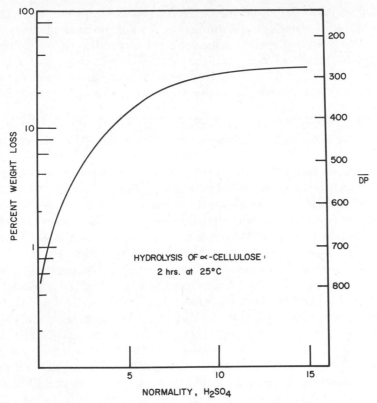

Fig. 3. Ant-Wuorinen and Visapaa's hydrolysis data for α-cellulose in H_2SO_4. Data from Ant-Wuorinen and Visapaa.[26]

$$CrR = (M_{std}/M_x)(A_x/A_{std}) \qquad (4)$$

where M_{std} and M_x are weights of materials in the beam. Because direct comparisons were made to standards, no corrections for absorption were made.[22] Segal's method for CrI is an example of what Miller[24] calls an internal x-ray method, as is CrA. The quantity CrR, in distinction, Miller would call an external method, because it involves a normalization and reference to another substance.

In his work on heterogeneous hydrolysis in strong acids, Ant-Wuorinen[25] used a somewhat different approach. His method used a measure related to the [002]-linewidth to calculate the *amorphous* character, and he then characterized crystallinity from that quantity.

Ant-Wuorinen and Visapaa (26) steeped cotton linters (presumably cellulose I) in H_2SO_4 at concentrations from $0.1N$ to $15N$. They measured CrI at the beginning and end of the series of hydrolyses. The degree of polymerization was also measured. The data are plotted in Figure 3. It is interesting to note that while the D.P. falls from ~790 to 280 during hydrolysis, the CrI values were all but unchanged, decreasing slightly from 0.73 before treatment to 0.71 after hydrolysis in $15N$ H_2SO_4. None of the x-ray data used to calculate CrI was reported, so that the effect of extreme hydrolysis on the shape of the diffraction maxima is unknown and the [002]-linewidth changes unknown.

Somewhat later, Ant-Wuorinen and Visapaa[27] established what they refer to as an index of order, *IO*. Assuming the crystalline/amorphous concept inadequate, they argued against using the term "crystallinity." The parameter they used, *IO*, was in all essentials the same as Segal's *CrI*. Statton (28) concluded that "order" and "crystallinity" were probably articulations of the same basic idea or notion, and in this paper we continue the use of "crystallinity" as a useful term.

In this laboratory, a simple experiment in hydrolysis of α-cellulose was done. Hydrolysis in $14.4N$ H_2SO_4 was carried out at 52°C for 36 hr. The material was entirely denatured, the liquor becoming brown to black in color. The retained material was thoroughly washed by repeated centrifugation to obtain a white, viscous suspension that appeared to be a dispersion of very small, translucent crystals when diluted. A small sheet was made by filtration and dried in air at 52°C. After equilibration with dry silica gel, the small sheet was subjected to x-ray diffraction analysis and to direct x-ray comparison to the starting material. The resultant x-ray diffraction patterns are shown in Figure 4.

As in the work of McKeown and Lyness,[15] the diffraction patterns are exceptionally like one another. Their "peptized" solids were produced in $2.5N$ H_2SO_4 by boiling and retained a considerable fiber-like character. The peptized solids prepared in this laboratory had no fiber-like character. The small sheet was brittle and horny in appearance, but it is, quite evidently, to be identified as cellulose I. The degree of crystallinity for the hydrocellulose was the same as for the raw material α-cellulose, the only difference being in [002]-linewidth and a "smearing-out" of [101]- and [10$\bar{1}$]-lines. If we assume that [002]-linewidth signifies "qualitative perfection,"[12] this experimental hydrocellulose is *more* crystalline than the α-cellulose raw material.

In a series of papers, Ant-Wuorinen and Visapaa (29) have attempted to show conclusively that order, or "crystallinity" as used here, dictates the essential reactivity of cellulose undergoing acid hydrolysis.

What is clear is not simply that strong hydrolytic agents appear to increase the intensive crystallinity of cellulose, but that hydrolysis residues retain their capacity for forming supermolecular structures of considerable integrity. It may be this integrity which gives long life to RBC separators in acid media.

EXPERIMENTAL

Resin-bonded cellulose separators were obtained from the Texon Corporation of South Hadley, Massachusetts. These materials were regular stock materials, ordinarily used in assembly of ESB, Incorporated, automotive batteries. They are thick paper stocks blended with very small amounts of synthetic fiber and impregnated, while wet, with water-borne phenol–formaldehyde resins. These are later cured by thermal treatment at temperatures of the order of 200°C. The α-cellulose used in this work was also obtained from Texon. Simple experiments using polymerized films of phenolic on crystalline materials indicated that their presence on cellulose fibers would not interfere with the x-ray diffraction spectrum. The phenolic crystallites are, apparently, too small to produce a coherent signal and do no more than slightly reduce the S/N ratio of the diffractometer output.

A large number of randomly selected separators were cut into 30 mm × 30 mm

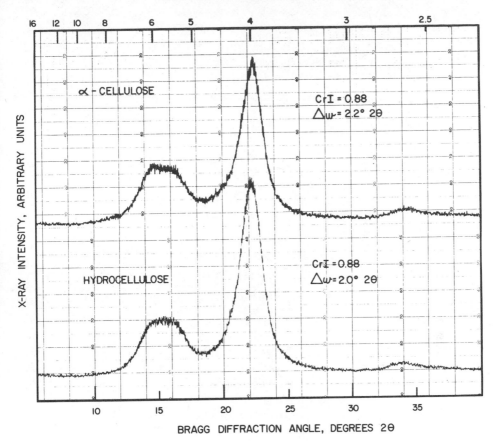

Fig. 4. X-ray diffraction spectra of α-cellulose compared to the product of fully denatured α-cellulose. This hydrocellulose was produced by 36 hr of hydrolysis in 1.400 specific gravity H_2SO_4 at 52°C.

pieces and stored in battery-concentration H_2SO_4. A second group of very carefully cut pieces was dried and preweighed before storage in acid. The unweighed samples were used solely for x-ray diffraction measurements. The weighed samples were used to study hydrolytic weight loss in H_2SO_4 of 1.265 specific gravity.

Approximately 40 to 60 chips were made up for each concentration of acid and shuffled before placing in the acid baths. The samples were put into 1-pound ointment jars of the solutions, and these were thermostated at 52°C (125°F) in an oil bath. At the end of specific storage times, four to seven samples were taken from each jar and rinsed in tap water, then in distilled water until free of sulfate. The chips were vacuum dried at 40°C and examined by x-ray diffraction. A Phillips Electronics Mark II X-Ray Diffractometer was used to obtain x-ray intensity data. All analyses were done at Cu-target parameters of 35–40 kVA and 15–20 mA x-ray current. Each series of measurements was concluded by analysis of a chip of virgin separator at the same x-ray parameters. These x-ray measurements were used to calculate both crystallinity and "qualitative perfection" of the separators after increasing periods of hydrolysis in acid.

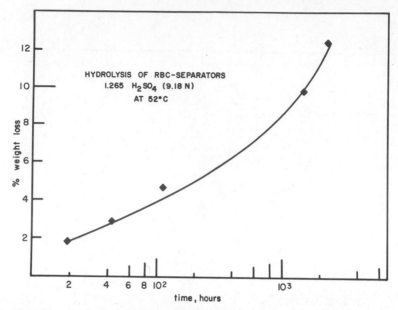

Fig. 5. Weight-loss data for RBC cellulose separators stored in 1.265 specific gravity H_2SO_4 for increasing periods. Temperature of storage was 52°C.

The carefully preweighed chips were put into 1.265 H_2SO_4 and hydrolyzed. Samples were withdrawn, in groups of five, at irregular intervals and washed and dried. The hydrolytic weight loss was calculated using these samples.

Reagent-grade chemicals were used throughout this work, and acid concentrations were determined by controlled-temperature hydrometry.

RESULTS AND DISCUSSION

Hydrolysis—Loss of Material

As in the case of unprotected α-cellulose,[1–6] hydrolysis of the cellulose in RBC separators is initially rapid, becoming slower as the time of reaction is extended. Preweighed separator pieces, soaked in $9.14N$ H_2SO_4 (specific gravity 1.265) showed fast initial reaction rates, losing 12.50% of their weight in 2410 hr at 52° ± 3°C. The weight loss data are shown in Figure 5 correlated using a polynomial curve-fitting equation.

Except for the very early work of Freudenberg and his colleagues,[30] hydrolysis in highly concentrated H_2SO_4 ($N>5$) seems only to have been measured by Ant-Wuorinen and his co-workers.[25–27] They treated α-cellulose in $5N$ and $8N$ H_2SO_4 at a temperature of 100°C and used the data to investigate the order and kinetics of heterogeneous cellulose hydrolysis. Using the amorphous/crystalline hypothesis, they also calculated crystalline fractions in the material by assuming that the rates of hydrolysis of the amorphous fraction were different, in terms of order, than the rate for the crystalline fraction. Their data are plotted in Figure 6 and compared directly to the hydrolysis data for RBC separators. One can see that RBC separators are far more stable in hydrolytic media than the usually quite reactive cellulose.

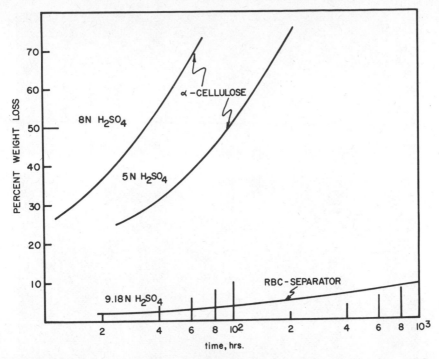

Fig. 6. Comparison of Ant-Wuorinen and Visapaa's data for α-cellulose with those for RBC separators. Ant-Wuorinen's data were generated by seriatim fixed-period hydrolyses at 100°C. The serial periods for $5N$ acid were 24 hr, and the serial periods for $8N$ acid were 12 hr. The RBC separator data were generated by continuous hydrolysis in $9.18N$ H_2SO_4 at 52°C. Ant-Wuorinen's data were abstracted from reference 26.

Conclusions from this particular comparison of hydrolysis data must be tempered. The present data were generated by stagnant hydrolysis at 52°C. Ant-Wuorinen's data, while generated at 100°C, were also done in a slowly flowing system and at lower H_2SO_4 concentrations. The conclusion that the phenolic resin acts to protect the cellulose from extensive, high-rate hydrolysis is, nonetheless, inescapable.

Scanning electron microscopy (SEM) was used to attempt a textural characterization of the fiber matrix in separators and the starting material. Figure 7 shows 1000× and 3000× SEM photos of the two matrixes. The differences are worth remarking. In the case of the α-cellulose, the fiber surfaces are rather sharply defined compared to RBC separator surfaces. In examination of separator SEM photos, there are also some characteristic "dimple-like" effects—absent on cellulose itself—that are probably due to a shrinking (surface free-energy minimization) of the polymerizing resin films. Except for those areas, the SEM pictures indicate the cellulose surfaces to be uniformly coated with the impregnating resins.

Crystallinity—Extensive and Intensive

The measure of CrR, the crystallinity ratio, indicates in an approximate sense the kinds of hydrolysis attack on the RBC separators. In this normalized scheme, the initial value is, by definition, 1.00, or 100%. What is interesting to note is

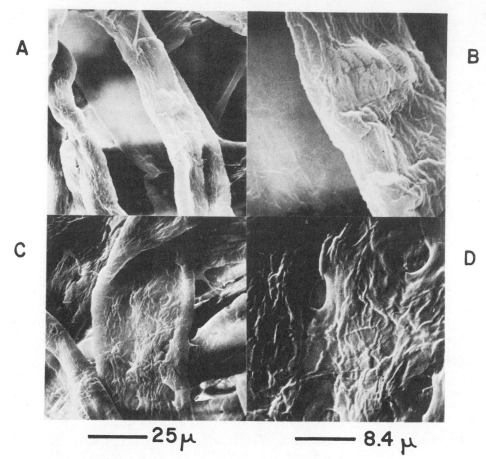

Fig. 7. Scanning electron micrographs of α-cellulose and RBC separators. A and B are micrographs of α-cellulose, and C and D are micrographs of RBC-separators. A and C and B and D are the same magnifications.

what happens to CrR as the hydrolysis time at 52°C becomes progressively longer. The data, derived from sample populations of five to seven numbers, are shown in Table I. The data show that only small changes occur in the retained cellulose material after extensive hydrolytic attack. In 3960 hr of hydrolysis in $9.00N$ H_2SO_4, RBC separators lose 15.7% of their weight, presumably cellulose only; yet after normalization by weight and direct comparison with virgin separators,

TABLE I
Crystallinity Ratio C and R of Hydrolyzed Separators

Acid strength		CrR			
Sp. gr.	N	691 hr[a]	1360 hr	2400 hr	3960 hr
1.260	9.00	0.887	0.965	0.939	0.916
1.280	9.75	0.855	0.839	0.925	0.841
1.325	11.48	0.878	0.900	0.833	0.847

[a] Period of hydrolysis.

the retained material is *more* crystalline in character than after only 691 hr of hydrolysis.

In the acids of increasing strengths, the trends are similar. All samples indicated increases in CrR with time of hydrolysis, but with monotonic decreases, then, as hydrolysis proceeded. The largest gain in CrR occurred, as expected, in the most dilute acid, the worst degradation being associated with the most concentrated acid.

What may be remarkable about these data is the degree of resistance to hydrolysis displayed. The question that deserves answer by further experimentation is how the cellulose maintains itself in media that do attack it as strongly as shown here.

In agreement with Ant-Wuorinen[29] and others,[15] these data indicate, despite considerable hydrolytic weight loss in the matrix, that the most hydrolysis-resistant material is that which is highly ordered, or crystalline. But it is also intuitively clear that what Ray and Bandyopadhay[12] called "qualitative perfection" changes considerably. Hermans and Weidinger[13] pictorialized this as a "splitting" of the fiber bundle parallel the fiber axis.[13] A broadening of the [002]-diffraction maxima would indicate the correctness of this picture, but what appears to happen is not simply a slight line broadening but a decrease in [002]-intensity (viz., fewer first-order [002]-diffractions). In the x-ray analysis done here, the [002]-linewidth changed less, relatively, than the [002]-line intensity.

Crystallinity Index and Qualitative Perfection

The crystallinity index CrI and a measure of "qualitative perfection," CrA, were calculated for the samples of RBC separators treated in H_2SO_4. The values for these measurements are shown in Table II. The datum levels for RBC separators before hydrolysis are $CrI = 0.781$ and $CrA = 6.55$. Hydrolysis in acids of increasing strengths increases the *intensive* crystallinity as calculated from Segal's index,[14] but as we have defined it here, hydrolysis leads to large losses

TABLE II
Intensive Crystallinity and "Qualitative Perfection"

Period of hydrolysis, hr	CrI	CrA
	1.260 H_2SO_4	
691	0.827	5.49
1300	0.801	4.40
2400	0.829	4.16
3960	0.784	3.54
	1.280 H_2SO_4	
691	0.828	5.07
1300	0.786	4.43
2400	0.817	4.42
3960	0.782	3.16
	1.325 H_2SO_4	
691	0.838	5.02
1300	0.779	4.08
2400	0.781	3.51
3960	0.767	2.77

of "qualitative perfection." (In all these measurements, the relative change in [002]-line intensity was as much as 50%, while the [002]-linewidth varied less than 16%.)

Immergut and Ranby[31] reported similar conclusions for native cotton, using D.P. measurements. They concluded that the *most ordered micelles* were proof to hydrolysis, except for the very strongest agents. These data would clearly support their conclusions, despite the interference of the impregnating phenolic resins used to protect the cellulose. In fact, these data fit very well into the amorphous/crystalline model *and* the fringed micelle model for cellulose.

The use of phenolic resins in battery technology has, however, lent us some additional insights into the possible synergistic action of cellulose and the phenolic impregnate. In large stationary battery use, phenolic resins of a similar kind are used to bind woven fiber-glass tubes used as active material supports and separators. In these batteries, the phenolic resin binding on the tubes is completely eroded after a few thousand hours of use.

The model that emerges is this: the phenolic coating is severely hydrolyzed in the absence of the chemical binding provided by the cellulose in the RBC separators. This means that both elements, cellulose and resin, cooperate in giving stability to the RBC separators. Recalling the work of Ruznak and Tanczos,[8] who pointed out that heating to ~190°C provides easily hydrolyzed —OH linkages in cellulose, we reasoned that during the curing step (~205°C) used in separator manufacturing, the cellulose linkages react with some labile resin linkages to form copolymers that both protect the cellulose linkages and afford the resin a more stable state with respect to acid hydrolysis.

We reasoned that, if this is correct, there should be a difference in degree of crystallinity, *CrI*, of heated α-cellulose and RBC separators before and after exposure to water vapor. Manjurath, Venkataraman, and Stephen[32] showed conclusively that the x-ray diffraction order of wet or damp cellulose was higher than that of dry cellulose. Morosoff[21] produced similar findings for "never-dried cotton."

We treated α-cellulose sheets to test temperatures in the order of 190°C and then equilibrated them with indicating silica gel. Samples of RBC separator material were also dried over silica gel.

Samples of both materials were also equilibrated with H_2O vapor at 25°C. When these samples were analyzed by x-ray diffraction, the degree of crystallinity of the RBC separators did not vary, within experimental error. However, the heated α-cellulose showed a consistent increase in *CrI* from 0.843 in the dry state to 0.921 in the moisture-equilibrated state. This indicates that any linkages created thermally in the curing separator were probably reacted with the impregnating resin. It is clear from the immense literature of the fabric industry that we can clearly expect copolymerization between the resin impregnate and the cotton fibers, but this x-ray test gives a particularly elegant demonstration.

It is also useful to compare these qualitative findings with Ant-Wuorinen and Visapaa's hypotheses on cellulose reactivity.[29] If, as they indicate, the intermolecular hydrogen bonded, —OH linkages are equally susceptible to attack by acid, then copolymerization of cellulose and phenolic impregnate, through these linkages made labile during the high temperature curing step should lend exceptional stability to the whole structure. It means that degradation is mainly through attack at the acetal linkages, and these are far less accessible because of the oriented fibrous character of the matrix.[13] This explanation agrees with the CrA data developed here. If $I(002)$ decreases while $W(002)$ changes little, then the average crystallite length has been decreased (parallel to the [002]-direction), while the crystallite size (perpendicular to the [002]-direction) is relatively unchanged. Attack at acetal linkages, followed by hydrolysis and weight loss, will lead to relatively fewer diffractors and necessarily to a reduction in $I(002)$. This means that the crystallite population, as time of hydrolysis continues, is made up of shorter crystallites, relatively unchanged in thickness.

In distinction, the fully hydrolyzed cellulose seen in Figure 4 indicates no change in CrA. While the ratio $I(002)/W(002)$ is the same, we know the particle deimensions are smaller. This indicates, conclusively, that the unimpregnated cellulose is attacked very generally (all labile —OH's and the acetal linkages), while the RBC separator is very selectively attacked.

CONCLUSIONS

Lead–acid battery separators made of cellulose and impregnated with thermosetting, phenolic resins display unusual resistance to attack by sulfuric acid. The cellulose *is* attacked and the separator matrix loses substantial material on prolonged storage in battery acid, but the degree of crystallinity decreases only slightly, though the decrease in CrI is related to increasing acid strength.

The "qualitative perfection" of the retained cellulose decreases, and presumably the average crystallite length is reduced during long storage of RBC separators in acid. X-ray measurements indicate that dry separator matrixes do not undergo any reorganization, as does α-cellulose, when the matrix is equilibrated with water. This is taken to indicate the intermolecular hydrogen-bonded —OH linkages enter into copolymerization reactions with the impregnating resin, and the cooperative, final structure has better acid resistance than either the cellulose or the phenolic impregnate.

X-ray diffraction measurements can be used to measure not only the *intensive* crystalline character of degraded RBC separators but also the degree of "qualitative perfection" and, with suitable, parallel chemical measurements, can quantify the *extensive* crystalline properties of the material.

The author wishes to thank ESB, Incorporated, for support of this work. Special thanks are due Barbara Campbell without whose assistance the experimental work would not have been completed. Ted Blickwedel and Karen Zimmerman provided computer analyses of special data.

References

1. R. F. Nickerson, *Ind. Eng. Chem.*, **33**, 1022 (1941); *ibid.*, **39**, 1507 (1947).
2. J. F. Saeman, *Ind. Eng. Chem.*, **37**, 43 (1945).
3. O. Ant-Wuorinen and A. Visapaa, *Paperi ja Puu*, **38**, 583 (1957).
4. A. Meller, *J. Polym. Sci.*, **4**, 619 (1949); *ibid.*, **10**, 213 (1959).
5. R. I. C. Michie, A. Sharples, and A. A. Walter, *J. Polym. Sci.*, **5**, 85 (1961).
6. Y. V. Brestkin and S. Y. Frenkel, *Vysokomol. Soedin.*, **11**, 2437 (1969).
7. J. Economy and L. Wohrer, in *Encyclopedia of Polymer Science and Technology*, Vol. 15, Wiley, New York, 1971, p. 373.
8. I. Rusznak and I. Tanczos, *J. Polym. Sci.*, **C42**, 1475 (1973).

9. J. J. Lander, *Proc. Symp. Battery Sep.*, Columbus, Ohio, Feb. 18–19, 1970, p. 4.

10. E. Sundberg, *Proc. Symp. Battery Sep.*, Columbus, Ohio, Feb. 18–19, 1970, p. 32.

11. B. A. Campbell and J. R. Dafler, *J. Electrochem. Soc.*, **122**, 1084 (1975).

12. P. K. Ray and S. B. Bandyopadhay, *J. Appl. Polymer Sci.*, **19**, 729 (1975).

13. P. H. Hermans and A. Weidinger, *J. Appl. Phys.*, **19**, 491 (1958); *J. Polym. Sci.*, **4**, 135 (1949).

14. L. Segal, J. J. Creely, A. E. Martin, Jr., and C. M. Conrad, *Text. Res. J.*, **29**, 786 (1959).

15. J. J. McKeown and W. I. Lyness, *J. Polym. Sci.*, **47**, 9 (1960).

16. A. Viswanathan, *J. Appl. Polym. Sci.*, **11**, 1027 (1967).

17. H. P. Klug and L. E. Alexander, *X-ray Diffraction Procedures*, 2nd ed., Wiley, New York, 1974, p. 687ff.

18. B. E. Warren and B. L. Averbach, *J. Appl. Phys.*, **21**, 595 (1950).

19. A. Bienenstock, *J. Appl. Phys.*, **32**, 187 (1961).

20. D. R. Buchanan and R. L. Miller, *J. Appl. Phys.*, **37**, 4003 (1966).

21. N. Morosoff, *J. Appl. Polym. Sci.*, **18**, 1837 (1974).

22. A. Venkateswaran and J. A. Van Den Akker, *J. Appl. Polym. Sci.*, **9**, 1149 (1965); A. Venkateswaran, *ibid.*, **13**, 2459 (1969).

23. D. F. Caulfield and R. A. Steffes, *Tappi*, **52**, 1361 (1969).

24. R. L. Miller, in *Encyclopedia of Polymer Science and Technology*, Vol. 4, Wiley, New York, 1966, p. 477ff.

25. O. Ant-Wuorinen and E. Lehtinen, *Paperi ja Puu* **38**, 523 (1956).

26. O. Ant-Wuorinen and A. Visapaa, *Paperi ja Puu*, **39**, 151, 229 (1957).

27. O. Ant-Wuorinen and A. Visapaa, *Paperi ja Puu*, **47**, 311 (1965).

28. W. O. Statton, *J. Polym. Sci.*, **C18**, 33 (1967).

29. O. Ant-Wuorinen and A. Visapaa, *Paperi ja Puu*, **51**, 107, 617, 737, 765 (1970).

30. K. Freudenberg et al., *Ber.*, **63**, 1510 (1930); **65**, 484 (1932); **68**, 2070 (1934).

31. E. A. Immergut and B. G. Ranby, *Ind. Eng. Chem.*, **48**, 1183 (1956).

32. B. F. Manjunath, A. Venkataraman, and T. Stephen, *J. Appl. Polym. Sci.*, **17**, 1091 (1973).

Received May 6, 1976
Revised August 4, 1976

JOURNAL OF APPLIED POLYMER SCIENCE   VOL. 21, 2565–2573 (1977)

Graft Copolymers of Starch–Polyacrylonitrile Prepared by Ferrous Ion–Hydrogen Peroxide Initiation

EDWARD I. STOUT, DONALD TRIMNELL, WILLIAM M. DOANE, and CHARLES R. RUSSELL, *Northern Regional Research Center, Agricultural Research Service, U.S. Department of Agriculture, Peoria, Illinois 61604*

Synopsis

The effects of concentration, reactant ratios, temperature, and starch pretreatment on grafting of acrylonitrile onto starch were studied. Grafting was efficient at high concentrations (8–12% starch) when granular starch was used. The molecular weights for grafted polyacrylonitrile (PAN) were higher when gelatinized starch was used, but grafting efficiencies (grafted PAN/total PAN) were much lower. The molecular weight of the grafted side chain increased with increased concentration of reactants. The grafting frequency was highest when the reaction mixture was kept at 5°C and decreased with increased swelling of the starch. The starch–polyacrylonitrile graft copolymers were saponified and dried to give products which absorbed 75–440 ml H_2O per gram and 20–70 ml synthetic urine per gram.

INTRODUCTION

The graft polymerization of acrylonitrile (AN) onto starch by cerium(IV) initiation has been extensively studied,[1–12] and products with considerable potential utility have been developed.[13] Because of the greater abundance and lower cost of ferrous salts compared to cerium salts, the ferrous ion–hydrogen peroxide initiation system was investigated for the preparation of the starch–polyacrylonitrile (S-PAN) graft copolymers. Fanta et al.[4] prepared S-PAN by ferrous ion–hydrogen peroxide initiation and found similar trends of molecular weight and grafting frequency compared to those obtained by cerium(IV) initiation. Brockway and Seaberg[14] have also reported on S-PAN graft copolymers prepared by ferrous ion–hydrogen peroxide initiation. However, when we prepared S-PAN graft copolymers by their method, we did not get reproducible results and found that the order and method of addition of the reactants were critical factors. Therefore, we have made a detailed study of this grafting reaction. The effects of concentration, starch pretreatment, temperature, and reactant ratios were studied. Some of the S-PAN copolymers were hydrolyzed with sodium hydroxide, and the properties of the resulting products were examined.

EXPERIMENTAL

Materials

Starch. Pearl corn starch (10–12% H_2O).

Monomer. AN (Eastman Kodak, practical grade) was used without further purification.

Initiator. Ferrous ammonium sulfate (Fisher Scientific Company, reagent grade) or ferrous sulfate (J. T. Baker Chemical Company, reagent grade) and hydrogen peroxide, 30% (J. T. Baker, reagent grade).

Other Reagents. All other reagents were reagent grade and used without further purification.

Graft Polymerization

The grafting reactions were run in a three-neck flask fitted with a nitrogen bubbler tube, stirrer, and dropping funnel. The starch, suspended in distilled water, was brought to the desired temperature and nitrogen bubbled through the suspension for 1 hr. The temperature of the mixture was then adjusted and the ferrous salt (dissolved in a small amount of H_2O) was added. After 10 min, AN was added and the mixture was stirred for 5 min. Then a dilute solution of hydrogen peroxide (0.3–1.5%) was added dropwise over a 20-min period. After the mixture had been stirred under nitrogen for 4 hr, it was filtered. The solid was washed twice with H_2O and three times with acetone, and then air dried. The homopolymer content was determined by extracting the product with DMF.[4]

Isolation of Grafted PAN

A portion (10 g) of the product, which had been extracted with DMF, was suspended in $1N$ HCl (50 ml) and the mixture kept on the steam bath for 4 hr to remove the starch moiety. The insoluble PAN was collected on a filter, washed thoroughly with H_2O, and dried. The intrinsic viscosity was determined at 25°C in DMF solution with Cannon-Fenske viscometers. The molecular weight was calculated from the equation[15] $[\eta] = 3.92 \times 10^{-4} \overline{M}_n{}^{0.75}$.

From the molecular weight of the grafted PAN and the nitrogen content of the DMF insoluble copolymer, the average number of anhydroglucose units (AGU) per grafted chain (grafting frequency) was determined.

RESULTS AND DISCUSSION

Graft Copolymerization Reaction

The results in Table I show that the amount of ferrous ion used to initiate polymerization may be varied considerably without greatly affecting the reaction. However, at the lower amounts (runs 1 and 2), the yields and grafting frequencies are decreased, while the molecular weights are increased; at the highest amount (run 6), total conversion of monomer to polymer is high, but the efficiency of grafting is considerably lowered. Therefore, at high iron ratio, homopolymerization is favored.

TABLE I
Effect of Fe^{2+} Concentration on Graft Polymerization Reaction[a]

Run no.	Fe^{2+} g[b]	Total polymer, g	DMF insol. g	% PAN	Mol. wt of graft	AGU per chain	% Conversion[c]	Grafting, efficiency, %[d]
1	0.05	32.2	31.0	29	43,200	655	29	95
2	0.1	38.5	36.0	36	50,697	505	50	81
3	0.2	40.8	35.1	39	29,500	286	60	71
4	0.2	43.4	35.6	39	29,500	233	63	70
5	0.5	45.0	34.5	40	27,600	267	69	63
6	1.0	44.0	26.8	22	23,400	591	70	26

[a] All runs were made using 21 g starch (granular), 31.8 g acrylonitrile (AN), and 1.0 ml 30% H_2O_2 diluted to 100 ml; reactions were run at 25°C and 4% starch concentration under nitrogen for 4 hr. DMF = Dimethylformamide; PAN = polyacrylonitrile; AGU = anhydroglucose units.
[b] Grams of $Fe(NH_4)_2(SO_4)_2 \cdot 6H_2O$.
[c] Weight of total PAN (homopolymer and grafted PAN)/weight of monomer.
[d] Weight of grafted PAN/total PAN.

TABLE II
Effect of H_2O_2 Concentration on Grafting Reaction[a]

Run no.	H_2O_2, ml[b]	Total polymer, g	DMF insol. g	% PAN	Mol. wt of graft	AGU per chain	% Conversion	Grafting efficiency, %
7	0.05	38.0	28.5	26.0	40,300	592	52	45
8	0.05	37.5	27.4	22.7	35,000	738	52	37
9	0.10	43.3	31.2	37.7	32,900	336	79	49
10	0.25	43.2	34.6	38.5	32,900	325	71	60
11	0.50	42.8	36.0	42.0	38,500	328	71	67
3	1.00	40.8	35.1	39.0	29,500	286	60	71

[a] All runs were made using 21 g starch (granular), 31.8 g AN, and 0.2 g $Fe(NH_4)_2(SO_4)_2 \cdot 6H_2O$; reactions were run at 25°C and 4% starch concentration under nitrogen for 4 hr.
[b] Volume of hydrogen peroxide (30%) which was diluted to 100 ml before addition.

TABLE III
Effect of Swelling the Starch on Grafting Reaction[a]

Run no.	Pretreatment, °C	Total polymer, g	DMF insol. g	% PAN	Mol. wt of graft	AGU per chain	% Conversion	Grafting efficiency, %
3	25	41.1	35.1	39	29,500	286	60	71
12	40	36.0	32.6	36	28,500	309	47	79
13	60	41.2	34.9	39	38,500	369	59	74
14	90	40.1	27.0	26	203,800	3338	58	40

[a] All runs were made using 21 g starch, 31.8 g AN, 0.2 g $Fe(NH_4)_2(SO_4)_2 \cdot 6H_2O$, and 1.0 ml 30% H_2O_2 diluted to 100 ml; the grafting reaction was run at 4% starch concentration under nitrogen at 25°C for 4 hr. Pretreatment consisted of treating the starch at the designated temperature for 1 hr.

TABLE IV
Dilution Effect on Grafting Reaction[a]

Run no.	% Starch	Total polymer, g	DMF insol.		Mol. wt of graft	AGU per chain	% Conversion	Grafting efficiency, %
			g	% PAN				
3	4	40.8	35.1	39	29,500	286	60	71
15	8	49.5	41.8	50	74,500	458	83	70
16	12	45.0	39.4	50	72,600	413	78	79
17	12	—	—	57	106,500	571	98	85

[a] All runs were made using 21 g starch (granular), 31.8 g AN, 0.2 g $Fe(NH_4)_2(SO_4) \cdot 6H_2O$, and 1.0 ml 30% H_2O_2 diluted to 100 ml; reaction temperature of the 8% and 12% mixtures rose to 40–45°C during first 30 min, but temperature of the 4% mixture only reached 30°C.

TABLE V
Effect of Reaction Temperature on Grafting[a]

Run no.	Reaction temperature, °C	Concentration, %	Total polymer, g	DMF insol.		Mol. wt of graft	AGU per chain	% Conversion	Grafting efficiency %
				g	% PAN				
18	5	4	35.5	27.2	28	11,500	188	51	46
3	25	4	40.8	35.1	39	29,500	286	60	71
19	40	4	41.5	34.9	42	56,100	471	72	65
20	60	4	44.0	31.3	34	100,000	1161	63	50
21	25	8	49.5	41.8	50	74,500	458	83	70
22	40	8	47.0	38.2	47	130,200	919	87	65
16	60	8	45.0	28.0	32	206,100	2743	69	42

[a] All runs were made using 21 g starch (granular), 31.8 g AN, 0.2 g $Fe(NH_4)_2(SO_4)_2 \cdot 6H_2O$, and 1.0 ml 30% H_2O_2 diluted to 100 ml; reactions were run under nitrogen for 4 hr.

The effect of varying the hydrogen peroxide ratio to other reactants on grafting and product properties is shown in Table II. As the amount of hydrogen peroxide is increased, the yield of grafted PAN, conversion, grafting efficiency, and frequency of grafting all increased, while the molecular weight of the grafted side chain decreased. However, the change in molecular weight was small and the yield appeared to reach a limiting value. The order and rate of addition of H_2O_2 was critical for obtaining reproducible results. Dropwise addition of the hydrogen peroxide gave the best results even though most of the polymerization appeared to occur before 25% of the total H_2O_2 solution was added.

It may be seen from the data in Table III that pretreatment of the starch in water at 25°, 40°, and 60°C causes relatively small differences in yield, molecular weight, or grafting frequency. However, gelatinization of the starch greatly reduces the grafting efficiency and the number of grafting sites, but the molecular weight of the grafted PAN is greatly increased.

The diluent effect is shown in Table IV. At the higher concentrations, the

TABLE VI
Effect of Monomer:Starch Ratio on Grafting Reaction[a]

Run no.	Amount of AN	Total polymer g	DMF insol.		Mol. wt of graft	AGU per chain	% Conversion	Grafting efficiency, %
			g	% PAN				
23	15.9	30.1	27.5	24.8	12,200	228	55	79
24	20.0	32.6	30.0	29.4	18,300	271	58	77
25	25.0	35.6	30.5	34.0	24,700	295	61	68
26	25.0	36.5	31.7	35.4	28,000	314	59	76
3	31.8	40.8	35.1	39	29,500	286	60	71

[a] All runs were made using 21 g starch (granular), 0.2 g $Fe(NH_4)_2(SO_4)_2 \cdot 6H_2O$, and 1.0 ml 30% H_2O_2 diluted to 100 ml; reactions were run under nitrogen at 25°C for 1 hr at 4% starch concentration.

conversion of monomer to polymer, the grafting efficiency, and the molecular weight of the grafted side chain increased. Increasing the concentration beyond 8% AN surpasses the solubility of AN in H_2O, which would account for the similar results between runs 15 and 16. However, another reaction at 12% AN gave a graft copolymer of 57% PAN, a grafting efficiency of 85%, and conversion of monomer to polymer of 98%. Some of the differences between the samples prepared at 4% concentration compared to those prepared at higher concentration may be due to the difference in temperature caused by the heat of reaction.

Reaction temperature greatly influences the grafting reaction as shown in Table V. The molecular weight increases considerably as the temperature is increased: At 4% starch concentration, the molecular weight increases from 11,000 at 5°C to 100,000 at 60°C; and at 8% starch concentration, from 74,000 at 25°C to 206,000 at 60°C. A large reduction in the grafting frequency occurred at the higher temperatures.

Results presented in Table VI show the effect of monomer:starch ratio on the grafting reaction. As the ratio of monomer to starch increased, the molecular weight of the graft increased while the number of AGU/chain, the conversion of monomer to polymer, and the grafting efficiency remained relatively constant.

The effect of other variables on the polymerization reaction are given in Table VII. In run 30, in which air was not excluded, the conversion of monomer to polymer was quite low even though the grafting efficiency remained high. Comparison of run 28 with run 27 indicates that CO_2 is essentially equivalent to N_2 for an inert atmosphere. Run 29 shows that tap H_2O reduces both the conversion and the grafting efficiency. When tap H_2O was used with no pH adjustment, very little polymerization occurred. The source of ferrous ion was not critical as indicated by run 31 compared to run 27. These data show ferrous sulfate gave higher conversion and efficiency than ferrous ammonium sulfate.

A number of preparations were made without the nitrogen atmosphere using starch which had been pregelatinized by injecting steam into the mixture to achieve a temperature of 98–99°C for 5 min. These results in Table VIII show

TABLE VII
Effect of Other Variables on Grafting Reaction

Run no.	Atmosphere	Type of H_2O	Total polymer, g	DMF insol.		Mol. wt. of graft	AGU per chain	% Conversion	Grafting efficiency, %
				g	% PAN				
27a	N_2	Distilled	40.8	35.1	39	29,500	286	60	71
28a	CO_2	Distilled	39.0	34.0	38	34,800	345	52	78
29a	N_2	Tap, pH 5	37.2	27.5	22	39,300	870	46	39
30a	Air	Distilled	33.5	29.4	28	21,500	343	35	73
31b	N_2	Distilled	47.3	38.8	45	36,600	276	78	71

[a] Made with 21 g starch (granular), 31.8 g AN, 0.2 g $Fe(NH_4)_2(SO_4)_2 \cdot 6H_2O$, 1.0 ml 30% H_2O_2; diluted to 100 ml; reactions were run at 25°C for 4 hr at 4% starch concentration.

[b] As in footnote above, but using 0.2 g $FeSO_4 \cdot 7H_2O$ instead of $Fe(NH_4)_2(SO_4)_2 \cdot 6H_2O$.

TABLE VIII
Dilution Effect on Grafting Reaction Using Gelatinized Starch[a]

Run no.	Starch conc. %	Reaction time, hr	Total polymer, g	DMF insol.		Mol. wt of graft	AGU per chain	% Conversion	Grafting efficiency, %
				g	% PAN				
32	4	1	31.0	23.7	13	27,600	1090	62.6	15
33	8	1	44.1	29.6	24	148,000	2820	71	31
34	8	2	48.0	34.2	36	191,000	2110	97	40

[a] Starch was gelatinized with "live steam" and polymerization reaction conducted at 60–70°C using 0.2 g Fe(NH$_4$)$_2$(SO$_4$)$_2$·6H$_2$O, 1.0 ml 30% H$_2$O$_2$ diluted to 100 ml, and 31.8 g AN.

TABLE IX
Absorbancy of Hydrolyzed Starch–PAN

			ml absorbed	
Run no.	% PAN	Mol. wt. of graft	H_2O	Synthetic urine[a]
35	14.2	31,100	80	20
36	15.6	31,400	125	30
37	20.1	28,000	125	25
38	34.9	63,500	130	30
39	45.3	89,200	440	70

[a] Synthetic urine, 1.28 g $CaCl_2$, 2.28 g $MgSO_4 \cdot 7H_2O$, 16.4 g NaCl, 40 g urea in 2 liters H_2O.

that the grafting efficiency is low (15–40%) under these conditions, but that a reasonable add-on (36%) can be achieved at the higher concentration of reactants.

The above results demonstrate that graft copolymers of starch–PAN with a wide range of add-on, molecular weight, and grafting frequency may be readily prepared with the ferrous ion–hydrogen peroxide initiator system.

Saponified Starch–PAN Copolymers

The fluid and synthetic urine uptake of saponified[16] starch–PAN copolymers were measured, and the results are given in Table IX. Products which contain more PAN of higher molecular weight absorbed more water.

Portions of the hydrolyzed gel were isolated by the method described by Gugliemelli et al.[16] The gel was acidified to pH 3.0, centrifuged, dehydrated with alcohol, and oven dried. The resulting powder was then redispersed in H_2O at pH 7.0–9.0 to give highly viscous dispersions.

Although the products reported here do not absorb as much water as the products reported by Weaver et al.,[13] the preparation from granular starch and the use of the less expensive initiator makes the ferrous ion–hydrogen peroxide-initiated graft polymerization an attractive alternative method of preparation of products of this type.

The mention of firm names or trade products does not imply that they are endorsed or recommended by the U.S. Department of Agriculture over other firms or similar products not mentioned.

References

1. L. A. Gugliemelli, C. L. Swanson, F. L. Baker, W. M. Doane, and C. R. Russell, *J. Polym. Sci., Polym. Chem. Ed.,* **12,** 2683 (1974).

2. Z. Reyes, C. F. Clark, F. Dreier, R. C. Phillips, C. R. Russell, and C. E. Rist, *Ind. Eng. Chem., Prod. Res. Dev.,* **12,** 62 (1973).

3. L. A. Gugliemelli, M. O. Weaver, C. R. Russell, and C. E. Rist, *Polym. Lett.,* **9,** 151 (1971).

4. G. F. Fanta, R. C. Burr, C. R. Russell, and C. E. Rist, *J. Macromol. Sci. Chem.,* 4(2), 331 (1970).

5. G. F. Fanta, R. C. Burr, C. R. Russell, and C. E. Rist, *Cereal Chem.,* **47,** 85 (1970).

6. G. F. Fanta, R. C. Burr, C. R. Russell, and C. E. Rist, *J. Polym. Sci. A-1,* **7,** 1675 (1969).

7. G. F. Fanta, R. C. Burr, C. R. Russell, and C. E. Rist, *J. Appl. Polym. Sci.,* **13,** 133 (1969).

8. R. C. Burr, G. F. Fanta, C. R. Russell, and C. E. Rist, *J. Macromol. Sci. Chem.*, **1**, 1381 (1967).

9. G. F. Fanta, R C. Burr, C. R. Russell, and C. E. Rist, *J. Appl. Polym. Sci.*, **11**, 457 (1967).

10. Z. Reyes, C. E. Rist, and C. R. Russell, *J. Polym. Sci. A-1*, **4**, 1031 (1966).

11. G. F. Fanta, R. C. Burr, C. R. Russell, and C. E. Rist, *J. Appl. Polym. Sci.*, **10**, 929 (1966).

12. G. F. Fanta, R. C. Burr, C. R. Russell, and C. E. Rist, *Polym. Lett.*, **4**, 765 (1966).

13. M. O. Weaver, E. B. Bagley, G. F. Fanta, and W. M. Doane, U.S. Pat. 3,935,099, Jan. 27, 1976.

14. C. E. Brockway and P. A. Seaberg, *J. Polym. Sci. A-1*, **5**, 1313 (1967).

15. P. F. Onyon, *J. Polym. Sci.*, **37**, 315 (1959).

16. L. A. Gugliemelli, M. O. Weaver, C. R. Russell, and C. E. Rist, *J. Appl. Polym. Sci.*, **13**, 2007 (1969).

Received July 12, 1976

JOURNAL OF APPLIED POLYMER SCIENCE   VOL. 21 2575–2581 (1977)

Poly(aryloxyphosphazenes) and a Flame Retardant Foam

JAMES E. THOMPSON and KENNARD A. REYNARD, *Horizons Research Incorporated, Cleveland, Ohio 44122*

Synopsis

Plastics and elastomers were prepared, physical state determined by the side chains attached to the phosphorus–nitrogen backbone. The poly(aryloxyphosphazenes) displayed a high degree of flame retardancy in the uncured, unfilled state. Limiting oxygen index (LOI) values varied from 27 to 33 for nonhalogenated materials and from 38 to 65 for halogenated materials. These values qualify all poly(aryloxyphosphazenes) studied as flame retardants according to the generally accepted definition ($LOI \geq 27$). Materials subjected to the National Bureau of Standards Smoke Test gave encouraging results. The $[(C_6H_5O)_2PN\text{-}(4\text{-}C_2H_5C_6H_4O)_2PN]_n$ elastomer was investigated for application as a fire retardant insulating foam. Closed-cell foams produced from this copolymer showed much improved fire retardancy and smoke generation compared to commercially available fire retardant foam insulations.

INTRODUCTION

The need for fire retardant polymers and polymer systems has increased markedly in recent years because of increased emphasis on safety and the increasing importance of enclosed environments. Elastomeric foams for thermal insulation are a basic requirement in environments such as naval vessels, aircraft, and space vehicles as well as in certain areas within ground-based structures. Poly(aryloxyphosphazenes) provide materials which have markedly reduced smoke evolution on combustion and improved fire retardancy over currently used materials.

Oligomeric phosphazene compounds have been studied for use in a variety of flame retardant applications.[1] The utility of the phosphazenes as flame retardants is due to the high percentage of phosphorus present, the simultaneous presence of large amounts of nitrogen, and the possibility of incorporation of halogen at the same time.[2] Polyphosphazene polymers, therefore, would be expected to be excellent flame retardant polymers.

A number of poly(aryloxyphosphazenes) with potentially useful properties have been synthesized,[3] and one of these, $[(C_6H_5O)_2PN\text{-}(4\text{-}C_2H_5C_6H_4O)_2PN]_n$, was developed into an elastomeric, closed-cell foam with superior flame retardancy and reduced smoke emission.

TABLE I
Typical Characterization of $[(C_6H_5O)_2PN\text{-}(4\text{-}C_2H_5C_6H_4O)_2PN]_n$ Copolymer

Yield, %	50–75	
$[\eta]_{C_6H_6}^{30°C}$	2–3	
Analysis	Found, %	Calculated, %
C	63.4–65.2	64.9
H	5.3–5.6	5.4
Cl	0.02–0.1	0.0
$C_6H_5O/4\text{-}C_2H_5C_6H_4O$	47/53–50/50 (by NMR)	50/50

TABLE II[3]
Limiting Oxygen Index (LOI) of $[(R_1C_6H_4O)_2PN\text{-}(R_2C_6H_4O)_2PN]_n$

R_1	R_2	LOI
H	H	33
4-Cl	4-Cl	44
3-Cl	3-Cl	41
4-CH$_3$	4-CH$_3$	27
3-CH$_3$	3-CH$_3$	28
4-Br	4-Br	65
3-CH$_3$	3-CH$_3$	38
4-Cl	4-Cl	
H	2,4-Cl$_2$	43
H	4-C$_2$H$_5$	28
4-Cl	2,4-Cl$_2$	59
3-CH$_3$	4-CH$_3$	27

EXPERIMENTAL

Synthesis of $[(C_6H_5O)_2PN\text{-}(4\text{-}C_2H_5C_6H_4O)_2PN]_n$ Polymer

Hexachlorophosphazene was purified by distillation (120°C/10 mm Hg) and recrystallization (n-heptane) and was polymerized under vacuum at 250°C, generally in the presence of HCl (1 mmole/2600 g monomer). The aryloxides were prepared by the addition of sodium methoxide (10 mole % excess over P-Cl equivalents) to an equimolar solution of phenol and 4-ethylphenol (5 mole-% excess over sodium methoxide) in bis(2-methoxyethyl) ether (ca. 1.5 l./mole NaOCH$_3$). The methanol produced was removed by azeotropic distillation with benzene. The $[Cl_2PN]_n$ polymer, essentially free from cyclic phosphazenes, was dissolved in dry benzene (ca. 1 l. solvent/100 g polymer) and added slowly over 3 to 5 hr to a refluxing (125°C) solution of the sodium aryloxides, and temperature was maintained at 125° ± 1°C for 50 to 55 hr. The reaction mixture was cooled to 80°C or lower, and copolymer was precipitated by addition to twice the total volume of methanol or ethanol/water (10/1 v/v) and stirred for one day. The polymer was dissolved three times in 8 to 16 liters tetrahydrofuran, precipitated into 10 to 15 gallons water, and washed with methanol or isopropanol. Ranges of values of intrinsic viscosity, elemental analyses, and $C_6H_5O/4\text{-}C_2H_5C_6H_4O$ ratios as determined by NMR (in deuterochloroform solvent) are shown in Table I.

TABLE III
Typical Properties of $[(C_6H_5O)_2PN-(4-C_2H_5C_6H_4O)_2PN]_n$ Foam

Property	Test reference	MIL P-0015280F (SHIPS) requirement	Typical $[(C_6H_5O)_2PN-(4-C_2H_5C_6H_4O)_2PN]_n$ foam properties
Density, lb/ft^3	ASTM D-1667-70	4.5 to 8.5	3.5 to 13
Compression resistance at 25% deflection	FED-STD-601, 12151 MOD.	2.0 to 6.0	2.0 to 7.0
Water absorption, psf, max.	4.3.6[a]	0.1	0.02 to 0.036
Compression set, %, max.	ASTM D-1667-70	24	—
Dimensional change, length %, max.	4.3.8[a]	7	3
Fire resistance, flame spread index, max.	ASTM E-162-67	30	14 to 24
Smoke density, flaming	NBS smoke chamber	250	49
Oil resistance	4.3.10[a]	no softening or visible swelling	no softening or visible swelling
Tensile strength, psi, min.	FED-STD-601, 4111	40	20 to 48
Ultimate elongation, %, min.	FED-STD-601, 4121	100	70 to 120
Tensile strength of cemented joints before aging, min.	4.3.13.1[a]	no bond failure	no bond failure
Flexibility at 28°F, initial, after heat aging	4.3.14.1[a]	no cracking	no cracking
7 days/180°F	4.3.14.2[a]	no cracking	no cracking
Thermal conductivity, Btu/in. (hr sq ft °F)$^{-1}$ K factor, max.	ASTM C-177-63	0.30	0.318
Water vapor permeability, perm-in., max.	ASTM C-355-64	0.30	0.16

[a] MIL P-0015280F (SHIPS).

Synthesis of Other Poly(aryloxyphosphazenes)

Other poly(aryloxyphosphazenes) were prepared using procedures similar to that for $[(C_2H_5O)_2PN-(4-C_2H_5C_6H_4O)_2PN]_n$ copolymer described above. Some of the polyphosphazenes synthesized are listed in Table II along with LOI values. Poly(alkylaryloxyphosphazenes) were decidedly more soluble than their unsubstituted or halogenated counterparts.

Preparation of Elastomeric Vulcanizates and Foams

Vulcanizates were prepared from $[(C_6H_5O)_2PN-(4-C_2H_5C_6H_4O)_2PN]_n$ copolymer using a high-intensity rubber mixer and a two-roll rubber mill. Polymer, pigments, and plasticizers were blended in the mixer, and peroxide curing agents

TABLE IV
$[(C_6H_5O)_2PN-(4-C_2H_5C_6H_4O)_2PN]_n$ Vulcanizate Formulations

	A	B	C
Copolymer, phr	100	100	100
Burgess KE, phr	100	—	—
Calwhite, phr	—	40	—
Hydral 710, phr	—	—	100
Elastomag 170, phr	6	5	5
DiCup 40KE, phr	4	—	—
Varox powder, phr	—	5	5.7
Benzoyl peroxide, phr	—	—	4
Cure			
Press, min/°F	15/300	15/290	15/290
Oven, hr/°F	24/212	24/212	24/212
Tensile strength,[a] psi	2410	1420	670
Elongation,[a] %	80	330	150

[a] ASTMD3196T.

were added to the mixed stock on the mill. Samples were molded in an electrically heated horizontal cut-off mold 0.050 in. deep.

Foams were prepared by mixing polymer and pigments in the mixer and adding peroxide curing agents, blowing agents, and activators on the mill at or below room temperature. Milled stock was molded in an electrically heated mold, using a full charge, under confining pressure for a short time (2 to 10 min) before being placed in a forced-air oven for final expansion. Foams were compounded to meet a U.S. Navy specification, MIL P-0015280F (SHIPS), shown in Table III.

RESULTS AN DISCUSSION

The $[(C_6H_5O)_2PN-(4-C_2H_5C_6H_4O)_2PN]_n$ copolymer was selected for development into an insulating foam because of its fire retardancy without the presence of halogen and because of its elastomeric character.

Prior to preparation of foam compositions, several vulcanizates were formulated to obtain physical/mechanical property data on the copolymer batches. Properties of three representative but unoptimized formulations are shown in Table IV. These results indicate that the $[(C_6H_5O)_2PN-(4-C_2H_5C_6H_4O)_2PN]_n$ copolymer shows promise for applications where moderate tensile strength and flame retardancy are required.

After a brief traverse of various foaming agents, curing agents, and foaming methods, foams of $[(C_6H_5O)_2PN-(4-C_2H_5C_6H_4O)_2PN]_n$ were prepared[4] using a mixed peroxide curing system and a chemical blowing agent, azodicarbonamide. Typical formulations and properties are shown in Table V. Formulation C in Table V was chosen as the most desirable for the intended application due to its excellent flame retardancy. Comparison of the NBS smoke test values of a foam prepared using this formulation with a commercial fire retardant foam is shown in Table VI. The maximum smoke density, D_{max}, of the $[(C_6H_5O)_2PN-(4-C_2H_5C_6H_4O)_2PN]_n$ foam is about one fifth that of the commercial foam. Also, the value for time to $D_s = 16$ for the $[(C_6H_5O)_2PN-(4-$

TABLE V
Typical $[(C_6H_5O)_2PN\text{-}(4\text{-}C_2H_5C_6H_4O)_2PN]_n$ Foam Formulations

	A	B	C
Copolymer, phr	100	100	100
Calwhite, phr	40	—	—
Hydral 710, phr	—	100	200
Elastomag 170, phr	5	5	5
Varox powder, phr	5	5	8
Benzoyl peroxide, phr	1	1.5	2
Zinc stearate, phr	—	0–10	8–26
Celogen AZ-130, phr	15	15–21	30
B IK, phr	10	10–15	20
Density, lb/ft^3	3.9–9.8	3.6–10	6–13
Compression resistance at 25% deflection, psi	1–4	2–5	2–7
Tensile strength, psi	—	20–50	20–30
Ultimate elongation, %	—	80–120	65–80
LOI	25–26	31	38–48

TABLE VI
NBS Smoke Test, Flaming Condition

	Commercial fire retardant foam	$[(C_6H_5O)_2PN\text{-}(4\text{-}C_2H_5C_6H_4O)_2PN]_n$ foam
Density, lb/ft^3	6	6.7
LOI	29	48
D_{max}	250	49
Time to $D_s = 16$, min	0.2	1.5
R_m, max. rate, min^{-1}	149	10
HCl, ppm	20	0
CO_2, %	0.5	0.3
CO, ppm	350	100
HCN, ppm	20	10
Weight loss, %	34.2	15.9

[a] Meets MIL P-0015280F (SHIPS).

$C_2H_5C_6H_4O)_2PN]_n$ represents a very considerable gain in egress time from a room in which a fire is consuming this foam as compared to the commercial foam. In addition, the surface flammability of this foam, as determined by ASTM E 162, was better than the surface flammability of a commercial material, as shown in Table VII.

Though $[(C_6H_5O)_2PN\text{-}(4\text{-}C_2H_5C_6H_4O)_2PN]_n$ foams were formulated to provide maximum flame retardancy, they also had to have adequate physical properties for their intended application as an insulating foam. A comparison of typical properties of $[(C_6H_5O)_2PN\text{-}(4\text{-}C_2H_5C_6H_4O)_2PN]_n$ foam to the military specification MIL P-0015280F is shown in Table III.

The foams also have long-term stability to at least 300°F as demonstrated by retention of resilience and density, as shown in Tables VII and VIII. These results suggest potential use at elevated temperatures.

TABLE VII
Surface Flammability of Foams

	$[(C_6H_5O)_2PN-(4-C_2H_5C_6H_4O)_2PN]_n$ foam	Commercial foam[a]
Flame spread factor F_s	4.4	4.9
Heat evolution factor Q	3.9	5.0
Flame spread index, $I_s = F_s \cdot Q$	17	24

[a] Meets MIL P-0015280F (SHIPS).

TABLE VIII
Compression Resistance at 25% Deflection After Isothermal Aging at 300°F

	Compression resistance, psi			
		$[(C_6H_5O)_2PN-(4-C_2H_5C_6H_4O)_2PN]_n$ Foams		
Hours	Commercial fire retardant foam[a]	I	II	III
0	2.5	1.7	4.0	6.7
2	1.9	1.6	—	—
6	2.3	1.7	—	—
24	12	0.7	—	—
96	25.7	1.7	—	—
	(no recovery)			
168	—	1.6	—	—
200	—	—	4.1	8.4
390	—	—	4.8	11.9
600	—	12.5	—	—
795	—	—	9.7	35.8
1128	—	—	15.5	48.2

[a] Meets MIL P-0015280F (SHIPS).

CONCLUDING REMARKS

Poly(aryloxyphosphazene) foams represent an advance over current commercial flame retardant closed-cell insulating foams. Foams were prepared on a larger laboratory scale to allow field testing, which is currently in progress. Other poly(aryloxyphosphazenes) show potential for advanced applications, particularly where reduced smoke generation and increased fire retardancy are important.

This work was done under Contract No. N00024-73-C-5474, Department of the Navy, Naval Ship Systems Command.

References

1. L. Godfrey and J. Schappel, *Ind. Eng. Chem., Prod. Res. Dev.*, **9,** 426 (1970).
2. J. Lyons, *The Chemistry and Uses of Fire Retardants*, Wiley, New York, 1970.

3. K. A. Reynard, A. H. Gerber, and S. H. Rose, Synthesis of Phosphonitrilic Plastics and Elastomers for Marine Applications, Horizons Inc., Final Report, Contract DAAG-71-C-0103, Dec. 1972, AD 755 188.

4. K. A. Reynard, R. W. Sicka, and J. E. Thompson, Poly(aryloxyphosphazene) Foams, Horizons Inc., Final Technical Report—Part 1, Contract No. N00024-73-C-5474, June 1974.

Received June 28, 1976
Revised July 19, 1976

TRANSACTIONS of
THE SOCIETY OF RHEOLOGY
—Journal of Rheology

Editor: Raymond R. Myers
Assistant Editors: Edward A. Collins
Shigeharu Onogi
J. George Savins
Charles L. Sieglaff
A. Silberberg
James L. White

This primary reference journal for unsolved problems in industry contains original papers on the science of the deformation and flow of matter. Serves especially those in plastics, rubbers, paints, coatings, fibers and structural materials. Coverage extends to the molecular features and morphology responsible for the properties in question, and also to the processes by which the compositions are shaped and made serviceable. Papers range over a wide variety of topics from theoretical to experimental basic studies to applied research, without regard for conventional limitations other than that the work be good science.

Although this is the official journal of the Society of Rheology, *Transactions* is not confined to papers presented at the Society's meetings.

Published Quarterly

Subscription: Volume 21, 1977: $55.00
Outside U.S. add $6.00 for postage and handling.

Mail to: **Subscription Department E5076-53**
John Wiley & Sons, Inc.
605 Third Avenue
New York, New York 10016

Please enter a one year subscription to *Transactions / Journal of Rheology,* Volume 21, 1977.

☐ Remittance enclosed $ ☐ Bill me.

Name

Address

City   State   Postal Code
Payment must be made in U.S. currency, by U.S. bank draft, international money order, or UNESCO coupons.

Photoaddition of Fluoroolefins on Aromatic Polyamide

MADELINE S. TOY and ROGER S. STRINGHAM, *Science Applications, Inc., Sunnyvale, California 94086,* and
FREDERIC S. DAWN, *National Aeronautics and Space Administration, Lyndon B. Johnson Space Center, Houston, Texas 77058*

Synopsis

A photografting method has been developed to surface treat aromatic polyamide fabrics in the presence of fluoroolefin vapors. The new fabrics are more flame resistant in oxygen-enriched environment than untreated commercial aramid fabrics. The photoaddition reaction of haloolefins has been shown to irreversibly modify the fabrics, which were analyzed by water wettability, scanning electron microscopy, x-ray analysis, and ^{19}F nuclear magnetic resonance spectroscopy.

INTRODUCTION

The objective of this work is to chemically modify commercial aromatic polyamide for providing flame-resistant fibrous materials in an oxygen-enriched environment. Such fibrous products are aimed for applications in space and deep-sea vehicles. Organic fibrous products, which possess highly aromatic backbone, are known to exhibit outstanding flame resistance.[1] Nomex, which is a high-temperature aromatic polyamide manufactured by du Pont, is self-extinguishing in air but burns in atmospheres with an elevated partial pressure of oxygen (e.g., 31/69 O_2/N_2 at 10 psia).

Prior work with Nomex fabric shows that improvement of flame resistance is feasible through chemical modification as phosphorylation[2] and halogenation.[3] However, such treatments strongly color the fibrous products and also degrade the aromatic polyamide.

This paper describes a photoaddition reaction of fluoroolefins to modify aromatic polyamide without the apparent change of physical properties and appearance of the fibrous material.

EXPERIMENTAL

Materials

Aromatic polyamide (Nomex HT-10-41, woven fabric, natural color) was purchased from Stern and Stern Textiles; tetrafluoroethylene and bromotrifluoroethylene were obtained from PCR; and nitrogen (99.999%), special gas mixture of 31% oxygen and 69% nitrogen, and fluorotrichloromethane were obtained from Matheson Gas. The fabric and reagents were used as received. The vapors of fluoroolefins were checked by infrared analysis.

2583

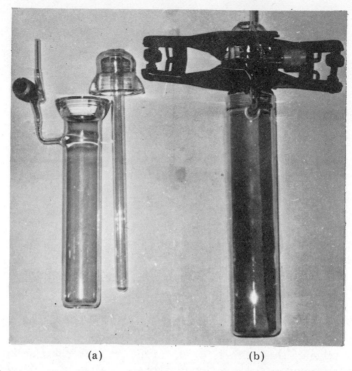

(a)   (b)

Fig. 1. Reaction vessel: (a) an opened cylindrical Pyrex reactor with side arm and valve for attachment to the manifold (to the left) and quartz sleeve (to the right); (b) a closed reaction vessel
with the fabric mounted around the centered quartz tube.

Apparatus

A copper vacuum manifold was used for transferring fluoroolefin vapors from
the storage cylinder to a piece of fabric specimen hanging in a reaction vessel (Fig.
1). The cylindrical Pyrex reaction vessel consists of a centered quartz sleeve
for receiving a 11-in. Pen Ray mercury-arc lamp (Ultraviolet Products). Pressures were measured with a Heise gauge, and the reaction temperature was
maintained by heating tape or infrared lamps.

Figure 2 shows the flammability test apparatus. The ignitor (Type B, Clen-
weld Products) was held in position by a coiled Nichrome ignition wire (1 ohm/
in.). The sample (2.5 × 5 in.) was mounted vertically between the stainless steel
sample holders, leaving 2 × 5 in. of exposed surface. The vertical flame test[4]
uses a mixture of 31% oxygen and 69% nitrogen at 10 psia.

Analytical Instruments and Sample Preparations

For IR transmission analysis, a strip of fabric was ground into 40 mesh, mixed
with KBr, and pressed into a pellet. A fabric sample for attenuated total re-
flectance (ATR) IR used a Wilkes double-beam ATR attachment at a 45° angle
of incidence in direct contact with a KRS-5 reflector plate (52.5 × 20 × 2 mm).
Both IR transmission and ATR spectra were recorded on a Perkin-Elmer Model
467 spectrometer.

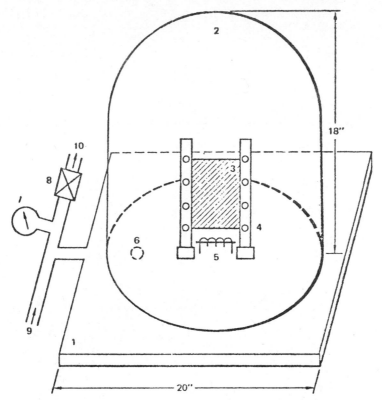

Fig. 2. Flammability test apparatus: (1) metal base plate; (2) bell jar (2 cu ft); (3) sample; (4) sample holders; (5) ignition wire and ignitor; (6) vacuum and gas inlet; (7) vacuum gauge; (8) valve to vacuum; (9) gas inlet; (10) to vacuum pump.

A Cambridge Mark IIA Stereoscan scanning electron microscope (SEM) equipped with an EDAX 505 energy dispersive x-ray probe was used for the photomicrographs and x-ray analysis. The SEM fabric samples were chilled and cut in liquid nitrogen for a clearer end view at the interphase and were subsequently deposited with a thin layer of gold–palladium. An antistatic solution (Ernest F. Fullam, Inc.) was added on the SEM fabric samples right before examination for improved resolution of the photomicrographs.

The ^{19}FNMR spectrum was measured by a Varian XL-100 spectrometer operating at 94.1 MHz. A piece of 4 × 9 in. (3.6 g) treated Nomex fabric was shredded into individual fibers and dissolved in 4 ml concentrated sulfuric acid with added deuterated water for the internal lock. The viscous solution was poured into a 12 mm O.D. NMR tube. Fluorotrichloromethane was used as an external standard.

Procedure

The fabric sample was mounted around the centered quartz tube (at 0 to 1 cm from the surface) in the photografting reaction vessel [Fig. 1(b)]. The side arm was attached to the copper manifold and evacuated. A measured amount of

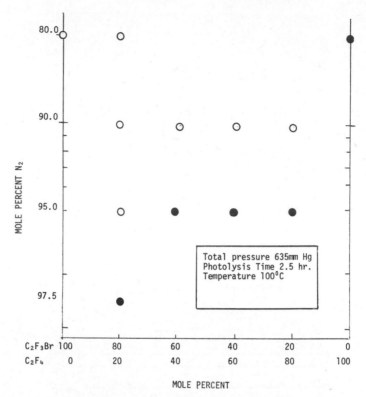

Fig. 3. Effect of fluoroolefin composition on flammability characteristics of photografted Nomex fabrics: (O) self-extinguishing; (●) burned.

gaseous fluoroolefins as neat or premixed fluoroolefins at specified ratio was introduced alternately for improved mixing with anhydrous nitrogen to a specified pressure, temperature, and photolysis time. The amounts of volatile reagents were determined by P-V-T measurements assuming ideal gas behavior.

At the end of the irradiation time, the reaction vessel was evacuated and air was introduced. The photografted fabric sample was washed with fluorotrichloromethane and dried under vacuum.

RESULTS AND DISCUSSION

The vertical flame test (Fig. 2) in a mixture of 31% oxygen and 69% nitrogen at 10 psia was used to show the difference of flammability characteristics of some photografted Nomex fabrics which were treated by varied fluoroolefin compositions in the presence of nitrogen. Figure 3 summarizes the results using one exposure to a medium-pressure mercury arc lamp (see under Apparatus). The photoaddition reaction of fluoroolefins chemically modified the aromatic polyamide surface and thus upgraded not only the flame resistant properties but also acid resistance.

An increase in light energy of the process shortens the fabric treatment time under photolysis, but high-energy ultraviolet source darkens the Nomex fabric rapidly.

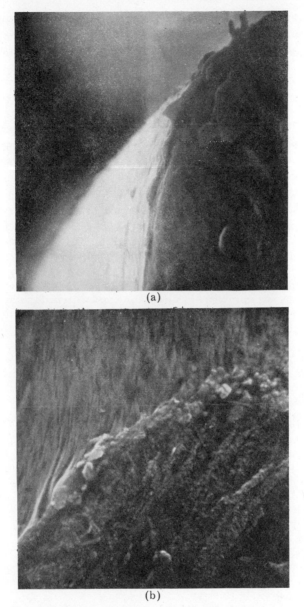

(a)

(b)

Fig. 4. Edge views (cut in liquid nitrogen) of treated Nomex fibers: (a) 12,000×, angle 75°, 20 kV; (b) after soaking in 70% H$_2$SO$_4$ for 80 sec, 11,000×, angle 30°, 20 kV.

In Figure 3, all samples are photografted and water nonwettable regardless of their flammability characteristics.   The water-nonwettability characteristic readily distinguishes them from the untreated samples.   However, the IR spectroscopy (transmission and ATR) failed to show any significant difference between the treated and untreated samples.   The absence of C—F bonds by ATR measurements for difluorocarbene-modified fiber surfaces has been previously reported.[5]   The lack of IR absorption for C—F bonds suggests the monomolecular-like character of the modified surface.

Figure 4 shows the edge views of treated Nomex fiber before (a) and after (b) soaking in 70% sulfuric acid for 80 sec. The SEM photomicrographs illustrate the ease of aromatic polyamide fiber to be strongly etched by the concentrated acid, while the surface of the treated fiber is affected at a substantially decreased rate.

The x-ray probe attached to the SEM is not a sensitive elemental analysis for the light elements,[6] but the presence of bromine on the photografted fabric shows a strong signal. Thus, several treated samples by varied ratios of tetrafluoroethylene and bromotrifluoroethylene were subjected to a gold evaporation process in the same vacuum chamber. Then the gold content of the various samples was assumed as identical and used as the standard. The higher ratios of C_2F_3Br to C_2F_4 in the premixed vapor composition show a corresponding higher bromine content on the treated sample.

The $^{19}FNMR$ spectrum shows the two major narrow absorptions, $\phi = 144$ and 170 ppm, from $CFCl_3$ at the relative intensities of 2:1. The spectrum rules out any significant quantity of the homopolymer[7] and confirms the presence of chemically bonded fluorocarbon-modified Nomex surface.

This work was supported by the National Aeronautics and Space Administration under Contract NAS9-14827. The authors are indebted to Mr. B. Lan for preliminary exploration, Mr. L. Cary for $^{19}FNMR$, and Mr. J. Terry for SEM and x-ray analysis.

References

1. J. H. Ross and R. M. Stanton, *High Temperature and Flame-Resistant Fibers*, J. Preston and J. Economy, Eds., Wiley, New York, 1973, pp. 109–119.

2. C. E. Hathaway and C. L. Early, *ibid.*, pp. 101–108.

3. S. S. Hirsch (to Monsanto Company), U.S. Pats. 3,549,307 (December 27, 1970) and 3,607,798 (September 21, 1971).

4. NASA Document NHB8060. 1A, *Flammability, Odor and Offgassing Requirements and Test Procedures for Materials in Environments That Support Combustion*, Office of Manned Space Flight, National Aeronautic and Space Administration, Washington, D. C., February 1974.

5. D. A. Olsen and A. J. Osteraas, *J. Appl. Polym. Sci.*, **13**, 1523 (1969).

6. O. Johari and A. V. Samudra, in *Characterization of Solid Surface*, P. F. Kane and G. B. Larrabee, Eds., Plenum Press, New York, 1974, p. 118.

7. C. W. Wilson, *J. Polym. Sci.*, **56**, 163 (1962).

Received May 25, 1976
Revised July 2, 1976

JOURNAL OF APPLIED POLYMER SCIENCE   VOL. 21, 2589–2596 (1977)

Synthesis of Copper(II) Complexes of Asymmetric Resins Prepared by Attachment of α-Amino Acids to Crosslinked Polystyrene

M. A. PETIT and J. JOZEFONVICZ, *Laboratoire de Recherches sur les Macromolécules, Université Paris-Nord, 93430 Villetaneuse, France*

Synopsis

In order to use ligand exchange resins for chromatographic resolution of racemic compounds, two series of asymmetric sorbents were prepared by attachment of various optically active α-amino acids onto crosslinked polystyrene. Chloromethylated and chlorosulfonated styrene–divinylbenzene copolymers were prepared and then treated with α-amino acids. Results show that reaction of α-amino acids with polystyrene could be carried to a substitution of 15% to 40% of the aromatic rings depending on many parameters. Stable copper(II) complexes of the asymmetric resins were prepared. Potentiometric methods were adapted to the case of insoluble materials such as resins. These methods indicate that bis-chelate complexes are formed.

INTRODUCTION

Attempts to resolve racemic compounds by ligand exchange chromatography have been carried out in a few cases with various sorbents. Davankov et al. have prepared metal complexes of asymmetric sorbents obtained by reacting chloromethylated polystyrene with α-amino acids[1] or α-amino acid methyl esters.[2] It can be concluded from their results that the most satisfactory chromatographic resolutions of α-amino acid racemates can be made using copper complexes of L-proline or L-hydroxyproline stationary ligands.[3–5] Other asymmetric sorbents obtained by reacting α-amino acids with chlorosulfonated polystyrene have been prepared by Vesa et al.[6] The authors obtained partial resolution of numerous α-amino acid racemates using the asymmetric sorbent poly(styrylsulfonyl-L-phenylalanine) charged with copper ions.[7] Snyder et al. reported the preparation of styrene–divinylbenzene copolymers containing the complex N-carboxymethyl-L-valine–copper(II). Their results show that partial resolution of several amino acids is possible on such a sorbent.[8]

In this paper, we report the preparation and the chemical properties of asymmetric sorbents similar to those prepared by Davankov and Vesa. The aim of this work was to elucidate the effect of certain parameters on the exchange capacities of the two series of asymmetric sorbents obtained from copper ions complexation of α-amino acids linked to chloromethylated or chlorosulfonated polystyrene:

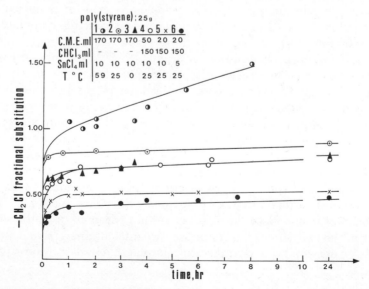

We also report the use of potentiometric methods which allow precise determinations of the sorbents composition.   Copper ions were chosen as complexing metal ions because of the high stability and the well-known structure of their α-amino acid complexes.   The influence of methylene or sulfone bridges on the ability of fixed α-amino acid ligands to interact with copper ions and other free ligands will be compared in a future paper.   The following describes the three successive experimental steps leading in each series to the final asymmetric, complexed sorbent: (1) preparation of chloromethylated or chlorosulfonated polystyrene; (2) attachment of α-amino acids onto the polymer, and (3) complexation of the asymmetric polymer by copper ions.

RESULTS AND DISCUSSION

Chloromethylation of Polystyrene

Crosslinked polystyrene was chloromethylated by pure or dilute chloromethyl methyl ether (CME) at various temperatures in the presence of different amounts of stannic chloride as catalyst.   Results are shown in Figure 1, where the frac-

Fig. 1. Rate of chloromethylation of polystyrene: effect of temperature, dilution of chloromethyl methyl ether (CME), and catalyst amount.

TABLE I
Properties of Chloromethylated Resins

Fixed α-AA	—CH$_2$Cl content, %[a]	α-AA/ PSS$^+$[b]	Reaction time, hr	α-AA content, %	α-AA capacity, meq/g[c]	Copper capacity, meq/g	
						Calcd.[d]	Found[c]
DL-Ala-1	116.1	2	52	17.2	1.10	—	—
DL-Ala-2	150.0	2.8	72	24.3	1.35	—	—
L-Ala-3	116.1	2	192	21.2	1.34	—	—
L-Ala-5	106.5	2	303	19.1	1.24	0.61	0.60
L-Phe-6	106.5	1.3	303	17.4	1.05	0.52	0.52
L-Tyr-10	98.0	2	63	16.7	1.04	0.51	0.78
L-Thr-9[e]	101.2	1.7	48	3.1	0.22	—	—
L-Thr-12	93.0	2	96	34.1	1.96	0.96	1.02
L-Try-13	93.5	2	96	11.4	0.73	0.36	0.59
L-OH Pro 17	31.0	2	22	12.9	0.99	0.49	0.53
L-OH Pro 19	49.2	1.3	19	12.6	0.93	0.46	0.48
L-OH Pro 15	52.8	2	18	16.0	1.13	0.56	0.64
L-OH Pro 7	98.2	2	720	37.4	2.03	1.01	0.98
L-Pro 16	31.0	2	22	13.0	1.01	0.50	0.49
L-Pro 18	49.2	2	19	16.5	1.19	0.59	0.60
L-Pro 14	52.8	2	46	17.9	1.23	0.59	0.60
L-Pro 8	98.2	2	95	36.4	2.06	1.02	0.99
L-Pro 11	129.3	2	63	28.4	1.61	0.79	0.82

[a] Percent —CH$_2$Cl content = 100 × fractional substitution of the polymer before attachment of α-amino acid (α-AA).

[b] Molar ratio of α-amino acid to sulfonium groups (PSS$^+$).

[c] As determined in experimental section.

[d] Calculated on the basis of one copper ion bound by two fixed α-amino acids.

[e] The chloromethylated resin was iodomethylated to an 80% extent before reaction with L-threonine.

tional substitution (number of chloromethyl groups per benzene ring) is plotted versus the reaction time. The chloromethyl content was determined according to a procedure described in the experimental part.

In the pure ether, no limit value of the substitution could be reached when refluxing at 59°C (curve 1). Furthermore, no striking difference was found between the runs at 25° and 0°C after 1 hr (curves 2 and 3).

When diluting the ether in chloroform (curves 4 and 5) at 25°C, the limit of substitution was lowered to 0.53.

When decreasing the amount of catalyst, the limit of substitution was slightly lowered (curves 5 and 6).

Attachment of α-Amino Acid to Chloromethylated Polystyrene

Significant attachment of α-amino acids to chloromethylated polystyrene implied the activation of the polymer. Three procedures have been used as follows:

The polymer was iodomethylated according to known conditions.[8,9] The exchange reaction of Cl by I proceeded to an extent of 80%. The resulting resin was not found to exhibit a sufficient reactivity toward α-amino acids (Table I, resin 9). Therefore, according to another procedure described elsewhere,[1] attempts were made to attach α-amino acids to chloromethylated polystyrene in the presence of sodium iodide and a tertiary amine.   Low attachment yields were found again.

Good yields could be obtained using the two following steps.   In the first step, chloromethylated polystyrene was treated with dimethyl sulfide in a water–isopropanol mixture following a preparation of sulfonium derivatives outlined by Snyder et al.[8]   The conversion rate is shown in Figure 2.   It is apparent that more than 80% of chloromethyl groups have reacted after 24 hr.   Changing the reaction temperature did not affect significantly the reaction yield.   The amount of displaced chlorine was determined using a method described in the experimental part.   The reaction is reversible; therefore, the sulfonium polymer was not isolated.   In the second step, the α-amino acid (sodium salt) dissolved in a water–isopropanol mixture was added to the sulfonium polymer suspension.   A sodium hydroxide amount corresponding to the number of sulfonium groups was simultaneously added in order to neutralize the hydrochloric acid amount displaced by the attachment reaction.   After refluxing for one to four days, the final polymer was filtered, washed, and titrated in order to determine the extent of α-amino acid attachment.

Results are summarized in Table I.   Comparison of samples 14, 18 and 1, 3, and 5 shows that the reaction tends to level off within approximately 40 hr.   Results observed on samples 15, 19 lead to the conclusion that there is no large influence of the molar ratio (α-amino acid/sulfonium groups) on the achieved α-amino acid content.

It may be pointed out that the determining parameter is the average number of chloromethyl groups per aromatic ring.   When changing this factor from 0.31 to 0.98, the percentage of aromatic rings having fixed a L-proline or L-hydroxyproline group increases from 13% to 37%.

The particle size range of final resins is strongly affected by the extent of α-amino acid attachment.   No significant change in the bead size of the starting polystyrene is observed when the percentage of substituted aromatic rings is less than 15%, which corresponds to a capacity of about 1 milliequivalent α-amino acid per gram resin (1 meq/g).   Resins with larger substitution percentages could be obtained; but, unfortunately, the beads generally break down to fine powders unsuitable in the chromatographic investigations.

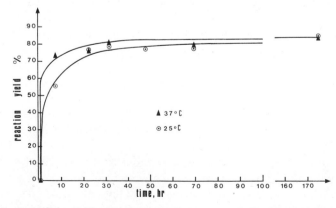

Fig. 2.   Rate of reaction of chloromethylated polystyrene with dimethyl sulfide: effect of temperature.

TABLE II
Properties of Chlorosulfonated Resins

Fixed α-AA	—SO$_2$Cl content, %[a]	α-AA/ —SO$_2$Cl[b]	α-AA content, %	α-AA capacity, meq/g[c]	Copper capacity, meq/g Calcd.[d]	Copper capacity, meq/g Found[c]
L-Phe-1	59.7	2	16.5	0.88	1.51	1.28
L-Pro-2	56.0	2	28.9	1.56	1.45	1.40
L-Phe-3	81.4	1.6	21.6	0.99	1.88	1.81
L-Thr-4	73.1	1.1	18.3	0.93	1.80	1.46
L-Ala-5	73.1	1.9	26.4	1.34	1.79	1.78
L-Pro-6	82.0	1	35.3	1.59	1.79	1.37
L-Glu-7	82.0	2	28.3	1.19	2.22	2.00
L-OH Pro-11	72.4	1.1	46.5	2.02	1.53	1.46

[a] Percent —SO$_2$Cl content = 100 × fractional substitution of the polymer before attachment of α-amino acid (α-AA).

[b] Molar ratio of α-amino acid to chlorosulfonated groups.

[c] As determined in experimental section.

[d] Calculated on the basis of one copper ion bound by two fixed α-amino acids or two sulfonate groups.

Chlorosulfonation of Polystyrene

Crosslinked polystyrene was chlorosulfonated according to a procedure previously described.[10] The chlorosulfonated materials were found to have in all cases a chlorosulfonyl content between 4 and 4.5 meq/g (see experimental section). Analysis indicated a slight excess of sulfur with respect to chlorine. This suggests that chlorosulfonation of polystyrene involves partial crosslinking due to sulfone formation since no sulfonate groups could be found. However, the percentage of bridged aromatic ring calculated from analysis of sulfur and chlorine is less than 10%. Because chlorosulfonated resins are sensitive to hydrolysis, reactions with α-amino acids were immediately carried out.

Attachment of α-Amino Acids to Chlorosulfonated Polystyrene

Chlorosulfonated polystyrene was treated in a water–dioxane mixture containing an α-amino acid in the presence of alkali according to a method described by Vesa et al.[6] The α-amino acid contents of the final resins were determined by acid–base titration (see experimental section). Results listed in Table II are expressed as the percentage of aromatic rings substituted by one α-amino acid group. The resin capacities are also reported in meq/g. Percentages have been calculated without considering crosslinkage by sulfone bridges since only few aromatic rings are bridged. The results show that the resins contain about 1 meq/g of α-amino acid. It can be calculated that approximately 20% to 30% of the aromatic rings of the polymer are substituted. It shall be pointed out that this substitution carried onto a chlorosulfonated resin is faster and more convenient than the one involving a chloromethylated resin.

Copper(II) Complexes of Polymer Derivatives

Two procedures were used to complex the α-amino acid groups linked to polystyrene. In the first procedure, a weighed portion of an asymmetric resin (sodium salt) was stirred in an aqueous solution containing a quantity of copper ions corresponding to half the amount of α-amino acid groups. This method was given up because the final complexed resin might be a mixture of the copper complex and insoluble copper hydroxide. Therefore, a second procedure was chosen.

The asymmetric resin was treated with an excess of $0.1M$ solution of copper nitrate in $0.5M$ aqueous ammonia. The complexed resin was filtered off after 24 hr and washed several times with $0.5M$ ammonia solution and then water. The copper content was determined as described in the experimental part.

Results listed respectively in Tables I and II for chloromethylated and chlorosulfonated polymers show that the experimental values of the copper capacity of the resins are in good agreement with the theoretical amounts calculated from the assumption that one copper(II) ion is bound with two α-amino acid groups. Our results agree well with previously reported studies[11] on the stoechiometry of the α-amino acid–copper(II) complexes. However, discrepancies occurred when L-tyrosine and L-tryptophan were fixed onto polystyrene. In the case of chlorosulfonated polymers, it was additionally discovered by copper content determinations that copper(II) ions are also bound with sulfonic sites giving the following structure:

$$CH-CH_2 \cdots \cdots CH-CH_2 \cdots \cdots CH-CH_2 \cdots$$

$$SO_2-NH-CHR \qquad\qquad SO_3^-$$
$$C=O$$
$$O----Cu----O$$
$$O=C \qquad\qquad Cu^{2+}$$
$$CHR-NH-SO_2 \qquad\qquad SO_3^-$$
$$\qquad\qquad\qquad SO_3^-$$

EXPERIMENTAL

Materials

Copolymers of styrene and divinylbenzene (2%) were Fluka samples in the form of 200–400 mesh beads. The commercial product was washed thoroughly with $1M$ sodium hydroxide, $1M$ hydrochloric acid, water, and methanol and then dried under vacuum at 60°C. The α-amino acids were Fluka reagents (puriss grade). They were used with other chemicals and solvents without further purification.

Chloromethylated Polystyrene

Copolymer styrene–divinylbenzene (25 g) was stirred at 25°C for 30 min in 150 ml chloroform. Pure or dilute chloromethyl methyl ether (CME) with stannic chloride was added. The reaction was then carried out at various temperatures for different times (Fig. 1). The resin was filtered off and washed with 3:1 dioxane–water and 3:1 dioxane–3N aqueous HCl. The polymer was further successively washed with solutions which changed gradually from water to pure dioxane and then progressively to pure methanol. Finally, it was dried under vacuum at 60°C.

The chloromethyl content was determined from the analytical value of Cl and through the following potentiometric procedure: a weighed portion (about 200 mg) of the resin was quaternized in 5 ml pure boiling n-butyl amine for 6 hr. The mixture was then poured into 50 ml water. After acidification of the heterogeneous medium with nitric acid, the Cl⁻ content was determined by potentiometric titration using a silver indicating electrode and a $0.1M$ silver nitrate solution as titrant. Good agreement was found between the values obtained from the two methods.

Sulfonium Polymer

A typical run was carried out according to the following procedure: a 20.0-g portion of dry chloromethyl polystyrene (130 mmoles Cl) was suspended in a mixture of 48 ml dimethyl sulfide (650 mmoles), 180 ml isopropanol, and 150 ml water. The solution was stirred at 25° or 37°C for several hours (Fig. 2). The reaction yield was determined using a potentiometric titration of the Cl⁻ ions contained in weighed aliquots of the suspension.

Attachment of α-Amino Acid to Sulfonium Polymer

To the preceding sulfonium polymer suspension containing about 100 meq —CH$_2$S$^+$(CH$_3$)$_2$Cl⁻ groups, a mixture of 100 meq NaOH and an amount between 100 and 200 mmoles α-amino acid (sodium salt) dissolved in about 100 ml water was added. After refluxing for variable times (Table I), the resin was filtered and refluxed for 4 hr in $4M$ NH$_4$OH to remove remaining dimethyl sulfide. The polymer was filtered and carefully washed with water, $1M$ HCl solution, water, and $1M$ NaOH solution. Then, it was several times suspended in water and filtered until the filtrate was found neutral. Finally, the polymer was dried under vacuum.

Chlorosulfonated Polystyrene

Crosslinked polystyrene beads (200–400 mesh), 30 g, were swelled for 1 hr at 25°C in 250 ml methylene chloride. Then, a mixture of 200 ml nitromethane and 180 ml chlorosulfonic acid was added. The solution was stirred at 40°C for 6 hr. The crude polymer was filtered and washed carefully with nitromethane and acetone. Then, the resin was washed again for a short time with water and methanol. Finally, it was dried under vacuum. The number of chlorosulfonyl groups —SO$_2$Cl was determined according to the following method: a weighed sample (200 mg) of resin was hydrolyzed at reflux for 24 hr in 50 ml aqueous $0.1M$ sodium hydroxide solution. After acidification, the Cl– ions were titrated by a $0.1M$ silver nitrate solution using a silver indicating electrode.

Attachment of α-Amino Acid to Chlorosulfonated Polymer

Between 100 and 200 mmoles α-amino acid was dissolved in 400 ml of a 5:3 water–dioxane mixture by adding the minimum amount of $4M$ NaOH. The pH was measured and about 25 g of the preceding chlorosulfonated resin (100 meq

—SO$_2$Cl) was added to the mixture. The pH was maintained at its original value by 4M NaOH additions. The reaction was stopped when no further NaOH was required. The polymer was filtered and carefully washed with water–dioxane mixtures, water, and 1M NaOH solution. Then, it was suspended several times in water and filtrated until the filtrate was found neutral. Finally, the polymer was dried under vacuum.

Determination of α-Amino Acid Contents

The following procedure was used for both chlorosulfonated and chloromethylated polystyrene resins containing α-amino acid groups. Polymers were suspended for 24 hr in an aqueous 0.1M sodium hydroxide solution, filtered, washed with aqueous 0.01M sodium hydroxide solution, and then dried. Under these conditons, all the α-amino acid groups were converted into their sodium salts. A weighed portion (1 g) of the sodium salt of the polymer was suspended in 30 ml water. An acidic titration was carried out very slowly by small additions of aqueous 0.1M hydrochloric acid. The observed equivalent point occurs for the amino group neutralization.

Determination of Copper Contents

A weighed portion (50 mg) of a copper complex of a resin was decomposed for a few hours in 50 ml of aqueous 1M nitric acid. After filtration, 1 ml of the solution was poured into the following mixture: 20 ml water, 10 ml 10% tartaric acid solution, and 10 ml 10% hydroxylamine hydrochloride solution. The pH was fixed between 5 or 6 by dropwise additions of concentrated ammonia. Then, 10 ml of 10^{-3}M bisquinolin solution in isoamyl alcohol was added. The water phase was discarded and the concentration of the copper(II)–bisquinolin complex was determined by spectroscopic measurements of the optical density at 547 nm (extinction coefficient ϵ_m = 7620 l./mole).

References

1. S. V. Rogozhin, V. A. Davankov, I. A. Yamskov, and V. P. Kabanov, *Vysokomol. Soedin. B,* **14,** 472 (1972); *C. A.,* **77,** 115 180 r, (1972).

2. V. A. Davankov, S. V. Rogozhin, and I. I. Piesliakas, *Vysokomol. Soedin. B,* **14,** 276 (1972); *C. A.,* **77,** 35 336 f (1972).

3. V. A. Davankov, S. V. Rogozhin, I. I. Piesliakas, A. V. Semechkin, and T. P. Sachkova, *Dokl. Akad. Nauk SSSR,* **201,** 854 (1971); *C.A.,* **76,** 100 010 (1972).

4. V. A. Davankov, S. V. Rogozhin, A. V. Semechkin, and T. P. Sachkova, *J. Chromatogr.,* **82,** 359 (1973).

5. V. A. Davankov, S. V. Rogozhin, and A. V. Semechkin, *J. Chromatogr.,* **91,** 493 (1974).

6. V. S. Vesa and R. K. Moroshchikas, *Tr. Akad. Nauk Lit. SSR, Ser. B,* **2**(69), 93 (1972); *C.A.,* **77,** 115 177 v (1972).

7. V. S. Vesa, *Zh. Ob. Shch. Khim, SSSR,* **42** (12), 2780 (1972); *J. Gen. Chem.,* **42** (12), 2771 (1972); *C.A.,* **78,** 136 637 f (1973).

8. R. V. Snyder, R. J. Angelici, and R. B. Meck, *J. Amer. Chem. Soc.,* **94,** 2660 (1972).

9. R. F. Hirsch, E. Gancher, and F. R. Russo, *Talanta,* **17,** 483 (1970).

10. S. Goldstein, A. Gulko, and G. Schmuckler, *Israel J. Chem.,* **10,** 893 (1972).

11. J. P. Greenstein and M. Winitz, *Chemistry of the Amino Acids,* Vol. 2, Wiley, New York, 1961, p. 1312.

Received March 29, 1976
Revised September 8, 1976

JOURNAL OF APPLIED POLYMER SCIENCE   VOL. 21, 2597-2607 (1977)

An Improved Technique for the Measurement of Dynamic Mechanical Properties of Viscoelastic Materials

A. F. YEE and M. T. TAKEMORI, *General Electric Corporate Research and Development, Synthesis & Characterization Branch, Chemical Laboratory, Schenectady, New York 12301*

Synopsis

An improved technique for the precision measurement of dynamic mechanical properties of viscoelastic materials is described. The instrumentation has been adapted for use with the commercial device Rheovibron, but can be used with any other similar device. An analysis of the technique, together with typical results, are presented. Analyses of error are included in the appendices.

INTRODUCTION

Many polymers have very low dynamic losses in temperature regions far below the glass transition temperature. In a recent study on several mixtures of poly(2,6-dimethyl-p-phenylene oxide) and polystyrene, the loss tangent tan δ was found to be less than 10^{-2} at low temperatures.[1] Using the commercially available dynamic-mechanical testing instrument Rheovibron (Model DDV-II-B, Toyo Baldwin Co., Japan), the resolution and the scatter of the results are such that interpretation is impossible. In this paper, we describe a new method to measure the dynamic mechanical properties of solid polymers. Although the modifications are on the Rheovibron, this method is generally applicable to the precision measurement of small phase shifts between two sinusoidal signals.

In the method to be described, we have retained the test bench of the Rheovibron, which includes the electromagnetic driver and the stress and strain gauges. We have modified the electronics by (a) providing closed-loop control so that the oscillation amplitude is constant, and (b) connecting the stress and strain gauges to a pair of low-noise chopper stabilized transducer conditioners so that stable, clean signals can be monitored continuously. We have also changed the analysis of the stress and strain signals from the "direct reading" manner of the Rheovibron with a more sensitive and simpler technique for the determination of the loss tangent and the storage modulus.

In the following section, we detail the experimental setup. In the subsequent sections, we present an analysis of our technique, and some results to illustrate the enhanced sensitivity obtained by this new technique. In Appendices I and II, we compute the errors involved in the measurements and show that they are indeed negligibly small. Finally, in Appendix III, we compare the modulus

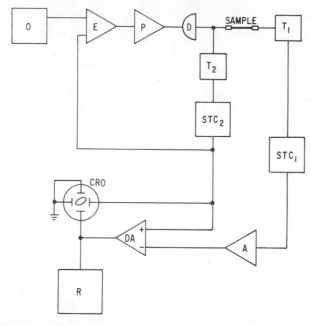

Fig. 1. Block diagram of the instrumentation: O = oscillator (0.01 Hz–1 KHz); E = error amplifier; P = dc power amplifier; D = driver; T_1 = stress gauge; T_2 = strain gauge; STC_1 = stress transducer conditioner; STC_2 = strain transducer conditioner; A = variable gain amplifier; DA = differential amplifier; CRO = oscilloscope; R = recording or measuring device.

measurements of the original Rheovibron and our modified version and show how we obtain the storage modulus E' directly.

EXPERIMENTAL SETUP

All the electronics with the original Rheovibron were replaced. The only parts that remain are (1) the bench, (2) the electromagnetic driver, (3) the stress and strain gauges, and (4) the sample positioning mechanism.

The electronics block diagram is shown in Figure 1. The instruments and the function they perform are described below:

1. Oscillator: Kikusui Electronics Corp. (Japan) Model 455. This oscillator generates a low-distortion, constant amplitude (better than 1 part in 4000) sine wave over the frequency range of 0.01 Hz to >1 KHz. It is used to provide a reference signal for the error amplifier.

2. Error Amplifier: MTS Corp. Model 440.13. This amplifier compares the reference signal from the oscillator with the strain signal from the strain transducer conditioner. The output of this amplifier is proportional to the difference signal such that the difference is driven toward zero. It enables us to maintain a constant oscillation amplitude irrespective of specimen stiffness as long as the amplitude is within the range of excursion allowed by the electromagnetic driver. Because of this strain feedback control, a constant gain on the strain signal is used. Once the strain amplitude is set, no further gain adjustments are necessary during subsequent phase measurements.

3. Power Amplifier: Hewlett Packard Model 6824A. This amplifier can provide ±1.0 amp at ±60 V from dc to >1 KHz. It converts the voltage signal

from the error amplifier into a proportionate current which excited the electro-magnetic driver.

4. Transducer Conditioners: MTS Corp. Model 440.21. These conditioners provide dc excitation as well as amplification for the strain gauges. The dc excitation is constant to better than 0.01%. Amplification is chopper stabilized.

The amplifiers have been modified to limit frequency response to −3 dB at 1 KHz in order to reduce the broad band noise. The two amplifiers are adjusted so that their relative phase shift is below the detection level.

5. Variable-gain Amplifier: Burr–Brown Model 3088. This is an instrumentation amplifier with relatively low noise and low drift. It is connected to the output of the stress transducer amplifier in order to vary the amplitude of the stress signal. This enables the establishment of the "horizontality" condition, to be defined in the next section.

6. Differential Amplifier: Burr–Brown Model 3088. This instrumentation amplifier amplifies the difference between stress and strain signals.

7. Amplitude Measurement: Nicolet Model 1090. This is a digital oscilloscope which can store two signals simultaneously in digital form. It incorporates a fast analog-to-digital converter (12 bit word/μsec) and a 4096-word memory. The signal amplitudes are easily determined digitally except where the signal-to-noise ratio is ~2. It is used to measure the amplitude of the difference signal.

The resolution and accuracy of our instrumentation is limited by two factors: 60 Hz noise and broad-band noise. The former can be minimized by careful grounding and shielding. The latter can be reduced by inserting a passive low-pass filter between the differential amplifier and the measuring devices. The error introduced by using a filter is small and will be discussed in Appendix II. In its present form, the instrument has a single point probable error of $\tan \delta = \pm 5 \times 10^{-4}$. The above-mentioned noise, however, limits the resolution to a minimum resolvable loss tangent value of 1.0×10^{-3}. For $\tan \delta > 2 \times 10^{-3}$, this noise is not a problem.

In the results section, we show the results of $\tan \delta$ measurement to demonstrate the resolution of the instrument.

METHOD

In this section, we describe the modified phase-shift determination that we have implemented for the Rheovibron. We have, for strain cycling at angular frequency ω,

$$\epsilon(t) = A \cos \omega t \tag{1}$$

and

$$\sigma(t) = B \cos (\omega t + \delta) \tag{2}$$

where δ is the desired phase shift between the stress and strain signals.

The difference of the stress and strain signals is given by

$$\Delta(t) = C \cos (\omega t + \beta) \equiv \epsilon(t) - \sigma(t)$$

$$= (A - B \cos \delta) \cos \omega t + B \sin \delta \sin \omega t \tag{3}$$

The Rheovibron uses this difference signal to obtain tan δ. This is accomplished by adjusting the gain on the stress signal until the amplitudes of the stress and strain signals are equal,[2]

$$A = B \tag{4}$$

a condition which is determined by taking appropriate RMS readings. When eq. (4) holds, the amplitude of the difference signal, $C_{A=B}$, is given by

$$\frac{C_{A=B}}{A} = 2 \sin \frac{\delta}{2} \tag{5}$$

where we have divided by A the amplitude of the strain signal.

The Rheovibron has a calibrated scale that converts the amplitude reading obtained in eq. (5) directly to tan δ; hence it is called a "direct reading" Rheovibron.

If we, on the other hand, adjust the gain on the stress signal until we obtain the condition

$$A = B \cos \delta \tag{6}$$

as opposed to that given by eq. (4), we obtain

$$\frac{C_{A=B\cos\delta}}{A} = \frac{B \sin \delta}{A} \tag{7}$$

where we have again divided by A the amplitude of the strain signal.

When we substitute eq. (6) for A, we obtain the very elegant result

$$\frac{C_{A=B\cos\delta}}{A} = \tan \delta \tag{8}$$

Equation (8), which should be compared with eq. (5), thus enables an exact measurement of tan δ.

In order to implement this exact measurement, the condition specified in eq (6) must be satisfied. We note that when this condition holds, the strain signal $\epsilon(t)$ and the difference signal $\Delta(t)$ are 90° out of phase. This condition is thus easily detectable by inputting these signals across the x- and y-axes of an oscilloscope, respectively. The semimajor axis of length A will then lie horizontal (parallel to the x-axis) when the gain of the stress signal is adjusted until eq. (6) holds. We, therefore, call this the "horizontality" condition. The semiminor axis is then given by $B \sin \delta$. When this is divided by A, we obtain an exact expression for the loss tangent, as given in eq. (8). Although one could theoretically measure the semiminor and semimajor axes of the ellipse on the oscilloscope, we use instead a Nicolet Model 1090 digital storage oscilloscope to record the difference signal and measure the amplitude, $C_{A=B\cos\delta}$. The amplitude of the strain signal, A, is held constant using a servo-feedback loop as discussed earlier and hence need be measured only once. In Appendix I, we show that a small error in establishing "horizontality" leads to a negligibly small error in the measured tan δ. Furthermore, in Appendix II, we show that an additional phase shift introduced by passing the $\Delta(t)$ signal through a low-pass filter does not lead to a detectable error in the establishment of the "horizontality" condition.

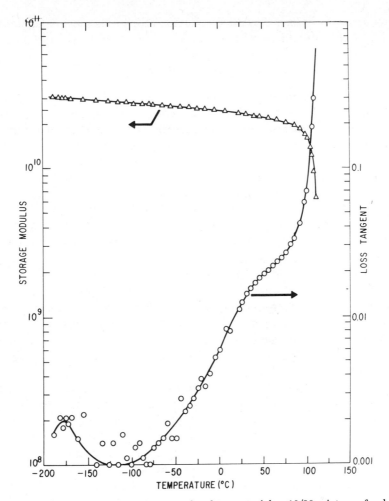

Fig. 2. Typical example of data taken on a low loss material, a 10/90 mixture of poly(2,6-di-methyl-*p*-phenylene oxide) and polystyrene.

RESULTS

We present in Figure 2 the results of one experiment which involves extremely small tan δ. The material is a 10/90 mixture of poly(2,6-dimethyl-*p*-phenylene oxide) and polystyrene. Details of the experiment and specimen preparation have been presented elsewhere.[1] The resolution limit caused by the noise is seen to be 1×10^{-3}. This is clearly shown in the temperature interval between −60° and −160°C. The existence of a peak at −180°C is suggested because the −190°C point represents several repeated measurements. The nature of this peak is discussed elsewhere.[1]

It should be noted that the level of noise is also somewhat dependent on the geometry and stiffness of the specimens. At certain temperatures, the specimen resonates with ambient vibrations emitted by humans as well as machines. It may become necessary to increase the tension on the specimen on such occasions. If the tan δ is changing rapidly, as is the case presented here, this type of noise is not usually a problem.

It should also be noted that all specimens were subjected to a pretension of about 0.2% to 0.3% steady strain.

CONCLUSIONS

As stated in the introduction, this paper arose out of our efforts to upgrade the Rheovibron. We feel that the "horizontality" method which we have presented has given us a first step in this direction and has provided many other benefits as well. Here we present the following achievements:

1. **Accuracy.** The "horizontality" condition provides a more sensitive determination of the loss tangent. A single adjustment is needed to establish "horizontality," and this measurement is attainable to a high degree of accuracy (See Appendix I). In the original Rheovibron approach, two RMS readings are required, to set $A = B$ in eq. (4), using a procedure more susceptible to larger errors. The results of the previous section bear out the increased sensitivity.

2. **Simplicity.** A measurement of "horizontality" requires a single adjustment of the gain of the stress signal amplifier, as opposed to the multiple manipulations required for the Rheovibron,[2] thus providing for ease of operation.

3. **No Unusual Equipment Necessary.** Our modification basically requires an $x-y$ oscilloscope and some means of measuring the amplitude of the difference signal, for example, an rms meter, an oscilloscope, a strip chart recorder, a data logger, etc. This equipment is commonly available in most academic and industrial laboratories.

4. **Monitoring Capability.** The ellipse on the $x-y$ oscilloscope is an excellent tool for monitoring the state of the sample. Insufficient tension, sample warpage, misalignment, or excessive noise are readily observable. In the original Rheovibron procedure, an oscilloscope is used in two ways: (a) to display the stress and strain signals to check for proper tension and *gross* warpage or misalignment; (b) to adjust the phase between oscillator and stress or strain amplitude measuring circuit. In our procedure, the oscilloscope displays the tan δ signal itself and is therefore much more sensitive to small warpages and misalignment.

5. **Amenable to Digital Processing.** The stress and strain signals may be directly digitized and analyzed to obtain the dynamic mechanical properties. In a paper to be published shortly, we will describe our digital analysis. This is the first step toward automation of the Rheovibron using microprocessor or computer technology.

6. **Understanding.** Finally, we feel that an important by-product of our approach is that it provides a better understanding of the procedure and the analysis of the dynamic mechanical measurements which might not otherwise be so readily apparent to the user of the Rheovibron.

The advantages of our technique are, to reiterate, fewer adjustments and switching operations, continuous signal monitoring to prevent "black box" induced errors, and higher resolution.

Appendix I

In this Appendix, we examine the uncertainty introduced in evaluating the loss tangent, tan δ, of eq. (8) due to an uncertainty in establishing the "horizontality" condition shown in eq. (6).

If the $x(t)$ and $y(t)$ signals on the oscilloscope (the strain and difference signals of Eqs. (1) and (3) are given by

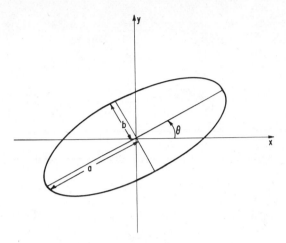

Fig. 3. General form of an ellipse: a = semimajor axis; b = semiminor axis; θ = angle with respect to x axis.

$$x(t) = A \cos wt$$
$$y(t) = A' \cos wt + B' \sin wt \qquad \text{(I-1)}$$

where

$$A' = A - B \cos \delta$$
$$B' = B \sin \delta$$

then the resultant ellipse is obtained by eliminating t:

$$C_1 x^2 + C_2 2xy + C_3 y^2 = 1 \qquad \text{(I-2)}$$

where

$$C_1 = \frac{1}{A^2}\left[1 + \left(\frac{A'}{B'}\right)^2\right]$$

$$C_2 = \frac{-A'}{AB'^2}$$

$$C_3 = \frac{1}{B'^2}.$$

The general form for an ellipse with semimajor and semiminor axes of lengths, a and b and which is tilted at angle θ with respect to the x-axis (see Fig. 3) is given by

$$D_1 x^2 + D_2 2xy + D_3 y^2 = 1 \qquad \text{(I-3)}$$

where

$$D_1 = \frac{\cos^2 \theta}{a^2} + \frac{\sin^2 \theta}{b^2}$$

$$D_2 = \left(\frac{1}{a^2} - \frac{1}{b^2}\right) \sin \theta \cos \theta$$

$$D_3 = \frac{\sin^2 \theta}{a^2} + \frac{\cos^2 \theta}{b^2}.$$

We can now compare the special ellipse of interest given by eq. (I-2) with the general ellipse given by eq. (I-3) by matching coefficients ($D_i = C_i$ for $i = 1, 2, 3$). We solve for a, b, and θ in terms of A, A', and B' and obtain

$$\tan 2\theta = \frac{2AA'}{A^2 - A'^2 - B'^2}$$
(I-4)

and

$$\left. \begin{array}{c} \dfrac{1}{a^2} \\[2mm] \dfrac{1}{b^2} \end{array} \right\} = \frac{1}{2}\left[\frac{1}{B'^2} + \frac{A'^2 + B'^2}{A^2 B'^2}\right] \mp \frac{A'}{AB'^2}\left[1 + \left(\frac{A^2 - A'^2 - B'^2}{2AA'}\right)^2\right]^{1/2}$$

Let us examine two cases:

(i) In the first case, we assume that we have adjusted the amplitudes of the stress and strain signals (B and A) so that

$$\theta = 0$$
(I-5)

that is, we attain perfect "horizontality" of the ellipse. Thus, from eq. (I-4),

$$2AA' = 0$$

Since $A \neq 0$,

$$A' = 0$$

or, from eq. (I-1),

$$A = B\cos\delta$$
(I-6)

which is, of course, our "horizontality" condition. Also, $a = A$ and $b = B'$ as expected.

(ii) Now, let us examine the more interesting case where θ is very small, but nonzero. This represents a deviation from "horizontality" by a small amount. From eqs. (I-1) and (I-4) we obtain

$$\tan 2\theta = \frac{2A(A - B\cos\delta)}{(2AB\cos\delta) - B^2}$$
(I-7)

Now let us define η by

$$\eta \equiv \frac{A - B\cos\delta}{B} \ll 1$$
(I-8)

where η is very small since we are very close to the "horizontality" condition, eq. (I-6). Then,

$$\tan 2\theta = \frac{2(\eta + \cos\delta)\eta}{2(\eta + \cos\delta)\cos\delta - 1}$$

and to lowest order in η,

$$\tan 2\theta \simeq \frac{2\cos\delta}{\cos 2\delta}\eta$$

Therefore,

$$\eta \simeq \frac{\cos 2\delta}{2\cos\delta}\tan 2\theta$$
(I-9)

Now, in our measurement for the loss tangent, we take the ratio

$$\frac{C_{A \simeq B\cos\delta}}{A} = \frac{(A'^2 + B'^2)^{1/2}}{A}$$

which, using eqs. (I-1) and (I-8), becomes

$$\frac{C_{A \simeq B\cos\delta}}{A} = \frac{\tan\delta\left[\left(\dfrac{\eta}{\sin\delta}\right)^2 + 1\right]^{1/2}}{\dfrac{\eta}{\cos\delta} + 1}$$
(I-10)

Using the approximation in eq. (I-9), we obtain

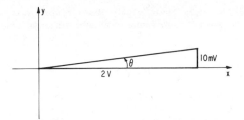

Fig. 4. Uncertainty in the horizontality condition.

$$\frac{C_{A \simeq B\cos\delta}}{A} \simeq \frac{\tan\delta\left[1 + \left(\dfrac{\tan 2\theta}{\tan 2\delta}\right)^2\right]^{1/2}}{1 + \dfrac{\cos 2\delta \tan 2\theta}{1 + \cos 2\delta}} \tag{I-11}$$

We distinguish two separate regimes:

(a) $\tan\theta \ll \tan\delta < 1$. For this region, eq. (I-11) becomes

$$\frac{C_{A \simeq B\cos\delta}}{A} \simeq \tan\delta\{1 - \theta\} \tag{I-12}$$

The error in our measurement of tan δ is thus given by θ, the error in establishing perfect "horizontality." For these larger values of tan δ (0.005 < tan δ < 0.2), we estimate our uncertainty to be certainly less than $\theta = 0.005$ (±10 mV on the y-axis when the x-axis amplitude is 2 V, see Fig. 4). This leads to insignificantly small errors.

(b) $\tan\theta \simeq \tan\delta \ll 1$ (0.001 < tan δ < 0.005). For this region, we obtain

$$\frac{C_{A \simeq B\cos\delta}}{A} \simeq \tan\delta\left[1 + \left(\frac{\theta}{\delta}\right)^2\right]^{1/2} \tag{I-13}$$

For these smaller values of δ, we estimate our uncertainty to be less than $\theta = 0.002$ (± 4 mV out of 2 V). (This smaller value for θ results from a combination of our observing ellipses which are less "fat" and hence more easily viewed and our switching to a more sensitive scale.) This may lead to a noticeable error in measuring tan δ as shown in eq. (I-13). However, this value of $\theta = 0.002$ is certainly a conservative overestimate as seen in the results shown in the paper. The few scattered points seen in the small tan δ region could reflect this error. A higher sensitivity could be achieved through additional filtering to reduce the noise (see Appendix II) and a more sensitive scale (our most sensitive scale at present is 50 mV/cm on the oscilloscope). However, the results we obtained were of sufficient accuracy that we did not implement these further improvements.

In conclusion, we have shown in this Appendix that the inability to attain perfect "horizontality" is not a serious problem and leads to negligible errors in our measurements of tan δ.

A comparable error analysis can be made of the original Rheovibron method, using eqs. (4) and (5) of the main text. If we define

$$\phi \equiv \frac{A - B}{B} \ll 1$$

to be the uncertainty in establishing the condition $A = B$ (ϕ is comparable to our θ or η), then we obtain

For $\phi \ll \delta < 1$:

$$\frac{C_{A \simeq B}}{A} \simeq 2 \sin\frac{\delta}{2}\left(1 - \frac{1}{2}\phi\right)$$

For $\phi \simeq \delta \ll 1$:

$$\frac{C_{A \simeq B}}{A} \simeq 2 \sin\frac{\delta}{2}\left[1 - \left(\frac{\phi}{\delta}\right)^2\right]^{1/2}$$

which are comparable to eqs. (I-12) and (I-13), respectively.

The increased sensitivity of our method arises from the smaller errors inherent to the "horizontality" approach of eq. (8) as compared to the "equal amplitude" approach of eq. (5). In other words, θ is smaller than ϕ, and this leads to more accurate values for the loss tangent.

Appendix II

The difference signal, eq. (3), is very small for small phase shifts, and hence noise may present significant problems. In this section, we show that use of a filter, even if it introduces a relatively large phase shift to the difference signal, nonetheless has a negligible effect on the desired loss tangent measurement.

The difference signal is given by [see eq. (3)]

$$\Delta(t) = C \cos (wt + \beta) \tag{II-1}$$

where

$$C = [(A - B \cos \delta)^2 + (B \sin \delta)^2]^{1/2} \tag{II-2}$$

and

$$\tan \beta = \frac{-B \sin \delta}{A - B \cos \delta} \tag{II-3}$$

Let us now suppose that this difference signal passes through a filter which introduces an additional phase shift ψ and attenuation ξ:

$$\Delta^f(t) = \xi C \cos (wt + \beta + \psi) \tag{II-4}$$

$$= \xi C \cos (\beta + \psi) \cos wt - \xi C \sin (\beta + \psi) \sin wt$$

We then place the filtered difference signal, $\Delta^f(t)$, instead of $\Delta(t)$ across the y-axis of the oscilloscope while keeping the strain signal, eq. (1), across the x axis. When we establish the "horizontality" condition by adjusting the gain of the stress signal, we make the coefficient of $\cos wt$ in eq. (II-4) vanish:

$$\xi C \cos (\beta + \psi) = 0 \tag{II-5}$$

Thus, using eqs. (II-5) and (II-3), we obtain

$$\tan \psi = \frac{1}{\tan \beta} = \frac{-(A - B \cos \delta)}{B \sin \delta} \tag{II-6}$$

When we calculate the phase angle by dividing the amplitude of the filtered difference signal by the amplitude of the strain signal, we obtain

$$\frac{C^f{}_{A=B\cos\delta}}{A} = \frac{\xi C \sin (\beta + \psi)}{A} \tag{II-7}$$

But from eq. (II-5), $\sin (\beta + \psi) = 1$; and using eqs. (II-2) and (II-6), we obtain

$$\frac{C^f{}_{A=B\cos\delta}}{A} = \frac{\xi B \sin \delta}{A} [1 + \tan^2\psi]^{1/2}$$

Further use of eq. (II-6) yields

$$\frac{C^f{}_{A=B\cos\delta}}{A} = \frac{\xi \tan \delta [1 + \tan^2\psi]^{1/2}}{1 - \tan \delta \tan \psi} \tag{II-8}$$

We consider two cases:

(a) $tan\ \delta \ll tan\ \psi \ll 1$. Retaining lowest order terms, we obtain

$$\frac{C^f{}_{A=B\cos\delta}}{A} \simeq \xi \tan \delta \left\{1 + \frac{1}{2} \tan^2\psi\right\} \tag{II-9}$$

Since $\xi \simeq 1$ and $\tan \psi$ is very small, the error in measurement of $\tan \delta$ due to filtering of the difference signal is negligibly small. In our experiments, we have used a filter for which $\tan \psi = 0.034$. The resultant error due to the $\frac{1}{2}\tan^2 \psi$ term is thus seen to be less than 0.1%.

(b) $tan\ \psi \lesssim tan\ \delta < 1$. For this case, eq. (II-8) becomes

$$\frac{C^f_{A=B\cos\delta}}{A} \simeq \xi \tan \delta \{1 + \tan \delta \tan \psi\} \tag{II-10}$$

The maximum value of $\tan \delta$ is roughly 0.2. The resultant error due to the $\tan \delta \tan \psi$ term is thus seen to be less than 0.7%.

Appendix III

In this Appendix, we describe the modulus measurement. The amplified strain signal is given by

$$A \text{ (volts)} = \epsilon_0 f(\epsilon) D(\epsilon) L \tag{III-1}$$

where A is the amplitude of the amplified strain gauge signal [eq. (1)], ϵ_0 is the strain amplitude, $f(\epsilon)$ is the amplification of the strain signal, $D(\epsilon)$ is the strain gauge conversion factor (volts/cm), and L is the sample length. The amplitude of the amplified stress gauge signal is given by

$$B \text{ (volts)} = \sigma_0 f(\sigma) D(\sigma) A_{cs} \tag{III-2}$$

where B is given in eq. (2), σ_0 is the stress amplitude, $f(\sigma)$ and $D(\sigma)$ are the corresponding amplification and conversion factors for the stress signal, and A_{cs} is the sample cross section. Thus,

$$\frac{A\sigma_0}{B\epsilon_0} = \frac{f(\epsilon)D(\epsilon)L}{f(\sigma)D(\sigma)A_{cs}} \tag{III-3}$$

In using the Rheovibron to measure the modulus of a sample, one adjusts B to equal A [eq. (4)] and thus obtains

$$E^* \equiv \frac{\sigma_0}{\xi_0} = \text{RHS of eq. (III-3) when } A = B. \tag{III-4}$$

A calculation of the RHS (right-hand side) of eq. (III-3) when $A = B$ thus yields the complex modulus E^*. Furthermore, the magnitude of A or B is not needed in the determination of the complex modulus once the $A = B$ condition is satisfied. The only information required are geometric terms, amplification factors, and conversion factors.

Using our "horizontality" method, however, we set $A = B \cos \delta$ [eq. (6)] and obtain

$$E' \equiv \frac{\sigma_0}{\epsilon_0} \cos \delta = \text{RHS of eq. (III-3) when } A = B \cos \delta \tag{III-5}$$

Thus, a calculation of the RHS of eq. (III-3) when $A = B \cos \delta$ yields the storage modulus E' directly, instead of the complex modulus E^*. The magnitude of A or B is again not required for a determination of E' as long as the "horizontality" condition ($A = B \cos \delta$) is satisfied.

References

1. A. F. Yee, *J. Polym. Eng. Sci.*, to be published.
2. *Rheovibron Instruction Manual 17*, Toyo Baldwin Co., Ltd., Tokyo, Japan August 1969.

Received June 22, 1976
Revised September 8, 1976

JOURNAL OF APPLIED POLYMER SCIENCE   Vol. 21, 2609–2619 (1977)

Viscoelastic Behavior of Partly Decrosslinked Polymer Networks. I. Acrylic Acid Anhydride-Crosslinked Poly(ethyl Acrylate)

S. YOMODA* and L. H. SPERLING

Materials Research Center No. 32, Lehigh University, Bethlehem, Pennsylvania 18015

Synopsis

Acrylic acid anhydride (AAA) and tetraethylene glycol dimethacrylate (TEGDM) were employed as labile and permanent crosslinking monomers for poly(ethyl acrylate), respectively. Upon partial or total hydrolysis of the AAA crosslinks, various states of viscoelastic creep and stress relaxation were brought about. The use of chemically active monomers for crosslinking permits new polymer structures to be synthesized. In this case, decrosslinking converts a thermoset polymer into its thermoplastic counterpart. The relationship between the present decrosslinking study and a new nomenclature theory of grafted and crosslinked polymers is explored.

INTRODUCTION

The viscoelastic behavior of imperfectly crosslinked polymer networks is both of practical and theoretical interest. On the practical side, polymers both above and below their glass transition temperatures exhibit excessive creep and flow when undercured or degraded. Epoxy adhesives, for example, are sometimes not fully cured following application; raising the temperature while in service may then cause the adhesive to fail.[1,2] Undercured elastomers also display excessive creep, as do materials that are subject to excessive heat.

The theoreticians have worried about polymerization and gelation kinetics,[3] about dangling chain ends,[4] and about molecular weights of chain segments between crosslinks.[5] The study of polymer degradation also has a long history; for example, the stress relaxation behavior of degrading elastomers has yielded new insights into the chemistry of oxidative scission. Most of these studies involved random degradation; in this study (and the papers that follow), specific bonds will be selectively degraded to produce easily characterizable network changes.

THEORETICAL ASPECTS

In a series of theoretical papers, Sperling and co-workers have been developing nomenclature schemes for polymer blends, grafts, and interpenetrating polymer

*Present address: Industrial Products Research Institute 21-2, 4-Chome Shimomaruko OTA-KU, Tokyo, Japan 144.

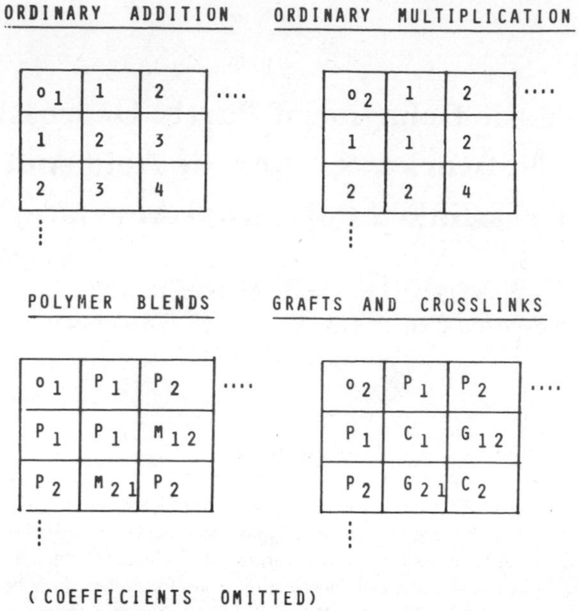

ORDINARY ADDITION   ORDINARY MULTIPLICATION

o_1	1	2	....
1	2	3	
2	3	4	

o_2	1	2	....
1	1	2	
2	2	4	

POLYMER BLENDS   GRAFTS AND CROSSLINKS

o_1	P_1	P_2	....
P_1	P_1	M_{12}	
P_2	M_{21}	P_2	

o_2	P_1	P_2	....
P_1	C_1	G_{12}	
P_2	G_{21}	C_2	

(COEFFICIENTS OMITTED)

Fig. 1. Illustration of the use of ring theory to describe polymer blends, grafts, and crosslinked homopolymers. Upper left and right, ordinary addition and multiplication. Lower left and right, polymer blends, and grafted and crosslinked systems.

networks.[6-8] Most recently, the mathematical ring-like characteristics of these materials were evolved.[8] A formal ring has two operations, which in ordinary algebra are addition and multiplication (see Fig. 1). In the case of interest presently, nonbonded polymer blends serve as the addition mode, while grafted and crosslinked polymers serve as the multiplication mode, as also shown in Figure 1. Under binary operation o_2, the combination

$$P_1 o_2 P_1 = C_1 \tag{1}$$

is found, where polymer 1 reacts with itself to yield the crosslinked product. Upon specifically removing the crosslink sites, the linear polymer 1 reappears. This procedure is the equivalent of transforming the element C_1 in the graft-crosslink table into its equivalent in the blends table, which, in this case, is just P_1. (Note that coefficients which denote quantities of materials involved are omitted for simplicity.) A formal function, β, was evolved[6] to describe the transformation:

$$\beta C_1 = \beta(P_1 o_2 P_1) = P_1 o_1 P_1 = P_1 \tag{2}$$

Concepts of this type have lead to a search for degradation reactions specific to the crosslink sites. The best reaction found so far involves the use of anhydrides, which can be easily hydrolyzed.[3]

It can be argued that incompletely crosslinked polymer materials can be made by straightforward syntheses. Systematic lowering of the crosslink unit concentration will bring forth a range of viscoelastic properties. However, preparation of fully crosslinked networks followed by selective decrosslinking may allow certain properties to be emphasized, thus enhancing our understanding of their particular roles. Either the polymer can be partly crosslinked, or fully

TABLE I
Characterization of PEA Networks[a]

	Sample no.						
	1	2	3	4	5	6	7
1-Doth, ml	0	0	0	0	0	0	0
AAA, ml	1.2	0.56	0.56	0.28	0	0	0
TEGDM, ml	0	0	1.4	0.70	2.9	1.4	0
$M_c(L) \times 10^4$	0.9	1.2	0.9	1.5	0.8	1.4	110
$M_c(Wg) \times 10^4$	1.2	1.7	0.9	1.6	0.7	1.5	90
$M_c(Th) \times 10^4$	1.0	2.0	1.0	2.0	1.0	2.0	∞
$M_c(E) \times 10^4$	0.9	1.2	0.9	1.3	0.7	1.2	1.7

[a] EA, 100 ml; benzoin, 0.4 g.

TABLE II
PEA Networks with 0.68% 1-Dodecanethiol[a]

	Sample no.						
	8	9	10	11	12	13	14
1-Doth, ml	0.68	0.68	0.68	0.68	0.68	0.68	0.68
AAA, ml	1,2	0.56	0.56	0.28	0	0	2.4
TEGDM, ml	0	0	1.4	0.7	2.9	1.4	0
$M_c(L) \times 10^4$	2.8	5.8	2.0	7.3	2.0	—	1.1
$M_c(Wg) \times 10^4$	2.6	4.6	2.4	6.6	2.1	—	1.2
$M_c(Th) \times 10^4$	1.9	3.9	2.0	4.0	2.0	4.1	1.0
$M_c(E) \times 10^4$	0.8	1.2	0.9	1.4	0.8	1.2	0.6
	After Hydrolysis (NH$_4$OH)						
$M_c(L) \times 10^4$	3.6	7.8	3.5	8.6	2.2	—	—
$M_c(Wg) \times 10^4$	4.8	7.5	3.1	7.3	2.0	—	—
$M_c(E) \times 10^4$	1.2	2.1	1.0	2.1	0.8	1.0	1.3

[a] EA; 100 ml; benzoin, 0.4 g.

crosslinked and then partly decrosslinked, to arrive at the same nominal point.
However the structures, and hence their viscoelastic behavior, may differ.

The reader will note that while the ring theory suggests selective crosslink site
attack, and presumes it complete, the incomplete reaction stage has much greater
interest to the students of viscoelasticity.

EXPERIMENTAL

The photochemical method of synthesizing poly(ethyl acrylate) (PEA) networks in bulk with UV light has been previously described.[9] In brief, benzoin
was used as the initiator, acrylic acid anhydride (AAA) was used as the labile
crosslinker, and tetraethylene glycol dimethacrylate (TEGDM) was used as the
permanent crosslinker. The chemical 1-dodecanethiol (1-Doth) was employed
as a chain transfer agent. This last was necessary because side reactions during
the polymerization of ethyl acrylate lead to gelation even without added crosslinker. The exact levels of TEGDM, AAA, and 1-Doth employed are shown
in Tables I–III.

Decrosslinking studies were done using ethylenediamine and ammonium
hydroxide. In another paper,[8] it was found that ethylenediamine was effective

TABLE III
PEA Networks Capable of Complete Hydrolysis[a]

	Sample no.					
	15	16	17	18	19	20
1-Doth, ml	1.36	1.36	1.36	1.36	1.36	2.7
AAA, ml	1.2	0.56	0.56	0.28	2.4	2.4
TEGDM, ml	0	0	1.4	0.7	0	0
$M_c(L) \times 10^5$	1.6	3.5	0.36	4.3	1.0	0.75
$M_c(Wg) \times 10^5$	1.6	3.6	0.37	3.8	0.7	0.54
$M_c(E) \times 10^4$	1.4	2.0	1.2	3.0	0.75	0.78
	After Hydrolysis (NH$_4$OH)					
$M_c(L) \times 10^5$	sol	sol	0.47	5.3	sol	sol
$M_c(Wg) \times 10^5$	sol	sol	0.44	5.0	sol	sol
$M_c(E) \times 10^5$	3.5	5.2	0.36	2.6	1.6	1.6

[a] EA, 100 ml; benzoin, 0.4 g.

in decrosslinking polystyrene networks; however, soaking the PEA for 24 hr in 28% NH$_4$OH was very effective, and this reagent was adopted for the present study.

The materials were characterized before and after hydrolysis by swelling them for one day in methyl ethyl ketone (MEK). Both the weight increase and the changes in length were recorded.

The creep properties were investigated using Gehman[10,11] and Clash-Berg[12] type creep testers; also tensile creep studies were performed.

RESULTS

Values of M_c, the molecular weight between crosslink sites, obtained by swelling the samples in MEK were calculated by the Flory–Rehner equation:[13,14]

$$\frac{1}{M_c} = \frac{\ln(1 - v_2) + v_2 + \chi_{12} v_2^2}{\rho V_0 [v_2^{1/3} - (v_2/2)]} \quad (3)$$

where v_2 represents the volume fraction of polymer in the sample at equilibrium; V_0 is the solvent molar volume, of density ρ; and the value of the interaction parameter χ_{12} was taken to be 0.46, which is the value for PEA in acetone.[15] While the value of χ for PEA in MEK has not been determined, the equilibrium swelling values of crosslinked PEA in acetone and MEK were determined on one sample and found to be nearly the same. Thus, χ for PEA in MEK was taken to be the same as in acetone.

In each case, volumes were assumed to be additive. Values reported in Tables I–III were based on actual weight gain, $M_c(Wg)$, and on length change, $M_c(L)$. In addition, values were estimated from Young's modulus E via the theory of rubber elasticity, $M_c(E)$:

$$M_c(E) = \frac{3\rho RT}{E} \quad (4)$$

By way of characterization, the density of several samples was measured by picnometer, and was found to vary from 1.10 to 1.19 g/cm^3, depending on the

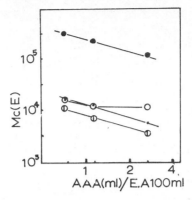

Fig. 2. Values of $M_c(E)$ as a funcion of AAA and 1-Doth levels, before and after hydrolysis: (O) 0.68% 1-Doth before hydrolysis; (Ø) 0.68% 1-Doth after hydrolysis; (●) 1.3% 1-Doth before hydrolysis; (◉) 1.3% 1-Doth after hydrolysis.

crosslink level.   During the swelling tests, only 1–2% of material was extracted, indicating reasonably crosslinked products.

Values of M_c via both swelling and modulus are compared to the theoretical values, $M_c(Th)$, calculated on the basis of actual amounts of crosslinker added, assuming infinite primary chain length.   Experimental values of M_c are shown to agree with theory in Table I, except for the far right-hand column.   With no added crosslinks, a value of M_c equal to the molecular weight itself is expected, but since infinite chains were assumed in the $M_c(Th)$ calculations, a value of ∞ is reported for the case of no crosslinks.   Finite values are noted experimentally, with much smaller values obtained via the modulus $[M_c(E)]$ experiment.   This last is because physical entanglements count effectively as crosslinks.   The values of $M_c(L)$ and $M_c(Wg)$ of sample 7, without any crosslinking agent added, is seen to be much larger than samples 1–6.   However, $M_c(E)$ for sample 7 is only slightly larger, the value for E being 5.1×10^6 dynes/cm^2 at 25°C.   This is due to the method of measurement, since Young's modulus E measures physical entanglements as well as actual chemical crosslinks.

In general, the relative effect of the physical entanglements increase in importance as the density of chemical crosslinks decreases.   For example, comparison of samples 4, 11, and 18 shows $M_c(Wg)$ increasing faster than $M_c(E)$ as more 1-Doth is added.   None of the materials shown in Table I would dissolve after hydrolysis, although increased swelling values were noted.

In an attempt to counteract the accidental gelation reactions, various quantities of 1-dodecanethiol were introduced to promote chain transfer reactions. As shown in Tables II and III, at a level of 1.36% 1-Doth or greater, the polymers are soluble after hydrolysis.   Using 1-Doth causes $M_c(L)$ and $M_c(Wg)$ of all samples to increase (reduced crosslinking), as illustrated in Tables II and III. After hydrolysis, the $M_c(L)$, $M_c(Wg)$, and $M_c(E)$ values of samples only containing TEGDM are not changed, but samples containing AAA are increased. The result is clear: the effect of 1-Doth is to cut the main chains during synthesis, but the ammonium hydroxide only attacks the AAA crosslink site.   The values of $M_c(E)$ on the bottom row of Table III represent the limiting level of physical crosslinks only.

To summarize the effects of AAA on $M_c(E)$, values are plotted in Figure 2

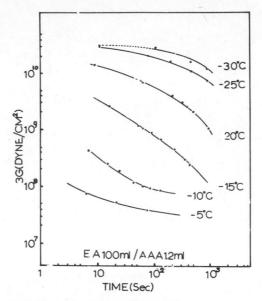

Fig. 3. Values of log three times the shear modulus G (log $3G$) vs time in the glass transition temperature range of PEA.

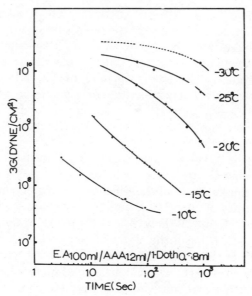

Fig. 4. Values of log $3G$ vs time for a series of temperatures for a material containing 0.68% 1-Doth.

before and after hydrolysis for two different 1-Doth levels.   (Note that a decreasing M_c value indicates an increased crosslinking level.)

As a last step in characterizing the PEA networks, a simple Gehman-type creep test is shown in Figure 3 for PEA containing 1.2% AAA, before hydrolysis.   The reported T_g of this material, $-22°C$, agrees well with the result, and a well-defined rubber plateau is approached at $-5°C$.   Addition of 0.68% of 1-Doth increases the rate of creep somewhat, as shown in Figure 4.   After hydrolysis, the

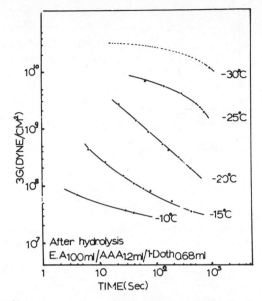

Fig. 5. Values of log $3G$ vs temperature for PEA, after hydrolysis, for a PEA containing 1.2 ml AAA and 0.68% 1-Doth.

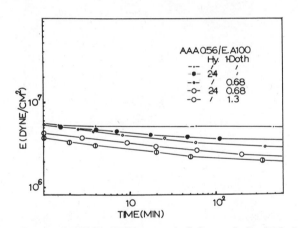

Fig. 6. Stress relaxation of PEA networks before and after hydrolysis.

rate of creep was increased still more, as shown in Figure 5. The creep rate of samples which contained only TEGDM and not any AAA was not appreciably changed after hydrolysis. The creep rates of samples containing both TEGDM and AAA was increased after hydrolysis (data not shown), but the magnitude of the change was not as large as is shown in Figures 4 and 5, which represents the limiting case of only AAA. Even though viscoelasticity increases from Figure 3 to Figure 5, the actual glass transition temperature probably remains nearly the same, only the molecular weight distributions in relation to the crosslink levels were changed.

Stress relaxation studies on a series of networks are shown in Figures 6 and 7. The modulus E was calculated from

$$\frac{w \times 981}{A} = \frac{E}{3}\left(\alpha - \frac{1}{\alpha^2}\right)$$

(5)

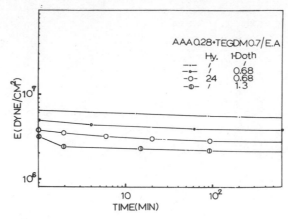

Fig. 7. Stress relaxation of PEA networks containing both permanent and temporary crosslinks sites.

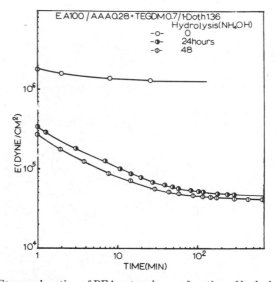

Fig. 8. Stress relaxation of PEA networks as a function of hydrolysis time.

where w equals the weight applied, A is the cross-sectional area of the sample, and α is the elongation, equal to the final length over the initial length. For high elongations, the engineering strain, $2\alpha^2 + (1/\alpha)$, was employed for modulus calculations. In each of the materials shown in Figures 6 and 7, the network remained intact after hydrolysis, although at a lower level of crosslinking.

The effect of hydrolysis time is shown in Figure 8. The level of 1-Doth, 1.36%, permits solubility after hydrolysis, as noted in Tables II and III. The TEGDM employed, however, kept the networks intact. Note that only a small effect is noted on the behavior between 24 and 48 hr of hydrolysis time.

The tensile creep modulus of several networks in shown in Figure 9. At a level of 1.36% 1-Doth, the network structures of the materials without TEGDM are seen to be completely destroyed. Creep was rapid enough to cause sample failure after only a few minutes. However, samples having TEGDM only behave as if the crosslink level remains unchanged. Figure 9 shows that only the AAA part

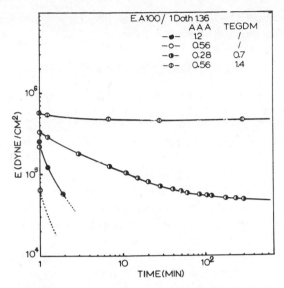

Fig. 9. Tensile creep modulus of several PEA samples, after hydrolysis, for 24 hr at 25°C.

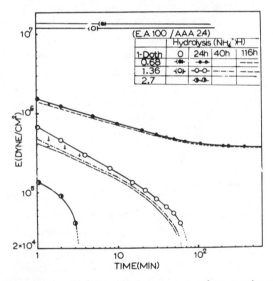

Fig. 10. Creep modulus of samples having little or no network properties after hydrolysis for 24 hr at 25°C in 28% NA₄OH.

of samples containing both AAA and TEGDM is broken by the ammonium hydroxide. After hydrolysis, the crosslink density depends on the TEGDM level, as shown in Table III and Figure 9.

While Figures 8–10 show creep behavior in the rubber and rubbery flow temperature regions of the samples, Figures 3–5 show the equivalent data in the glassy and glass transition region.

Finally, Figure 10 summarizes the creep modulus behavior of hydrolyzed samples having various levels of 1-Doth. At 0.68% 1-Doth, a network is retained, and the modulus does reach a plateau. At 1.36% 1-Doth, the polymer is just soluble, and failure occurred after about 1 hr. At 2.7% 1-Doth, creep is much more rapid, due undoubtedly to the lower molecular weight remaining, and the sample failed after only a few minutes.

DISCUSSION AND CONCLUSIONS

In this first paper on selective decrosslinking and degrafting, the behavior of acrylic acid anhydride crosslinked poly(ethyl acrylate) was explored. Figure 1 shows four tables in summary form. The top two show the ordinary arithmetic operations of addition and multiplication. The bottom two tables show the equivalent operations of blending and crosslinking or grafting. While the analogy is obviously inexact, it provides a basis for many combinations and transformations. Through use of these tables, arbitrarily complex materials can be conceived and named and their relationship to other materials described. The decrosslinking reaction described herein is one of the simplest transformations possible. Equation (2) described the ring theory transformation from a crosslinked polymer to a linear polymer with the use of the β function. In this case, the specific degradation of the crosslink sites themselves, rather than a random-type degradation, is specified. The simple case of total decrosslinking has already been briefly explored.[8] The more interesting case from a viscoelastic point of view involves selective partial decrosslinking.

Hydrolysis of AAA can be effected by ethylenediamine,[8] sodium hydroxide in water, or ammonium hydroxide in water. For PEA crosslinked with AAA, the hydrolysis of the AAA was found to be substantially complete after 24 hr of soaking with 28% ammonium hydroxide solutions, making this a practical reagent for PEA/AAA systems.

Even after hydrolysis, the samples containing only AAA but also only modest amounts of 1-Doth did not flow. These samples apparently had some remaining gelation, due to the side reactions during synthesis. Note that the materials in Figures 2 and 10, which should have flowed in the absence of side reactions, in fact did not.

Thus, without a sufficient amount of chain transfer agent (1-Doth), side reactions which normally occur in the free-radical polymerization of PEA created a gelled sample even in the absence of deliberately introduced crosslinking agents. With 1-Doth present, a branched polymer must be present because 1-Doth does not suppress the side reactions; it only causes the chains to be cut at random points.

By controlling the AAA and 1-Doth levels, materials just at the critical gel point were created. These materials exhibited low moduli and large creep values.

The authors are pleased to acknowledge the partial support of Grant AFOSR-76-2945 and Wright-Patterson AFB Contract No. F33615-75-C-5167. S. Yomoda also wishes to thank the Sciences and Technology Agency of the Japanese Government for fellowship support.

References

1. J. K. Gillham, J. A. Benci, and A. Noshay, *J. Appl. Polym. Sci.*, **18,** 951 (1974).
2. A. S. Kenyon and L. E. Nielsen, *J. Macromol. Sci.*, **A3,** 275 (1969).
3. P. J. Flory, *Principles of Polymer Chemistry,* Cornell University Press, Ithaca, N.Y., 1953, Chap. IX.
4. J. Scanlan, *J. Polym. Sci.*, **43,** 501 (1960).
5. A. V. Tobolsky, *Properties and Structure of Polymers,* Wiley, New York, 1960, Chap. 2.

6. L. H. Sperling, in *Recent Advances in Polymer Blends, Grafts, and Blocks*, L. H. Sperling, Ed., Plenum Press, New York, 1974.

7. L. H. Sperling and K. B. Ferguson, *Macromolecules*, **8**, 691 (1975).

8. L. H. Sperling, K. B. Ferguson, J. A. Manson, E. M. Corwin, and D. L. Siegfried, *Macromolecules*, **9**, 743 (1976).

9. V. Huelck, D. A. Thomas, and L. H. Sperling, *Macromolecules*, **5**, 340 (1972).

10. ASTM Standards, ASTM D 1053-58T, American Society for Testing Materials, Philadelphia, Pa., 1958.

11. ASTM Standards, ASTM D-1043, American Society for Testing Materials, Philadelphia, Pa., 1974.

12. R. F. Clash, Jr., and R. M. Berg, *Ind. Eng. Chem.*, **34**, 1218 (1942); ASTM Standards, ASTM D 1043-51, American Society for Testing Materials, Philadelphia, Pa.

13. P. J. Flory and J. Rehner, *J. Chem. Phys.*, **11**, 512 (1943).

14. P. J. Flory, *Chem. Rev.*, **35**, 51 (1944).

15. J. E. Hanson, M. G. McCarthy, and T. J. Dietz, *J. Polym. Sci.*, **7**, 77 (1951).

Received May 17, 1976
Revised August 4, 1976

JOURNAL OF APPLIED POLYMER SCIENCE   VOL. 21, 2621–2629 (1977)

Effect of Pressure on Melting Temperature and Other Associated Thermodynamic Functions of Polyethylene

R. N. GUPTA, P. C. JAIN, and V. S. NANDA, *Department of Physics and Astrophysics, University of Delhi, Delhi-110007, India,* and A. S. RESHAMWALA, *National Aeronautical Laboratory, Bangalore, India*

Synopsis

The melting temperature of polyethylene was determined at pressures up to 30 kbar. Using these results and the calculated values of the volume change on melting in the Clausius–Clapeyron equation, the enthalpy and entropy of fusion as a function of pressure were also determined.

INTRODUCTION

The melting behavior of polyethlyene under pressure has been investigated by a number of authors.[1–8] Most of these studies, however, were confined to pressures below 6 kbar. Only Osugi and Hara[3] carried out their measurements up to 30 kbar. These authors detected the phase transition below 5 kbar by the volume discontinuity method. This involved the isothermal compression of polyethylene melt and the determination of the pressure at which the volume discontinuity occurred. The temperature of the isotherm was taken as the melting point corresponding to that pressure. The solidified samples, however, showed a variation in crystallinity by about 8%. Since in the case of polymers the melting temperature is dependent to a certain extent on the degree of crystallinity, the procedure of Osugi and Hara cannot be regarded as really satisfactory. For pressures above 5 kbar, a different technique, using a cubic press and differential thermal analysis, has been employed to determine the melting temperature. The results obtained by this method are less reliable due to the nonhydrostatic character of the pressure involving very large pressure gradients.

In this paper, the results of our study of the melting behavior of polyethylene at pressures up to 30 kbar are reported. The samples used in all the measurements were characterized by the same degree of crystallinity. Furthermore, the experimental arrangement and the technique for locating the melting temperature were also the same over the entire pressure range. We also determined the enthalpy and the entropy of fusion up to 9 kbar by the help of the Clausius–Clapeyron equation.

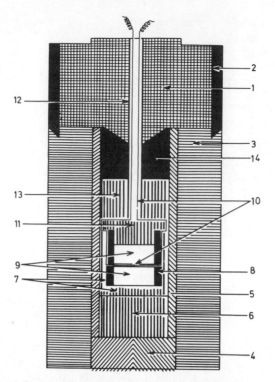

Fig. 1. Constructional details of the cell used in the melting experiment: (1) stainless steel seal; (2) pyrophillite ring; (3) talc cylinder; (4) graphite disc; (5) graphite heater; (6) talc disc; (7) talc cup; (8) pyrophillite rings; (9) polyethylene sample; (10) thermocouple; (11) talc cap; (12) ceramic tubing; (13) talc seal; (14) pyrophillite conical seal.

EXPERIMENTAL

The polymer used for this investigation was linear polyethylene (GF 5750) supplied by Hoechst Dyes and Chemicals Ltd., India. The commercial material, in granular form, was first melted and then allowed to crystallize at 120°C for 2 hr, after which it was cooled to the room temperature at a rate of 2°C/min. The density of the sample so formed was found to be 0.951 g/cc at 25°C. According to the procedure adopted in our earlier work,[9] this density corresponds to 72% crystallinity.

The melting experiment was carried out in a piston cylinder assembly. The required pressures were generated with the help of a 1000-ton hydraulic press. The sample was located in a specially designed talc-pyrophyllite cell. The constructional details are shown in Figure 1. The cell, along with the sample, was placed in the cylinder where it was compressed to the desired pressure by the advancing piston. The value of the pressure was calculated from the oil pressure in the press by area multiplication. No effort was made to calibrate the system by using standard pressure points. However, the error involved in pressure determination, due to the frictional loss and the deformation of the piston as a result of heating, is estimated to be not greater than 2%. The heating of the sample was carried out isobarically with the help of the cylindrical graphite heater shown in Figure 1. Different heating rates were tried; a rate of 6°C/min was found to be the most suitable for locating the transition. Similar heating

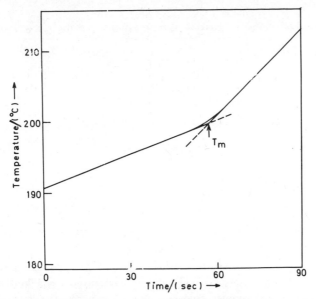

Fig. 2. Sample temperature vs time in a typical isobaric run at 3 kbar (choice of reference for time is arbitrary).

rates have also been employed by other workers.[6] A Chromel–Alumel thermo-couple was used to read the temperature of the polyethylene sample. The output of the thermocouple was fed to an X–Y recorder which plotted the thermo-emf and hence the temperature as a function of time.

A typical plot at 3 kbar pressure is shown in Figure 2. Here, the curve shows only that part of the melting curve where the melting is near completion. In polymers, unlike other substances, melting is not a sharp phenomenon but is extended over a range of temperatures. The crystallinity slowly starts disap-pearing till it vanishes completely. The temperature at which the crystallinity disappeared completely was taken as the melting temperature (T_m). The un-certainty involved in the determination of T_m was never larger than $\pm 1.5°C$.

RESULTS AND DISCUSSION

The smoothed values of the melting temperature for polyethylene as a function of temperature obtained from our raw experimental data are shown in Table I. The melting temperature at atmospheric pressure is in agreement within a degree with the value quoted by the suppliers of the material used in the present ex-periment. It is rather low as compared to the reported values for a high-density polyethylene. Such a low value could be due to some branching present in the sample.

The plot in Figure 3 shows ΔT_m, the change in melting temperature, as a function of pressure. Here, the results of Osugi and Hara,[3] Davidson and Wunderlich,[6] and Bassett and Turner[8] are also shown. Since the melting tem-perature at atmospheric pressure is slightly different in various cases considered, the role of pressure in changing T_m is brought out better by taking ΔT_m instead of T_m as the dependent variable. It may be noted that the smoothed values of Osugi and Hara on the low-pressure side lie below the curve while, above 20 kbar

TABLE I
Smoothed Values of Melting Temperature as a Function of Pressure

P, kbar	T_m, °C
0	126
1	154
2	180
3	200
4	217
5	234
8	277
10	296
15	333
20	357
25	378
30	396

the trend is opposite.   The results of Davidson and Wunderlich, available only below 6 kbar for folded chain crystals, show an even more marked disagreement. Their data for extended-chain crystals (not shown in the figure) surprisingly are in conformity with this curve.   On the other hand, results of Basset and Turner, for folded-chain crystals, show good agreement with the present work.

The enthalpy of fusion, ΔH, as a function of pressure can be obtained from the results of the melting experiment using the Clausius–Clapeyron equation

$$\frac{dP}{dT_m} = \frac{(\Delta H/T_m)}{\Delta V} \tag{1}$$

provided ΔV, the volume change on melting, is known.   Osugi and Hara mea-

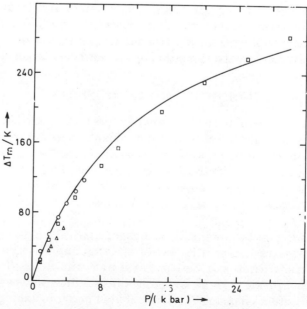

Fig. 3. Variation of melting temperature as a function of pressure: full curve, present results; (□) Osugi and Hara; (△) Davidson and Wunderlich; (○) Bassett and Turner.

TABLE II
Coefficients of Eq. (2) with kbar as Unit of Pressure and °C as Unit of Temperature

Coefficient	Value
a_0	125.98
a_1	32.168
a_2	−3.2071
a_3	0.27651
a_4	−0.010549

TABLE III
Values of dP/dT_m[a]

P, kbar	dP/dT_m		
	1	2	3
0	31.1	40	—
1	37.7	45	46.1
1.5	—	—	48.3
2	44.8	50	50.8
3	51.9	55	56.5
4	58.5	61	63.7
5	64.3	65	73.0
6	69.3		85.5
7	74.4		
8	81.0		
9	92.0		

[a] 1: Present results; 2: results of Osugi and Hara; 3: results of Bassett and Turner; rest as for Table II.

sured the volume change on melting for their semicrystalline sample for pressures up to 4 kbar. Knowing the degree of crystallinity of the sample, it is possible to determine from their results the true volume change on melting of a completely crystalline sample. In this work, we followed a different procedure for determining ΔV for pressures up to 9 kbar. It is based on the knowledge of the equation of states of the crystalline and the amorphous phases. The uncertainty involved in the estimation of ΔV by this method varies between 0.5% and 1% for the lowest and the highest pressure limits. The necessary details are given in the Appendix.

For the determination of dP/dT_m, the smoothed experimental values of T_m for pressures up to 10 kbar were fitted into a fourth-degree polynomial:

$$T_m = a_0 + a_1P + a_2P^2 + a_3P^3 + a_4P^4 \qquad (2)$$

The values of the coefficients are given in Table II. The error in the determination of dP/dT_m, taking account of the errors in T_m and P, is estimated to be about 3% for pressures up to 7 kbar, and it becomes 6% at higher pressures. The results for dP/dT_m are given in Table III. The results of our calculation of ΔH from eq. (1) are plotted in Figure 4 along with the results of other workers. The values of Osugi and Hara in this figure have been duly corrected to apply to a completely crystalline sample.

It is observed that the results from various sources show quantitatively marked differences. For a clear understanding of the reasons, reference may be made

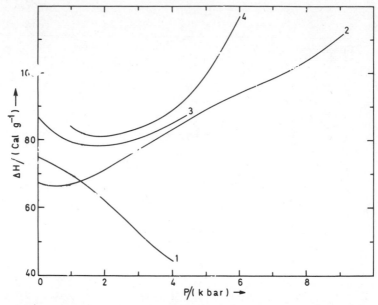

Fig. 4. Variation of ΔH (cal/g) with pressure: (1) Osugi and Hara; (2) present work; (3) Osugi and Hara, with our ΔV values; (4) Basset and Turner.

to Tables III and IV where dP/dT_m and ΔV values used in these references are compared. It may be observed that the ΔV values of Osugi and Hara are lower* than ours, and percentagewise, this difference widens with P. For $P \simeq 0$, where the crystalline and amorphous specific volumes are known experimentally with greatest accuracy, we should have $\Delta V = 0.224$ cc/g.[6] The results of Osugi and Hara[3] show here a serious disagreement. On the other hand, our equation-of-state procedure gives a ΔV value in close agreement with this result. The departures in dP/dT_m values in the various cases could be partly ascribed to the differences in the samples employed. It can be shown that the qualitative trend

TABLE IV
Volume Change on Melting, ΔV, for Fully Crystalline Polyethylene[a]

P, kbar	ΔV, cc/g	
	1	2
0	0.227	0.195
1	0.174	0.154
2	0.147	0.116
3	0.132	0.086
4	0.121	0.063
5	0.115	
6	0.109	
7	0.103	
8	0.097	
9	0.090	

[a] As in Table III.

* The volume discontinuity method used by these authors tends to underestimate the volume change because of lack of sharpness in the melting or freezing process for polymers.

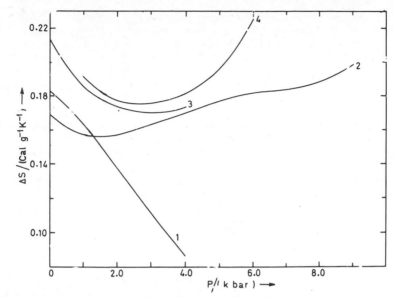

Fig. 5. Variation of ΔS (cal g^{-1} °K^{-1}) with pressure. The remainder as in Fig. 4.

of variation of ΔH with P depends markedly on the ΔV values. For example, it may be noted from Figure 4 that the ΔH results of Osugi and Hara, based on our ΔV values, show a variation with pressure which agrees qualitatively with our results. Further, it may be mentioned that in the limit $P \simeq 0$, our ΔH result is very close to the currently accepted value,[10] which is 70 cal/g.

Finally, in Figure 5, the entropy of melting, ΔS, as a function of pressure is shown. The differences between the results from various sources are seen to be qualitatively similar to the ΔH case. It is seen from our results that the entropy of fusion after a slow initial decrease with pressure increases comparatively more steeply beyond 2 kbar. This implies that pressure is less effective in producing order in the liquid phase beyond this pressure.

CONCLUSIONS

In the determination of thermodynamic functions of fusion, the weakest link in the purely experimental determination seems to be the measurement of volume change on melting. We have in this study bypassed this difficulty by making use of theoretical or semitheoretical equations of state. An experimental confirmation of the ΔV results is, however, desirable. This would be possible by carrying out unit cell measurements[14] at elevated pressure as close to T_m as possible and PVT measurements of the melt on the other side of the transition.

The authors would like to thank Dr. S. Ramaseshan for allowing the use of high-pressure equipment at the N.A.L. for this investigation.

Appendix

Here, we shall describe the procedure adopted for determining the volume change upon melting as a function of pressure from the knowledge of the melting temperature and the equation of states of the melt and the crystal.

The procedure for the calculation of the melt volume from the Tait equation at a given temperature and pressure has been discussed by us in an earlier publication.[11]   The range of applicability of eq. (4b) of this reference implies that for polyethylene, the temperature should not exceed 300°C.   Since the melting pressure for polyethylene corresponding to this temperature is nearly 10 kbar, the amorphous specific volume, and hence ΔV, calculations were carried out below this pressure.

For the polymer crystal phase, we have recently developed an equation of state[12] which is based on the quantum mechanical version of the cell model.   Such a theory in the harmonic approximation has already been used by us for explaining the low-temperature thermal expansivities of the polymer glasses.[13]   In our recent PVT studies of polymer crystal phase, since the interest was in the relatively higher-temperature region, the theory involved two important differences.   First, an account of anharmonicity was taken by including the first anharmonic term in the expansion of the cell potential.   Secondly, for the sake of simplicity, the vibrational frequency spectrum for the volume-dependent degrees of freedom was replaced by a single frequency.   This approximation is known to be good except at very low temperatures.

The resulting equation of state has the form

$$\tilde{P}\tilde{V} = 2(A\tilde{V}^{-4} - B\tilde{V}^{-2}) + 3\gamma\tilde{\theta}F_1\left(\frac{\tilde{\theta}}{\tilde{T}}\right) + \frac{9}{8}\gamma\beta\tilde{V}^2\tilde{\theta}^2F_2\left(\frac{\tilde{\theta}}{\tilde{T}}\right) - \frac{9}{4}\alpha\beta\tilde{V}^2\tilde{\theta}^2F_3\left(\frac{\tilde{\theta}}{\tilde{T}}\right) \tag{A.1}$$

here $\tilde{P}$, $\tilde{V}$, and $\tilde{T}$ are the reduced pressure, reduced volume, and reduced temperature, respectively, while

$$F_1\left(\frac{\tilde{\theta}}{\tilde{T}}\right) = \frac{1}{2} + \frac{1}{e^{\tilde{\theta}/\tilde{T}} - 1} \tag{A.2}$$

$$F_2\left(\frac{\tilde{\theta}}{\tilde{T}}\right) = \frac{1}{2} + \frac{3e^{\tilde{\theta}/\tilde{T}} + 1}{(e^{\tilde{\theta}/\tilde{T}} - 1)^2} - \frac{\tilde{\theta}}{\tilde{T}}\frac{e^{\tilde{\theta}/\tilde{T}}(e^{\tilde{\theta}/\tilde{T}} + 3)}{(e^{\tilde{\theta}/\tilde{T}} - 1)^3} \tag{A.3}$$

$$F_3\left(\frac{\tilde{\theta}}{\tilde{T}}\right) = \frac{1}{2} + \frac{2e^{\tilde{\theta}/\tilde{T}}}{(e^{\tilde{\theta}/\tilde{T}} - 1)^2} \tag{A.4}$$

$$\alpha = 1 + \frac{2A_1\tilde{V}^{-2}}{(A_1\tilde{V}^{-2} - 2B_1)} - \frac{A_2\tilde{V}^{-2}}{(A_2\tilde{V}^{-2} - 2B_2)} \tag{A.5}$$

$$\beta = \frac{A_2\tilde{V}^{-2} - 2B_2}{(A_1\tilde{V}^{-2} - 2B_1)^2} \tag{A.6}$$

$$\gamma = \gamma_0\left[1 - \beta\tilde{\theta}_0\tilde{V}^2\left\{F_1\left(\frac{\tilde{\theta}_0}{\tilde{T}}\right) - \frac{(\tilde{\theta}_0/\tilde{T})e^{\tilde{\theta}_0/\tilde{T}}}{(e^{\tilde{\theta}_0/\tilde{T}} - 1)^2}\right\}\right] - \alpha\beta\tilde{\theta}_0\tilde{V}^2F_1\left(\frac{\tilde{\theta}_0}{\tilde{T}}\right) \tag{A.7}$$

$$\gamma_0 = \left[\frac{4}{3} + \frac{A_1\tilde{V}^{-2}}{(A_1\tilde{V}^{-2} - 2B_1)}\right] \tag{A.8}$$

and

$$\tilde{\theta} = \tilde{\theta}_0\left\{1 + \beta\tilde{\theta}_0\tilde{V}^2F_1\left(\frac{\tilde{\theta}_0}{\tilde{T}}\right)\right\}^{1/2} \times \left[1 + \frac{3}{8}\beta\tilde{V}^2\theta_0\left\{1 + \beta\tilde{\theta}_0\tilde{V}^2F_1\left(\frac{\tilde{\theta}_0}{\tilde{T}}\right)\right\}^{1/2}\right] \tag{A.9}$$

where $\tilde{\theta}_0 = h\nu_0/kT^*$ is the reduced characteristic temperature corresponding to the harmonic oscillation frequency ν_0, and T^* is the temperature-reducing parameter.   Further, A and B are numerical constants with values $A = 1.011$, $B = 1.2045$, $A_1 = 22.1060$, $B_1 = 5.2797$, $A_2 = 200.6530$, and $B_2 = 14.3340$.

It was found that, for polyethylene, if we take $\tilde{\theta}_0 = 0.054$, $T^*/K = 6918$, and the volume-reducing parameter V^* (cc/g) $= 0.9954$, the experimental VT results of Davis, Eby, and Colson[14] for the crystal phase are explained accurately above 130°K.   Further, the PVT results of Hellwege et al.[15] and Olabisi and Simha[16] for semicrystalline polyethylene below 60°C could be explained nicely by making the reasonable assumption that the degree of crystallinity is not affected by pressure.

The results of calculation of volume change upon melting as a function of pressure are given in Table IV.

References

1. S. Matsuoka, J. Polym. Sci., **57**, 569 (1962).
2. E. Baer and J. L. Kardos, J. Polym. Sci., **A-3**, 2827 (1965).

3. J. Osugi and K. Hara, *Rev. Phys. Chem. Jpn.*, **36**, 28 (1966).

4. F. E. Karasz and L. D. Jones; *J. Phys. Chem.*, **71**, 2234 (1967).

5. D. V. Rees and D. C. Basset, *J. Polymer Sci.*, **B7**, 273 (1969).

6. T. Davidson and B. Wunderlich, *J. Polym. Sci. A-2*, **7**, 377 (1969).

7. P. D. Calvert and D. R. Uhlmann, *J. Polym. Sci. A-2*, **10**, 1811 (1972).

8. D. C. Bassett and B. Turner, *Phil. Mag.*, **29**, 925 (1974).

9. R. K. Jain, R. N. Gupta, and V. S. Nanda, *J. Macromol. Sci. Phys.*, **B11**, 411 (1975).

10. B. Wunderlich, *Macromolecular Physics*, Academic Press, New York, 1973, Chap. 4, p. 388.

11. V. S. Nanda and R. Simha, *J. Chem. Phys.*, **41**, 3870 (1964).

12. Y. R. Midha and V. S. Nanda, to be published; Y. R. Midha, Equation of State and Related Properties of Polymeric and Monomeric Materials, Ph.D. Thesis, University of Delhi, 1975.

13. R. Simha, J. M. Roe, and V. S. Nanda, *J. Appl. Phys.*, **43**, 4312 (1972).

14. G. T. Davis, R. K. Eby, and T. R. Colson, *J. Appl. Phys.*, **41**, 4316 (1970).

15. K. H. Hellwege, W. Knappe, and P. Lehmann, *Kolloid-Z.*, **183**, 110 (1962).

16. O. Olabisi and R. Simha, *Macromolecules*, **8**, 206 (1975).

Received April 2, 1976
Revised August 4, 1976

JOURNAL OF APPLIED POLYMER SCIENCE   VOL. 21, 2631–2644 (1977)

A Relationship Between Steady-State Shear Melt Viscosity and Molecular Weight Distribution in Polystyrene

B. H. BERSTED and J. D. SLEE, *Research and Development Department, Amoco Chemicals Corporation, Amoco Research Center, Naperville, Illinois 60540*

Synopsis

A model that relates to the molecular weight distribution (MWD) of high-density polyethylene to the steady-state shear melt viscosity has been applied to polystyrene melts. Relations are developed for predicting the rheological flow curve from the molecular weight distribution. Relationships are also developed to predict the MWD from the flow curve, although practical limitations to this procedure are given. From a consideration of predictions of the model and experimental data, it is concluded that the transition for a given molecular species from Newtonian to non-Newtonian flow is sharp. Additionally, the calculated empirical parameter that partitions the MWD into molecules that act in a Newtonian fashion and those that do not is shown to be equivalent to the largest molecular weight homolog that can still undergo Newtonian flow at a given shear rate for monodisperse fractions. The temperature dependence of the relaxation times is found to be somewhat higher than that predicted by the Rouse theory. An activation energy of 30 kcal/mole for η_0 was used to fit the experimental viscosity data adequately at 190° and 225°C. The terminal relaxation spectrum for a narrow-MWD polystyrene standard is calculated and found to agree well for long relaxation times with that reported in the literature.

INTRODUCTION

A model relating the non-Newtonian steady-shear melt viscosity, relaxation spectrum, and elastic properties of high-density polyethylene to the molecular weight distribution, MWD, has been described in earlier publications.[1,2] *The model is based upon the concept that viscoelastic functions at zero shear rate are valid at nonzero shear rates if the shear-dependent contributions of the molecular components are individually taken into account.* The model can best be described in terms of four major assumptions about the effect of shear rate on the spectrum of relaxation times. First, it is assumed that the spectrum of relaxation times is cut off at a maximum allowed relaxation time, $\tau_m(\dot\gamma)$. Second, it is assumed that the τ_m is a function of shear rate such that $\tau_m \propto 1/\dot\gamma$. The third assumption is that, in addition to the longest relaxation time for a given molecule, the molecular chain undergoes relaxations characteristic of all molecular weight molecules less than its own molecular weight. Lastly, it is assumed that the relaxation times associated with a given molecular species are independent of communal properties in a polydisperse sample. This last assumption is restricted to entangled systems.

2631

The first assumption given above suggests that the general relation[3] for the zero shear viscosity to the relaxation spectrum may be modified to

$$\eta(\dot\gamma) = \int_0^{\tau_m} H(\tau)d\tau \qquad (1)$$

The effect of shear rate on the relaxation spectra for two monodisperse species of differing molecular weight is schematically shown in Figure 1. The third assumption implies that, for relaxation times less than or equal to the longest relaxation time of the smaller molecular weight species M_1 in Figure 1, the relaxation spectra of the two samples of differing molecular weight are identical. Furthermore, the behavior depicted in the figure indicates that the effective (operative) relaxation spectra will be the same at any shear rate where both samples are undergoing non-Newtonian flow. However, from eq. (1), this implies that both samples will have identical viscosities (equivalent to that of a sample of molecular weight M_c, which has as its longest relaxation time τ_m). In other words, at a given shear rate, all molecular weight species larger than M_c act as though they were of molecular weight M_c, and species having molecular weights less than M_c act as they do at zero shear. M_c can be thought of as the largest molecular weight homolog that can be undergoing Newtonian flow at a given shear rate.

The above argument also suggests that the onset of non-Newtonian flow is due to the rendering inoperative of the longest relaxation time associated with the sample. Similar ideas have been expressed by Vinogradov[3] in explaining the effects of blending of narrow-MWD polybutadienes on the land fracture phenomenon. Vinogradov suggests that each component of the mixture acts independently and that each component either contributes to the viscous losses as it does in the Newtonian region or acts with diminished effect in the high elastic state.

In order to calculate the steady-state shear viscosity at any shear rate for broad-MWD polymers, the relation between zero shear viscosity and molecular weight was assumed to be known. An empirical relationship for polyethylene at 190°C reported in the literature[4] was used:

$$\log \eta_0 = -12.296 + 3.36 \log \overline{M}_w + 0.51 \log (\overline{M}_z/\overline{M}_w) \qquad (2)$$

The steady shear melt viscosity at any shear rate was assumed to be related to the MWD through the relation

$$\log \eta(\dot\gamma) = -12.296 + 3.36 \log \overline{M}_w{}^* + 0.51 \log [\overline{M}_z{}^*/\overline{M}_w{}^*]$$

where

$$\overline{M}_w{}^* = \sum_{i=1}^{i=c-1} w_i M_i + M_c \sum_{i=c}^{i=\infty} w_i$$

$$\overline{M}_z{}^* = \sum_{i=1}^{i=c-1} w_i M_i{}^2 + M_c{}^2 \sum_{i=c}^{\infty} w_i \Big/ \sum_{i=1}^{i=c-1} w_i M_i + M_c \sum_{i=c}^{\infty} w_i \qquad (3)$$

and w_i is the weight fraction of the ith component. For high-density polyethylene, the relation between M_c and $\dot\gamma$ was found to be

$$M_c = 540,000 \ (\dot\gamma^{-0.300}) \qquad (4)$$

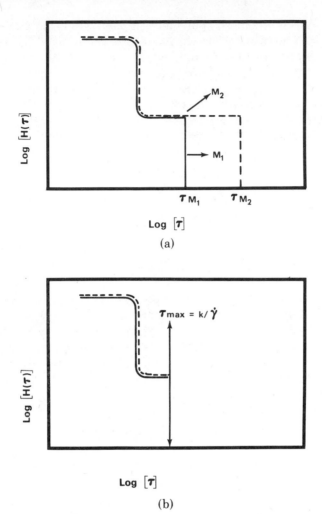

Fig. 1. (a) Schematic view of the relaxation spectra at zero shear rate of two monodisperse samples having molecular weights M_1 and M_2, where $M_2 > M_1$. (b) Postulated effect of shear rate on the relaxation spectra of the two samples in (a). In the case depicted, both samples would be undergoing non-Newtonian flow.

In spite of the model's success in accounting for the variation of viscosity and first normal stress difference as a function of shear rate, a number of important questions remain unanswered. The most pressing question involves the definition of M_c. In our model, the empirically determined relation of M_c to shear rate for polydisperse samples is assumed to be the variation of the onset of non-Newtonian flow for monodisperse samples of varying molecular weight with shear rate. Unfortunately, no essentially monodisperse samples of HDPE are readily available to test the above assumption. At this point, M_c (as calculated from a broad-MWD sample) must be regarded as an empirical parameter whose exact meaning remains to be defined. This is one of the goals of this publication. We shall attempt to give meaning to M_c by generating a M_c-versus-shear rate relationship similar to eq. (4) for a broad MWD and comparing this relationship with the onset of non-Newtonian behavior in very narrow-MWD samples.

Polystyrene is an ideal polymer with which to test the definition of M_c since quite narrow-MWD anionically polymerized polystyrene materials are readily available.   Using these materials, the model's assumption of a sharp transition from Newtonian to non-Newtonian flow can also be tested.   Further, the generality of the "partition" model can be assessed, and inversion of the model to predict the MWD from rheological data will be demonstrated.   In a manner similar to that used for HDPE,[2] the terminal relaxation spectrum for a narrow-MWD polystyrene standard will also be shown to be predictable from the parameteric relations as obtained from a broad-MWD sample.

EXPERIMENTAL

The sample labeled PS-350 is a commercial crystal polystyrene.   The polystyrene standards were anionically polymerized materials obtained from ArRo Laboratories.

Rheological data were obtained at 190° and 225°C using an Instron rheometer with a capillary having an L/D of 33:1.   Rabinowitsch corrections were applied to the data.

Molecular weight data were obtained on a Waters Model 200 GPC at 135°C using 1,2,4-trichlorobenzene as a solvent and four Styrogel columns of porosities 10^6, 10^5, 10^4, and 10^3 Å.   Polystyrene standards polymerized by Pressure Chemical and characterized by ArRo Laboratories were used for calibration. Spreading corrections[5] were applied to the molecular weight distribution data for the anionically polymerized standards used in this study to obtain the polydispersities as given by ArRo Laboratories.

RESULTS AND DISCUSSION

Calculation of the Relation Between M_c and Shear Rate for Polystyrene

In order to calculate the relation between M_c and shear rate, the relationship between zero shear viscosity and molecular weight must be known.   The relationship given by Zosel[6] was chosen as

$$\log \eta_0 = -12.8 + 3.4 \log \overline{M}_w \qquad \text{at } 190°C \qquad (5)$$

To find the relation at 225°C, an activation energy of 30 kcal/mole as given by various authors[7-9] was used to give

$$\log \eta_0 = -13.8 + 3.4 \log \overline{M}_w \text{ at } 225°C \qquad (6)$$

Log–log plots of η versus $\dot{\gamma}$ for sample PS-350 at 190 and 225°C are given in Figure 2, where the points represent experimental data from the capillary rheometer.   The MWD data for this sample are given in Table I.   The value of M_c was determined at each shear rate and temperature by means of an interval halving computer program and the equation

$$\log \eta(\dot{\gamma}) = \log K + 3.4 \log \overline{M}_w^* \qquad (7)$$

where $\overline{M}_w^* = \Sigma_{i=1}^{c-1} w_i M_i + M_c \Sigma_{i=c}^{\infty} w_i$, w_i is the weight fraction of the ith component from the MWD curve, and K is the constant in the zero shear viscosity relationship (i.e., $\log K = -12.8$ and -13.8 at 190° and 225°C, respectively).   The

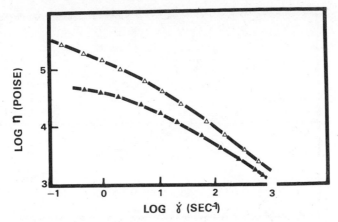

Fig. 2. Apparent viscosity η as a function of shear rate for the polystyrene sample PS-350. Solid (▲) and open triangles (△) are experimental data at 225° and 190°C, respectively. The curves are the calculated relations based on eqs. (7), (8), and (9).

results of the calculations are plotted in Figure 3. The equations relating M_c and shear rate at 190° and 225°C, respectively, are given by

$$M_c = 330,000 \, (\dot{\gamma}^{-0.2602}) \qquad (8)$$

and

$$M_c = 640,000 \, (\dot{\gamma}^{-0.2602}) \qquad (9)$$

Comparison with High-Density Polyethylene

Figure 3 shows that, at 190°C and a given shear rate, the M_c value for polyethylene is slightly larger than that of polystyrene. Because M_c has previously been defined as the largest molecule that can still relax at a given shear rate, it may be concluded that, at 190°C and at a given shear rate, a larger molecular weight molecule of polyethylene may more fully relax than that of polystyrene. However, because the activation energies for polyethylene and polystyrene are so different (i.e., approximately 6.3 kcal for polyethylene vs approximately 30 kcal for polystyrene), the relative M_c values change substantially with temperature.

The relations of log M_c vs log $\dot{\gamma}$ for polystyrene at 190° and 225°C have the

TABLE I
Molecular Weight Distribution Data for the Polystyrene Samples

Sample	$\overline{M}_n$	$\overline{M}_w$	$\overline{M}_z$	$\overline{M}_w/\overline{M}_n$
PS-350	72,000	290,000	580,000	5.4
PS-1	158,000[a]	179,000[a]		1.13
PS-2	375,000[a]	411,000[a]		1.10
PS-3	735,000[a]	852,000[a]		1.16

[a] Average values given by ArRo Laboratories.

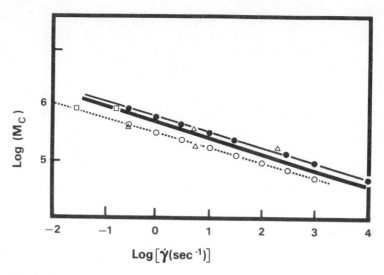

Fig. 3. Relation between partitioning molecular weight M_c and shear rate. Solid black and open circles are calculated points from polystyrene sample PS-350 at 225° and 190°C, respectively. Triangles are points based on the narrow-MWD Pressure Chemical polystyrene standards of $\overline{M}_w$ = 411,000 and $\overline{M}_w$ = 160,000. These points were obtained from the data of Graessley and Penwell.[11] Squares were calculated from the data of Chee and Rudin. Heavy solid line is that obtained earlier for high-density polyethylene.[2]

same slope. Calculating[1] the limiting power law relation between viscosity and shear rate for polystyrene as 3.4 × slope, we obtain a value of −0.88, which is higher than the −0.818 as predicted by Graessley[10] and somewhat lower than the value of −1.0 predicted from the model presented for polyethylene[1] of −1.0.

Prediction of the Flow Curve for "Essentially Monodisperse Samples"

The model assumes that M_c is a unique (for a given polymer structure) function of shear rate and that there is a sharp transition from Newtonian to non-Newtonian flow for either a monodisperse sample or a homolog in a polydisperse sample. These assumptions can be tested by applying the M_c-versus-shear-rate relationship as obtained on a broad-MWD polystyrene sample to essentially monodisperse, anionically polymerized polystyrene standards of known molecular weight.

Experimental data for a Pressure Chemical standard of $\overline{M}_w$ = 411,000 from Graessley's[11] cone-and-plate rheometer and our Instron rheometer at 190°C are given in Figure 4. The data of Graessley are those obtained at 193.5°C. The data have been shifted both vertically and horizontally to correspond to 190°C data assuming an E_a of 30 kcal/mole for η_0. The solid curve is that predicted on the basis of molecular weight distribution data corrected for spreading[5] so as to yield $\overline{M}_w/\overline{M}_n$ = 1.1 and $\overline{M}_w$ = 411,000. The agreement is quite good. Because the predictions are based on a sharp transition from Newtonian to non-Newtonian behavior for each homolog in the very narrow-MWD sample, the assumption of a sharp transition is reinforced. Furthermore, the generality of the M_c-versus-shear-rate relation is demonstrated. Additionally, the

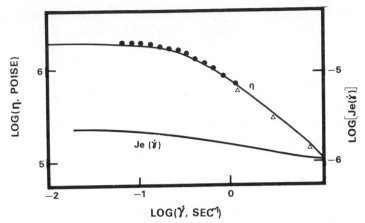

Fig. 4. Aparent viscosity η and steady shear elastic compliance J_e at 190°C for the Pressure Chemical standard having $\overline{M}_w$ = 411,000 and $\overline{M}_w/\overline{M}_n$ = 1.1. Solid circles are experimental viscosity data from Graessley[11] obtained on the cone-and-plate viscometer. Triangles are experimental data obtained on the capillary rheometer.

agreement obtained here on the Pressure Chemical sample having $\overline{M}_w$ = 411,000 should be general for the other narrow-MWD standards, since at equivalent polydispersities the shapes of the viscosity–shear-rate curves can be quantitatively superimposed.[11]

Comparison of Partitioning Molecular Weight M_c (as Calculated from a Polydisperse Sample) with Onset of non-Newtonian Flow Observed for Essentially Monodisperse Samples

Ideally, it would be desirable to obtain the shear rate at which flow changes from Newtonian to non-Newtonian for a group of monodisperse polystyrene samples of different molecular weights in order to verify that M_c (as calculated from a broad-MWD sample) is the same as the onset of non-Newtonian flow for a monodisperse sample of molecular weight M_c. However, narrow-MWD polystyrene samples of $\overline{M}_w/\overline{M}_n \simeq 1.1$ do not suit this type of analysis since even this small amount of polydispersity leads to a fairly broad transition from Newtonian flow to power law behavior. In principle, the shear rate at which non-Newtonian behavior just begins could be used to calculate the corresponding M_c, and the result could be compared with the largest molecular weight observed by GPC. However, neither the shear rate for the onset of non-Newtoninan flow nor the largest molecular weight homolog in the sample can be accurately determined.

As a result of the difficulties, a better approach is to use $\overline{M}_w$, which is presumably more accurately known. A log normal MWD will be assumed. It is shown in the Appendix that the melt viscosity for samples of $\overline{M}_w/\overline{M}_n$ = 1.10 and 1.16 and having log normal MWD's will drop to 65% and 57%, respectively, of the viscosity at zero shear when the shear rate is reached such that $M_c = \overline{M}_w$. Consequently, since $\overline{M}_w$ is known and the $\dot{\gamma}$ at which η/η_0 = 0.65 (or 0.57 for $\overline{M}_w/\overline{M}_n$ = 1.16) can be measured, a point is independently determined that can be compared to the relationship obtained for the broad-MWD sample in Figure 3.

Using the criterion that $M_c = \overline{M}_w$ when $\eta/\eta_0 = 0.65$ (or 0.57 for $\overline{M}_w/\overline{M}_n = 1.16$), the shear rate at which $\eta/\eta_0 = 0.65$ vs $\overline{M}_w$ is plotted in Figure 3 for three polystyrene standards at 190° and 225°C. The 190°C data on PS-1 and PS-2 were interpolated from the data of Graessley.[11] The 225°C data were obtained from an extrapolation of Graessley's[11] data and are not as accurate as those at 190°C. The data at 190° and 225°C for PS-3 were calculated from the data of Chee and Rudin.[12] As can be seen in Figure 3, these points as determined for the three narrow-MWD standards agree well with the log M_c-vs-log $\dot{\gamma}$ relations established from the broad-MWD sample PS-350. It, therefore, may be concluded that M_c is well defined as the largest molecular weight species that acts in a Newtonian fashion at a given shear rate.

Relaxation Times

As shown in an earlier publication[2] on the prediction of elastic properties from MWD, the steady shear elastic compliance can be calculated in terms of the unknown parameter β, which represents the proportionality constant in the assumed relation between the maximum allowed relaxation time τ_m and $1/\dot{\gamma}$. (The onset of non-Newtonian flow is interpreted as the disappearance of a relaxation time proportional to $1/\dot{\gamma}$.) Using the experimental results of Mieras and Rijn,[13] we found β to be 1.65. Consequently, for polystyrene,

$$\tau_m = 1.65/\dot{\gamma} \tag{10}$$

and from eq. (8),

$$\tau = 1.0 \times 10^{-21} M^{3.84} \tag{11}$$

The constant of 1.65 for polystyrene at 190°C in eq. (10) is almost identical to that of 1.7 obtained for polyethylene at 190°C. While the agreement between these two constants suggests a unique value for β, which is independent of polymer type, the sensitivity of this constant to the choice of zero shear relations for the two different polymer systems and the sensitivity of this constant to the various calculations made in obtaining it make the agreement seem fortuitous.

The temperature dependence of the relaxation times can be calculated from eqs. (8) and (9). From the assumed proportionality between the maximum allowed relaxation time and $1/\dot{\gamma}$ for a given molecular weight M_c, the effect of temperature can be represented as

$$\frac{\tau_{190°C}}{\tau_{225°C}} = \left(\frac{640,000}{330,000}\right)^{1/0.2602} = 12.75$$

Temperature independence of the proportionality constant between the maximum allowed relaxation time and $1/\dot{\gamma}$ is assumed. For an $E_a = 30$ kcal/mole, the temperature variation of $\tau = \eta_0/\rho T$ from the Rouse theory is

$$\frac{\tau_{190°C}}{\tau_{225°C}} = \frac{(\eta_0)_{190°C}}{(\eta_0)_{225°C}} \times \frac{498}{463} \times \frac{\rho_{225°C}}{\rho_{190°C}} = 11.1$$

The temperature effect of the density ρ used here was that given by Chee and Rudin.[14] Although the effect of temperature in the Rouse theory is somewhat less than predicted here, the predictions of the two models are in substantial

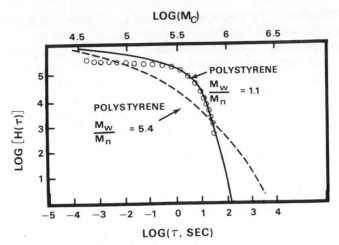

Fig. 5. Relaxation spectra for polystyrene samples PS-350 and $\overline{M}_w$ = 411,000 Pressure Chemical standard as a function of relaxation time τ and partitioning molecular weight M_c. Calculated spectra for the PS-350 and Pressure Chemical standard at 190°C are given by dashed and solid line, respectively. Experimental data of Prest[17] at 192°C for the Pressure Chemical material are given by circles.

agreement. The larger "shift factor" than predicted by the Rouse theory[15] agrees well with the results of Graessley and Penwell[11] on the temperature behavior of narrow-MWD polystyrenes.

By use of the proportionality constant between relaxation time and molecular weight, α, the relaxation spectrum may be calculated (2). A similar relation to that given earlier for polyethylene is obtained as

$$H(\tau_m) = \frac{d\eta}{d\tau_m} = \frac{3.4K}{3.84\alpha} \frac{(\overline{M}_w{}^*)^{2.4}\overline{A}_2}{(M_c)^{2.84}} \qquad (12)$$

where

$$\overline{M}_w{}^* = \sum_{i=1}^{C-1} \overline{h}_i M_i + M_c \sum_{i=C}^{\infty} \overline{h}_i \text{ and } \overline{A}_2 = \sum_{i=C}^{\infty} \overline{h}_i$$

The calculated relaxation spectra for the broad-MWD PS-350 and the 411,000 narrow-MWD samples are compared in Figure 5. Narrowing of the MWD cuts off the long relaxation times, and the terminal spectrum approaches that of a "box" as used in the theory of Maruyama et al.[16] to relate the steady flow viscosity and the dynamic viscosity. The experimental data of Prest[17] at 192°C are included for comparison with the calculated relaxation spectrum of the 411,000 polystyrene standard at 190°C. This agreement at the terminal end of the spectrum supports the interpretation of the shear rate for the onset of non-Newtonian behavior as the disappearance of a particular relaxation mechanism at a given shear rate. This concept is embodied in the "thixotropy theory" of Leonov and Vinogradov[18] and the "network rupture theory" of Tanner.[19] Furthermore, Staverman et al.[20] conclude that this feature is consistent with dynamic experiments superimposed on steady shearing flow.

As demonstrated for polyethylene,[2] the steady shear elastic compliance $J_e(\dot{\gamma})$ can be calculated once α is known. $J_e(\dot{\gamma})$ as calculated is shown in Figure 4 to be a slowly varying function of $\dot{\gamma}$. This small shear rate dependence is consistent with those reported[21,22] for polystyrene solutions and poly(vinyl acetate) samples. However, in contrast to the predicted decrease of $J_e(\dot\gamma)$ with $\dot\gamma$, $J_e(\dot\gamma)$ was reported by Graessley and Segal[21] to increase slightly. Endo, Fujimoto, and Nagasawa[23] present data on poly(α-methylstyrene) consistent with the theory of Tanaka, Yamamoto, and Takino[24] describing the shear dependence of the shear dependent elastic compliance. Like Graessley's data, $J_e(\dot\gamma)$ was found by Nagasawa et al. to increase with shear rate for very narrow-MWD samples.

Speculation Regarding Entanglements

In view of the "partition" model's success in describing the elastic properties and non-Newtonian viscosity behavior of both polyethylene and polystyrene melts, some discussion of the model's implications in terms of entanglements seem in order.

Although entanglements are generally accepted as the cause of the strong dependence of the zero shear viscosity on molecular weight, the origin of the non-Newtonian behavior is not so clear. If entanglements are accepted as the dominant contribution (i.e., intermolecular interactions predominate over intramolecular interactions), then the non-Newtonian behavior of high molecular weight polymers can be qualitatively accounted for in three general ways: (1) the number of entanglements vary with shear rate when a critical shear rate is exceeded; (2) the number remains the same but their effectiveness changes with shear rate; or (3) some combination of the number and effectiveness of the entanglements changes with shear rate.

If the first possibility is accepted, non-Newtonian flow implies a reduced number of couples for molecules at increased shear rates. However, in terms of the basic assumption of the partition model, the validity of application of characteristics of monodisperse to polydisperse samples, molecules in a polydisperse sample that are not undergoing non-Newtonian flow participate in the same number of couples that they do at zero shear. Therefore, we have a paradoxical situation where the number of entanglements in a presumably homogeneous sample are changed for some molecules and not for others, but they would have to participate in mutual couples for the sample to be homogeneous. As a result, one must conclude that either the concept of variation of entanglement density with shear rate is inconsistent with the assumptions of the partition model, or else homogeneity does not exist in the non-Newtonian region. The third possibility can be ruled out on the same basis.

As a result, it is concluded that the partition model appears to be consistent with an entanglement concept only for constant entanglement density and reduced entanglement effectiveness as the mechanism for non-Newtonian flow.

Calculation of the MWD from Rheological Data

The calculation of the MWD from rheological data has been reported by various authors. Locata et al.[25] use intrinsic viscosity and the zero shear melt viscosity to obtain estimates of $\overline{M}_w$ and $\overline{M}_z/\overline{M}_w$. However, the method is restricted to log-normal MWD's and polymer systems in which η_0 has a dependence on polydispersity (not just $\overline{M}_w$). Menefee[26] uses stress relaxation data and a modified Rouse based model to calculate the MWD.

It should be possible by inversion of eq. (7) to predict the MWD from data on the steady shear melt viscosity. The inversion of eq. (7) may be effected as follows: Let the index c in eq. (7) be shear-rate dependent. Then, for a specific shear-rate, the viscosity $\eta(\dot{\gamma})$ may be expressed as

$$\eta(\dot{\gamma}_c) = K \left[\sum_{i=1}^{c-1} w_i M_i + M_c \sum_{i=c}^{\infty} w_i \right]^{3.4} \equiv \eta_c \tag{13}$$

or

$$\left[\left(\frac{\eta_{c+1}}{K} \right)^{1/3.4} - \left(\frac{\eta_c}{K} \right)^{1/3.4} \right] = (M_{c+1} - M_c) \sum_{i=c+1}^{\infty} w_i \tag{14}$$

or

$$\sum_{i=c+1}^{\infty} w_i = \frac{\left[\left(\frac{\eta_{c+1}}{K} \right)^{1/3.4} - \left(\frac{\eta_c}{K} \right)^{1/3.4} \right]}{M_{c+1} - M_c} \tag{15}$$

As c increases, $\dot{\gamma}_c$ decreases. By definition, $\sum_{i=c+1}^{\infty} w_i$ is the relative weight percent of the sample above the molecular weight M_{c+1}. In order to reconstruct the MWD, the w_i values corresponding to each molecular weight species are needed. This can be accomplished by noting that

$$\sum_{i=c}^{\infty} w_i - \sum_{i=c+1}^{\infty} w_i = w_c \tag{16}$$

and, therefore,

$$w_c = \left(\frac{1}{K} \right)^{1/3.4} \left[\frac{(\eta_c)^{1/3.4} - (\eta_{c-1})^{1/3.4}}{M_c - M_{c-1}} - \frac{(\eta_{c+1})^{1/3.4} - (\eta_c)^{1/3.4}}{M_{c+1} - M_c} \right] \tag{17}$$

where η_{c-1}, η_c, and η_{c+1} represent the viscosities at closely spaced shear-rate intervals. Consequently, the normalized weight percent of M_c in the sample can be calculated from eq (17). From w_c and the corresponding M_c calculated from eq. (8) or (9), the entire MWD can be calculated.

The method outlined above has been applied to sample PS-350 described in Table I for the purpose of illustration. The rheological data given in Figure 2 at 225°C were used and the molecular weight distribution averages calculated. The results are given in Table II.

Reasonably good agreement between the averages obtained by means of gel permeation chromatography and those calculated using eq. (17) and rheological data at 225°C is obtained. The absence of a calculated value for $\overline{M}_n$ arises out of the lack of the very high shear-rate rheological data necessary to obtain estimates from eq. (17) of the weight percent of the lower molecular weight homologs.

TABLE II
Comparison of Experimentally Determined and Calculated Molecular Weight Averages
of Sample PS-350

	$\overline{M}_w$	$\overline{M}_z$
Predicted	310,000	520,000
Experimental (GPC)	290,000	580,000

In fact, eqs. (8) and (9) suggest that information regarding $\overline{M}_n$ is unattainable from rheological measurements of steady shearing flow for broad-MWD samples or for monodisperse samples of very low molecular weight.

ASSESSMENT OF RESULTS IN TERMS OF THE RELATION OF η_0 TO MOLECULAR WEIGHT

Throughout the preceding discussion, specific literature relations of η_0 to molecular weight were employed. However, considering the primary importance ascribed to these relations for relating both viscous and elastic properties to the MWD in the non-Newtonian region, some evaluation of the results in terms of the choice of the η_0–MWD relation is in order.

Table III contains the experimental and calculated values for η_0. The η_0 values for the narrow-MWD polystyrenes were obtained from the data of Penwell and Graessley[11] by extrapolation and interpolation. A plot of log η_0 vs $1/T$ gave approximately straight lines, curving slightly at the higher temperatures. Values for η_0 at 190° and 225°C are shown in the table for both the linear and second-degree polynomial fits. The values of η_0 for the PS-350 were estimated by fitting the data at 190° and 225°C to the Sabia[27] model. Besides the relations used in this paper for calculating η_0 from the MWD, calculations of η_0 using an older but widely used relation[28] are given. As can be seen from the table, the Zosel[6] relation gives better agreement with the experimental data used in applying the partition model. While the calculated values of η_0 are not as close to the experimental as one might wish, the agreement is judged satisfactory in light of the rather substantial variations in literature relations.

An error in the zero shear relation can only affect the agreement shown between M_c (as calculated from a broad-MWD sample) and the "onset" on non-Newtonian behavior of "monodisperse" samples by affecting the calculated M_c value at a particular shear rate for the broad-MWD sample. This is true since the molecular weights of the monodisperse materials are independently determined and the absolute values of the viscosities are not used. We have made calculations for PS-350 and determined that by letting K, the constant in the MWD–zero shear relation, vary by 60%, M_c varied by less than 40% over the range of $\dot{\gamma} = 10^{-2}$ to 10^2 sec^{-1}. For a K that is 60% larger than that used by us, α and β, the constants in the relations between the relaxation time and molecular weight

TABLE III

Sample	Method of obtaining η_0	η_0 (190°C), poises	η_0 (225°C), poises
PS-350	Experimental (E)	6.50×10^5	5.98×10^4
	Zosel[6] equation (Z)	5.92×10^5	5.92×10^4
	Nielsen[28] equation (N)	9.31×10^5	9.95×10^4
PS-2	E (linear fit)	1.98×10^6	1.26×10^5
	(Polynomial fit)	2.10×10^6	1.77×10^5
	Z	1.94×10^6	1.94×10^5
	N	3.05×10^6	3.26×10^5
PS-1	E (linear fit)	8.32×10^4	3.16×10^3
	(polynomial fit)	1.01×10^5	7.94×10^4
	Z	1.15×10^5	1.15×10^4
	N	1.80×10^5	1.93×10^4

and shear rate, respectively, varied such that α and β were found to be 32×10^{-21} and 2.2. This change in the relation for η_0 changes β from 1.65 to 2.2. Therefore our conclusion as to the apparent agreement between the β for polyethylene and polystyrene at 190°C is relatively insensitive to the choice of relation for η_0. It should be noted that in order to fit the viscosity data the exponents in eqs. 8 and 9 had to be changed.

Even if there exists a unique relation between η_0 and MWD for a given polymer type, errors involved in the determination of the MWD could be serious to the use of the partition model since $\overline{M}_w$ is being raised to the 3.4th power. As a result, errors in $\overline{M}_w$ will be greatly magnified in calculating η_0. We believe it is the errors in measuring the MWD that will make agreement between independent investigators difficult. We, therefore, recommend that for a given polymer type, the M_c-vs-shear-rate relation be regarded as relative to the η_0 relation and MWD used. Consequently, in applying our model, an η_0 relation should be chosen that is consistent with the experimental MWD data. After this has been accomplished, the M_c-vs-$\dot{\gamma}$ relation can be determined.

CONCLUSIONS

The ability to predict the rheological curve for an "essentially monodisperse" polystyrene standard, together with the demonstration that M_c values calculated (at given values of the shear rate) from a broad-MWD sample correspond to extremely narrow-MWD polystyrene standards of molecular weight M_c (which are experiencing the onset of non-Newtonian flow at the corresponding shear rates), lends credence to "partition" model assumptions, namely, that (1) the transition from Newtonian to non-Newtonian flow is sharp; (2) M_c, as calculated from polydisperse samples, is indeed the largest molecular weight that can respond in a Newtonian fashion, regardless of polydispersity; and (3) M_c for a given polymer type is a unique function of shear rate, independent of communal properties of the sample as a whole. Further, credence is lent to the model by showing that the temperature dependence of the calculated relaxation spectrum is close to that predicted by the Rouse theory.

The zero shear relation, the material constant α relating relaxation time to molecular weight, and the shear rate dependence of the parameter M_c must be known in order to calculate the viscoelastic functions from the MWD.

The concept of a reduction in entanglement density accounting for non-Newtonian behavior appears to be inconsistent with the assumptions of the model presented here, unless sample homogeneity does not exist under non-Newtonian conditions.

Calculation of the molecular weight distribution from rheological measurements using this model is probably not useful because, unlike the calculation of the rheological flow curve from the complete MWD data, the whole flow curve is impossible to obtain. Certainly, no prediction of $\overline{M}_n$ for broad-MWD samples is possible because the shear rates necessary to obtain the data are unobtainable.

Appendix

The calculation of η/η_0 at the shear rate where $M_c = \overline{M}_w$ can be simplified by noting that any of the MWD's of the anionically polymerized can be approximated by log normal molecular weight distributions.[2] From the earlier definition of $\overline{M}_w{}^*$, and assuming a log normal molecular weight distribution[2] which varies continuously with molecular weight, $\overline{M}_w{}^*$ can be redefined as

$$\overline{M}_w{}^* = \overline{A}_2 M_c + \frac{\overline{M}_w}{\sqrt{2\pi}} \int_{-\infty}^{(\sqrt{2}\,\ln(M_c/M_0)/\beta)-\beta/\sqrt{2}} \frac{\beta}{} e^{-z^2/2} dz$$

where

$$\overline{A}_2 = \frac{1}{\sqrt{2\pi}} \int_{\sqrt{2}\,\ln(M_c/M_0)/\beta}^{\infty} e^{-z^2/2} dz$$

$$z = \frac{\sqrt{2}(\ln M - \ln M_0)}{\beta}$$

and

$$\beta = [2\ln(\overline{M}_w/\overline{M}_n)]^{1/2}$$

For $\overline{M}_w/\overline{M}_n = 1.1$ and $M_c = \overline{M}_w$, $\overline{M}_w{}^* = 0.88\overline{M}_w$ ($\overline{M}_w$ is the actual weight-average molecular weight). Consequently, $\eta/\eta_0 = k[(\overline{M}_w{}^*)^{3.4}]/k[(\overline{M}_w)^{3.4}] = 0.65$ for $M_c = \overline{M}_w$.

The authors would like to thank Ken Stanish for his assistance in the computer programs used here. Also appreciated are the useful discussions with Professor W. W. Graessley and the valuable comments of Dr. J. R. Knox.

References

1. B. H. Bersted, *J. Appl. Polym. Sci.*, **19**, 2167 (1975).
2. B. H. Bersted, *J. Appl. Polym. Sci.*, **20**, 2075 (1976).
3. G. V. Vinogradov, *Rheol. Acta*, **12**, 273 (1973).
4. G. Locati and L. Gargani, *Polym. Lett.*, **11**, 95 (1973).
5. S. T. Balke and A. E. Hamielec, *J. Appl. Polym. Sci.*, **13**, 1381 (1969).
6. A. Zosel, *Rheol. Acta*, **10**, 215 (1971).
7. T. G. Fox and P. J. Flory, *J. Amer. Chem. Soc.*, **70**, 2384 (1948).
8. G. H. Wist, R. N. Howard, and B. Wright, *Adv. Polym. Sci. Technol.*, **26**, 348 (1967).
9. W. P. Cox, L. E. Nielsen, and R. Keeney, *J. Polym. Sci.*, **26**, 365 (1957).
10. W. W. Graessley, *J. Chem. Phys.*, **47**, 1942 (1967).
11. R. C. Penwell and W. W. Graessley, *J. Polym. Sci.*, **12**, 1771 (1974).
12. K. K. Chee and A. Rudin, *Trans. Soc. Rheol.*, **18**, 103 (1974).
13. H. Mieras and Van Rijn, *Nature*, **218**, 865 (1967).
14. K. K. Chee and A. Rudin, *J. Macromol. Sci.-Phys.*, **B-7**, 497 (1973).
15. P. E. Rouse, *J. Chem. Phys.*, **21**, 1272 (1953).
16. T. Maruyama, Y. Takano, and M. Yamomoto, *Rep. Progr. Polym. Sci., Jpn.*, **11**, 99 (1968).
17. W. M. Prest, *Polym. J.*, **4**, 163 (1973).
18. A. I. Leonov and G. V Vinogradov, *Doklady Akad. Nauk SSSR*, **155**, 406 (1964).
19. R. J. Tanner and J. M. Simmons, *Chem. Eng. Sci.*, **22**, 1803 (1967).
20. A. J. Staverman, Z. Laufer, and H. L. Jalink, *Rheol. Acta*, **14**, 650 (1975).
21. W. W. Graessley and L. Segal, *Macromolecules*, **2**, 47 (1969).
22. W. W. Graessley and W. C. Uy, *Macromolecules*, **4**, 458 (1971).
23. H. Endo, T. Fujimoto, M. Nagasawa, *J. Polym. Sci. A-2*, **9**, 345 (1971).
24. T. Tanaka, M. Yamamoto, and V. Takano, *J. Macromol. Sci.*, **B4**, 931 (1970).
25. G. Locati, L. Gargangi, and De Chirico, *Rheol. Acta*, **13**, 786 (1974).
26. E. Menefee, *J. Appl. Polym. Sci.*, **16**, 2215 (1972).
27. R. Sabia, *J. Appl. Polym. Sci.*, **7**, 347 (1963).
28. L. E. Nielsen, *Mechanical Properties of Polymers*, Rheinhold, New York, 1962.

Received May 27, 1976
Revised August 4, 1976

JOURNAL OF APPLIED POLYMER SCIENCE   VOL. 21, 2645–2660 (1977)

Thermomechanical Behavior of Poly(vinyl Chloride) in the Process of Degradation

SHOICHIRO YANO, *Industrial Products Research Institute, 21-2,4-Chome Shimomaruko, Ota-ku, Tokyo, Japan*

Synopsis

The thermomechanical behavior of poly(vinyl chloride) (PVC) was investigated during its thermal degradation by using torsional braid analysis. In thermomechanical behavior as a function of temperature, the relative rigidity G_r decreased initially with increasing temperature, then began to increase passing through a minimum at about 200°C, and finally decreased at 340°C. Increase in G_r from 200°C was caused by formation of a conjugated polyene chain accompanied by dehydrochlorination and by crosslinking reaction, and decrease in G_r at 340°C was related to scission reactions of the crosslinking network by oxidation. In the change in logarithmic decrement Δ, three peaks were observed: at 90°C, coinciding with the glass transition of the polymer; at about 200°C, due to the melting transition of crystallites, and at about 300°C, due to a loss of mechanical energy in the rheological transition of the polymer from a liquid state to a glassy state passing through a viscoelastic region. The thermomechanical properties of PVC with different molecular weights were also measured, and the effect of molecular weight on G_r and Δ are discussed. In isothermal measurements of the relative rigidity in air, exponentially increasing curves were observed as a function of time. These curves were analyzed kinetically as a first-order reaction, and an activation energy of 22.7 kcal/mole was obtained.

INTRODUCTION

Thermal degradation of poly(vinyl chloride) (PVC) has been studied by a number of workers using various methods, such as the measurement of hydrogen chloride evolved in the early stage of degradation;[1–7] intrinsic viscosity and gel permeation chromatography (GPC);[8–10] infrared, nuclear magnetic resonance, and ultraviolet/visible spectroscopy;[4,9–13] thermogravimetry;[14–19] and dielectric spectroscopy.[20]

Dehydrochlorination of PVC occurs by zipper-like elimination of hydrogen chloride,[21] a radical mechanism[22] by which rupture takes place initially at a comparatively weak C–Cl bond, and ionic mechanism[23] resulting in the formation of a conjugated polyene chain. The conjugated polyene chain leads to crosslinking reactions such as copolymerization between polyene chains, chain transfer between a polyene chain and a normal polymer chain, a Diels-Alder reaction, and cross-dehydrochlorination.[22]

From the viewpoint of mechanical property, an increase in modulus of elasticity or rigidity is expected when the conjugated polyene chain and the crosslinking network chain are formed in the polymer chains, because molecular motion of a segment is restricted and its mobility decreases.

In this paper, the thermomechanical behavior of PVC having various molecular weights was measured in the temperature range of 30° to 480°C using torsional braid analysis (TBA) developed by Gillham[24–26] and the effects of molecular weight and atmosphere on thermomechanical properties were investigated. Furthermore, isothermal TBA measurement was made in the temperature range of 180° and 200°C, and kinetic analysis was carried out.

EXPERIMENTAL

Materials

The PVC samples used were supplied by Nippon Zeon Co., Ltd., and Sumitomo Chemical Co., Ltd. These polymers were without any additives and were characterized by viscosity measurement.

Number-average molecular weights of these polymers were calculated by the following equation,[16,27] and the results are given in Table I:

$$[\eta] = 20.4 \times 10^{-4} M_n^{0.56} \tag{1}$$

where $[\eta]$ is the intrinsic viscosity and M_n is the number-average molecular weight.

The polymers were purified by extraction with methanol and dried *in vacuo.*

Composite specimens of PVC and glass braid for TBA measurements were prepared by immersing glass braid in a 10% tetrahydrofuran solution of PVC. Sufficient solvent was removed by heat treatment for three days at about 70°C *in vacuo* (below 10^{-5} mm Hg).

Torsional Braid Analysis

A TBA apparatus equipped with a data analyzer to print out digitally the amplitudes and periods of oscillation was used for investigating the thermomechanical behavior of PVC. Detail of the TBA apparatus was reported previously.[28] The thermomechanical behavior for the composite specimens of PVC and glass braid was observed in the temperature range of 30° to 480°C. The relative rigidity G_r and logarithmic decrement Δ were calculated by the following relations:

$$G_r = (P_0/P)^2 \tag{2}$$

$$\Delta = \ln (A_1/A_3) = \ln (A_3/A_5) = \ldots \tag{3}$$

or

$$\Delta = \ln (A_2/A_4) = \ln (A_4/A_6) = \ldots \tag{4}$$

TABLE I
Data of Investigated Polymers

Polymer	Sample no.	M_n	Supplier
Zeon 103EP8	P-800	46,500 ⎫	
Zeon 103EP	P-1050	61,300 ⎬ Nippon Zeon	
Zeon 101EP	P-1450	87,600 ⎭ Co., Ltd.	
Sumilit SX-D	P-1900	109,000 ⎫ Sumitomo Chemical	
Sumilit SX-DH	P-2600	166,000 ⎭ Co., Ltd.	

where A_1, A_2, A_3, and so on, are the digital printed amplitudes; P_0 is the period at 30°C; and P is the period at an arbitrary temperature. The period is converted from the printed total time dividing it by a preset number of cycles.[28]

For isothermal measurement of TBA, the relative rigidities were presented by $1/P^2$ at each time, since P_0 at time $t = 0$ was difficult to determine accurately.

Temperature control of the furnace of the TBA apparatus was carried out by using a program control unit (Chino Works Co., Ltd., Model NP 163) equipped with thyristor regulator (Chino Works Co., Ltd., Model OL-12); the temperature errors were then within ±1°C. The heating rate for measuring the thermomechanical properties of PVC was 1°C/min.

For the isothermal TBA measurement, the furnace was preheated to an arbitrary temperature and the composite specimen was introduced. About 5 min or less were needed to reach the required temperature. The distance between chucks of the TBA apparatus was 80 mm.

Thermogravimetry and Differential Thermal Analysis

Thermogravimetry (TG) was carried out by using a microelectrobalance equipped with a DTA unit in a vertical tubular oven (Rigaku Denki Co., Ltd.). These thermal analyses were done in an atmosphere of air and nitrogen gas for the granular PVC samples of 8–10 mg each which were contained in platinum pans (5 mm in diameter). Heating rates were 1°C/min and 5°C/min for TG and DTA measurement, respectively.

RESULTS AND DISCUSSION

Figure 1 shows the curves of the thermomechanical behavior and TG for P-800 (M_n = 46,500) in air at 1°C/min. Decrease in G_r and a peak in Δ at about 90°C are due to the glass transition of PVC. In the vicinity of 200°C, a minimum in G_r and a peak in Δ occur. Salovey and Badger[17] observed an endothermic peak caused by melting of crystallites at about 200°C in DTA measurements. Bateille and Van[16] also reported a peak in the DTA curve at 280°C where all the crys-

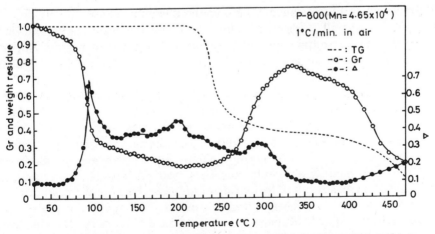

Fig. 1. Thermomechanical behavior and thermogravimetry for P-800 in air at 1°C/min.

tallinity was lost.   Therefore, a peak in Δ at 200°C coincides with the melting transition of the crystallites contained in PVC.

The relative rigidity G_r begins to increase gradually after passing through a minimum and then increases rapidly at 260°C corresponding to weight loss (dotted line in Fig. 1).   The increment in G_r may be related to a stiffening process of the molecular chain according to dehydrochlorination and crosslinking reactions of the PVC.

Winkler[22] reported that dehydrochlorination of PVC proceeds with the following radical mechanisms resulting in the formation of a conjugated polyene chain:

$$R\cdot + -\underset{\underset{Cl}{|}}{CH}-CH_2-\underset{\underset{Cl}{|}}{CH}-CH_2-\underset{\underset{Cl}{|}}{CH}-CH_2- \longrightarrow$$

$$RH + -\underset{\underset{Cl}{|}}{CH}-\overset{\cdot}{CH}-\underset{\underset{Cl}{|}}{CH}-CH_2-\underset{\underset{Cl}{|}}{CH}-CH_2- \quad (5)$$

$$-\underset{\underset{Cl}{|}}{CH}-\overset{\cdot}{CH}-\underset{\underset{Cl}{|}}{CH}-CH_2-\underset{\underset{Cl}{|}}{CH}-CH_2- \longrightarrow$$

$$Cl\cdot + -\underset{\underset{Cl}{|}}{CH}-CH=CH-CH_2-\underset{\underset{Cl}{|}}{CH}-CH_2- \quad (6)$$

$$Cl\cdot + -\underset{\underset{Cl}{|}}{CH}-CH=CH-CH_2-\underset{\underset{Cl}{|}}{CH}-CH_2- \longrightarrow$$

$$HCl + -\underset{\underset{Cl}{|}}{CH}-CH=CH-\overset{\cdot}{CH}-\underset{\underset{Cl}{|}}{CH}-CH_2- \quad (7)$$

$$-\underset{\underset{Cl}{|}}{CH}-CH=CH-\overset{\cdot}{CH}-\underset{\underset{Cl}{|}}{CH}-CH_2- \longrightarrow$$

$$-\underset{\underset{Cl}{|}}{CH}-CH=CH-CH=CH-CH_2- + Cl\cdot \quad (8)$$

It is believed that the mean length of the polyenes formed during dehydrochlorination is small, i.e., seven to eight double bonds because of readdition of hydrogen chloride to the double bonds formed[29] and termination of zipper reactions at a change in structure of the chain caused by oxidation, chain branching, or some other defect.[22]

If the length of the polyene chain is small, a significant increase in rigidity is not expected.   However, crosslinking reactions occur by copolymerization between polyene chains, by chain transfer between a polyene chain and a segment of a normal polymer chain, by a Diels-Alder reaction, and by cross-dehydrochlorination.[6,7,10,11,22,31]   Furthermore, in air, alkoxy radicals and alkylperoxy radicals are formed by oxidation, and these radicals also lead to crosslinking reactions.[11,29]   As a result of formation of polyene chains and crosslinking network chains during the thermal degradation of PVC, molecular motion is restricted and the rigidity of the polymer is markedly increased.   During the reaction described above, the polymer transforms into a glassy state from a liquid

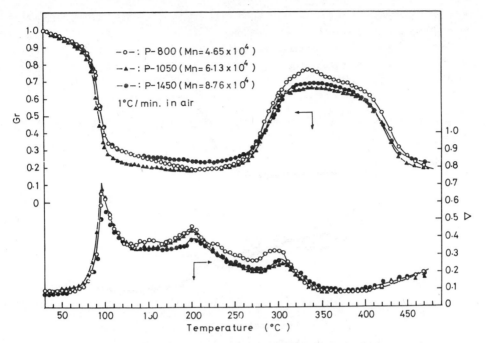

Fig. 2. Thermomechanical behavior for P-800, P-1050, and P-1450 in air at 1°C/min.

state passing through a viscoelastic region, and, accordingly, a peak in Δ at 295°C appears together with an increase in G_r.

At 330°C, G_r decreases gradually and then rapidly from 410°C. Stronberg, Straus, and Bernard[18] analyzed the decomposition products by mass spectrometry and detected carbon chain breakdown products such as low molecular weight saturated and unsaturated hydrocarbons, benzene, and toluene at 400°C. Iida, Nakanishi, and Gotō[32] also analyzed the decomposition products by using a gas chromatograph, detecting small amounts of benzene at 300°C and benzene, toluene, ethylbenzene, o-xylene, styrene, and naphthalene above 400°C. Consequently, the gradual decrease in G_r at 330°C may be due to the formation of low molecular weight materials based on the scission reaction of the network chain formed; and the rapid decrease in G_r from 410°C reflects marked scission reaction including vaporization of low molecular weight materials from the glass braid. These results are consistent with the data of TG (dotted line in Fig. 1) and DTA (Fig. 5).

The thermomechanical properties in the temperature range of 30° to 480°C for PVC with number-average molecular weights of 46,500 (P-800), 61,300 (P-1050), and 87,600 (P-1450) are shown in Figure 2. Those of PVC with number-average molecular weights of 109,000 (P-1900) and 166,000 (P-2600) are shown in Figure 3. All G_r curves resemble each other; G_r decreases initially with increasing temperature, subsequently increases owing to the dehydrochlorination and crosslinking reactions, and finally decreases with temperature. Because of different dehydrochlorination rates for each PVC, minimum points in the G_r-versus-temperature curves for PVC with the higher molecular weights shift to the higher temperature side. These minimum points for P-800, P-1050, P-1450, P-1900, and P-2600 are at 215°, 225°, 235°, 240°, and 245°C, respectively.

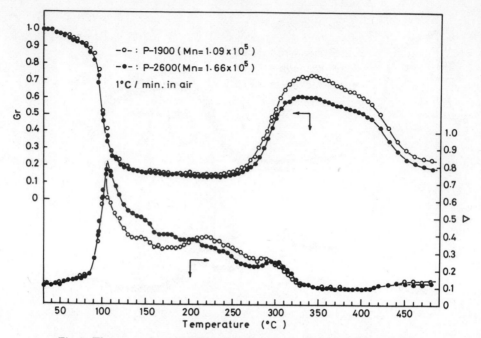

Fig. 3. Thermomechanical behavior for P-1900 and P-2600 in air at 1°C/min.

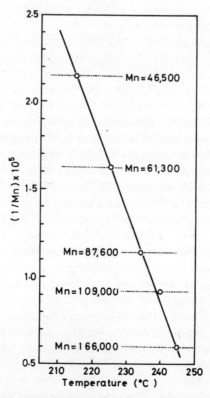

Fig. 4. Plot of temperature at minimum in G_r in Figs. 2 and 3 against reciprocal of number-average molecular weights.

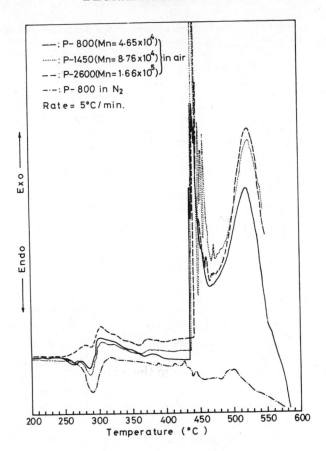

Fig. 5. DTA curves for P-800, P-1450, and P-2600.

Talamani and Pezzini[33] and Bataille and Van[16] reported that the plot of the rate of dehydrochlorination against the reciprocal of molecular weights gave a linear relation.

Thus, plotting the temperature at minimum points in G_r-versus-temperature curves against the reciprocal of number-average molecular weights gives a straight line as shown in Figure 4. It is found that the temperature where G_r begins to increase, i.e., the temperature of a minimum in G_r, is controlled by the dehydrochlorination rate, and PVC with the higher molecular weights has a slower rate of dehydrochlorination. This result is consistent with that of isothermal measurements (Fig. 11) described later.

The temperature of formation of low molecular weight products due to the scission of the network chain molecules, namely, the temperature of the decrease in G_r, is 345°C for P-800, but for other polymers this temperature is in the range of 350° to 355°C, and there is no remarkable difference corresponding to the molecular weights. The temperature of rapid decrease in G_r is also independent of molecular weight, being from about 400° to 410°C.

As to change in Δ arising from the melting transition, a peak appears at about 200°C for P-800, P-1050, and P-1450, but for P-1900 it appears at about 220°C shifting to the higher-temperature side. For P-2600, no peak appears in this

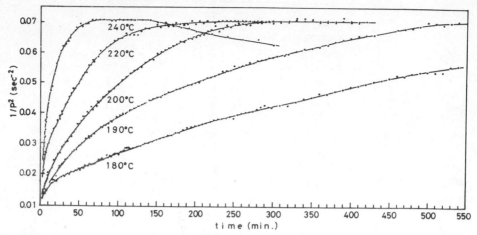

Fig. 6. Isothermal curve of relative rigidity for P-800 in air at temperatures between 180° and 240°C.

temperature region. The peak appearing in the temperature range of 270° to 320°C is independent of molecular weight.

Figure 5 shows DTA curves of P-800, P-1450, and P-2600 in air and of P-800 in nitrogen at a heating rate of 5°C/min. An endothermic peak of P-800 and P-1450 at about 260°C is attributable to the melting transition of crystallites of PVC.[17] This peak does not appear in P-2600, since it may be difficult to crystallize because of its higher molecular weight (M_n = 166,000). Consequently, a peak in Δ for P-2600 is not observed at about 200°C. An endothermic peak in the vicinity of 290°C is assigned to dehydrochlorination.[17] Marked peaks

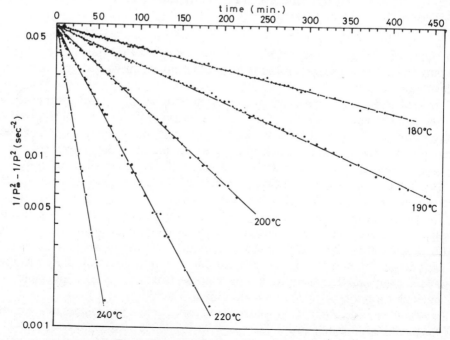

Fig. 7. Plot of ln ($1/P_\infty^2 - 1/P^2$) vs t for P-800.

TABLE II
Rate Constants for P-800 at Different Temperatures

Temperature, °C	k, min^{-1}
180	2.84×10^{-3}
190	5.06×10^{-3}
200	1.01×10^{-2}
220	2.06×10^{-2}
240	6.09×10^{-2}

in air at temperatures between 440° and 600°C are due to the formation of low molecular weight products by oxidation, and these peaks are not observed in nitrogen.

Figure 6 shows isothermal measurements of relative rigidities for P-800 in air at 180°, 190°, 200°, 220°, and 240°C. The relative rigidity increases exponentially with elapsed time owing to formation of polyene chains, chain branching, crosslinking between double bonds, and cross-dehydrochlorination, and then reaches equilibrium asymptotically. At 180°C, equilibrium is not reached in the range of time observed. At 240°C, after equilibrium is reached, the relative rigidity decreases with time after 140 min according to the scission of the network chains as shown in the case of the temperature dependence of G_r (Figs. 1, 2, and 3).

For these isothermal curves as a function of time, a first-order reaction is assumed just as in the case of thermosetting plastics,[34] and they are analyzed kinetically. When rigidity at time $t = 0$, G_0, increases to G_t at time t and reaches equilibrium rigidity G_∞, then the equation for a first-order reaction is

$$d(G_\infty - G_t)/dt = k(G_\infty - G_t) \qquad (9)$$

Integrating eq. (9) gives eq. (10):

$$\ln (G_\infty - G_t)/(G_\infty - G_0) = -kt \qquad (10)$$

where k is the rate constant. As $G_0 \propto 1/P_0^2$, $G_t \propto 1/P^2$, and $G_\infty \propto 1/P_\infty^2$, eq. (10) is converted into eq. (11):

$$\ln (1/P_\infty^2 - 1/P^2) = -kt + \ln (1/P_\infty^2 - 1/P_0^2) \qquad (11)$$

where P_0, P, and P_∞ are the period at $t = 0$, $t = t$, and $t = \infty$, respectively. Thus, plotting of $\ln (1/P_\infty^2 - 1/P^2)$ against t gives a linear relation, and the rate constant k is obtained from the slope of the straight line. In Figure 7, a plot of $\ln (1/P_\infty^2 - 1/P^2)$ against t from the data of Figure 6 is represented. For 180°C, calculation is done by using the equilibrium value of $P_\infty = 0.0703$ for measurements at other temperatures, since equilibrium is not reached in the range of time observed. As shown in Figure 7, linear relations are obtained at each temperature, and from the slope of the straight lines, the rate constants are obtained as collected in Table II.

As shown in Figure 8, the plot of the rate constant k versus the reciprocal of the absolute temperature, $1/T$, is linear; and from the slope of the straight line, an activation energy of 22.7 kcal/mole is calculated according to the Arrhenius relation. The activation energies for the thermal degradation of PVC have been observed by a number of workers and they agree with our result: Abbãs and

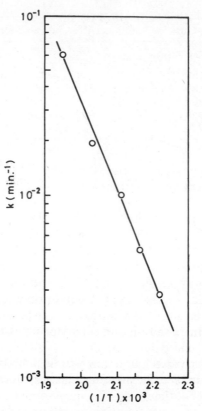

Fig. 8. Arrhenius plot.

Sörvik[9] reported that no significant difference was found between the activation energies in oxygen and nitrogen and obtained values of 26–28 kcal/mole. Hedvig[20] found a value of 32 kcal/mole by using dielectric spectroscopy. Stronberg, Straus, and Achhammer[18] and Salovey and Bair[19] analyzed kinetically the weight loss-versus-time data as a $\frac{3}{2}$-order reaction and obtained values of 26–32 kcal/mole in vacuo and 27 kcal/mole in nitrogen, respectively. Imoto and Otsu[31] analyzed the relation between the insoluble part in tetrahydrofuran and degradation time as a first-order reaction to obtain a value of 25 kcal/mole. And Furusho, Komatsu, and Nakagawa[35] investigated the isothermal TBA curve as a zero-order reaction and obtained an activation energy of 24 kcal/mole.

In Figure 9, the relative rigidities measured isothermally at 200°C in air are plotted for PVC with different number-average molecular weights. Exponential

TABLE III
Rate Constants for PVC with Different Number-Average Molecular Weights at 200° C

Sample no.	M_n	k, min⁻¹
P-800	46,500	1.01×10^{-2}
P-1050	61,300	8.05×10^{-3}
P-1450	87,600	6.64×10^{-3}
P-1900	109,000	6.23×10^{-3}
P-2600	166,000	4.73×10^{-3}

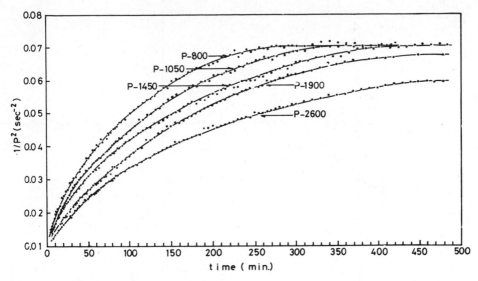

Fig. 9. Isothermal curve of relative rigidity for P-800, P-1050, P-1450, P-1900, and P-2600 in air at 200°C.

increase in relative rigidity as a function of time reaches equilibrium asymptotically for P-800, P-1050, and P-1450, but not for P-1900 and P-2600 in the range of observation time scale. When $\ln (1/P_\infty^2 - 1/P^2)$ is plotted against t for the data of Figure 9 according with eq. (2), then linear relations are obtained as shown

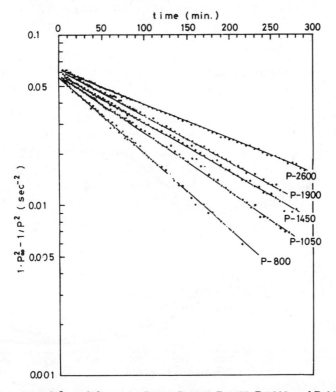

Fig. 10. Plot of $\ln (1/P_\infty^2 - 1/P^2)$ vs t for P-800, P-1050, P-1450, P-1900, and P-2600 at 200°C.

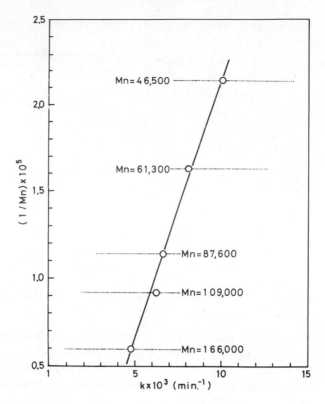

Fig. 11. Plot of rate constant vs reciprocal of number-average molecular weight.

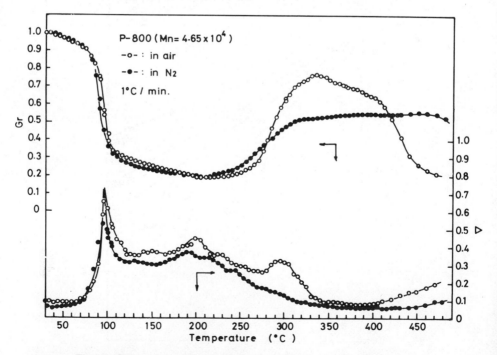

Fig. 12. Comparison of thermomechanical behavior in air and nitrogen.

in Figure 10. From the slope of each straight line, the rate constants k are calculated as listed in Table III. It is found that the increase in the rate of the relative rigidity is slower the higher the molecular weight of PVC.

As shown in Figure 11, the plot of the rate constant against the reciprocal of the molecular weight gives a straight line as reported by Talamani and Pezzini[33] and Bataille and Van.[16] This result agrees with the data shown in Figure 4 where the temperature of the minimum in G_r was plotted against the reciprocal of the molecular weights. It is concluded that the increase in rigidity measured by TBA is controlled by the dehydrochlorination rate of PVC.

In Figure 12, the thermomechanical behavior in air is compared with that in nitrogen for P-800. Measurement of the thermomechanical behavior in nitrogen was carried out flowing highly pure nitrogen gas (above 99.999% pure) at a rate of 200 ml/min. Changes in thermomechanical behavior in nitrogen are the same as those in air until 200°C. Above 200°C, G_r increases rapidly in air, while in nitrogen it increases gradually. At temperatures between 200° and 270°C, the rate of increase in G_r in nitrogen is faster than in air. However, between 270° and 340°C, the rate in air is faster than in nitrogen and the value of G_r in air is larger than in nitrogen. These are explained by the following mechanisms. Winkler[22] proposed the following oxidative scission mechanisms:

$$R\cdot + -\underset{\underset{Cl}{|}}{C}H-CH_2-\underset{\underset{Cl}{|}}{C}H-CH_2-\underset{\underset{Cl}{|}}{C}H-CH_2-- \longrightarrow$$

$$RH + -\underset{\underset{Cl}{|}}{C}H-CH_2-\underset{\underset{Cl}{|}}{\overset{.}{C}}-CH_2-\underset{\underset{Cl}{|}}{C}H-CH_2- \quad (12)$$

$$-\underset{\underset{Cl}{|}}{C}H-CH_2-\underset{\underset{Cl}{|}}{\overset{.}{C}}-CH_2-\underset{\underset{Cl}{|}}{C}H-CH_2- + O_2 \longrightarrow$$

$$-\underset{\underset{Cl}{|}}{C}H-CH_2-\underset{\underset{O}{\overset{|}{\underset{.}{\overset{|}{O}}}}}{\overset{\underset{Cl}{|}}{C}}-CH_2-\underset{\underset{Cl}{|}}{C}H-CH_2- \quad (13)$$

$$-\underset{\underset{Cl}{|}}{C}H-CH_2-\underset{\underset{O}{\overset{|}{\underset{.}{\overset{|}{O}}}}}{\overset{\underset{Cl}{|}}{C}}-CH_2-\underset{\underset{Cl}{|}}{C}H-CH_2- + RH \longrightarrow$$

$$-\underset{\underset{Cl}{|}}{C}H-CH_2-\underset{\underset{O}{\overset{|}{\underset{H}{\overset{|}{O}}}}}{\overset{\underset{Cl}{|}}{C}}-CH_2-\underset{\underset{Cl}{|}}{C}H-CH_2- + R\cdot \quad (14)$$

$$-\underset{\underset{Cl}{|}}{C}H-CH_2-\underset{\underset{O}{\overset{|}{\underset{H}{\overset{|}{O}}}}}{\overset{\underset{Cl}{|}}{C}}-CH_2-\underset{\underset{Cl}{|}}{C}H-CH_2-- \longrightarrow$$

$$-\underset{\underset{Cl}{|}}{C}H-CH_2-\underset{\underset{.}{\overset{|}{O}}}{\overset{\underset{Cl}{|}}{C}}-CH_2-\underset{\underset{Cl}{|}}{C}H-CH_2- + OH\cdot \quad (15)$$

$$\text{—}\overset{\overset{\displaystyle Cl}{|}}{CH}\text{—}CH_2\text{—}\overset{\overset{\displaystyle Cl}{|}}{\underset{\underset{\displaystyle \cdot}{O}}{C}}\text{—}CH_2\text{—}\overset{\overset{\displaystyle Cl}{|}}{CH}\text{—}CH_2\text{—} \longrightarrow \text{—}\overset{\overset{\displaystyle Cl}{|}}{CH}\text{—}CH_2\text{—}\overset{\overset{\displaystyle Cl}{|}}{C}{=}O + \cdot CH_2\text{—}\overset{\overset{\displaystyle Cl}{|}}{CH}\text{—}CH_2\text{—}$$

(16)

Sobue, Tabata, and Tajima[11] also proposed the following mechanisms:

$$\text{—}CH{=}CH\text{—}\underset{\underset{\underset{\displaystyle H}{O}}{O}}{CH}\text{—}CH{=}CH\text{—} \longrightarrow \text{—}CH{=}CH\text{—}\underset{\underset{\displaystyle H}{C}}{=}O + O{=}CH\text{—}CH_2\text{—} \quad (17)$$

$$\text{—}CH{=}CH\text{—}\underset{\underset{\underset{\displaystyle H}{O}}{O}}{CH}\text{—}CH_2\text{—} \longrightarrow \text{—}CH{=}CH\text{—}\underset{\underset{\displaystyle H}{C}}{=}O + HO\text{—}CH_2\text{—} \quad (18)$$

Radicals formed during scission reactions abstract hydrogen atoms from other polymer chains and accelerate the formation of double bonds:[9]

$$\text{—}CH_2\text{—}\overset{\overset{\displaystyle Cl}{|}}{CH}\text{—}CH_2\text{—}\overset{\overset{\displaystyle Cl}{|}}{CH}\text{—} \xrightarrow{\cdot OH, \cdot CH_2\text{—}} \text{—}CH_2\text{—}\overset{\overset{\displaystyle Cl}{|}}{CH}\text{—}\overset{\cdot}{CH}\text{—}\overset{\overset{\displaystyle Cl}{|}}{CH}\text{—} \quad (19)$$

$$\text{—}CH_2\text{—}\overset{\overset{\displaystyle Cl}{|}}{CH}\text{—}\overset{\cdot}{CH}\text{—}\overset{\overset{\displaystyle Cl}{|}}{CH}\text{—} \longrightarrow \text{—}CH_2\text{—}\overset{\overset{\displaystyle Cl}{|}}{CH}\text{—}CH{=}CH\text{—} + Cl\cdot \quad (20)$$

$$Cl\cdot + \text{—}\overset{\overset{\displaystyle Cl}{|}}{CH}\text{—}CH{=}CH\text{—}CH_2\text{—}\overset{\overset{\displaystyle Cl}{|}}{CH}\text{—}CH_2\text{—} \longrightarrow$$

$$HCl + \text{—}\overset{\overset{\displaystyle Cl}{|}}{CH}\text{—}CH{=}CH\text{—}\overset{\cdot}{CH}\text{—}\overset{\overset{\displaystyle Cl}{|}}{CH}\text{—}CH_2\text{—} \quad (21)$$

$$\text{—}\overset{\overset{\displaystyle Cl}{|}}{CH}\text{—}CH{=}CH\text{—}\overset{\cdot}{CH}\text{—}\overset{\overset{\displaystyle Cl}{|}}{CH}\text{—}CH_2\text{—} \longrightarrow$$

$$\text{—}\overset{\overset{\displaystyle Cl}{|}}{CH}\text{—}CH{=}CH\text{—}CH{=}CH\text{—}CH_2\text{—} + Cl\cdot \quad (22)$$

According to these mechanisms, the scission reactions accompanied by dehydrochlorination occur at the initial stage of the thermal degradation of PVC in

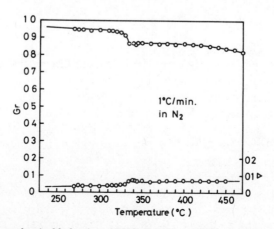

Fig. 13. Thermomechanical behavior of PVC (P-800) cooled from 480° to 30°C in nitrogen.

air.[9,22] Abbås and Sörvik[9] reported that weight-average molecular weights increased with progressing dehydrochlorination, but in air these decreased initially and then increased. Consequently, between 200° and 270°C, the rate of increase in G_r in air is slower than in nitrogen owing rather to the effect of scission in air than to formation of double bonds; and between 270° and 340°C, the formation of the double bonds which are accelerated according to eqs. (20), (21), (7), and (8) causes a marked increase in G_r. Above 340°C in air, G_r decreases owing to the formation of low molecular weight products, while in nitrogen the remarkable scission reaction of the molecular chain does not occur, as shown in the DTA curve (Fig. 5).

Shimokawa et al.[36] suggested that the structure of pyrolysis products in nitrogen by using NMR and ESR is as follows:

At 200–350°C:

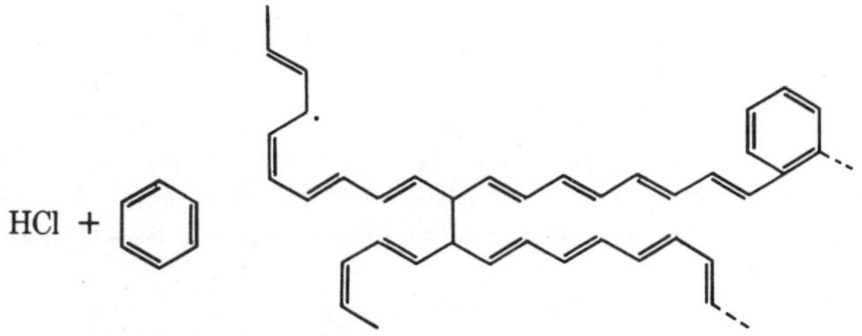

HCl +

I

At 350–410°C:

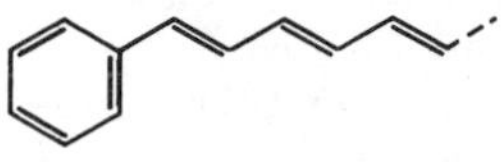

II 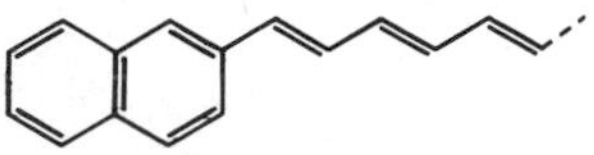 III

Above 420°C:

IV 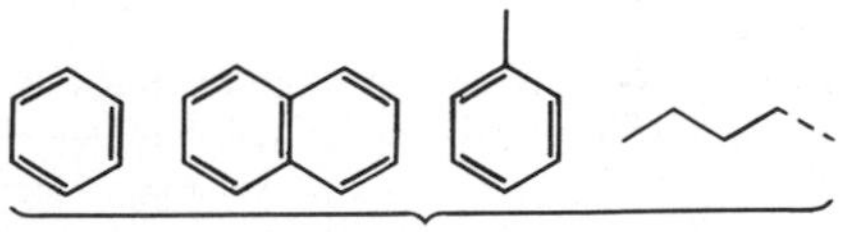 V

Increase in G_r above 200°C in nitrogen may be due to the formation of a structure such as I, which is produced by dehydrochlorination and crosslinking reactions. A small decrease in G_r at 470°C in nitrogen is considered to be due to the formation of structure II or III.

Changes in Δ in nitrogen are approximately the same as those in air up to 280°C, but a peak at about 300°C in air is not observed in nitrogen. This may be due to the gradual increase in G_r in nitrogen, and transition from a liquid state to a glassy state may not occur.

For a composite specimen heated to 480°C and allowed to cool to room temperature in nitrogen, the thermomechanical behavior is measured again as shown in Figure 13. The decrease in G_r and a small peak in Δ are observed at 335°C. This may be due to the melting transition of a dense structure such as IV. Shimokawa et al.[36] and Otani[37] reported that when PVC was heated at a rate of 10°C/min, residues of thermally decomposed PVC melt rapidly at about 410°C. The difference between our results (335°C) and their results (410°C) may be due to the heating rate, i.e., 1°C/min in our measurements and 10°C/min in their measurements.

References

1. J. H. L. Henson and F. J. Hybart, *J. Appl. Polym. Sci.*, **16**, 1653 (1972).

2. W. I. Bengough and H. M. Share, *Makromol. Chem.*, **66**, 31, 45 (1963).

3. A. H. K. Yousufzai, M. M. Zafar, and Shabih-UL-Hasan, *Eur. Polym. J.*, **8**, 1231 (1972).

4. J. Millan, E. L. Madruga, M. Bert, and A. Guyot, *J. Polym. Sci., Polym. Chem. Ed.*, **11**, 3299 (1973).

5. K. B. Abbås and E. M. Sörvik, *J. Appl. Polym. Sci.*, **17**, 3567 (1973).

6. M. Ohta and M. Imoto, *Kogyo Kagaku Zasshi* (*J. Chem. Soc. Japan, Ind. Chem. Sect.*), **54**, 470 (1951).

7. M. Imoto and T. Otsu, *Kogyo Kagaku Zasshi* (*J. Chem. Soc. Jpn., Ind. Chem. Sect.*), **54**, 771 (1951).

8. K. B. Andersson and E. M. Sörvik, *J. Polym. Sci.*, **C**(33), 247 (1971).

9. K. B. Abbås and E. M. Sörvik, *J. Appl. Polym. Sci.*, **17**, 3577 (1973).

10. D. Druesedow and C. G. Gibbs, *Natl. Bur. Stand. Circular*, **No. 525**, 69 (1953).

11. H. Sobue, Y. Tabata, and Y. Tajima, *Kogyo Kagaku Zasshi* (*J. Chem. Soc. Jpn., Ind. Chem. Sect.*), **61**, 106 (1958).

12. I. Ouchi, *J. Polym. Sci. A*, **3**, 2685 (1965).

13. D. Baun and M. Thallmair, *Makromol. Chem.*, **108**, 241 (1967).

14. A. Guyot and J. P. Benevise, *J. Appl. Polym. Sci.*, **6**, 98 (1962).

15. J. D. Matlack and A. P. Metzger, *J. Appl. Polym. Sci.*, **12**, 1745 (1968).

16. P. Bataille and B. T. Van, *J. Polym. Sci. A-1*, **10**, 1097 (1972).

17. R. Salovey and R. G. Badger, *Proc. Symp. Ecol. Probl. New York City*, 1973, p. 109.

18. R. R. Stromberg, S. Straus, and B. G. Achhammer, *J. Polym. Sci.*, **35**, 355 (1959).

19. R. Salovey and H. E. Bair, *J. Appl. Polym. Sci.*, **14**, 713 (1970).

20. P. Hedvic, *J. Polym. Sci.*, **C**(33), 315 (1971).

21. C. S. Marvel, J. H. Sample, and M. F. Roy, *J. Amer. Chem. Soc.*, **61**, 3241 (1939).

22. D. E. Winkler, *J. Polym. Sci.*, **35**, 3 (1959).

23. B. Baum, *S.P.E. J.*, **17**, 71 (1961).

24. A. F. Lewis and J. K. Gillham, *J. Appl. Polym. Sci.*, **6**, 422 (1962).

25. J. K. Gillham, in *Thermoanalysis of Fibers and Fiber-Forming Polymers, Appl. Polym. Symposia*, No. 2, R. F. Shwenker, Jr., Ed., Interscience, New York, 1966, p. 45.

26. J. K. Gillham, *C.R.C. Crit. Rev. Makromol. Sci.*, **1**, 83 (1972).

27. Z. Mencik, *Chem. Listy*, **49**, 598 (1955); *C. A.*, **50**, 650 (1956).

28. S. Yano, *J. Appl. Polym. Sci.*, **19**, 1087 (1975).

29. T. Kelen, G. Balint, G. Galambos, and F. Tüdös, *J. Polym. Sci.*, **C**(33), 211 (1971).

30. E. J. Arlman, *J. Polym. Sci.*, **12**, 547 (1954).

31. M. Imoto and T. Otsu, *Kogyo Kagaku Zasshi* (*J. Chem. Soc. Jpn., Ind. Chem. Sec.*), **56**, 802 (1953).

32. T. Iida, M. Nakanishi, and K. Gotō, *J. Polym. Sci., Polym. Chem. Ed.*, **12**, 737 (1974).

33. G. Talamani and G. Pezzini, *Makromol. Chem.*, **39**, 26 (1960).

34. D. H. Kaelble and E. H. Cirlin, *J. Polym. Sci.*, **C**(35), 79 (1971).

35. N. Furusho, T. Komatsu, and T. Nakagawa, *Nippon Kagaku Kaishi* (*J. Chem. Soc. Jpn., Chem. Ind. Chem.*), **No. 6**, 1166 (1973).

36. S. Shimokawa, Y. Ohno, J. Sohma, H. Hirano, and K. Endoh, *Nippon Kagaku Kaishi* (*J. Chem. Soc. Jpn., Chem. Ind. Chem.*), **No. 10**, 2016 (1973).

37. S. Ohtani, *Kogyo Kagaku Zasshi* (*J. Chem. Soc. Jpn., Ind. Chem. Sec.*), **61**, 447 (1958); *ibid.*, **66**, 122 (1963).

Received November 25, 1974
Revised August 10, 1976

JOURNAL OF APPLIED POLYMER SCIENCE   VOL. 21, 2661–2673 (1977)

Reverse Osmosis Characteristics of Composite Membranes Prepared by Plasma Polymerization of Allylamine. Effects of Deposition Conditions

D. PERIC,* A. T. BELL, and M. SHEN, *Department of Chemical Engineering, University of California, Berkeley, California 94720*

Synopsis

A study has been conducted to determine the effects of flow configuration and reaction conditions on the performance of composite reverse osmosis membranes prepared by plasma polymerization of allylamine over a porous polymer substrate. It was established that superior membranes were obtained by using a gas-flow configuration avoiding direct monomer flow over the substrate. High rejections of NaCl could be attained when the plasma-deposited film was sufficiently thick to bridge all of the pores in the substrate. It was observed that in addition to influencing the rate of polymerization, the conditions used to sustain the plasma also affected the reverse osmosis characteristics of the deposited film. The effects of these conditions and other preparation procedures are discussed. Attempts to use infrared spectroscopy and ESCA to identify the relationship between polymer structure and reverse osmosis performance were not successful. ESCA did prove useful, though, in confirming an earlier postulated hypothesis that degradation of reverse osmosis performance is associated with the hydrolysis of nitrogen-containing structures in the plasma-deposited film.

INTRODUCTION

The preparation of composite reverse osmosis membranes by plasma deposition of a thin polymer film over a porous substrate has recently been demonstrated by several authors.[1–4] Work by Yasuda and Lamaze[2] established that membranes exhibiting high salt rejection and water flux can be obtained provided the monomer used to produce the rejecting layer contains nitrogen. An investigation of allylamine as a candidate monomer conducted by Bell et al.[4] revealed that the quality of the membranes produced also depends strongly on the nature of the substrate and the conditions used to prepare the rejecting layer. The present studies were undertaken to further extend the work of Bell et al. Major objectives included a more extensive determination of the effects of deposition parameters on membrane performance. Investigations were also performed to determine the relationship between preparation conditions and the chemical structure of the plasma-deposited film.

EXPERIMENTAL

The reactor used in the present work is shown in Figure 1. It consisted of two 8-in.-diameter stainless steel electrodes enclosed in an 18-in.-diameter bell jar. The central portion of the lower electrode was hollow and could be cooled or

*Present address: Dow Chemical Co., Pittsburg, California.

2661

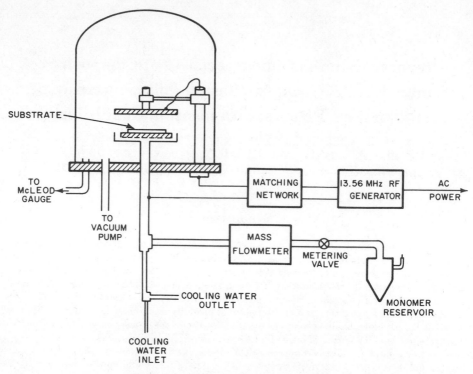

Fig. 1. Schematic of experimental apparatus.

heated by passing water through it. Surrounding the holder was a hollow cup which could be used to supply monomer or to evacuate the bell jar. The upper electrode was solid and could not be heated or cooled. The discharge was sustained between the two electrodes by a 13.56 MHz rf generator (Tracerlab Co.), capable of delivering up to 300 W. The gap between electrodes could be changed by moving either electrode upward or downward.

The monomer used was allylamine (CH_2=CH—CH_2NH_2, Aldrich Chemical Co., bp 53°C). Prior to use, it was degassed by repeated freezing and thawing while pumping on it. The substrate used was an asymmetric cellulose acetate–nitrate film manufactured by Gulf Environmental Systems.[5] This material had a shiny side containing pores of 0.025 μm average diameter and a water permeability of 170×10^{-5} g/cm²-sec-atm.

The liquid monomer was stored in a small glass reservoir and fed to the system as a vapor. The vapor flow rate was monitored by a mass flowmeter (Matheson Model F50M). Unreacted vapor and volatile byproducts of polymerization were evacuated by a mechanical vacuum pump. The system pressure was monitored by a McLeod gauge connected to a port in the reactor base plate and also by means of a thermocouple gauge located in the line connecting the vacuum pump to the system.

The reactor was designed so that monomer could be fed and removed in a number of ways, as shown in Figure 2. The possible flow configurations were as follows: (1) monomer fed through the upper electrode and removed through the lower electrode, (2) monomer fed through the lower electrode and removed through the upper electrode, (3) monomer fed through the base plate and re-

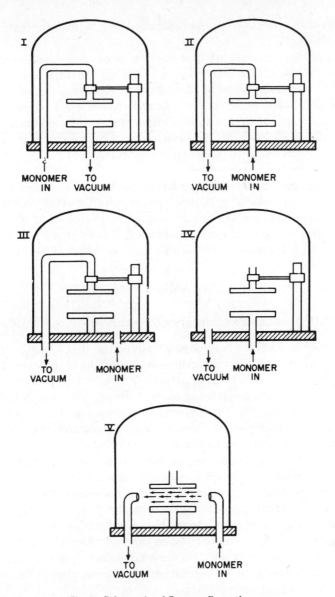

Fig. 2. Schematic of flow configurations.

moved through the upper electrode, (4) monomer fed through the lower electrode
and removed through the base plate, and (5) monomer fed from one side of the
electrodes and removed from the other side.

Membranes were prepared by placing a 4-in. disk of the substrate under a brass
ring on the lower electrode. The bell jar was put in place and the system evacuated to about 0.010 torr pressure. The desired flow of monomer to the system
was established, and the pressure was allowed to increase by closing a valve on
the vacuum line until the desired pressure was reached. The discharge was initiated by turning on the rf generator and adjusting the matching network for
minimum reflected power. During deposition, the lower electrode was water
cooled to maintain the substrate surface temperature near 20°C. After depo-

sition, a 2-in. disk was cut from the center of the 4-in. disk for testing in the reverse osmosis loop.

The membranes were tested in a reverse osmosis test cell connected to a high-pressure brine recirculation loop. In all of the experiments, the brine concentration was maintained at 1% and the applied pressure across the membrane was kept at 1500 psi. Each membrane was allowed to operate for a minimum of 20 hr before the first sample of effluent was collected for determination of salt rejection and flux. The techniques used for measurement of rejection and flux were identical to those described by Hossain et al.[6]

Chemical characterization was accomplished by use of infrared spectroscopy and ESCA (Electron Spectroscopy for Chemical Analysis). Samples for infrared spectroscopy were prepared by deposition on a NaCl crystal. A Perkin–Elmer 137 spectrometer was used to record the spectra. Samples for ESCA were obtained by depositing polymer on aluminum foil or by using sections of actual membranes. Spectra were recorded on a du Pont Model 650 spectrometer.

RESULTS AND DISCUSSION

Effect of Deposition Parameters on Reverse Osmosis Performance

As mentioned earlier, the reactor was designed so that a number of flow patterns could be obtained. To determine which of the flow patterns produced membranes with the best reverse osmosis characteristics, membranes were prepared at various conditions using each of the possible flow configurations.

Configuration IV (see Fig. 2) was found to produce membranes with the best reverse osmosis performance of those tested. Configurations I, II, and III all produced membranes which exhibited poor rejection (less than 40%) and high flux. The films obtained with these configurations were observed to crack and break up when wetted, and, in some cases the films had an oily appearance. The crossflow configuration, V, produced membranes with better reverse osmosis characteristics than those obtained with configurations I, II, or III. The rejections for these membranes were generally lower, however, than those obtained using configuration IV. A comparison of the performance of membranes prepared using configurations IV and V is shown in Table I. While the results given in the table relate to one set of deposition conditions, similar results were obtained for other deposition conditions.

The results of the experiments just described suggest that superior reverse osmosis membranes are obtained when direct monomer flow over the substrate is avoided. A possible explanation for this conclusion is the observation that the rate of deposition is slower in the absence of flow over the surface on which deposition occurs. As a result, freshly deposited polymer has a longer period of exposure to the effects of the plasma and hence a greater opportunity to crosslink. These effects have been noted during the plasma polymerization of ethylene.[7]

On the basis of the flow configuration studies, it was decided to use configuration IV for the balance of the experiments which were devoted to the effects of deposition conditions on the reverse osmosis characteristics of the membranes. The first deposition parameter studied, deposition time, was found to have a significant effect on both flux and rejection, as shown in Figure 3. For deposition

TABLE I
Effect of Flow Configuration on Membrane Performance[a]

Membrane no.	Configuration[b]	Rejection, %[c]	Flux, gfd[c]
392	V	79.3	10.3
393	V	70.0	11.6
394	V	96.5	8.1
414	V	69.5	17.0
413	V	82.5	20.0
415	V	74.6	22.0
361	IV	85.0	12.0
341	IV	97.0	5.0
355	IV	87.0	8.0

[a] Membrane preparation conditions: flow config., IV; pressure, 200–250 μHg; power, 24 W; monomer flow, 4.4 cm^3/min; elec. gap, $2^7/_8$ in.; dep. time, 13 min.
[b] See Fig. 2.
[c] Feed concentration, 1% NaCl; feed temperature, 20 °C; applied pressure, 1500 psi.

times greater than 800 s, the flux and rejection approach asymptotic limits of 10 gfd and 95%, respectively. The trends observed are similar to those noted by Bell et al.[4] and are associated with the gradual closure of the pores present on the surface of the substrate. At short times, insufficient polymer is deposited to cover all of the surface pores, leaving holes in the surface through which salt solution can pass. At high deposition times, the deposited film completely covers all of the pores, leading to maximum rejection.

In the course of studying the effects of deposition time, it was found that higher salt rejections could be obtained by wetting freshly prepared membranes in

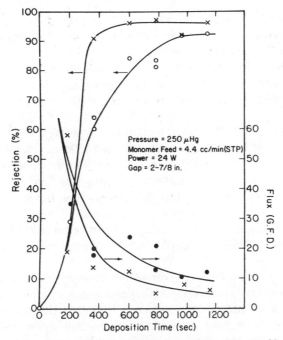

Fig. 3. Effect of deposition time on membrane rejection and flux (x) wetted before cutting. (●,○) not wetted.

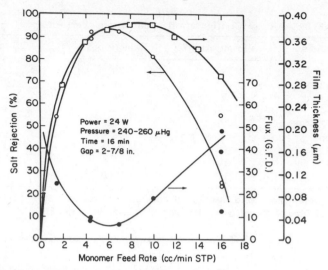

Fig. 4. Effect of monomer flow rate on membrane rejection (—○—), flux (—●—), and film thickness (—□—).

distilled water for 10 to 15 min prior to cutting out the 2-in. sample. The samples were then dried and stored until tested for their reverse osmosis performance. Figure 3 shows the results obtained with membranes treated in this fashion. Significant increases in salt rejection are observed for membranes prepared at intermediate deposition times. However, the improvement in rejection is accompanied by a decline in flux. Based upon these observations, all subsequent studies were performed using membranes which had been wetted before cutting.

Figure 4 shows the effect of monomer flow rate on membrane flux and rejection. The rejection passes through a maximum for flow rates between 4 and 7 cm³/min. The flux, on the other hand, decreases with increasing flow rate, passing through a minimum when the rejection is at its maximum. Also shown in Figure 4 is a curve of the calculated thickness of the plasma-polymerized film. This curve is based on deposition rate studies performed on an aluminum foil substrate.

For flow rates below 6 cm³/min, the observed dependence of rejection and flux on flow rate appears to be associated with the thickness of the deposited film. At low flow rates, the film thickness achieved in 16 min is inadequate to provide good rejection (see Fig. 3). At higher flow rates, the film thickness decreases gradually, but the rejection is seen to fall off much more rapidly than would be expected solely due to a decline in film thickness. It would, therefore, appear that the structural characteristics of films deposited at high flow rates are different from those of films of equivalent thickness deposited at lower flow rates.

The effect of the deposition pressure on membrane performance is shown in Figure 5. The rejection passes through a maximum at a pressure of about 250 μ and then levels off at higher pressures. The flux decreases rapidly as the pressure increases at low pressure and then levels off at higher pressures. A curve of the predicted film thickness is also shown in Figure 5.

For pressures below 250 μ, the effect of pressure on the reverse osmosis char-

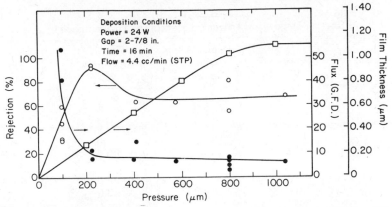

Fig. 5. Effect of pressure on membrane rejection (—○—), flux (—●—), and film thickness (—□—).

acteristics of the membranes can be attributed to the increasing thickness of the plasma-deposited film. At higher pressures, the film thickness continues to increase but the rejection declines. This behavior might possibly be explained by the presence of very fine faults or cracks in the film. Alternatively, the chemical and/or structural characteristics of the films prepared at higher pressures may be less favorable for good salt rejection.

The effect of the electrode gap on the rejection and flux of the membranes is shown in Table II. In preparing the membranes listed in this table, the deposition time was adjusted so that the same amount of polymer was deposited in each case. All other deposition conditions were held constant. The rejection of the membranes is found to increase as the gap size is decreased, although the overall variation is not large. The flux is found to be largest for a gap size between 1.5 and 2.0 in.

Finally, to test the effect of discharge power, membranes were prepared at 24 W, 42 W, and 62 W. The time of deposition was adjusted so that the same amount of film was deposited in each case. The results are shown in Table III. The rejection of the membranes is highest for films produced at a power of 42 W, although the overall variation with power is not large. The flux of the films

TABLE II
Effect of Electrode Gap on Membrane Performance[a]

Membrane no.	Gap, in.	Deposition time, min	Rejection, %[b]	Flux, gfd[b]
408	1.0	21.6	94.2	10.2
409	1.0	21.6	94.4	12.9
406	1.5	19.1	94.2	10.4
407	1.5	19.1	91.1	15.4
410	2.25	19.1	91.3	15.4
411	2.25	19.1	94.4	15.2
390	2.85	16.0	89.0	7.2
401	2.85	16.0	87.5	11.7

[a] Membrane preparation conditions: flow config., IV; pressure, 200–250 μ Hg; power, 24 W; monomer flow, 5.0 cm³/min; dep. time, see table.

[b] Feed concentration, 1% NaCl; feed temperature, 20°C; applied pressure, 1500 psi.

TABLE III
Effect of Deposition Power on Membrane Performance[a]

Membrane no.	Power, W.	Deposition time, min	Rejection, %[b]	Flux, gfd[b]
341	24	16.0	97.0	5.0
355	24	16.0	87.0	8.0
395	42	13.4	90.5	10.2
397	42	13.4	98.5	6.8
400	42	13.4	96.3	7.9
396	62	13.0	80.4	13.7
398	62	13.0	92.5	14.4
403	62	13.0	93.0	10.4

[a] Membrane preparation conditions: flow config., IV; pressure, 200–250 μ Hg; monomer flow, 4.4 cm^3/min; elec. gap, 2$\frac{7}{8}$ in.; dep. time, see table.

[b] Feed concentration, 1% NaCl; feed temperature 20 °C; applied pressure, 1500 psi.

increases with increasing power, and again the effect of power is not large. Bell et al.[4] observed similar trends with deposition power in their studies and also found 40 W to be the optimum power. The occurrence of an optimum power was ascribed to a balance between increased deposition rate and increased substrate degradation which occurs as the power is increased.

Additional improvements in membrane performance could be obtained by feeding monomer to the reactor prior to the initiation of the discharge and by heating the base plate supporting the substrate. The first of these techniques was found to improve rejection without having any effect on flux. These results are summarized in Table IV which compares rejection and fluxes for membranes prepared with and without prefeeding of monomer. Similar results have been observed by Wydeven.[8] A possible explanation for the improved rejection is that prefed monomer adsorbs on the substrate surface and, once the discharge is initiated, rapidly polymerizes forming an intimate bond with the substrate.

TABLE IV
Effect of Feeding Monomer Before Initiation of Discharge
on Membrane Performance[a]

Membrane no.	Rejection, %[b]	Flux, gfd[b]
381 (monomer fed for 15 min before discharge)	94.1	10.9
383 (monomer fed for 15 min before discharge)	94.5	11.3
416 (monomer fed for 15 min before discharge)	95.3	7.4
417 (monomer fed for 15 min before discharge)	90.0	10.3
361 (monomer not prefed)	85.0	12.0
341 (monomer not prefed)	97.0	5.0
355 (monomer not prefed)	87.0	8.0

[a] Membrane preparation conditions: flow config., IV; pressure, 200–250 μ Hg; power, 24 W; monomer flow, 4.4 cm^3/min; elec. gap, 2$\frac{7}{8}$ in.; dep. time, 13 min.

[b] Feed concentration, 1% NaCl; feed temperature, 20 °C; applied pressure, 1500 psi.

TABLE V
Effect of Using a Heated or Cooled Base Plate
on Membrane Performance[a]

Membrane no.	Rejection, %[b]	Flux, gfd[b]
386 (heated base plate, $T = 38°C$)	90.4	16.9
387 (heated base plate, $T = 38°C$)	87.0	18.0
388 (heated base plate, $T = 38°C$)	87.7	18.0
361 (cooled base plate, $T = 20°C$)	85.0	12.0
341 (cooled base plate, $T = 20°C$)	97.0	5.0
355 (cooled base plate, $T = 20°C$)	87.0	8.0

[a] Membrane preparation conditions: flow config., IV; pressure, 200–250 μ Hg; power, 24 W; monomer flow, 4.4 cm³/min; elec. gap, 2⅞ in.; dep. time, 13 min.

[b] Feed concentration, 1% NaCl; feed temperature, 20 °C; applied pressure, 1500 psi.

Heating the lower electrode to a temperature of 38°C had a significant effect on the flux through the membranes, but little effect on salt rejection. Table V compares the results for membranes prepared on a heated and cooled base plate.

On the basis of results obtained with prefed monomer and using a heated base plate, a series of membranes were prepared using both techniques together. The monomer was prefed to the reactor at the same flow rate and pressure used during deposition. The base plate was heated only during deposition. Rather than obtaining membranes with both improved salt rejection and higher flux, as was hoped for, the performance of the membranes prepared using both techniques was poorer than if neither of the techniques had been used. These results are summarized in Table VI.

The infrared spectra recorded of plasma-polymerized allylamine deposited on a NaCl crystal resembled those reported by Bell et al.[4] The assignment of the bands observed in these spectra are given in Table VII. Spectra taken of films prepared at different pressures and flow rates were practically indistinguishable, suggesting that although films prepared at different conditions have different reverse osmosis characteristics, their chemical structures are essentially the same.

In an effort to detect differences in membrane surface composition as a function of deposition conditions, a series of samples were examined by ESCA.

TABLE VI
Effects of Heating Substrate Holder and Feeding Monomer Before Initiation of
Discharge on Membrane Performance[a]

Membrane no.	Rejection, %[b]	Flux, gfd[b]
404	86.0	7.9
405	75.6	9.9
412	82.5	5.2
418	96.0	5.3
417	87.2	15.0

[a] Membrane preparation conditions: flow config., IV; pressure, 200–250 μ Hg; power, 24 W; monomer flow, 4.4 cm³/min; elec. gap, 2⅞ in.; dep. time, 13 min.

[b] Feed concentration, 1% NaCl; feed temperature, 20 °C; applied pressure, 1500 psi.

TABLE VII
Infrared Frequencies and Band Assignments

Frequency, cm^{-1}	Band assignments
3340	ν(N—H)
2960	ν(CH$_3$)
2930	ν(CH$_2$)
2870	ν(CH$_3$)
2840	ν(CH$_2$)
2200	ν(C≡N)
1620	ν(C≡N) and δ(N—H)
1440	δ(CH$_3$) and δ(CH$_2$)
1380	δ(CH$_3$)

The binding energies for 1s electrons in carbon, nitrogen, and oxygen and the ratios of peak areas are shown in Table VIII. The positions of the three bands were found to be independent of film deposition conditions, and the ratios of peak areas exhibited no significant trends. Thus, it would appear that ESCA, like infrared spectroscopy, is incapable of identifying the structural characteristics of the plasma-deposited films which control their reverse osmosis performance.

In the study performed by Bell et al.,[4] it was noted that the reverse osmosis performance of the membranes tended to degrade with the duration of use. ESCA studies performed on the membranes before and after they were used for reverse osmosis revealed a decrease in the amount of nitrogen and increase in the amount of oxygen on the membrane surface after the membrane had been used for reverse osmosis. This same behavior was also observed by Yasuda.[10] It was proposed by Bell et al. that the degradation observed was due to the hydrolysis of imine and ketimine groups in the film to form carboxylic acid groups. The hydrolysis reaction was believed to be responsible for the destruction of crosslinks in the film and weakening of the film structure. To further verify this interpretation, additional studies were conducted.

In performing the monomer flow rate studies noted earlier, it was observed that membranes produced at high monomer flow rates had a greater tendency to degrade than those produced at the optimum flow rate of 4–7 cm^3/min S.T.P. To determine whether exposure to water produced differences in film structure, membranes were prepared using monomer flow rates of 5 and 16 cm^3/min S.T.P. Samples of each film were placed overnight in a dish of salt water maintained at 20° or 40°C. A third sample of each membrane was stored dry in a desiccator. The wetted samples were allowed to dry, and then all of the samples were analyzed by ESCA. The results are shown in Table IX.

TABLE VIII
ESCA Binding Energies and Peak Area Ratios

Binding energy, eV[a]			Peak area ratio[b]		
C(1s)	O(1s)	N(1s)	O/C	N/C	O/N
284.6	532.6	399.6	0.34	0.20	1.7

[a] Adjusted to E_B = 284.6 eV for C(1s) to account for charging of sample.[4]
[b] Average values.

TABLE IX
ESCA Results for Dry and Wetted Membranes[a]

Sample	Binding energy, eV			Peak area ratio		
	C(1s)	O(1s)	N(1s)	O/C	N/C	O/N
365 Dry	284.6	532.2	399.7	0.31	0.20	1.5
365 Wetted in 40°C water	284.6	532.6	399.8	0.28	0.15	1.9
365 Wetted in 20°C water	284.6	532.2	399.9	0.37	0.16	2.3
378 Dry	284.6	532.5	399.6	0.30	0.22	1.3
378 Wetted in 20°C water	284.6	532.9	400.1	0.37	0.18	2.1
378 Wetted in 20°C water	284.6	532.6	399.5	0.26	0.18	1.5
366 Dry	284.6	532.6	399.6	0.35	0.36	1.1
366 Wetted in 40°C water	284.6	532.5	399.9	0.34	0.18	1.9
366 Wetted in 20°C water	284.6	532.6	399.9	0.37	0.02	17.0
384 Dry	284.6	532.6	399.6	0.35	0.15	2.3
384 Wetted in 20°C water	284.6	532.6	399.8	0.40	0.01	32.0
384 Wetted in 20°C water	284.6	532.7	399.9	0.50	0.04	13.0
Gulf substrate dry	284.6	533.8	400.1	1.5	0.03	52.0
	286.1					
Gulf substrate wetted in 20°C water	284.6	533.5	399.8	2.1	0.02	92.0
	286.2					

[a] Membrane preparation conditions:

	365 and 378	366 and 384
Flow configuration	IV	IV
Pressure	230 μ Hg	240 μ Hg
Power	24 W	24 W
Monomer flow	5 cm³/min	16 cm³/min
Electrode gap	2⅞ in.	2⅞ in.
Deposition time	16 min	16 min

A comparison of the positions of the C(1s), N(1s), and O(1s) peaks for dry membranes and membranes wetted in either 20° or 40° salt water shows only small differences. A change can be noted in the elemental ratios of the membranes as a result of wetting them. The membranes produced at the optimum flow rate (membranes 365 and 378) show a slight increase in oxygen and a decrease in nitrogen on the surface of the films after wetting in both 20° and 40°C water. The membranes produced at the higher monomer flow rate (366 and 384) show a large decrease in the amount of nitrogen on the surface of the films after being wetted in 20°C water. A decrease in nitrogen was also noted when the films were wetted in the 40°C salt water, but the effect was surprisingly much smaller. A sample of the substrate alone was also analyzed by ESCA before and after being wetted. The results obtained were quite different from those obtained with the membranes, indicating that the spectra obtained with the membranes are characteristic of the plasma-polymerized allylamine film alone (see Table IX).

Further tests of the correlation between membrane degradation and changes in the surface contents of oxygen and nitrogen were carried out with membranes prepared at different pressures. These membranes were analyzed by ESCA before and after they were used for reverse osmosis. In Table X, it is seen that all of the membranes which degraded (it should be noted that degradation in all cases corresponded to a decline in rejection of less than 1% in 24 hr) showed

TABLE X
ESCA Analyses of Membranes Before and After Testing of
Reverse Osmosis Performance[a]

Sample	Binding energy, eV			Peak area			Deposition pressure, μ Hg	Degree of degradation
	C(1s)	O(1s)	N(1s)	O/C	N/C	O/N		
368 Before RO	284.6	532.4	399.4	0.41	0.25	1.64	95	beginning
368 After RO	284.6	532.4	399.6	0.68	0.12	5.66		to degrade
369 Before RO	284.6	532.6	399.3	0.30	0.17	1.76	410	no
369 After RO	284.6	532.0	399.5	0.33	0.12	2.75		
370 Before RO	284.6	532.2	399.5	0.26	0.19	1.37	575	yes
370 After RO	284.6	532.3	399.4	0.35	0.11	3.18		
371 Before RO	284.6	532.6	399.4	0.32	0.17	1.88	850	yes
371 After RO	284.6	532.4	399.8	0.75	0.16	4.70		
372 Before RO	284.6	532.6	400.3	0.29	0.15	1.93	850	yes, after
372 After RO	284.6	532.3	399.3	0.39	0.09	4.34		25 hr
373 Before RO	284.6	532.5	399.5	0.28	0.23	1.22	1050	yes,
373 After RO	284.6	532.6	399.9	0.62	0.16	3.89		slightly
374 Before RO	284.6	532.6	399.7	0.37	0.17	2.18	225	yes,
374 After RO	284.6	532.5	399.4	0.56	0.11	5.10		slightly
375 Before RO	284.6	532.6	399.3	0.33	0.20	1.65	440	no
375 After RO	284.6	532.2	399.5	0.43	0.20	2.32		

[a] Membrane preparation conditions: flow config., IV; pressure, see table; power, 24 W; monomer flow, 4.4 cm³/min; elec. gap, 2⅞ in.; dep. time, 16 min.

a fairly large increase in the O/C ratio and a concurrent decrease in the N/C ratio. Membranes 369 and 375, which did not degrade, also showed increases in the O/C ratio, and membranes 369, in addition, showed a decrease in N/C ratio after use for reverse osmosis. The changes in the elemental ratios for these membranes were smaller, though, than those noted for membranes which did degrade.

From the data given in Tables IX and X, it is evident that the rejecting layer of all of the membranes undergo hydrolysis to some degree upon contact with water and that membranes which degrade undergo a greater degree of hydrolysis. The extent to which hydrolysis occurs does depend on the conditions under which the membrane is prepared. However, it is still not apparent why some of the membranes degrade and others do not.

CONCLUSIONS

The present work has further confirmed that the reverse osmosis characteristics of membranes prepared by plasma polymerization of allylamine are a sensitive function of the preparation conditions. Superior membranes were obtained by using a gas flow configuration which avoided direct monomer flow over the substrate. To achieve high rejections, the plasma-deposited film must be sufficiently thick. It was determined that while monomer flow rate, pressure, interelectrode gap distance, and discharge power influence the rate of polymerization, these variables also influence reverse osmosis characteristics of the deposited film. Thus, films of equivalent thickness prepared under different conditions exhibited difference in their reverse osmosis performance.

The effects of several variations in the membrane preparation procedure were also explored. Wetting membranes with distilled water and then allowing them to dry before testing their reverse osmosis performance resulted in an improved performance over membranes which had not been treated in this fashion. Higher water fluxes, without loss of salt rejection, could be obtained by heating the substrate holder during deposition. On the other hand, the salt rejection characteristic of the membranes could be improved by passing monomer over the substrate prior to initiating the discharge. Attempts to use both of the methods just mentioned on a single membrane, however, did not result in a simultaneous improvement in flux and rejection.

Characterization of the plasma-polymerized films by infrared spectroscopy and ESCA has established that neither of these techniques can identify significant differences in the chemical composition and structure of films prepared under different conditions. As a result, these techniques do not help to explain the variations in reverse osmosis performance observed. ESCA, however, has been useful in confirming the hypothesis that degradation in reverse osmosis performance is associated with the hydrolysis of nitrogen-containing structures in the plasma-deposited film.

This work was supported by NASA under Grant NSG-2043. The authors also wish to thank Dr. M. Millard of the USDA Western Regional Laboratory for providing use of his ESCA facilities.

References

1. D. R. Buck and V. K. Davar, *Br. Polym. J.*, **2**, 238 (1970).
2. H. Yasuda and C. E. Lamaze, *J. Appl. Polym. Sci.*, **17**, 201 (1973).
3. J. R. Hollahan and T. Wydeven, *Science*, **179**, 500 (1973).
4. A. T. Bell, T. Wydeven, and C. C. Johnson, *J. Appl. Polym. Sci.*, **19**, 1911 (1975).
5. R. L. Riley, G. Hightower, and C. R. Lyons, in *Reverse Osmosis Membrane Research*, H. K. Lonsdale, Ed., Plenum, New York, 1972.
6. S. Hossain, R. L. Goldsmith, M. Tan, T. Wydeven, and M. I. Leban, *J. Eng. Ind.*, 1023 (1973).
7. J. M. Tibbitt, A. T. Bell, and M. Shen, submitted to *J. Macromol. Sci.-Chem.*
8. T. Wydeven, Biotechnology Division, NASA Ames Research Center, Moffett Field, California, personal communication.
9. J. Delhalle, J. M. Andre, S. Delhalle, J. J. Pireaux, R. R. Caudano, and J. J. Verbist, *J. Chem. Phys.*, **60**, 595 (1974).
10. H. Yasuda, in *Reverse Osmosis and Membranes. Theory–Technology–Engineering*, S. Sourirajan and M. Dekker, Eds., in press (private communication).

Received April 27, 1976
Revised August 18, 1976

JOURNAL OF APPLIED POLYMER SCIENCE   VOL. 21, 2675–2682 (1977)

Halogen-Modified Impact Polystyrene. II. Evidence for Condensed-Phase Reactions by Thermogravimetry

B. L. JOESTEN and E. R. WAGNER, *Union Carbide Corporation, Bound Brook, New Jersey 08805*

Synopsis

Blends of high-impact polystyrene with decabromodiphenyl oxide and/or antimony trioxide were characterized by thermogravimetry. The observed weight loss for the blends was compared with a calculated weight loss which was determined from a weighted sum of the weight loss of the individual materials in the blend. This comparison of observed and calculated weight loss provided a method to determine if condensed-phase reactions occur among the materials in the blend. Definite evidence for condensed-phase reactions was observed when polybutadiene (impact modifier), decabromodiphenyl oxide, and antimony trioxide were present simultaneously. In that case, the observed weight loss exceeded the calculated weight loss above 330°C. When one of the three materials was absent, the observed weight loss was less than or equal to the calculated weight loss. The condensed-phase reactions involving polybutadiene, decabromodiphenyl oxide, and antimony trioxide occurred in nitrogen as well as in air.

INTRODUCTION

The synergistic effect of antimony trioxide on the flame-quenching efficiency of organic halides, which has been recognized for 40 years, was reviewed in 1972.[1] More recently, the role of the polymeric matrix in the synergistic interaction of antimony trioxide and decabromodiphenyl oxide in high-impact polystyrene was described.[2] The present paper describes data obtained by thermogravimetry which indicate that the synergism originates with reactions that occur in the condensed phase and that involve decabromodiphenyl oxide, antimony trioxide, and polybutadiene. Condensed-phase reactions control the rate of fuel generation, and they must be in equilibrium with the consumption of the fuel in the gas phase to sustain combustion.[3] The condensed-phase reactions which occur in high-impact polystyrene that contains decabromodiphenyl oxide and antimony trioxide upset the equilibrium by flooding the gas phase with bromine-containing, flame-quenching molecules.[2]

EXPERIMENTAL

Materials

The impact polystyrene (IPS) was a commercial Union Carbide Corporation product. The decabromodiphenyl oxide (DBDPO) was supplied by the Dow Chemical Co. The antimony trioxide (Sb_2O_3) was Matheson, Coleman & Bell, reagent grade.

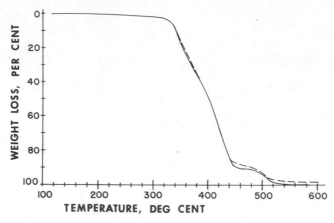

Fig. 1. Thermogravimetry of 86/10/4 blend of IPS, DBDPO, and Sb_2O_3 (HM-IPS): heating rate, 10°C/min; atmosphere, air.

Blends containing IPS, DBDPO, and Sb_2O_3 were prepared on a compounding extruder. Blends of IPS and one of the other two components were prepared on a two-roll mill. Blends of DBDPO and Sb_2O_3 were dry blends mixed with a mortar and pestle.

Thermogravimetry

The thermogravimetric data were obtained with a Perkin-Elmer TGS-1 Thermobalance. The initial sample weight was approximately 2 mg. Samples were heated at 10°C/min with air or nitrogen flowing past the microfurnace at 30 cc/min.

Data were recorded on paper tape for subsequent analysis by computer.

RESULTS AND DISCUSSION

Impact Polystyrene Blended With DBDPO and Sb_2O_3

Impact polystyrene blended with DBDPO and Sb_2O_3 will be called halogen-modified impact polystyrene (HM-IPS). Figure 1 shows duplicate weight loss curves for HM-IPS when it is heated in air at 10°C/min. Rapid weight loss does not occur until the temperature exceeds 340°C.

The weight loss of HM-IPS in air is compared to the weight loss of IPS in air in Figure 2. Below 330°C, both materials have the same weight loss. Above 330°C, the weight loss of HM-IPS exceeds that of the IPS.

To determine the significance of the greater weight loss for HM-IPS relative to IPS, the weight loss of the individual materials in HM-IPS must be compared with the weight loss of HM-IPS. Therefore, a computer program was written to calculate the weight loss for a blend of materials from the weight loss curves for each of the materials in the blend:

$$W_{cal}(T) = \text{calculated weight loss of blend} = \sum_i \alpha_i W_i(T) \tag{1}$$

where α_i = weight fraction of material i in the blend, and $W_i(T)$ = weight loss

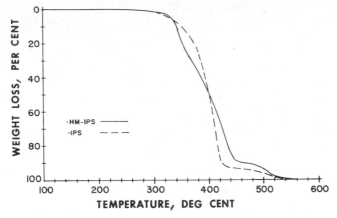

Fig. 2. Thermogravimetry of IPS and HM-IPS: heating rate, 10°C/min; atmosphere, air.

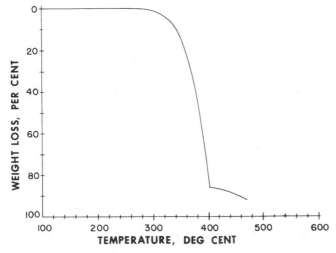

Fig. 3. Thermogravimetry of DBDPO: heating rate, 10°C/min; atmosphere, air or N₂.

of material i at temperature T. The calculated weight loss for the blend should be equal to the observed weight loss of the blend if the materials in the blend do not react among themselves.

Figure 3 shows the weight loss curve for DBDPO. This weight loss curve was the same in either air or nitrogen. Weight loss becomes detectable near 280°C and is accompanied by the formation of white crystals on relatively cool parts of the thermogravimetric apparatus. The melting temperature of DBDPO is approximately 300°C. The weight loss illustrated in Figure 3 most likely represents sublimation and voltalization rather than fragmentation.

Figure 4 shows the weight of Sb_2O_3 as a function of temperature. Weight loss is not detected until the temperature reaches 500°C. The weight loss is the same in either air or nitrogen until it amounts to approximately 20% near 550°C. The weight shows no further change above 550°C in air but continues to decrease in nitrogen.

Figure 5 illustrates that the weight loss observed for a blend of DBDPO and

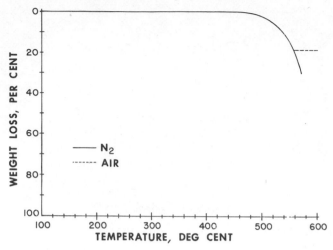

Fig. 4. Thermogravimetry of Sb$_2$O$_3$: heating rate, 10°C/min; atmosphere, air and N$_2$.

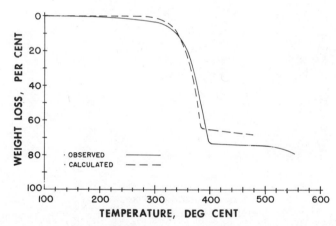

Fig. 5. Thermogravimetry of a 70/30 blend of DBDPO and Sb$_2$O$_3$ compared with calculated weight loss: heating rate, 10°C/min; atmosphere, air.

Sb$_2$O$_3$ is very similar to the weight loss calculated by eq. (1) from the individual weight loss curves of DBDPO and Sb$_2$O$_3$. The similarity of the observed and calculated weight loss curve in Figure 5 does not rule out the possibility that DBDPO and Sb$_2$O$_3$ react. If they do react, the reaction does not change the temperature dependence of the weight loss very much relative to what is expected for nonreacting materials.

Figure 6 compares the weight loss observed for HM-IPS in air with a calculated weight loss curve which was synthesized by eq. (1) from individual weight loss curves of IPS and a DBDPO/Sb$_2$O$_3$ blend in air. The observed weight loss of HM-IPS exceeds the calculated weight loss near 330°C. That is, the observed weight loss is greater than expected for a blend of nonreacting materials. Therefore, IPS, DBDPO, and Sb$_2$O$_3$ must interact above 330°C. Chemical reactions must occur in the condensed phase and generate products which volatilize above 330°C.

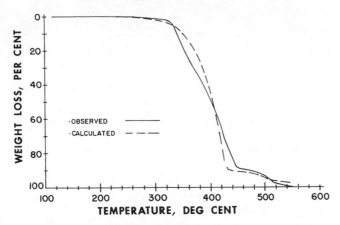

Fig. 6. Thermogravimetry of HM-IPS compared with calculated weight loss: heating rate, 10°C/min; atmosphere, air.

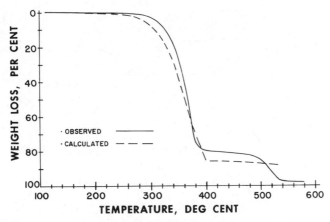

Fig. 7. Thermogravimetry of a 50/35/15 blend of polystyrene, DBDPO, and Sb_2O_3 compared with calculated weight loss: heating rate, 10°C/min; atmosphere, air.

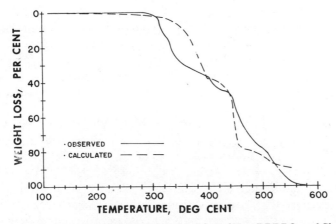

Fig. 8. Thermogravimetry of a 50/35/15 blend of polybutadiéne, DBDPO, and Sb_2O_3 compared with calculated weight loss: heating rate, 10°C/min; atmosphere, air.

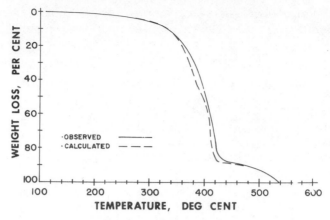

Fig. 9. Thermogravimetry of a 80/20 blend of IPS and DBDPO compared with calculated weight loss: heating rate, 10°C/min; atmosphere, air.

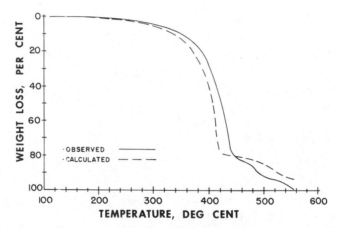

Fig. 10. Thermogravimetry of a 92/8 blend of IPS and Sb_2O_3 compared with calculated weight loss: heating rate, 10°C/min; atmosphere, air.

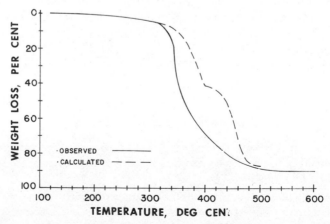

Fig. 11. Thermogravimetry of a 50/35/15 blend of IPS, DBDPO, and Sb_2O_3 compared with calculated weight loss: heating rate, 10°C/min; atmosphere, N_2.

Several additional blends were characterized to determine the necessary and sufficient conditions for the condensed-phase reactions to occur.

Polystyrene Blended With DBDPO and Sb_2O_3

The observed weight loss of a polystyrene/DBDPO/Sb_2O_3 blend is compared to its calculated weight loss in Figure 7. The observed weight loss is less than the calculated weight loss until the weight loss exceeds 70%. If the polystyrene, DBDPO, and Sb_2O_3 react, the reaction products are less volatile than the individual materials in the blend.

Polybutadiene Blended With DBDPO and Sb_2O_3

Polybutadiene is present in IPS as the impact modifier. Polybutadiene having the microstructure 35% cis-1,4, 55% trans-1,4, and 10% 1,2-addition was blended with DBDPO and Sb_2O_3.

Figure 8 compares the observed and calculated weight loss in air for a polybutadiene/DBDPO/Sb_2O_3 blend. In this case, the observed weight loss exceeds the calculated weight loss near 300°C. Therefore, the condensed-phase reactions are definitely indicated.

IPS Blended With Either DBDPO or Sb_2O_3 Separately

Figures 9 and 10 show the observed and calculated weight loss in air for IPS/DBDPO and IPS/Sb_2O_3 blends, respectively. The observed and calculated weight loss curves are similar for both blends, with the observed weight loss being less than the calculated weight loss.

Therefore, the observed weight loss exceeds the calculated weight only when polybutadiene, DBDPO, and Sb_2O_3 are present simultaneously. That is, a definite indication for condensed-phase reactions is observed only when all three materials are present.

Figure 11 compares the observed and calculated weight loss in nitrogen for an IPS/DBDPO/Sb_2O_3 blend. Even in nitrogen, the observed weight loss exceeds the calculated weight loss. Therefore, oxygen is not necessary for the condensed-phase reactions involving polybutadiene, DBDPO, and Sb_2O_3.

CONCLUSIONS

Synergism in the IPS/DBDPO/Sb_2O_3 system results from reactions that occur in the condensed phase and which require the simultaneous presence of polybutadiene, DBDPO, and Sb_2O_3.

The condensed-phase reactions do not require oxygen.

As described in an earlier paper,[2] the condensed-phase reactions are initiated by thermally generated polymeric free radicals which occur at lower temperatures for polybutadiene than for polystyrene.

References

1. J. J. Pitts, *J. Fire Flamm.*, **3,** 51 (1972).
2. E. R. Wagner and B. L. Joesten, *J. Appl. Polym. Sci.*, **20,** 2143 (1976).
3. D. E. Stuetz, A. H. DiEdwardo, F. Zitomer, and B. P. Barnes, *J. Polym. Sci., Polym. Chem. Ed.*, **13,** 585 (1975).

Received April 27, 1976
Revised August 20, 1976

JOURNAL OF APPLIED POLYMER SCIENCE   VOL. 21, 2683-2693 (1977)

Radiation-Induced Polymerization of Styrene at High Dose Rates

J. TAKEZAKI, T. OKADA, and I. SAKURADA, *Osaka Laboratory for Radiation Chemistry, Japan Atomic Energy Research Institute, Mii-minamimachi, Neyagawa City, Osaka, 572 Japan*

Synopsis

A kinetic equation was derived for the radiation-induced polymerization of styrene under the assumption that both radical and cationic polymerizations take place concurrently throughout the whole range of the dose rate of radiation and the water content of the styrene. The equation enables one to calculate rates of the total, radical, and cationic polymerization at a given dose rate and water content and agrees satisfactorily with experimental results, which cover dose rates from 4.2×10 to 2.1×10^5 rad/sec and water contents from 3.2×10^{-3} to 3.5×10^{-2} mol/l. Experimental estimation of the contribution of radical and cationic mechanisms was done by GPC curves of polymers obtained under various conditions. When the contribution of ionic mechanism is expressed in weight percent, it changes from 0% to 100% in the range of the experiment; on the other hand, if it is expressed in mole percent, it is independent of the dose rate and remains constant throughout the whole range of the experiment.

INTRODUCTION

A number of reports on the radiation-induced polymerization of styrene have appeared in the literature, and a full account of the polymerization of styrene under ordinary conditions of purity, dryness, and dose rate can be found in Chapiro.[1] It appeared that the polymerization proceeds mainly by radical mechanism. Since then, however, it has been shown that ionic mechanism plays a predominant part in the polymerization of extremely dry styrene.[2,3]

Squire et al.[4] investigated radiation-induced polymerization of not rigorously dried styrene at higher dose rates up to 3 Mrads/sec, and a substantial contribution to the polymerization of concurrent cationic process was observed. We have also carried out similar experiments[5] in a dose rate range of 4.2×10 to 2.1×10^5 rad/sec. The water content of styrene was varied between 3.2×10^{-3} and 3.5×10^{-2} mole/l.; the latter value corresponds to the saturation water content of styrene at room temperature.

It was shown that the total rate of polymerization, R_p, may be written as the sum of radical R_r and ionic polymerization rate R_i:

$$R_p = R_r + R_i = B_r I^{1/2} + B_i [X]^{-1} I$$

where I and $[X]$ are dose rate and water content, respectively; and B_r and B_i are constants which contain G-values for radical and ion formation and rate constants of radical and ionic polymerization, respectively. Essential applicability of the equation to the experimental results was recognized.

2683

The present paper is also concerned with radiation-induced polymerization of styrene, and it is intended to divide polymerization product into two components, i.e., into radical and ionic polymers, by gel permeation chromatography (GPC). It is expected that by combined kinetic analysis of the polymerization reaction and GPC analysis of the product we will get more detailed and quantitative information about the radiation-induced polymerization than we have at present.

EXPERIMENTAL

Styrene Sample

Styrene monomer was washed with sodium hydroxide and then with water to remove any inhibitor. The washed styrene was dried overnight with $CaCl_2$ and distilled. The distilled styrene was brought into contact with CaH_2, kept at least two weeks to dry further, and then distilled for the irradiation. The water content of the finally distilled styrene was about 3×10^{-3} mole/l. This is called, hereafter, moderately dried styrene; most of the experiments were carried out with the moderately dried styrene.

Irradiation Procedure

Irradiation for the polymerization was carried out with electron beams from a 1.5-MeV Van de Graaff accelerator in a dose rate range of 1.1×10^4 to 2.1×10^5 rad/sec, and gamma rays from a 2000-Ci cobalt 60 source was also employed for irradiation at a lower range, 3.7×10^2 to 4.2×10 rad/sec. The stainless steel irradiation cell is the same as that used in the previous report.[5] The inner size of the cell is 50 mm × 25 mm × 1 mm, and the thickness of the liquid monomer is 1 mm.

The irradiation was carried out at room temperature, and the cell was cooled by an electric fan during the irradiation. When necessary, the irradiation was performed intermittently (50 sec irradiation and 60 sec interval), so that the temperature rise could be limited to less than 4°C.

Separation of Polymers

As was pointed out in the previous report, separation of polymers from the solution of the reaction products by precipitation with methanol is unsatisfactory because a very large amount, occasionally more than 30%, of low polymers which cannot be precipitated with methanol are formed by the irradiation, especially when the rate is very high. In the present work, all polymers were separated by pumping out the unreacted monomer and solvent at room temperature under vacuum. This precaution is very important.

Sample Analysis

The molecular weights and their distribution were determined by gel permeation chromatography using a high-speed liquid chromatograph HLC-801A of Toyo Soda Kogyo K.K.

TABLE I

Rate of Polymerization of Moderately Dried Styrene as a Function of Dose Rate

Dose rate, rad/sec	Total dose, Mrad	Conversion, %	R_p, mole/l.-sec	Wt. fraction of polymers, %		
				Radical	Cationic	Oligomeric
4.2×10	1.8	6.0	1.22×10^{-5}	—	—	1
3.7×10^2	1.9	5.4	9.17×10^{-5}	49	49.5	1.5
1.05×10^4	3.1	3.5	1.02×10^{-3}	10.5	87.0	2.5
2.1×10^5	10.3	11.3	1.97×10^{-2}	6.5	90.5	3

TABLE II

Rate and Molecular Weight for Polymerization of Moderately Dried Styrene in the Presence of Ammonia (6.0×10^{-1} mole/l.)

Dose rate, rad/sec	Total dose, Mrad	Conversion, %	R_p, mole/l.-sec	Molecular wt. at peak[a]
4.2×10	1.7	3.64	8.00×10^{-6}	56.000
3.7×10^2	23	27.4	4.10×10^{-5}	27.500
1.05×10^4	21	1.00	4.68×10^{-5}	6.000
2.1×10^5	420	5.78	2.70×10^{-4}	3.000

[a] The values are virtually the same as the number-average molecular weight calculated from the area of the GPC curve.

RESULTS

Experimental results of dose rate dependence of the rate of polymerization of styrene are shown in Table I. It may be seen that the rate of polymerization increases with increasing dose rate.

Polymerization at various dose rates in the presence of ammonia was also carried out, and the results are shown in Table II. The rate of polymerization in the presence of ammonia (0.60 mole/l.) decreases with increasing dose rate because ammonia is a strong inhibitor for the cationic polymerization which plays a more important part at higher dose rates.

GPC measurements were carried out on polystyrenes formed in the experiments shown in Tables I and II, and typical molecular weight distribution curves are shown in Figures 1(a)–1(d) and 2.

The curve in Figure 1(a) for the polymerization at a dose rate of 4.2×10 rad/sec is, if we neglect small amounts of oligomers, a simple distribution curve with a peak at $M = 5.6 \times 10^4$. Polymerization at the same dose rate in the presence of ammonia gives a similar distribution curve with a peak at the same molecular weight as may be seen in the curve a of Figure 2. Therefore, it is apparently simple to conclude that the polymerization at such a dose rate proceeds by radical mechanism. This is true, roughly speaking; there is some difficulty, however, for the interpretation because polymers produced by ionic mechanism have also a peak at nearly the same position, and there is a possibility that ionic polymer is contained in an amount which cannot be neglected.

The curve in Figure 1(d) for the polymerization without ammonia at 2.1×10^5 rad/sec has a distinct peak at $M = 3.6 \times 10^4$ and a shoulder at $M = 5 \times 10^3$. It is interesting that there are small maxima at molecular weights corresponding

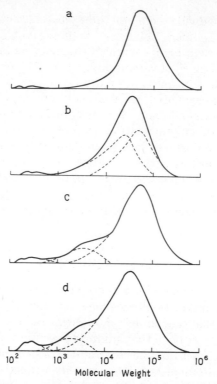

Fig. 1. Molecular weight distribution curves by GPC measurements of polystyrenes obtained by polymerization of moderately dried styrene at various dose rates (rad/sec): (a) 4.2×10; (b) 3.7×10^2; (c) 1.05×10^4; (d) 2.1×10^5.

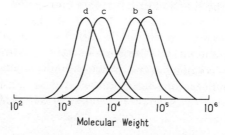

Fig. 2. Molecular weight distribution curves by GPC measurements of polystyrenes obtained by polymerization of moderately dried styrene in the presence of ammonia at various dose rates (rad/sec): (a) 4.2×10; (b) 3.7×10^2; (c) 1.05×10^4; (d) 2.1×10^5.

apparently to oligomers such as dimers, trimers, and tetramers, and the peaks of these maxima become more distinct with increasing dose rate.

Curves of molecular weight distribution of polymers obtained at various dose rates in the presence of ammonia have shapes similar to one another, differing only in the position of peaks. These curves correspond to radical polymerization at various dose rates. Molecular weights at the peaks of curves are also given in Table II. It is seen that the molecular weight decreases with increasing dose rate.

It was intended to divide the distribution curves in Figure 1 into two parts, but it was necessary to divide them into three parts, i.e., into areas corresponding to radical, ionic, and oligomeric polymers. An important guideline of the graphic division was the curves in Figure 2, which show molecular weight distribution of radical polymers obtained at various dose rates. The procedure is shown with dotted lines for curves b, c, and d in Figure 1; the weight fractions of the three kinds of polymer were calculated, and the results are shown in Table I. It is true that the basis of the division is not sufficiently firm, because master distribution curves for the cationic polymerization are not yet clearly established. It is self-consistent, however, as may be seen in Figures 1(b), 1(c), and 1(d) and will be shown later. Regarding curve a in Figure 1, adoption of the procedure to divide into three components was given up, because of the above-mentioned difficulty that the peaks of radical and ionic polymers were located practically at the same molecular weight, and the ionic polymer content is presumed to be very small.

DISCUSSION

The equation in the introduction was derived under the assumption that both radical and ionic polymerization take place concurrently throughout the whole dose-rate range, and that the number of initiating radicals or ions created by the radiation is dependent only on the radiation dose but independent of the dose rate. The well-known fact that the contribution of ionic mechanism is dominant in the higher dose-rate range is due to our conventional way of calculating the contribution not by the number but by the weight of polymer molecules.

In the present paper, the theoretical derivation of eq. (1) and comparison of the experimental results with theory will be shown in some detail. It is assumed that the overall reaction rate R_p is the sum of the reaction rate by radical mechanism, R_r, and the reaction rate by ionic mechanism, R_i:

$$R_p = R_r + R_i. \tag{1}$$

In the radical polymerization of styrene in bulk, it is known that the termination mechanism is a coupling of two growing chains and that no chain transfer reaction takes place under ordinary experimental conditions. The rate of radical polymerization may be expressed by the following well-known equation:

$$R_r = k_{pr} k_{tr}^{-1/2} (R_{ir})^{1/2} [M] \tag{2}$$

where R_r is the rate of radical polymerization in terms of monomer consumption, in moles/l.-sec; k_{pr} and k_{tr} are rate constants of polymerization and termination, respectively; and $[M]$ means concentration of monomer, in moles/l. R_{ir} is the rate of initiating radical formation, in moles/l.-sec; and can be written as follows:

$$R_{ir} = \frac{10 G_r d \varphi}{N} I = \Phi_r I \tag{3}$$

where G_r is the G-value (radiation chemical yield in number of molecules per 100 eV absorbed energy) for the initiating radical formation; I is the dose rate, in rad/sec; N is Avogadro's number; d is the density of styrene; and φ is a factor for normalizing the unit of radiation energy. All the above constants are summarized into one symbol and are denoted by Φ_r.

From eqs. (2) and (3), the following expressions are obtained:

$$R_r = k_{pr}k_{tr}^{-1/2}\Phi_r^{1/2}[M]I^{1/2} \tag{4}$$

$$D.P._r = 2k_{pr}k_{tr}^{-1/2}\Phi_r^{-1/2}[M]I^{-1/2} \tag{5}$$

In the right-hand side of the above equations, all symbols except $[M]$ and I are constants; $[M]$ also may be regarded to be unchanged because we deal with the initial rate and degree of polymerization, and G_r is assumed to be constant throughout the whole range of radiation dose. Therefore, all symbols in eq. (4) except I is summarized in one and denoted by B_r; so we get

$$R_r = B_rI^{1/2} \tag{6}$$

The degree of polymerization is

$$D.P._r = \text{const. } I^{-1/2} \tag{7}$$

Experimental results in Table II for the polymerization of styrene in the presence of ammonia show fair agreement with eqs. (6) and (7).

For the case of radiation-induced polymerization of highly dried styrene, where cationic polymerization dominates, Williams et al.[6] have proposed a kinetic scheme in which a monomer cation was an initiator and propagation proceeded in the usual manner by addition of monomer; transfer to monomer and termination both by impurity X (e.g., water) and anions were also taken into account. In the present discussion, termination by anions was neglected because the reaction is carried out in the presence of a moderately large amount of water, so that termination by water may be regarded to be dominant. The rate and degree of polymerization are given by the following equations:

$$R_i = k_{pi}R_{ii}\frac{[M]}{k_{tx}[X]} \tag{8}$$

$$D.P._i = \frac{k_{pi}[M]}{k_{tm}[M] + k_{tx}[X]} \tag{9}$$

where R_{ii}, k_{pi}, k_{tx}, and k_{tm} are rate of formation of initiating cation, rate constants of propagation and termination by impurity (water), and transfer constant to monomer, respectively.

The rate of initiating cation formation is

$$R_{ii} = \frac{10G_id\varphi}{N}I = \Phi_iI \tag{10}$$

where G_i has a similar meaning as G_r in eq. (3) and is the G-value for the formation of initiating cation. As in the case of radical polymerization, we get the following equation:

$$R_i = k_{pi}k_{tx}^{-1}\Phi_iM\frac{I}{[X]} \tag{11}$$

We may summarize all symbols except I and $[X]$ into one symbol and denote by B_i:

$$R_i = B_i\frac{I}{[X]} \tag{12}$$

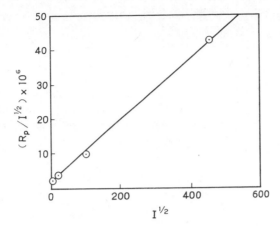

Fig. 3. Effect of dose rate I (rad/sec) on rate of polymerization of moderately dried styrene, R_p (mole/l.-sec).

Equations (1), (6), and (12) lead to the following expression for the overall rate of polymerization:

$$R_p = B_r I^{1/2} + B_i \frac{I}{[X]} \qquad (13)$$

This is the equation which has already been shown in the introduction.

To check the applicability of this equation for the polymerization of styrene of constant water content at various dose rates, the equation is transformed to

$$\frac{R_p}{I^{1/2}} = B_r + \frac{B_i}{[X]} I^{1/2} \qquad (13')$$

A plot of $R_p/I^{1/2}$ as a function of $I^{1/2}$ is expected to give a straight line. The graphic representation of the experiment in Table I is shown in Figure 3, and a straight line is obtained. This is quantitative evidence that radical and ionic polymerizations take place concurrently throughout the dose rate range of the present experiment. It is found from the intercept and the inclination of the curve that B_r and $B_i/[X]$ are 1.8×10^{-6} and 8.9×10^{-8}, respectively; $B_i = 2.84 \times 10^{-10}$, because the water content of the moderately dried styrene is 3.2×10^{-3} mole/l.

The effect of water content on the rate of polymerization was already reported in a previous paper as time–conversion curves. Table III shows numerically the rate of polymerization of styrene having various water contents at a constant dose rate of 2.1×10^5 rad/sec. According to eq. (13), R_p changes linearly with the reciprocal of the water content. Figure 4 is a graphic representation of the experimental results, and it is seen clearly that R_p shows the expected change with

TABLE III
Rate of Polymerization R_p of Styrenes of Various Water Contents
at a Dose Rate of 2.1×10^5 rad/sec

[H₂O], mole/l.	3.2×10^{-3}	5.7×10^{-3}	2.0×10^{-2}	3.5×10^{-2}
R_p, mole/l.-sec	1.65×10^{-2}	9.1×10^{-3}	1.78×10^{-8}	9.1×10^{-4}

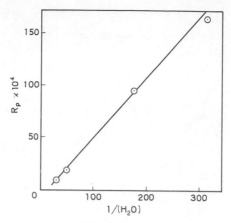

Fig. 4. Influence of water content $1/[H_2O]$ (l/mole) on polymerization rate of styrene.

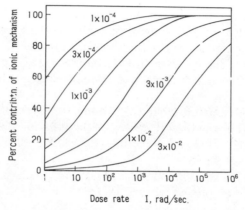

Fig. 5. Influence of water content of styrene and dose rate of irradiation on percent contribution of ionic mechanism in weight percent of polymer. Curves correspond to water contents from 1×10^{-4} to 3×10^{-2} mole/l.

$[H_2O]^{-1}$. The value of B_i found by this method is 2.72×10^{-10}, which agrees satisfactorily with that obtained from Figure 3.

We can now calculate the contributions of the radical and ionic mechanisms for a wide range of dose rate and water content in terms of weight of polymer based upon eq. (13). The calculated values are shown in Figure 5. It covers dose rate and water content ranges from 1 to 1×10^6 rad/sec and from 1×10^{-4} to 3×10^{-2} mole/l., respectively. Water-saturated styrene contains about 3×10^{-2} mole/l. water at room temperature. It may be seen from the figure that the contribution of ionic mechanism at lower water content increases at first very rapidly with increasing dose rate to show a value greater than 80%. On the other hand, in the case of styrene of rather high water content, the curves are S-shaped and the initial increase in ionic mechanism is slow. The figure shows further that at a very high dose rate, such as 10^6 rad/sec, the ionic mechanism is dominant, even in the case of water-saturated styrene.

There are three methods for the estimation of the contribution of radical or cationic mechanism in the polymerization at various dose rates: (1) The polymerization rate in the presence of ammonia is regarded to be due to radical

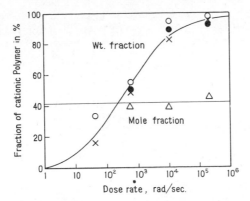

Fig. 6. Fraction of cationic polymer in wt-% and mole-% for polymerization of moderately dried styrene at various dose rates: (O) wt-%, method 1; (●) wt-%, method 2; (✕) wt-%, method 3; (△) mole-%, GPC method.

mechanism, so the difference of polymerization rates in the absence and presence of ammonia is a result of cationic polymerization.   (2) Based on the GPC analysis of polymers, it is possible know the fractions of radical and cationic polymers. (3) Via employment of the theoretical eq. (13) for the rate of polymerization, the contribution of the two mechanisms in the polymerization at any dose rate and water content can be calculated.

Figure 6 shows the contribution of the cationic mechanism, in weight percent, of the polymer found by the three different methods for moderately dried styrene at various dose rates.   The values obtained by different methods show fair agreement to one another.

Though we are not of the opinion that the GPC method gives the most reliable result, this method is employed for further discussion because number-average molecular weights are found from GPC curves.   In the following calculation, molecular weights at the peaks of the curves are used, since they are virtually the same as the graphically calculated number-average molecular weight and are less influenced by the graphic division into components than the former.

The rates of radical and cationic polymerizations are calculated from the overall rate of polymerization and contributions of the mechanisms.   The rates of radical and cationic polymerizations divided by the number-average degrees of polymerization and dose rate give the number of moles of radical and cationic polymers formed per 1 rad irradiation per liter styrene.   The calculated values are shown in Table IV.   It may be seen that the numbers of polymer molecules formed by each mechanisms are virtually independent of the dose rate, though the numbers at lower dose rates are somewhat larger than the others.   In the case of radical polymerization, eqs. (4) and (5) leads to

$$\frac{R_r}{D.P._r I} = \frac{10 G_r d \varphi}{2N} = \text{const.} \qquad (14)$$

and so experiment and theory show essentially good agreement.

From the numbers of radical and cationic polymer molecules formed per rad irradiation per liter styrene, we can calculate the contribution of cationic (or radical) mechanism in mole percent.   The calculated values are graphically shown in Figure 6.   It is seen that the contribution is independent of the dose

TABLE IV
Rate and Number-Average Degree of Polymerization for Radical and
Cationic Polymerization of Moderately Dried Styrene

Dose rate, I, rad/sec	4.2×10^a	3.7×10^2	1.05×10^4	2.1×10^5
Rate of polymerization, mols/l.-sec				
R_r	(8.1×10^{-6})	4.5×10^{-5}	1.07×10^{-4}	1.28×10^{-3}
R_i	—	4.55×10^{-5}	8.85×10^{-4}	1.78×10^{-2}
Number-average degree of polymerization				
$\overline{D \cdot P \cdot r}$	(4.9×10^2)	2.7×10^2	3.85×10	2.4×10
$\overline{D \cdot P \cdot i}$	—	4.3×10^2	5×10^2	3.4×10^2
Number of polymer molecules, mols/l. rad				
$R_r/(D \cdot P \cdot r \cdot I)$	(3.9×10^{-10})	4.5×10^{-10}	2.7×10^{-10}	2.7×10^{-10}
$R_i/(D \cdot P \cdot i \cdot I)$	—	2.9×10^{-10}	1.7×10^{-10}	2.4×10^{-10}
G_r	(0.78)	0.90	0.54	0.54
G_i	independent of dose rate			

a This calculation is based on the polymerization in the presence of ammonia.

rate and has an average value of about of 40% in a wide range of dose rates from 1 to 10^5 rad/sec, in which the contribution of the cationic mechanism in weight per cent changes practically from 0% to 100%.

The G-value for the initiating radical formation, i.e., G_r, is calculated by eq. (14) and shown in Table IV. The average G_r value is 0.68, which agrees with the value of 0.69 calculated by Chapiro[1] from data of different authors for dose rates below 2–3 rad/sec. According to Chapiro, G_r decreases with increasing dose rate to show a value of 0.3–0.46 in a dose rate range of 10–500 rad/sec. In the present paper, the scattering in G_r is regarded to be due to experimental error; the conclusion of Chapiro may be due to the fact that it was not known in 1961 that an appreciable amount of cationic polymers are formed at higher dose rates even with "wet" styrene. According to our experimental results on moderately dried styrene, cationic polymers show higher molecular weights than radical polymers above a dose rate of about 100 rad/sec. Therefore, if the contribution of cationic polymers is not taken into account, we obtain apparently lower G_r values at higher dose rate.

In the case of cationic polymerization, it is somewhat complicated, as eqs. (9) and (14) suggest, to know the number of polymer molecules produced by one initiating cation, because the degree of polymerization is controlled by two factors, namely, chain transfer to monomer and termination by water as eq. (9) shows. The experimental results, however, that the number of cationic polymers produced by a unit dose and their number-average molecular weight are independent of the dose rate show that G_i is also independent of the dose rate of irradiation.

The formation of oligomers in the course of the polymerization was neglected in the discussion. As has already been shown in Table I, the fraction of oligomers increases with dose rate, and it is plausible that they are formed in the initiating stage of cationic polymerization. Further investigation into the field of polymerization of styrene under high dose rates is now in progress. It has already been found that polystyrene of molecular weight about one million is formed not in moderately dried but in water-saturated styrene or in styrenes which contain a small amount of simple additives. This high molecular weight polystyrene is formed by some other mechanism than the radical and cationic polymers which are discussed in the present paper.

References

1. A. Chapiro, *Radiation Chemistry of Polymeric Systems,* Interscience, New York, 1962, pp. 150–167.

2. D. J. Metz and C. L. Johnson, *Polym. Prepr.,* **4,** 2295 (1966).

3. K. Ueno, Ko. Hayashi, and S. Okamura, *J. Polym. Sci., Polym. Lett. Ed.,* **3,** 363 (1965).

4. D. R. Squire, J. A. Cleave, T. M. A. Hossain, W. Oraby, E. P. Stahel, and V. Stannett, *J. Appl. Polym. Sci.,* **16,** 645 (1972).

5. J. Takezaki, T. Okada, and I. Sakurada, *Jpn. Atomic Energy Res. Inst. Rept.,* **5029,** 66, 73 (1974).

6. F. Williams, Ka. Hayashi, K. Ueno, Ko. Hayashi, and S. Okamura, *Trans. Faraday Soc.,* **63,** 1501 (1967).

Received August 3, 1976

JOURNAL OF APPLIED POLYMER SCIENCE   VOL. 21, 2695–2709 (1977)

Kinetics of Thermal Polymerization of Shellac. V. Turbidimetric and Fractionation Studies

A. KUMAR, *Indian Lac Research Institute, Namkum, Ranchi, Bihar, India*

Synopsis

In the present investigation, the changes in precipitation of the shellac condensates with curing time have been followed turbidimetrically. The experimental data support the saturation limit law. Further, the fractionation of a polymer with low degree of polymerization has been effected by the integral method, and the relation between W_x (the weight fraction of the precipitate) and v (the volume of precipitant added) has been established. In addition, the fractions have been characterized in terms of inherent viscosity. The experimental data, which exhibit alternation behavior, have been confirmed by a number of statistical tests.

INTRODUCTION

A knowledge of molecular weight and size is essential for an understanding of the physical behavior of high polymers.[1] Generally, the polymers consist of molecules with a more or less broad range of sizes.[2] It should be pointed out that the size disparity arises from the random nature of chemical reaction and equal reactivity of the same class.[3] In heterogenous polymers, the molecular size is not sufficiently characterized by an average value.[4] Therefore, it seems indispensible to determine the distribution of molecular weights or sizes about the mean value for correlating with reaction kinetics[5] and also for tailoring polymers so as to have desired physical properties.[6] In fact, there are several methods for the determination of the molecular weight distribution function, but the turbidimetric titration is commonly used for a variety of reasons.[7] On this account, an effort has been made to determine the molecular weight distribution function turbidimetrically.

EXPERIMENTAL

Reagents. Methanol B.D.H. (Laboratory reagent). Potassium chloride—pure (Merck).

Polymerization. Dewaxed, decolorized shellac samples (dried and desiccated, 10 g each) were polymerized at $150° \pm 1°C$ by the usual method.[8] The condensates were powdered, passed through a 40-mesh sieve, and kept in the dark prior to use.

Turbidimetric Titration. For the determination of the precipitation point, 5 ml of 1.0% polymer solution in methanol was introduced in a clean 100-ml glass-stoppered (Pyrex) conical flask suspended in a thermostated bath main-

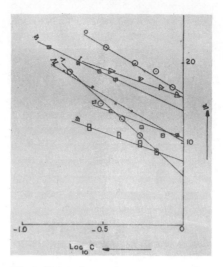

Fig. 1. Dependence of v on concentration.

tained at 35° ± 0.5°C. After the attainment of the bath temperature, the non-solvent (water) was slowly added until a haze appeared. The amount of the nonsolvent required for the onset of precipitation (v) was calculated in terms of percentage. The precipitation points at several concentrations were determined likewise. The results are presented in Figure 1.

Isolation of Fractions. There are many methods for polymer fractionation, viz., fractional precipitation, extraction, elution, thermal diffusion, zone refining, ultrafiltration, selective absorption, Brownian diffusion, chromatography (precipitation and absorption), and turbidimetric titration. Out of all these methods, the turbidimetric titration has been used as an analytical tool.[9] The underlying principle rests on the observation that the less soluble high molecular weight polymers precipitate out first, followed by low molecular weight species.[3] The results are altered by aging or agglomeration or coagulation of the precipitate.[2] The turbidity in all these cases varies without any change in the amount of polymer precipitated. Therefore, an attempt has been made to weigh out the precipitate gravimetrically.

For the study, 5 ml 1% solution of shellac condensate designated as polymer II in methanol was charged into several thin-walled, flat-bottomed specimen tubes and corked. The nonsolvent addition was carried out in a bath thermostated at 35° ± 1°C. To the first aliquot, the amount of nonsolvent added was just sufficient to bring the solution to the verge of precipitation.

It is known that a minimum concentration of electrolyte is required for flocculation of a suspension.[10] Therefore, 0.2 g solid KCl was used to coagulate the stable suspension. After allowing to stand overnight, the material was filtered through a clean glass-sintered Pyrex crucible. The precipitate was repeatedly washed with water till free of KCl, dried under vacuum, and accurately weighed in a weighing bottle. From this amount and the initial concentration of the polymer solution, the weight fraction (W_x) of the precipitate was calculated. To the remaining aliquots, the increased amounts of nonsolvent were added, and the weight fractions of the precipitates were determined likewise. The results are contained in Table I.

TABLE I
Fractionation Data of a Typical Shellac Condensate

Fraction	V, ml	$100/$ $(100+v)$	Weight fraction W_x	$\log W_x$-$(1-W_x)$	Intrinsic viscosity $[\eta]$	Cumulative intrinsic viscosity $\Sigma[\eta]$	$[\eta]/$ W_x	$\log [\eta]/$ W_x
a	10	0.909	0.142	−0.7812	0.08	0.08	0.56	−0.2518
b	12	0.893	0.178	−0.6645	3.10	3.18	17.42	1.2410
c	14	0.877	0.240	−0.5006	2.23	5.41	9.29	0.9680
d	16	0.862	0.284	−0.4016	0.40	5.81	1.41	0.1492
e	18	0.847	0.309	−0.3495	2.46	8.27	7.96	0.9009
f	20	0.833	0.337	−0.2939	1.47	9.74	4.36	0.6395
g	22	0.820	0.363	−0.2442	1.55	11.29	4.27	0.6304
h	24	0.806	0.397	−0.1815	2.44	13.73	6.15	0.7889
i	26	0.794	0.459	−0.0714	0.64	14.37	1.39	0.1430
j	28	0.781	0.461	−0.0679	0.71	15.08	1.54	0.1875
k	30	0.761	0.497	−0.0052	0.74	15.82	1.49	0.1732
l	32	0.758	0.523	−0.0400	0.44	16.26	0.84	−0.0757
m	40	0.714	0.577	0.1349	0.06	16.32	0.10	−0.0000
n	50	0.667	0.669	0.3056	0.90	17.22	1.34	0.1271
o	60	0.625	0.767	0.5174	0.10	17.32	0.13	−0.8861

TABLE II
Values of $f(M)$ and K as Function of Polymerization Time for Shellac Condensates Polymerized at 150°C

Polymer designation	Polymerization, time, min	K	$f(M)$
O	0	12.73	16.2
I	5	7.50	15.8
II	10	7.37	10.7
III	15	7.06	7.8
IV	20	12.00	10.2
V	25	18.00	6.0
VI	30	10.00	14.0

Viscosity Measurements. The intrinsic viscosity of each fraction was determined in methanol at 35° ± 0.5°C. The results are included in Table I.

RESULTS AN DISCUSSIONS

The saturation limit law[11] states that:

$$v = K \log C + f(M)$$

where v is percent nonsolvent added for incipient precipitation of the polymer, C is the concentration at the precipitation point, and $f(M)$ is the function of molecular weight.

According to the above equation, the plot of v vs $\log C$ should be a straight line. Such plots of turbidimetric data are shown in Figure 1. The value of $f(M)$ and K are given in Table II.

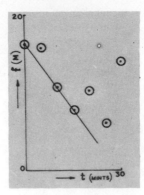

Fig. 2. Dependence of $f(M)$ on time of polymerization.

Dependence of $f(M)$ and K on Polymerization Time in the Pregelation Stage

The dependence of $f(M)$ and K on polymerization time is shown in Figures 2 and 3. Since the intermolecular reaction of the pregelation stage is of zero order,[8] it is expected that $f(M)$, being a function of molecular weight, should vary linearly with time. This is the case up to the gel point (Fig. 2). Figure 3 indicates that the parameter K, which decreases gradually with polymerization time, becomes constant at the gel point.

Dependence of $f(M)$ on Number- and Weight-Average Molecular Weights (M_n and M_w)

According to Brønsted and Schulz, the precipitation point v at constant concentration is linearly related to the reciprocal molecular weight; but Harris and Miller[12] have observed that the plot of v vs $1/M$ is not linear. They have suggested that the plot of log M vs log $f(M)$, which is nearly linear, can be used as the calibration curve for the determination of molecular weight.

More recently,[13] it has been proposed that

$$v = a \log \frac{1}{[\eta]} + b$$

This can be rewritten as

$$v = b - a \log [\eta]$$

Also, $[\eta] = KM^\alpha$ (Mark–Houwink–Sakurada equation). Therefore,

$$\log [\eta] = \log K + \alpha \log M$$

On substitution,

$$v = b - a \log K - a\alpha \log M$$

Let $b - a \log K = A$ and $a\alpha = B$. Then, $v = A - B \log M$. Therefore, the plot of v against log M (at constant concentration) should be a straight line. Again,

$$v = K \log C + f(M)$$

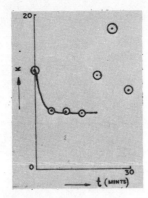

Fig. 3. Dependence of K on time of polymerization.

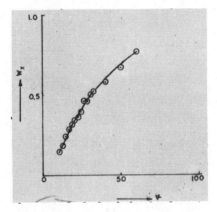

Fig. 4. Dependence of weight fraction W_x on v.

Therefore,

$$K \log C + f(M) = A' - B \log M$$

Since C is constant, we can write that $f(M) = A' - B \log M$.

If these relations hold, a plot of $f(M)$ vs $\log \overline{M}_n$ or $\log \overline{M}_w$ should be a straight line. Secondly, as M would increase, $f(M)$ would decrease. That is to say, the greater the molecular weight, the smaller would be the corresponding $f(M)$ value.

Dependence of W_x on v

The plot of the weight fraction of the polymer precipitated, W_x, against the percentage of precipitant added, v, is shown in Figure 4. A relation between W_x and v is now deduced.

Let C_0 be the initial concentration (in g/100 ml) of the shellac condensate and v be the per cent nonsolvent added for the onset of precipitation; C represents the concentration at the saturation point. Then,

$$C = \frac{100C_0}{100 + v} = \frac{C_0}{1 + v/100}$$

Suppose C_p is the amount of polymer precipitated (in g) and v be increased to $v + dv$. Let C' (in g/100 ml) represent the concentration at the next saturation point. Then,

$$C' = \frac{100(C_0 - C_p)}{100 + v + dv} = \frac{(C_0 - C_p)}{1 + (v + dv)/100}$$

Hence,

$$\frac{C'}{C} = \frac{1 + (v/100)}{1 + (v/100) + (dv/100)} \cdot [1 - (C_p/C_0)]$$

From the saturation limit law,

$$v = K \log C + f(M)$$

or

$$\log C = \frac{v - f(M)}{K}$$

Therefore,

$$C = 10^{[v-f(M)]/K} = 10^{v/K} \times 10^{-f(M)/K}$$

If $dv \ll v$, then the solution at both dilutions v and $v + dv$ would be saturated with respect to species M_i. From the above-derived equation, it follows that

$$C' = 10^{(v+dv)/K} \times 10^{-f(M)/K}$$

Hence,

$$\frac{C'}{C} = 10^{dv/K}$$

On equating the two C'/C terms, one obtains

$$1 - (C_p/C_0) = 10^{dv/K} \times \frac{1 + (v/100) + (dv/100)}{1 + (v/100)}$$

$$= 10^{dv/K} \times \left[1 + \frac{dv}{(100 + v)}\right]$$

or

$$C_p/C_0 = 1 - 10^{dv/K} \times [1 + dv/(100 + v)]$$

$$= 1 - 10^{dv/K} - \frac{dv}{100 + v} \times 10^{dv/K}$$

If dv is experimentally kept constant, then

$$C_p/C_0 = A - \frac{B}{100 + v}$$

The term C_p/C_0 is the weight fraction of the polymer precipitated, i.e., W_x. Therefore,

$$W_x = A - \frac{B}{100 + v}$$

Evidently, a plot of W_x against $1/(100 + v)$ would be a straight line. Such a plot

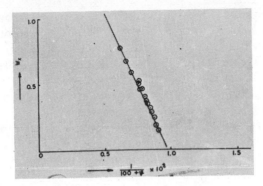

Fig. 5. Relation between W_x on v.

of the fractionation data is shown in Figure 5, which is strictly linear. This supports the above relationship showing the dependence of W_x on v.

Basic Theories of Precipitation

For the precipitation to occur, the solution must be supersaturated with respect to the solute so that the metastable state of supersaturation may revert back to the stable state by the release of excess solute as a precipitate.[14] There are two stages involved in the initial formation of a precipitate: (i) the induction period required for the first nuclei to form, and (ii) the period of crystal growth until a stable state is reached.[14]

The nucleation begins when the concentration of different ions reaches values equal to or higher than those of the solubility product.[15] In the beginning, the nuclei grow rapidly, diminishing supersaturation and solubility, but subsequent growth is slower.[14] The rate of nucleation[16] has been expressed as

$$R = Ae^{-\Delta G/kT}$$

where ΔG is the free energy of activation, k is the Boltzmann constant, T is absolute temperature, and A represents the frequency factor. Very recently, the phenomenon of nucleation has been discussed in terms of heterophase fluctuations[17] called embryos, that is, minute, unstable, temporary aggregations constantly forming and disappearing.

The energy required for embryo growth increases only up to a critical size and then falls off rapidly with increasing particle diameter. The embryos of critical size are called three-dimensional nuclei.[17] As soon as one or more stable nuclei are formed, the crystallization begins. It stops when the potential of the liquid phase equals that of the solid phase.[17]

The theories of crystal growth are now discussed. According to the migration theory,[18] the incoming unit is not immediately incorporated in the growing phase even if it has arrived on the site by diffusion. It sticks only to a place of stronger attachment, viz., edge, corner, surface, hole, etc. On the other hand, according to the spiral growth theory,[18] the surface of most crystals contains dislocations with a screw component, and the spiral growth takes place at such dislocated sites resulting from surface nucleation, high supersaturation, incorporated or absorbed impurity, mechanical stress, fluctuations in temperature, etc.

The crystals can also develop by heterogeneous nucleation at the surface of the suspended insoluble impurity or on the walls of the container or at the surface of a liquid or at a liquid–liquid boundary.[17] It should be pointed out that the ratio of crystal growth to nucleation rate is a measure of crystal size.[16] The larger the ratio, the coarser the product. Secondly, the rate of crystal growth at lower concentration is diffusion controlled, and the resulting crystals are reasonably perfect.[14] This is one of the reasons why a polymer solution of less than 1% concentration is chosen for the fractionation study.

In the light of the above discussion, it can be inferred that on the gradual addition of a nonsolvent to the shellac condensate solution, a metastable state is created which, by way of nucleation and crystal growth, gives the cloudy precipitate.

Distribution of Molecular Species

The molecular weight of a precipitate depends on the nonsolvent/solvent ratio.[19] The distribution of molecules[20] between the dilute solution phase and the precipitate phase is dependent on the chain length (i.e., molecular weight). According to Spencer,[21] the polymers with molecular weights above M_{solid} remain in the precipitate phase, and polymers with molecular weights below $M_{solution}$ pervade the solution phase. Brønsted and Schulz[22] have proposed the following formula for the distribution of molecular species into two phases:

$$v'_x/v_x = e^{\sigma x}$$

where v'_x and v_x are the volume fractions of polymer of the degree x of polymerization in the precipitate and dilute solution phase, respectively, and σ is a complex function of the Flory–Huggins interaction constant, the molecular weight distribution, and the concentration. Schulz[23] has also suggested another formula based on the relative potential energy of a chain molecule in the solution and the precipitate phase. That is,

$$C''_i/C'_i = \exp \frac{rE}{RT}$$

where rE represents the gain of energy on transferring a polymer molecule of chain length r from one phase to the other. The conditions of phase separation[24] have been also predicted in terms of thermodynamic activity.

The plot of log $(W_x/1 - W_x)$ against $[\eta]$, which is a function of chain length r, is shown in Figure 6. Except for a few scatters, the points fall upon two straight lines in support to the Schulz's theory and the theory of alternation as discussed later.

Characterization of Fractions

A number of methods for determining molecular weight can be employed for the characterization of the functions. Generally, the density, index of refraction, and inherent viscosity are used for this purpose.

The density of a polymer is an index of the region of primary valence in the lattices[25] and does not vary significantly with $\overline{M}_n$. But this method has limited scope. The plots of n_D vs $(\overline{M}_n)^{-1}$ are undoubtedly straight lines,[26] but the changes in n_D with M_n are very small. However, on account of the direct dependence on M and ease of determination, the inherent viscosity is commonly

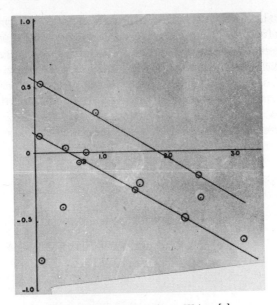

Fig. 6. Plot of log $W_x/(1 - W_x)$ vs $[\eta]$.

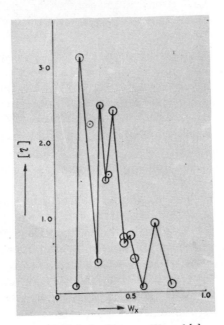

Fig. 7. Relation between W_x and $[\eta]$.

used for the characterization of the polymers. In the present case, the fractions have been characterized by inherent viscosity. The plot of W_x vs $[\eta]$ is shown in Figure 7. The graph contains multiple peaks and thus represents a multimodal distribution.

Molecular Weight and Distribution Function

For the determination of molecular weight distribution function, the polymer is dissolved in a suitable solvent at sufficiently dilute concentration and fractionated either by the repetitive addition of nonsolvent or by lowering the temperature of the solution. Then, the cumulative weights of the fractions are plotted against their molecular weights so as to define the integral weight distribution function. In actual practice, one half of the weight percent of the fraction plus the sum of the weight percentages of the preceding fraction is plotted versus the molecular weight of the ith fraction. The differential weight distribution are obtained by graphic differential of the integral curve. The procedure assumes that each fraction has a symmetric molecular weight distribution, and the overlapping of fractions does not take place to any appreciable extent.

Tung[27] has proposed the following equation for correlating the integral molecular-weight distribution:

$$I(M) = I - \exp(-aM^b)$$

where a and b are two adjustable parameters. The corresponding differential distribution is

$$W(M) = abM^{b-1} \exp(-aM^b)$$

Wassleu has proposed the following distribution function:

$$I(M) = \frac{1}{B\sqrt{\pi}} \int_{-\alpha}^{\ln M} \exp\left[-1/B^2 \cdot \ln^2 \frac{M}{M_0}\right] d\log M$$

where B and M_0 are two adjustable parameters. The corresponding differential distribution function is

$$W(M) = \frac{1}{B\sqrt{\pi}} \cdot \frac{1}{M} \exp\left[-1/B^2 \cdot \ln^2 \frac{M}{M_0}\right]$$

Recently, a method[28] of directly determining the differential distribution has been developed. The method entails the construction of a triangle of $dw/d(\log M)$ vs $\log M$ with three parameters representing three characteristic molecular weights.

In the integral method, the fractions are collected by the addition of the increased amounts of nonsolvent to a given volume of the polymer solution. The technique has been developed by Billmeyer and Stockmeyer[29] and others. From the weight-average molecular weight and mass of the fraction, the distribution width is calculated in terms of a parameter H which, in turn, is related to another parameter of the distribution width such as $\overline{M}_w/\overline{M}_n$. It should be added that the distribution curves at small conversion permit the determination of the true forms of the distribution functions.[30]

Statistical Analysis of Fractionation Data

An inspection of Figure 7 shows that it is difficult to offer an explanation for such a disposition of data. However, an attempt has been made to confirm the experimental data by a number of statistical tests. There are several statistical methods[31] for displaying the distribution data diagrammatically (i.e., the construction of histogram or polygon). The most common and convenient method is the cumulative frequency diagram. In this method, a number of intervals, usually of equal lengths, are marked on a horizontal axis. The midpoint of each

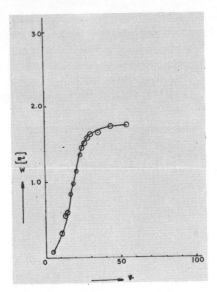

Fig. 8. Cumulative inherent viscosity polygon.

interval is labeled with the value of the variate to which it corresponds. Then, an ordinate measuring the "accumulated" frequency (up to and including that value of the variate) is erected at the midpoint of each such interval and the upper endpoints of the neighboring ordinates are joined. The resulting figure represents the cumulative frequency polygon.

The cumulative inherent viscosity polygon is shown in Figure 8. The S-shaped graph justifies the viscosity data. Apart from this, a simple mathematical tool has been designed to test the validity of the fractionation data.

The weight-average intrinsic viscosity of the aliquots, obtained on admixing two, three, four, etc., fractions together, can be given by the equation of the type

$$[\eta]_w = \frac{\Sigma W_x [\eta]}{W_x}$$

The value of $[\eta]_w$ together with the number of fractions admixed (n_f) are contained in Table III. The plot of $[\eta]_w$ against n_f is shown in Figure 9. The linearity of the plot provides additional evidence in favor of the generated fractionation data.

The Variation of $[\eta]$ with W_x

The physicochemical properties of the fatty acids, when plotted against their carbon number, exhibit alternation.[32] Moreover, it has been found that the experimental points fall on two smooth curves corresponding to even and odd number of carbon atoms. The situation bears a close analogy to the present case.

As can be seen, the upper and lower points in Figure 10 tend to fall on two different curves. Therefore, the incorporation of even and odd numbers of carbon atoms into these fractions may be responsible for the alternation of in-

TABLE III
Weight-Average Inherent Viscosities $[\eta]_w$ and Fraction
Numbers n_f of the Hypothetical Admixtures in Question

n_f	$[\eta]_w$
1	0.8
2	1.78
3	1.96
4	1.43
5	1.71
6	1.66
7	1.63
8	1.78
9	1.58
10	1.46
11	1.36
12	1.24
13	1.17
14	1.13
15	1.01

herent viscosity. Further, it has been found that

$$\log \frac{[\eta]}{W_x} = a + b[\eta]$$

A plot of log ($[\eta]/W_x$) vs $[\eta]$ is shown in Figure 11. All points (except a few) fall on two straight lines. This provides an additional proof in favor of the data and treatment of the subject matter.

CONCLUSIONS

The following conclusions can be drawn from the foregoing paragraphs.

The solubility is depressed on the addition of a nonsolvent, and upon the attainment of supersaturation, the precipitation occurs.

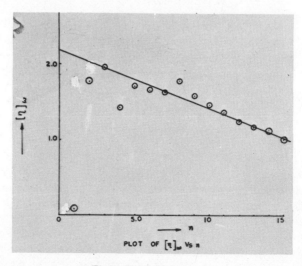

Fig. 9. Plot of $[\eta]_w$ vs n_f.

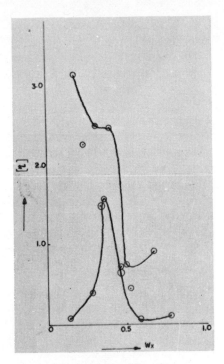

Fig. 10. Plot of $[\eta]$ vs W_x.

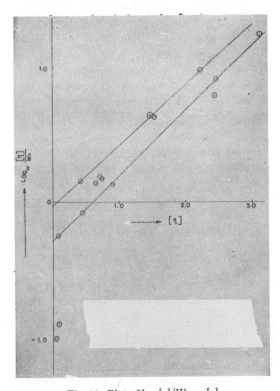

Fig. 11. Plot of log $[\eta]/W_x$ vs $[\eta]$.

The volume of the nonsolvent required for the incipient precipitation depends on the concentration of the polymer solution.

The weight fraction of the precipitate depends on the volume of the nonsolvent added.

The inherent viscosities of the fractions exhibit a natural mode of distribution.

The manifestation of alternation in the present instance proves the presence of even and odd numbers of carbon atoms in the isolated fractions.

It is suggested that the integral method of fractionation allows the tailoring of the polymer molecules in accordance with the chain length suitable for enduse. On the other hand, the differential method of fractionation facilitates identification of macromolecular species of different chain lengths present in the polymerization product.

The author wishes to thank Professor S. R. Palit, D.Sc., F.R.I.C., F.N.A., for valuable suggestions and to Dr. J. N. Chatterjea, D.Sc., D.Phil., F.R.As.C., F.R.I.C., F.N.A., for kind permission to publish this paper.

References

1. D. J. Harmon, *J. Polym. Sci. C*, **8**, 243 (1965).
2. J. H. Badley, *J. Polym. Sci. C*, **8**, 305 (1965).
3. G. M. Guzman, *Progress in High Polymers*, Vol. I, Heywood and Company, London, 1961, pp. 115–183.
4. H. Campbell and P. Johnson, *Trans. Faraday Soc.*, **XL** (6), 221 (1944).
5. A. S. Kenyon, I. O. Salyer, J. E. Kurz, and D. R. Brown, *J. Polym. Sci. C*, **8**, 205 (1965).
6. F. W. Billmeyer, Jr., *J. Polym. Sci. C*, **8**, 161 (1965).
7. R. W. Hall, *Techniques of Polymer Characterization*, Butterworth, London, 1959, pp. 53–58.
8. A. Kumar, *J. Appl. Polym. Sci.*, **8**, 1186 (1964).
9. N. S. Schneider, *J. Polym. Sci. C*, **8**, 179 (1965).
10. S. Ghosh, Presidential Address, Section of Physical Sciences, The National Academy of Sciences, India, Twenty-eighth Annual Session, Agra, Feb. 6–8, 1959.
11. D. R. Morey and J. W. Tamblyn, *J. Appl. Phys.*, **16**, 419 (1945).
12. I. Harris and R. G. J. Miller, *J. Polym. Sci.*, **7**, 377 (1951).
13. S. Tanaka, A. Nakamura, and H. Morikawa, *Makromol. Chem.*, **85**, 164 (1965).
14. E. W. Berg, *Physical and Chemical Methods of Separation*, McGraw-Hill, New York, 1963, pp. 250–295.
15. J. A. Palermo and G. F. Bennett, *Ind. Eng. Chem.*, **57**, 58 (1965).
16. D. B. Wilson, *Chem. Eng.*, 119 (1965).
17. R. S. Tipson, *Technique of Organic Chemistry*, Vol. III, Part I, Interscience, New York, 1956, Chap. III, pp. 395–414.
18. R. S. Tipson, *Anal. Chem.*, **37**, 26A (1965).
19. H. Campbell and P. Johnson, *Trans. Faraday Soc.*, **XL**, 223 (1944).
20. R. L. Scott, *Ind. Eng. Chem.*, **45**, 2532 (1953).
21. R. S. Spenser, *J. Polym. Sci.*, **3**, 606 (1948).
22. R. W. Hall, *Techniques of Polymer Characterization*, Butterworth, London, 1959, p. 20.
23. H. Tompa, *Polymer Solutions*, Butterworth, London, 1956, pp. 219–232.
24. C. M. Conrad, *Ind. Eng. Chem.*, **45**, 2511 (1953).
25. H. Mark, *Physical Chemistry of High Polymeric Systems*, Interscience, New York, 1940, p. 131.
26. J. D. Ingham and D. D. Lawson, *J. Polym. Sci.*, **A3**, 2707 (1965).
27. L. H. Tung, *High Polymers*, Vol. XX, Wiley-Interscience, New York, 1965, pp. 513–575.
28. F. Rodriguez and O. K. Clark, *Ind. Eng. Chem.*, **57**, 13 (Nov. 1965).
29. F. W. Billmeyer, Jr. and W. H. Stockmayer, *J. Polym. Sci.*, **V**, 121 (1950).

30. E. F. G. Herington, *Trans. Faraday Soc.*, **XL**, 237 (1944).

31. R. Goodman, *Teach Yourself Statistics*, The English Language Book Society and the English University Press, London, 1965, pp. 21–26.

32. A. W. Ralston, *Fatty Acids and Their Derivatives*, Wiley, New York, 1948, pp. 322–395.

Received September 19, 1975
Revised August 27, 1976

The Kinetics of Polyesterification. I. Adipic Acid and Ethylene Glycol

CHEN CHONG LIN and KUO HUANG HSIEH, *Department of Chemical Engineering, National Taiwan University, Taipei, Taiwan, China*

Synopsis

The polyesterification between adipic acid and ethylene glycol in nonequimolar ratios was investigated. The kinetic equations obtained were quite different from those obtained by Flory in equimolar systems. The kinetic equations obtained in this study were $-d[COOH]/dt = k[COOH][OH]^2$ for uncatalyzed polyesterification and $-d[COOH]/dt = k[COOH]^2$ for catalyzed polyesterification. The mechanism of the polyesterification of a dibasic acid and a glycol can only be explained by the dissociation effect of hydrogen ion from dibasic acid in glycol.

INTRODUCTION

Many experimental studies on the polyesterification between dibasic acids and glycols have been reported by various authors. Recent textbooks[1,2] dealing with polymer chemistry treat polyesterification as a simple third-order, irreversible reaction as originally proposed by Flory.[3] As Goldschmidt[4] has shown, the esterification reactions are generally hydrogen ion catalyzed. Therefore, the following rate equation is considered for polyesterification:

$$-d[COOH]/dt = k[COOH][OH][H^+] \qquad (1)$$

According to Flory, polyesterification in the absence of a foreign acid, owing to the catalytic effect of the dibasic acid molecule, is a third-order reaction. The rate of the polyesterification reaction should be written as

$$-d[COOH]/dt = k[COOH]^2[OH] \qquad (2)$$

On the other hand, in the presence of foreign acid, the hydrogen ion derives mainly from the added acid. The polyesterification is thus a second-order reaction:

$$-d[COOH]/dt = k[COOH][OH][H^+]$$
$$= k'[COOH][OH] \qquad (3)$$

where the rate constant k' includes the catalyst concentration. During the past 20 years, several investigators have published data which appear to show that Flory's assumption is invalid.

Tang and Yao[5] have examined nonequimolar ratio systems and proposed a new kinetic equation. Campbell et al.[6] have shown that the rate of esterification can be affected by film thickness and water content of the atmosphere. Thus, the view by earlier workers that the polyesterification corresponds to a continuous increase in kinetic order, becoming approximately third order at the later stage of reaction in the absence of catalyst or that it is a simple second order in the presence of catalyst or that the order of reaction is more complicated in the nonequimolar ratio, are all refuted, and the long-disputed question of the order of the polyesterification is clarified in this work.

EXPERIMENTAL

Materials. Adipic acid of reagent grade was recrystallized from conductivity water; mp 151.5°C. Ethylene glycol was obtained by distillation of a chemical grade. As catalyst, p-toluenesulfonic acid of reagent grade was used with no further purification.

Apparatus. The apparatus consisted of a Pyrex bulb of about 100-cc capacity sealed to the bottom of a 2.5-cm-diameter tube about 20-cm long. Through a stopper at the top of this tube, a pipet was inserted. The pipet was used to remove samples, and also for admitting a slow stream of nitrogen through the reaction mixture in order to facilitate removal of water formed. The effluent stream of nitrogen and water vapor passed through a long reflux condenser, by which the loss of glycol was minimized. The stream was then led downward from a side tube at the top of condenser, where the temperature was kept at about 110°C, to a cooling graduated bottle to collect water.

Procedure. The mixture of glycol, to which the p-toluenesulfonic acid was added in the case of acid-catalyzed reaction, and adipic acid in nonequimolar ratio was placed in the reaction bulb. The reactants should be preheated before they are placed together in the reaction bulb. Nitrogen was bubbled through the mixture, which was quickly raised to reaction temperature. The reaction mixture can be withdrawn, weighed, dissolved with mixed solvent (benzene, isopropanol, and methanol in equivolume), and titrated with methanolic KOH, using phenolphthalein as indicator. A sharp endpoint was always observed. If the concentration change due to the removal of water is taken into consideration, the acid concentration may be calculated according to the following equation:

$$C = \frac{C_e(W_0 - 18) \times 1000}{W_0(1000 - 18C_e)} \tag{4}$$

where C is the actual acid concentration, in equivalent moles per kg sample, including water produced; C_e is the apparent acid concentration, in equivalent moles per kg sample; and W_0 is the total mass of reaction mixture based on one equivalent mole of adipic acid. The degree of polymerization can be calculated by the following equation.

$$\text{D.P.} = \frac{1 + r}{1 + r - 2P} \tag{5}$$

where r represents the initial molar ratio between [OH] and [COOH] and is always set to be more than unity in this investigation.

THEORETICAL CONSIDERATIONS

It has been suggested in the past that the esterification reactions are hydrogen ion catalyzed. The rate of polyesterification as expressed in eq. (2) for an uncatalyzed reaction in nonequimolar ratio can be written as

$$-dC/dt = kC^2(C + a) \tag{6}$$

where $C = [COOH]$, $C + a = [OH]$, and $a = (r - 1)C_0$. Upon integration, we obtain

$$\frac{a}{C} - \ln \frac{C+a}{C} = a^2kt + k_a = k_1t + k_a \tag{7}$$

where $k_a = (a/C_0) - \ln r$ and $k_1 = a^2k$. In terms of $P = (C_0 - C)/C_0$ and $a = (r - 1)C_0$, eq. (7) becomes

$$\frac{r-1}{1-P} - \ln \frac{r-P}{1-P} = k_1t + k_a \tag{8}$$

For an equimolar reaction, i.e., $a = 0$, eq. (6) is simplified to

$$-dC/dt = kC^3 \tag{9}$$

Upon integration, it becomes

$$2kt = \frac{1}{C^2} - \frac{1}{C_0^2} \tag{10}$$

and

$$2C_0^2kt = \frac{1}{(1 - P)^2} - 1 \tag{11}$$

This is the equation obtained by Flory.[3] If the polyesterification proceeds by another type of kinetics as shown in the following equation:

$$-d[COOH]/dt = k[COOH][OH]^2 \tag{12}$$

then, analogous to eq. (6), the net rate of reaction would be

$$-dC/dt = kC(C + a)^2 \tag{13}$$

Upon integration, it yields

$$\ln \frac{r-P}{1-P} - \frac{r-1}{r-P} = a^2kt + k_b = k_1t + k_b \tag{14}$$

where $k_b = \ln r - (r - 1)/r$ and $k_1 = a^2k$. A plot of $\ln [(r - P)/(1 - P)] - [(r - 1)/(r - P)]$ vs t should be linear.

In the case of acid-catalyzed polyesterification, the rate of reaction according to Flory's concept of eq. (3) will be

$$-dC/dt = k'C(C + a) \tag{15}$$

Such a rate is given by

$$\ln \frac{r-P}{1-P} = ak't - \ln \frac{1}{r} = k_2t + k_c \tag{16}$$

where $k_c = -\ln(1/r)$ and $k_2 = ak'$. If this acid-catalyzed reaction proceeded by the following kinetic type instead of eq. (3),

$$-d[COOH]/dt = k''[COOH]^2 \tag{17}$$

then it is a second-order reaction with respect to [COOH]. This equation integrates to

$$\frac{1}{C} - \frac{1}{C_0} = k''t \tag{18}$$

When $C = C_0(1 - P)$ is substituted, eq. (18) becomes

$$C_0 k'' t = \frac{1}{1 - P} - 1 \tag{19}$$

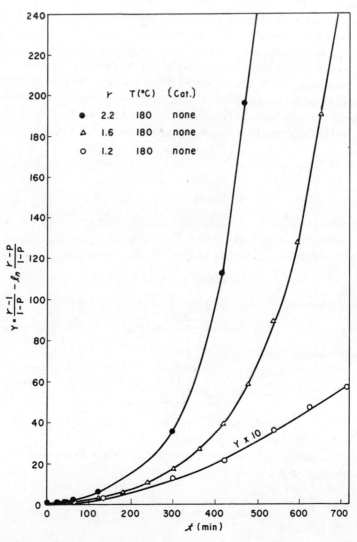

Fig. 1. Uncatalyzed polyesterification of nonequimolar quantities of adipic acid and ethylene glycol. Plots of $(r - 1)/(1 - P) - \ln[(r - P)/(1 - P)]$ vs reaction time all give no straight lines.

Flory's kinetics of eq. (3) can coincide fortuitously with the result of eq. (19) only for the system of equimolar reactants.

RESULTS AND DISCUSSION

The typical experimental data of the polyesterification between nonequimolar quantities of adipic acid and ethylene glycol of $r = 1.6$ in the absence of foreign acid at a constant temperature of 180°C are listed in Table I. For brevity, the analytical data of subsequent experiments under various r values are not tabulated.

All the results plotted as indicated by eq. (8) are shown in Figure 1. On the other hand, the results plotted as indicated by eq. (14) are shown in Figure 2. At first glance, the data seem fairly well represented by eq. (14) rather than eq. (8) over the range of $P = 0$ up to $P = 0.99$. Evidently, these are third-order kinetics not according to eq. (2), but eq. (12). The correspondence between theory and data in Flory's experiments[3] can be regarded as fortuity of an equimolar reaction, to which eq. (9) is applicable for both kinetic types of eqs. (2) and (12).

The apparent agreement between theory and experiment of Flory has resulted in a misconception. It is interesting to point out that the polyesterification for a larger molar ratio (for instance, $r = 4$) indicates a linear relationship when it is plotted only on the basis of the proposed mechanism as indicated by eq. (17). This means that the reaction is now second order with respect to [COOH]. We

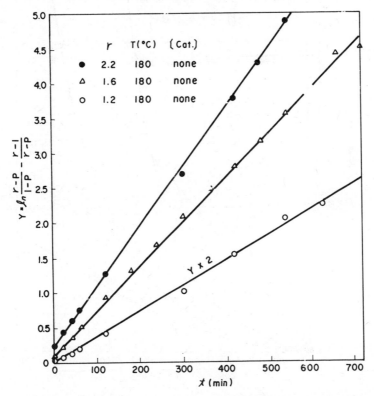

Fig. 2. Uncatalyzed polyesterification of nonequimolar quantities of adipic acid and ethylene glycol. Plots of ln $[(r - P)/(1 - P)] - (r - 1)/(r - P)]$ vs reaction time all give straight lines.

TABLE I
Adipic Acid—Ethylene Glycol[a]

t, min	C, equiv. moles kg sample	P	D.P.	$\dfrac{r-1}{1-P} - \ln\left(\dfrac{r-P}{1-P}\right)$	$\ln\left(\dfrac{r-P}{1-P}\right) - \dfrac{r-1}{r-P}$
0	8.149	0.000	1.000	0.130	0.095
20	4.490	0.449	1.528	0.352	0.216
40	2.865	0.648	1.994	0.710	0.365
60	2.059	0.747	2.351	1.158	0.512
120	1.108	0.875	3.059	3.045	0.930
180	0.603	0.926	3.476	5.899	1.319
240	0.374	0.954	3.757	10.428	1.715
300	0.244	0.970	3.939	16.991	2.094
365	0.165	0.980	4.063	26.208	2.455
420	0.116	0.986	4.140	38.382	2.788
480	0.078	0.990	4.194	58.525	3.170
540	0.0526	0.994	4.248	88.404	3.554
600	0.0369	0.995	4.262	127.600	3.901
660	0.0250	0.997	4.290	190.279	4.286
720	0.0180	0.998	4.305	266.003	4.512
780	0.00852	0.999	4.319	833.680	5.356

[a] $r = 1.6$, $T = 180°C$, [Cat.] = none.

believe that hydrogen ion has resulted from the dissociation of acid in combination with the solvent. Ethylene glycol will act as the solvent in this case. Since adipic acid dissociates in ethylene glycol very incompletely only in the magnitude of 0.390 mole/mole ethylene glycol even at 180°C, the concentration of hydrogen ion does not depend on the concentration of adipic acid added, but on the concentration of ethylene glycol presented in the system. Thus,

$$[H^+] = k_h[OH] \tag{20}$$

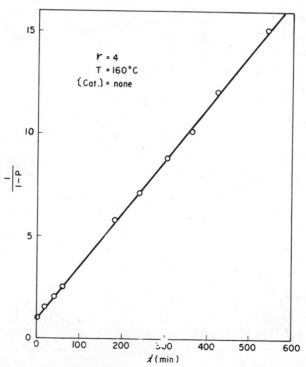

Fig. 3. Uncatalyzed polyesterification of adipic acid and ethylene glycol in large excess of ethylene glycol. Plot of $1/(1 - P)$ vs reaction time gives a straight line.

TABLE II
Adipic Acid—Ethylene Glycol[a]

t, min	C, equiv. moles kg sample	P	D.P.	$\ln\left(\dfrac{r-P}{1-P}\right)$	$\dfrac{1}{1-P}$
0	8.133	0.0000	1.000	0.4700	1.0000
20	1.0478	0.8712	3.032	1.7331	7.7620
40	0.3994	0.9509	3.724	2.5817	20.3630
90	0.2126	0.9739	3.987	3.1776	38.2549
150	0.1232	0.9849	4.126	3.7071	66.0146
180	0.0941	0.9884	4.172	3.9651	86.4293
240	0.0787	0.9903	4.198	4.1408	103.3418
300	0.0624	0.9923	4.225	4.3685	130.3365
360	0.0547	0.9933	4.239	4.5059	148.6837
420	0.0461	0.9943	4.253	4.6659	176.4208
480	0.0393	0.9952	4.265	4.8363	206.9466

[a] $r = 1.6$, $T = 151°C$, [Cat.] = 0.0105 equiv./kg.

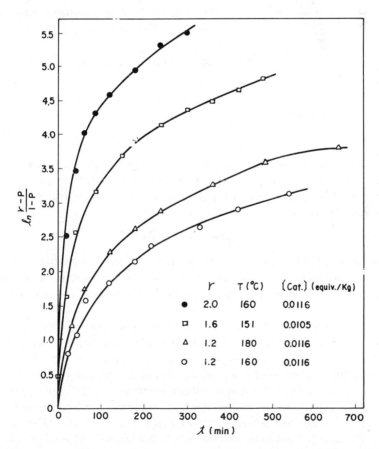

Fig. 4. Catalyzed polyesterification of adipic acid and ethylene glycol. Plots of $\ln[(r-P)/(1-P)]$ vs reaction time all give no straight lines.

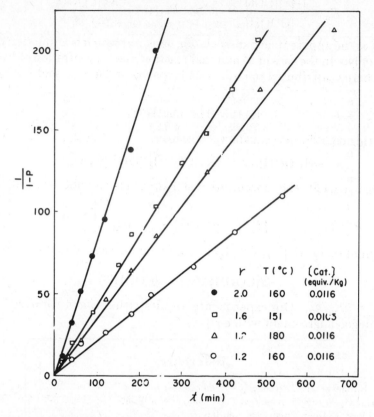

Fig. 5. Catalyzed polyesterification of adipic acid and ethylene glycol. Plots of $1/(1 - P)$ vs reaction time all give straight lines.

Substituting eq. (20) into eq. (1), we can obtain eq. (12). In the case of excess of ethylene glycol (generally, $r > 4$), the concentration of hydrogen ion is not saturated and the concentration of hydrogen ion depends on the concentration of acid itself; therefore,

$$[H^+] = k_h'[COOH] \tag{21}$$

Substituting eq. (21) into eq. (1) and neglecting the concentration change of glycol, we can obtain eq. (17). Figure 3 shows the typical data for an uncatalyzed system in the case of excess in ethylene glycol, which is plotted as indicated by eq. (19).

Several experiments on the reaction of adipic acid with ethylene glycol catalyzed by a small amount of p-toluenesulfonic acid (about 0.012 mole per kg mass) were carried out. The typical experimental data of the polyesterification between nonequimolar quantities of adipic acid and ethylene glycol of $r = 1.6$ in the presence of foreign acid at a constant temperature of 151°C are listed in Table II. Figures 4 and 5 show the results plotted as indicated by eq. (16) and eq. (19), respectively. All the results fail to give straight lines with eq. (16) and clearly demonstrate that the reactions do not follow the kinetic type of eq. (3) as proposed by Flory but of eq. (17) proposed by us. The equilibrium expression for the dissociation of an acid in ethylene glycol may be written

$$K_a = \frac{[H^+][COO^-]}{[COOH]} \quad \text{or} \quad [H^+] = \frac{K_a[COOH]}{[COO^-]} \tag{22}$$

where K_a is the apparent acid dissociation constant which is a function of temperature only. In the case of a catalyzed reaction, the concentration of hydrogen ion $[H^+]$ here is attributed to both added catalyst and adipic acid. This leads to

$$[H^+] = [H_h^+] + [H_a^+]$$

Substituting eq. (22) into eq. (1), we obtain

$$-d[COOH]/dt = kK_a[COOH]^2[OH]/[COO^-] \tag{23}$$

According to eq. (20), the concentration of hydrogen ion attributed to adipic acid, $[H_a^+]$, is

$$[H_a^+] = [COO^-] = k_h[OH]$$

The elimination of $[OH]$, $[COO^-]$ and $[H_a^+]$ among these equations leads to

$$-d[COOH]/dt = k''[COOH]^2$$

where $k'' = kK_a/k_h$. Our experimental results with the acid-catalyzed system are also in good agreement with eq. (17).

References

1. F. W. Billmeyer, Jr., *Textbook of Polymer Science,* Wiley, New York, 1962, Chap. 8.
2. C. Tanford, *Physical Chemistry of Macromolecules,* Wiley, New York, 1961, pp. 588–596.
3. P. J. Flory, *J. Amer. Chem. Soc.,* **59,** 466 (1937).
4. H. Goldschmidt et al., *Z. Phys. Chem.,* **60,** 728 (1907); *ibid.,* **70,** 627 (1910); *ibid.,* **81,** 30 (1913).
5. A. C. Tang and K. S. Yao, *J. Polym. Sci.,* **35,** 219 (1959).
6. G. A. Campbell, E. F. Elton, and E. G. Bobalek, *J. Appl. Polym. Sci.,* **14,** 1025 (1970).

Received August 10, 1976

JOURNAL OF APPLIED POLYMER SCIENCE   VOL. 21, 2721–2733 (1977)

Secondary Electron Emission from Polymers and its Application to the Flexible Channel Electron Multiplier

YOSHIO KISHIMOTO, *Central Research Laboratory, Matsushita Electric Industrial Co., Ltd., Osaka 570, Japan*, and

TOMONAO HAYASHI, MASASHI HASHIMOTO, and TSUTOMU OHSHIMA, *Institute of Space and Aeronautical Science, University of Tokyo, Tokyo 153, Japan*

Synopsis

The basic characteristics of secondary electron emission (SEE) from various organic compounds have been investigated, and a channel electron multiplier with high gain and flexibility has been developed. The maximum SEE yield is higher for the aliphatic compound than for the aromatic, and is higher for the organic solid with high ionization potential. By studying the SEE yields from the electron-conductive polymeric compositions which consist of plasticized poly(vinyl chloride) and electroconductive particles (NaTCNQ or carbon black), it is shown that the SEE yield depends mainly on the characteristics of the matrix polymer and is almost independent of the addition of electroconductive particles which inherently have low SEE yields. Adding less than 5% stabilizers to these polymeric compositions has little effect on the SEE yields. A flexible channel electron multiplier (FCEM) made of the electron-conductive polymeric composition shows the following characteristics: gain $\simeq 10^8$ (applied voltage of 3 kV); rise time $\simeq$ a few nanoseconds; background count rate < 0.1 cps; and maximum output current $\simeq 10^{-6}$ A. As a photon detector in the vacuum UV region, the FCEM shows a threshold value of 8.4 eV for photoelectric emission.

INTRODUCTION

The study of secondary electron emission (SEE) from organic compounds was first carried out by Matskevich et al.,[1] and the general characteristics were reported by Martsinovskaya.[2] A detailed report on SEE from some aromatic hydrocarbons by Bubnov et al.[3] showed that the SEE yield from anthracene depends on both the crystal state and the angle of incident primary electrons. Willis et al.[4] studied the relation between the normalized SEE characteristics of some polymers and their densities. Detailed studies and theories on SEE from organic compounds have not yet been reported. The authors have tried to review and analyze the trend of the maximum SEE yields from various organic compounds on the basis of these reported data. This paper describes the SEE characteristics not only for pure polymers, but also for electron-conductive polymeric compositions comprising polymer, conductive particles, and stabilizer.

As an application of the SEE effect of electron-conductive polymeric com-

2721

TABLE I
Maximum SEE Yields of Various Organic Compounds
I. Molecular Crystal

Abbreviation	Material	Chemical structure	δ_{max}	$E_{p\ max}$, eV	Ref[a]
BE	Benzene		1.66	200	2
NA	Naphthalene		1.52	300	2
AN	Anthracene		1.38	400	2
				200	3
PH	Phenanthrene		1.55	300	2
DI	Diphenyl		1.7	400	2
TE	Tetracene		1.46	200	3
PY	Pyrene		1.50	250	3
LT	LiTCNQ		1.33	200	EX
NT	NaTCNQ		1.6	200	EX
KT	KTCNQ		1.6	200	EX
C	Graphite		1.0	300	1
IC	Ice	H—O—H	2.3	300	2

II. Polymers

PI	Polyimide		2.1	150	4
			1.5	180	EX
XY	Xylene resin		1.8	200	EX
PS	Polystyrene		3.0	250	4
			2.1	250	1
PE	Polyethylene		2.85	250	1
PVC	Poly(vinyl chloride)		2.2	250	EX

continued

TABLE I

Abbreviation	Material	Chemical structure	δ_{max}	$E_{p\ max}$, eV	Ref[a]
PTFE	Poly(tetrafluoroethylene)	$-\!\!+\!CF_2\!-\!CF_2\!\!+\!\!-$	3.0	300	4
PET	Poly(ethylene terephthalate)	$-\!\!\big(OC\!-\!\bigcirc\!\!-\!COOCH_2CH_2O\big)_n$	4.8 3.2	175 250	4
TSi	Tetraphenyl-tetramethyl-trisiloxane		2.0	200	7
PDSi	Poly(dimethylsiloxane)		2.35	200	EX

[a] EX = Experimental data by authors.

positions, a flexible channel electron multiplier (FCEM) has been fabricated.[5,6]

In general, there are two types of channel electron multipliers (CEM); one is a thin film-type CEM made of lead glass and the other, a bulk-type CEM made of ceramics such as $BaTiO_3$ and $ZnTiO_3$. This FCEM is a bulk-type CEM made of polymeric composition and can be easily fabricated by an extrusion-molding method because of the excellent molding qualities of the electron-conductive polymeric composition. As compared with the fragile CEM made of glass or ceramics, the FCEM resists mechanical shock and vibration and can be set in any curvature in order to avoid "ionic feedback." In this paper, the performance and advantages of FCEM are also described.

SECONDARY ELECTRON EMISSION YIELD

Experimental

The SEE yields from polymers were measured not only for pure polymers, but also for electron-conductive polymeric compositions applicable to the materials for FCEM. The SEE yields from organic semiconductors which could be used as conductive particles in the polymer matrix were also measured.

In preparing the test samples, crystal powders of organic semiconductors (LT, NT, and KT shown in Table I) were molded into tablets 1.5 mm thick and 1 cm in diameter under high pressure, and polymers with high resistivity (PI, XY, PVC, and PDSi shown in Table I) were made into films a few microns thick on aluminum plates.

As raw materials for test samples of electron-conductive polymeric compositions applicable to FCEM, the following compounds were selected. As matrix polymer, poly(vinyl chloride) (PVC) was selected because of its high SEE capability and excellent blending and molding qualities. As polymeric plasticizer, polyurethane (PU) was employed because of its low vapor pressure and effectiveness on flexibility. As stable electroconductive particles for importing

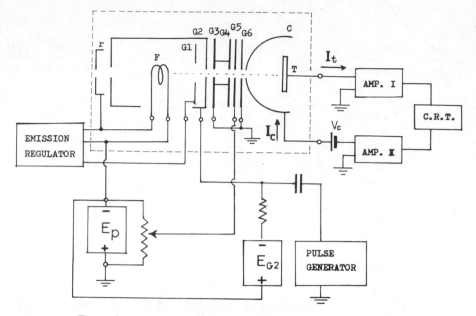

Fig. 1. Apparatus for measuring secondary electron emission yield.

electronic conductivity to the polymer, sodium 7,7,8,8-tetracyanoquinodi-methane (NaTCNQ) or carbon black was used. The former is an organic semiconductor which has a volume resistivity of 10^5 ohm·cm and molecular dispersibility in the polymer matrix; and the latter has a resistivity of 0.2 ohm·cm and granular dispersibility. PVC, PU, electroconductive particles (NaTCNQ or carbon black), and stabilizers (tribasic lead sulfate and barium cadmium coprecipitation salts of lauryl acid) are blended by heated rollers and then formed into a sheet 1.5 mm thick. Each sample is cut into a disk 1 cm in diameter and is mounted on a target.

The SEE yield is measured by the dc method for the organic semiconductors, and by the pulse beam method for the polymers and their compositions in order to avoid charge buildup on the sample surface. The block diagram of the pulse beam method is shown in Figure 1. The electron beam from the cathode F is accelerated to E_p eV by an electron lens system (G_1–G_6) and bombards the target T. The electron beam current used was less than 10^{-9} A, and its pulse width was 1 msec. The secondary electrons emitted from the sample are collected at the collector C and are measured; measurement was carried out under pressure less than 10^{-8} torr.

The SEE yield δ is defined by the following equation:

$$\delta = I_c/(I_c - I_t) \tag{1}$$

where I_c and I_t are the collector current and the target current, respectively.

Results and Discussion

The maximum SEE yields δ_{max} and the corresponding primary electron energy $E_{p\,max}$ of some organic compounds are shown in Table I. Most of the $E_{p\,max}$ values

TABLE II
Maximum SEE Yields and Ionization Potentials of Various Organic Solids

Material	δ_{max}	I_s, eV	Ref.	π_e	σ_b	σ_b/π_e
Benzene	1.66	—	—	6	6	1.0
Naphthalene	1.52	6.76	11	10	8	0.8
		6.84				
Anthracene	1.38	5.65	11	14	10	0.71
Phenanthrene	1.55	6.45	11	14	10	0.71
Tetracene	1.46	5.28	11	18	12	0.67
Pyrene	1.50	5.6	11	16	10	0.62
		5.8				
Diphenyl	1.7	—	—	12	11	0.92
Graphite	1.0	4.83	12	∞	0	0
Polyethylene	2.85	8.5	9	0	6	∞
Poly(vinyl chloride)	2.2	6.0	10	—	—	—
Polystyrene	2.1	7.0	10	6	11	1.83
NaTCNQ	1.6	5.6	8	—	—	—

are 200–300 eV, and the δ_{max} values are higher for aliphatic than for aromatic compounds.

In simple hydrocarbon compounds, the relationship between the maximum SEE yields and the chemical bonds is shown in Table II and is graphically plotted in Figure 2. In this Figure, π_e is the number of π electrons in the molecule and σ_b is the number of σ bonds existing in the outside of the π electron clouds. It is evident that the higher the value of σ_b/π_e, the higher the maximum SEE yield. This is exemplified by comparison between diamond and graphite both of which consist of the same carbon atoms. The former is a σ bond crystal with δ_{max} of 2.8, and the latter is a π bond crystal with δ_{max} of 1.0. As seen from the difference of conductivity between diamond and graphite, the electronic conduction of the organic compound can be attributed to the π electrons in the molecule, and it

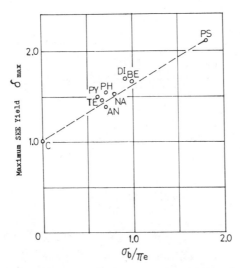

Fig. 2. Relationship between maximum SEE yield and chemical bonds in simple hydrocarbons.

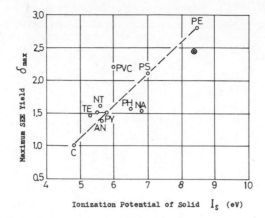

Fig. 3. Relationship between maximum SEE yield and ionization potentials of solids: (⊙) NaTCNQ-type FCEM.

is plausible that the compound with the high electronic conductivity shows the lower SEE yield. However, electronic conductivity is a macroscopic property which reflects the long-distance order of molecular configuration, while the SEE yield is a microscopic and statistical property which reflects the nature of the chemical bond and structure. Therefore, an organic compound which shows a low SEE yield is not necessarily electron conductive.

The data on the maximum SEE yields from organic compounds in relation to the ionization potential of solid are shown in Table II and are graphically plotted in Figure 3, where these values are ionization potentials determined by photoelectric emission from the solid. It is apparent that a high maximum SEE yield corresponds to a high ionization potential. This result is similar to the relationship between work function and maximum SEE yield for metals.[13] For a more detailed discussion of the SEE yield from organic compound, the relation of the SEE yield both to ionization potential and electron affinity would have to be considered.

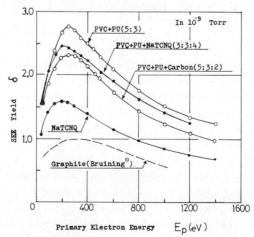

Fig. 4. SEE yields from electron-conductive polymeric compositions as function of primary electron energy.

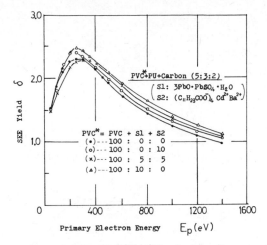

Fig. 5. Effect of stabilizers on SEE yields of polymeric compositions.

The SEE characteristics of the electron-conductive polymeric compositions applicable to the materials for FCEM are shown in Figure 4. It shows that the SEE yield depends on the characteristics of the matrix polymer, but is almost independent of the addition of electroconductive particles which inherently have low SEE yields. This fact can be understood if one assumes that the surface of the polymeric compositions becomes polymer rich by an "exudation" effect of polymer or plasticizer during the process of molding. Figure 5 shows that the SEE characteristics of the electron-conductive polymeric compositions are not affected by adding less than 5% stabilizer.

The maximum SEE yields from organic compounds are generally lower than those from inorganic insulators. However, since the values of $E_{p\,max}$ of organic compounds are low (200–300 eV), the SEE yield in low primary electron energy regions is relatively high. This makes the application of organic polymers to CEM possible.

FLEXIBLE CHANNEL ELECTRON MULTIPLIER (FCEM)

Experimental

Some of organic polymeric compositions having an appropriate electrical resistivity of 10^6–10^{10} ohm·cm are applicable to the materials for FCEM. In this paper, three types of FCEM are made of the above-mentioned electron-conductive polymeric compositions where NaTCNQ and/or carbon black are dispersed in the plasticized PVC matrix. The sheet of the electron-conductive polymeric composition was cut into small pellets, which were then shaped into a tube through a die by the extrusion molding method. The tube obtained by this process is schematically illustrated in Figure 6 together with its dimensions. As electrode, colloidal carbon (aquadag) was first coated to both ends of the FCEM, and silver wires wound on their coated carbon were fixed by silver paint with an epoxy resin binder for obtaining low-resistance ohmic contacts.

The characteristics of the FCEM are measured in the pulse counting mode under vacuum ($<10^{-5}$ torr) by using the apparatus shown in Figure 6, where the

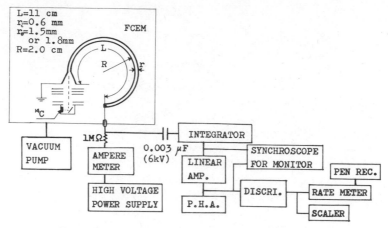

Fig. 6. Measuring system of the characteristics of FCEM.

FCEM is bent in a circular arc of radius 20 mm in order to avoid ionic feedback effect. As primary electrons for the test, secondary electrons emitted by β-ray irradiation from ^{14}C to a metal plate (Cu) were accelerated up to 300 eV and led to an input cone of the FCEM. The gain is obtained by measuring the total charge included in each output pulse. The count rate and the total counts are monitored by a rate meter and a scaler, respectively, as shown in Figure 6. This pulse counting mode is advantageous since the gain obtained is independent of the detection efficiency.

The gain G of the FCEM is given by the following equation:

$$G = \int j_0(t)dt/e = CV/e \tag{2}$$

where $j_0(t)$ is the output current at time t, C is the capacity of the condenser, and V is the peak voltage value when the condenser is charged by the output current. Mean gain $\overline{G}$ is defined as

$$\overline{G} = \sum_j G_j n_j \bigg/ \sum_j n_j \tag{3}$$

where G_j and n_j are the gain and the number of pulses, respectively, in channel j of the pulse hight analyzer.

As a typical case, the electron-conductive polymeric composition is extruded through a die into a tube 10 cm in length, 1.2 mm in inner diameter, and 3.0 mm in outer diameter. A high dc voltage V_a, around 3 kV, is applied between both ends of the tube. A single electron introduced near the cathode of the tube makes hopping motions in the tube and reaches the anode. As the SEE yield of the tube material is higher than unity, the electrons at the entrance increase in number by every collision with the tube wall, and an FCEM is obtained. Under the applied voltage V_a, when the number of collisions of secondary electrons with the tube wall is n for a pass through the channel, an energy eV_a/n is imported to the secondary electrons per hopping. The SEE yield δ at the tube wall depends on the electron energy eV_a/n, and the gain G of FCEM is given by $G = \delta^n$. For a typical case, the following value of G is expected under conditions when $V_a = 3$ kV, $n = 30$, $V_a/n = 100$ V, and $\delta = 1.9$:

$$G = (1.9)^{30} = 2.3 \times 10^8.$$

Results and Discussion

The size and characteristics of each FCEM made of electron-conductive polymeric composition are tabulated in Table III. The electrical resistance of the NaTCNQ-type FCEM made of PVC, PU, NaTCNQ, and stabilizers lies within the 10^{11}–10^{12} ohm range (volume resistivity $\rho = 10^9$–10^{10} ohm·cm), and its temperature coefficient has a large negative value, as shown in Figure 7. The high resistance of this FCEM is caused by the high resistivity ($\rho = 10^5$ ohm·cm) of NaTCNQ itself. However, the resistance is very stable and is independent of the thermal histories and molding conditions. In the case of the carbon-type FCEM made of PVC, PU, carbon black, and stabilizer, the resistance lies within the 10^8–10^{10} ohm range ($\rho = 10^6$–10^8 ohm·cm), and its temperature coefficient is slightly positive. Though these characteristics are suitable for FCEM, the resistance is somewhat affected by the thermal histories and molding conditions. The dispersibility of chain-structure carbon black particles in the polymer matrix may be responsible for these effects. The electrical resistance of the NaTCNQ carbon-type FCEM made of PVC, PU, NaTCNQ, carbon black, and stabilizer lies within the 10^8–10^{10} ohm range ($\rho = 10^6$–10^8 ohm·cm), and its temperature coefficient is slightly negative. This type of FCEM is excellent in the stability of its resistance, and is one of the most promising FCEM's for this development.

The voltage–current characteristics of all FCEM's are ohmic in a wide range, and the electric field strength in operation is 250–300 V/cm.

Figure 8 shows the relationship between mean gain measured and applied voltage, where a high mean gain of $\overline{G} = 10^8$ is obtained at $V_a = 3$ kV.

Figure 9 shows the count-rate dependence of the mean gain and the output current ratio I_0/I_d, where I_0 is the output current and I_d is the tube current at the time of no count. With increase in the count rate, a saturation of the output current ratio results, and the mean gain decreases. The resistance of the NaTCNQ-type FCEM is as high as 10^{11}–10^{12} ohm, and the FCEM is not adequate for high rate counting; but the output current ratio I_0/I_d reaches 10^{-1}, which would be the upper limit expected theoretically. The resistance of the carbon-type FCEM is adequately low (10^8–10^{10} ohm); but the decrease in mean gain starts at a count rate of $N_c = 10^3$ cps, as shown in Figure 9. The output current ratio tends to saturate at $I_0/I_d = 10^{-2}$–10^{-3}, which is well below the theoretical limit, and the mean gain is characterized by a gradual decrease with the increase in count rate.

TABLE III
Sizes and Characteristics of FCEM

	NaTCNQ-type FCEM	Carbon-type FCEM	NaTCNQ + Carbon type FCEM
Inner diameter, mm	1.2	1.2	1.2
Outer diameter, mm	3.0	3.6	3.6
Tube length, cm	11	11	11
Electrical resistance, ohm	10^{11}–10^{12}	10^8–10^{10}	10^8–10^{10}
Maximum output current, A	10^{-10}	10^{-7}	10^{-6}
Gain ($V_a = 3$ kV)		10^8	
Background		< 0.1 count/sec	

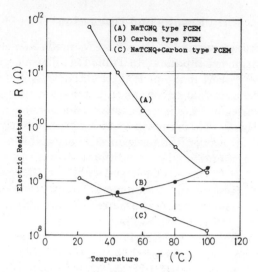

Fig. 7. Temperature dependence of electrical resistance of FCEM.

The difference in these characteristics can be attributed mainly to the charge-up effect of the high-resistance domains distributed on the inner surface of the tube, and is related to the respective electroconduction mechanisms of these FCEM materials. Because the conductivity of the FCEM materials is due to the channeling effect among electroconductive particles in the polymer matrix,

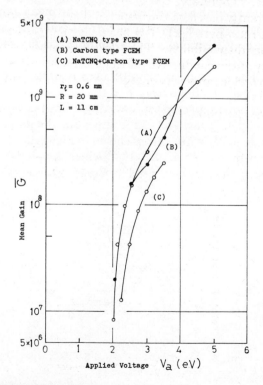

Fig. 8. Relationship between mean gain of FCEM and applied voltage.

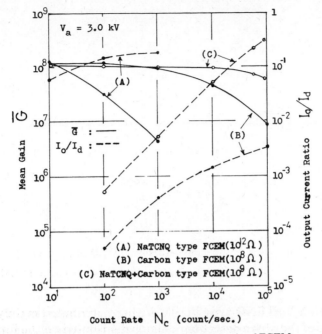

Fig. 9. Dependence of mean gain and output current ratio of FCEM on count rate.

the conductivity is determined by the quantity and dispersibility of the conductive particles. Therefore, the charge-up effect of the domains of these FCEM's is apparently based on the dispersibility of the conductive particles in the polymer matrix, where NaTCNQ has molecular dispersibility and carbon black has granular dispersibility. The NaTCNQ carbon-type FCEM, in which the dispersibility of the conductive particles is improved, shows excellent gain characteristics in a wide range of count rates, and the I_0/I_d ratio measured reaches 10^{-1} adequately.

The FCEM has also photon sensitivity in the vacuum UV region, and the UV

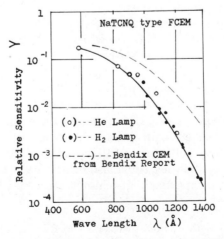

Fig. 10. Photon sensitivity of FCEM in vacuum UV region.

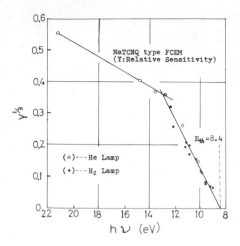

Fig. 11. Cube root plots of photon sensitivity of FCEM in vacuum UV region.

sensitivity of the NaTCNQ-type FCEM is shown in Figure 10. It is adequate for the vacuum UV photon detection. The threshold value E_{th} for photoelectric emission is given in Figure 11. This was determined by applying the cube root law,[9] where the UV sensitivity is interpreted as the quantum yield for photoelectric emission. The value of E_{th} = 8.4 eV found in the figure is taken as the ionization potential of solids, and is plotted in Figure 3 since the maximum SEE yield δ_{max} of this FCEM is 2.45, as shown in Figure 4. The plot does not show discrepancies with the general tendency of other plots.

It is confirmed that the lifetime of FCEM is 10^{10} counts in total counts, which is comparable to that of the CEM made of lead glass.[14] From this result, it is deduced that the chemical change of the FCEM materials caused by SEE would be negligibly small because of the protective effects such as the "sponge" and the "cage" effects against radiant rays.[15] Studies on the vacuum-released gases from FCEM are being carried out by the authors.

Thus, the FCEM has high flexibility, can be set in any curvature in order to avoid ionic feedback effect, and can be easily mounted in an instrument. Moreover, because of its high flexibility, the FCEM is most suitable for a space-borne electron or photon detector which is subject to considerably strong shocks and vibration. The NaTCNQ-type FCEM has already been loaded on sounding rockets of the University of Tokyo for detecting vacuum UV photon radiation in space,[16] and the carbon-type FCEM has been borne on a scientific satellite,[17] where favorable results were obtained.

The NaTCNQ carbon-type FCEM is the most promising FCEM developed recently, and shows excellent gain characteristics in a wide range of count rate. The electron-conductive polymeric composition used for this FCEM, because of its excellent molding qualities, could also be utilized as material for a channel plate whose channels are arranged. Its channel plate may be used, for example, as an image intensifier.

The authors wish to express their sincere thanks to Dr. M. Fukuda, Dr. F. Oda, and Dr. F. Nakao for helpful discussions and assistance in preparing the manuscript.

References

1. T. L. Matskevich and E. G. Mikhailova, *Sov. Phys.-Solid State*, **2**, 655 (1960).
2. E. G. Martsinovskaya, *Sov. Phys.-Solid State*, **7**, 661 (1965).
3. L. Ya. Bubnov and E. L. Frankevich, *Phys. Status Solidi B Basic Res.*, **62**, 281 (1974).
4. R. F. Willis and D. K. Skinner, *Solid State Commun.*, **13**, 685 (1973).
5. T. Hayashi, M. Hashimoto, and K. Yamamoto, *Rev. Sci. Instrum.*, **40**, 1239 (1969).
6. T. Hayashi, M. Hashimoto, and K. Yamamoto, in *Proc. 8th Int. Symp. Space Tech. Sci.*, Tokyo, 1969, p. 781.
7. K. Ishikawa and K. Goto, *Jpn. J. Appl. Phys.*, **6**, 1329 (1967).
8. P. Nielson, A. J. Epstein, and D. J. Sandman, *Solid-State Commun.*, **15**, 53 (1974).
9. M. Fujihira and H. Inokuchi, *Chem. Phys. Lett.*, **17**, 554 (1972).
10. F. I. Vilesov, A. A. Zagrubskii, and D. A. Sukhov, *Sov. Phys.-Solid State*, **11**, 2775 (1970).
11. M. Batley and L. E. Lyons, *Mol. Cryst.*, **3**, 357 (1968).
12. F. Gutmann and L. E. Lyons, *Organic Semiconductors*, Wiley, New York, 1967, p. 693.
13. E. M. Baroody, *Phys. Rev.*, **78**, 780 (1950).
14. T. Hayashi and M. Hashimoto, in *Proc. 10th Int. Symp. Space Tech. Sci.*, Tokyo, 1973, p. 745.
15. A. Charlesby, *Atomic Radiation and Polymers*, Pergamon Press, New York, 1960, p. 492.
16. T. Ogawa and T. Tohmatsu, *J. Geophys. Res.*, **76**, 6136 (1971).
17. T. Tohmatsu, K. Suzuki, and T. Ogawa, *J. Geomagn. Geoelectr.*, **27**, 295 (1975).

Received June 30, 1976
Revised September 10, 1976

JOURNAL OF APPLIED POLYMER SCIENCE   VOL. 21, 2735–2743 (1977)

Investigation of High-Density Polyethylene Film Surface Treated with Chromic Acid Mixture by Use of 2,4-Dinitrophenylhydrazine. II. Film Surfaces Treated at 70°C

KOICHIRO KATO, *Material Division, Industrial Products Research Institute, Tokyo, Japan*

Synopsis

High-density polyethylene films were treated with chromic acid mixture at 70°C. The treated films were then reacted with 2,4-Dinitrophenylhydrazine. The changes in the amounts of carbonyl groups and 2,4-dinitrophenylhydrazones formed in the films were estimated by comparing their absorptions in the infrared and ultraviolet spectra, respectively. Scanning electron micrographs of the treated film surfaces were taken. Oxidation of the film surface zone, etching of the film surface zone, and oxidation of surface zone bared from the film inner zone seem to have occurred with increase in treatment time. High-density polyethylene film surfaces were oxidized to a greater extent than low-density polyethylene film surfaces; however, the rate of etching of the low-density polyethylene film surface zone was larger than that of the high-density polyethylene film surface zone.

INTRODUCTION

In a previous paper,[1] high-density polyethylene film surfaces treated with chromic acid mixture at 30°C for different periods of time and surfaces treated with chromic acid mixture heated to different temperatures in a range of 30° to 70°C had been compared with low-density polyethylene film surfaces produced by the chromic acid mixture treatment.

Industrially, treatment of polyethylene film surfaces with chromic acid mixture is frequently carried out at a high temperature, that is, at about 70°C, to strengthen the adhesive bonds of the films to paints and adhesives.

In this work, high-density polyethylene films were treated with chromic acid mixture at 70°C, and 2,4-dinitrophenylhydrazine was allowed to react with the treated films. The changes of content of carbonyl groups in the treated films, the contact angles of water on the treated films, and the amount of 2,4-dinitrophenylhydrazones formed in the treated films were compared with comparable changes in treated low-density polyethylene films. Scanning electron micrographs of the treated film surfaces were taken. The results are reported in this paper.

EXPERIMENTAL

Films

High-density polyethylene film and low-density polyethylene film (used in a previous work[1]) received from Showa Yuka Company were used in this work. The densities of the high-density polyethylene (HDPE) and low-density polyethylene (LDPE) films were 0.949 g/ml and 0.926 g/ml, respectively. The HDPE and LDPE crystallinities obtained by the x-ray method[2-4] according to the specifications of the samples received from Showa Yuka Company were 80% and 67%, respectively. The HDPE and LDPE crystallinities obtained by using infrared spectroscopy[5] were 69% and 44%, respectively. The unsaturated group content of the films obtained by infrared spectroscopy[5,6] (according to the specifications of the samples received from Showa Yuka Company) are as follows:

	HDPE	LDPE
$-CH=CH_2/1000$ C	0.8	trace amount
$-CH=CH_2-/1000$ C	trace amount	trace amount
$>C=CH_2/1000$ C	trace amount	0.2

These films contained no additives. The HDPE and LDPE thicknesses were 0.087 mm and 0.10 mm, respectively.

Treatment with Chromic Acid Mixture

Chromic acid mixture was prepared by mixing a 10% aqueous solution of potassium dichromate with a solution prepared from sulfuric acid (97%) and water at a ratio of 30:10 by volume. Cleaned polyethylene films were immersed in the chromic acid mixture at 70°C for different periods of time. The films were then withdrawn from the chromic acid mixture, washed thoroughly with distilled water, and dried in a desiccator.

Formation of 2,4-Dinitrophenylhydrazones in Treated Polyethylene Film

The reagents were prepared by methods carried out in previous work.[7] 2,4-Dinitrophenylhydrazine solution was prepared by mixing 1 g 2,4-dinitrophenylhydrazine, 5 ml hydrochloric acid, 5 ml water, and 100 ml ethyl alcohol. The solution was prepared just before use in every experiment. The polyethylene films treated with the chromic acid mixture were immersed in the 2,4-dinitrophenylhydrazine solution for 15 min. The films were then withdrawn from the hydrazine solution, repeatedly washed with ethyl alcohol until the hydrazine absorption at the 1200 cm^{-1} band in the infrared spectrum had disappeared, and dried.

Measurement of Wettability with Water of Treated Film Surfaces

A drop of distilled water was carefully placed on the surface of the sample, and the contact angle of the drop was measured by using an Erma Model G-1 contact

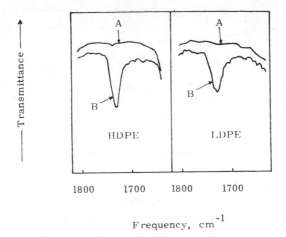

Fig. 1. Carbonyl stretching region of polyethylene films treated with chromic acid mixture: (a) original films; (b) treated films.

angle meter. The mean of ten measurements was taken with each sample. All measurements were made at about 50% R.H. and 20°C, within 10 sec of placing each drop.

Absorption Spectra

Ultraviolet absorption spectra of the samples were recorded by means of a Hitachi Model 356 recording ultraviolet spectrometer. Infrared absorption spectra of the samples were recorded by means of a Perkin–Elmer Model 180 infrared spectrophotometer.

Scanning Electron Microscopy

The scanning electron micrographs of the polyethylene film surfaces were taken with a Hitachi–Akashi Model MSM-4 scanning electron microscope.

RESULTS AND DISCUSSION

The infrared spectra of the polyethylene films treated with chromic acid mixture at 70°C showed that the absorptions[8–11] of the C=O stretching vibration appeared at about 1750 to 1700 cm^{-1}, as shown in Figure 1. The spectral changes in the infrared spectra show that carbonyl groups were formed in the molecular chains when the polyethylene films were oxidized at 70°C by chromic acid mixture.

The ultraviolet spectra of the chromic acid-treated polyethylene films allowed to react with 2,4-dinitrophenylhydrazine showed absorptions[12,13] of 2,4-dinitrophenylhydrazones near 365 nm, as shown in Figure 2 (where HDPE-DNPH is the abbreviation for the HDPE reacted with 2,4-dinitrophenylhydrazine and LDPE-DNPH is the abbreviation for the LDPE reacted with 2,4-dinitrophenylhydrazine). The spectral change in the ultraviolet spectra shows that 2,4-dinitrophenylhydrazones were formed in the polyethylene films by the re-

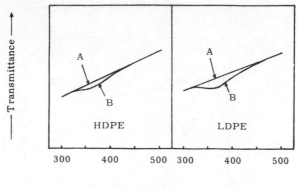

Fig. 2. Ultraviolet spectra of HDPE-DNPH and LDPE-DNPH: (a) films treated with chromic acid mixture; (b) films treated with chromic acid and then reacted with 2,4-dinitrophenylhydrazine (HDPE-DNPH and LDPE-DNPH).

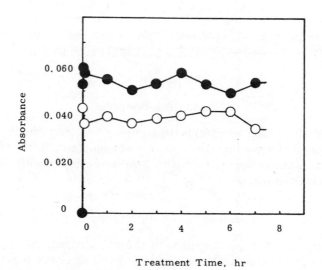

Fig. 3. Plots of absorbances at 1730 cm^{-1} in treated HDPE (●) and LDPE (○) vs treatment time.

action of 2,4-dinitrophenylhydrazine with the carbonyl groups in the polymer chains when the 2,4-dinitrophenylhydrazine was reacted with the films oxidized by chromic acid mixture.

Plots of absorbances at 1730 cm^{-1} in treated polyethylene films versus treatment times of the films with chromic acid mixture are shown in Figure 3. Plots of contact angles of water on the treated polyethylene films versus treatment times of the films with chromic acid mixture are shown in Figure 4. Plots of absorbances at 365 nm in HDPE-DNPH and LDPE-DNPH versus treatment times with chromic acid mixture are shown in Figure 5. In the early stages of the treatment, the absorbances at 1730 cm^{-1} and 365 nm increased with increase in treatment time, as shown in Figures 3 and 5, and the contact angles of water decreased with increase in treatment time, as shown in Figure 4. These phe-

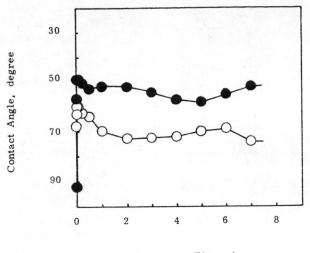

Fig. 4. Plots of contact angles of water on treated HDPE (●) and LDPE (○) vs treatment time.

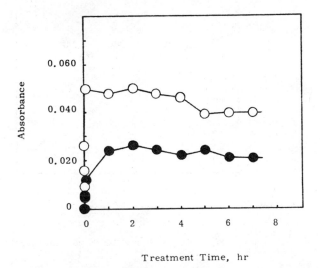

Fig. 5. Plots of absorbances at 365 nm in HDPE-DNPH (●) and LDPE-DNPH (○) vs treatment time.

nomena show that the polyethylene film surfaces are oxidized in the early stages of the treatment. The rate of increase of absorbance at 365 nm in HDPE-DNPH with increase in treatment time was lower than the rate of increase of the absorbance in LDPE-DNPH with increase in treatment time, as shown in Figure 5. The crystalline region in HDPE is larger than the crystalline region in LDPE. Therefore, it is possible that hindrance to 2,4-dinitrophenylhydrazine penetration into spaces between molecular chains in the HDPE surface is larger than the hindrance to 2,4-dinitrophenylhydrazine penetration into spaces between the molecular chains in LDPE surfaces, until partial breakdown of the molecular chains in the HDPE surface increases.

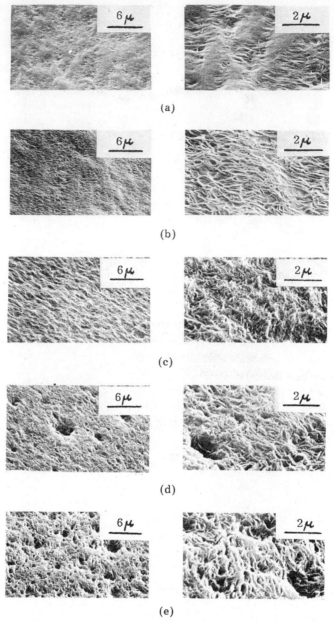

Fig. 6. Scanning electron micrographs of the surfaces of HDPE treated with chromic acid mixture.

The absorbances at 1730 cm^{-1} in HDPE were larger than the absorbances at 1730 cm^{-1} in LDPE, as shown in Figure 3. The decreases in the contact angles on HDPE surfaces produced by chromic acid treatment were larger than the decreases in the contact angles on comparably treated LDPE surfaces, as shown in Figure 4. These phenomena show that the HDPE surfaces were oxidized to a greater extent than the LDPE surfaces. It has been known[14,15] that the rate of oxidation of olefins is affected by the content of olefinic double bonds in the

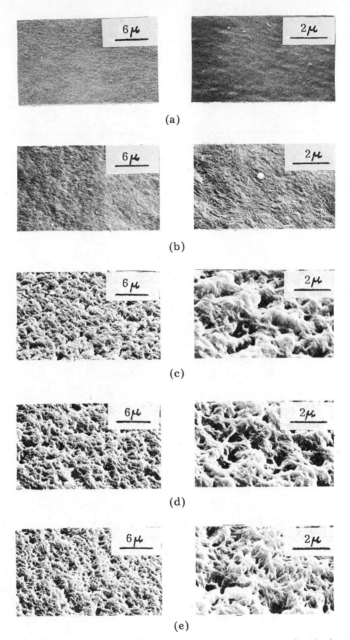

Fig. 7. Scanning electron micrographs of the surfaces of LDPE treated with chromic acid mixture.

olefins. It is within the range of possibility that the difference between HDPE and LDPE in the rate of oxidation of the respective polymer film surface was caused by a difference in the content of olefinic double bonds in the polymers.

The absorbances at 365 nm in LDPE-DNPH were larger than the absorbances at 365 nm in HDPE-DNPH, as shown in Figure 5. It is probable that the hindrance to 2,4-dinitrophenylhydrazine penetration into spaces between the mo-

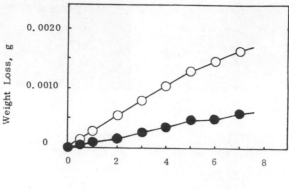

Fig. 8. Plot of weight loss of HDPE (●) and LDPE (○) per 2 cm² of film area vs treatment time.

lecular chains in HDPE was larger than the hindrance to hydrazine penetration into spaces between the molecular chains in LDPE, because the amorphous region in HDPE was smaller than the amorphous region in LDPE.

After the early stages of treatment, the absorbances at 1730 cm⁻¹ and 365 nm in the films decreased slightly and thereafter seemed to repeat the slight decrease and the slight increase of the absorbances with increase in treatment time, as shown in Figures 3 and 5. The contact angle of water on the HDPE surface increased slightly and the contact angle of water on the LDPE surface seemed to increase with increase in treatment time over about 2 hr. Thereafter, the contact angles on the films seemed to repeat the slight decrease and the slight increase of the contact angles with increase in treatment time, as shown in Figure 4.

In order to look at the film surfaces produced after the early stages of the treatment, scanning electron micrographs of the treated film surfaces were taken. The scanning electron micrographs of the treated film surfaces are shown in Figures 6 and 7. When the polyethylene films were treated with chromic acid mixture for 1 min, lamellar packets were apparent in the LDPE surface and clearly apparent in the HDPE surface. It is probable that lamellar packets were bared from the film inner zones by the increase in breakdown in the polymer film surfaces. It is probable that lamellar packets were clearly apparent in the HDPE surface because the crystalline region in HDPE is large. It is suggested that the chromic acid mixture was hindered from reacting with the polymer in the crystalline region bared from the film inner zone.

When the polyethylene films were treated for 1 hr, numerous voids were observed on the LDPE surface, but clear voids were not observed on the HDPE surface. Clear voids were observed on the HDPE surfaces treated for 5 hr. The weight of the films decreased with increase in treatment time, and the weight loss of LDPE was larger than the weight loss of HDPE, as shown in Figure 8. These phenomena show that the polyethylene film surfaces were etched with increase in treatment time and that the rate of etching of the LDPE surface by chromic acid was larger than the rate of etching of the HDPE surface. It is within the range of possibility that this difference in rate of etching of the film surfaces was caused by a difference in the amounts of amorphous regions in the films.

From these results, it can be assumed that the decrease in absorbance at 1730 cm^{-1} and 365 nm and the increase in contact angle of water after the early stages of the treatment were caused by a decrease in the amount of carbonyl groups in the film surfaces caused by an increase in the surfaces bared from the inner zones in the films. The large decrease in contact angle of water on the LDPE surface after the early stages of the treatment may have been caused by large etching of the LDPE surface.

It can be inferred that the surfaces bared from the inner zones in the films are oxidized and that, thereafter, the etching and oxidation of the film surfaces are repeated. It is probable that repeated absorbances at 1730 cm^{-1} and 365 nm and contact angles of water slightly increase and slightly decrease, respectivly, with increase in treatment time because of the above-mentioned changes in the films.

The author would like to thank H. Noji of the Nissei Sangyo Company for the scanning electron microscopy.

References

1. K. Kato, *J. Appl. Polym. Sci.*, **20**, 2451 (1976).
2. S. Krimm and A. V. Tobolsky, *J. Polym. Sci.*, **7**, 57 (1951).
3. I. Nitta and H. Tadokoro, *Kobunshi*, **5**, 296 (1956).
4. I. Nitta and H. Tadokoro, *Kobunshi*, **5**, 345 (1956).
5. E. Cernia, C. Mancini, and G. Montaudo, *Polym. Lett.*, **1**, 371 (1963).
6. L. H. Cross, R. B. Richards, and H. A. Wills, *Disc. Faraday Soc.*, **9**, 235 (1950).
7. K. Kato, *J. Appl. Polym. Sci.*, **15**, 2115 (1971).
8. F. M. Rugg, J. J. Smith, and R. C. Bacon, *J. Polym. Sci.*, **13**, 535 (1954).
9. J. P. Luongo, *J. Polym. Sci.*, **42**, 139 (1960).
10. H. C. Beachell and G. W. Tarbet, *J. Polym. Sci.*, **45**, 451 (1960).
11. M. Ōki, *Infrared Spectra*, Tokyo University, Tokyo, 1967, p. 80.
12. L. A. Jones, J. C. Holmes, and R. B. Seligman, *Anal. Chem.*, **28**, 191 (1956).
13. C. J. Timmons, *J. Chem. Soc.*, 2613 (1957).
14. Y. Kamiya, *Oxidation of Organic Compounds*, Gihodo, Tokyo, 1973, p. 295.
15. T. Nozoe, *Chemical Experiment*, Vol. II, Kawaide Shobo, Tokyo, 1942, Chap. 4, p. 105.

Received June 14, 1976
Revised September 14, 1976

JOURNAL OF APPLIED POLYMER SCIENCE   VOL. 21, 2745-2768 (1977)

Photophysical Processes and Interactions Between Poly(ethylene Terephthalate) and 1-Amino-2-(2-methoxyethoxy)-4-hydroxy-9,10-Anthraquinone

ROBERT G. MERRILL and CARLETON W. ROBERTS, *Textile Department, Clemson University, Clemson, South Carolina 29631*

Synopsis

The effect of 1-amino-2-(2-methoxyethoxy)-4-hydroxy-9,10-anthraquinone (C. I. Disperse Red 59) on the phototendering of poly(ethylene terephthalate) (PET) was assessed. The photophysical processes occurring in the polymer, the dye, and the dyed polymer were determined. The energy and nature of the dye and polymer electronic excited states were assigned on the basis of absorption and luminescence properties. Irradiation failed to produce dye-sensitized phototendering of PET; however, the titanium dioxide delusterant in commercial PET did function as a sensitizer in the presence of moist air. The phototendering of blank-dyed PET yarn was found to obey (pseudo-) zero-order kinetics $k = 1.69 \times 10^{-19}$ per cent breaking strength loss/quantum absorbed/cm^2. The dye exhibited fluorescence from a lowest, ~51.5 kcal/mole, singlet charge-transfer (C-T) excited state but did not phosphoresce. The PET possessed a complex fluorescence spectrum attributed to similar $^1(n,\pi^*)_1$ excited states, ~78.1 kcal/mole, while its phosphorescence derives from a proposed $^3(\pi,\pi^*)$ state, ~69.8 kcal/mole, populated by intersystem crossing from a $^1(\pi,\pi^*)$ state, ~92.3 kcal/mole. The dyed polymer exhibited a PET-sensitized delayed fluorescence from the dyestuff involving triplet–singlet transfer by a dipole–dipole (Coulombic) long-range resonance excitation mechanism. The transfer process was characterized by an experimentally determined critical transfer distance, R_0, of approximately 40 Å.

INTRODUCTION

For most textile products, actinic exposure initiates photodegradation reactions that result in a general weakening of the polymer, commonly referred to as phototendering. In addition to their inherent phototendering tendency, many polymers undergo more rapid photodegradation in the presence of certain substances which act as photosensitizers for the polymer degradation. A complete study of polymer phototendering and the effects of photosensitizers on the tendering process requires, first of all, that the general mechanism of photochemical degradation be determined for the polymer in the absence of sensitizers. The sensitized phototendering process is characterized by analysis of the effects of the sensitizer on the molecular weight and/or mechanical properties of the irradiated polymer. Determination of the manner in which a sensitizer enhances the normal polymer phototendering process requires a knowledge of the polymer and sensitizer electronic energy states (most photochemical and photophysical processes occur from the lowest excited states for organic molecules).

A sensitizing substance may function as a direct or indirect photosensitizer,

2745

a photo-initiator, or a photo-optical sensitizer of polymer degradation. Direct (photophysical) sensitization requires a donor–acceptor electronic energy transfer process in which the polymer plays the part of the acceptor. Indirect (photophysical) sensitization employs a third species as the acceptor. Photo-initiators, on the other hand, react directly with the polymer or undergo photochemical decomposition first, with the photochemical products then initiating degradation reactions of the polymer. Photo-optical sensitizers require the formation of a polymer–sensitizer complex resulting in a new absorbing chromophore.

The photochemical aspects of the degradation of poly(ethylene terephthalate) (PET) have recently been investigated extensively by Day and Wiles[1-6]; however, to our knowledge, no previous studies of PET photophysical processes or the effects of possible sensitizing phototenderers on PET photodegradation have been published except for the preliminary work with model phthalate esters by Cheung.[7]

Cheung examined the photophysical processes of dibutyl terephthalate, bis(2-ethoxyethyl) terephthalate, and bis[2-(2-ethoxyethoxy)ethyl] terephthalate, and the dyestuff C. I. Disperse Red 59 [1-amino-2-(2-methoxyethoxy)-4-hydroxy-9,10-anthraquinone] (structure obtained through courtesy of E. I. du Pont de Nemours & Co., Wilmington, Del., 1973). The model esters exhibited fluorescence at room temperature and phosphorescence when cooled to 77°K. The electronic absorption leading to the observed luminescence was tentatively assigned as a $^1(n,\pi^*)$ transition of the ester chromophore. Cheung proposed that in solution, the dye fluoresced from a $^1(n,\pi^*)$ electronic state. The fact that no phosphorescence was detected for the dyestuff, under any conditions, indicated that it should be a poor sensitizer for photosensitized oxidation.[8] Solutions of the dye in the model compounds exhibited no evidence of intermolecular electronic energy transfer or complex formation.

This research involved the accelerated phototendering of C. I. Disperse Red 59-dyed and blank-dyed PET yarns irradiated under carefully controlled oxidative conditions with artificial 3000-Å light. The extent of phototendering was assessed by measuring the yarn breaking strength, not as a function of irradiation time, but as a function of the total incident radiation. Other factors considered included the effect of titanium dioxide delusterant (TiO_2) and water vapor on the extent of phototendering.

The dye and polymer lowest excited states were identified with regard to their respective energies and transitions responsible for each state. The energy states and photophysical processes for the polymer and dyestuff alone were compared with those for the dyed polymer, and the results were used to explain the observed sensitizing properties of the dyestuff.

EXPERIMENTAL

Ultraviolet and visible absorption spectra were obtained using a Cary Model 14 or Model 118C spectrophotometer. Routine determinations of absorbance for concentration measurements by Beer's law were made using a Bausch and Lomb Spectronic 20 spectrophotometer. Yarn samples were knit on a Lawson Fiber Analysis Knitter (FAK) which features an automatic compensating yarn feed to ensure identical sample preparation. Atmospheric scouring and pressure dyeings were carried out in an Ahiba AG Model G6B dyeing machine. A Rayonet

Type RS Model RPR-208 preparative photochemical reactor was used to irradiate the samples. An MGR-100 merry-go-round assembly, in the center of the reactor, rotated the samples inside a circular bank of eight RUL-3000 Å low-pressure mercury, phosphor conversion lamps. Yarn tensile testing was performed on an Instron Model 1101 (TM-M) constant rate of extension testing machine. Luminescence measurements were obtained with a Perkin–Elmer Model MPF-3 fluorescence spectrophotometer equipped with corrected spectra, phosphorescence, and front surface accessories. A Tektronix Model 5103N storage oscilloscope was used to display luminescence decay curves and to measure the corresponding mean lifetimes. Low-temperature luminescence sample tube-spinning rates were measured using a Pioneer Photo-Tach Model 1030 tachometer. Elemental analyses were performed by Galbraith Laboratories, Inc., Knoxville, Tennessee.

Purification of "Latyl" Cerise B

One gram of commercial "Latyl" Cerise B [C. I. Disperse Red 59, 1-amino-2-(2-methoxyethoxy)-4-hydroxy-9,10-anthraquinone, crude wet, du Pont] was extracted with 250 ml ethyl acetate in a Soxhlet extractor and recrystallized twice to give pyramidal metallic-brown crystals with mp 174.5–175.5°C.

ANAL. Calcd for $C_{17}H_{15}NO_5$: C, 65.16; H, 4.83; N, 4.47; O, 25.53. Found: C, 65.22; H, 4.88; N, 4.53; O, 25.37 (diff).

Aqueous Dyeing of Poly(ethylene Terephthalate) Yarn and Film

The yarn samples were mounted in the form of knit tubes while the film samples were rolled and fastened in the shape of a cyclinder. The samples were scoured to remove any spin finish, knitting oil, or external contaminant that might be present. The samples were scoured for 20 min at 75–82°C with a 1% (by weight) aqueous solution of tetrasodium pyrophosphate (TSPP) in an Ahiba dyeing machine. The samples were then cooled to 69–75°C, removed from the machine, and rinsed with distilled water.

The dyeings were carried out in sealed pressure dyeing containers. The dyeing containers were filled (90%) with distilled water, heated to 60–75°C, and a measured weight of the commercial dye "Latyl" Cerise B was added. After 10 min, two to four samples were entered, the containers were sealed, and the temperature was raised slowly to 92–100°C and held for 15 min for exhaustion purposes. The bath temperature was then raised slowly to 121–124°C and held for 1 hr. The bath was then cooled to 69–75°C and the samples were removed, rinsed with distilled water, and dried at 70–80°C for 1 hr.

The same preparation and dyeing procedures, with the exception of the addition of the dye, were used to prepare the "blank-dyed" control samples.

Determination of Dye Concentration in Yarns and Films

One sample from each dyeing was analyzed to determine the concentration of dye present. The dye was stripped from the PET substrate using a method suggested by Monkman.[9] The stripped yarn sample was dried at 70–80°C and weighed. The percent by weight dyeing was calculated from the above data and was converted to molar concentration employing the corresponding density for the PET sample.

Irradiation Conditions

The dyed and blank-dyed knit samples were unraveled and mounted on separate wire frames (41 × 3 cm). Each frame held eight yarns attached by means of masking tape at each end. Each yarn was pretensioned prior to mounting with a 4.2-g weight (0.25 g/tex)[10] to remove crimp and ensure uniform mounting tension.

The yarns, mounted on the wire frames, were placed into four identical Pyrex tubes (45 × 4.5 cm) equipped with a gas inlet at the bottom and an outlet at the top.

Compressed air was filtered (13 × 4 Å molecular sieves) and dried (Drierite towers) and delivered at 2.5 SCFH to each Pyrex tube at 40°C. [SCFH (air) = standard cubic feet of air per hour, where standard refers to the conditions of 70°F (21.1°C) and atmospheric pressure (760 mm Hg).]

For one experiment, it was desired to introduce water vapor into the air flow at a known concentration. This was accomplished by inserting a Milligan gas washer half-filled with distilled water into the air line between the rotameter and the sample irradiation tubes. The amount of water vapor picked up by the dry air as it passed through the gas washer was determined by measuring the weight gain of a known amount of Drierite in a small drying tube placed in the line on the exit side of the gas washer. Using the flow rate, adjusted to standard conditions, the time of flow, and the concentration of saturated aqueous vapor at the temperature of the exiting air flow, the percent relative humidity of the resultant air was determined.

For each dye concentration, a set of eight dyed and blank-dyed yarns were each irradiated simultaneously but in separate irradiation tubes. Irradiation times ranged from 5 to 60 hr.

Yarn Breaking Strength

The dyed and blank-dyed yarn breaking strengths were determined according to ASTM Standard D2256-69[10] using a 25-cm gauge length and a 20-cm/min rate of extension which gave a time to break of 20 ± 3 sec for the unirradiated blank-dyed yarns. The samples were allowed to equilibrate at ambient conditions in the dark for at least 24 hr.

Actinometry

The light intensity of the irradiating lamps and its variation as the lamps aged was monitored using the potassium ferrioxalate chemical actinometer developed by Hatchard and Parker[11,12] and modified by Baxendale and Bridge,[13] Lee and Seliger,[14] and Rurien.[15] A Beer's law plot of the standard calibration data was linear, yielding a molar extinction coefficient ϵ of 1.22×10^4 l./mole·cm (literature value 1.11×10^4 l./mole·cm).[16] The measured lamp intensities were found to decrease from a maximum of 6.82×10^{15} to 2.18×10^{15} quanta/cm^2/sec after 733.5 hr.

U.S.P. grade 95% ethanol was purified by fractional distillation and the purity checked by luminescence on excitation at 250 nm.[17]

Analysis of the yarn samples was found to show variable results in terms of reproducibility due mainly to the inherent inhomogeneity of the sample. The above problem was remedied by a technique similar to that described by Hollifield and Winefordner.[18] The basic technique involves the rotation (1600–3300 rpm) of the sample tube within the Dewar during analysis so that any sample inhomogeneities are averaged, producing a steady emission.

Materials

The spectrophotometric-grade solvents ethyl acetate and N,N-dimethylformamide were purchased from Matheson, Coleman, and Bell; carbon tetrachloride, from J. T. Baker Chemical Co.; and dichloromethane, from Aldrich Chemical Co., Inc. U.S.P.-grade 95% ethanol, after further purification, was used for luminescence experiments. A ferrous ammonium sulfate vial for standard volumetric solution preparation was supplied by Anachemia Chemicals Ltd. Quartz phosphorescence sample tubes were custom fabricated by Wilmad Glass Company, Inc. "Latyl" Cerise B and "Latyl" Cerise B crude wet dye (C. I. Disperse Red 59) and Mylar Type A poly(ethylene terephthalate) film were gifts of E. I. du Pont de Nemours & Co. The poly(ethylene terephthalate) 150 denier, 32 monofilaments yarn was donated by the American Enka Corporation, while the 150 denier, 35 monofilaments sample was a gift from Dow Badische (Table I).

RESULTS AND DISCUSSION

Photophysical Processes in Poly(ethylene Terephthalate)

The absorption spectrum of a ~0.90-mil Mylar PET film (film I) versus air exhibited a slight attenuation of light at all wavelengths; the spectrum was

TABLE I
Yarn and Film Sample Properties

	Yarn I[a]		Yarn II[b]		Film I[c]	
	Mfg. data	Exp. data	Mfg. data	Exp. data	Mfg. data	Exp. data
Denier/filaments	150/32		150/35		—	
Gauge	—		—		92	
Thickness mil	—		—		0.92	0.9[d]
Twist, TPI	½ Z		¼ Z		—	0.90[e]
Density, g/cc	—		1.361		1.395	
Draw ratio	3.47		—		—	
Refractive index, Abbe	—		—		1.64	
Birefringence	—		0.196		—	
Plasticizers	—		—		none	
% TiO$_2$	none?	<9 ppm Ti <1.5 × 10⁻³ calcd.	0.30	0.144 Ti 0.240 calcd.	none?	

^a Enka "clear" PET yarn.
^b Dow Badische PET yarn.
^c DuPont Mylar R Type A PET film.
^d Micrometer caliper.
^e Infrared interference fringe pattern.

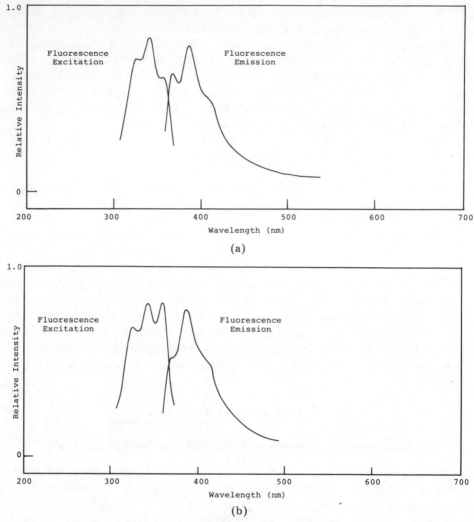

Fig. 1. (a) Corrected fluorescence excitation and emission spectra of poly(ethylene terephthalate) yarn containing less than 9 ppm Ti (yarn I), at room temperature. Excitation scan: Em λ 388 nm, Ex slit 3 nm, Em slit 10 nm. Emission scan: Ex λ 342 nm, Ex slit 10 nm, Em slit 3 nm. (b) Corrected fluorescence excitation and emission spectra of poly(ethylene terephthalate) yarn containing 0.240% TiO$_2$ (yarn II), at room temperature. Excitation scan: Em λ 388, Ex slit 3 nm, Em slit 10 nm. Emission scan: Ex λ 342, nm, Ex slit 10 nm, Em slit 3 nm. (c) Corrected fluorescence excitation and emission spectra of poly(ethylene terephthalate) film containing no TiO$_2$ (film I), at room temperature. Excitation scan: EM λ 388 nm, Ex slit 3 nm, Em slit 10 nm. Emission scan: Ex λ 342 nm, Ex slit 10 nm, Em slit 3 nm.

dominated by the intense absorption of wavelengths less than ~312 nm. The onset of absorption near 310 nm agrees with the results of Marcotte et al.[19] The presence of similar absorption bands have also been reported[7,19] for various model terephthalate esters.

Employing the data of Marcotte et al.[19] and assuming a film density of ~1.385 g/cm^3 (partly crystalline nonoriented PET)[20] and also assuming that each PET repeat unit contains only one chromophore (or at the most two, in the case of carbonyl chromophores), the following approximate molar extinction coefficients

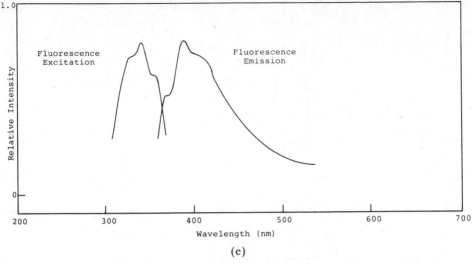

(c)

Fig. 1 (*continued*)

were calculated for the PET absorption bands: 240 nm ($\epsilon \sim 1.37 \times 10^4$ l./mole·cm), 270 nm ($\epsilon \sim 2.10 \times 10^3$ l./mole·cm), and 290–310 nm ($\epsilon \sim 1.27$–0.64×10^3 l./mole·cm).   These values are of the same general magnitude as those reported by Cheung[7] for methanol solutions of model phthalate esters.

The corrected fluorescence excitation and emission scans for the various PET samples are presented in Figure 1(a), 1(b), and 1(c).   The spectra are all quite similar with respect to position of the excitation and emission bands, with most of the differences arising from variations in peak intensities.   Excitation bands were noted at ~326, 342, and 358 nm, while emission bands were located at ~369, 390, and 412 nm.

The fluorescence emission data for film I compare favorably with the uncorrected spectrum by Day and Wiles[2] for a Mylar PET film.   In addition, the PET fluorescence properties are, in general, similar to those found for PET model phthalate esters by Cheung.[7]

The low-temperature (77°K) luminescence spectrum for yarn I, Figure 2(a), exhibited the expected increased band sharpness and small 0–0 band separation.

Figure 2(b) and 2(c) represent the uncorrected* phosphorescence excitation and emission spectra for the PET yarn I and yarn II samples at 77°K.   Both samples are similar, each possessing a 310-nm excitation and a ~454-nm emission with a mean lifetime τ of 1.0–1.4 sec.   No room temperature phosphorescence was detected for any of the PET samples.

The low-intensity phosphorescence excitation plateau, ranging from 340 to 370 nm for the yarn II sample [see Fig. 2(c)] is attributed to the presence of TiO$_2$ in the polymer since it is absent in the TiO$_2$-free sample [yarn I, see Fig. 1(c)] and because it becomes more evident in PET samples containing increasing amounts of TiO$_2$.   In addition, the excitation wavelengths, i.e., 340–370 nm, agree

---

* The phosphorescence accessory of the Perkin-Elmer Model MPF-3 fluorescence spectrophotometer is used for measuring low-temperature fluorescence and phosphorescence spectra. The corrected spectra accessory is inoperable under these conditions.

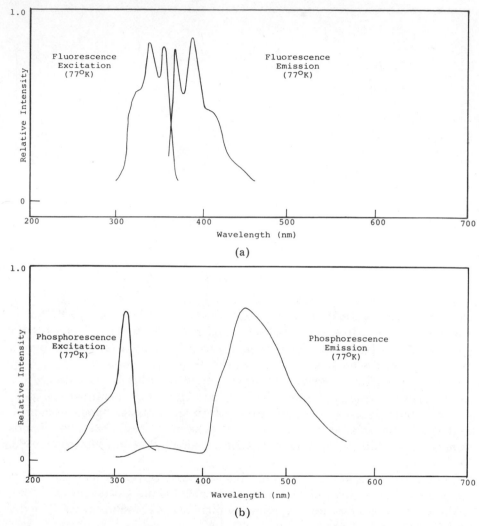

Fig. 2. (a) Uncorrected fluorescence excitation and emission spectra for poly(ethylene tereph-thalate) yarn containing less than 9 ppm Ti (yarn I), at 77°K. Excitation scan: Em λ 390 nm, Ex slit 2 nm, Em slit 10 nm. Emission scan: Ex λ 345 nm, Ex slit 10 nm, Em slit 2 nm. (b) Uncorrected phosphorescence excitation and emission spectra for poly(ethylene terephthalate) yarn containing less than 9 ppm Ti (yarn I), at 77°K. Excitation scan: Em λ 450 nm, Ex slit 10 nm, Em slit 10 nm. Excitation scan: Em λ 310 nm, Ex slit 10 min. Spinning sample, lifetime (τ) 1.4 sec. (c) Uncorrected phosphorescence excitation and emission spectra for poly(ethylene terephthalate) yarn containing 0.240% TiO₂ (yarn II), at 77°K. Excitation scan: Em λ 454 nm, Ex slit 2 nm, Em slit 16 nm. Emission scan: Em λ 312 nm, Ex slit 8 nm, Em slit 5 nm. Lifetime (τ) 1.0 sec.

well with the 365-nm excitation reported by Taylor et al.[21] for TiO_2 delusterant in nylon 6,6.

The PET fluorescence and emission bands do not appear to be due to the vi-brational structure characteristic of a single chromophore since the bands do not occur at equal wave-number intervals. In addition, the relative excitation and emission-band intensities were found to be wavelength dependent, giving further evidence that more than one chromophore is involved. A detailed analysis of the interrelationships of the excitation and emission bands revealed

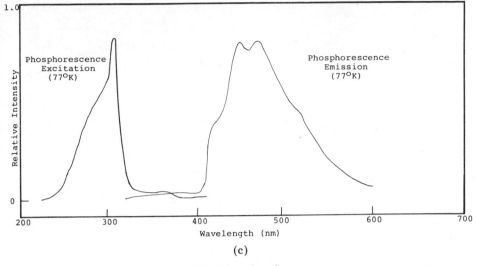

Fig. 2 (*continued*)

that there were at least two independent contributions. The fact that the fluorescence and phosphorescence excitation bands do not coincide also implies that PET phosphorescence is due to a different chromophore.

The possibility that the PET fluorescence or phosphorescence is derived from trace impurities within each polymer sample is unlikely. This conclusion is based on the similarity of the luminescence properties of diverse PET polymer samples, ranging from yarn to film and produced by different manufacturers, and on agreement of the spectral data with the luminescence properties of model terephthalate esters.

Pacifici and Straley[22] have reported that the mono- and dihydroxyterephthalate moieties in surface-oxidized PET possess fluorescent properties with emission maxima at 459 (mono) and 435, 510 (w) (di) with excitation at 340 and 309 nm. Our data lead us to conclude that these are not the chromophores which are responsible for the luminescent properties of the film and fiber samples reported here.

If it is assumed that the crystalline and amorphous regions of PET possess different luminescence properties, the complex nature of the luminescence spectra may be assigned to differences in the degree of crystallinity of the samples. It could also arise from different isolated luminescent chromophores situated along the polymer chain or from the characteristic luminescence from various molecular weight species in the distribution, ranging from oligomer to polymer, present in each sample.

The approximate extinction coefficients calculated for PET, coupled with the absorption data for model phthalate esters, suggest that the PET absorption bands at 240, 270, and 290–310 nm are due to π,π^* transitions. Considering these band assignments, the PET phosphorescence excitation band at 310 nm would also be a π,π^* state, while the fluorescence excitations, 326–358 nm, would have to be attributed to an n,π^* state located under the long wavelength shoulder of the 290–310 nm absorption. The phosphorescence emission band at 454 nm is most likely a $^3(\pi,\pi^*)$ state because of the long phosphorescence lifetime[23] and the large S_1-T_1 energy splitting ($\sim$8000 cm^{-1}).[24]

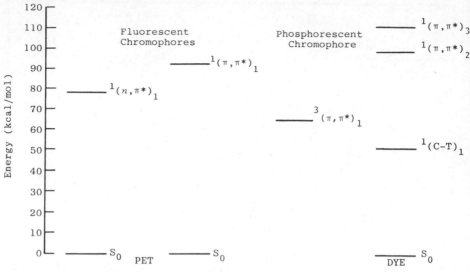

Fig. 3. The major electronic energy levels and band assignments for poly(ethylene terephthalate) (PET) and 1-amino-2-(2-methoxyethoxy)-4-hydroxy-9,10-anthraquinone (C. I. Disperse Red 59).

The O–O bands for PET fluorescence and phosphorescence yield the following electronic state energies: $S_1 \cong 78.1$ kcal/mole (n,π^*); $S_1' \cong 92.3$ kcal/mole (π,π^*) (fluorescent chromophores); $T_1' \cong 69.8$ kcal/mole (phosphorescent chromophore). The lowest electronic energy levels and their band assignments are diagrammed in Figure 3.

In terms of the phototendering of PET alone, analysis of its absorption spectrum reveals that the onset of absorption at ~310 nm, which lies within the high-energy range of terrestrial sunlight, coincides with the critical wavelength for PET photodegradation.[5] The same wavelength, 310 nm, also produces phosphorescence from the polymer, which implies that the triplet state may be involved in the photodegradation of PET.

Photophysical Processed in C. I. Disperse Red 59

C. I. Disperse Red 59, 1-amino-2-(2-methoxyethoxy)-4-hydroxy-9,10-anthraquinone,

was initially developed[25] as an anthraquinone dye for cellulose acetate. It is reported to act as a phototendering sensitizer when used to dye PET. The ultraviolet-visible absorption spectrum of the purified dyestuff, $5.60 \times 10^{-5} M$ in dichloromethane, reveals three main absorption regions, i.e., ~256, ~287, and 450–550 nm.

The corrected fluorescence excitation and uncorrected emission spectra of

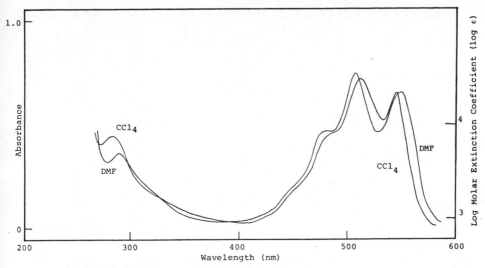

Fig. 4. Absorption spectra of $5.00 \times 10^{-5}M$ solutions of C. I. Disperse Red 59 in carbon tetrachloride (CCl$_4$) and N,N-dimethylformamide (DMF), respectively, measured in 1-cm cells with corresponding pure solvents as reference.

a dichloromethane solution of the dyestuff are shown in Figure 5. The band maxima for the excitation spectrum were nearly identical to those obtained by absorption measurements, while the emission spectrum exhibited a structured band with a maximum of 568 nm.

Figure 6 illustrates the effect of lowering the temperature to 77°K on the band structure of the uncorrected fluorescence excitation and emission spectra of a rigid solution of the dye in 95% ethanol. Both spectra exhibit what appears to be strong vibrational structure with a separation of 1350 cm^{-1} for the emission spectra.

In agreement with the work reported previously by Cheung,[7] no phosphorescence attributable to the dyestuff was obtained from dye solutions in 95% ethanol at room temperature or glassed at 77°K. In addition, saturation of the above solution with nitrogen gas prior to phosphorescence measurement produced no dye phosphorescence. An attempt to obtain phosphorescence using benzophenone as a sensitizer was also unsuccessful.

Although the dyestuff used for this study is somewhat complex, containing three auxochromic substituents, it is still possible to draw general conclusions concerning the origin of its absorption and luminescence bands and, as a result, its expected phototendering activity.

Analysis of the absorption spectra (Fig. 4) of the dye used in this study, 1-amino-2-(2-methoxyethoxy)-4-hydroxy-9,10-anthraquinone, in terms of band intensity and solvent shift data, and comparison with the absorption data and band assignments for similar, 1,4-disubstituted 9,10-anthraquinones[26–34] led to the following band assignments: The two longest wavelength absorption bands, ~546 and ~510 nm, are assigned as charge transfer (C-T) bands involving the intramolecular hydrogen bonding of the amino and hydroxy substituents with the anthraquinone carbonyls, while the remaining bands in the visible region, ~483 and 451 nm, are either C-T or π,π^* in nature. The two bands in the ultraviolet region, ~287 and ~256 nm, are relatively unaffected by the attached

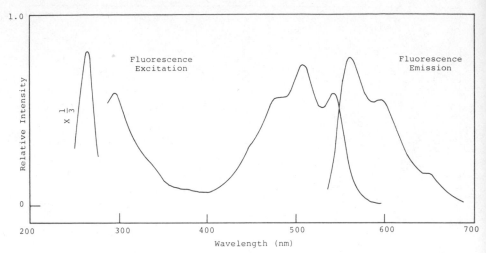

Fig. 5. Corrected fluorescence excitation and uncorrected emission spectra of $5 \times 10^{-6}M$ C. I. Disperse Red 59 in dichloromethane at room temperature. Excitation scan: Em λ 580 nm, Ex slit 10 nm, Em slit 5 nm. Emission scan: Em λ 510 nm, Ex slit 10 nm, Em slit 5 nm.

auxochromes and are therefore assigned as π,π^* bands, as in the unsubstituted 9,10-anthraquinone.

Anthraquinones possessing a lowest n,π^* excited state are highly reactive toward hydrogen abstraction, thus allowing them to initiate photo-oxidation reactions. This is due to the change in the carbonyl polarity that occurs when a nonbonding electron, situated on the carbonyl oxygen, is promoted to an antibonding π^* orbital having a significant spatial contribution at the carbonyl carbon atom, thus resulting in a partial positive charge residing on the carbonyl oxygen.

The converse situation arises for the case where the lowest excited state is C-T

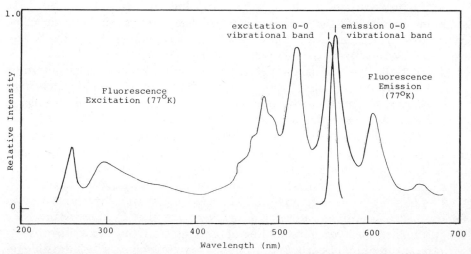

Fig. 6. Uncorrected fluorescence excitation and emission spectra of C. I. Disperse Red 59 in 95% ethanol at 77°K. Excitation scan: Em λ 608 nm, Ex slit 4 nm, Em slit 10 nm. Emission scan: Ex λ 520 nm, Ex slit 10 nm, Em slit 4 nm.

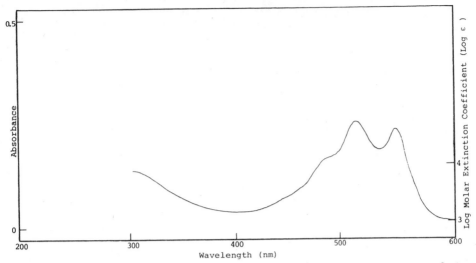

Fig. 7. Absorption spectrum of 6.70 × 10⁻³M C. T. Disperse Red 59 in ~0.90 mil Mylar [poly-(ethylene terephthalate)] film (film I), with blank-dyed film I as reference.

in nature, such as occurs when the carbonyl is intramolecularly hydrogen bonded to another substituent. Under these conditions, the electron movement in the carbonyl is opposite to the electron shift in an n,π^* transition and, therefore, the C-T state has little hydrogen abstraction tendency. Since the lowest excited state of C. I. Disperse Red 59 is also C-T in nature, the dye would be expected to exhibit a negligible tendency to function as a photo-initiator of PET photo-tendering by hydrogen abstraction.

The lack of detectable phosphorescence from the dyestuff C. I. Disperse Red 59 and its structural similarity to other known "poor sensitizers" [8] give further evidence that it should not act as a sensitizer to PET phototendering. Applying the usual criteria to the spectra for C. I. Disperse Red 59 yields the following main excited electronic energy levels: $S_1 \cong 51.1$ kcal/mole; S_2 (287 nm band) $\cong 98.6$ kcal/mole; S_3 (256 nm band) $\cong 111$ kcal/mole. The dye energy levels and band assignments are shown diagrammatically in Figure 3.

Photophysical Processes in Poly(ethylene Terephthalate) Dyed with C. I. Disperse Red 59

The absorption spectrum of the dye within the polymer matrix (film I) is displayed in Figure 7. An identical blank-dyed PET film was employed as the reference material. In the wavelength region for which PET is transparent, the dye absorption spectrum is nearly identical to its solution spectrum (see Fig. 4), although the bands are slightly red shifted, ~300 cm⁻¹, in the polymer. The apparent lack of absorption of the dyed film below ~303 nm is due to the strong attenuation of both the sample and reference beams by the PET for wavelengths less than ~310 nm. The similarity of the absorption spectra for the dye in solution and in the polymer matrix and the absence of any new absorption bands preclude the formation of an absorbing species due to a dye–polymer complex and, therefore, the operation of the dye as a photo-optical sensitizer.

Figures 8 and 9 are examples of the dye–polymer fluorescence, indicating that

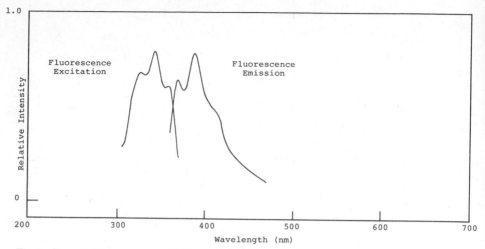

Fig. 8. Corrected fluorescence excitation and emission spectra for 0.0287% (by weight) C. I. Disperse Red 59-dyed poly(ethylene terephthalate) yarn containing less than 9 ppm TiO₂ (yarn I), at room temperature. Excitation scan: Em λ 388 nm, Ex slit 3 nm, Em slit 10 nm. Emission scan: Ex λ 342 nm, Ex slit 10 nm, Em slit 3 nm.

the PET and the dyestuff retain their original fluorescence properties even when combined. The dye-corrected fluorescence excitation scan reaffirms the bathochromic shift noted previously for its absorption spectra in PET. The dye fluorescence emission was also "red" shifted in the polymer ~450 cm⁻¹ to ~538 and ~610 nm.

The phosphorescence excitation and emission spectra of a 0.421% (by weight) C. I. Disperse Red 59 dyed yarn (yarn I) at 77°K is depicted in Figure 10. The phosphorescence emission is characterized by a band at ~454 nm, corresponding to the normal phosphorescence of blank-dyed PET, and a second emission band

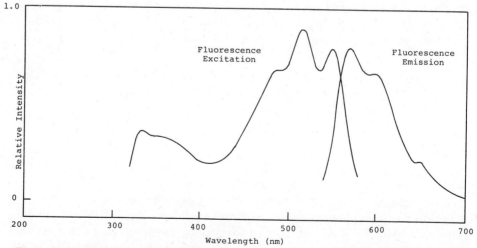

Fig. 9. Corrected fluorescence excitation and uncorrected fluorescence emission spectra for 0.0287% (by weight) C. I. Disperse Red 59-dyed poly(ethylene terephthalate) yarn containing less than 9 ppm Ti (yarn I), at room temperature. Excitation scan: Em λ 610 nm, Ex slit 3 nm, Em slit 10 nm, filter 350 nm. Emission scan: Ex λ 520 nm, Ex slit 10 nm, Em slit 3 nm.

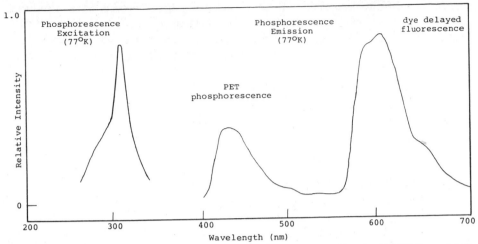

Fig. 10. Uncorrected phosphorescence excitation and emission spectra for 0.421% (by weight) C. I. Disperse Red 59-dyed poly(ethylene terephthalate) yarn containing less than 9 ppm Ti (yarn I), at 77°K. Excitation scan: Em λ 585 nm, Ex slit 10 nm, Em slit 10 nm. Emission scan: Ex λ 310 nm, Ex slit 10 nm, Em slit 10 nm; lifetime (τ) 0.3 sec (430 nm), 0.2 sec (610 nm).

appearing at the same wavelength (~585 and 610 nm) and with the same band shape as the fluorescence emission of the dyestuff. Increasing the dye concentration quenched the 454-nm PET phosphorescence band and increased the emission due to the dye relative to the PET emission band, as shown in Figure 11. The mean lifetime of the PET phosphorescence was also found to decrease with the dye concentration, while the lifetime for the dye emission paralleled that of the PET phosphorescence.

The phosphorescence spectra indicated that energy transfer, not from the dye to the PET as would be expected for a sensitizer of polymer photodegradation, but from the polymer to the dye had occurred. Analysis of the phosphorescence

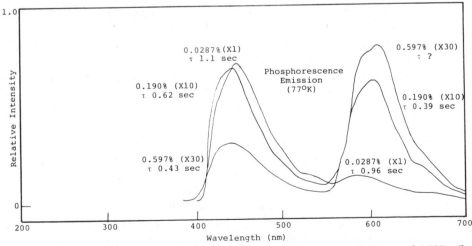

Fig. 11. Uncorrected phosphorescence emission spectra for 0.0287%, 0.190%, and 0.597% (by weight) C. I. Disperse Red 59-dyed poly(ethylene terephthalate) yarn containing less than 9 ppm Ti (yarn I), at 77°K. Emission scan: Ex λ 310 nm, Ex slit 10 nm, Em slit 10 nm; spinning samples.

spectra and lifetimes coupled with the data for the dye fluorescence revealed that energy transfer was occurring from the triplet state of the polymer, $^3PET^*$, causing the dye to be raised to its first excited singlet state, $^1Dye^*$, resulting in the emission of PET-sensitized dye delayed fluorescence as diagrammed below:

$$^1PET + h\nu \rightarrow {}^1PET^*$$

$$^1PET^* \xrightarrow{ISC} {}^3PET^*$$

$$^3PET^* + {}^1Dye \; {}^1PET + {}^1Dye^* \; (T\text{--}S \text{ energy transfer})$$

$$^1Dye^* \rightarrow {}^1Dye + h\nu' \text{ (sensitized delayed fluorescence)}$$

$$^3PET^* \rightarrow {}^1PET + h\nu'' \text{ (phosphorescence)}$$

Triplet–singlet (T–S) energy transfer from PET to the dyestuff is spin forbidden for electron exchange iteration and exciton migration radiationless transfer mechanisms.[38] The decrease in the mean lifetime of the donor species (PET) with increasing acceptor (dye) concentration and the invariance of the donor emission spectrum with increasing acceptor concentration indicate that the transfer involves a long-range dipole–dipole interaction.

The majority of experimental cases where T–S transfer has been shown to occur involve the incorporation of the donor and acceptor in either a glassed solvent or a polymer matrix. However, in these cases, the dispersing medium generally does not participate in the energy transfer process. The work by Dearman and Lang[36] concerning the energy transfer occurring in proflavine-dyed nylon 6,6 films is apparently the only previously reported case of T–S energy transfer in which the donor species was a man-made polymer.

In order to provide further evidence that the delayed fluorescence of C. I. Disperse Red 59 is due to long-range T–S energy transfer from PET and to further characterize this transfer process, kinetic experiments were carried out in order to determine the experimental critical transfer distance R_0. A series of PET yarn I samples were dyed with C. I. Disperse Red 59 to give dye concentrations of 0.256 (0.0058), 0.686 (0.0156), 1.26 (0.0287), 2.82 (0.064), 5.32 (0.121), 8.36 (0.0190), and $8.71 \times 10^{-3} M$ (90.198% by weight), respectively. The uncorrected PET phosphorescence emission spectra and mean lifetimes were obtained for the above samples and a blank-dyed yarn sample. The ratio of the donor lifetime in the absence of acceptor to the lifetime in the presence of the acceptor, $\tau_D/\tau_D{}^0$, and the corresponding donor emission quantum yield ratio, $\phi_D/\phi_D{}^0$ (determined by measuring the areas under the appropriate donor emission curves), were calculated. The resulting data were plotted versus the acceptor concentration according to the method employed by Ermolaev and Sveshnikova[37] and are reproduced in Figure 12. The donor lifetime data gave a critical acceptor concentration, $[A]_{1/2}$, of 6.45×10^{-3} mole/l. which yields an experimental critical transfer distance of 39.5 Å. The magnitude of the critical transfer distance definitely indicates the existence of long-range energy transfer. In addition, the ratio of the initial slope of $\phi_D/\phi_D{}^0$ to that of $\tau_D/\tau_D{}^0$ is approximately equal to 2, as predicted for resonance excitation energy transfer by Galanin.[38]

The critical transfer distance R_0 calculated above is merely a measure of the

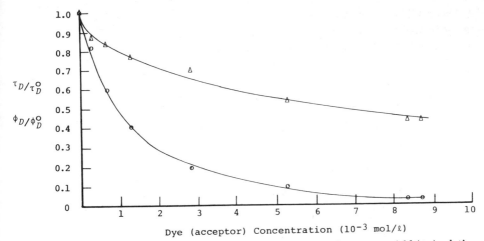

Fig. 12. Ratio of PET (donor) phosphorescence lifetime (τ_D) and quantum yield (ϕ_D) relative to values in the absence of acceptor, $\tau_D/\tau_D{}^0$ and $\phi_D/\phi_D{}^0$, respectively, as a function of C. I. Disperse Red 59 (acceptor) concentration: (Δ) $\tau_D/\tau_D{}^0$; (0) $\phi_D{}^0/\phi_D$.

distance dependence of an energy transfer mechanism for a given donor–acceptor pair and should be a constant under these conditions. For most donor–acceptor pairs, there are at least two types of radiationless electronic energy transfer mechanisms which may apply, with the dominant one depending upon the donor–acceptor separation, viscosity, and/or temperature. For the C. I. Disperse Red 59-dyed poly(ethylene terephthalate), the only other possible energy transfer would be S–S energy transfer. However, the PET fluorescence does not appreciably overlap the dye absorption spectrum, and therefore its contribution should be small [see Fig. 1(a)–1(c)]. Under these conditions, T–S energy transfer should occur not only over donor–acceptor separations of 20–60 Å but also for much smaller separations. The transfer of electronic energy from the PET to C. I. Disperse Red 59 proves that the reverse process cannot occur and therefore does not produce dye-sensitized phototendering of PET by electronic energy transfer.

In summary, referring to the electronic excited states characteristic of the dye C. I. Disperse Red 59 and the polymer poly(ethylene terephthalate) (see Fig. 3), it is apparent that direct (photophysical) energy transfer from the dye to the polymer is unlikely due to the unfavorable energy dispositions, i.e., $E_{PET^*} \gg E_{Dye^*}$, and to the observed energy transfer in the opposite direction. An analysis of the expected photoactivity of the dyestuff, in terms of hydrogen abstraction or the generation of a third photoreactive species, indicates that it ought to be unreactive and function as a photoprotective agent by dissipating absorbed radiant energy photophysically through its intramolecularly hydrogen-bonded states.

Photo-oxidation of Dyed and Blank-Dyed Poly(ethylene Terephthalate)

Our initial photodegradation experiments were designed to investigate the effect of dye concentration on the phototendering of poly(ethylene terephthalate) (PET). Many factors other than the incorporation of dye molecules into a

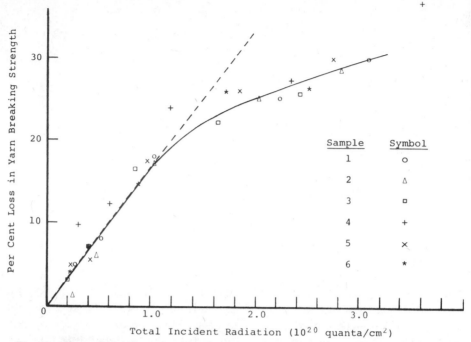

Fig. 13. Percent loss in yarn breaking strength as a function of total incident radiation for blank-dyed PET yarns (yarn I) irradiated in dry air.

polymer matrix may also have a sensitizing effect on the photodegradation of a polymer, e.g., the presence of titanium dioxide (TiO_2) delusterant, carriers for dyeing, atmospheric and/or internal moisture, etc. Therefore, the first experiments were carried out under conditions in which as many as possible sensitizing agents, other than the dye itself, were eliminated.

The PET yarn samples (yarn I) employed were essentially free of TiO_2 (anatase), containing less than 9 ppm Ti. The scoured yarn samples were dyed at 121–124°C under pressure without the aid of a carrier and were flushed with dry air.

A series of six dyed yarn samples (yarn I, samples 1–6) containing 0.064%, 0.121%, 0.198%, 0.344%, 0.597%, and 0.811% (by weight) C. I. Disperse Red 59 were irradiated, along with the corresponding blank-dyed samples, from 5 to 60 hr in the photochemical chamber.

With increasing exposure to radiation the dyed and blank-dyed samples, in general, became weaker and more brittle and exhibited lower percent elongations at break. No visible photofading of the dyed yarns was apparent (not quantized).

The variation in the radiation intensity within the photolysis chamber due to lamp aging was monitored periodically by actinometry. The variation of the incident-light intensity during the course of the experiments was taken into account by measuring the resultant extent of photo-oxidation, expressed as the percent loss in yarn breaking strength, as a function of the total incident quanta rather than as a function of irradiation time. This, in effect, approximates conditions of irradiation at constant light intensity.

Reference to Figure 13 shows the excellent correlation between the PET

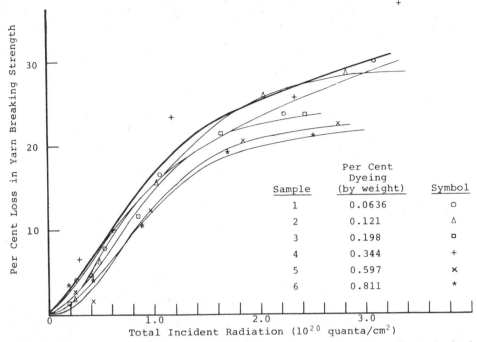

Fig. 14. Percent loss in yarn breaking strength as a function of total incident radiation for dyed PET yarns (yarn I) irradiated in dry air: (—) dyed yarns; (—) average curve for blank-dyed yarn (yarn I).

photodegradation data obtained for the various blank-dyed samples when plotted on a total incident radiation scale. The first sample irradiated in the series, sample 4, deviates somewhat from the "general" curve presumably because it was exposed during the initial period when the lamp intensities were rapidly changing. Therefore, the data obtained for this sample will be neglected for all comparative purposes.

The photo-oxidation rate curves for the dyed PET yarns are given in Figure 14. Comparison of the data for the dyed yarns with the "general" photo-oxidation curve for the blank-dyed PET yarn reveals that although the degradation curves are similar in shape, none of the dye concentrations produced a sensitized phototendering of the polymer. In fact, the dye was found to act increasingly as a photoprotective agent as its concentration in the polymer increased.

The lack of any evidence for dye-sensitized phototendering of PET under the conditions of the first experiment was surprising since C. I. Disperse Red 59 is reported by the supplier to be a possible sensitizer of poly(ethylene terephthalate) phototendering. Inasmuch as the initial experiments were designed to analyze the interactions of the polymer and dyestuff alone, it seemed quite possible that some other species or agent was required in order for the dye to sensitize PET photodegradation.

Commercial PET fibers normally contain TiO_2 (anatase) dispersed throughout the polymer as a delusterant in the range of 0.05% to 2.0%.[39] To determine if there was a synergistic photosensitizing effect between TiO_2 and the dyestuff, a commercial PET yarn sample (yarn II) containing 0.24% TiO_2 was dyed to give a concentration of 0.181% (by weight) C. I. Disperse Red 59. The dyed and

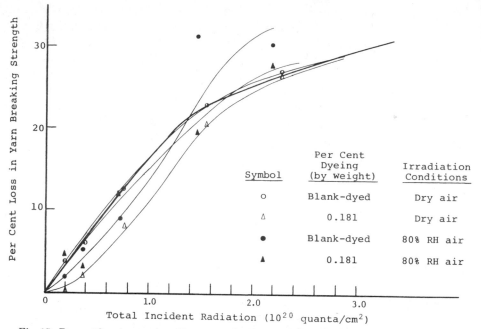

Fig. 15. Percent loss in yarn breaking strength as a function of total incident radiation for dyed and blank-dyed PET yarn (yarn II) irradiated in dry and 80% relative humidity air: (—) yarn II; (—) average curve for blank-dyed yarn I, irradiated in dry air.

blank-dyed samples were irradiated under the same conditions employed for the previous samples. The resulting rate of photo-oxidation curves are depicted in Figure 15. Analysis of the dyed versus the blank-dyed data again indicates that no sensitized phototendering occurred. In addition, comparing the photodegradation curve for the blank-dyed yarn II with the average curve for the blank-dyed yarn I samples, the TiO_2 did not seem to have a sensitizing effect on the rate of PET phototendering.

In the TiO_2-sensitized phototendering of polymers, water vapor may play an important, if not necessary, role.[40] Therefore, another set of samples, identical to those used in the above experiment, were irradiated as before except that the system was flushed with air containing water vapor (80% R.H.). The photodegradation curves for these samples are also depicted in Figure 15. Although the data for these samples exhibit more scatter than for the previous samples, it is still obvious that dye-sensitized phototendering has not occurred. Relating the photodegradation curve for the blank-dyed yarn II irradiated at 80% R.H. to the curve for the same yarn irradiated in dry air indicates, however, that TiO_2-sensitized phototendering of PET does occur when irradiation takes place in the presence of water vapor.

Kinetics of PET Photodegradation

In addition to indicating the reproducibility of the tensile test data when plotted on a total incident radiation abscissa, Figure 13 shows an initial (pseudo-) zero-order rate of PET phototendering (see Appendix).

Using a method of least-squares analysis of the initial data in Figure 13, a value of $k_{h\nu}$ = 1.69 × 10^{-19}% breaking strength loss/quantum absorbed/cm^2 = 1.02 × 10^5% breaking strength loss/einstein absorbed/cm^2, where einstein = 6.02 × 10^{23} quanta, was obtained. This rate constant calculated above may represent a true zero-order rate constant reflecting the primary photolytic reaction occurring in PET photo-oxidation, or it may be a pseudozero-order rate constant characterizing the overall rate of PET photo-oxidation.

The change in the slope of the PET photodegradation curve, at a total incident radiation level of about 10^{20} quanta/cm^2, may be caused by several possible factors. Since the photodegradation of PET with irradiation wavelengths less than 310 nm occurs primarily at the polymer surface,[2] extended exposure results in the formation of a thin layer or "skin" of photo-oxidized polymer. This surface layer is capable of functioning as a radiation-absorbing barrier, thus protecting the underlying undegraded polymer. The inflection in the rate curve could also be due, in part, to a photodegradation mechanism in which scission of the weakest polymer links predominates initially, followed by the breaking of stronger chain links at a reduced rate after the weak links have all been broken.

CONCLUSIONS

The fluorescence and phosphorescence properties of poly(ethylene terephthalate) (PET) have been determined, and the corresponding electronic transitions have been tentatively assigned and quantified. The identification of the lowest excited electronic states, from which most photochemical and photophysical processes occur, provides an insight into PET photodegradation reactions and the possible interactions with other excited electronic species.

Analysis of the absorption and luminescence characteristics of C. I. Disperse Red 59 [1-amino-2-(2-methoxyethoxy)-4-hydroxy-9,10-anthraquinone], compared with those reported for similar compounds, indicated that the dyestuff, which fluoresces but does not phosphoresce, possesses a lowest singlet C–T excited state. Comparing the expected photosensitizing properties of the dyestuff to 9,10-anthraquinone, which possesses a lowest $^1(n,\pi^*)$ excited state and undergoes intersystem crossing to the triplet state in high yield (ϕ_{ISC} = 0.90),[35] one finds a complete reversal of sensitizing behavior. The ability to initiate photoreactions by hydrogen abstraction or by energy transfer from the triplet state is great for 9,10-anthraquinone, but almost nonexistent for the dye.

At room temperature, the luminescence characteristics of the C. I. Disperse Red 59-dyed PET were nearly identical to those of the individual components. At 77°K, triplet–singlet energy transfer from PET to the dyestuff resulted in a sensitized delayed dye fluorescence. A kinetic analysis of the transfer process yielded a critical acceptor (dye) concentration $[A]_{1/2}$ of 6.45 × 10^{-3} mole/l., which gave a critical transfer distance R_0 of 39.5 Å. The large transfer distance, linked with the spectral and lifetime characteristics of the donor (PET) and acceptor (dye) emissions, identified the energy transfer mechanism as being due to a long-range dipole–dipole (Coulombic) interaction.

The photo-oxidation studies of dyed and blank-dyed poly(ethylene terephthalate) yarns revealed that the dyestuff did not sensitize the photodegradation of TiO_2-containing or TiO_2-free PET over a wide range of dye concentrations and irradiation conditions designed to approximate natural exposure. Furthermore, at high concentrations, the dye exhibited a photoprotective effect.

The only evidence obtained for sensitized PET phototendering was for a blank-dyed titanium dioxide-containing yarn irradiated in 80% relative humidity air, thus emphasizing the importance of moisture in the TiO_2-sensitized process. Kinetic analysis of the phototendering data for blank-dyed PET indicated an initial (pseudo-) zero-order reaction with a rate constant of 1.69×10^{-19}% breaking strength loss/quantum absorbed/cm^2.

The photo-oxidation activity of C. I. Disperse Red 59 found experimentally is consistent with the results obtained from the study of the photophysical processes occurring in the dye and polymer. Analysis of the dyed polymer absorption and luminescence spectra indicates that a dyed–polymer complex is not formed and, therefore, the dye cannot function as a photo-optical sensitizer. Due to the inverted relationship of the dye–polymer lowest excited energy levels,

$$^3(\pi,\pi^*)_1 \; ^1(C\text{-}T)_1$$
$$>$$
$$(E_{PET^*} \; E_{Dye^*})$$

the dye should be incapable of efficient direct (photophysical) energy transfer to the polymer. Further evidence for this was found when it was was determined that energy transfer actually took place in the opposite direction, from the polymer to the dye, by a dipole–dipole long-range resonance excitation energy transfer mechanism.

Based on the electronic energy levels characteristic of PET, dyes in general should be incapable of sensitizing photoreactions in PET by a direct (photophysical) energy transfer process. In order for a dye to appear colored, it must absorb visible radiation, therefore limiting the energy of its lowest electronic excited state to a maximum of approximately 70 kcal/mole. Therefore, a few dyes would possess lowest excited states with sufficient electronic energy to allow efficient transfer of PET. Of course, this does not eliminate the possibility of photosensitization by other mechanisms.

Appendix

Kinetics of Chain Scission Photodegradation of Polymers

For a polymeric system in which photodegradation occurs randomly and all bonds are identical, the zero order reaction rate is given by[41]

$$-\frac{dn}{dt} = \phi I_a \tag{1}$$

where n is the number of intact chain links, I_a is the intensity of light absorbed by the polymer (quanta/sec), ϕ is the quantum yield of photodegradation (chain scissions/quantum absorbed), and t is the time (sec).

If it is assumed that the breaking strength b of a textile yarn is proportional to the number of unbroken chain bonds present in a polymer;[42] and if the other stipulations applying to eq. (1) are approximated, then the zero-order reaction rate for PET phototendering can be written as

$$-\frac{db}{dt} = k\phi I_a \tag{2}$$

$$= k' I_a$$

where k is a proportionality constant and $k' = k\phi$. Integration of eq. (2) yields

$$b_0 - b_t = k'I_a t \tag{3}$$

where b_t represents the yarn breaking strength at time t and b_0 is the initial yarn breaking strength.

According to the Beer–Lambert law,

$$I = I_0\, e^{-alc} \tag{4}$$

where I_0 if the monochromatic light intensity (quanta/sec) incident at the surface of an absorbing sample of concentration c (moles/l.), I is the light intensity transmitted through a thickness l (cm) of the sample, and a (l./mole·cm) is the molar extinction coefficient which depends upon the wavelength of the light and the nature of the absorbing species.

The light intensity absorbed by a sample, I_a, is defined by

$$I_a = I - I_0 \tag{5}$$

Combining eqs. (4) and (5) and substituting for I_a in eq. (3) gives

$$b_0 - b_t = k'I_0(1 - e^{-alc})t \tag{6}$$

For the case of strong absorption, which should apply to PET yarn irradiated at 300 nm,

$$1 - e^{-alc} \cong 1$$

and, therefore,

$$b_0 - b_t \cong k'I_0 t \tag{7}$$

Converting the left side of eq. (7) to the percent loss in yarn breaking strength, $[(b_0 - b_t)/b_{02}] \times 100$, and the incident light intensity to units of quanta/cm^2 yields

$$\left(\frac{b_0 - b_t}{b_0}\right) \times 100 = \frac{100k'A}{b_0}\left(\frac{I_0}{A}t\right)$$

$$= k_{h\nu}\left(\frac{I_0}{A}t\right)$$

where A is the area of the sample (cm^2), I_0/A is the incident-light intensity (quanta/cm^2), and $k_{h\nu} = 100k'A/b_0$ is the phototendering rate constant.

Since $(I_0 t)/A$ represents the total radiation intensity (quanta/cm^2) incident on the sample at time t, a plot of the loss in the yarn breaking strength versus the total incident radiation intensity should be linear, with a slope equal to the phototendering rate constant $k_{h\nu}$.

One of the authors, R.G.M., gratefully acknowledges the support of the J. E. Sirrine Textile Foundation during a portion of this work. This manuscript was taken from a dissertation submitted by R. G. Merrill to Clemson University in partial fulfillment of the requirements for the degree of Doctor of Philosophy in Textile and Polymer Science, May 1976.

References

1. M. Day and D. M. Wiles, *J. Polym. Sci., Polym. Lett. Ed.*, **9**, 665 (1971).
2. M. Day and D. M. Wiles, *J. Appl. Polym. Sci.*, **16**, 175 (1972).
3. M. Day and D. M. Wiles, *J. Appl. Polym. Sci.*, **16**, 203 (1972).
4. M. Day and D. M. Wiles, *Can. J. Chem.*, **49**, 2916 (1971).
5. M. Day and D. M. Wiles, *J. Appl. Polym. Sci.*, **16**, 191 (1972).
6. P. Blais, M. Day, and D. M. Wiles, *J. Appl. Polym. Sci.*, **17**, 1895 (1973).
7. P. R. Cheung, M.S. thesis, Clemson University, Clemson, S.C., Dec. 1974.
8. H. Dearman and A. Chan, *J. Chem. Phys.*, **44**, 416 (1966).
9. J. R. Monkman, *J. Soc. Dyers Colour.*, **87**, 16 (1971).
10. American Society for Testing Materials, D2256-69, ASTM Standards, 1971, Supplement Part 24, p. 364.
11. C. A. Parker, *Proc. R. Soc. London, Ser. A*, **220**, 104 (1953).
12. C. G. Hatchard and C. A. Parker, *Proc. R. Soc. London, Ser. A*, **235**, 518 (1956).
13. J. H. Baxendale and N. K. Bridge, *J. Phys. Chem.*, **59**, 783 (1955).

14. J. Lee and H. Seliger, *J. Chem. Phys.*, **40,** 519 (1964).

15. K. C. Kurien, *J. Chem. Soc. B* **10,** 2081 (1971).

16. J. G. Calvert and J. N. Pitts, Jr., *Photochemistry*, Wiley, New York, 1966.

17. C. A. Parker, *Proc. Soc. Anal. Chem.*, **3,** 158 (1966).

18. H. C. Hollifield and J. D. Winefordner, *Anal. Chem.*, **40,** 1959 (1968).

19. F. B. Marcotte, D. Campbell, J. A. Cleaveland, and D. T. Turner, *J. Polym. Sci., Polym. Chem. Ed. A-1*, **5,** 481 (1967).

20. A. B. Thompson and D. W. Woods, *Nature*, **176,** 78 (1955).

21. H. Taylor, W. Tincher, and W. Hamner, *J. Appl. Polym. Sci.*, **14,** 141 (1970).

22. J. G. Pacifici and J. M. Straley, *J. Polym. Sci. B*, **7,** 7 (1969).

23. A. Somersall and J. Guillet, *J. Macromol. Sci., Rev. Macromol. Chem.*, **C13**(2), 135 (1975).

24. R. P. Wayne, *Photochemistry*, American Elsevier, New York, 1970.

25. R. C. Johnson (to du Pont), U.S. Pat. 2,768,052 (Oct. 23, 1956).

26. W. Flaig, J. C. Salfeld and E. Baume, *Justus Liegigs Ann. Chem.*, **618,** 117 (1958).

27. R. Peters and H. Sumner, *J. Chem. Soc.*, **Part 2,** 2101 (1953).

28. H. Meir, in *The Chemistry of Synthetic Dyes*, Vol. 4, K. Venkataraman, Ed., Academic Press, New York, 1971, Chap. 7.

29. G. Porter and P. Suppan, *Trans. Faraday Soc.*, **61,** 1664 (1965).

30. G. Porter, in *Reactivity of the Photoexcited Organic Molecule*, Wiley-Interscience, New York, 1967, pp. 70–110.

31. S. Nagakura and A. Kuboyama, *J. Amer. Chem. Soc.*, **76,** 1003 (1954).

32. J. W. Sidman, *J. Amer. Chem. Soc.*, **78,** 4567 (1956).

33. R. Morton, *Biochemistry of Quinones*, Academic Press, New York, 1965.

34. L. Lang, Ed., *Absorption Spectra in the Ultraviolet and Visible Region*, Vols. VI and VIII, Academic Press, New York, 1965.

35. A. Lamola and N. J. Turro, in *Technique of Organic Chemistry*, Vol. XIV, P. A. Leermakers and A. Weissberger, Eds., Interscience, New York, 1969.

36. H. Dearman, F. Lang, and W. Neely, *J. Polym. Sci., Polym. Phys. Ed. A-2*, **7,** 497 (1969).

37. V. L. Ermolaev and E. B. Sveshnikova, *Sov. Phys.-Dokl.* (Engl. Transl.), **8,** 373 (1963); *Dokl Akad. Nauk SSSR*, **149,** 1295 (1963).

38. M. D. Galanin, *Sov. Phys.-JETP* (Engl. Transl.), **1,** 317 (1955); *Zh. Eksp. Teor. Fiz.*, **28,** 485 (1955).

39. M. J. Wall and G. C. Frank, *Text. Res. J.*, **41,** 32 (1971).

40. G. S. Egerton and K. M. Shah, *Text. Res. J.*, **38,** 130 (1968).

41. B. Ranby and J. Rabek, *Photodegradation, Photooxidation, and Photostabilization of Polymers*, Wiley, New York, 1975.

42. T. Alfrey, Jr., in *High Polymers*, Vol. VI, Interscience, New York, 1948.

Received June 22, 1976
Revised September 14, 1976

JOURNAL OF APPLIED POLYMER SCIENCE   VOL. 21, 2769–2790 (1977)

The NORDFORSK PVC Polymer Characterization Project

ERLING M. SÖRVIK, *The Polymer Group, Department of Organic Chemistry, Chalmers University of Technology and University of Gothenburg, Göteborg, Sweden*

Synopsis

Nordic research and industrial laboratories under the auspices of NORDFORSK performed a series of round-robin tests on characterization methods for PVC. Ten samples of commercial-type emulsion and suspension PVC were used. The resins covered a broad range of molecular weight. Gel permeation chromatography (GPC) was used to determine molecular weight distribution and molecular weight averages, $\overline{M}_n$ and $\overline{M}_w$. These were also determined by osmometry and light scattering measurements, respectively. A good correlation was found for these three methods but GPC was by far the most versatile. Intrinsic viscosity was determined and viscometric routine analysis were investigated to evaluate the precision and informative value of such analysis. Solution viscometry according to the ISO or DIN standard proved to be quite adequate, being accurate, fast, versatile, and inexpensive. NMR spectroscopy was found to be much more accurate for quantitative tacticity determinations than infrared or Raman spectroscopy. For most characterization methods, remarkably good agreement between the laboratories was reached. The thorough investigations of the methods used resulted in detailed recommendations for viscometric, osmometric, and GPC determinations.

INTRODUCTION

In the year 1969, representatives of research and industrial laboratories from the Nordic countries (Denmark, Finland, Norway, and Sweden) came together under the auspices of NORDFORSK (Scandinavian Council for Applied Research) to start a common project concerning structure and properties of industrially important synthetic polymers. In connection with this project, a subgroup, NORDFORSK Polymer Characterization Group, was formed with the aim of studying characterization methods important to current industrial activities and academic research in the Nordic countries. The work was first directed toward poly(vinyl chloride) (PVC) and polyethylene (PE).

In this report, the work on PVC during the years 1970–1973 is summarized. It involves the determination of molecular weight distribution MWD, molecular weight averages $\overline{M}_n$ and $\overline{M}_w$, intrinsic viscosity $[\eta]$, and tacticity. Besides these determinations used in scientific work, viscometric routine analysis was investigated in order to evaluate the precision and informative value of such analysis and to find out whether alternative procedures could be suggested. A further object of these investigations was to characterize a set of batches of PVC resins useful in other NORDFORSK research activities.

A series of round robin tests was carried out involving steps of successive refinements in the measuring technique. During the work, three different sets of PVC resins were characterized, totaling ten resins. The results were discussed at eight meetings. Detailed recommendations have been worked out for viscometric, osmometric, and gel-chromatographic (GPC) determinations on PVC. These recommendations were intended to be published separately. Due to changes in the policy of NORDFORSK, this work had to be canceled. Nor could the other plans for cooperative work within the group be carried through.

EXPERIMENTAL AND RESULTS

Characterization Methods, Samples, and Investigators

The participating laboratories and the methods used are listed in Table I. The PVC resins used are listed in Table II. They include suspension- and emulsion-polymerized resins of commercial and experimental type. The polymers are grouped according to the order in which they were investigated.

In the first round, the work concerned one commercially available standard quality suspension resin and one research quality emulsion resin of similar molecular weight. These polymers were kindly supplied by Dr. H. Leth-Pedersen (A/S Nordiske Kabel- og Traadfabrikker, Kemisk Forskningslaboratorium, La Coursvej 7, DK-2000 Copenhagen, Denmark) and Prof. J. Ugelstad (SINTEF, N-7034 Trondheim-NTH, Norway), respectively. During the NORDFORSK work, they stored an appropriate quantity of respective polymer batches.

In the second round, a series of suspension and emulsion polymers with three different levels of molecular weight was investigated. The material, one commercial and five experimental polymers, was kindly delivered by KemaNord AB (Fack, S-850 13 Sundsvall, Sweden) and Norsk Hydro A/S (Porsgrunn Fabrikker, N-3901 Porsgrunn, Norway) in close cooperation. The experimental polymers were produced in pilot plant quantities exclusively for this investigation. Typical standard procedures for suspension and emulsion polymerization were followed (see Appendices 1 and 2). Changes in molecular weight were achieved by changes in polymerization temperature (PT).

In the third round, some of the recommended characterization procedures were tested on two commercial suspension polymers of similar molecular weight. The resins were kindly supplied by Norsk Hydro A/S and KemaNord AB, respectively. During the NORDFORSK work, samples of group 2 and 3 resins could be ordered from these companies.

Solvents and Dissolution Methods

Tetrahydrofuran (THF), purum, and cyclohexanone (CH) were used as solvents throughout the investigation. A few tests with dimethylformamide (DMF) and dimethylacetamide (DMA) gave inconsistent results, as expected.

Retention of molecular aggregates of PVC even in good solvents is well known and has been studied elsewhere (see, for example, Andersson et al.[1]) As confirmed in this investigation, the presence of aggregates will noticeably influence GPC and light-scattering (LS) measurements but not osmometric or viscometric measurements.

TABLE I
Participating Laboratories and Method Used

	$\overline{M}_n$ (osmom.)	$\overline{M}_w$ (LS)	$\overline{M}_n, \overline{M}_w,$ MWD (GPC)	(viscometry)	$[\eta]$ η_{rel} (viscometry)	Tacticity Raman	IR	NMR
1. Danmarks Tekniske Højskole, Sect. of Polymer Technology, Lyngby, Denmark	x	–	x	x	x	–	–	–
2. Nordisk Kabel-og Traadfabriker, København, Denmark	x	x	x	x	–	–	–	–
3. Dept. of Wood and Polymer Chemistry, Univ. of Helsinki, Finland	x	–	–	x	–	x	x	x
4. Neste OY, Kulloo, Finland	x	x	x	–	–	–	–	x
5. Finnish Pulp and Paper Research Institute, Tapiola, Finland	–	x	–	–	–	–	–	–
6. Pekema OY, Kulloo, Finland	–	–	–	–	x	–	–	–
7. Norsk Hydro A/S, Porsgrunn, Norway	–	–	–	–	x	–	–	–
8. SINTEF, Trondheim, Norway	x	–	–	–	–	–	–	–
9. Chalmers Tekniska Högskola, Polymergruppen Göteborg, Sweden	–	–	x	x	x	x	x	x
10. KemaNord AB, Sundsvall, Sweden	–	–	–	–	x	–	–	–
11. L.M. Ericsson AB, Stockholm, Sweden	–	–	x	–	x	–	–	–

TABLE II
Investigated PVC Resins

Chronologic group	Designation	Polymerization		K value[b]	Delivered by
		System[a]	Temp, °C		
1.	Corvic D65/8, X-AB	S	—	65	Dr. H. Leth-Pedersen, NKT Prof. J. Ugelstad, SINTEF
2.	S-54	E_{expt} S_{expt}	75	53.1	KemaNord AB
	Pevikon R-24[c]	S	55	66.5	KemaNord AB
	S-80	S_{expt}	43	78.6	KemaNord AB
	E-54	E_{expt}	75	54.6	Norsk Hydro A/S
	E-67	E_{expt}	57	68.7	Norsk Hydro A/S
	E-80	E_{expt}	43	81.2	Norsk Hydro A/S
3.	Pevikon S-685	S	—	68	KemaNord AB
	Norvinyl S9-70	S	—	68	Norsk Hydro A/S

[a] E = Emulsion polymerization; S = suspension polymerization, expt = experimental quality.
[b] K value according to Fikentscher reported by supplier.
[c] Present designation of this resin type: Pevikon S-657.

In order to disintegrate PVC aggregates in THF solutions, autoclaving for 3 hr at 120°C is recommended.[2] An inexpensive autoclave specially designed for this purpose has been constructed. Drawings and autoclaves may be ordered from Chalmers University of Technology (Chalmers University of Technology, Polymer Group, Fack, S-402 20 Gothenburg, Sweden).

As a safety precaution, peroxides should be removed from THF by refluxing over sodium borhydride followed by distillation over sodium.[1] The solvent and solutions should be kept under nitrogen. Presence of peroxides may influence spectrometric determinations on PVC obtained from THF solutions but does not seem to influence the other determinations investigated.

Light Scattering (LS)

Absolute determinations of $\overline{M}_w$ were performed by LS at 5460 Å of THF and CH solutions at 20–25°C. The THF solutions were autoclaved 2 hr at 120°C. The results and further experimental details are given in Table III. Values from the same laboratory using the same technique are given in the same row in the table even when the measurements were performed on different occasions. However, when different techniques were used, the data are given in separate rows. This method of presentation is used throughout the report if not otherwise stated.

As rather few LS measurements were undertaken, few statements can be made. At the most, one resin, Corvic D65/8, was investigated by four laboratories. In this case the coefficient of variation between the mean $\overline{M}_w$ values is only 2.0%. Measurements on CH and THF solutions show reasonable agreement whenever comparison is possible, i.e., for Corvic D65/8, X-AB, and Pevikon R24. No differences between results from various measuring equipment are observable. It might be concluded that the LS measurements on CH and THF solutions of PVC were more easy to perform and gave more conformity of results than expected.

Membrane Osmometry

Absolute determinations of $\overline{M}_n$ were performed with high-speed automatic membrane osmometers using CH and DMF solutions.

Experimental details and results are given in Table IV. DMF proved to be a bad solvent compared with CH. Membranes of the type Sartorius SM 11539 and Schleicher & Schüll 08 gave equivalent results, while Sartorius SM 11536 was too permeable for low molecular weight species. This explains the high $\overline{M}_n$ values given in the last row of the table. Apart from these results, the measurements show excellent agreement. For Corvic D65/8, the coefficient of variation for the $\overline{M}_n$ determinations at four laboratories is 5.1%. No difference between different measuring equipment is observed.

Determination of θ Temperature

A special investigation concerning the determination of the θ temperature was undertaken at the University of Helsinki. The Flory θ temperature is an important thermodynamic quantity which may, in principle, be determined by

TABLE III
Results Obtained by Light Scattering ($\overline{M}_w \times 10^{-3}$)[a]

Corvic D65/8	X-AB	S-54	Pevikon R-24	S-80	E-54	E-67	E-80	Solution	dn/dc, ml/g	Remarks
103.3	96.8							CH	0.074	SOFICA-40B
106.0[b]								THF	0.1108	SOFICA-4200
107.0	101.0							THF	0.107	Brice-Phoenix-2000
108.0	118.0									
		43.6	104.0	124.5	44.5	99.0	177.8	THF	0.1065	SOFICA-40B
			83.6					THF	0.109	Brice-Phoenix-2000
Average 106.0	105.3	43.6	93.8	124.5	44.5	99.0	177.8			

[a] All measurements at ambient temperatures.
[b] Extrapolation to zero angle from constant C/R_θ values.

TABLE IV
Results Obtained by Osmometry ($\overline{M}_n \times 10^{-3}$)

Corvic D65/8	X-AB	S-54	Pevikon R-24	S-80	E-54	E-67	E-80	Pevikon S-685	Norvinyl S9-70	Solvent, measuring temp., °C, and membrane type
49.5	54.5	27.2	41.9	73.1	28.5	50.2	67.4	45.7	44.6	CH 35 Sartonius SM 11539
54.0	53.6	26.0	44.8	71.2	28.7	45.6	68.5	48.8	49.6	CH 25 Sartonius SM 11539
49.0	57.0				29.0	43.9	69.0			CH 35 Schleicher & Schüll 08
53.5	49.1				34.8	51.0	67.0			CH 35 Schleicher & Schüll 08
		31.7	43.4	69.1						CH 35 Sartonius SM 11539
Average 51.5	53.6	28.3	43.3	71.1	30.3	47.7	68.0	47.3	47.1	
75.6	58.7									DMF 25 Sartonius SM 11536
67.7	60.9									DMF 25 Sartonius SM 11536
		33.0	53.2	80.9	31.8	50.1	86.2			CH 25 Sartonius SM 11536

TABLE V
First Virial Coefficient A_1, Second Virial Coefficient A_2, and Flory's Theta
Temperature θ for PVC in Cyclohexanone Determined by Membrane Osmometry at
308–322°K (35–49°C) Using Sartonius SM 11539 Membranes

Parameter	S-54	Pevikon R-24	S-80	E-54	E-67	E-80
$A_1 \times 10^5$	3.534	2.309	1.408	3.300	2.096	1.471
A_2, mole·cm³/g²						
308°K	2.306	3.322	1.989	2.293	1.058	2.307
311°K	3.979	—	—	3.567	3.508	—
315°K	4.989	4.753	2.461	5.055	4.040	2.723
322°K	—	5.758	(2.473)	—	—	3.492
θ, °K	302	288	282	303	306	291

osmometric measurements.[3] In polymer solutions at $T = \theta$ (θ conditions), the polymer chain dimensions are unperturbed by intramolecular interactions. Measurements on polymer solutions at θ are ideal from a thermodynamic point of view. Thus, theory predicts α in the Mark-Houwink equation,

$$[\eta_\theta] = K_\theta \overline{M}_w{}^\alpha$$

to be 0.5, independent of polymer and solvent type. K_θ should be nearly independent of the solvent type. From theoretical considerations, Van Krevelen and Hoftyzer[4] have estimated the K_θ value of PVC to be 12.4×10^{-4}.

An estimate of θ may theoretically be determined from the temperature dependence of the second virial coefficient, A_2, by extrapolating A_2 to zero. A_2 is given by the virial equation for osmotic pressure,

$$\frac{\Pi}{CRT} = A_1 + A_2 \cdot C + \cdots$$

where $A_1, A_2 \ldots$ are virial coefficients, C is solute concentration, and Π is osmotic pressure.

To test this seemingly simple method, a separate series of measurements on "group 2 resins" in CH was utilized for a calculation (see Table V). A_1 was taken as the reciprocal of $(\overline{M}_n)_{average}$, Table IV. The data of Table V indicate that the scatter of the A_2 values is quite high. This adversely affects the estimate of θ. A definite trend toward lower θ values with increasing molecular weight (lower PT) is indicated.

The scatter in A_2 will not influence the calculated average value of θ to a great extent, however. The $\theta_{calculated}$ was found to be 295° ± 12°K for the samples investigated. This is apparently too high a value. A θ temperature around 295°K for the PVC/CH system implies that ordinary viscometric and osmometric determinations on PVC at room temperature would be carried out near θ conditions. This is not in accordance with general experience, which can be seen, e.g., by comparing the theoretical values of α and K_θ given above with experimentally found values: Theoretical values: $\alpha = 0.5$, $K_\theta = 12.4 \times 10^{-4}$. Experimental values[5] in CH at 25°C: $\alpha = 0.78$, $K = 1.38 \times 10^{-4}$.

The reason why such a high value for the θ temperature was obtained in this case is not fully understood. In fact, a θ temperature of 303°K is reported[6] for PVC. This may well be correct, however, as it refers to the system THF–water

(100:11.9), which is a commonly used precipitation system for PVC at room temperature.

Gel Permeation Chromatography (GPC)

Determination of molecular weight distribution (MWD) and molecular weight averages was performed by GPC using a Waters GPC Model 200 and, in one case, a Model Ana-Prep. All participants followed the ordinary experimental procedure recommended by Waters: solvent, THF; temperature, 25°C; sample volume, 2 ml; sample concentration, 2–3 mg/ml; injection time, 2 min; flow rate, 1.0 ml/min; columns, 4–5 Styragel columns, plate count > 700 plates/ft, range 10^3–10^5 Å or higher.

During the work, some laboratories changed their column combinations in order to increase the resolution in the high molecular weight part of the MWD. The need for heat treatment of the sample solutions (3 hr at 120°C) was also investigated by some workers. Considerable attention was paid to alternative procedures for calibration and data treatment.

Calibration

In the calibration procedure, all participants used the same narrow-distribution standards of polystyrene (PS) delivered by Waters. Transformation of the relation found for PS between elution volume (V_e) and the molecular weight (M) into a calibration curve for PVC was performed either by the universal calibration principle[7] or the Q-factor method.[8]

Most workers preferred the universal calibration method. This implies that the separation in GPC is governed by the hydrodynamic volume of the solute and that $[\eta]M$ is a measure of the hydrodynamic volume. The Mark–Houwink equation relates $[\eta]$ to M for flexible, unbranched polymers and thus provides a simple means to convert a PS calibration into a PVC calibration. Most workers used the relations[9]

$$[\eta]_{PS} = 1.179 \times 10^{-4} \, \overline{M}_w{}^{0.72}$$

$$[\eta]_{PVC} = 1.35 \times 10^{-4} \, \overline{M}_w{}^{0.77}$$

One laboratory used a slightly different equation for PVC[5]:

$$[\eta]_{PVC} = 1.5 \times 10^{-4} \, \overline{M}_w{}^{0.77}$$

This laboratory also measured $[\eta]$ directly for the PS standards used. It turned out that these two approaches gave about the same GPC results.

A few workers used the Q-factor method. This is based on the assumption that separation in GPC is related to the extended chain length of the solute molecules. Although this assumption is not generally valid, the results confirm that the method may be used for unbranched, undegraded PVC (see Table VI and ref. 9).

GPC Data Treatment

The GPC curves for all samples were quite similar in shape, showing the regular, fairly narrow distribution characteristic for undegraded PVC. Computing

TABLE VI
Comparison Between Universal Calibration Principle (U) and Q-Factor Method (Q)[a]

	Corvic D65/8			Pevikon S-54	R-24	S-80	E-54	E-67	E-80
$\overline{M}_{nU} \times 10^{-3}$	52.2	51.7	53.1	26.1	40.7	50.6	26.7	42.4	54.2
$\overline{M}_{nQ} \times 10^{-3}$	46.0	47.5	48.5	23.4	36.8	44.8	23.6	38.7	48.5
$\overline{M}_{nU}/\overline{M}_{nQ}$	1.13	1.09	1.09	1.12	1.11	1.13	1.13	1.10	1.12
$\overline{M}_{wU} \times 10^{-3}$	122.0	115.0	117.0	53.2	86.2	127.0	56.7	97.4	146.0
$\overline{M}_{wQ} \times 10^{-3}$	113.0	108.5	109.0	47.2	77.6	117.0	50.6	89.8	135.0
$\overline{M}_{wU}/\overline{M}_{wQ}$	1.08	1.06	1.08	1.13	1.11	1.09	1.12	1.08	1.08

[a] Corvic D65/8 measured with three different column combinations. All other samples analyzed with still another column combination.

MWD and molecular weight averages from the GPC curves was performed according to Waters recommendations using different computer facilities. The difference in results when using two well-known computer programs on the same experimental data is illustrated in Table VII. Drott's program allows for the calculation of long-chain branching if values of the intrinsic viscosity are included.

In Waters recommendations, no correction for axial dispersion is included. Calculations have shown that the gain in precision is of importance only for narrow distributions but not when $\overline{M}_w/\overline{M}_n > 2$. There is also a considerable risk for introducing errors when using these corrections. Our results clearly illustrate these different aspects: After correction, $\overline{M}_n$ should increase and $\overline{M}_w$ decrease. In Table VIII, examples of the effect of unintentionally introduced errors are given. In another investigation, Table IX, using the same data program, the corrections were in the proper direction but quite insignificant compared with the experimental errors.

Reproducibility

The reproducibility of the GPC measurements is quite good. The coefficient of variation within a single laboratory using standardized technique was 2–6% over an extended period of time (Table X). Between the participating laboratories, the variation was also very small although the samples represented different polymerization systems and molecular weight ranges. This is still more remarkable because different pretreatments of the sample solutions were used as well as different methods for GPC calibration (Table XI). In fact, the results

TABLE VII
Comparison Between Results Obtained When Using Different Computer Programs
on the Same Experimental GPC Data

	Program	$\overline{M}_n \times 10^{-3}$	$\overline{M}_w \times 10^{-3}$
Pevikon S-685	Drott[a]	44.8	91.8
	Pickett[b]	46.0	96.5
Norvinyl S9-70	Drott[a]	43.9	95.2
	Pickett[b]	45.0	99.6

[a] E. E. Drott and R. A. Mendelson, *J. Polym. Sci. A-2*, **8**, 1361 and 1373 (1970).

[b] H. E. Pickett, M. J. R. Cantow, and J. F. Johnson, *J. Appl. Polym. Sci.*, **10**, 917 (1966).

are much more uniform in this round robin test than in the IUPAC round[10] performed in 1969. This is an effect of the close cooperation between the Nordic laboratories made possible by the active work in the NORDFORSK Polymer Characterization Group.

TABLE VIII
Erratic Influences of Correction for Axial Dispersion on GPC Data[a]

	S-54	Pevikon R-24	S-80	E-54	E-67	E-80	Pevikon S-685	Norvinyl S9-70
$\bar{M}_n$ uncorr. $\times 10^{-3}$	26.1	40.7	50.6	26.7	42.4	54.2	44.8	43.9
$\bar{M}_n$ corr. $\times 10^{-3}$	29.1	47.0	59.7	29.9	49.1	64.3	38.8	44.1
$\bar{M}_w$ uncorr. $\times 10^{-3}$	53.2	86.2	127.0	56.9	97.4	146.0	91.8	95.2
$\bar{M}_w$ corr. $\times 10^{-3}$	54.1	88.6	134.0	57.6	100.0	153.0	83.6	89.6

[a] For Pevikon S-685 and Norvinyl S9-70, the correction method and data program used were according to S. T. Balke and A. E. Hamielec, 6th Int. Seminar on GPC, Miami Beach, Oct. 1968. For all other samples, the correction procedure applied was according to S. T. Balke and A. E. Hamielec, *J. Appl. Polym. Sci.*, 13, 1381 (1969).

TABLE IX
Expected Influence of Correction for Axial Dispersion on GPC-Data
Sample: Corvic D65/8. Correction program used: S. T. Balke and A. E. Hamielec, 6th Int. Seminar on GPC, Miami Beach, Oct. 1968. (Compare Table VIII.)
Three different column combinations were used.

Column combination	A	B	C
$\bar{M}_n$ uncorr. $\times 10^{-3}$	52.2	51.7	52.7
$\bar{M}_n$ corr. $\times 10^{-3}$	52.3	51.7	53.5
$\bar{M}_w$ uncorr. $\times 10^{-3}$	122.0	115.0	120.0
$\bar{M}_w$ corr. $\times 10^{-3}$	112.0	108.0	109.0

Remark: Column combination A: $3 \times 10^5, 1 \times 10^5, 3 \times 10^4, 1.5 \times 10^4$ A
Remark: Column combination B: $1 \times 10^6, 3 \times 10^5, 1 \times 10^5, 3 \times 10^4, 1.5 \times 10^4$ A
Remark: Column combination C: $1 \times 10^6, 2 \times 10^4, 1 \times 10^4, 1 \times 10^3$ A

TABLE X
Reproducibility of GPC Measurements Within One Laboratory[a]

Solution pretreatment	Date of test		$\bar{M}_n \times 10^{-3}$	$\bar{M}_w \times 10^{-3}$	$\bar{M}_z \times 10^{-3}$
—	5/29/70		49.3	118.4	249.4
—	6/30/70		45.9	116.5	238.2
—	10/5/70		42.3	113.8	220.5
—	10/8/70		45.4	115.6	227.6
		Average	45.7	116.1	233.9
		Coeff. of var., %	6.3	1.6	5.4
120°C, 2 h	6/1/70		44.2	109.3	195.9
120°C, 3 h	9/21/70		45.1	113.4	205.3
120°C, 3 h	10/5/70		46.6	111.5	202.2
120°C, 3 h	10/7/70		45.4	111.3	202.2
		Average	45.3	111.4	201.4
		Coeff. of var., %	2.2	1.5	2.0

[a] Sample: Corvic D65/8.

TABLE XI

Reproducibility of GPC Measurements Among Different Laboratories. Autoclaved and Nonautoclaved Solutions. Calibration According to Universal Calibration Procedure or Q-Factor Method

	Corvic D65/8	X-AB	S-54	Pevikon R-24	S-80	E-54	E-67	E-80	Pevikon S-685	Norvinyl S9-70
$\bar{M}_n \times 10^{-3}$	—	—	26.1	40.7	50.6	26.7	42.4	54.2	41.0	41.8
	53.5	47.0	26.4	44.7	61.7	30.8	47.2	67.5	44.0	47.0
	—	—	26.1	49.3	61.4	27.5	39.2	72.0	42.3	44.7
	45.3	47.1	26.5	39.8	57.3	26.8	42.4	57.7	46.0	45.0
	50.2	52.3	26.1	43.3	59.4	27.2	43.7	63.1	47.5	50.0
Average	49.7	48.8	26.2	43.6	58.1	27.8	42.9	62.9	44.2	45.7
Coeff. of var., %	8.3	6.2	0.7	8.6	7.8	6.1	6.0	11.5	6.0	6.6
$\bar{M}_w \times 10^3$	—	—	53.2	86.2	127.0	56.7	97.4	146.0	93.3	96.0
	115.0	113.4	48.7	82.7	133.8	54.9	97.4	153.5	98.0	101.3
	—	—	57.2	104.2	161.1	63.2	111.1	183.1	91.1	91.0
	111.4	108.3	51.2	89.5	143.0	57.7	99.1	162.4	96.5	99.6
	106.1	115.9	53.3	91.6	142.9	57.4	99.5	166.5	101.1	104.3
Average	110.8	112.5	52.7	90.6	141.6	58.0	100.9	162.3	96.0	98.4
Coeff. of var., %	4.0	3.4	5.9	8.1	9.1	5.4	5.7	8.7	4.1	5.2

TABLE XII
Effect of Heat Treatment (3 h, 120°C) of Sample Solutions on GPC Measurements

	$\overline{M}_n \times 10^{-3}$		$\overline{M}_w \times 10^{-3}$	
	Nonautocl.	Autocl.	Nonautocl.	Autocl.
Corvic D65/8	45.7	45.3	116.1	111.4
	49.9	53.5	118.7	115.0
	49.7	50.2	106.3	106.1
X-AB	46.0	47.1	120.7	108.3
S-54	26.6	26.1	54.0	53.2
	24.8	22.7	51.2	48.4
Pevikon R-24	49.2	49.3	104.2	104.7
	40.0	40.7	89.2	86.2
	42.1	39.3	87.7	82.7
S-80	55.1	50.6	144.0	127.0
	55.5	54.9	139.9	133.8
E-54	27.2	26.7	57.2	56.7
	26.4	26.8	57.2	54.9
E-67	43.4	42.4	105.0	97.4
	40.1	41.6	94.5	97.4
E-80	58.0	54.2	175.0	146.0
	63.8	60.1	151.0	153.5

Column Combination and Resolution

As pointed out earlier, the column combination should be chosen in such a way that a good resolution is obtained within the molecular weight range of interest. The $\overline{M}_w$ values of group 2 resins, row 3 Table XI, illustrates the effect of inferior resolution in the high molecular weight part of the MWD. In the subsequent testing round, an improved column combination was used (see group 3 resins, row 3, Table XI). On the other hand, as shown in Table IX, there is little reason to further improve an already acceptable resolution.

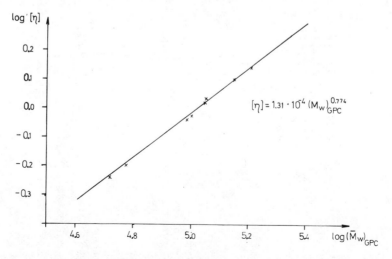

Fig. 1. Relation between $[\eta]_{THF}^{25°C}$ and $(\overline{M}_w)_{GPC}$.

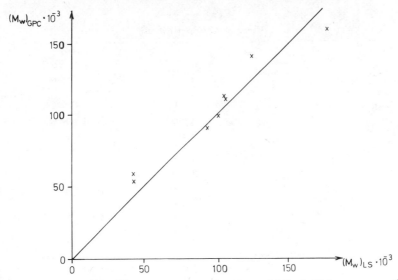

Fig. 2. Comparison between $\overline{M}_w$ values obtained by LS and GPC. Solid line represent $(\overline{M}_w)_{GPC}$ = $(\overline{M}_w)_{LS}$.

Heat Treatment of Sample Solutions

Retention of molecular aggregates of PVC even in good solvents is well known and has been studied elsewhere.[2,11] This investigation confirms that molecular aggregation influences the GPC measurements (Table XII). For practical purposes, however, heat treatment (3 hr at 120°C) is not necessary for undegraded samples of ordinary commercial PVC, only for high molecular weight resins. Even for such polymers, $\overline{M}_n$ is hardly influenced (see also Table X). On the other hand, high molecular weight fractions, degraded samples, and samples of high tacticity always call for heat treatment of the sample solutions.[1,2]

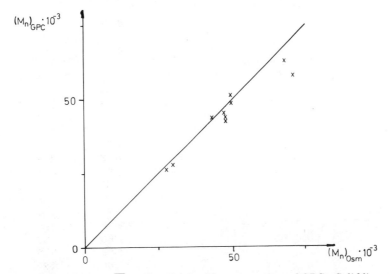

Fig. 3. Comparison between $\overline{M}_n$ values obtained by osmometry and GPC. Solid line represent $(\overline{M}_n)_{GPC}$ = $(\overline{M}_n)_{osm}$.

TABLE XIII
Viscosity Measurements

PVC resin	[η]		η_{rel}	No.[b,c] η_{red}[b]	K[b,d]
	in THF	in CH			
Corvic D65/8	1.05	1.11			
		1.12			
		1.07			
		1.09			
		1.09			
Average	1.05	1.10			
X-AB	1.08	1.16			
		1.08			
		1.09			
		1.01			
Average	1.08	1.08			
S-54	0.66 (corr)[a]	0.63	1.34	68	
	0.58	0.61	1.35	69	
			1.34	68	
			1.35	69	
Average	0.58	0.62	1.35	69	53.6
Pevikon R-24	0.96 (corr)[a]	0.90	1.56	112	
			1.54	108	
		0.95	1.56	112	
		0.88			
		0.90			
Average		0.91	1.56	111	66.9
S-80	1.36 (corr)[a]	1.28	1.84	162	
		1.23	1.81	168	
			1.81	162	
			1.81	161	
				162	
Average		1.26	1.82	165	78.9
E-54	0.69 (corr)[a]	0.65	1.36	73	
	0.66 (corr)[a]	0.63	1.36	72	
	0.64		1.37	73	
	0.63		1.36	73	
				72	
Average	0.64	0.64	1.36	73	54.3
E-67	1.02 (corr)[a]	1.00	1.59	118	
	1.06	0.93	1.59	118	
	(0.80)		1.59	117	
			1.60	117	
				119	
Average	1.06	0.97	1.59	118	68.5
E-80	1.46 (corr)[a]	1.36	1.85	175	
	1.39	1.42	1.88	170	
			1.88	176	
			1.90	175	
				179	
Average	1.39	1.39	1.88	175	81.3
Pevikon S-685	1.04 (corr)[a]	—	1.59	118	
	1.00		1.60	119	
			1.59	117	
			1.60	120	

continued

TABLE XIII

| PVC resin | $[\eta]$ | | η_{rel} | No.[b,c] η_{red}[b] | K[b,d] |
	in THF	in CH			
Average	1.00		1.60	118	69.0
Norvinyl S9-70	1.04 (corr)[a]	—	1.61	122	
	1.00		1.62	125	
			1.60	120	
			1.61	121	
Average	1.00		1.61	122	69.5

[a] Corrected for kinetic energy loss.

[b] Determined according to ISO standard R 174.

[c] ISO viscosity number $= \dfrac{\eta - \eta_0}{\eta_0 \cdot C} = (\eta_{rel} - 1)\dfrac{1}{C}$ where C = concentration in g/100 ml.

[d] K-value according to H. Fikentscher, *Cellulosechemie*, 13, 58 (1932)

$$\log \eta_{rel} = C \cdot \left[\frac{75\ K^2}{1 + 1,5\ KC} + K \right]$$

where C = concentration in g/100 ml.

Accuracy of the GPC Data

In Table XI, relevant GPC data of the investigated samples are summarized. The Mark–Houwink relation given in Figure 1 is based on these data and the $[\eta]$ values given in Table XIII. This relation,

$$[\eta] = 1.31 \times 10^{-4}\ (\overline{M}_w)_{GPC}^{0.774}$$

is in excellent agreement with the relation used for the universal calibration procedure[9] (see above). It is a strong indication that the GPC and viscometric measurements have been carried out with great accuracy and precision. Comparing Tables XI, III, and IV show good agreement between GPC, osmometric, and light-scattering measurements. This is also illustrated in Figures 2 and 3.

Solution Viscometry

Viscometric measurements were carried out in CH and THF at 25°C using Ubbelohde viscometers and, in one case, Ostwald viscometers. The bulk of the investigations was carried out according to the ISO standard R 174, i.e., determining η_{rel} at a concentration of 0.005 g/ml in CH. Intrinsic viscosity was also determined. The results are summarized in Table XIII.

The viscometric determinations show an extraordinarily good agreement between the different laboratories. Furthermore, there are virtually no differences between CH and THF in these measurements, irrespective of concentration and molecular weight. The results of the viscometric measurements according to the ISO standard are given in three ways, which, in fact, are equivalent:
Relative viscosity:

$$\eta_{rel} = \eta/\eta_0$$

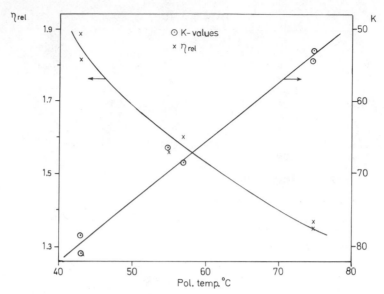

Fig. 4. η_{rel} and K value according to Fikentscher plotted as a function of polymerization temperature PT of PVC.

ISO Viscosity number:

$$\text{``}\eta_{\text{red}}\text{''} = \frac{\eta - \eta_0}{\eta_0 \cdot C} = (\eta_{\text{rel}} - 1)\frac{1}{C}$$

K Value according to Fikentscher[12]:

$$\log \eta_{\text{rel}} = C \cdot \left[\frac{75K^2}{1 + 1.5KC} + K\right]$$

where C = concentration in g/100 ml.

The ranking of these measures was not discussed seriously. In spite of its empiric and complicated relation to measured quantities, the use of K is firmly established in industry, presumably due to its linear relation to PT (Fig. 4).

The η_{rel} and viscosity number are not simply related to PT. In one laboratory, an Ubbelohde viscometer of about the same construction as an approved ISO viscometer was used. The uncorrected results obtained with this viscometer were in good agreement with the rest of the measurements. According to Andersson,[13] a correction for kinetic energy loss was calculated from the dimensions of the viscometer. When this correction was applied, slightly higher viscosity values were obtained, well outside the scatter of the rest of the measurements. It may be concluded that correction terms should not be calculated but estimated experimentally. It may be further concluded that no special correction is necessary if the ISO or DIN standards are applied. For proper characterization work, $[\eta]$ must be used (see concluding paragraph).

In Figure 5, $[\eta]_{\text{THF}}^{25°C}$ is related to $(\overline{M}_w)_{\text{LS}}$ in a log–log diagram in order to illustrate the correlation between the viscometric and LS measurements performed. Although the data points are very few, a Mark–Houwink equation was calculated via a linear regression analysis. The result is compared with the most widely accepted Mark–Houwink relation for PVC.[14] The deviation between

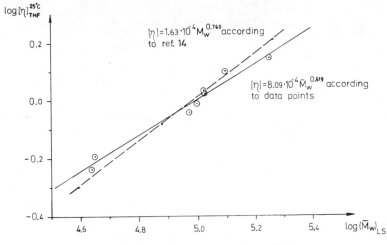

Fig. 5. Relation between $[\eta]_{THF}^{25°C}$ and $(\overline{M}_w)_{LS}$.

this function and the data points in the middle of the diagram is small, while the few points at both extremes show a considerable deviation, presumably due to the LS measurements (cf. Fig. 2). As to the high accuracy of the $[\eta]$ measurements, this is illustrated in Figure 1.

Measurements of Tacticity

Determination of tacticity was performed by infrared, Raman, and NMR spectroscopy. In connection with this work, a special investigation was carried out at the University of Helsinki. In the report,[15] a thorough discussion of the experimental technique is given. As the steric structure of PVC has only little influence on the position of the absorption bands, tacticity determinations are hampered by extensive overlapping of spectral peaks. This may result in wrong assignments in the relation between structure and band position. It also calls for intricate curve resolution methods in quantitative determinations. NMR spectroscopy is by far the most accurate method for measurements of tacticity. Using this technique, both qualitative and quantitative investigations were carried out.

NMR spectra were determined with Varian 60 and 100 Mc instruments on o-dichlorobenzene solutions at 140°C. A qualitative comparison between the spectra obtained from both instruments shows that the variation in the degree of syndiotacticity is very small among polymers E-54, E-67, E-80, S-54, R-24, and S-80. No exact correlation to the PT can be deduced from the present data owing to the narrow range of temperatures. However, it is well known that the syndiotacticity increases with decreasing Pt.[16]

In the quantitative determinations, the NMR spectrum of the methylene groups of polymer S-80 was resolved graphically into six bands, which were assigned to syndiotactic, isotactic, and combined sequences. By comparing the areas of the syndiotactic bands to the area of the total band complex, a measure, α, of the amount of syndiotactic dyades was obtained. A computer-based curve resolving technique was also tested on polymer R-24. For polymer S-80, α was found to be 0.56. Accordingly, slightly more than half of the dyades were syn-

TABLE XIV
Tacticity Measurements

PVC resin	IR A_{1428}/A_{1435}[a]	Raman A_{1428}/A'_{1435}[a]	NMR α[b]
S-54	1.05 1.10	1.17	0.52
Pevikon R-24	1.10 1.17	1.20	0.54
S-80	1.15 1.21	1.23	0.56
E-54	1.04 1.09	—	0.51
E-67	1.12 1.16	1.21	0.55
E-80	1.15 1.22	—	0.56

[a] Tacticity evaluations using absorbance ratio 1428 cm^{-1}/1435 cm^{-1} in IR and Raman spectroscopy according to H. Germar, K.-H. Hellwege, and U. Johnsen, *Makromol. Chem.*, **60**, 106 (1963), and P. J. Hendra, *Adv. Polym. Sci.*, **6**, 151 (1969).
[b] Amount of syndiotactic dyades, see text.

diotactic. Using this value as a standard, a simplified, relative calculation method was used for the other polymers. As expected, the syndiotacticity is decreasing with PT, but the tendency is quite weak (Table XIV).

Infrared spectra were determined on films cast from THF solutions using Beckman IR-9 and Perkin-Elmer 457 grating spectrometers. The ratio between the absorbances at 1428 and 1437 cm^{-1} was taken as a rough measure of syndiotacticity.[17,18] A slight tendency toward an increase in syndiotacticity was found with decreasing PT (see Table XIV). Other absorbance ratios were also tested with about the same result.

Raman spectra were determined on PVC powders with a Spectra Physics Model 147 Kr ± laser at 6471.0 Å, 100–200 mW, coupled to a Jarrel–Ash 25-107 double-slit monochromator with digital output. The obtained absorbance ratios at 1428/1436 cm^{-1} are given in Table XIV. They show the same tendency as the infrared measurements. Other absorbance ratios were also tested.

CONCLUSIONS

Table XV gives a summary of the experimental work, i.e., of the PVC resins used, the characterization methods tested, and the data obtained. By this study, a unique set of well-characterized PVC samples was made available for further work. The samples constitute a series of emulsion- and suspension-polymerized PVC resins within a broad range of molecular weights representative of commercial PVC qualities. For many of the resins the polymerization procedure is known.

For most characterization methods tested, remarkably good agreement between participating laboratories was reached. This applies even to such intricate methods as light scattering, LS, and osmometric determinations. A good correlation was also found between the results obtained with these methods and with gel permeation chromatography. As GPC has higher precision and accu-

TABLE XV
Summary of Sample Characterization Data Obtained

Group	Sample	PT, °C[a]	η_{rel}	K[b]	$[\eta]_{THF}^{25°C}$, dl/g	$\overline{M}_n \times 10^{-3}$		$\overline{M}_w \times 10^{-3}$		$\overline{M}_w/\overline{M}_n$		α^c
						Osm.	GPC	LS	GPC	LS/Osm.	GPC	
1	Corvic D65/8	—	—	—	1.05	51.5	49.7	106.0	110.8	2.06	2.23	—
	X-AB	—	—	—	1.08	53.6	48.8	105.3	112.5	1.96	2.31	—
2	S-54	75	1.35	53.6	0.58	28.3	26.2	43.6	52.7	1.54	2.01	0.52
	Pevikon R-24	55	1.56	66.9	0.91d	43.3	43.6	93.8	90.6	2.17	2.08	0.54
	S-80	43	1.82	78.9	1.26d	71.1	58.1	124.5	141.0	1.75	2.44	0.56
	E-54	75	1.36	54.3	0.64	30.3	27.8	44.5	58.0	1.47	2.09	0.51
	E-67	57	1.59	68.5	1.06	47.7	42.9	99.0	100.9	2.08	2.35	0.55
	E-80	43	1.88	81.3	1.39	68.0	62.9	177.8	162.3	2.61	2.58	0.56
3	Pevikon S-685	—	1.60	69.0	1.00	47.3	44.2	—	96.0	—	2.17	—
	Norvinyl S9-70	—	1.61	69.5	1.00	47.1	45.7	—	98.4	—	2.15	—

[a] Polymerization temperature.
[b] K value calculated from η_{rel} according to Fikentscher; η_{rel} determined in CH at 25°C, concn. 0.5 g/100 ml.
[c] Amount of syndiotactic dyades determined by NMR.
[d] $[\eta]_{CH}^{25°C}$.

racy, gives much more information (molecular weight distribution and long-chain branching), and is far more versatile to use, there seems to be no advantage in using LS and osmometry if GPC is available. Knowledge of MWD and LCB is of great importance not only in scientific work but also in many industrial applications, i.e., in degradation studies, when developing new resins and in the analysis of unknown samples.

However, at present, few Nordic industries use any of the above-mentioned methods when characterizing PVC resins. Instead, they rely on simple viscometric methods, which give no information about MWD or LCB. They are thus insufficient for the above-mentioned type of work. In routine production control, however, solution viscometry according to the ISO or DIN standard procedure is quite adequate, being accurate, fast, versatile, and inexpensive. According to information from KemaNord AB,[19] a standard deviation of 0.01 in relative viscosity is to be expected in normal production control.

Reporting the results as Fikentscher K values has no physical sense, but is a concession to conservative commercial usage. The viscosity number or the relative viscosity is a more direct and proper measure. Use of the intrinsic viscosity $[\eta]$ for routine production control is much more time consuming and is not necessary when the samples are quite similar in structure. However, when elucidating the molecular weight and structure of unknown samples, $[\eta]$ must be used as only this viscometric measure is related to structure peculiarities such as LCB and segments of abnormal mobility.

Because tacticity in PVC is restricted to very short chain sequences, only spectroscopic methods are available for such determinations. These methods are, however, hampered by extensive overlapping of spectral peaks. This calls for intricate curve resolution methods. NMR spectroscopy is much more accurate for quantitative tacticity determinations than infrared or Raman spectroscopy. According to the present measurements, PVC resins of ordinary commercial type show only small differences in tacticity. When working with such polymers, there is obviously little need for tacticity determinations.

Appendix I

Polymerization Procedure for S-54 and S-80

Extract from letter in Swedish written by Dr. Sten Porrvik, KemaNord AB 1971-08-13:

The polymerizations were carried out in 14-liter stainless steel autoclaves. Six runs were made at 43°C and ten at 75°C. The polymers obtained at each temperature (24 kg) were separately homogenized.

S-54	Parts by weight
6.9 kg Distilled water	135
5.1 kg Vinyl chloride	100
5 g Hydroxypropylmethylcellulose	0.098
1 g Azobisisobutyronitrile	0.020
Agitation	475 rpm
Temperature	75°C
Time	9 hr (average)
Pressure	15.5 kg/cm^2
Polymerization stopped at	6.0 kg/cm^2
Particle size	100–400 μm

Charge filtered off and washed. Dried at 50°C. Moisture content 0.03%.

S-80	Parts by weight
6.5 kg Distilled water	128
5.1 kg Vinyl chloride	100
1.9 g Hydroxypropylmethylcellulose	0.037
8.5 g Dicetyl peroxydicarbonate	0.17
Agitation	475 rpm
Temperature	43°C
Time	8 h (average)
Pressure	7.3 kg/cm^2
Polymerization stopped at	4.5 kg/cm^2
Conversion	90 %
Particle size	100–400 μm

Charge filtered off and washed. Dried at 50°C. Moisture content 0.03%.

Impurities in Vinyl Chloride:

Butadiene	~10 ppm
1-Chloromethane	~50 ppm
Acetylenes	<1 ppm
1,2-Dichloroethane	~1 ppm

Impurity content of the polymer equals added suspensionstabilizer and initiator, i.e., S-54, 0.1%; S-80, 0.2%.

Appendix II

Polymerization Procedure for E-54, E-67, and E-80

Extract from letter in Norwegian written by Dr. Odd Palmgren, Norsk Hydro A/S 1971-07-14:
The polymerizations were carried out in a pilot plant reactor. Two runs were made at each temperature. The latices from the same temperature level were mixed and spray dried at 60°C.

Polymer	Polymerization temperature, °C	Initiator content, % of monomer
E-54	75	0.011
E-67	57	0.033
E-80	43	0.270
Conversion		~89%
Size of primary particles		~0.3 μm
Size of particles formed during spray drying		5–30 μm
pH		3–4
Moisture content		0.15–0.20%

Impurities in Vinyl Chloride:

Butadiene	~10 ppm
1-Chloromethane	~200 ppm
Content of aid chemicals	~1.5%
Emulsifier:	dialkyl sulfosuccinate, alkyl sulfate
Buffer:	phosphate
Initiator:	K$_2$S$_2$O$_8$

Initiator and buffer added before heating.

On behalf of the members of NORDFORSK Polymer Characterization Group, the author wishes to thank NORDFORSK for supporting the project and Miss Ann-Christin Wentzel and Mr. Stig Pettersson NORDFORSK for administrative work. The author also wishes to thank Professor Johan Lindberg, University of Helsinki, for making internal report material available prior to publication and for stimulating discussions and support. Professor J. Kops, Technical University of Denmark, is gratefully acknowledged for initiating and encouraging the work. The author also wishes to thank Dr. A. Holmström for valuable support.

References

1. K. B. Andersson, A. Holmström, and E. M. Sörvik, *Makromol. Chem.*, **166**, 247 (1973).

2. K. B. Andersson and E. M. Sörvik, *J. Polym. Sci. C*, **33**, 247 (1971).

3. P. J. Flory, *Principles of Polymer Chemistry*, Cornell University Press, Ithaca, N.Y., 1953, p. 547.

4. D. W. van Krevelen and P. J. Hoftyzer, *Properties of Polymers. Correlation with Chemical Structure*, Elsevier, Amsterdam, London, New York, 1972.

5. M. Bohdanecký, K. Solc, P. Kratochvíl, M. Kolinský, M. Ryska, and D. Lim, *J. Polym. Sci. A-2*, **5**, 343 (1967).

6. J. Brandrup and E. H. Immergut, Eds., *Polymer Handbook*, 2nd ed., Wiley, New York, 1975.

7. S. Grubisic, P. Rempp, and H. Benoit, *J. Polym. Sci. B*, **5**, 753 (1967).

8. J. C. Moore, *J. Polym. Sci. A*, **2**, 835 (1964).

9. J. Lyngaae-Jørgensen, Undersøgelser over polyvinylklorids fremstilling, molekylstruktur of mekaniske egenskaper. Thesis, Technical University of Denmark, 1970.

10. C. Strazielle and H. Benoit, *Pure Appl. Chem.*, **26**, 451 (1971).

11. J. Lyngae-Jørgensen, *J. Chromatogr. Sci.*, **9**, 331 (1971).

12. H. Fikentscher, *Cellulosechemie*, **13**, 58 (1932).

13. K. B. Andersson, Rekommendation avseende bestämning av gränsviskositeten för PVC-lösningar, The Polymer Group, Chalmers University of Technology, 1972; revised by E. M. Sörvik and L. O. Sundelöf, 1973.

14. A. J. de Vries, C. Bonnebat, and M. Carrega, *Pure Appl. Chem.*, **26**, 209 (1971).

15. J. J. Lindberg, M. Lucander, P. Seppänen, and F. Stenman, IUPAC Int. Symp. on Macromol., Madrid, 1974.

16. H. U. Pohl and D. O. Hummel, *Makromol. Chem.*, **113**, 190 (1968).

17. H. Germar, K.-H. Hellwege, and U. Johnsen, *Makromol. Chem.*, **60**, 106 (1963).

18. P. J. Hendra, *Adv. Polym. Sci.*, **6**, 151 (1969).

19. T. Jonsson, KemaNord AB, Stenungsund, Sweden, personal communication.

Received July 29, 1976
Revised September 14, 1976

JOURNAL OF APPLIED POLYMER SCIENCE   VOL. 21, 2791–2815 (1977)

The Tensile Fatigue Behavior of para-Oriented Aramid Fibers and Their Fracture Morphology

L. KONOPASEK and J. W. S. HEARLE, *Department of Textile Technology, University of Manchester Institute of Science and Technology, Manchester, England*

Synopsis

Samples of Fiber B and PRD 49 which were the forerunners of current Kevlar aramid fibers were subject to a limited number of tensile tests and tensile fatigue tests in order to determine their fracture morphology. The fibers were examined by optical and scanning electron microscopy. Both tensile and fatigue failure occurs by axial splitting, with the fatigue splits being much longer. Compressive effects in snap-back cause kink bands to form. The fatigue strength is only marginally less than the tensile strength.

INTRODUCTION

This paper describes studies of high-modulus aramid organic polymer fibers of a type which are now produced and sold by du Pont under the trade name Kevlar. These fibers are included in a type now known by the generic title aramid fibers.[1] When first introduced by du Pont, they were referred to as Fiber B and PRD 49: they are now given the trade name of Kevlar.

The types of Kevlar available are: Kevlar, intended for use in rubber tires, etc., and Kevlar-29, intended for use in high-strength textiles, both former Fiber B; and Kevlar-49, intended for use in rigid reinforced materials and other uses needing high stiffness, former PRD 49. The definition of an aramid fiber as given in the Textile Institute's "Textile Terms and Definitions," based on the U.S. Federal Trade Commission is: A fiber in which the fiber-forming substance is a long-chain synthetic polyamide in which at least 85% of the amide linkages are attached directly to two aromatic rings.

Two forms of Fiber B are believed to be the same in fiber constitution but different in finish; PRD 49 is a higher-stiffness version of the material. The samples tested were presumably typical of production some time ago, possibly on an experimental plant, but it must be realized that in a developing technology of this type, the structure of fibers supplied may be changed from time to time— either intentionally or otherwise. Lack of experience may also have led to fiber damage in handling. The constitution and method of manufacture of these fibers have not been disclosed, though statements by authors from other companies have appeared in the literature.[2,3] Their chemical structure is presumed to

2791

consist of para-oriented benzene rings linked by —CONH— groups; Black and Preston[2] quote the following formulae:

$$\left[\text{NH}\left\langle\bigcirc\right\rangle\text{NH--CO}\left\langle\bigcirc\right\rangle\text{CO}\right]_n$$

or

$$\left[\text{NH}\left\langle\bigcirc\right\rangle\text{CO}\right]_n$$

Meredith[4] states that Kevlar is poly(p-phenyleneterephthalamide), which is the first of the two formulae above.

Molecules of this type will be relatively stiff and strongly interactive with one

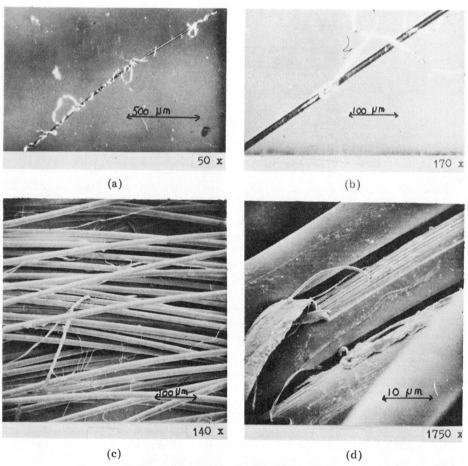

(a)   (b)

(c)   (d)

Fig. 1. SEM and optical microscope views of untested Fiber B and PRD 49 surface: (a), (b) Optical microscope views of Fiber B filaments as received at different magnifications. Note detached ribbon-like fibrillar layer separated from the filament and wound around it. (c), (d) SEM general views of Fiber B filaments as received at different magnification, showing many fibrils and fibrillar strands separated from the surface of the filaments. Note a "peeling" effect in (d). (e) Optical micrograph revealing the dark lines in Fiber B filaments, as seen in polarized light. (f), (g) SEM micrographs showing longitudinal splits and slightly bulging lines around the surface, in Fiber B and PRD 49, respectively.

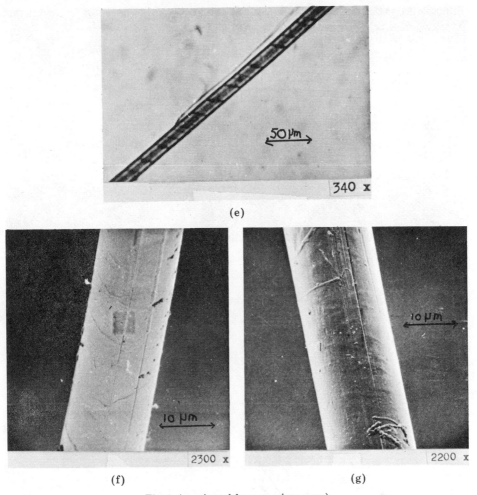

Fig. 1. (*continued from previous page*)

another. This, with the method of manufacture, leads to highly oriented fibers, with very high modulus, tenacity, and thermal stability. Several papers and bulletins describing their applications have appeared.[5,6]

The emphasis in the present work has been on a study of the tensile fatigue of these fibers using the fatigue tester developed by Bunsell et al.[7] and on the morphology of their fracture.

PRELIMINARY STUDIES

Fibers Examined

Two types of high-modulus, wholly aromatic polyamide fibers, designated as Fiber B and PRD 49, were obtained from du Pont in the form of multifilament yarns. The diameter of single filaments of both samples was found by optical microscopy to be approximately 12.4 μm. The linear density of single filaments was calculated to be 0.18 tex (1.61 den), by taking the density to be 1.44 g/cm^3 and assuming a circular cross section of filaments.

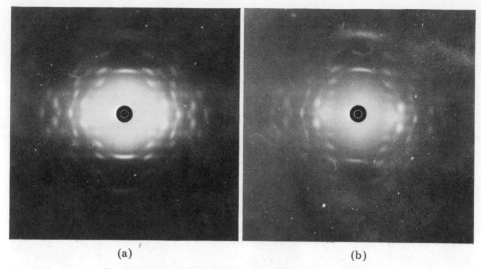

(a)   (b)

Fig. 2. X-ray diffraction pictures of Fiber B and PRD 49.

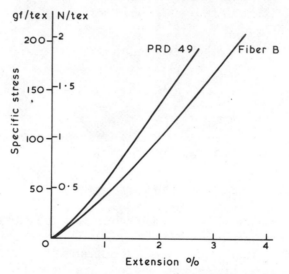

Fig. 3. Typical stress–strain curves of Fiber B and PRD 49.

The surfaces of untested filaments under the optical microscope and in the SEM show a generally smooth structure, but there are longitudinal splits in places, with many separated fibrils and ribbon-like fibrillar strands wound around the filament as shown in Figures 1(a), 1(b), 1(c), and 1(d). The existence of many fibrils and fibrillar strands separated from the outer layer of the filaments indicates a weak cohesion between fibrils. It is clearly necessary to take care in processing Kevlar in order to minimize the development of this type of damage. There is also evidence of slightly bulging lines around the surface located at various places along the filament, as shown in Figure 1(f) and 1(g). Dark lines of two different intensities may be seen when viewed in polarized light under the optical microscope; they are located at various angles between +45° and −45° to the filament cross-sectional plane [Fig. 1(e)].

The high orientation of the filaments was shown by the fact that their birefringence Δn was found to be 0.445. An x-ray diffraction picture (Fig. 2) confirms the high crystallinity and orientation.

Simple Tensile Tests

Simple tensile tests were carried out on the Instron tester with a cross-head speed of 5 cm/min and a gauge length of 5 cm. The tests produced in both materials a very high breaking load and low breaking extension.

The load–extension curves of PRD 49 and Fiber B show a rapid rise up to the breaking point (Fig. 3); there is no yield region such as is characteristic of most polymer fibers. The tenacity of Fiber B and PRD 49 is more than twice as high as that of polyester tire filaments and superhigh-tenacity nylon and more than three times as high as that of medium-tenacity nylon. The initial tensile modulus of Fiber B is approximately 15 times that of medium-tenacity nylon and six times higher than that of polyester. The initial modulus of PRD 49 is approximately 20 times higher than that of medium-tenacity nylon and seven times higher than that of polyester. The above comparison is based on the values from Figure 3 and Shirley Institute data.[8]

TABLE I
Tensile Properties of Fiber B and PRD 49

	Fiber B	PRD 49
Diameter, measured in optical microscope, μm	12.4	12.4
Linear density, calculated, tex(den)	0.179(1.61)	0.180(1.62)
Instron Tests:		
Number of tests	24	20
Mean breaking load, N(gf)	0.361(36.8)	0.341(34.8)
Standard deviation, N(gf)	0.041(4.1)	0.068(6.9)
Variation coefficient, %	11.2	19.9
Max. value, N(gf)	0.422(43)	0.569(58)
Min. value, N(gf)	0.275(28)	0.196(20)
Tenacity, N/tex(gf/tex)(gf/den)	2.015(205.4)(22.9)	1.894(193.0)(21.5)
Standard deviation, N/tex (gf/tex)(gf/den)	0.226(23.1)(2.6)	0.377(38.4)(4.3)
Max. value, N/tex (gf/tex)(gf/den)	2.35(240)(26.7)	3.16(322)(35.8)
Min. value, N/tex (gf/tex)(gf/den)	1.53(156)(17.4)	1.09(111)(12.4)
Breaking extension, %	3.67	2.77
Standard deviation, %	0.45	0.25
Variation coefficient, %	12.2	9.2
Max. value, %	4.60	3.20
Min. value, %	3.00	2.30
Mean breaking secant tensile modulas, N/tex (gf/tex)(gf/den)	55.3(5635)(626)	69.0(7038)(782)
Standard deviation, N/tex (gf/tex)(gf/den)	4.63(472)(524)	17.7(1804)(200)
Variation coefficient, %	8.4	25.6
Initial tensile modulus from stress—strain curve, N/tex (gf/tex)(gf/den)	38.4(3900)(433)	427(4250)(472)

Table I summarizes mean values and other statistical characteristics of the results in the simple tensile tests made on Fiber B and PRD 49. Fiber B shows approximately the same irregularity in breaking load and breaking extension. The irregularity of extension in PRD 49 is similar to that in Fiber B, but the irregularity of breaking load is twice as high. It may be noted that the maximum strength value for PRD 49 was greater than that of Fiber B.

These test results should not be regarded as more than indicative of the fiber properties: a much more extensive statistical survey would be needed to obtain definitive results. Furthermore, in a material of such high stiffness, there may be errors due to softness of the measuring system, with a consequent underestimate of modulus and overestimate of breaking extension.

Fracture Morphology of Simple Tensile Failure

After tensile failure on the Instron tester, we examined the samples using the optical microscope and the SEM. All examined samples show a very long fracture with extensive splitting in a longitudinal direction. The optical microscope views show that the fracture occurs by prolonged axial splitting, but little detail is visible. In order to get complete views of the breaks at a reasonable magnification it is necessary to make montages of about ten SEM pictures. These are difficult to reproduce. SEM views of simple tensile fracture of the Fiber B filament are shown in Figure 4. Long montages of both broken ends are supplemented by some sections at higher magnification. The appearance is typical of both Fiber B and PRD 49. The fracture appears to develop along a plane at a very small angle to the filament axis. The length of fractures varies between approximately 500 and 800 μm (40 to 70 filament diameters). As the diameter of a filament is about 12 μm, the angle between the plane of the fracture and the filament axis must average about 1° to 1.5°.

The two broken ends usually differ in appearance: one end shows extensive splitting [Fig. 4(b)], while the other is a single, solid piece [Fig. 4(a)]. The "solid" end has split off from the other end and tapers in an elliptical cross section from the full filament cross section, where the split starts, to a small tip. In the other portion, there are many tips from separate splits which run back to two or more major splits at the beginning of the failed region. This splitting is usually accompanied by loose fibrillar bundles projecting from the surface of the fracture in several directions. A more recent series of tests by B. Lomas shows that there is no correlation between the direction of these ends and the direction of extrusion or winding on the package. Out of a total of 20 tests, the solid end was on the piece nearer the surface of the package in eight specimens and on the piece nearer the center of the package in another eight specimens; one specimen showed V-shaped ends, and three had both ends solid without multiple splits.

A possible mechanism of fracture development is shown schematically in Figure 5. An imperfection on the surface of the filament [such as shown in Fig. 1(d)] may act as the initiation point in the breakup of the fibrillar unit under the increasing load. The longitudinal shear stresses, induced at the root of the initial gap, cause longitudinal splitting of the first bundle of fibrils. There are also tensile stresses acting around the root. The tensile modulus and strength are much higher than shear modulus and strength; therefore, the crack develops under the above-mentioned steep angle. After the next layer of fibrils has

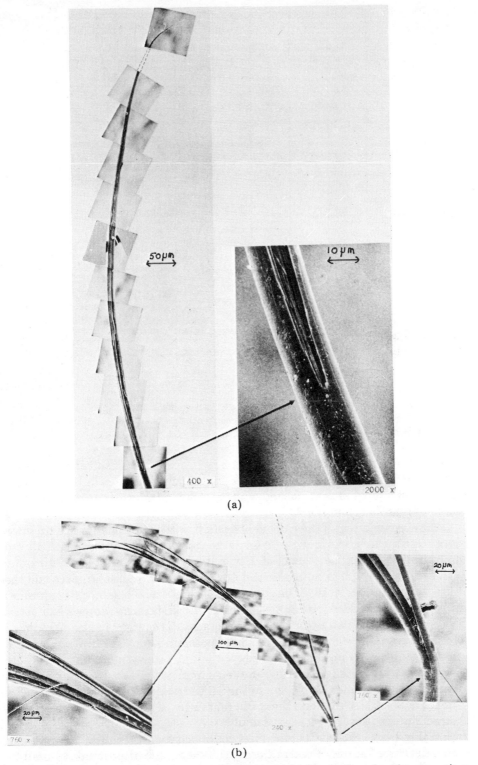

Fig. 4. Fiber B simple tensile fracture: (a), (b) SEM montages of opposite ends with some sections at higher magnification (breaking strength 42 gf, breaking extension 4.4%).

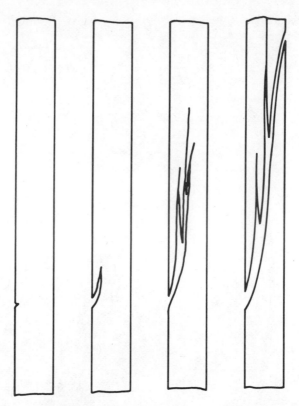

Fig. 5. Schematic representation of simple tensile fracture development in Fiber B and PRD 49. Note the transverse dimensions are expanded for clarity; actual breaks extend over longer lengths relative to filament diameter.

broken, a new gap is opened up, and there is again a concentration of shear stresses at the new root which results in splitting the next layer of fibrils. Likewise, the break is transmitted from one fibrillar unit to the next until the filament is broken completely.

It may be noted that if the crack propagation, with splitting, is in one direction along the fiber, and provided the main crack continues to propagate at a rate not appreciably less than the other cracks, then this main crack must reach the other surface first: thus, it is not surprising to find one end as a solid piece and the other with multiple cracks. The only conditions in which both ends would show multiple splits would be *either* if separate branching cracks propagating in opposite directions joined up *or* if the main crack (to the right in Fig. 5) stopped while the branches grew: and both these possibilities would lead to forms of splitting different from that observed.

When the whole lengths of the broken samples were examined, we found (under the optical microscope and in the SEM) bulging lines located some distance from the fractured end. Two different forms of these lines were observed: distinct dislocations [Fig. 6(a)] and double dislocations giving a "bow" configuration [Fig. 6(c)]. These bulging lines could occur as a result of compression forces developed in the filament during the snap-back after break. Possibly, there might be a relationship between the slightly bulging lines in untested filaments and the more pronounced bulging lines after break. If we compare the spacing between dark lines observed in untested filaments under the optical microscope with the spacing of bulging lines in Figure 6(b) (optical micrograph) and Figure 6(a) (SEM micrograph), we can see that it is approximately the same.

The partially broken, sharply bent, split sections of the filament and transverse bands located just below the bend in the fracture region [Fig. 6(d)] may be seen

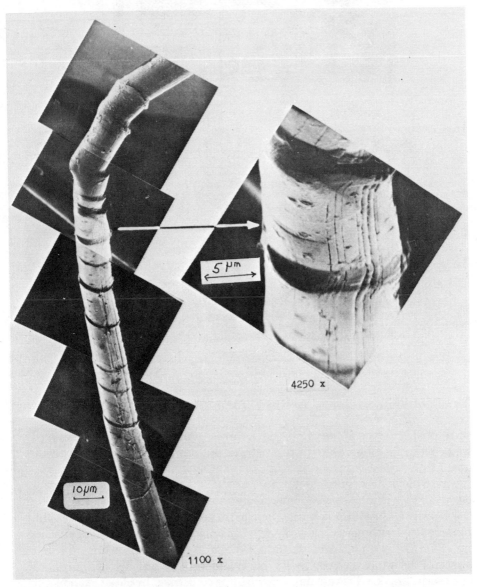

(a)

Fig. 6. SEM and optical views of various types of structural dislocations—"bulging lines"—discovered at some distance back from ends of tensile fracture: (a) SEM micrographs showing "ring-like" bulging lines in Fiber B. (b) Optical micrograph showing bulging lines in Fiber B. (c) SEM micrograph presenting "bow" configuration bulging lines in PRD 49. (d) SEM micrograph of sharply bent, split sections of PRD 49 filament with distinct transverse bands located just below the bend in the fractured region.

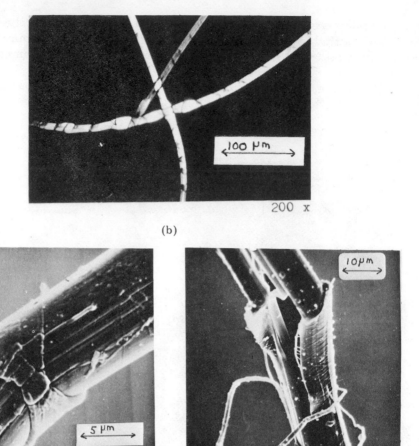

(b)

(c)   (d)

Fig. 6. (*continued from previous page*)

as additional evidence of the compression forces.   Another remarkable example
of snap-back of a ribbon-like fibrillar strand into opposed helices is shown in
Figure 7.

Figure 8 shows the internal surfaces of the split sections within a tensile
fracture of Fiber B filament.   Comparing internal surfaces with the outer surface
of the filament, the difference may be clearly seen: internal surfaces exhibit
transverse lines with periodically repeated spacing approximately 0.5 μm, while
an outer surface is smooth and uniform.   We propose that these lines are characteristic of the internal structure of Fiber B and PRD 49 and do not appear only
after a tensile break.   This assumption might be confirmed by closer examination
of an internal surface of peeled filaments (thicker than those we had obtained)
before any tests.

In the fiber fracture classification given by Hearle,[9,10] there is a group called
"fracture with axial splitting."   Tensile fracture of Fiber B and PRD 49 could
be included in that group, showing extensive axial splitting approximately 70
times longer than a filament diameter.

Fig. 7. SEM micrograph of PRD 49 tensile fracture, showing effects of snap-back on a ribbon-like fibrillar strand which has separated from the filament.

A fracture of Fiber B in liquid nitrogen also shows break by axial splitting, with very marked transverse lines in the internal surface (Fig. 9). Fiber B exhibited an extremely high breaking strength in liquid nitrogen and on extensibility much lower than at room temperature.

FATIGUE TESTS

Test Method

A study of fatigue properties of Fiber B and PRD 49 was carried out on Bunsell's fatigue tester, of which a detailed description has been given elsewhere.[7]

A working gauge length of 40 mm was chosen for our experiments. The sample was subjected to a load cycling with a maximum load in each cycle lower than the breaking load of the material in a simple tensile test. The cycling frequency was 50 Hz. The working speed of the upper-jaw vertical movement from the motor through the gears was 1.3 cm/min.

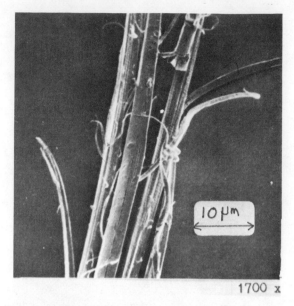

1700 x

Fig. 8. Internal transverse lines in the tensile fractured region of Fiber B.

On starting the experiment, the motor stretches the sample until the selected maximum load is reached. An oscillatory load amplitude is being set up during the initial period.

After the initial period the lower jaw vibrates sinusoidally with the set amplitude, and the filament undergoes periodical or quasi-periodical loading with the load P varying within the interval:

$$\max(P_{mean} - P_{osc}; 0) < P < P_{max}$$

where $P_{mean} = 1/T \int_t^{t+T} P\,dt$ is the mean load; $P_{osc} = (P_{max} - P_{mean})$ is oscillatory load; P_{max} is maximum load; t is time; and T is period.

Different load conditions which may take place are schematically illustrated in Figure 10. The real signal corresponding to the applied load is observed on the oscilloscope. The apparatus was designed in such a manner that whenever, during the test, the maximum load on the sample drops below a required value, the motor switches on to compensate it by stretching the sample.

The behavior of Fiber B and PRD 49 during the fatigue test was different from that of nylon and other fibers. Nylon and other textile fibers display a certain amount of viscous flow (or plastic deformation) which results in progressive stretching of the fiber during the whole period of the fatigue test in order to maintain the set maximum load. By contrast, Fiber B and PRD 49 appear to behave during the fatigue test like perfectly elastic springs. After producing the required maximum load at the beginning of the test, the motor stops and the sample length and mean load remain constant. After a period of vibration, the filament breaks and there is only a small inertial movement of the upper jaw at the moment of final filament break.

In general, the filaments during the fatigue test were repeatedly copying relevant parts of the steep stress–strain curves from the Instron, and, correspondingly, the amplitudes of the lower jaw had to be set to less than 0.5 mm.

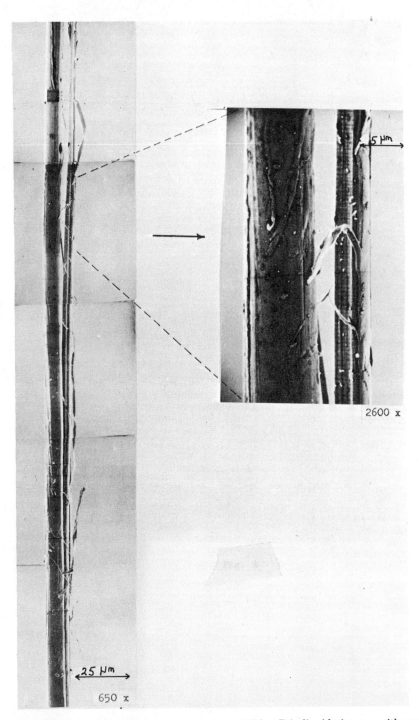

Fig. 9. SEM micrographs showing tensile fracture of Fiber B in liquid nitrogen, with separate section at higher magnification.

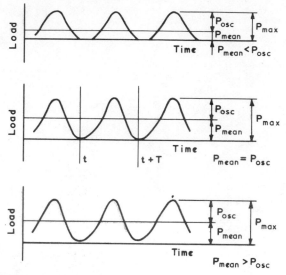

Fig. 10. Different loading conditions of fatigue testing.

The static extension observed was about 2–3%, depending on the set maximum load.

Some possible outcomes of the fatigue tests may be as follows: (a) break during the initial period (i.e., before or just after reaching the chosen maximum load); (b) break after a certain number of cycles (i.e., after a minimum of 9000 cycles under set loading conditions); (c) absence of a break at the chosen testing period.

Only samples broken in the middle are taken into account; breaks near the

TABLE II
Summary of Results of Fatigue Tests of Fiber B and PRD 49

Test no.	Fiber B				PRD 49			
	Oscillatory load, gf	Mean load, gf	Maximum load, gf	Life time, no. of cycles	Oscillatory load, gf	Mean load, gf	Maximum load, gf	Life time, no. of cycles
1	11	9	20	immediate break	12	9	21	1.8×10^5
2	12	10	22	0.15×10^5	14	10	24	immediate break
3	12	10	22	0.51×10^5	12.5	12	24.5	0.45×10^5
4	13	12	25	not broken after 30.75×10^5	13	12	25	0.62×10^5
5	14	12	26	0.09×10^5	13	12	25	9.10×10^5
6	13.5	13	26.5	not broken after 162.2×10^5	12	14	26	immediate break
7	14.5	13.5	28	2.85×10^5	13	14	27	0.62×10^5
8	14.5	14	28.5	0.09×10^5	14.5	12.5	27	2.40×10^5
9	15.5	13	28.5	8.77×10^5	14	13	27	4.05×10^5
10	15	14	29	immediate break	14	13	27	7.80×10^5
11	15	14	29	immediate break	14.5	14	28.5	0.75×10^5
12	15	14	29	0.08×10^5	15	14	29	immediate break
13	12	17	29	6.57×10^5	15	14	29	immediate break
14	15	14	29	21.90×10^5	15	14.5	29.5	immediate break
15	15.5	14	29.5	9.75×10^5	18	16	34	immediate break
16	15.5	14.5	30	0.27×10^5				
17	16	15	31	immediate break				
18	16	15	31	immediate break				
19	16	15	31	0.27×10^5				
20	16.5	15.5	32	0.09×10^5				
21	17.5	17	34.5	2.30×10^5				

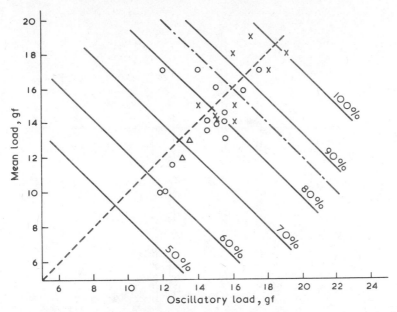

Fig. 11. Results of Fiber B fatigue tests in relation to various chosen values of mean load and oscillatory load: (O) fatigue failure; (x) immediate failure; (△) not broken; (—) lines of equal maximum load (% of Instron breaking load); (— · —) mean maximum load of immediate failures; (- - -) line of zero minimum load.

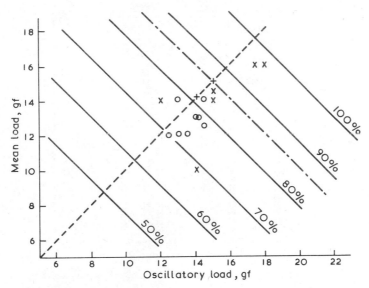

Fig. 12. Results of PRD 49 fatigue tests in relation to various chosen values of mean load and oscillatory load (symbols as in Fig. 11).

jaws are discarded. The summary of the results of fatigue tests of Fiber B and PRD 49 is shown in Table II. These data are shown in Figures 11 and 12 in relation to various chosen values of mean load P_{mean} and oscillatory load P_{osc}. The broken line shown in these figures divides the plane into upper left segment with $P_{mean} > P_{osc}$ and lower right segment with $P_{mean} < P_{osc}$. Perpendicular

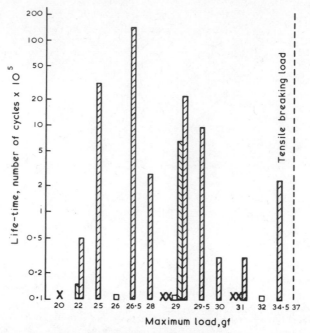

Fig. 13. Diagram of Fiber B fatigue lifetime: (x) immediate break; (—) lifetime 0.1×10^5 cycles; blocks show individual results with lifetime 0.1×10^5 cycles.

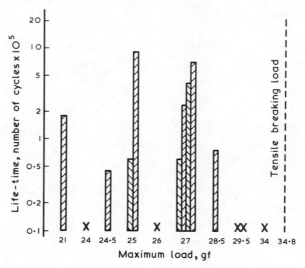

Fig. 14. Diagram of PRD 49 fatigue lifetime (symbols as in Fig. 13).

to the broken line in each figure are the lines of equal maximum load $P_{\max} = P_{\text{mean}} + P_{\text{osc}}$ corresponding to 100%, 90%, ... 50% of the mean value of the breaking load in simple tensile tests.

As may be seen in Figure 12, all the five samples of PRD 49 subjected to a maximum load larger than 82% of mean breaking load and also three samples below 82% have broken during the initial period. Something in the method of mounting or application of load in the apparatus, thus, seems to lead to a lower

TABLE III
Results of fatigue tests using different procedures

Tensile breaking load, gf	Max. load in Fatigue test, gf	Tensile breaking load, %	Life time, no. of cycles × 10^5
34	22 (normal speed)	65	0.51
30	slow increase 18–24 (normal speed)	77	7.2
30	22–29 (movement by hand)	100	11.7

breaking load. All the other samples of PRD 49 under maximum load of less than 82% have broken after various periods of cycling.

In the case of Fiber B (Fig. 11), the nine breakages during the initial period are dispersed between 80.5% and 100% of the mean breaking load, and the 14 fatigue breakages, between 60.5 and 90.4%. The two samples tested under maximum loads of 69.5% and 73.5% (of the mean breaking load) survived 17 and 79 hr of cycling, respectively. The dispersion of the experimental results may be seen as reflecting a high irregularity of the tensile properties of the materials.

Although the results are considerably scattered and do not show the distinct areas of the three above-mentioned outcomes as clearly as in the case of nylon 66,[11] it may be concluded that the breaking resistance of the filaments of both types (Fiber B and PRD 49) is to a limited degree adversely affected by cycling.

The performance of Fiber B under our fatigue testing seems to be better and the rate of deterioration of mechanical properties lower than that of PRD 49. This conclusion is supported by comparing the lifetime (Figs. 13 and 14), which is higher for Fiber B than for PRD 49. The experimental values, however, are very uneven, and especially striking is the apparent absence of correlation between the lifetime of the samples and the set maximum load.

As a matter of interest, we carried out fatigue tests on three filaments of Fiber B using the following different procedures: (a) quick application of maximum load at normal speed of extension during about 1 min; (b) gradual increase of maximum load during the period of a few hours, each increase being made at the normal speed of extension; (c) slow increase of maximum load by hand operation. Tensile tests were also performed on other portions of each filament. The results of these tests are shown in Table III. These tests show that while in the first test the applied maximum load was 70% of the breaking load, in the second and third tests filaments seem to become stronger during the load cycling, and we were able to increase the maximum load up to 77% and 100% of the breaking load, respectively. This is an interesting finding but it should be supported by further testing.

Fracture Morphology of Fatigue Failure

All the filaments broken in fatigue tests were examined under the optical microscope, and a few of them were subjected to a detailed investigation in the SEM. We could not identify in Fiber B and PRD 49 such a basic difference

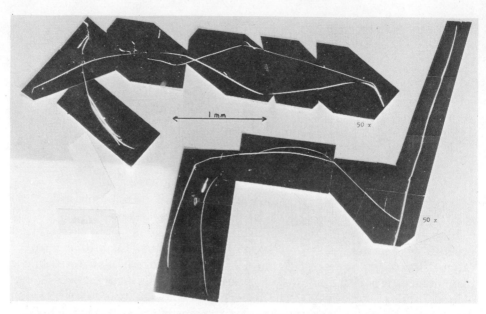

Fig. 15. (a), (b) Montages of Fiber B fatigue fracture (both broken ends) taken under the optical microscope (failed after 2.85×10^5 cycles at max. load = 28 gf).

between the fracture morphology of simple tensile failure and fatigue failure as we did in nylon 66 and other textile fibers.[11,12] This finding seems to agree with the absence of plastic deformation during the fatigue test as shown in the previous chapter. The fact that the filament behaves during the fatigue test as a nearly perfect spring implies little change of mechanical properties in the longitudinal direction. Consequently, little difference between the fracture patterns in tensile and fatigue tests was to be expected.

On the other hand, all the filament failures following the cycling on the fatigue tester occurred under a maximum load which was lower than the average breaking load in a simple tensile test. Our investigation of the fatigue-broken filaments was aimed to reveal possible structural causes and signs of the deterioration of breaking resistance during cycling.

The most remarkable difference between tensile and fatigue-broken filaments is in the much deeper and longer splits occurring in fatigue breaks compared with normal tensile breaks; in addition, this longitudinal splitting is much more extensive and appears often at both broken ends. This may be seen as a consequence of loosening the comparatively weak interfibrillar bonds during the high-frequency loading and unloading.

Figures 15(a) and (b) show montages, taken through the optical microscope, which illustrate the fatigue failure (both broken ends) of Fiber B. The fracture extends over a total length approximately of 6 mm (485 times the fiber diameter), which is about seven times longer than in a simple tensile break. Sometimes, due to the extensive splitting of the filaments, portions of the fracture are lost. An example of this is shown in Figure 15(b) where the broken portion of the fiber lies across the fractured end. In this case, the broken part is still present, but in most cases losses of this kind are not discovered until the fracture is examined in the SEM.

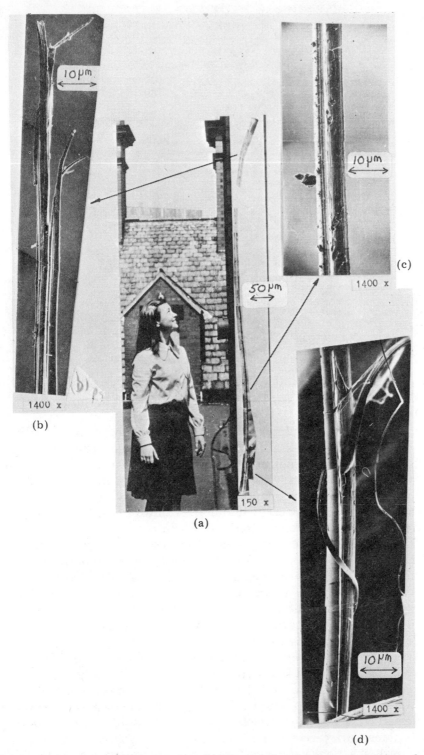

Fig. 16. Montage comparing the length of the Fiber B fatigue fracture with the human height, and SEM micrographs showing some sections of the fracture at higher magnification.

Fig. 17. SEM micrograph showing a section of PRD 49 fracture. Note a thin layer peeled from the main body and splits within this thin layer.

We also observed a similar type of fatigue fracture morphology in PRD 49. Because of the enormous length of the fracture, it was difficult to record as a whole in the SEM at magnifications high enough to detect fine details within the fracture surface. In some cases montages were made consisting of 25 or more different sections, but they still only covered part of the full-fracture length, and we often missed some sections; Figure 16(a) illustrates graphically the problems involved in making these montages.

Figure 16(b) illustrates the top section of a typical Fiber B fatigue fracture with multiple splits (this is only a part of a montage taken in the SEM in 27 stages). Figure 16(c) shows the inner surface of the same fracture (about 3 mm from the top) with transverse lines going along the whole length with about the same spacing as in a simple tensile break. In this illustration, the thickness of this split portion of the fracture represents only about half of the diameter of the filament. The shape of the cross section in this part of the fracture is semi-circular with a reentrant portion in the middle of the inner surface. Figure 16(d) shows a part further from the broken end. In Figure 17, a thin layer peeling from the main body of a filament of PRD 49 can be seen; there are also splits within this thin layer. Another example of multiple splits in Fiber B occurring in the middle portion of the fatigue fracture, with many fibrillar bundles projecting from the inner surface, is shown in Figure 18.

The result of loosening the interfibrillar bonds due to cycling loading in PRD 49 is illustrated in Figure 19 where, in the middle portion of the fracture, the filament has broken into two distinct parts forming a hole in the filament re-

Fig. 18. SEM micrograph showing multiple splits in the middle portion of the Fiber B fatigue fracture.

sembling the eye of a needle. This unbroken split portion of the filament is an example of an earlier stage of development of the splits during the cycling (it is likely that most of the broken split portions went originally through that stage).

In fatigue-broken samples as in tensile ones, bulging lines (dislocations) were found some distance from the fracture during a detailed examination in the SEM; they were located at various angles to the filament axis [Fig. 20(a)]. Most of these

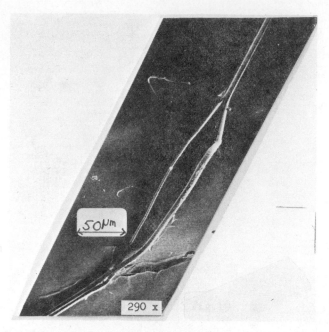

Fig. 19. SEM micrograph showing isolated split portion within the fractured region of PRD 49 fatigue failure.

bulging lines, in contrast to those observed in tensile broken filaments show many cracks extending from the lip of the bulge (dislocation) approximately parallel with the filament axis [Fig. 20(a) and (b)].

Distinct dislocations (sharp bends) were also often found in the middle of the split portion of the fracture, as illustrated in Figure 21(a) (PRD 49). A possible consequence of compression forces (as in tensile break) can be seen at closer investigation of this dislocation in Figure 21(b), which also shows closely spaced transverse lines.

The fatigue fracture morphology of Fiber B and PRD 49 could be included in the same group of fracture forms[9] as tensile fracture of these fibers, i.e., fracture with axial splitting, though this has been subdivided into tensile and fatigue groups.[10]

Creep Tests of Fiber B

Fiber B and PRD 49 as mentioned above did not show any appreciable plastic deformation or creep when tested on the fatigue tester during and up to 50 h or so. The absence of significant viscoelastic or plastic deformation was also observed when testing Fiber B under a steady load on the creep tester, whose description is given by Bunsell.[13]

Immediately after applying the load (8, 13, or 26.5 g), the filament stretched to the extent corresponding roughly to the stress–strain curve from the Instron. The extension remained almost constant for about 2 hr. During the next two to three days, we observed a barely noticeable additional extension of 0.1–0.2% in each of the three cases.

The small value of static creep as compared with total absence of dynamic creep might be explained by the fact that on the fatigue tester, the filament is

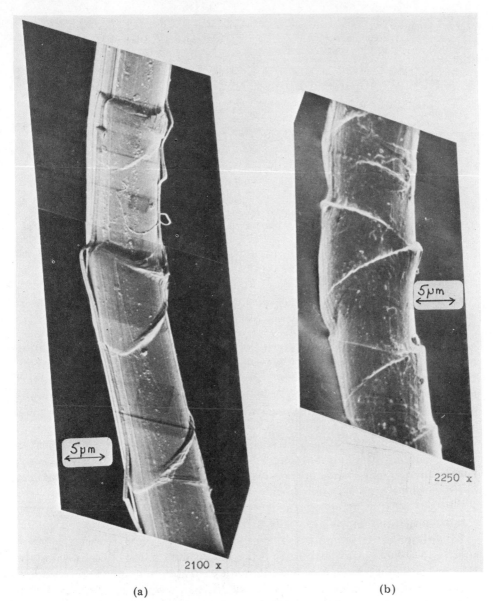

Fig. 20. (a), (b) SEM micrographs showing bulging lines at some distance from the fractured end of a Fiber B filament after fatigue failure. Longitudinal cracks are also apparent.

under a load near to the maximum only during a short interval in each cycle, after which it is allowed to relax. Our observation of dynamic and static creep, however, should not be taken as final and conclusive because of insufficient accuracy of the deformation readings on both fatigue tester and creep tester as measured against generally low deformability of the Fiber B and PRD 49.

CONCLUSIONS

The tests which we have made confirm the remarkably high stiffness and strength of Kevlar fibers. The fracture morphology shows, furthermore, that

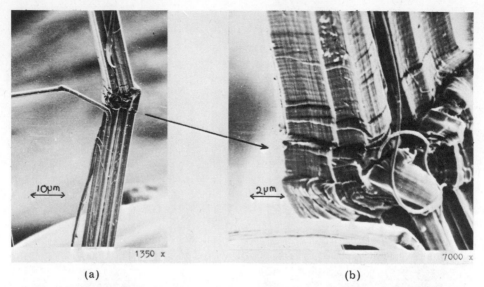

(a)   (b)

Fig. 21. (a), (b) SEM views of dislocations within the fatigue fracture region of PRD 49 at different magnifications.

when failure comes, it is not the result of fracture across the axis of orientation but of splitting along the axis. This axial splitting will derive from any discontinuity, such as a surface flaw, which must give rise to shear stresses. The fact that there are no chain molecules crossing and supporting axial planes, but only weak intermolecular forces between these planes, will then lead to the axial splitting.

If the splitting, or multiple splitting, is even slightly off axis (by 1° or 2°), then it will eventually over long lengths cross the fiber and lead to a loss of continuity; before this happens, there may be a transverse failure of the small residual area of fibers which bear the whole load.

The easy axial splitting has also been shown in Kevlar fibers broken down by compressive forces in the x-press test.[14]

In addition to its theoretical interest, the fact that Kevlar breaks by axial splitting is also of great practical importance. Filaments are not used separately; they are part of a bundle in a multifilament yarn and, in many uses, contained within a matrix. Under these conditions, filaments which have split will still contribute greatly, throughout their length, to the load-bearing capacity of the assembly. The aspect ratio of the split fibrils is high and so they will be effective as "staple fibers." Kevlar in use is thus likely to be effectively stronger than would be expected from tests on single filaments.

This advantage will be even more marked in the even longer axial splits which result from fatigue tests. It is now a general experience of our tensile fatigue testing of fibers that even when tensile breaks occur transversely, fatigue breaks usually occur by axial splitting; and where tensile breaks show axial splitting, fatigue breaks are longer and more split. This applies also to Kevlar. However, the effects of tensile fatigue on reducing the load-bearing capacity of Kevlar appear to be quite small, little more than would be allowed for in variability of test data and hardly worthy of counting separately in determining safety factors.

In view of the considerable scatter of the results, and the range of possible combinations of load, it is difficult to make firm comparisons without carrying out very large numbers of tests. However, the following tentative conclusions seem justified in their application to the particular Fiber B and PRD 49 samples tested: (a) The method of application of load in the fatigue tester appears to lead to a breaking load which is lower than in an Instron tensile test. (b) The application of an oscillatory load does appear to cause a further small drop in the maximum load needed to cause failure; this effect appears to be more marked when the fiber is allowed to go slack. (c) Nevertheless, the fatigue effect is much less severe than in nylon or polyester fibers; allowing for the variability of results, it appears that the rated loading under fatigue conditions comparable to those used in these tests should be taken to be about 75% of the Instron breaking load or 90% of the load for immediate failure under these conditions. A comparable figure for the other synthetics would be around 60%.

The results presented in this paper, which concentrate on the failure morphology, are in general agreement with the studies of mechanical properties reported recently by Bunsell.[15]

This work has been carried out with support from Procurement Executive, Ministry of Defence. The authors also acknowledge the help of E.I. du Pont de Nemours & Co., Inc., in supplying yarn samples and of Miss B. Lomas (U.M.I.S.T., Manchester) for useful discussions.

References

1. *Text. Inst. Ind.*, **12**, 380 (1974).
2. W. B. Black and J. Preston, High-modulus wholly aromatic fibers, M. Dekker, INC., New York, 1973, p. 5.
3. C. B. Chapman, *Fibres,* Butterworth, London, 1974, pp. 80–81.
4. R. Meredith, *Text. Progr.,* **7** (No. 4), (1975).
5. J. W. Rothuizen, *Text. Inst. Ind.,* **11**, 142 (1973).
6. du Pont de Nemours & Co., *Information Bulletins No. 4, 5, 6, 7*, 1974.
7. A. R. Bunsell, J. W. S. Hearle, and E. Hunter, *J. Phys. Ed.,* **4**, 868 (1971).
8. *Fibre Data Summaries*, Shirley Institute, Manchester, July 1966.
9. J. W. S. Hearle, B. Lomas, and A. R. Bunsell, *Appl. Polym. Symp.,* **23** 147 (1974).
10. J. W. S. Hearle, in *Contributions of Science to the Development of the Textile Industry,* M. Cordelier and P. W. Harrison, Eds. Textile Institute and Institut Textil de France, 1975.
11. A. R. Bunsell and J. W. S. Hearle, *J. Mater. Sci.,* **6**, 1303 (1971).
12. A. R. Bunsell and J. W. S. Hearle, *J. Appl. Polym. Sci.,* **18**, 267, 1974.
13. A. R. Bunsell, Ph.D. dissertation, Univ. Manchester Inst. Sci. Technol., 1972.
14. J. W. S. Hearle and S. C. Simmens, *Polymer,* **14**, 273 (1973).
15. A. R. Bunsell, *J. Mater. Sci.,* **10**, 1300 (1975).

Received June 11, 1976

Peel Mechanics for an Elastic-Plastic Adherend

A. N. GENT and G. R. HAMED, *Institute of Polymer Science,
The University of Akron, Akron, Ohio 44325*

Synopsis

The force required to propagate a 180° bend in an elastic-plastic strip has been calculated from elementary bending theory. Measured forces for Mylar strips of various thicknesses, bent to various degrees, were in good agreement with these calculated values. The corresponding additional stripping force in a peeling experiment will depend upon the thickness of the elastic-plastic adherend, becoming zero both for infinitesimally thin adherends and for those exceeding a critical thickness t_c and passing through a maximum value at intermediate thicknesses. Published data are in good agreement with these conclusions. For a strongly adhering strip, higher peel strengths are found for a peel angle of 180°, compared to 90°, and the effect is greater than can be accounted for solely by plastic yielding of the adherend. It is attributed in part to greater energy dissipation within the adhesive layer.

INTRODUCTION

Several investigators have analyzed the peeling test assuming that both the adherend and the adhesive obey linear elastic mechanics.[1–7] However, it is now widely recognized that in a peeling experiment the stripping member may undergo plastic yielding if the bending stresses imposed by the peel force are sufficiently large.[8–13] Plastic yielding provides an energy dissipation mechanism, and thus a higher peel force is required than if yielding does not occur. The magnitude of this additional energy dissipation has now been determined experimentally for a simple elastic-plastic strip adhering to a rigid substrate. Results are given below for the peel force component arising from yielding of the adherend. They are compared with the predictions of an approximate theoretical treatment. Conclusions are drawn as to the effect of yield stress, thickness, and elastic modulus of the adherend, and of the strength of adhesion to the substrate.

In a further series of experiments, the contribution to the work of detachment arising from plastic yielding of a strip adhering to a deformable elastomeric substrate has been measured. Peeling experiments have been carried out at peel angles of 90° and 180°; the results are compared with values obtained when plastic yielding of the strip was prevented. Large differences were observed for both peel angles. They are attributed only in part to energy expended in plastic deformation of the adherend; part of the additional energy losses must arise within the elastomeric substrate when plastic yielding occurs in the detaching layer. Dissipative processes within the adhesive layer have previously been shown to account for much of the observed peel strength of adhesive joints, in the absence of plastic yielding.[14–17] These processes are not discussed in the

2817

present paper, which deals solely with the conditions for, and consequences of, plastic yielding in the detaching layer.

EXPERIMENTAL

As shown later, Mylar [poly(ethylene terephthalate) film, E. I. du Pont de Nemours and Co.] undergoes plastic yielding at a well-defined yield stress and conforms closely to ideal elastic-plastic behavior, at least in tension. Strips of Mylar were, therefore, used as model elastic-plastic adherends. The force P per unit width of strip required to propagate a bend was measured for varying degrees of curvature of the strip during detachment from a weakly adhering substrate. As shown in Figure 1, two Mylar strips were detached simultaneously by peeling them away from two rubber-covered metal plates. Adhesion to the rubber was relatively small, the peel force P being only about 4 N/m in the absence of plastic yielding. The thickness of the rubber layer was also small, about 0.3 mm, so that no significant deformation of the rubber was expected. The rubber layers served merely to prevent slipping and buckling of the Mylar strips under the force P.

The degree of bending of the Mylar strips was characterized by the distance D between the central planes of the adhering and fully removed portions of the film, Figure 1. Various values of D were obtained by altering the separation of the two steel backing plates, which were held parallel to each other at a given distance by means of adjustable spacer rods. When the spacing D was reduced below a critical value, the force P was found to increase greatly, and the amount, denoted P_y, by which it exceeded the small value required to detach the unrestrained strip is attributed to energy dissipated in plastic yielding. Values of P_y were measured for a wide range of spacings D, and for various thicknesses of film, in the range of 25–360 μm. In addition, the effect of varying the speed of propagation of the bend was examined over the range of 3×10^{-4} mm/sec to 3 mm/sec.

In order to examine the effect of plastic yielding under conditions of strong adhesion, Mylar strips 76 μm thick were adhered to a 1 mm thick layer of an elastomeric SBS triblock copolymer (Shell Kraton 1101) by pressing the two materials together for 90 min at a temperature of 150°C. The Kraton layer was held flat by bonding its lower surface to a steel plate. On peeling the Mylar strip off the elastomer, failure occurred at the Mylar–elastomer interface, as represented schematically in Figure 2, and the detached strip was tightly curled, indicating that it had undergone severe plastic yielding during detachment.

Peeling experiments were also carried out with the same strongly adhering materials, i.e., Mylar and Kraton 1101, under conditions where no plastic deformation of the Mylar strip occurred. The experimental arrangement for this, suggested by Dr. D. I. Livingston of the Goodyear Tire and Rubber Company Research Division, is shown in Figure 3. It resembles that employed in ASTM Test Method D 3167-73T. The Mylar strip in the detachment region was bent around a freely rotating roller having a sufficiently large radius of curvature so that bending stresses in the Mylar would not cause yielding. With a 12.7-mm-diameter roller, the maximum tensile strain in the outer regions of the Mylar strip was calculated to be only 0.006, considerably smaller than the yield strain, as discussed later.

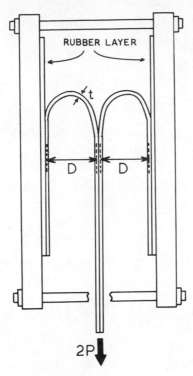

Fig. 1. Experimental arrangement for determining the work expended in plastic deformation of a peeling strip.

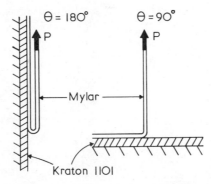

Fig. 2. Peeling an adhering Mylar strip from a Kraton 1101 substrate at 180° and 90°.

Weights were applied to the roller axle, as shown in Figure 3, so that the Mylar film would conform closely to the surface of the roller as detachment occurred. It was also found necessary to pull at a slight angle to the vertical in order to assure that the Mylar film was in good contact with the roller. Once the weights were in place and before starting to peel, the force measured by the load cell due to the weights and roller arrangement was noted. This value was then subtracted from the force measured during detachment to give the true peel force. When removed in this way, the Mylar strip showed no residual curvature, indicating that no plastic yielding had occurred during detachment.

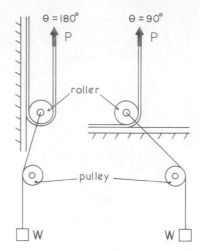

Fig. 3. Experimental arrangement for peeling at 180° and 90° without plastic yielding of the detaching strip.

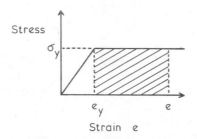

Fig. 4. Stress–strain relation for an ideal elastic-plastic solid.

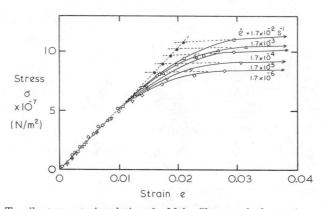

Fig. 5. Tensile stress–strain relations for Mylar film stretched at various rates $\dot{e}$.

THEORETICAL CONSIDERATIONS: PEELING AN ELASTIC-PLASTIC ADHEREND

An ideal elastic-plastic solid follows a linear stress–strain relation until the yield stress σ_y and yield strain e_y are attained. It then deforms at constant stress, as shown schematically in Figure 4. Mylar film shows elastic-plastic behavior in tension resembling this ideal pattern, (Fig. 5), although the transition from

TABLE I
Values of Yield Stress σ_y and Yield Strain e_y for Mylar Film Stretched at Various Rates

$\dot{e}$, sec^{-1}	σ_y, MN/m^2	e_y
1.7×10^{-6}	82	0.016
1.7×10^{-5}	89	0.0175
1.7×10^{-4}	95	0.0185
1.7×10^{-3}	101	0.0195
1.7×10^{-2}	107	0.021

elastic to plastic behavior is more gradual than in the ideal case. Moreover, the yield stress and yield strain increase somewhat with rate of deformation, even though the elastic modulus appears to remain substantially unchanged (Fig. 5).

Approximate values for yield stress and strain were obtained from the intercept of the two linear relations which describe the wholly elastic and wholly plastic regimes, represented by the broken lines in Figure 5. The filled-in circles in Figure 5 denote yield points deduced in this way; the numerical values are given in Table I and are plotted in Figure 6 against the rate of extension $\dot{e}$ on a logarithmic scale. As is commonly found,[18] these semilogarithmic plots yielded linear relationships. When values of yield stress and strain were required in order to calculate the plastic work expended in peeling, using the approximate theory developed below, the corresponding rate of strain was approximated by

$$\dot{e} = \dot{c}/t$$

where $\dot{c}$ is the rate of peel and t is the thickness of the strip. Values of σ_y and e_y were then read from Figure 6.

A schematic diagram of one of the peeling Mylar strips is shown in Figure 7, with the distribution of stress across the thickness shown for a particular section which has undergone partial plastic yielding. It is assumed that the yield behavior in compression is the same as that in tension, so that the neutral axis is still located at the center of the strip. As a section of the strip traverses the bend, it passes from an undeformed state in the adhering region through a maximum

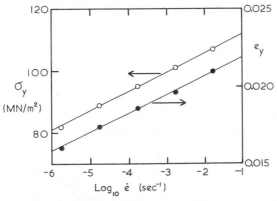

Fig. 6. Experimental relations between yield stress σ_y, yield strain e_y, and rate of extension $\dot{e}$, from Fig. 5.

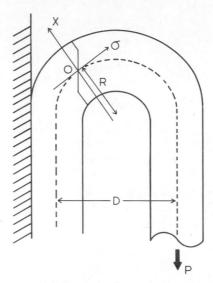

Fig. 7. Schematic diagram of peeling strip showing neutral axis (broken curve), local radius of curvature R, and the variation of tensile stress σ with distance x from the neutral axis.

bending deformation where the radius of curvature of the neutral axis is a minimum, at the point O in Figure 7, say. The maximum strain e imposed on a layer at a distance x from the neutral axis is then given by

$$e = x/R \tag{1}$$

where R is the minimum radius of curvature of the neutral axis. If this strain exceeds the yield strain e_y, then energy is dissipated per unit volume equal to the shaded area in Figure 4 in taking the layer past the point O. If e is less than e_y, then it is assumed that no energy is expended in taking the layer around the bend, i.e., all the elastic energy expended in deforming the layer is recovered again when it is straightened. Also, any further plastic work expended as the plastically deformed layers move on into regions of lesser curvature and are straightened again is neglected. In practice, the peeled strips were found to show residual curvature after plastic deformations had been encountered, suggesting that any plastic work expended subsequently in straightening them was less than that expended in deforming them.

Thus, the total energy expended in plastic deformation during peeling of unit length of the strip is given approximately by

$$W = 2 \int_{e_y R}^{t/2} \sigma_y (e - e_y) dx \tag{2}$$

per unit width of strip, where t is the thickness. This energy is supplied by the component P_y of the peel force arising from plastic work:

$$W = 2P_y \tag{3}$$

Hence, from eq. (1), (2), and (3),

$$P_y = \frac{1}{4} (\sigma_y e_y t) \left[\left(\frac{t}{2Re_y} \right) + \left(\frac{2Re_y}{t} \right) - 2 \right] \tag{4}$$

It is now necessary to find the relationship between the minimum radius of curvature R and the imposed spacing D in order to compute the corresponding peel forces P_y by means of eq. (4). Two limiting cases will be considered. For an elastic strip peeled at 180°, the distance D is obtained from elementary bending theory[19]:

$$D = 2(EI/P)^{1/2} \qquad (5)$$

where E is Young's modulus and I is the second moment of area of cross section per unit width of the strip, given by

$$I = t^3/12$$

The minimum radius of curvature in this case is developed at the point of separation; it is

$$R = EI/PD \qquad (6)$$

Combining eqs. (5) and (6), we obtain a relation for the minimum radius of curvature in terms of the spacing D for a perfectly elastic strip,

$$R = D/4 \qquad (7)$$

The other limiting case occurs when the peeling strip folds back on itself to form a fully developed plastic hinge at the point of detachment. The minimum possible value of the radius of curvature of the neutral axis in this case is $t/2$, when the separation D of the neutral axes becomes equal to the strip thickness t. Thus,

$$R \approx t/2 \approx D/2 \qquad (8)$$

In practice, the minimum radius R will lie between the extremes given by eqs. (7) and (8), tending toward the former relation when the amount of plastic deformation is small and toward the latter, when it is substantial.

It is instructive to examine eq. (4) in greater detail. At small values of the spacing D and radius of curvature R, the first term in the brackets in eq. (4) becomes dominant and the equation simplifies to

$$P_y \approx \sigma_y t^2/8R \qquad (9)$$

When the radius of curvature takes its minimum possible value, $t/2$, the corresponding maximum possible contribution to the peel force per unit width is obtained as

$$P_{y,\text{max}} = \sigma_y t/4 \qquad (10)$$

It should be noted that the peeling strip will fail by plastic yielding in tension at a force of $\sigma_y t$ per unit width. The maximum peel force contribution from plastic bending effects is thus comparable in magnitude to the ultimate strength of the adherend.

At the other extreme, eq. (4) predicts that P_y becomes zero when the radius of curvature exceeds a critical value, denoted R_0, given by

$$R_0 = t/2e_y$$

The corresponding critical spacing D_0 for elastic films is given by eq. (7):

$$D_0 = 2t/e_y \qquad (11)$$

and the corresponding critical thickness t_c is given by

$$t_c = 12 \, EP_0/\sigma_y{}^2 \tag{12}$$

from eqs. (5), (6), and (11), where P_0 denotes the peel force per unit width in the absence of plastic yielding. No contribution to the observed peel force from plastic yielding will occur for adhering strips having a thickness greater than t_c.

Calculations up to this point have dealt with peeling at an angle of 180°. It is instructive to consider what changes would be necessary for peeling at 90°. Equation (9) becomes

$$P_y \approx \sigma_y t^2/4R$$

for the peel force contribution at small values of the radius of curvature R. When the radius takes its minimum feasible value, $t/2$, the corresponding maximum possible value of P_y becomes

$$P_{y,\mathrm{max}} = \sigma_y t/2$$

in place of eq. (10), even closer than before to the ultimate strength of the peeling strip. When the thickness of the peeling strip exceeds a critical value, given by

$$t_c = 6EP_0/\sigma_y{}^2 \tag{13}$$

plastic yielding will not occur. At first sight, eq. (13) appears to predict a smaller value of critical thickness for an adherend peeled at 90° than for one peeled at 180°, eq. (12). However, because the peel force at 90° is twice as large as that at 180° for the same work of detachment, eq. (12) and (13) actually correspond to the same value of critical thickness.

EXPERIMENTAL RESULTS FOR A WEAKLY BONDED ELASTIC–PLASTIC ADHEREND

In Figure 8, the total peel force P per unit width of strip is plotted as a function of peel rate for a Mylar film weakly adhered to a rubber-coated steel plate and held at various degrees of bending during detachment, Figure 1. The peel forces for an unrestrained strip (where the value of the spacing distance D is approximately 15 mm) are also shown in Figure 8. As D was reduced down to about 4 mm, the peel forces remained small and constant. But for values of D below this critical level, i.e., for higher degrees of bending of the Mylar strip, a dramatic increase in P was found.

The additional peel force P_y was measured for various values of the imposed spacing D below the critical value (denoted D_0). The results are shown in Figure 9 for four different thicknesses of Mylar film at a constant peeling speed of 0.04 mm/sec. For a fixed spacing, P_y was found to be greater the thicker the Mylar film. Also, the values obtained dropped rapidly to zero as the spacing approached the corresponding critical value D_0 for each film.

In order to obtain theoretical values of P_y for quantitative comparison with these experimental results, several steps are necessary. First, values of yield stress σ_y and strain e_y were read from Figure 6 at the appropriate rate of extension. The minimum radius R of curvature appropriate to the spacing D was

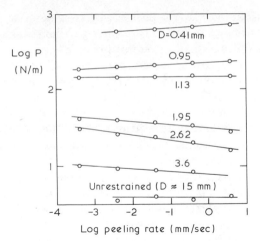

Fig. 8. Peel force P per unit width vs rate of peeling for a Mylar film 76 μm thick, peeled at various degrees of bending. D denotes the imposed bending spacing, as shown in Fig. 1.

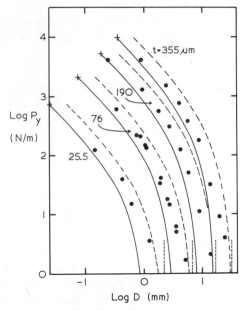

Fig. 9. Additional peel force P_y per unit width arising from plastic yielding vs imposed bending spacing D, for Mylar films of various thickness t peeled at 0.04 mm/sec. Vertical broken lines denote calculated values of the critical spacing D_0, from eq. (11).

determined from eq. (7) or (8). Values of P_y were then calculated from eq. (4). The two theoretical relations shown in Figure 9 for each thickness of Mylar film were obtained in this way. The broken curves, using R from eq. (7), should be more appropriate at small amounts of plastic work and the full curves, using R from eq. (8), at large degrees of plasticity.

Maximum values of P_y were also calculated from eq. (10). They are plotted in Figure 9 (crosses) against the appropriate values of D for each film, i.e., when $D = t$, and form the terminal points for the theoretical relations representing large degrees of plasticity, the full curves in Figure 9. Values of the spacing D_0

at which the contribution P_y to the peel force becomes zero were calculated from eq. (11). They are shown in Figure 9 as the right-hand vertical asymptotes of the relations representing small amounts of plastic work, i.e., the broken curves in Figure 9. Experimentally observed spacings at which a plastic contribution to the peel force was first observed were in good agreement with these calculated values in all cases.

Indeed, the experimental results for P_y are seen to be in good agreement with the theoretical predictions over the entire range of measured values and for all thicknesses of adherend. Moreover, they tend to lie closer to the broken relations at large spacings D and closer to the full relations at small values of D, in accord with expectation. Contributions to the observed peel forces arising from plastic work are thus successfully accounted for, both qualitatively and quantitatively, by the present theoretical treatment.

Effects of rate of peeling on the observed peel force can also be explained in terms of contributions from plastic work. At values of the spacing distance D just below the critical level D_0, the peel force was found to decrease as the peel rate increased, whereas at much smaller values of D than this, the peel force increased somewhat with increasing peel rate, Figure 8. Both of these contrasting effects appear to be direct consequences of the rate dependence of yield stress and yield strain, Figure 6. At large values of D, i.e., at strains near the onset of plasticity, yielding will be more extensive at low rates because the yield strain is smaller at low rates of deformation. The contribution P_y to the observed peel force will be correspondingly greater at low rates of peel and decrease as the rate increases. However, when plastic yielding is already extensive, i.e., at small values of the spacing D, then the peel force will increase with increasing rate of peel because of the corresponding increase in yield stress and strain with rate of deformation.

EXPERIMENTAL RESULTS FOR A STRONGLY ADHERING STRIP

Measurements were made of the work of detachment for a Mylar strip 76 μm thick adhering to a layer of Kraton 1101. For peeling at 90°, the work of detachment is given directly by the peel force per unit width, but for peeling at 180°, it is given by twice the peel force per unit width because, in order to detach a length L, the point of application of the peel force must travel a distance $2L$.

The experimental results at both peel angles are plotted in Figure 10 against the rate of peeling. As shown there, the work of detachment was found to be considerably larger at a peel angle of 180°, compared to 90°. Moreover, after detachment at 180°, the Mylar strip exhibited a high degree of permanent curvature, indicating that extensive plastic yielding had occurred during the peeling process, whereas after peeling at 90°, the residual curvature was much less pronounced.

The theoretical treatment given earlier does not predict any difference between the contribution of plastic yielding to the observed work of detachment at 90° and 180°. The present observations cannot, therefore, be accounted for in terms of that theory, and an explanation must be sought in other directions.

It is illuminating in this connection to compare the observed works of detachment with that required in the absence of plastic yielding. Detachment of the Mylar strip at 90° and 180° without plastic deformation was achieve by

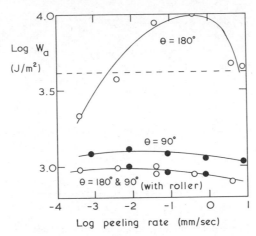

Fig. 10. Work W_a of detachment vs. rate of peeling for a Mylar strip 76 μm thick adhering to a Kraton 1101 substrate: (O) peeled at 180°; (●) peeled at 90°. Broken horizontal line represents the maximum energy expended in plastic deformation of the Mylar strip at 180°, calculated from eq. (10).

peeling around a large-diameter roller, as shown in Figure 3. The results obtained in this way are included in Figure 10. They were much smaller than before, and the values for 90° and 180° peel angles now coincided. Also, no permanent curvature of the Mylar strips was found. Thus, the difference found previously between the work of detachment at 90° and 180° peel angles can be attributed, at least in part, to different levels of plastic work in the two cases, although it is not yet apparent why they should differ.

The maximum contribution that yielding in the Mylar strip can make to the detachment energy may be calculated by means of eq. (10). The value obtained is represented by the broken horizontal line in Figure 10. When it is added to the lower curve in Figure 10, representing the detachment energy when no yielding of the Mylar strip occurs, the sum is still not as large as the highest values obtained experimentally for peeling at 180°. This discrepancy is even greater when the actual contribution to the detachment energy arising from plastic yielding of the Mylar strip is employed in place of the maximum possible value. The actual work expended in plastic yielding was deduced from measurements of the bending distance D, obtained from photographs of the peeling strip in the process of detachment. A value for D of 0.32 mm was determined in this way for peeling at 180° under the largest peel forces. The corresponding contribution of plastic yielding to the work W_a of detachment was obtained from Figure 9; it is only about 1.3×10^3 j/m^2. This is far too small to account for the difference between the value of W_a when no plastic yielding occurs, about 1×10^3 j/m^2, and the value obtained when the Mylar strip is allowed to bend sharply during detachment, about 1×10^4 j/m^2 (Fig. 10).

There are, therefore, two anomalous features of the present experimental results: the Mylar strip does not undergo fully plastic bending, even though the peel forces are sufficiently large to cause this condition, and the peel energy at 180° is considerably greater than the sum of the plastic work expended in the Mylar and the work of detachment in the absence of plastic yielding. These discrepancies appear to be associated with deformations of the adhesive layer

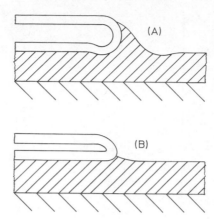

Fig. 11. Detachment from a deformable substrate (a) and from a stiffer, less extensible substrate (b).

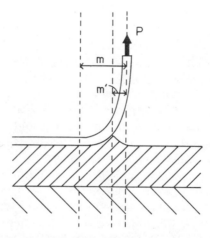

Fig. 12. Reduction in bending moment for peeling at 90° from a deformable substrate (schematic). The moment arm of the peel force P is represented by m for a rigid substrate and by m^1 for the deformable substrate shown.

in the immediate vicinity of the detachment front. Part of the adhesive material was observed to follow around the sharply bent region of the Mylar strip before detaching, as shown schematically in Figure 11(a). Thus, the Mylar strip was stiffened by this still-adhering part of the substrate layer, and it did not undergo such severe bending as it otherwise would have done [Fig. 11(b)]. This is apparently the reason why it did not become fully plastic, even though the peel forces were large enough to make an unsupported Mylar film yield completely.

Deformation of the substrate layer will be still more effective in lessening the effects of plastic yielding at a peel angle of 90°. In this case, a relatively small deformation of the substrate will allow a significant *rotation* of the still-attached portion of the adherend toward the line of action of the peel force. Thus, the bending moment acting at the point of detachment will be decreased and yielding of the adherend will be delayed or reduced (Fig. 12). We conclude that strongly-adhering substrates which also have sufficient extensibility to conform to the shape of the adherend in the region of detachment will reduce the severity

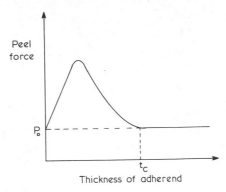

Fig. 13. Dependence of the peel force P on thickness t of an elastic-plastic adherend. Broken horizontal line represents the work of detachment in the absence of plastic yielding.

of bending and hence reduce the contribution of plastic yielding of the adherend to the work of detachment, especially at 90°.

The question remains, why are the observed energies of detachment for peeling at 180° so large? An important contribution appears to come from energy dissipation within the substrate material in the highly deformed region around the point of detachment. The present substrate, although basically elastomeric in character, is stiffer for small deformations and then yields at a tensile stress of about 1.5 MN/m^2, to become softer and highly extensible. Thus, additional energy dissipation by a yielding process within the substrate will occur when the local stress reaches a value of about 1.5 MN/m^2. This circumstance may well arise in the vicinity of a sharply bent peeling strip. Moreover, dissipation of energy by this mechanism is likely to depend strongly upon the rate of deformation because the substrate material shows rate-dependent mechanical properties. Thus, the pronounced effect of the rate of peel upon the work of detachment at 180° (Fig. 10), is consistent with rate effects within the substrate material rather than within the Mylar adherend.

We conclude that inelastic deformation of the substrate layer was mainly responsible for the higher peel strengths observed at a peel angle of 180°. Plastic deformation of the stripping member can thus lead to an increase in peel strength in two ways: (i) directly, by an additional force representing the work required to propagate the bend in an elastic-plastic strip as peeling proceeds, and (ii) indirectly, by causing a larger deformation in the elastomeric substrate under the higher peel forces and bringing about greater energy losses in this layer as a result.

EFFECT OF THICKNESS OF THE ADHEREND

It is apparent from Figures 9 and 10 that the energy expended in bending the stripping layer may make a large contribution to the total work of detachment. The extent of this contribution will depend upon the strength of adhesion, however. If the interfacial adhesion is sufficiently weak or if the adhering layer is sufficiently thick or strong, the conditions for plastic yielding will not arise and there will be no contribution to the peel force from this source. On the other hand, with strong adhesion, or thin ductile adhering layers, yielding will occur readily and contribute to the total work of detachment.

These considerations account for published reports[20-22] that the peel force passes through a maximum as the adherend thickness is increased. For a given level of adhesion, a very thin adherend will yield during peeling, but the total energy dissipated will be small because t is small, and the contribution of plastic yielding to the peel force will be negligible. As the thickness is increased, more energy will be dissipated and the peel force will increase, eq. (10). However, at sufficiently large thicknesses, the detaching layer will become too stiff to undergo yielding throughout its thickness and the peel force will begin to decrease as the thickness is increased further. Eventually, when the thickness exceeds t_c, the detaching layer will not undergo plastic yielding at all and the peel force will return to its original value. Thus, the peel force at both zero and large thicknesses of adherend should be equal, and they should both reflect the work of detachment in the absence of plastic yielding. This general dependence upon thickness is shown schematically in Figure 13; published results are in good agreement with these deductions.[20,21]

CONCLUSIONS

The peel force required to propagate a bend in an elastic-plastic strip has been calculated using elementary bending theory. Measured forces for Mylar strips of various thicknesses, bent to various degrees, have been found to be in good agreement with these calculated values. The extent to which these forces contribute to the total stripping force in a peeling experiment is governed by the strength of adhesion, relative to the thickness and yield stress of the adherend. While energy expended in the stripping member can clearly make a major contribution to the total peel force (Fig. 9 and 10), the contribution will be zero when the interfacial adhesion is relatively small and the adherend is sufficiently thick so that it does not undergo plastic yielding at all.

The deformability of the adhesive will also affect the extent to which plastic yielding contributes to the total peel force. For instance, consider the two peel systems shown in Figure 11, which both peel under the same force P. Case A shows peeling with a soft, deformable adhesive, whereas in case B, the adhesive is nearly rigid. In case A, the detaching strip may be kept from undergoing a sharp bend because the adhesive effectively stiffens it in the peeling region. Thus, the contribution of yielding to the total peel force will be reduced in this case. In case B, the same peel force may cause the detaching strip to pass through a sharp bend, with a consequent large contribution to the total peel force arising from plastic yielding.

This work forms part of a program of research on failure processes supported by a research grant from the National Science Foundation. The authors are indebted to Dr. J. Schultz of the Centre de Recherches sur la Physico-Chimie des Surfaces Solides, Mulhouse, France, for helpful discussions and some preliminary results on plastic yielding of Mylar films during detachment.

References

1. G. J. Spies, *Aircraft Eng.*, **25**, 64 (1953).
2. J. J. Bikerman, *J. Appl. Phys.*, **28**, 1484 (1957).
3. J. J. Bikerman, *J. Appl. Polym. Sci.*, **2**, 216 (1959).
4. D. H. Kaelble, *Trans. Soc. Rheol.*, **3**, 161 (1959).
5. D. H. Kaelble, *Trans. Soc. Rheol.*, **4**, 45 (1960).

6. S. Yurenka, *J. Appl. Polym. Sci.*, **6,** 136 (1962).

7. J. L. Gardon, *J. Appl. Polym. Sci.*, **7,** 643 (1963).

8. C. Mylonas, in *Proc. 4th Int. Congr. Rheology,* Part 2, Interscience, New York, 1963, pp. 423–447.

9. A. J. Duke and R. P. Stanbridge, *J. Appl. Polym. Sci.*, **12,** 1487 (1968).

10. M. D. Chang, K. L. DeVries, and M. L. Williams, *J. Adhesion,* **4,** 221 (1972).

11. A. N. Gent and J. Schultz, in *Proc. Int. Rubber Conf., Brighton, May 1972,* Instn. Rubber Industry, London, 1973, pp. C1. 1–6.

12. W. T. Chen and T. F. Flavin, *IBM J. Res. Dev.,* **16,** 203 (1972).

13. A. J. Duke, *J. Appl. Polym. Sci.*, **18,** 3019 (1974).

14. A. N. Gent and R. P. Petrich, *Proc. R. Soc.,* **A310,** 433 (1969).

15. A. N. Gent, *Bull. Soc. Chim. France,* 3237 (1970).

16. A. N. Gent and A. J. Kinloch, *J. Polym. Sci. A-2,* **9,** 659 (1971).

17. A. N. Gent, in *Dynamic Crack Propagation,* G. C. Sih, Ed., Nordhoff Internatl. Publishing, Leyden, 1973, pp. 157–163.

18. P. B. Bowden, in *The Physics of Glassy Polymers,* R. N. Haward, Ed., Wiley, New York, 1973, Chap. 5.

19. R. V. Southwell, *An Introduction to the Theory of Elasticity,* 2nd ed., Oxford University Press, London, 1941, reprinted by Dover Publications, New York, 1969, Chap. 13.

20. D. Satas and F. Egan, *Adhesives Age,* **9**(8), 22 (1966).

21. J. Johnston, *Adhesives Age,* **11**(4), 20 (1968).

22. D. W. Aubrey, G. N. Welding, and T. Wong, *J. Appl. Polym. Sci.*, **13,** 2193 (1969).

Received July 28, 1976
Revised September 27, 1976

Branching and Molecular Weight Distribution of Polyethylene SRM 1476

HERMAN L. WAGNER and FRANK L. McCRACKIN, *Institute for Materials Research, National Bureau of Standards, Washington, D.C. 20234*

Synopsis

A method of determining the distribution of branching in a polymer is developed employing limiting viscosity numbers (intrinsic viscosity), gel permeation chromatography (GPC), and absolute molecular weight determinations of fractions of the whole polymer. A molecular weight calibration of the GPC column set is first determined employing these fractions. From the limiting viscosity number measurements of these fractions and their molecular weight distribution determined from the GPC chromatogram, the viscosity–molecular weight relationship is determined by a nonlinear least-squares fitting procedure. For the same molecular weight, the limiting viscosity number of the branched polymer is less than the limiting viscosity number of the linear polymer. From the ratio of the two, the number of branches per unit molecular weight of the branched polymer is calculated. This method was applied to SRM 1476, the standard reference branched polyethylene issued by the National Bureau of Standards. The branching density for the constituents of SRM 1476 rise from zero at molecular weights less than 10,000 to about 6 to 8×10^{-5} at molecular weights of 50,000 and above. The branching of SRM 1476 was also determined by the method of Drott and Mendelson, giving a result in fair agreement with the above method.

INTRODUCTION

Although it has long been recognized that not only molecular weight distribution but also long-chain branching significantly affects polymer properties, particularly rheological behavior, the quantitive assessment of branching has remained a difficult task. Gel permeation chromatography (GPC) has become a commonly employed method of determining molecular weight distribution, but its use is generally limited to linear polymers. This is due to the dependence of the method on hydrodynamic volume, which varies, for polymers of the same molecular weight, with the degree of branching. However, by combining GPC with other techniques, it is possible to obtain information not only about molecular weight distribution but branching as well. In the method proposed by Drott and Mendelson,[1] it is assumed that the branching frequency is the same for all species of varying molecular weight in the sample and that "universal calibration" of the GPC column is valid for branched polymers. In this investigation, a method of determining the molecular weight distribution and the dependence of branching on molecular weight of the species in the polymer without these assumptions is given. The method was applied to SRM 1476,[2] a standard reference material of the National Bureau of Standards. This polymer was fractionated; and, from an examination of many of these fractions

2833

by a combination of GPC, dilute solution viscosity, light scattering, and osmometry, we obtained information about its branching distribution.

EXPERIMENTAL

SRM 1476 was fractionated by the column elution procedure previously described.[3] The Celite column was heated to 127°C, and polymer dissolved in xylene was permitted to flow onto the column, which was then allowed to cool to 50°C overnight. All of the polyethylene, except for a small amount (called fraction 1 AS), precipitated on the column. The xylene at 50°C was then displaced by a poor solvent, 2-butoxyethanol, and the column containing the bulk of the polyethylene was reheated to 127°C. The fractionation proceeded by extraction with mixtures by xylene and 2-butoxyethanol which were successively richer in the better solvent, xylene. Recovery was 97–98%. To obtain sufficient material for this study, ten batches of 20 g each were fractionated separately and corresponding fractions from each fractionation were grouped together into 12 main fractions. These were then refractionated into 122 subfractions.

Most of the fractions and subfractions were characterized by GPC and, in addition, by one or more of the following techniques: dilute solution viscosity to measure limiting viscosity number; light scattering, to measure weight-average molecular weight; and osmometry, to measure number-average molecular weight.

Light-scattering measurements were made in 1-chloronaphthalene at 135°C using a Sofica light scattering photometer previously calibrated with benzene. Unpolarized light at 546 nm was employed with solutions which had been clarified with a Millipore filter of 0.22 μm nominal pore size. Weight-average molecular weights were determined from extrapolation of the scattering data at five concentrations and 11 angles by the Zimm method. The other details of the measurement are similar to those reported[4,5] for the work on SRM 1475.

Light-scattering measurements made on the whole polymer, filtered in the same way through a 0.22-μm Millipore filter, did not yield a satisfactory Zimm plot, showing a severe downturn in the reciprocal scattering function at low viewing angle. Moore and Peck[6] have attributed this to the presence of very high molecular weight polyethylene species. However, when the whole polymer, dissolved in xylene, was first eluted through the Celite column employed in the fractionation and then filtered through the 0.22-μm Millipore, this downturn was much reduced. An estimate of the weight-average molecular weight of the material was made, but the uncertainty is at least 15%. Zimm plots for the fractions were satisfactory.

Osmotic pressure determination of number-average molecular weight were made in a Hewlett–Packard membrane osmometer in 1-chloronaphthalene at 130°C using a 450 D Arro Laboratory gel cellophane membrane. Data from five concentrations were extrapolated to zero concentration. The details of technique and data analysis are essentially similar to what has been described previously.[7]

GPC data were obtained on a Waters Model 200 apparatus. Styragel columns were employed with nominal exclusion limits ranging from 100 to 10^7 Å. Two column sets were used; column set A was used to give good resolution for high molecular weight polymers, and column set B was used to give good resolution for lower molecular weight polymers. The calibration of the columns will be discussed below.

The limiting viscosity number $[\eta]$ was measured in 1,2,4-trichlorobenzene at 130°C. The method has also been described elsewhere.[8]

A listing of the subfractions with associated data is given in Table I.

DATA ANALYSIS

Subfractions

Since the elution volume in GPC depends on the hydrodynamic volume of the polymer, which is a function not only of molecular weight but also of degree of branching, calibration with linear fractions in the usual way does not suffice for the study of branched materials. Instead, each of the two column sets used for the subfraction analysis was calibrated with those subfractions of SRM 1476 for which molecular weight averages were determined by light scattering or osmometry. The molecular weight M was assumed to be related to the retention volume v by

$$\log M = A + Bv + Cv^2 \tag{1}$$

where A, B, and C are determined by a least-squares fitting procedure to give the best agreement among the values of M_w, the weight-average molecular weight as determined by light scattering, and M_n, the number-average molecular weight determined by osmometry. The weight- and number-average molecular weights are given in terms of the chromatograms by

$$M_w = \int_0^\infty H(v) \, M(v) \, dv \tag{2}$$

and

$$M_n = 1 \bigg/ \int_0^\infty H(v) \, M^{-1}(v) \, dv \tag{3}$$

where H is the height of the chromatogram normalized to unit area. This method of calibration has been described previously.[9]

For column set A, the following subfractions were used: 7AS6, 10AS12, 12AS3, 12AS8, and 12AS9. This yielded the following calibration of column A:

$$\log M = 19.1603 - 0.7454v + 0.00808v^2 \tag{4}$$

with a mean-square residual of 11%. For the column set B, subfractions 3AS2, 4AS3, 5AS5, 6AS6, 7AS13, 8AS9, 9AS2, 9AS10, and 11AS2 were used to give the following calibration for column B:

$$\log M = 13.484 - 0.1666v - 0.00213v^2 \tag{5}$$

with a mean-square residual of 17%. The calibration depends, of course, on the degree of branching as well as the molecular weight, so that the coefficients in eqs. (4) and (5) depend not only on the column but the degree and distribution of branching of SRM 1476.

The column elution procedure used to prepare the fraction is known to fractionate linear polymers according to molecular weight. On the other hand, in

TABLE I
Branched Subfractions of SRM 1476

Subfraction	M_w	M_n	$[\eta]$, ml/g	Subfraction	M_w	M_n	$[\eta]$, ml/g	Subfraction	M_w	M_n	$[\eta]$, ml/g
3AS2	7,000	4800	23.8	7AS8			60.0	11AS2	186,000	81,800	134
3AS3			30.4	7AS9			59.5	11AS3			158
				7AS10			67.5				
4AS2			26.1	7AS11			78.8	12AS3	75,400		94.6
4AS3	9,830	9,560	30.3	7AS12			71.6	12AS5	376,000	115,800	169
4AS4			35.6	7AS13		44,400	101.8	12AS6	923,000		205
				7AS14			105.7	12AS8	912,000		286
5AS4			34.4	7AS15			104.3	12AS9	772,000	146,000	254.1
5AS5	15,600	14,000	40.0								
5AS6			45.2	8AS8			70.8				
				8AS9			81.6				
6AS4			38.7								
6AS5			41.0	9AS1			138				
6AS6	17,500		45.0	9AS2	120,000		101				
6AS7			48.7	9AS10	116,000	71,600	114				
6AS8			54.6								
				10AS11			123				
7AS5			50.6	10AS12		117,000	150				
7AS6	24,000	24,100	54.6	10AS13			172				
7AS7			57.9	10AS14			175				

the case of branched polymers, the separation into fractions probably occurs on the basis of branching as well as molecular weight of the species so that the fractions and subfractions probably differ in branching as well as in molecular weight. However, a single calibration curve of molecular weight versus elation volume was obtained for each set of columns despite the fact that the elution volume depends on both the branching and molecular weight of the polymer. We conclude, therefore, that the branching of the fractions are dependent mainly on their molecular weight, so that their chromatograms are determined mainly by their molecular weight. Some of the differences between the molecular weight averages of the subfractions calculated from the calibrating eqs. (4) or (5) and their measured values may be due to variations in branching of the subfractions.

We now wish to find a relationship between limiting viscosity number $[\eta]_b$ and molecular weight for the species which constitute SRM 1476. We assume that this relationship may be represented by the empirical relationship

$$\log [\eta]_b = P + Q \log M + R (\log M)^2 \tag{6}$$

The limiting viscosity number of a fraction may be computed from its chromatogram by integrating over the species in the fraction:

$$[\eta]_c = \int_0^\infty H(v) [\eta]_b \, dv \tag{7}$$

where $[\eta]_b$ is the limiting viscosity number of the species with retention volume v. By eqs. (6) and (7),

$$[\eta]_c = \int_0^\infty H(v) \exp [P + Q \log M + R (\log M)^2] \, dv \tag{8}$$

The limiting viscosity number $[\eta]_c$ of a fraction may be computed from eqs. (1) and (8) for assumed values of P, Q, and R. A series of values of v are chosen, and the molecular weight M corresponding to each value of v is calculated. Then the integrand of eq. (8) in computed for each value of v, and the integral is numerically evaluated to give the calculated limiting viscosity number $[\eta]_c$ of the fraction. This value may be compared to the measured value $[\eta]_m$ of the subfraction.

In order to determine the relationship of limiting viscosity number to molecular weight, the constants P, Q, and R in eq. (6) must be determined. This was done by the procedure shown in Figure 1. The limiting viscosity numbers $[\eta]_m$ of 40 fractions were measured and GPC chromatogram of the fractions were obtained. Then, the limiting viscosity numbers of each of the fractions were computed from their chromatograms by eqs. (1) and (8). These calculated values were compared with the measured values of limiting viscosity numbers. The values of P, Q, and R were then changed and new values of $[\eta]_c$ computed from the chromatograms. This iteration is continued until the values of P, Q, and R that yield the best possible agreement between the calculated and measured limiting viscosity numbers are obtained and the relationship given by eq. (6) is determined.

The viscosity-average molecular weight of these 40 fractions ranged from 9000 to 400,000, and the limiting viscosity numbers ranged from 23.9 to 205 ml/g. The viscosity–molecular weight relation obtained in this way is given by

$$\log [\eta]_b = -1.4587 + 0.8658 \log M - 0.0326 (\log M)^2 \tag{9}$$

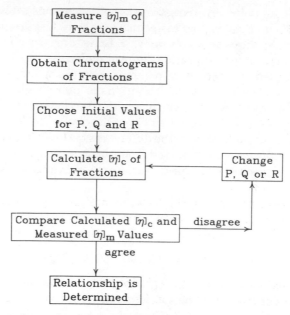

Fig. 1. Flow chart of procedure used to determine the relationship between limiting viscosity number and molecular weight of branched polyethylene.

and is shown by the solid curve in Figure 2. The viscosity-average molecular weight M_v of a subfraction is defined as the solution of the equation

$$\log [\eta]_c = P + Q \log M_v + R (\log M_v)^2 \tag{10}$$

The points in Figure 2 represent the observed values of limiting viscosity number plotted against the viscosity-average molecular weight obtained from the solution of eq. (9) with final values of P, Q, and R. The relative error of $[\eta]$ (residual standard deviation) is 9%. Also shown is the Mark–Houwink relation for linear polyethylene,[10] plotted as a dashed line and given by

$$[\eta]_l = 0.0392 \, M^{0.725} \tag{11}$$

The linear and branched curves are coincident for $M < 10,000$, so that species of molecular weight up to 10,000 have little or no detectable long-chain branching.

The extent of branching may be expressed by the ratio G of the limiting viscosity number of a branched polymer species to that of the linear species of the *same molecular weight*:

$$G = [\eta]_b/[\eta]_l \tag{12}$$

G is plotted as a function of molecular weight for SRM 1476 in Figure 3. The relationship of G to the ratio g of the mean squares of the radii of gyration, $\langle s \rangle^2$, of branched to linear polymer of the same molecular weight has not been settled, but we have employed the relationship proposed by Zimm and Kilb[11]:

$$G = g^{1/2} = \{\langle s \rangle_b{}^2/\langle s \rangle_l{}^2\}^{1/2} \tag{13}$$

Zimm and Stockmayer[12] have derived the following relationship between g and

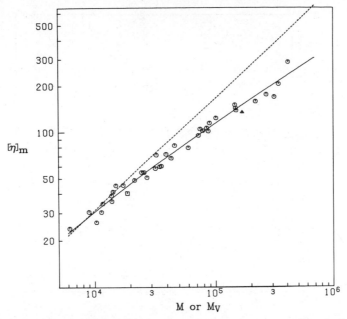

Fig. 2. Relationship of limiting viscosity number to molecular weight of branched polyethylene SRM 1476. Subfractions 5AS5 and 11AS2 are shown by a square and triangle, respectively; other subfractions are shown by circles, and the calculated relationship is shown by the curve. The limiting viscosity number of linear polyethylene is shown by the dotted line.

the number of branch points n_w for a randomly branched polydisperse polymer having trifunctional branch points:

$$g = \frac{6}{n_w} \frac{1}{2} \left(\frac{2 + n_w}{n_w}\right)^{1/2} \ln \left[\frac{(2 + n_w)^{1/2} + n_w^{1/2}}{(2 + n_w)^{1/2} - n_w^{1/2}} - 1\right] \quad (14)$$

From eqs. (10) to (14), n_w was calculated as a function of molecular weight. Then, the number of branch points per unit molecular weight

$$\lambda = n_w/M \quad (15)$$

was calculated and is shown in Figure 4. The curve shows that $\lambda = 0$ for molecular weights less than 10^4, as expected from the results of Figure 2, and that λ then rises quickly to $(5–8) \times 10^{-5}$, but does not change appreciably after that. Because of the sensitivity of λ to errors in the experimental data, we cannot assert that the maximum is real.

The branching of subfractions 5AS5 and 11AS2 has been studied by Bovey et al.[13] using ^{13}C nuclear magnetic resonance. They measured 1.0 and 8.3 long branches per weight-average molecule for subfractions 5AS5 and 11AS2, respectively. By averaging values of n_w over the molecular weight distributions (as determined from their chromatograms) of these subfractions, we computed values of 0.9 and 12 for subfraction 5AS5 and 11AS2, respectively. Considering the uncertainties in both methods, the agreement is good.

MAIN FRACTIONS

The values of λ were also calculated from the chromatograms of the main fractions in order to provide a check of the previous calculations. These chro-

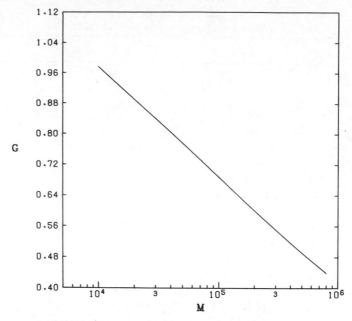

Fig. 3. Ratio, G, of limiting viscosity numbers of branched to linear polymer vs molecular weight.

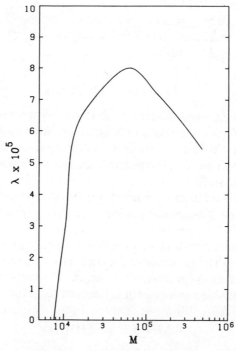

Fig. 4. Number of branch points, λ, per unit molecular weight for branched polyethylene SRM 1476.

TABLE II
Branched Main Fractions of SRM 1476

Fraction	$\lambda \times 10^5$	M_v	$[\eta]_{obs}$
3AS	0	7,200	24.6
4AS	0	9,800	30.6
5AS	0	13,500	38.6
6AS	6.2	19,300	45.5
7AS	7.4	27,800	56
8AS	7.6	40,600	70
9AS	3.6	76,500	112.5
10AS	8.3	1,940,000	152.5
11AS	4.7	1,680,000	164.2

matograms were not obtained on the same column set as the subfractions, but instead were obtained on a set calibrated with linear polyethylenes. Hence, it was necessary to use the Drott–Mendelson method to find values of λ.

The calibration was carried out with four linear polyethylene fractions and a sample of $C_{94}H_{190}$. Weight- and number-average molecular weights had been determined for the fractions by light scattering and osmometry, giving a 9-point calibration curve computed by the method referred to previously. The values of λ for each of the main fractions from 3AS to 11AS and viscosity-average molecular weights found by this method are shown in Table II. Fraction 1AS, which, as indicated above, was xylene soluble at 50°C, and fraction 2AS, which was made up of inhomogeneous particles, were not analyzed. The results for sample 12AS are questionable because the chromatogram went beyond the column calibration and are not included.

These values of λ are in general agreement with the values found for the subfractions (Fig. 4), considering the sensitivity of λ to errors in the limiting viscosity number and in chromatography.

WHOLE POLYMER

GPC measurements were also made on the whole polymer filtered in two different ways. In Figure 5, the solid chromatogram was obtained with ordinary filtration through a 0.45-μm pore size Millipore filter, and the dashed chromatogram was obtained with the polymer put through the Celite column in xylene solution, and then filtered through the same size filter before injection. This was the same Celite column used for fractionation. The Celite apparently removes some of the higher molecular weight species which are not removed by filtration.

The column set employed was calibrated with only linear fractions. In order not to assume, as in the Drott–Mendelson method, a constant λ, we employed a method which utilizes "universal calibration" in conjunction with the relationship between molecular weight and viscosity, eq. (10), found for subfractions of this polymer. The calibration of the column with linear fractions is represented by

$$\log M = A_l + B_l v + C_l v^2 \tag{16}$$

The universal calibration assumption holds that the hydrodynamic volume

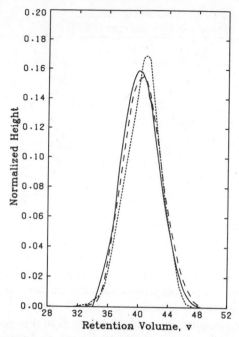

Fig. 5. GPC chromatograms of whole polymer SRM 1476 after filtration through a 0.45-μm Millipore filter (solid curve) and after filtration through a Celite column and a 0.45-μm Millipore filter (dashed curve). The dotted curve was obtained by summing the chromatograms of the main fractions 3AS to 12AS. All chromatograms are normalized to unit area.

$$U_v = M[\eta] \tag{17}$$

at a particular elution volume v is the same for branched and linear polymer. Combining eqs. (16) and (17) with the Mark–Houwink equation, eq. (11), we find for the linear polymer

$$\log U_v = \log [\eta] [M] = \log k + (a + 1)A_l + (a + 1)B_l v + (a + 1)C_l v^2 \tag{18}$$

From eqs. (9) and (15), we obtain for the branched polymer

$$\log U_v = P + (Q + 1) \log M + R(\log M)^2 \tag{19}$$

Molecular-weight averages of the branched polymer were computed from its chromatogram by use of eqs. (18) and (19). For every retention volume v included in the chromatogram, the value of $\log U_v$ was computed by eq. (18). Then, the corresponding value of the molecular weight was found by solving eq. (19). Thus, the molecular weight corresponding to each retention volume in the chromatogram was determined; so that by integrating the molecular weight over the chromatogram, the molecular weight averages were obtained. Also, the molecular weight distribution of the whole polymer was calculated from the chromatogram obtained with filtration only through a 0.45-μm Millipore filter, and it is shown in Figure 6. The limiting viscosity number for the whole polymer is also similarly obtained from the chromatogram and eqs. (6), (18), and (19). The results are shown in Table III in the first three columns. The weight-average molecular weight obtained by light scattering is higher than that obtained by GPC and is at least partially due to the very large uncertainties in the results

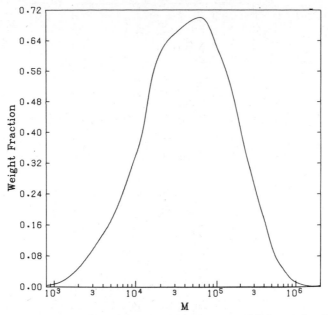

Fig. 6. Molecular weight distribution in log molecular weight of SRM 1476 after filtration through a 0.45-μm Millipore filter.

attributable to the influence of high molecular-weight particles on the light scattering data. The variation in molecular weight with filtration procedure shown in the table is also not surprising for branched polyethylenes, since the number and size of these particles are a function of the filtration procedure.

We compare in Table III the results obtained as described above with those obtained by the Drott–Mendelson method, which assumes constant λ. The difference in the average molecular weights between the two methods is small.

As a check on the consistency of these methods, the chromatograms of the main fractions from 3AS to 12AS were weighted by their fractional composition as determined by the original fractionation data for SRM 1476, yielding the dotted curve shown in Figure 5. The chromatogram of SRM 1476 filtered through Celite is seen to agree best with the summation of the main fractions, very likely because both were filtered by the Celite. The lower molecular weight (high retention volume) tail of the fraction-summed chromatogram contains a smaller amount of material than either of the whole polymer chromatograms, probably because fractions 1AS (2.7% of the total) and 2AS (3.7% of the total) were not included. We have no explanation of why there is disagreement at the high molecular weight end, with the summation chromatogram showing a somewhat narrower distribution. The chromatogram for the sum of main fractions was analyzed as above, employing eq. (10) to give the results shown in Table III.

SUMMARY

We have obtained an estimate of the branching and molecular weight distribution of SRM 1476, the branched polethylene standard reference material issued by the National Bureau of Standards. This was obtained by combining

TABLE III
Analysis of SRM 1476

| Filtration method | By eq. (10) | | | By Drott–Mendelson | | | By sum of fractions | | Light scattering |
	M_w	M_n	$[\eta]$, ml/g[a]	M_w	M_n	$\lambda \times 10^5$	M_w	M_n	M_w
0.45-μm Millipore	96,500	22,700	94.0	102,500	23,700	8.8	105,000	25,000	140,000
Celite column + 0.45-μm Millipore	90,700	19,500	89.5	90,900	20,100	6.3			

[a] Certificate value is 90.24 ml/g.

data from a detailed examination of fraction by light scattering, osmometry, viscosity, and GPC techniques. Although the results show reasonable internal consistency, they are subject to the many sources of error which are usual with these techniques, such as 10–15% errors in light scattering and osmometry as well as errors that are caused by the presence of the very high molecular weight species in branched polyethylene. The quantity of these species removed by filtration will vary with technique and is not easily controlled. In many of the fractions, their presence is shown by high molecular weight tails in the chromatograms, so that a small uncertainty in the baseline of a chromatogram can result in a large error in distribution. Nevertheless, these estimates of branching and molecular weight should enhance the usefulness of SRM 1476 and provide a starting point for further investigation of branched polyethylenes.

The authors wish to thank R. G. Christensen, J. R. Maurey, and J. E. Brown for assistance in the fractionation and characterization of the branched polyethylene fractions. Certain commercial equipment, instruments, and materials are identified in this paper in order to adequately specify the experimental procedure. In no case does such identification imply recommendation by the National Bureau of Standards, nor does it imply that the material or equipment identified is necessarily the best available for the purpose.

References

1. E. E. Drott and R. A. Mendelson, *J. Polym. Sci. A2*, **8**, 1361 (1970).

2. National Bureau of Standards Certificate, SRM 1476, Nov. 6, 1969, Office of Standard Reference Materials, NBS, Washington, D.C. 20234.

3. R. G. Christensen, *J. Res. Nat. Bur. Stand. (U.S.)*, **76A** (*Phys. Chem.*) (No. 2), 149 (1972).

4. L. J. Frolen, G. S. Ross, A. M. Wims, and P. H. Verdier, *J. Res. Nat. Bur. Stand. (U.S.)*, **76A** (Phys. Chem.) (No. 2), 156, (1972).

5. H. L. Wagner, *J. Res. Nat. Bur. Stand. (U.S.)*, *76A* (Phys. Chem.) (No. 2), 151 (1972).

6. L. D. Moore and V. G. Peck, *J. Polym. Sci.*, **36**, 141 (1959).

7. J. E. Brown and P. H. Verdier, *J. Res. Nat. Bur. Stand. (U.S.) 76A* (*Phys. & Chem.*) (No. 2), 169 (1972).

8. R. G. Christensen, *J. Res. Nat. Bur. Stand. (U.S.)*, **76A** (*Phys. Chem.*), (No. 2), 147 (1972).

9. F. McCrackin, *J. Appl. Polym. Sci.*, **21**, 191 (1977).

10. H. L. Wagner and C. A. J. Hoeve, *J. Polym. Sci., Polym. Phys. Ed.*, **11**, 1189 (1973).

11. R. W. Kilb and R. H. Zimm, *J. Polym. Sci.*, **37**, 19 (1959).

12. W. H. Stockmayer and B. H. Zimm, *J. Chem. Phys.*, **17**, 301 (1949).

13. F. A. Bovey, F. C. Schilling, F. L. McCrackin, and H. L. Wagner, *Macromolecules*, **9**, 76 (1976).

Received May 28, 1976
Revised August 13, 1976

Surface Free Energy Analysis of Polymers and its Relation to Surface Composition

TOSHIAKI MATSUNAGA, *Chemical Research Institute of Non-Aqueous Solutions, Tohoku University, Sendai 980, Japan*

Synopsis

The dispersion force component of surface free energy, γ_S^d, and the nondispersive interaction free energy between solid and water, I_{SW}^n, were determined by the two-liquid contact-angle method, i.e., by the measurement of contact angles of water drops on plain solids in hydrocarbon, for commercially available organic polymers such as nylons, halogenated vinyl polymers, polyesters, etc. A method to estimate the I_{SW}^n values from the knowledge of the polymer composition is also proposed, on the basis of the assumption of the spherical monomer unit and the sum of interactions between functional groups and water molecules at the surface.

INTRODUCTION

Since Fowkes had proposed experimental methods for doing so,[1] many investigations have been conducted to evaluate the components of surface and interfacial free energies due to intermolecular forces in order to understand interfacial phenomena of organic polymers. The surface and interfacial tensions mainly for molten polymers has recently been reviewed by Wu.[2] For solids, unfortunately, an intrinsically correct method has not yet been elucidated.

As an extension of Fowkes' approach, the dispersion force component as well as the po term of surface free energy have been approximated by contact angle measurement of polar and nonpolar liquids in air (the one-liquid contact-angle method).[3-6] Another extension of Fowkes approach has been proposed by Tamai et al.[7] from contact angle measurement of water drops on solids in hydrocarbon (the two-liquid contact-angle method).

A different approach from the solubility parameters has also been reported to evaluate the dispersion and the polar components.[8] The dispersion force component of surface free energy γ_S^d obtained by Tamai et al.[7] seems to be comparatively larger than others, as pointed out by Panzer.[8] There may be many yet unknown factors for this discrepancy, but one possible reason may be that the neglect of the surface pressure in the one-liquid method could have given the apparently smaller γ_S^d values, as discussed elsewhere in detail.[9]

In this investigation, the two-liquid method was applied to commercially available organic polymers, and γ_S^d and I_{SW}^n (the nondispersive interaction free energy between solid and water) were determined. A method of estimation of I_{SW}^n from the surface composition of polymers is also proposed. Since I_{SW}^n values can give useful surface energy information on polar terms, it may be of value for such applications as adhesion phenomena if the I^n_{SW} values can be estimated from the knowledge of polymer composition.

EXPERIMENTAL

Materials

Isooctane and cyclohexane of absorption-spectoscopic grade were used as saturated hydrocarbons. Water was redistilled from alkaline permanganate solution in a Pyrex glass apparatus.

Most polymers were commercially available plates as follows:

Nylon 6, CM-1031, Toray Industries Inc.

Nylon 6,6, "Zytel" 101; Nylon 6,12, "Zytel" 151, E.I. du Pont Far East Co.

Poly(vinylidene Fluoride) (PVDF), Kureha Chemical Industries Co.

Poly(trifluoromonochloroethylene) (PFCE), "Daiflon," and poly(tetrafluoroethylene–hexafluoropropylene) copolymer (PFEP$_{cop}$), "Neoflon," Daikin Kogyo Co.

Poly(oxymethylene) (POM), "Delrin" 5000, E.I. du Pont Far East Co.

Poly(ethylene terephthalate) (PET), "Lumilar" 100, Toray Industries Inc.

Polycarbonate (PC), Polycarbonate A-3000, Idemitsu Petrochemical Co.

Phenol (PPh) and Melamine (PMe) resin laminated plates, Sumitomo Bakelite Co.

The densities[d], determined from their sizes and weights, and the characteristics of the crystal structures, investigated by x-ray diffractometer (Shimadzu Seisakusho, VD-1), for these plate samples were as follows: PVDF: $d = 1.76$, small peaks of (010) and (200) of orthogonal structure. PFCE: $d = 2.10$, small peak of hexagonal (100). PFEP: $d = 2.07$, sharp peak of poly(tetrafluoroethylene). POM: $d = 1.39$, large and sharp peak of orthogonal structure. PC: $d = 1.19$, very broad peak. PET: $d = 1.38$, large peak of triclinic (100). Nylon 6: $d = 1.19$. Nylon 6,6: $d = 1.14$. Nylon 6,12: $d = 1.05$.

The x-ray diffraction patterns for nylons will be discussed later. Since phenol and melamine resins are laminated, their densities could not be determined.

Surface Preparation and Measurement of Contact Angles

The size of the sample plates was about 1×3 cm. Thicknesses were from 1 to 5 mm according to polymers, except PET, which was 0.1 mm thick.

These samples were cleaned before each measurement, by slight rubbing with a piece of gauze soaked in detergent solution and then thoroughly washing with distilled water. After drying for 1 hr in a desiccator with phosphorus pentoxide, these samples were transferred to an optical cell and covered with hydrocarbon.

The contact angles of water drops on the polymers were measured with a goniometer–telescope system at $20 \pm 0.5°C$. For each measurement, 12 to 18 contact angles were averaged, changing the size and place of the water drops.

The surface and interfacial tensions of liquids were measured by the Wilhelmy plate method.

TABLE I
Contact Angles and Analytical Results (20°C)[a]

Polymers	θ, degrees		γ_S^d, erg/cm²	$I/_{SW}^n$, erg/cm²	γ_S^p, erg/cm²	γ_S, erg/cm²
	c-Hex	i-Oct				
Nylon 6	105.6 ± 0.5	99.4 ± 0.6	78' ± 7	37.8 ± 0.3	7.2	85
Nylon 6,6	94.1 ± 0.6	87.6 ± 0.6	81 ± 7	47.8 ± 0.3	11.5	93
Nylon 6, 12	113.9 ± 1.0	109.0 ± 0.8	62 ± 9	30.7 ± 0.4	4.7	67
PVC[b]	139.9 ± 1.5	134.2 ± 1.0	56 ± 5	12.5 ± 0.3	0.8	57
PVDF	125.7 ± 1.1	123.2 ± 0.8	40 ± 4	21.1 ± 0.3	2.3	42
PFCE	170.4 ± 0.9	164.6 ± 0.6	36 ± 3	0.9 ± 0.1	0.0	36
PTFE[b]	174.7 ± 0.9	173.4 ± 0.8	25 ± 2	0.1 ± 0.1	0.0	25
PFEP$_{cop}$	174.2 ± 0.5	175.4 ± 0.6	26 ± 2	0.1 ± 0.1	0.0	26
POM	123.7 ± 1.1	117.6 ± 1.2	71 ± 6	23.4 ± 0.3	2.7	74
PET	118.8 ± 0.5	114.5 ± 1.0	56 ± 5	26.7 ± 0.3	3.6	60
PC	143.2 ± 0.4	137.9 ± 1.0	54 ± 5	10.6 ± 0.3	0.6	55
PPh	102.1 ± 1.0	95.6 ± 0.9	81 ± 7	40.9 ± 0.4	8.4	89
PMe	111.1 ± 0.7	106.8 ± 0.5	57 ± 5	32.8 ± 0.4	5.4	62

[a] Surface and interfacial tensions for liquids at 20°C: $\gamma_{\text{c-Hex}} = 25.0$, $\gamma_{\text{i-Oct}} = 18.9$, $\gamma_{\text{c-Hex}/W} = 50.0$; $\gamma_{\text{i-Oct}/W} = 49.3$, $\gamma_W = 72.7$, $\gamma_W^d = 23.0$ dynes/cm.
[b] From ref. 9.

RESULTS AND DISCUSSION

The analysis of the two-liquid contact-angle method is according to Tamai et al.[7]

The Young-Dupré equation of the contact angle θ of water drops (W) on plain solid (S) in hydrocarbon (H) is

$$\gamma_{SH} = \gamma_{SW} + \gamma_{HW} \cos \theta \tag{1}$$

where γ is the surface or interfacial free energy and the subscripts SH, SW, and HW mean the interface of solid/hydrocarbon, solid/water, and hydrocarbon/water, respectively.

According to Fowkes' theory for the expansion of surface free energy in regard to intermolecular forces and the geometric mean assumption for the dispersive interaction free energy at the interface, eq. (1) can be rearranged:

$$I_{SW}^n - 2(\gamma_S^d)^{1/2}[(\gamma_H)^{1/2} - (\gamma_W^d)^{1/2}] = \gamma_W - \gamma_H + \gamma_{HW} \cos \theta \tag{2}$$

where I_{SW}^n is the nondispersive interaction free energy between solid and water. The two unknowns, γ_S^d and I_{SW}^n, in eq. (2) can be solved by measurement of contact angles in two different hydrocarbons.

The accuracy of the γ_S^d determination by the two-liquid method is not very high, estimated about ±10%, because of its high sensitivity to the error in contact angle measurement. However, the accuracy of I_{SW}^n is considered to be sufficiently adequate, within around ±0.3 erg/cm².

The contact angles and their analytical results by the two-liquid method are listed in Table I. The sign ± for contact angles indicates the standard deviations, and those for γ_S^d and I_{SW}^n represent the 90% confidence limits of accuracy. The surface and interfacial tensions for liquids are shown in this table. The dis-

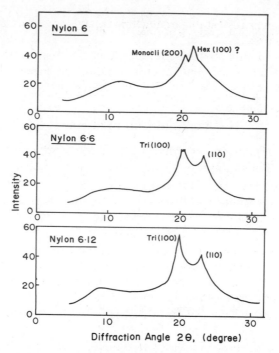

Fig. 1. X-ray diffraction patterns for nylons (Cu $K\alpha$).

persion component of the surface tension of water γ_W^d was calculated according to Fowkes' method from the interfacial tensions between the hydrocarbon and water interfaces. Although Fowkes has given 21.8 dynes/cm as the average value of γ_W^d, 23.0 dynes/cm was adopted in this paper from the interfacial tensions obtained here and in the previous study.[9]

Nylons

Since nylon 6,6 has a larger amount of amide groups than nylon 6,12, the former may well have a larger I_{SW}^n value. Moreover, that γ_S^d of nylon 6,6 is larger may be reasonable, because the functional groups such as amides, hydroxyls, carboxyls, etc., have larger polarizabilities than C—H or C—C bonds,[10] which should contribute to an increase in the dispersion force, if other factors remain constant.

Nylon 6 and nylon 6,6 have different I_{SW}^n values, even though their γ_S^d values are almost equal. This difference may be somewhat unexpected, considering that these nylons have equal amounts of amide groups though different arrangements in the polymer chains.

According to Fort,[11] nylon 6 and nylon 6,6 have similar wetting behavior and equal critical surface tensions γ_c, 42 dynes/cm. Baier and Zisman,[12] however, have indicated that γ_c of nylon 11 was sometimes even larger than that of nylon 6 according to their preparation methods.

The difference in crystal structure of these polymers might affect their surface properties. The x-ray diffraction patterns are shown in Figure 1. Although nylon 6,6 and 6,12 present similar patterns of stable triclinic crystals, nylon 6 display a diffraction peak of stable monoclinic crystals as well as that due to some quasi-stable structure.

This difference in bulk structure might affect the surface structure and the configuration or conformation of functional groups at the surface, and consequently the I_{SW}^n values.

Halogenated Vinyl Polymers

The γ_S^d values of halogenated vinyl polymers are comparatively larger than reported values. For example, γ_S^d values reported are 32.0 erg/cm^2 for PVC,[3] 14.5 erg/cm^2 for PTFE,[4] and 26.2 erg/cm^2 for PVDF.[4]

However, γ_S^d values obtained here for PTFE and PFCE, 25 and 36 erg/cm^2, respectively, correspond very well to the surface free energies theoretically calculated by Good,[14] 24 and 38 erg/cm^2 respectively. As these polymers have very small polarities, as shown in Table I, γ_S^d should be considered to be almost equal to γ_S. There may be many reasons for the disagreement between the results of the two-liquid method and other experimental methods. For one, this discrepancy may be due, at least partly, to the neglect of the surface pressure effect (π) in the one-liquid method. A detailed discussion of this point has been reported elsewhere.[9]

In comparison with those of investigated molten polymers,[2] the γ_S^d values for all polymers investigated here seem to be larger. However, since a correct, reliable method to determine surface free energies for solids is not yet available and some discontinuity of surface free energy between solid and liquid might still possibly exist, it cannot be claimed at present which results are accurate.

Polyesters and Other Polymers

The polyesters, such as PET and PC, and those polymers in the lower part of Table I have, in general, many functional groups, and so it would be natural that I_{SW}^n as well as γ_S^d are comparatively large, as discussed above for nylons.

Estimation of I_{SW}^n from the Composition of Polymers

In the one-liquid method, the nondispersive interaction free energy between solid and polar liquids have been frequently used to obtain the polar surface free energy γ_S^p, assuming the geometric mean for the interfacial force[3,4,5,6] or the harmonic mean.[15]

For the results of the two-liquid method, Kaelble[16] has shown that the geometric mean rule would be applicable. He has rearranged eq. (2) into the following form:

$$\frac{W_{23} + \gamma_{2V} - \gamma_{1V} - \gamma_{12}}{2(\beta_2 - \beta_1)} = \beta_3 + \alpha_3 \left(\frac{\alpha_2 - \alpha_1}{\beta_2 - \beta_1} \right) \tag{3}$$

where the subscripts 1, 2, 3, and V are hydrocarbon, water, solid, and vapor, respectively, and W is the work at the interface, and α and β are the square roots of the dispersion and polar component of the surface tension of each phase, respectively. By application of this equation to Tamai and co-workers' data, Kaelble obtained a linear line for each solid, which should mean that the geo-

TABLE II
Estimation of $I_{SW}{}^n$ from Polymer Structure

Polymer	x	$I/_{SW}^{n}(x)$[a]	$s(x)$[b]	$I/_{SW}^{n}(x) \cdot s(x)$, erg/cm²	$I/_{SW}^{n}$, erg/cm² Calcd.	Obsd.
Nylon 6	—CONH—	17	2.7[c]	45.9	45.9	37.8
Nylon 6, 6	—CONH—	17	2.7[c]	45.9	45.9	47.8
Nylon 6, 12	—CONH—	17	1.8[c]	30.6	30.6	30.7
PMMA[d]	—COO—	4.5	3.7	16.7	16.7	27.4
PSt[e]	—Benz.	1	3.3	3.3	3.3	5.9
PVC[d]	—Cl	2	5.7	11.4	11.4	12.5
PVDF	—F₂	3	6.5	19.5	19.5	21.1
PET	—COO—	4.5	5.3	23.9	26.5	26.7
	—Benz.	1	2.6	2.6		
PC	—COO—	4.5	2.1	9.5	13.7	10.6
	—Benz.	1	4.2	4.2		
POM	—O—	2.5	9.2	23.0	23.0	23.4
PPh[f]	—OH	10	3.7	37.0	40.7	40.9
	—Benz.	1	3.7	3.7		

[a] In units of 10^{-14} erg/molecule.

[b] In units of 10^{14} cm^{-2}.

[c] Only for nylons, $s(x)$ was calculated assuming the nylon chains to be rod-like, not spherical. Then, since the volume of one monomer unit can be obtained as $v = (M/dN)$, the occupied surface area by one monomer unit a is given as $a = l(v/l)^{1/2} = (lv)^{1/2}$, if polymer chains lie parallel to the surface plane, where l is the length of monomer unit along the polymer chain, 8.7, 8.7, and 13.1 Å for nylon 6, 6, 6, and 6, 12, respectively.

[d] $I/_{SW}^{n}$ values from ref. 9.

[e] Unpublished data.

[f] For phenol resin, a network-structured polymer, an average monomer unit was assumed as $+C_6H_3 \cdot (OH) \cdot CH_2 +_n$, and $d = 1.27$ was adopted as the bulk density. Melamine resin was excluded, because its average monomer unit is considered more vague.

metric mean rule is applicable to the polar terms, and could obtain $\alpha_3 (= \gamma_S^d)$ and $\beta_3 (\gamma_S^p)$ values. Therefore, applying this idea to I_{SW}^{n} values here obtained, γ_S^p values were calculated for the present polymers which are also listed in Table I with the total surface free energy γ_S, the sum of γ_S^d and γ_S^p.

However, as Tsutsumi has revealed,[16] the nondispersive interaction energy between mica and water deviates from the geometric mean, although those between mica and several organic polar liquids obey rather well the geometric mean assumption. At any rate, since I_{SW}^{n} itself can be used as a measure of surface polarities, the estimation of I_{SW}^{n} values from the surface composition of polymers has been attempted.

I_{SW}^{n} is considered to be mainly due to hydrogen bonding, and in some cases also due to dipole–dipolde interaction, between functional groups on a given surface and water molecules. Because of the short-range characteristics of hydrogen bonding, effective interaction may be restricted to that between the functional groups and tlhe nearest water molecules. If this is the case, I_{SW}^{n} may be estimated from the kinds and amounts of functional groups as the sum of the interactions, as follows.

$$I_{SW}^{n} = \sum_{x} I_{SW}^{n}(x) \cdot s(x) \qquad (4)$$

where x denotes functional groups, $I_{SW}^n(x)$ is the contribution of one x group to I_{SW}^n, and $s(x)$ is the surface density of x. This equation means that a functional group x may similarly contribute to I_{SW}^n in any polymer, regardless of its specific properties in each polymer. Even with this assumption, it is difficult to know exactly the surface density $s(x)$.

As a first approximation, $s(x)$ was calculated assuming the spherical monomer unit of a given polymer as

$$s(x) = k(M/dN)^{-2/3} \tag{5}$$

where k is the number of x in one monomer unit, M is the molecular weight of the monomer unit, d is the bulk density, and N is Avogadro's number.

The I_{SW}^n values so calculated are listed in Table II and compared with observed values. The contribution of each functional group $I_{SW}^n(x)$ was appropriately chosen so that the calculated values should agree with the observed ones as far as possible.

These $I_{SW}^n(x)$ values seem to be rather reasonable in two ways. The first is that some $I_{SW}^n(x)$ values such as those for ester and aromatic groups can be used for several polymers, as seen in Table II. The second is that the $I_{SW}^n(x)$ values may be considered reasonable when compared with that for water surface. Since the interaction free energy between the imaginary water/water interface I_{WW}^n is calculated to be 99.6 erg/cm^2 (as $I_{WW}^n = 2(\gamma_W - \gamma_W^d)$), and the surface density $s(H_2O)$ by eq. (5) is 10.4×10^{14} cm^{-2}, $I_{WW}^n(H_2O)$ is obtained as 10×10^{-14} erg/molecule. This value corresponds well to that of the OH group, $I_{SW}(OH)$. Moreover, the $I_{SW}^n(x)$ for ester and ether groups, about $\frac{1}{2}$ and $\frac{1}{4}$ of $I_{SW}^n(OH)$, respectively, may be reasonable. For instance, the solubilities in water of polar organic compounds consisting of similar alkyl chain structures, 2-pentanol $(C_2H_4OHC_3H_7)$, butyl acetate $(CH_3COOC_4H_9)$, and ethyl propyl ether $(C_2H_5OC_3H_7)$ are 0.54, 0.37, and 0.21 mole/kg H_2O at 25°C, respectively.[18]

To refine this approach, however, further research for many polymers should be done, and if in some cases specific information on functional groups at the given polymer surface can be added for $I_{SW}^n(x)$, more accurate and applicable I_{SW}^n values would be obtained.

The author wishes to express his thanks to Prof. Y. Tamai for his valuable discussions and continual encouragement. Prof. K. Murakami and Dr. K. Ono are appreciated for their suggestions on polymers. The author is indebted to those companies that have supplied polymer samples.

References

1. F. M. Fowkes, *Ind. Eng. Chem.*, **56** (12), 40 (1964).
2. S. Wu, *J. Macromol. Sci.*, **C 10**, 1 (1974).
3. D. K. Owens and R. C. Wendt, *J. Appl. Polym. Sci.* **13**, 1741 (1969).
4. D. H. Kaelble, *Physical Chemistry of Adhesion*, Wiley-Interscience, New York, 1971, p. 164.
5. Y. Kitazaki and T. Hata, *J. Adhesion Soc. Jpn*, **8**, 131 (1972).
6. E. H. Andrews and A. J. Kinloch, *Proc. R. Soc. London*, **A332**, 385 (1973).
7. Y. Tamai, K. Makuuchi, and M. Suzuki, *J. Phys. Chem.*, **71**, 4176 (1967).
8. J. Panzer, *J. Colloid Interface Sci.*, **44**, 142 (1973).
9. Y. Tamai, T. Matsunaga, and K. Horiuchi, *J. Colloid Interface Sci.*, to be published.
10. C. P. Smith, *Dielectric Behavior and Structure*, McGraw-Hill, New York, 1955.
11. T. Fort, Jr., *Adv. Chem. Ser.*, **43**, 302 (1964).
12. R. E. Baier and W. A. Zisman, *Macromolecules*, **3**, 462 (1970).

13. D. H. Kaelble and E. H. Cirlin, *J. Polym. Sci.,* **A2,** 363 (1971).

14. R. J. Good, *Adv. Chem. Ser.,* **43,** 74 (1964).

15. S. Wu, *J. Polym. Sci. C,* **34,** 19 (1971).

16. D. H. Kaelble, *XXIIIrd Int. Congress Pure Appl. Chem.,* **8,** 265 (1971).

17. K. Tsutsumi, Preprint of 34th Annual Meeting of Chem. Soc. Jpn., April 1976.

18. Chem. Soc. Japan, *Kagaku-Benran* (*Handbook of Chemistry*), Maruzen, Tokyo, 1972, pp. 816, 832, 836.

Received July 13, 1976
Revised September 14, 1976

Uptake of Tridodecylmethylammonium Chloride by PVC

P. E. FROEHLING, D. M. KOENHEN, C. A. SMOLDERS, and A. BANTJES, *Laboratory for Macromolecular Chemistry, Twente University of Technology, Enschede, The Netherlands*

Synopsis

The uptake of tridodecylmethylammonium chloride (TDMAC) by poly(vinyl chloride) has been investigated to provide a more quantitative basis for the preparation of blood-compatible surfaces based on TDMAC–heparin coatings. Sorption isotherms of TDMAC from toluene–cyclohexane and toluene–methanol mixtures have been measured. In toluene–cyclohexane mixtures, the TDMAC uptake is proportional to the degree of swelling of the polymer. From ion-exchange experiments with $^{36}Cl^-$, it appears that only a small fraction of the TDMAC remains near the PVC surface to provide the heparin binding capacity. Methanol forms a strong H-bonded complex with TDMAC in toluene and prevents its sorption by PVC.

INTRODUCTION

The quaternary ammonium salt tridodecylmethylammonium chloride (TDMAC) has been extensively used in biomedical materials technology for the preparation of nonthrombogenic surfaces. The compound can be applied to polymeric materials by adsorption from organic solvents, resulting in a small ion exchange capacity on the surface of the material, which can be used to bind ionically the anticoagulant polyelectrolyte heparin.[1] Materials which are "heparinized" in this way have very favorable properties with respect to the absence of initiation of blood coagulation, and their application in a variety of therapeutic and diagnostic fields is currently under investigation.[2,3] A quantitative description of the attachment of TDMAC to polymers has been lacking up to now.

Within the scope of our research in the field of blood-compatible surface coatings, we report here on the solution and adsorption behavior of TDMAC. As a polymeric adsorbent, poly(vinyl chloride) was chosen. Several solvent systems have been investigated to relate the TDMAC uptake to polymer swelling and to solution behavior.

EXPERIMENTAL

Materials

TDMAC was obtained from Polysciences Inc. Poly(vinyl chloride) powder was Breon S 110/10, a very pure preparation according to elementary analysis

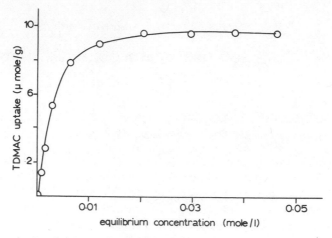

Fig. 1. Sorption isotherm of TDMAC by PVC from toluene solution at 20°C.

and IR spectrum. From gel permeation chromatography (solvent, tetrahydro-furan; stationary phase, Styragel, Waters Associates), the molecular weight distribution was calculated[4,5] as $\bar{M}_n$ = 28,000, $\bar{M}_w$ = 56,000, using calibration samples of PVC from Pressure Chemical Co. The surface area of the PVC powder was determined as 1.0 m^2/g by the BET method with nitrogen adsorption, using a Perkin-Elmer Model 212D Sorptometer.

Methods

Adsorption experiments at which 5 g PVC was equilibrated with 25 ml of the appropriate solutions were carried out at 20° ± 0.5°C. TDMAC-loaded PVC powders were separated from toluene solutions by filtration, followed by repeated rapid washings with small quantities of toluene, and dried *in vacuo* at 45°C for 48 hr. TDMAC concentrations were determined by the titration method described by Cross[6] and Patel.[7] Swelling experiments were carried out as described before.[8] Radiotracer experiments to determine ion exchange capacity of TDMAC adsorbates were performed at the Interuniversitary Reactor Institute, Delft, The Netherlands, using an aqueous ^{36}Cl$^-$ solution (Na^{36}Cl, The Radio-

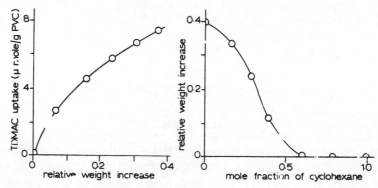

Fig. 2. Swelling of PVC and TDMAC sorption in 5.25 × 10^{-3}M solution in toluene–cyclohexane mixtures at 20°C.

TABLE I
Chloride Exchange of TDMAC Adsorbates with $^{36}Cl^-$

Total TDMAC present, μmole/g PVC	Exchangeable Cl^-, μmole/g PVC
4.247	0.0515
6.056	0.2167
7.125	0.3051

chemical Centre) with a specific activity of 0.340 Ci/mole. Radioactivity measurements were carried out on a Packard TriCarb Model 3320 liquid scintillation counter, using the Packard "Instagel" scintillation medium. Gas-chromatographic separations of toluene–methanol mixtures were performed at 152°C on Porapak Q columns. Light-scattering measurements were performed at 25°C on a Fica-50 photogoniodiffusiometer with unpolarized light of 546 mm. IR spectra were recorded on a Beckmann IR-33 spectrometer equipped with Beckmann liquid cells with NaCl windows and Teflon spacers, optical path 1.2 mm.

RESULTS AND DISCUSSION

The adsorption isotherm of TDMAC on PVC from toluene solution is given in Figure 1. The plateau value of adsorption, 10.27 μmole/g, combined with the BET area of 1.0 m²/g, corresponds to an improbably small area of 16 Å²/molecule, assuming monolayer adsorption on the polymer surface. It can be concluded that the TDMAC is not only present on the PVC surface, but does actually dissolve into the toluene-swollen polymer. This is confirmed by the relation between degree of swelling and TDMAC uptake of PVC in toluene–cyclohexane mixtures (Fig. 2).

The fraction of TDMAC remaining near the polymer surface, thus contributing to the ion-exchange capacity, was determined by $^{36}Cl^-$ exchange of TDMAC-loaded PVC. Let there be x exchangeable Cl^- ions on the PVC surface and m $^{36}Cl^-$ ions in solution before equilibration. After equilibration, there remain n $^{36}Cl^-$ ions in solution. At equilibrium, the $^{36}Cl^-/Cl^-$ ratio on PVC and in solution should be equal:

$$\frac{x - m + n}{m - n} = \frac{m - n}{n} \tag{1}$$

TABLE II
Light Scattering of TDMAC in Toluene/Methanol[a]

Methanol concentration, mole/l.	TDMAC concentration, mole/l.	Dissymmetry factor
0	0.0525	1.706
1.312	0.0525	1.204
0	0.00525	1.081
0.1312	0.00525	1.035

[a] λ = 546 mm (unpolarized).

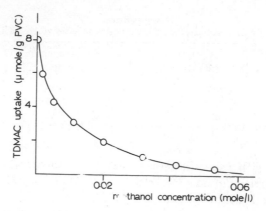

Fig. 3. TDMAC sorption by PVC from $5.25 \times 10^{-3}M$ solution in toluene–methanol mixtures at 20°C.

from which follows that

$$x = (m/n)\,(m - n) \tag{2}$$

The results with three different TDMAC loads are given in Table I. It is obvious that only a small fraction of the TDMAC is present on the PVC surface.

The TDMAC uptake in toluene–methanol mixtures is given in Figure 3. Nothwithstanding the enhanced swelling caused by added methanol,[8] the TDMAC uptake is greatly reduced by small amounts of methanol and approaches already a zero level at methanol concentrations at which swelling is hardly influenced. This is not caused by selective adsorption of methanol which might prevent the TDMAC uptake, as was shown by gas chromatography of toluene–methanol mixtures before and after treatment with PVC. The swelling behavior is not influenced by TDMAC.

It is well known that trialkylammonium salts with eight or more C atoms per carbon chain do not form well-defined "inverted micelles" in toluene or cyclohexane solution, contrary to smaller oil-soluble surfactant molecules, but rather tend to form stepwise aggregates depending on surfactant concentration.[9,10] Light-scattering data of TDMAC in toluene with added methanol are given in Table II. From the dissymmetry factor, i.e., the ratio of light-scattering intensities at angles of 45° and 135°, the size of particles of known shape may be determined.[11] From the decrease of the dissymmetry factor when methanol is added, it can be concluded that the TDMAC aggregates in toluene are largely broken up by methanol. The formation of a strong hydrogen-bonded complex between methanol and TDMAC was demonstrated by IR spectroscopy[12] of $0.1M$ CD_3OD in toluene, which showed a wavelength shift of the O—D adsorption from $2680\ cm^{-1}$ to $2510\ cm^{-1}$ when TDMAC was added to a concentration of $4.3 \times 10^{-3}M$. It is probable that the formation of the methanol–TDMAC complex makes the interaction between PVC and TDMAC thermodynamically unfavorable, thus diminishing the TDMAC uptake.

The authors thank G. van de Ridder, L. Broens, and H. Bevers (Twente University of Technology) and L. van Westing (Interuniversiform Reactor Institute, Delft) for experimental contributions, and Z. Kolar (I.R.I) for valuable suggestions concerning the radiochemical experiments.

References

1. G. A. Grode, S. J. Anderson, H. M. Grotta, and R. D. Falb, *Trans. Amer. Soc. Artif. Int. Organs,* 15, 1 (1969).
2. R. I. Leininger, J. P. Crowley, R. D. Falb, and G. A. Grode, *Trans. Amer. Soc. Artif. Int. Organs,* 18, 312 (1972).
3. J. Ehrlich, *Polym. Eng. Sci.,* 15, 281 (1975).
4. J. M. Evans, *Polym. Eng. Sci.,* 13, 401 (1973).
5. J. N. Cardenas and K. F. O'Driscoll, *J. Polym. Sci., Polym. Lett. Ed.,* 13, 657 (1975).
6. J. T. Cross, *Analyst,* 90, 315 (1965).
7. D. M. Patel and R. A. Anderson, *Drug Stand.,* 26, 189 (1958).
8. P. E. Froehling, D. M. Koenhen, A. Bantjes, and C. A. Smolders, *Polymer,* 17, 835 (1976).
9. K. A. Allen, *J. Phys. Chem.,* 62, 1119 (1958).
10. H. Gutmann and A. S. Kertes, *J. Colloid Interface Sci.,* 51, 406 (1975).
11. G. Oster, in *Physical Methods of Chemistry,* A. Weissberger and B. Rossiter, Eds., Wiley-Interscience, New York, 1972, Part IIIA, pp. 81–85.
12. W. Gordy, *J. Chem. Phys.,* 7, 93 (1939).

Received July 12, 1976

JOURNAL OF APPLIED POLYMER SCIENCE   VOL. 21, 2861–2866 (1977)

Prefatigue Hysteresis Effects on Viscoelastic Crack Propagation

AKIRA KOBAYASHI and NOBUO OHTANI, *Institute of Space and Aeronautical Science, University of Tokyo, Tokyo, 153, Japan*

Synopsis

Prefatigue hysteresis effects on viscoelastic crack-propagation velocity were investigated through velocity-gauge techniques at different temperature levels. It was found that prefatigue effects accelerate elastic predominance in viscoelastic dynamic crack propagation, approaching elastic brittle fracture as shown by Berry's equation. This results in greater dynamic crack-propagation velocity at any given test temperature level.

INTRODUCTION

Viscoelastic dynamic crack propagation was studied by the present authors.[1,2,3] However, these studies were carried out under virgin material conditions and no prefatigue effects were investigated. It is already known that the fatigue effects make the material brittle as in the case of metals; therefore, such prefatigue effects might also be expected to make several contributions to the dynamic crack-propagation behavior in viscoelastic materials; the elastic predominance, caused by an increasing brittle condition, might surely be expected to have an influence on the viscoelastic dissipation properties governing the dynamic crack-propagation velocity. The present paper describes the prefatigue effects on viscoelastic dynamic crack propagation at different temperature levels.

EXPERIMENTAL

Specimen

Poly(methyl methacrylate) (PMMA) sheet, Sumipex, produced by Sumitomo Chemical Company, Japan, is used as the specimen material (lot number 107-641). The individual specimen configuration is shown in Figure 1, in which the starting notch is machined after prefatigue hysteresis.

Prefatigue Hysteresis

The prefatigue hysteresis (Table I) was achieved at room temperature (22°C) through the use of a servopulser, EHF-10, manufactured by Shimadzu Seisakusho, Ltd., Japan. In the preliminary test, the number of cycles to failure at 12 Hz = $1.3 \times 10^5 \sim 3.5 \times 10^5$ and the static breaking stress $\sigma_b = 7$ kg/mm^2 were obtained for unnotched specimens.

2861

Dynamic Crack Propagation Measurements

The specimen shown in Figure 1 was subjected to constant cross-head speed tension of 2 mm/min (equivalent strain rate of 1.85×10^{-4}/sec) at 22° and 50°C, respectively, in an Instron tensile tester in order to initiate dynamic crack propagation from the starting notch. The relative humidity was $60 \sim 63\%$.

The breaking stress was measured by the load cell attached to the tensile tester.

The velocity-gauge technique[4] was used to obtain the dynamic crack propagation velocity. Velocity gauges consist of a series of conducting wires, du Pont No. 4817 conductive silver coating material, placed at certain intervals on the projected path of the crack and perpendicular to the direction of crack propagation, as shown in Figure 2. These wires form one leg of a bridge (Fig. 3) which

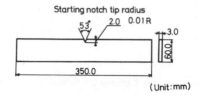

Fig. 1. Specimen dimensions.

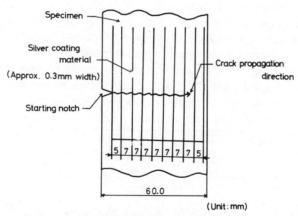

Fig. 2. Velocity-gauge arrangement.

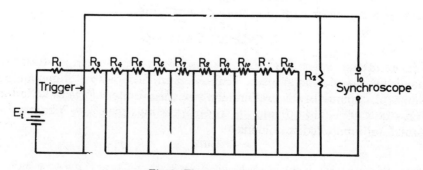

Fig. 3. Electronic circuit.

is connected to a Synchroscope DS-5305B, made by Iwatsu Electric Co., Ltd., Japan. The times at which these wires break, owing to the propagating crack, were obtained from the trace on the Synchroscope. Thus, the average crack-propagation velocity between wires can be obtained. The virgin specimens, which were free of prefatigue hysteresis, were also examined for comparison.

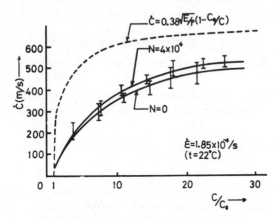

Fig. 4. Dynamic crack-propagation velocity profiles at 22°C.

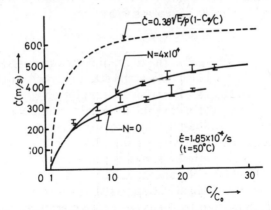

Fig. 5. Dynamic crack-propagation velocity profiles at 50°C.

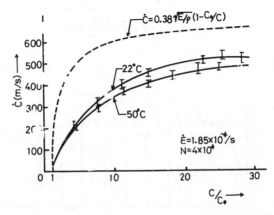

Fig. 6. Dynamic crack-propagation velocity profiles in the prefatigue hysteresis condition.

TABLE I
Prefatigue Hysteresis

Stress amplitude	Wave pattern	Prefatigue cycles
$0 \rightleftharpoons 2.8$ kg/mm²	sine (12 Hz)	4×10^4

TABLE II
Number of Specimens

Prefatigue hysteresis	22°C	50°C
4×10^4	4	2
0	3	3

RESULTS AND DISCUSSION

Experimental results on the dynamic crack-propagation velocity are shown in Figures 4–7, and those on the breaking stresses for notched specimens are shown in Figures 8 and 9. It is well known that Berry's equation[5] can be applied for the dynamic crack-propagation velocity in the brittle elastic solid with any starting notch tip radius. In Figures 4–7, Berry's equation is also plotted for comparison. Berry's equation is expressed as

$$\dot{C} = 0.38 \sqrt{E/\rho} \, (1 - C_0/C)$$

for the lower boundary, where $\dot{C}$ is the dynamic crack-propagation velocity, E is Young's modulus, ρ is the density, C_0 is the starting notch length, and C is the arbitrary running crack length. Berry's curve is plotted with $E = 299$ kg/mm² and $\rho = 122.4$ kg.sec²/m⁴, obtained in the uniaxial tension creep test assuming a three-parameter model and the density measurement, respectively, at 22°C. Numbers of specimens are as shown in Table II.

The prefatigue hysteresis effects on the dynamic crack propagation velocity $\dot{C}$ in PMMA at 22°C and 50°C are shown in Figures 4 and 5, respectively. The dynamic crack-propagation velocity in the prefatigued condition is higher than in the virgin-state condition, irrespective of temperature, although several

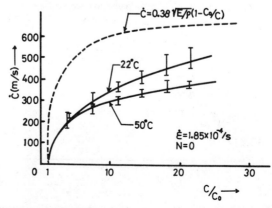

Fig. 7. Dynamic crack-propagation velocity profiles in the virgin-state condition.

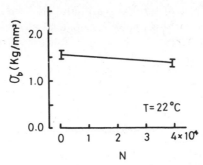

Fig. 8. Breaking stress vs number of prefatigue cycles at 22°C.

scatters are observed. Especially at 50°C, the distinct tendency dependent on the prefatigued condition can be recognized in the crack-propagation velocity. The fact may be explained on the basis that the material becomes brittle due to prefatigue hysteresis resulting in a decrease in viscoelasticity, thus enhancing the elastic characteristics and approaching Berry's equation. The prefatigue contribution may be recognized to be similar to the case of metals.

The effects of temperature on the dynamic crack-propagation velocity are shown in Figure 6 for the prefatigue hysteresis condition of 4×10^4 cycles and in Figure 7 for the virgin-state condition. It is recognized that the effects of temperature on the dynamic crack-propagation velocity are more pronounced in the virgin-state specimens than in the prefatigue hysteresis ones.

The prefatigue hysteresis effects on the breaking stresses are shown in Figure 8 for 22°C and in Figure 9 for 50°C. At 22°C, the breaking stresses are dependent on the prefatigue hysteresis, decreasing as the prefatigue hysteresis increases (Fig. 8). At 50°C, however, no prefatigue hysteresis contribution on the breaking stresses is observed (Fig. 9). The virgin specimen is distinctly affected by the temperature contribution on the breaking stress value.

CONCLUSIONS

Prefatigue hysteresis effects on viscoelastic crack-propagation velocity were investigated and compared with the virgin-state case by velocity-gauge techniques at different temperature levels. It was found that the dynamic crack-propagation velocity in the viscoelastic solid becomes greater at the prefatigued

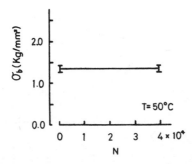

Fig. 9. Breaking stress vs number of prefatigue cycles at 50°C.

condition irrespective of test temperature, and that the dynamic crack-propagation velocity in the prefatigue hysteresis specimens approaches the theoretical in Berry's equation $\dot{C} = 0.38 \sqrt{E/\rho} \, (1 - C_0/C)$ for elastic brittle fracture.

The authors are grateful to Professor Kozo Kawata for his encouragement. Messrs. Morio Okuyama, Shigeharu Akita, Nobuo Ida, and Kuniaki Ohmori are acknowledged for their assistance in the experimental work, and Mr. Yasuhiro Katsuta for preparing the figures.

References

1. A. Kobayashi and N. Ohtani, *J. Jpn. Soc. Aero. Space Sci.*, **20,** 301 (1972) (in Japanese).
2. A. Kobayashi, N. Ohtani, and T. Sato, *J. Appl. Polym. Sci.*, **18,** 1625 (1974).
3. A. Kobayashi and N. Ohtani, *Bull. Inst. Space Aero. Sci. Univ. Tokyo,* **11,** 4(B), 49 (1976) (in Japanese).
4. H. Liebowitz, Ed, *Fracture,* Vol. II, Academic Press, New York, 1968, p. 545.
5. J. P. Berry, *J. Mech. Phys. Solids,* **8,** 194 (1960).

Received July 2, 1976

Volumetric Properties of Block and Random Copolymers of Butadiene and Styrene at Pressures to 1 Kilobar

J. A. R. RENUNCIO and J. M. PRAUSNITZ, *Chemical Engineering Department, University of California, Berkeley 94720*

Synopsis

Densities of thermally annealed copolymers were measured at 75° and 100°C at pressures to 1 kilobar. The compositions ranged from pure polybutadiene to pure polystyrene, from completely random to completely block copolymers. The experimental results are well represented by the Tait equation. To a first approximation, specific volumes and compressibilities are linear functions of weight per cent styrene. For a fixed composition, the effect of structure on volumetric properties is small. However, it appears that, when compared at the same overall composition, the specific volume and compressibility are larger for the random copolymer; specific volume and compressibility decline slightly when the styrene is in block rather than random form.

INTRODUCTION

While volumetric properties (PVT data) have been reported for a variety of homopolymers, relatively few data have been published for random copolymers; data for block copolymers are extremely rare.[1] Here, we report experimental density measurements for copolymers of butadiene and styrene at 75° and 100°C and at pressures to 1 kilobar. Measurements have been made for various copolymers from completely random to completely block copolymers.

EXPERIMENTAL

Experimental studies were made on 12 polymers as indicated in Table I. Our measurements were conducted on the first 11 polymers; the data of Quach and Simha[2] were used for the 12th polymer.

All polymer samples were obtained from commercial sources and, therefore, they may include small amounts of impurities. We estimate that the maximum impurities are less than 1 wt-% volatile matter, less than 1 wt-% soap, and at most 0.2 wt-% ash.

Small cubic samples of copolymer (about 2 mm per edge) were degassed for at least 3 h to remove volatile impurities.

First, density measurements were made at atmospheric pressure, using a conventional glass dilatometer briefly described elsewhere.[3] The dilatometer was previously calibrated with known densities of hydrocarbons. Experimental

TABLE I
Butadiene–Styrene Copolymers

Identification no.	Sample[a]	% Bound styrene	% Block styrene	$M_w \times 10^{-3}$	$M_n \times 10^{-3}$	Other details
1	Solprene 235	0	0	~270	~135	10% 1,2-butadiene
2	Europrene cis	0	0	327	153	100% cis-butadiene
3	Stereon 702	18–21	0.5–2.0	240	100	random copolymer
4	Europrene R130	25	0	481	239	random copolymer
5	Solprene 1206	25	0	210	120	random, 30% 1,2-butadiene
6	Solprene 1205	25	18	80	65	random with blocks 10% 1,2-butadiene
7	Europrene S140	48	15	—	—	random with blocks
8	Europrene S141	48	32	76.1	61.8	random with blocks
9	Europrene S142	70	45	126.4	97.6	random with blocks
10	TR-41-2425	25.4	all block		7–43–7	block copolymer S–B–S 40% cis-butadiene 50% trans-butadiene 10% 1,2-butadiene
11	Europrene T161	30	all block	229.6	130.5	block copolymer S–B–S
12	pure styrene	100	0			Taken from Quach and Simha[2]

a Solprene series from Phillips Petroleum Company; Europrene series from ANIC, Milan, Italy; Stereon from Firestone Synthetic Rubber & Latex Co.; TR from Shell Development Company.

tests with mercury at 75° and 100°C gave excellent agreement with the density data of Bigg;[4] experimental error was always less than ±0.01%.

Second, density measurements were made at high pressure. For high-pressure studies, the experimental equipment is the same as that used by Beret;[5] the central component is a high-pressure cell with a flexible bellows to contain the sample and to isolate it from the pressure-transmitting fluid.[6] The apparatus is calibrated with highly accurate PVT data for mercury and for heptane. Pressures are measured with a precision Heise gauge whose accuracy is 0.1% of full scale (±1 bar).

The high-pressure cell is located in a constant-temperature bath using silicone oil as heating fluid. The bath is controlled to ±0.01°C by a Hallikainen proportional temperature controller. Calibrated thermometers used for temperature measurements are accurate to ±0.05°C. Taking into consideration errors in temperature and pressure measurements as well as errors in calibration, the overall uncertainty of our relative volume measurements is 0.04%.

Densities of mercury at normal pressure were taken from Bigg,[4] and densities at high pressure were obtained from fitted values of Beret.[7]

After the polymer sample was weighed, it was placed inside the dilatometer or the bellows; the sample containers were then connected to the vacuum line for another 2 h of degassing and filling the empty space with previously degassified mercury.

All measurements were conducted under isothermal conditions at 75° and 100°C. In the high-pressure experiments, the pressure was always raised approximately 50 bars for each measurement. The change of volume with pressure was plotted as the data were obtained to determine possible discontinuities in slope caused by phase transitions. No discontinuities were observed.

For atmospheric-pressure measurements and for high-pressure measurements, constant temperature was maintained with a white-oil bath controlled by a Hallikainen proportional temperature controller. The temperature was measured by NBS-calibrated thermometers.

TABLE II
Specific Volumes at 1 Atmosphere

Sample no.	Specific volume, cc/g	
	75°C	100°C
1	1.1587	1.1791
2	1.1434	1.1630
3	1.1559	1.1760
4	1.1074	1.1260
5	1.1087	1.1276
6	1.1103	1.1291
7	1.0614	1.0787
8	1.0607	1.0770
9	1.0298	1.0148
10	1.0989	1.1177
11	1.0972	1.1158

While measurements reported here are at 75° and 100°C, measurements were also made at temperatures slightly lower and slightly higher than 75° or 100°C. These additional measurements were undertaken to see if there were unusual changes with temperature indicating phase transitions. No unusual changes were observed.

Early measurements indicated a lack of reproducibility, especially for those polymers containing a large amount of styrene. To obtain reproducibility, all samples were annealed prior to final experimental measurements. Annealing was done *in situ* at 120°C for 2 h, the samples were then cooled to 70°C at a rate of 2°C per hour. After annealing, measurements were always made with increasing temperature. Upon repeating the annealing cycle several times, excellent reproducibility ($\pm 10^{-4}$ cm^3/g) was obtained for all measurements.

RESULTS

Table II gives specific volumes at 1 atm and at two temperatures. Figure 1 shows these results at 75°C.

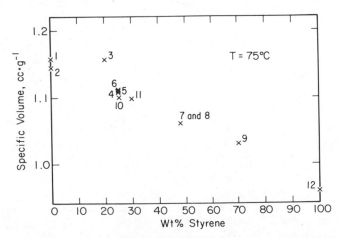

Fig. 1. Specific volumes of copolymers of butadiene and styrene at 1 atm. Samples are identified in Table I.

TABLE III
Parameters in the Tait Equation[a]

Sample no.	$T = 75°C$			$T = 100°C$		
	C	$B \times 10^{-4}$, bar^{-1}	$\sigma \times 10^4$	C	$B \times 10^{-4}$, bar^{-1}	$\sigma \times 10^4$
1	0.1221	0.1627	1.25	0.1083	0.1324	1.81
2	0.1288	0.2216	0.62	0.1228	0.1729	1.09
3	0.09695	0.1362	1.52	0.1009	0.1224	2.02
4	0.1029	0.1301	1.79	0.1182	0.1371	1.82
5	0.1147	0.1929	0.78	0.07983	0.09976	2.52
6	0.09021	0.1358	1.42	0.2500	0.3649	0.33
7	0.1344	0.2321	0.58	0.1151	0.1743	1.01
8	0.1078	0.1681	1.03	0.08794	0.1211	1.81
9	0.08723	0.1772	0.73	0.07611	0.1262	1.42
10	0.07866	0.1171	1.75	0.08936	0.1188	1.91
11	0.1303	0.2225	0.62	0.1142	0.1650	1.14

[a] σ is the standard deviation.

Specific volumes at high pressures are well represented by the Tait equation:

$$\frac{v}{v_0} = 1 - C \ln \left(1 + \frac{P}{B}\right) \tag{1}$$

where v/v_0 is the ratio of specific volume at pressure P to that at 1 atm. Constants C and B are shown in Table III. The pressure is in bars. Detailed experimental results are available from the authors. Equation (1) represents the data within experimental error.

For our purposes here, we define the compressibility β by

$$\beta \equiv -\frac{1}{v_0} \left(\frac{\partial v}{\partial P}\right)_T \tag{2}$$

TABLE IV
Compressibility β [See eqs. (2) and (3)]

Sample no.	β at $T = 75°C$, bars$^{-1} \times 10^5$				β at $T = 100°C$, bars$^{-1} \times 10^5$			
	400 bars	600 bars	800 bars	1000 bars	400 bars	600 bars	800 bars	1000 bars
1	6.02	5.48	5.03	4.65	6.28	5.63	5.10	4.66
2	4.92	4.57	4.27	4.00	5.77	5.27	4.86	4.50
3	5.50	4.94	4.48	4.11	6.22	5.53	4.99	4.54
4	6.05	5.41	4.90	4.47	6.68	6.00	5.45	4.99
5	4.92	4.53	4.20	3.91	5.71	5.00	4.44	4.00
6	5.13	4.61	4.18	3.82	6.17	5.88	5.62	5.38
7	4.94	4.60	4.31	4.05	5.37	4.92	4.53	4.20
8	5.18	4.72	4.34	4.02	5.46	4.85	4.37	3.98
9	4.02	3.68	3.39	3.15	4.58	4.09	3.69	3.37
10	5.01	4.44	3.99	3.62	5.63	5.00	4.49	4.08
11	4.96	4.61	4.31	4.04	5.57	5.08	4.66	4.31
12[a]	2.78	2.62	2.48	2.35				

[a] From Quach and Simha.[2]

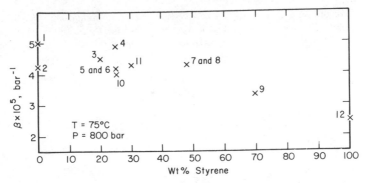

Fig. 2. Compressibilities of copolymers of butadiene and styrene at 800 bars. Samples are identified in Table I.

This compressibility is readily found from eq. (1):

$$\beta = C(B + P)^{-1} \tag{3}$$

Table IV shows values of β at 75° and 100°C at 400, 600, 800, and 1000 bars.

When Barlow's data[8] for poly-*cis*-butadiene between 4° and 55°C are extrapolated to 75° and 100°C, the results are in good agreement with our measurements.

Figure 1 shows specific volumes at 1 atmosphere as a function of weight percent styrene. There is a clear trend indicating that the specific volume falls as the percent styrene rises; but, in addition, some structural effects are also evident. For example, sample 2 is pure poly-*cis*-butadiene, while sample 1, also pure polybutadiene, is a mixture of the cis and trans forms of polymerized 1,2-butadiene.

Samples 4, 5, 6, and 10 all have the same overall composition; but, as shown in Table I, there are differences in structure. Samples 4 and 5 are random copolymers but with different molecular weights. Sample 6 has 18% styrene in block form, and sample 10 is a radial (S-B-S) copolymer.

Figure 2 shows compressibility β at 800 bars as a function of weight percent styrene. Again, it is evident that β tends to decline as the percent styrene rises, and again some structural differences are apparent.

Unfortunately, it is not possible to draw clear quantitative conclusions from the PVT data assembled here. However, the results shown in Figures 1 and 2 at 75°C (and those at 100°C are very similar) suggest that both the specific volume and the compressibility decline when, at constant overall composition, the styrene is added to the butadiene in block rather than random form. It appears that block copolymers can pack more efficiently than random copolymers and thereby more strongly resist compression.

While the results obtained here leave many questions unanswered, they provide at least an initial view into the relatively unexplored territory of PVT properties of copolymers. The results obtained here indicate that while structure affects these properties, at any fixed overall composition, structural effects are not large in magnitude but in the direction suggested by simple geometric considerations.

For polymer samples used, the authors are grateful to Shell Development Company, Firestone Synthetic Rubber and Latex Company, Phillips Petroleum Company, and Anic Corporation. For financial support, the authors are grateful to the National Science Foundation, to the Donors of the Petroleum Research Fund administered by the American Chemical Society, and to the Commission of Educational Exchange Between the United States of America and Spain, for a fellowship received by one of us (J.A.R.R.).

References

1. J. Brandrup and E. H. Immergut, Eds., *Polymer Handbook,* 2nd ed., Wiley, New York, 1975; Bibliography of Rubber Literature, Division of Rubber Chemistry of the Amer. Chem. Soc., J. M. Huber Corporation, Edison, New Jersey, 1938–67.

2. A. Quach and R. Simha, *J. Appl. Phys.,* **42,** 4592 (1971).

3. J. A. R. Renuncio and J. M. Prausnitz, *Macromolecules,* **9,** 324 (1976).

4. P. H. Bigg, *Brit. J. Appl. Phys.,* **15,** 1111 (1964).

5. S. Beret and J. M. Prausnitz, *Macromolecules,* **8,** 536 (1975).

6. J. W. M. Boelhouwer, *Physica,* **26,** 1021 (1959); A. K. Doolittle, I. Simon, and R. W. Cornish, *A.I.Ch.E. J.,* **6,** 150 (1960); A. Quach and R. Simha, *J. Appl. Phys.,* **42,** 4592 (1971).

7. S. Beret, Ph.D. Thesis, University of California, Berkeley, 1975.

8. J. W. Barlow, *J. Poly. Sci.,* to appear.

Received January 23, 1976
Revised August 18, 1976

JOURNAL OF APPLIED POLYMER SCIENCE   VOL. 21, 2873–2876 (1977)

Lignin Gels as a Medium in Gel Permeation Chromatography

TOM LINDSTRÖM, CHRISTER SÖREMARK, and LENNART WESTMAN, *Swedish Forest Products Research Laboratory, S-114 86 Stockholm, Sweden*

Synopsis

The preparation of spherical lignin gel beads, based on the crosslinking reaction between epichlorohydrin and kraft lignin (Indulin AT), is described. The lignin gels prepared were found to be an efficient resin in gel permeation chromatography. The separation of polystyrenes in dimethylformamide is described. The resin was found to separate polystyrenes with molecular weights up to 110,000. An inverse linear relationship between log M and elution volume or the partitioning coefficient was established.

INTRODUCTION

Our knowledge of lignin has evolved over a period of more than one hundred years, and their importance is widely recognized. It is now known that lignins exist as a polymeric wall constituent in almost all dry land plants and, among the natural polymers, lignins are second only to carbohydrates in natural abundance.

Black liquors from the conventional kraft (sulfate) pulping process contain lignin (kraft lignin), hemicelluloses, acids derived from carbohydrates, and small amounts of extractives. Of these, only lignin is precipitated on acidification, and it can thus be easily separated. Lignin is recognized as a polyphenolic resin. The chemical and polymeric properties of lignin have been described in textbooks on the subject.[1]

This paper describes a technique to prepare spherical crosslinked lignin beads suitable for gel permeation chromatography (GPC). The use of these gels to separate polystyrenes in dimethylformamide (DMF) is also demonstrated.

EXPERIMENTAL

Preparation of Gel Beads

A commercially available kraft lignin (Indulin AT, manufactured by Westvaco Co., Charleston, U.S.A.) was used in this investigation. Some characteristic data of the lignin can be found in Sarkanen and Ludwig.[1] All chemicals used were of analytical grade.

Lignin, 200 g, was dissolved in 600 g 2M sodium hydroxide. The solution was stirred for 4 h in order to ensure complete dissolution. This solution was then

2873

thoroughly filtered on glass frits and finally on a glass fiber filter (Whatman GF/A) in order to remove small amounts of residual cellulosic fibers and colloidal material.

The lignin solution was added to a three-necked 5-l. reaction vessel equipped with a high-intensity stirrer. Freshly distilled 1,2-dichloroethane (bp 88–90°C), 3 l., was then added and the two-phase system was stirred for 15 min. During the stirring, some (<10%) of the lignin was dissolved in the dichloroethane phase. After this period of stirring, 15 g emulsifier (Cremophor EL, BASF) was added and the mixture stirred for another 2 h.

At this point, the crosslinking agent (60 g epichlorohydrin) was added to the reaction vessel. The crosslinking reaction was run in two steps, first for 48 h at the same temperature as before (21°C) and then for 24 h at an elevated temperature (40°C), with continuous stirring. After cooling to room temperature, the reaction product was picked up on a screen with 0.18 mm in open diameter and washed thoroughly, first with 2M sodium hydroxide and then with tap water. Finally, a small quantity of coarse beads was removed on a 0.35-mm screen. The gel beads were stored in tap water under slightly alkaline conditions in a refrigerator. The total yield in the preparation of the gel beads was approximately 85%.

Prior to column packing, the lignin gel beads were washed with 0.5M sulfuric acid in order to convert the acidic groups to the hydrogen form. The gels were then washed with distilled water to neutral pH and finally with DMF. The gel beads in DMF were spherical and of fairly uniform size (Fig. 1). The mean diameter was found to be 220 μm.

Gel Permeation Chromatography

The gel beads were deaerated and packed in a glass column (height 65 cm, diameter 1 cm) equipped with two Teflon seals. The column was connected between a peristaltic pump and a differential refractometer (Waters Associates, Milford, Massachusetts, U.S.A.) and a drop counter (LKB-Produckter AB,

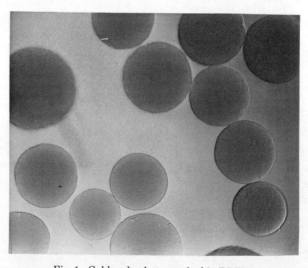

Fig. 1. Gel beads photographed in DMF.

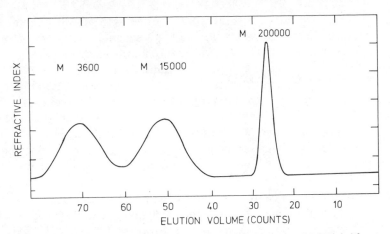

Fig. 2. Elution pattern for a polystyrene mixture (M 200,000, 15,000, and 3,600) (without correction for broadening).

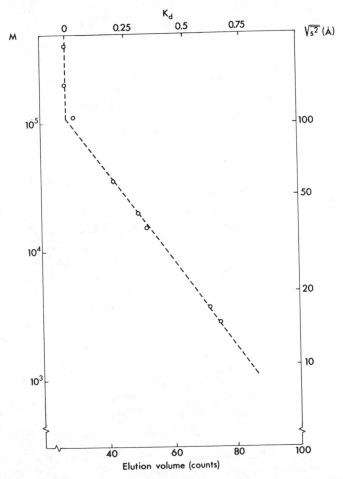

Fig. 3. Elution volume of polystyrenes of different molecular weights. The radius of gyration has been calculated by use of the Flory-Fox equation with a value of 2.1×10^{21} for the universal parameter.[2] The intrinsic viscosities of polystyrenes in DMF have been determined by Tsimpris et al.[3]

Bromma, Sweden) in series.   A total of 3.0 m silicone tubings (diameter 1 mm) was used.   The drop counter was adjusted to give a chart mark (= 1 count) for every 16 drops, which is equal to 0.484 ml.   The column was thermostated to 25°C and protected from UV radiation with aluminum foil.

Narrow-molecular weight distribution polystyrene standards (Pressure Chemical Co., Pittsburgh, Pennsylvania, U.S.A.) of weight-average molecular weights (M) 2,900, 3,600, 15,000, 19,500, 35,000 110,000, 200,000, and 470,000 were used.   The void volume was found to be 100 counts as determined from DMF labeled with C14 (The Radiochemical Center, Amersham, Buckinghamshire, England) and excluded volume 28.5 counts as determined with polystyrene 470000.

A change in sample concentration from 1 to 10 g/l. (sample load 1 count) did not affect the elution volume.   At the highest concentration, no change in elution volume was detected at flow rates between 1.06 and 11.07 ml/h·cm². Normally, the flow rate was 3.75 ml/h·cm² and the sample concentration 5.0 g/l.   The reproducibility was checked over a period of six months and was found to be M = 110,000: ±0.2 counts; and M = 2,900: ±0.5 counts.

A typical elution pattern for a polystyrene mixture (M 200,000, 15,000, and 3,600) is given in Figure 2.

DISCUSSION

Results from GPC measurements are commonly presented as log M versus elution volume or the partitioning coefficient, K_d, defined by

$$K_d = \frac{V - V_{excl}}{V_{void} - V_{excl}}$$

where V = elution volume; V_{excl} = exclusion volume; and V_{void} = void volume (elution volume of solvent).   As shown in Figure 3, an inverse linear relationship is obtained within the separation region.   From Figure 2 and 3, it can be concluded that the lignin beads are well suited for use in GPC.   The separation ability can be expressed as plate counts.[4]   For o-dichlorobenzene, a value of 360 (plates per foot) was found.   This must, however, be too low since no correction for experimental broadening in tubings was made.

In this study, DMF has been used as an elution liquid since it is known to be a good solvent for lignin.   It is, of course, possible to use other solvents and thereby change the behavior of the lignin gel as a GPC medium.

Thanks are due to Dr. W. Brown, University of Uppsala, Sweden, for valuable discussions during the course of this work.   The authors are also indebted to Westvaco Corporation, Charleston, South Carolina, U.S.A., for sponsoring this work.

References

1. K. V. Sarkanen and C. H. Ludwig, Eds., *Lignins,* Wiley-Interscience, New York, 1971.

2. P. J. Flory, *Principles of Polymer Chemistry,* Cornell University Press, Ithaca, New York, 1953, pp. 611, 616.

3. C. W. Tsimpris, B. Surayanarayan, and K. G. Mayhan, *J. Polym. Sci. A-2,* **10,** 1837 (1972).

4. K. H. Altgelt and L. Segal, Eds., *Gel Permeation Chromatography,* Marcel Dekker, New York, 1971, p. 40.

JOURNAL OF APPLIED POLYMER SCIENCE   VOL. 21, 2877–2884 (1977)

Degradation of Aqueous Poly(vinylpyrrolidone) Solution by High-Speed Stirring*

AKIHIKO NAKANO† and YUJI MINOURA, *Department of Polymer Chemistry, Research Institute for Atomic Energy, Osaka City University, Osaka, Japan*

Synopsis

The effect of concentration on scission of poly(vinylpyrrolidone) ($\overline{p}_v$ = 6,700) in aqueous solution by high-speed stirring at a speed of 30,000 rpm at 30°C was investigated. Concentration was varied from 0.04 to 2% g/ml. Polymer chains were ruptured to lower molecular weights with decreasing concentration. The rate constant of scission, k, and the limiting degree of polymerization, P_l, in Ovenall's equation calculated for the results were considerably changed in the polymer concentration range from 0.2 to 1% g/ml. The effect of addition of methyl orange on polymer scission was then studied, because the dye had been reported to increase the viscosity of aqueous poly(vinylpyrrolidone) solution because of unfolding of the macromolecule chains. However, no significant effect was found in the concentration range from 0.034 to 0.34 in the molar ratio of methyl orange to poly(vinylpyrrolidone).

INTRODUCTION

The authors have been studying degradation by high-speed stirring of solutions of various polymers such as poly(methyl methacrylate),[1–4] poly(methyl acrylate),[5] poly(α-methylstyrene),[5] polystyrene,[2,3,5] polyisobutylene,[2,5] and poly(ethylene oxide)[1,2,5,6] and the effects of polymer concentration[3,4,5] and solvent.[2,3,5] It was found that the rate of scission of the polymer chains was higher and the final chain length was shorter at lower polymer concentrations for all solvents.[3,5] It was also found that, at a certain low polymer concentrations, the rate of scission was higher and the final chain length was shorter in good solvents than in poor solvents.[3,5] In the previous paper, those results were discussed in terms of hydrodynamic volumes.[5]

In this study, poly(vinylpyrrolidone) (PVP) was chosen as a polymer for degradation because of its interesting property. PVP has a marked ability to bind a variety of small molecules to change its conformation. It is revealed that PVP stands far above any of the other synthetic macromolecules in binding.[7] Killmann and Bittler[8] studied the interaction between PVP and Blancophor dyes and found an expansion of the PVP molecule caused by electrostatic repulsion of the absorbed dye ions by means of viscosity and light scattering

---

* Part of this study was presented at the 34th Annual Meeting (Spring) of the Japan Chemical Society on April 4, 1976 at Hiratsuka in Kanagawa Pref.

† Present address: Wireless Research Laboratory, Matsushita Electric Industrial Co., Ltd., 1006, Kadoma, Osaka, Japan.

measurements. Nakagaki and Shimabayashi[9] investigated the interaction between PVP and amino acids. Takagishi and Kuroki et al.[7,10] have been re-
searching the interaction of PVP with methyl orange and its homologs in aqueous
solution. According to the studies, addition of the dyes into aqueous PVP solution increases the viscosity of the solution, showing unfolding of the random
coil of the polymer. They attributed these facts to the hydrophobic interaction
between hydrocarbon portions of the dyes and nonpolar parts of the macromolecule.

The effect of polymer concentration of scission of the polymer chain was first
investigated. Then, the effect of addition of methyl orange on the scission of
PVP in solution by high-speed stirring was also investigated in order to ascertain
the previous interpretation,[5] namely, that there is a relation between mechanical
scission of polymer chains in solution and their hydrodynamic volumes. The
effect of additives on the degradation of polymer solutions has only rarely been
investigated.

EXPERIMENTAL

Materials

Poly(vinylpyrrolidone), PVP (K-90), was obtained from Tokyo Kasei Kogyo
Corp. The nominal average molecular weight was 360,000. The intrinsic viscosity $[\eta]$ of aqueous solutions of the polymer at 30°C measured by the authors
was 1.82 dl/g, and the viscosity-average molecular weight $\overline{M}_v$ was 740,000 according to[11]

$$[\eta] = 14 \times 10^{-5} \, \overline{M}_v{}^{0.70} \tag{1}$$

Water was used as solvent after purification through ion exchange resin.
Methanol was used after distillation.

Specially pure-grade methyl orange was supplied by Wako Pure Chemical
Industries, Ltd. Polymer and methyl orange were used without purification.

Stirring Apparatus and Method of Stirring

A T.K. Homomixer of HS-M type made by Tokushu-Kika Kogyo Co., Ltd.,
was used as high-speed stirrer. The stator, turbine, and vessel of the mixer were
the same as those used in the previous experiment.[6]

A solution containing a given weight of polymer in 200 ml water was stirred
in a 300-ml vessel made of stainless steel. Stirring speed was 30,000 ± 500 rpm.
For keeping the temperature of the solution at 30° ± 5°C and to keep the mixer
safe from harm by superheating, 5 min of stirring and 5- to 10-min pauses for
cooling were alternated. After stirring for a given time, about 10 ml stirred solution was removed and stirring was then continued. Dilute solutions of less
than 0.2% g/ml were stirred batchwise.

Polymer Separation and Method of Measuring $[\eta]$
and Molecular Weight

Polymer solutions stirred for a given time were dried by a warm-air drier until
their weights became constant. Intrinsic viscosities $[\eta]$ of recovered polymers
with or without methyl orange were all measured in methanol at 30° ± 0.02°C

using an Ubbelohde viscometer. Methyl orange is practically insoluble in methanol, but can be considerably soluble in the presence of PVP. It was ascertained beforehand that, fortunately, methyl orange does not affect $[\eta]$ of PVP in any way. Viscosity-average molecular weight $\overline{M}_v$ was calculated from $[\eta]$ in methanol at 30°C by eq. (2), which was obtained by the authors using PVP's with different $\overline{M}_v$ calculated by eq. (1):

$$[\eta] = 15.6 \times 10^{-5} \, \overline{M}_v{}^{0.70} \tag{2}$$

Since the molecular weight distribution is considered to vary owing to scission of chains during stirring, it is most appropriate to estimate the number-average molecular weight $\overline{M}_n$ for calculation of the number of scissions, but $\overline{M}_v$ was used here according to custom for the sake of convenience.

Rate Constant of Scission, k, and Limiting Degree of Polymerization, P_l

Rate constant of scission, k, and limiting degree of polymerization, P_l, in Ovenall's[12] eq. (3) for obtained results were determined by the method described in the previous paper:[6]

$$\frac{dB_i}{dt} = k(P_i - P_l)n_i \qquad (P_i > P_l)$$
$$\frac{dB_i}{dt} = 0 \qquad (P_i \leq P_l) \tag{3}$$

where dB_i/dt is the rate of scission of molecules of degree of polymerization P_i; n_i is the number of such molecules; k is the rate constant of scission; and P_l is the limiting degree of polymerization below which molecules cannot be degraded.

RESULTS

Effect of Concentration on PVP Scission

Aqueous solutions containing 0.04% to 2% g/ml PVP were prepared and stirred at a speed of 30,000 rpm. Decrease in $[\eta]$ of recovered polymers is shown in Figure 1. The value of $[\eta]$ decreased rapidly at first and then slowly, reaching a constant value depending on the polymer concentration. It is found that the rate of decrease in $[\eta]$ increased and that the final $[\eta]$ decreased with decrease in polymer concentration. The tendency resembles results obtained for polystyrene, and other polymers.[3,5]

The relationship between number of scission per polymer molecule and stirring time is shown in Figure 2. The number of scissions per molecule, B_t/n_0, was calculated by eq. (4):

$$B_t/n_0 = P_0/P_t - 1 \tag{4}$$

where P_0 and P_t are the degrees of polymerization before stirring and after stirring for time t, respectively. The number of scissions increased rapidly at first and then slowly.

The k and P_l values obtained for the above B_t/n_0-versus-time curves are plotted versus polymer concentration in Figure 3. It is found that P_l becomes smaller and k larger with decreasing concentration and that changes in P_l and

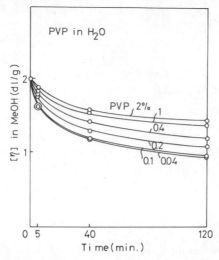

Fig. 1. Degradation of PVP by high-speed stirring (30,000 rpm, 30°C).

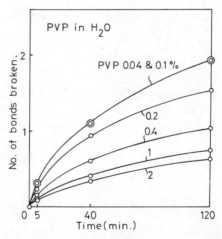

Fig. 2. Number of bonds broken per polymer molecule during high-speed stirring (30,000 rpm, 30°C).

k values are remarkable in the concentration range of 0.2% to 1% g/ml. The former tendency had been found for other polymers in several solvents.[3,5]

Effect of Addition of Methyl Orange on Viscosity of Aqueous PVP Solution

As described above, addition of methyl orange to aqueous PVP solution was found to increase the viscosity of the solution.[10] The effect of methyl orange on viccosity of aqueous PVP solutions is shown in Figure 4, where the ordinate indicates the falling times of aqueous PVP solutions with or without methyl orange through a capillary (viscosities), and the abscissa shows molar ratios of methyl orange to PVP. Viscosity was scarcely increased with methyl orange at low concentrations, while it increased remarkably at high polymer concentrations.

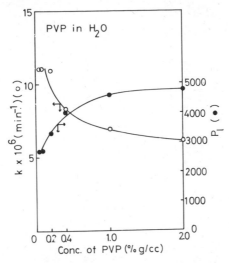

Fig. 3. Effect of concentration on PVP on k and P_l (30,000 rpm, 30°C).

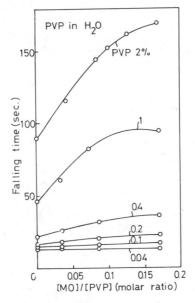

Fig. 4. Effect of methyl orange on viscosity of aqueous PVP solution.

It is noted that 0.1%, 0.2%, and 0.4% g/ml PVP solutions containing methyl orange at a molar ratio of 0.17 had nearly the same viscosities as 0.2%, 0.4%, and 1.0% g/ml PVP solutions without methyl orange, respectively. The molar ratio of 0.17 is equal to a weight ratio of 0.5 of methyl orange to PVP.

The effect of methyl orange on the viscosity can be observed from another viewpoint, as shown in Figure 5, where relative viscosities are plotted on the ordinate. The effect was found largest for the solution containing 1% g/ml PVP, while the effect was little for the solution of 0.04% g/ml.

In order to elucidate the effect of addition of methyl orange on $[\eta]$ of aqueous PVP solution, methyl orange and PVP at a certain molar ratio were dissolved

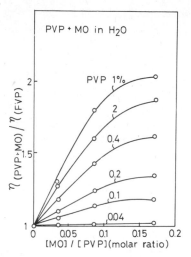

Fig. 5. Effect of methyl orange on viscosity of aqueous PVP solution.

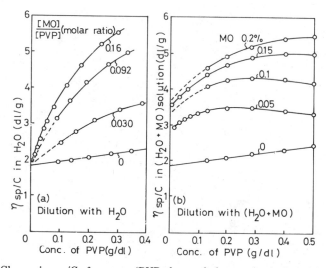

Fig. 6. Change in η_{sp}/C of aqueous (PVP plus methyl orange) solution with dilution.

in water, and $[\eta]$ was measured diluting the solution with pure water. The results are shown in Figure 6(a), where η_{sp}/C-versus-C curves (where C is polymer concentration) are not linear except for the solution containing only PVP; but all of the curves seem to converge to a point by extrapolation. When a certain weight of PVP was dissolved in aqueous methyl orange solution with a certain concentration and diluted with the methyl orange solution, the relationship between η_{sp}/C and C showed complicated curves as shown in Figure 6(b). In this case, the molar ratio of methyl orange to PVP increased with dilution, reaching infinity at zero polymer concentration, but it seemed that higher intrinsic viscosities were measured for PVP solutions which were diluted with higher concentrations of methyl orange solution.

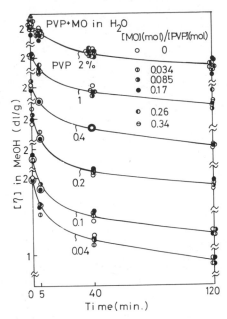

Fig. 7. Degradation of aqueous (PVP plus methyl orange) solution in various molar ratios of methyl orange to PVP by high-speed stirring (30,000 rpm, 30°C).

Effect of Addition of Methyl Orange on PVP Scission by High-Speed Stirring

Degradation of an aqueous PVP solution containing methyl orange by high-speed stirring at a speed of 30,000 rpm at 30°C is shown in Figure 7, where $[\eta]$ of recovered mixtures of PVP and methyl orange in methanol at 30°C is plotted as the ordinate. It was established beforehand that addition of methyl orange does not affect the value of $[\eta]$ of PVP solution in methanol as described above. It was also confirmed by superposition of starting points that any deviations are within experimental error. Not only starting points but also all the degradation curves can be superposed within experimental error, regardless of addition of methyl orange, for each solution with identical PVP concentration. In the case of 1% g/ml PVP solution, an equivalent weight of methyl orange to PVP (that is, 100 parts per 100 parts resin) was indeed added to the solution at highest methyl orange concentration. 100 phr methyl orange corresponds to a molar ratio of 0.34. 2% g/ml PVP solution could dissolve 75 phr methyl orange at highest at 30°C (molar ratio of methyl orange to PVP, 0.26). The other solutions contained 50 phr methyl orange at highest (molar ratio 0.17). Aqueous PVP solutions containing methyl orange at such high concentrations were stirred, and $[\eta]$ of the stirred polymers was measured. The curves were slightly scattered, but no tendency with addition of methyl orange was found. Consequently, it was concluded that the addition of methyl orange does not meaningfully affect scission of PVP chain by high-speed stirring.

In contrast to the above, the effect of concentration of the polymer can be clearly found in Figure 7, that is, the lower the concentration, the faster the degradation.

DISCUSSION

The effect of concentration of the macromolecule PVP on scission of the polymer by high-speed stirring was found as observed above, but no significant effect of addition of the small molecules methyl orange was found. The latter results are reminiscent of the findings that the scission of long-chain poly(methyl methacrylate) was little if at all suppressed by addition of short-chain PMMA.[4] The authors' expectation that there might be a certain effect of methyl orange on the scission of PVP if it unfolded the random chains of the polymer could not be detected.

Reasons for the results can be postulated as follows. (1) The effect of expansion of the polymer chain on scission can more easily be detected for the solution with lower polymer concentration;[3,5] however, the increase in viscosity or the expansion of polymer chain by the addition of methyl orange was not so high for such solution that the effect of the dye could not be detected. (2) Increase in viscosity by adding methyl orange to aqueous PVP solution may result from complicated factors such as intermolecular and intramolecular interactions. If unfolding (expanding) of conformation of polymer chains is not so large as the increase in viscosity, the effect of the expansion on the scission is difficult to detect. (3) Absorption (binding) of methyl orange by PVP is not so strong because of hydrophobic interaction that the binding can no longer hold under enough high shear to rupture polymer chains. In other words, viscosities of PVP solutions containing methyl orange might be shear dependent like poly(acrylic acid) and poly(methacrylic acid).[13,14] It might be expected that the viscosities approach the ones without methyl orange. Unfortunately, probably due to a relatively narrow shear-rate variation range, the authors could not find a shear dependence for 1% g/ml aqueous PVP solutions containing methyl orange in molar ratios from 0 to 0.17 under shear rates from 7.16 to 71.6 sec^{-1}. If so, the effect of methyl orange on unfolding the chains may be decreased. Thus, the effect of the dye on the scission was decreased or eliminated. The authors consider that the third possibility is more probable than the others.

The authors intend to investigate the effect of change in the conformation of polymer chains on scission by another method.

References

1. A. Nakano and Y. Minoura, *J. Appl. Polym. Sci.*, **15**, 927 (1971).
2. A. Nakano and Y. Minoura, *J. Appl. Polym. Sci.*, **16**, 627 (1972).
3. A. Nakano and Y. Minoura, *J. Appl. Polym. Sci.*, **19**, 2119 (1975).
4. A. Nakano and Y. Minoura, *J. Appl. Polym. Sci.*, **19**, 2749 (1975).
5. A. Nakano and Y. Minoura, *Macromolecules*, **8**, 677 (1975).
6. Y. Minoura, T. Kasuya, S. Kawamura, and A. Nakano, *J. Polym. Sci. A-2*, **5**, 125 (1967).
7. T. Takagishi and N. Kuroki, *J. Polym. Sci., Polym. Chem. Ed.*, **11**, 1889 (1973).
8. E. Killmann and R. Bittler, *J. Polym. Sci. C*, **39**, 247 (1972).
9. M. Nakagaki and S. Shimabayashi, *Nippon Kagaku Kaishi*, 1914 (1972).
10. T. Takagishi, K. Imajo, Y. Matsudaira, and N. Kuroki, *Preprint I for 31st Annual Meeting of Chemical Society of Japan*, 1974, p. 584.
11. W. Scholtan, *Makromol. Chem.* **7**, 209 (1951).
12. D. W. Ovenall, G. W. Hastings, and P. E. M. Allen, *J. Polym. Sci.*, **33**, 207 (1958).
13. R. Sakamoto and K. Yoshioka, *Nippon Kagaku Zasshi*, **83**, 517 (1962).
14. P. Alexander and K. A. Stacey, *Trans. Faraday Soc.*, **51**, 299 (1955).

Received June 21, 1976
Revised August 31, 1976

JOURNAL OF APPLIED POLYMER SCIENCE   VOL. 21, 2885–2897 (1977)

Crystalline Characteristics of Ethylene/Propylene/ 1,4-Hexadiene Terpolymers and Related Ethylene Copolymers

C. K. SHIH and E. F. CLUFF, *Elastomer Chemicals Department, Research Division, Experimental Division, E. I. du Pont de Nemours & Co., Inc., Wilmington, Delaware 19898*

Synopsis

An improved differential thermal analytical technique which permits the rapid, convenient characterization of the thermal behavior of crystalline polymers free of any influence of prior thermal history is presented. Characterization of both crystallization and fusion phenomena is described for ethylene/propylene copolymers subjected to well-controlled thermal scanning techniques. Parameters describing these phenomena are derived. While they are nonequilibrium parameters, they are reproducible and capable of correlation with polymer composition. The crystallization onset temperature determined by this cooling technique was found to relate to the molar ethylene content of the copolymers by an equation similar to the one derived by Flory[5] based on equilibrium melting point. The relationship was found to hold true for a number of ethylene copolymers, including samples of linear and branched polyethylene, commercial EPDM, and ethylene/vinyl acetate copolymers.

INTRODUCTION

We wish to describe an improved differential thermal analytical technique which permits the rapid, convenient characterization of the thermal behavior of crystalline polymers free of any influence of prior thermal history. The technique was demonstrated in the characterization of various ethylene copolymers, mostly with the class of EPDM's which are constituted mainly of ethylene, propylene, and a small amount of a diene such as ethylidene norbornene, 1,4-hexadiene, or dicyclopentadiene. The crystalline behavior of these materials has been reviewed recently by Baldwin and VerStrate.[1] From density and x-ray measurements at room temperature, the degree of crystallinity was found to depend upon composition, with polymers of higher ethylene content exhibiting higher crystallinity. The degree of crystallinity at a given composition can also vary depending upon the catalyst and synthesis conditions, presumably as a result of changes in the monomer sequence length or compositional distribution. Some heat of fusion data have also been presented[2] based on samples annealed at room temperature.

Clegg, Gee, and Melia[3] presented heating thermograms of a number of ethylene/propylene dipolymers. Unfortunately, the thermal history of the samples was not given.

TABLE I
Thermal Characteristics of E/P/HD, EPDM, and Polyethylene Samples

Sample	Polymer	E, mole-%	M_v [a]	T_f, °C	Melting range, °C [c]	T_m [c,d]	ΔH_f [e]	Remarks
A1	polyethylene	100		120	75 to 145	135	50	"Marlex" 5003, linear PE, Phillips Petroleum Co.
A2		100		123	75 to 150	140	58	linear PE, experimental sample
A3		100(5)		100	25 to 120	112	36	branched PE, experimental sample
A4		100(5)		100	40 to 120	112	30	DYNH-1, branched PE, Union Carbide Co.
B1	E/P/HD	84.3	87,000	52	-40 to 105	62	24.9	2.0 mole % HD
B2		79.5	190,000	40	-42 to 125	48	20.9	1.3 mole % HD
B3		69.6	150,000	6	-50 to 75	0	11.0	1.3 mole % HD
B4		64.7	110,000	-17	-55 to 15	-25	1.5	1.7 mole % HD
B5		73.2	—	18.5	-50 to 65			1.3 mole % HD
B6		71.8		13	-45 to 75			1.3 mole % HD
B7		63.2		-22	-55 to 15			1.8 mole % HD
B8		61.3	80,000	—	—	—	0	2.0 mole % HD
B21		78.0		32	-45 to 65	43	17.7	1.5 mole-% HD fraction of B2 (55% wt)

B22		80.0		32	−45 to 65	45	19.6	1.1 mole-% HD fraction of B2 (25% wt)
B23		81.7		55, 95	−45 to 120	50	24.4	1.1 mole-% HD fraction of B2 (20% wt)
C1	EPDM	76.0	200,000	45	−45 to 125	50	10.1	1.2 mole-% ENB "Vistalon" 3708, Enjay Chemical Co.
C2		77.0	160,000	33	−35 to 65	45	12.3	1.2 mole-% ENB "EPsyn" 5508, Copolym. Corp.
D1	Blend	50.0		123	75 to 175	135, 165		melt blend of polyethylene (sample A-2) and polypropylene (Avison GP)
E1	E/VAc	79		33	−30 to 75	50		experimental samples
E2		84		45	−30 to 80	50		
E3		86.5		60	−20 to 95	70		
E4		88		67	−20 to 95	80		
E5		92		73		87		

a Viscosity-average molecular weight, based on $[\eta] = 1.38 \times 10^{-4} (M_w)^{0.81}$. Intrinsic viscosity $[\eta]$ determined in perchloroethylene at 30°C.

b Onset temperature for crystallization, sample control cooled at 20°C/min.

c From DSC heating curve scanned immediately after the sample has been control cooled (20°C/min) from molten state.

d Minimum peak temperature of the endotherm.

e Not corrected for side-chain content. Assuming there are 2.5 branches/100 C atom, then E = 95 mole %.

In the work presented here, rapid reproducible characterization of both crystallization and fusion phenomena free of the influence of prior thermal history is described for ethylene/propylene copolymers subjected to well-controlled thermal scanning techniques. Parameters describing these phenomena are derived. While they are nonequilibrium parameters, they are reproducible and capable of correlation with polymer composition. Deviations from random copolymer structures appear to be detectable.

EXPERIMENTAL

Polymer Samples

The materials studied include both linear and branched polyethylenes (PE, Series A), a series of ethylene/propylene/1,4-hexadiene terpolymers (E/P/HD, Series B), and two samples of commercial ethylene/propylene/ethylidenenorbornene terpolymers (E/P/ENB, Series C). Five experimental samples of ethylene/vinyl acetate copolymers (E/VAc, Series E) have also been included in this study.

The experimental E/P/HD polymers (B1 to B7) were produced by solution polymerization with Ziegler catalysis. Other samples, including series A, C, and D, were commercial polymers, with manufacturers listed in Table I.

The polymer fractions (B21, B22, and B23) were obtained by fractional extraction of sample B2. Samples B21 and B22 are the successive extracts using hexane at 25° and 50°C. The remaining insoluble fraction is designated as B23.

Differential Thermal Analysis

Measurements were carried out with a du Pont 900 DTA instrument equipped with a DSC (differential scanning calorimetric) cell. The cooling scan of the DSC measurement was carried out using either of the two following attachments:

1. The standard cooling can supplied by the du Pont Company: The scan was lifted approximately $1/8$ in. from the platform with a brass ring in order to avoid direct contact between the silver heating block and the cooling surface. Cooling was provided by pumping liquid nitrogen continuously into the screened well of the cooling can.

2. Cooling block: As shown in Figure 1, a double-jacket heat exchanger was tightly mounted on top of the silver heating block of the du Pont DSC cell. Gaseous nitrogen coolant was directed to the cooling assembly during measurements with a controlled rate of cooling.

The stability of the cooling arrangement is extremely important, because any slight thermal or vibrational disturbance in the system may introduce a false output signal. The modifications described above greatly improve the stability over the commercial design in this particular model. The baseline is essentially linear over the broad temperature range examined. The second system is judged even better in this aspect, although the cooling capacity is somewhat reduced due to the use of gaseous coolant. Thus, it was only used for scans above DSC measurements.

In order to eliminate the influence of prior thermal history, the samples were equilibrated for 3 min at 150°C to ensure removal of residual crystallinity; the

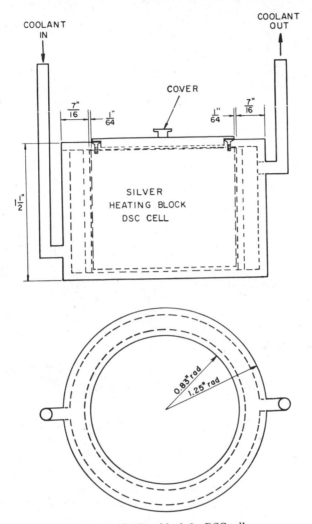

Fig. 1. Cooling block for DSC cell.

cooling scans were then run at 20°C/min immediately after the cooling scans. Without the high-temperature equilibration, nonreproducible crystallization temperatures were observed during the cooling scan; and in the heating thermograms, endotherms with varied peak temperature and peak size depending upon the prior thermal history were observed, to be described in a later section. In the studies on effect of annealing time and temperature, the samples were heated for 3 min at 150°C and placed on a metal surface at the annealing temperature. Following completion of the annealing period, the samples were rapidly quenched in liquid nitrogen, and then the DSC heating scans were taken.

RESULTS

The effects of annealing time and temperature on the DSC thermograms of E/P/HD terpolymers are illustrated in Figures 6 and 7. In view of the strong thermal history effects, thermograms determined with samples equilibrated in

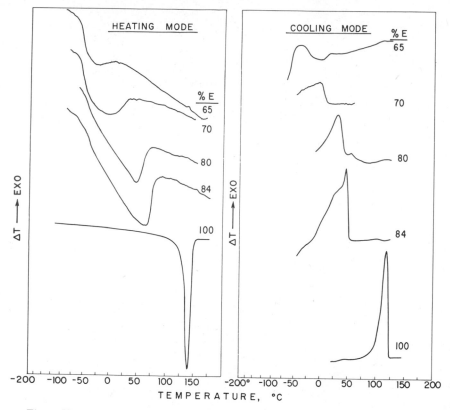

Fig. 2. Heating and cooling thermograms of E/P/HD terpolymers and polyethylene.

the molten state followed by a controlled scanning rate are presented in Figure 2. Various features derived from the heating and the subsequent cooling scans are shown in Table I. In the heating scans, a slope change occurs at $-60°C$ for all the EPDM samples. This corresponds to the glass transition temperature and is followed immediately by a very broad endotherm as the temperature is increased. The size of this endotherm is dependent on polymer composition. The degree of crystallinity, as evidenced by the size of the endotherm, decreases as the ethylene content of the polymer decreases. This is in general agreement with the observations in the literature summarized in reference 1 for other types of EPDM and ethylene/propylene dipolymers. As temperature is further increased, the curve returns to its baseline. Some waviness does occur with some of the polymers (e.g., sample B2, Fig. 6). The thermogram of hexane-soluble fraction B21 (Fig. 2) has an exceptionally linear baseline in the high-temperature region resulting from the removal of the more crystalline and perhaps blockier polymer fractions where two endotherms were observed (Fig. 4). The thermogram of sample B8, a terpolymer containing 61.5 mole% ethylene, the least crystalline polymer of the series, is shown in Figure 5. Essentially no endotherm was observed.

In the cooling thermogram, a sharp exotherm occurs about 10° to 15°C below the peak temperature of the corresponding endotherm in the heating curve. The exotherm can be characterized by the crystallization onset temperature T_f. The latter is defined by the initial departure of the exotherm from the baseline as

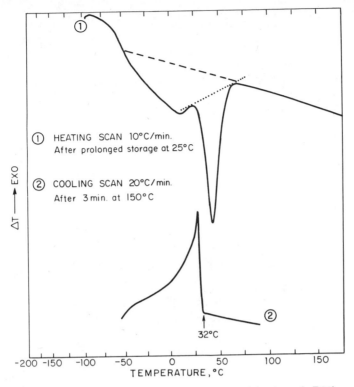

Fig. 3. Thermogram of E/P/HD terpolymer fraction (sample B21).

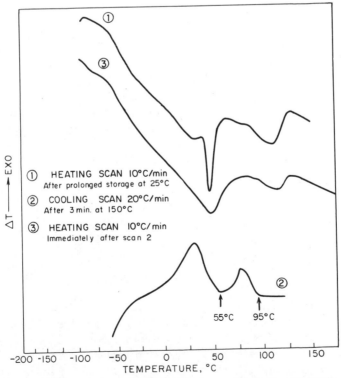

Fig. 4. Thermogram of E/P/HD terpolymer fraction (sample B23).

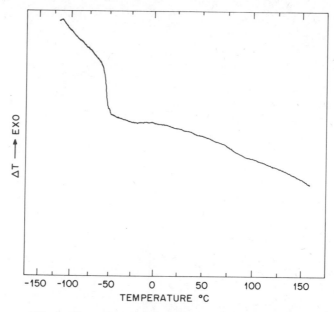

Fig. 5. Thermogram of E/P/HD terpolymer (sample B8).

shown by an arrow in Figure 3. It is reproducible to within 1°C. T_f data for the various samples are also shown in Table I.

DISCUSSION

Heating Thermograms of E/P/HD Terpolymers

As described previously, the thermogram of an E/P/HD terpolymer containing 63 mole % or more ethylene is rather complex. It is linear below its glass transition temperature (~−60°C); but as the temperature is raised, it immediately plunges into a broad endotherm before returning to its baseline. The endotherm is interpreted as the melting of crystallites. This is in agreement with the behavior of ethylene/propylene copolymers and other terpolymers reported in the literature.[3,4] The crystallinity is believed to be associated with ethylene sequences.[1] All samples showed a rather broad endotherm, probably owing to the existence of a broad ethylene sequence length distribution which results in crystals of different sizes with varying degrees of defects and imperfections. The melting range of the polymers is shown in Table I for samples scanned right after being control cooled from the molten state.

Effect of Thermal History

The shape of the endotherm as well as the location of the peak temperature is extremely sensitive to the thermal history of the polymer sample. This is indicated in Figures 6 and 7, which show the important effect of time and temperature of annealing. As shown in Figure 7, the DSC thermograms for samples annealed atroom temperature for 10 min at 1 or 20 hr are considerably different from that of the same sample after prolonged room-temperature storage. Both

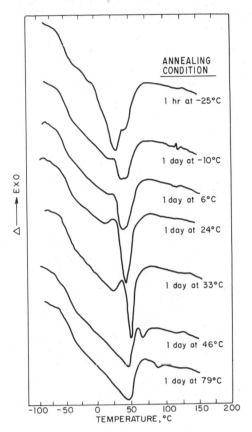

Fig. 6. Thermogram of annealed E/P/HD terpolymer (sample B2).   Heating rate, 10°C/min.

the size and the peak temperature of the endotherm increased with the annealing time.   The effect of annealing temperature is illustrated with sample B2, as shown in Figure 6.   The polymer contains 79.5 mole % ethylene; its thermogram has a broad endotherm covering −42° to 125°C, with a peak temperature of 40°C. The peak temperature can be varied from 30° to 50°C as shown in Table II by varying the annealing temperature.   Samples annealed within the 25–45°C range result in double endotherms.   The peak melting temperature and its intensity increase with the annealing temperature and time, as shown in Table II.   An additional endotherm beyond the temperature range of the major melting region was also induced by annealing sample B2 at 79°C (see Fig. 6).   This could be due to the presence of a highly crystalline fraction.   Examination of the hexane-soluble and hexane-insoluble fractions revealed this could indeed be true, as shown in Figures 3 and 4.   The DSC curve is very linear and free of waviness at 55–175°C for sample B21, the portion soluble in hexane at 25°C.   An additional endotherm centered at 90° to 125°C occurred with sample B23, the portion insoluble in hexane at 50°C.   Furthermore, the cooling curve of the latter also showed an additional exotherm corresponding to the higher melting peak.

Cooling Thermograms of E/P/HD Terpolymers

Because of the strong effect of thermal history on the DSC thermograms, crystallinity of the polymer is best analyzed by examining the DSC cooling curve

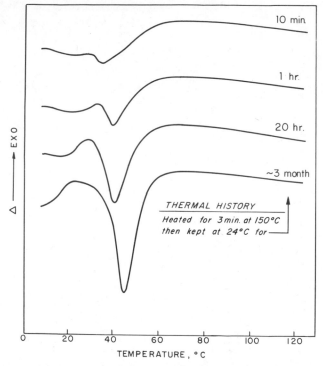

Fig. 7. Thermograms of annealed E/P/ENB terpolymer (sample C2). Heating rate, 10°C/min.

after the sample has been heated above its melting point to eliminate all vestiges of crystallinity.   This is not a common technique, because facilities for obtaining a controlled rate of cooling are required.   By means of the two attachments described in the experimental section, we were able to examine the crystallization behavior of the polymer samples cooled from the molten state where they were

TABLE II
Effect of Annealing on Melting Temperature of EPDM's[a]

Sample	Annealing temperature, °C	Time	Peak temperature, °C[b]	
B2	−25	1 hr	30 (s)	42 (shr)
	−10	24 hr	20−25 (shr)	35−45 (m)
	6	24 hr	25 (shr)	38 (m)
	24	24 hr	15 (m)	43 (s)
	33	24 hr	25 (m)	50 (s)
	46	24 hr	45 (s)	65 (w)
	79	24 hr	45 (s)	86 (w)
C2	25	10 min	36 (w)	
	25	1 hr	40 (m)	
	25	20 hr	41 (s)	
	25	3 months	45 (s)	

[a] Sample was heated for 3 min at 150°C, then quenched to the annealing temperature. Relative intensity of the endotherm: s = strong, m = medium, w = weak, shr = shoulder.
[b] Minimum point of the endotherm.

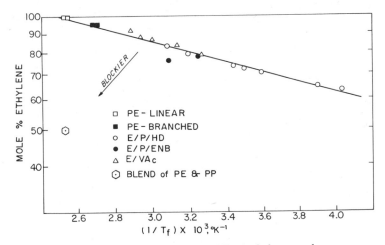

Fig. 8. Compositional dependence of T_f of ethylene copolymers.

free from effects of previous thermal history. Typical cooling curves are shown in Figure 2. The crystallization behavior can be characterized by the temperature (T_f) at which a sharp rise of ΔT occurred.

Effect of Comonomer Composition

The onset of temperature of crystallization (T_f) as defined previously for the various polymers is strongly dependent on composition, as shown in Table I. As a matter of fact, T_f can be correlated with the mole-% of ethylene (E) as shown in Figure 8 and may be represented by

$$1/T_f = k_1 \ln E + k_2 \qquad (k_1 \text{ and } k_2 = \text{constants})$$

for all the EPDM's and polyethylene samples examined. The relationship is similar to the one derived by Flory[5] based on the theory of random copolymers. However, the constants k_1 and k_2 lack theoretical significance because a non-equilibrium freezing temperature instead of the thermodynamic melting point was used. Note that the latter involves difficult and tedious measurements as compared to the simple cooling scan in determining the crystallization onset temperature. The equation relates T_f to polymer composition, and T_f increases as ethylene concentration increases. As shown in Figure 8, the line passes right through the point for linear polyethylene. If we assume that there are 2.5 branches per 100 backbone carbons in branched polyethylene,[6] the data of the latter fall on the line also. These results conform with the concept that the crystallinity in E/P copolymers with more than 60 mole % ethylene are ethylenic in origin.

We have also examined the crystallization behavior of some ethylene/vinyl acetate copolymers, which are known to have random sequence length distributions.[7] Their T_f–E relationships are also in line with the correlation. As was discussed previously, the ethylene/propylene copolymers could have different sequence length distributions due to the varied synthesis conditions and catalyst used.[1,8] This would result in polymers of different crystallinity for a given composition. It is postulated that polymers of a blockier ethylene sequence length distribution will yield a higher freezing point and hence will fall below the line in Figure 8. For example, sample D1, a physical blend of polyethylene and polypropylene with 50 mole % of the former, has a T_f value of 123°C, and the data point is far below the correlated line. One of the two E/P/ENB samples also falls slightly below the correlated line. The sample is probably somewhat blockier than the rest of the E/P/HD and E/P/ENB terpolymer or E/VAc copolymer samples. The relative chain blockiness defined in such a scheme is, of course, grossly simplified. However, the technique is rather simple and may provide a relative measure of the monomer sequence blockiness in the ethylene copolymers. One is cautioned in the use of the cooling technique in polymer characterization that only pure and uncontaminated samples be used since small amounts of nucleating agent may produce an erroneously high crystallization onset temperature.

The relationship between T_f and composition observed with the copolymer samples suggests that the effect of all the comonomers, including propylene, hexadiene, ethylidenenorbornene, and vinyl acetate, are roughly equivalent, and the variation in T_f can be accounted for solely by the molar ethylene content in the polymer.

The compositional dependence of polymer crystallinity can also be characterized by other thermal parameters, e.g., the heat of fusion (ΔH_f) and the peak temperature of the endotherm (T_m). As discussed previously, these parameters are highly dependent upon the thermal history of the polymer. VerStrate and Wilchinisky[2] chose to anneal the sample at room temperature for an extended period of time (up to 20 days) before making their measurements. We decided to use heat scanning immediately after a sample is control cooled (20°C/min) from its molten state. The ΔH_f and T_m values of the samples are reported in Table I. ΔH_f was determined from the area of the endotherm below the baseline, and the latter was drawn by extending the baseline of the polymer in the high-temperature region as illustrated by the dashed line in Figure 3. Note that, if the baseline is drawn conventionally as the tangent to the two sides of the endotherm, as illustrated by the dotted line in Figure 3, the value obtained would be considerably lower, even when one is comparing the part of the endotherm above room temperature. This method of drawing baselines is further supported by the heating scan of a noncrystalline sample shown in Figure 5, where the thermogram is essentially linear from −50° to 150°C and the baseline in the lower temperature portion (say, −50° to 100°C) can be represented closely by an extrapolated line from those in the higher temperature range. The results so obtained are shown in Table I. Both T_m and ΔH_f increase as ethylene content is increased.

The parameters T_f, T_m, ΔH_f, and the melting temperature range of the E/P/HD terpolymers appear to change continuously with ethylene concentration right through to 100% ethylene, i.e., polyethylene. The changes in T_f and T_m are rather smooth near polyethylene composition; but rather sharp changes occur with ΔH_f and the melting temperature range when ethylene content is increased from 85% to 100%.

SUMMARY

An improved differential, thermal analytical technique which permits the rapid, convenient characterizations of the thermal behavior of crystalline polymers free of any influence of prior thermal history is presented. By mechanical modification of a du Pont Model 900 differential thermal analyzer, stable baselines were obtained during the cooling mode. High-temperature equilibration prior to thermal analysis eliminated the influence of prior thermal history on the crystallization and fusion behavior of the polymers.

The technique was demonstrated in the characterization of various ethylene copolymers, mostly with the class of EPDM's which are copolymers of ethylene, propylene, and a small amount of a diene such as 1,4-hexadiene, ethylidene-norbornene, or dicyclopentadiene. Also studied were random ethylene/vinyl acetate copolymers and branched and linear polyethylene. The effect of annealing time and temperature was further demonstrated with this improved technique.

Rapid, reproducible characterizations of both crystallization and fusion phenomena were carried out on these ethylene copolymers subjected to well-controlled thermal scanning techniques. The crystallization onset temperature (T_f) determined by this technique was found to relate to the molar ethylene content of the E/P/HD polymers by an equation similar to the one derived by Flory using equilibrium melting point. The substitution of the latter with the crystallization onset temperature simplifies greatly the experimental measurements. The relationship was found to hold true for samples of linear and branched polyethylene, commercial EPDM, and ethylene/vinyl acetate copolymers. It is suggested that the relative chain blockiness of the ethylene copolymers may be estimated by comparing their crystallization onset temperatures.

The authors are indebted to Dr. Jen Chiu of E. I. du Pont de Nemours & Co. for his suggestion of the cooling technique in the thermal measurements.

References

1. F. P. Baldwin and G. VerStrate, *Rubber Chem. Technol.*, **45,** 709 (1972).
2. G. VerStrate and Z. W. Wilchinsky, *J. Polym. Sci. A2*, **9,** 127 (1971).
3. G. A. Clegg, D. R. Gee, and T. P. Melia, *Makromol. Chem.*, **116,** 130 (1968).
4. J. R. Richards, R. G. Mancke, and J. D. Ferry, *Polym. Lett.*, **2,** 197 (1964).
5. P. J. Flory, *Principles of Polymer Chemistry*, Cornell University Press, Ithaca, N.Y., 1953, pp. 570, 573.
6. R. A. V. Raff and K. W. Doak, Eds., *High Polymers*, Vol. XX, Interscience, New York, 1965, p. 678.
7. J. Schaefer, *J. Phys. Chem.*, **70,** 1925 (1966).
8. C. Cozewith and G. VerStrate, *Macromolecules*, **4,** 482 (1971).

Received May 11, 1973
Revised May 13, 1976

JOURNAL OF APPLIED POLYMER SCIENCE   VOL. 21, 2899–2904 (1977)

Effect of Pressure on CO_2 Transport in Poly(ethylene Terephthalate)

W. J. KOROS and D. R. PAUL, *Department of Chemical Engineering, The University of Texas at Austin, Austin, Texas 78712,* and M. FUJII, H. B. HOPFENBERG, and V. STANNETT, *Department of Chemical Engineering, North Carolina State University, Raleigh, North Carolina 27607*

Synopsis

The CO_2 solubility, permeability, and diffusion time lag in poly(ethylene terephthalate) are reported at 35° and 65°C for CO_2 pressures ranging from 0.07 to 20 atm. The subatmospheric time lag and permeability measurements were made with a glass system at North Carolina State University, while the measurements between 1 and 20 atmospheres, using an identical polymer sample, were made at The University of Texas with a metal system capable of tolerating gauge pressures up to 30 atm. The measured solubility, permeability, and time lag all show strong deviations from the well-known simple expressions for gases in rubbery polymers. The solubility isotherm is nonlinear in pressure, and both θ and P are quite pressure dependent, with each showing tendencies to approach low and high pressure asymptotic limits. These effects decrease as temperature increases and would be expected to disappear at or near the glass transition where the amorphous regions become rubbery. The importance of reporting the pressure levels used in transport measurements is emphasized for gas/glassy polymer systems where transport process do not follow linear laws.

INTRODUCTION

The simplest model for gas sorption and permeation in polymers envisions the equilibrium sorption isotherm to follow Henry's law,

$$C = k_D p \qquad (1)$$

and the transport to follow Fick's first law with a concentration-independent diffusion coefficient[1] D. In this case, the resulting differential equations which describe both transient and steady-state transport processes are linear; and, as a result, it is possible to define and measure simple parameters which are independent of the external pressure boundary conditions. The most common and useful of these are the permeability P and time lag θ, which for the above-mentioned model are related to fundamental quantities via

$$P = k_D D \qquad (2)$$

$$\theta = l^2/6D \qquad (3)$$

Both P and θ can be deduced from a single transient permeation experiment,[2] thus giving k_D and D provided the membrane thickness l is known. Generally, the experiment is done with a very high vacuum on the downstream side of the membrane while a finite driving pressure, p_2, is used upstream. For the simple model described above, which is evidently quite valid for rubbery polymers, the value of p_2 selected for this experiment should not matter, and usually its range is dictated by details of equipment design while the exact value is selected to provide a convenient rate of gas transmission. Because of this presumed independence of the measured parameters on this pressure, it has become common practice to not even report it.

There is substantial evidence, however, that this simple model is inadequate for a number of gas/glassy polymer systems. For example, there are now many published sorption isotherms which show substantial nonlinear behavior even at modest or low pressures.[3-22] Theoretical interpretation of these results has led to models that suggest either P or θ or both might depend on p_2.[23,24] Some recent data for CO_2 in polycarbonate have shown[22] that P and θ both depend on p_2. These data were obtained with a permeation apparatus designed specifically for the purpose of varying p_2 in rather high ranges. The upstream side of the equipment must, therefore, be a rather robust metal design and construction. Such equipment is not well suited for measurements with p_2 much below atmospheric pressure because small air leaks may contaminate the upstream compartment which was designed to contain high gas pressures. Conversely, small outward leaks are of no concern when operating as a high-pressure cell. As a result, the earlier polycarbonate/CO_2 data do not extend below 1 atm, although there is considerable evidence for this system and others presently being studied that P and θ may show considerable pressure dependence below 1 atm. In general, there may not be a practical low-pressure range where it is always safe to assume pressure independence of these measured parameters.

Most laboratories equipped for gas permeation research use equipment constructed entirely of glass, and consequently p_2 is restricted to subatmospheric values. Therefore, if one chooses to study the effect of p_2 on the transport parameters, these equipment design considerations restrict most investigators to cover the range below 1 atm although it would be desirable to cover the entire range in some instances. A joint project was, therefore, carried out to measure P and θ as a function of p_2 on the same polymer sample over a broad pressure range traversing 1 atm. The laboratories at North Carolina State University and The University of Texas which are well equipped for measurements with p_2 below and above 1 atm, respectively, cooperated in this project. Results for the system poly(ethylene terephthalate)/CO_2 at 35° and 65°C are reported here.

The data presented are intended to demonstrate the effect of upstream pressure on P and θ for systems in which transport processes are not described by linear differential equations. Presently, there is evidence which suggests that all gas/glassy polymer systems fall into this category. The results will not be analyzed or discussed extensively in terms of any specific model; however, such an analysis is now underway for this same system using much more extensive data and will be reported in a later paper.

EXPERIMENTAL

Permeation

The apparatus and operating procedures for both the low-pressure and high-pressure experiments used in this study have been described in the literature.[22,27] Both cells used large downstream gas receiver volumes and a sensitive MKS Baratron as the downstream pressure sensor to permit maintenance of a very small pressure as the boundary condition at the downstream membrane face. The vacuum system at North Carolina State was constructed of glass, while the system at The University of Texas was constructed of metal to permit application of upstream driving pressures up to 30 atm.

For the high-pressure system, the diffusion area was determined ($\pm2\%$) by masking both membrane faces with either vapor-deposited aluminum or carefully cut aluminum foil tape. To seal against high pressures without imposing undue stress on the glassy membrane, it was convenient to adopt a double-sealing arrangement. A piece of filter paper, cut to the same size as the unmasked diffusion area, was placed on the sintered metal support to facilitate gas flow to the downstream receiver. The membrane was then adhered to the bottom metal plate with an epoxy resin, and a good vacuum seal was easily achieved. To seal against high-pressure leaks to the outside from the cell top, a Teflon gasket with sufficiently large inside diameter was placed on the metal plate so that it surrounded, but did not contact, the epoxy–membrane assembly. The gasket was compressed by tightening six symmetrically placed nuts. This double-seal system has proven to be adequate in fairly high temperature and pressure service. Degassing times at least ten times longer than the largest observed time lag were used between runs. The time lag was not affected by more protracted degassing.

For the low-pressure system, standard sealing techniques and previously reported operating procedures[27] worked well.

Sorption

Design and operation of the sorption cell are described elsewhere.[21] The cell was a dual-volume, dual-transducer design similar to that reported in an earlier paper[22] with modifications to improve the signal-to-noise ratio.

RESULTS

Poly(ethylene terephthalate) (PET) was selected for this work because of its potential importance in carbonated beverage packaging[25] and its strongly non-linear sorption behavior.[7,14,15,19] The particular sample chosen was a commercially available 2-mil film which is optically quite transparent although very crystalline. More detailed characterization of this polymer is available elsewhere.[26]

The PET/CO$_2$ sorption isotherms measured in The University of Texas laboratories at 35° and 65°C are presented in Figure 1. It is clear that these isotherms are quite nonlinear and cannot be described by Henry's law; however, they can be accurately described by, and understood in terms of, the dual sorption model[3,9] extensively discussed in the literature.[6–25] From these sorption results, various models[9,23,24] would predict either or both the permeability and the time lag to depend on pressure.

Figures 2 and 3 show the time lag and permeability plotted versus the upstream CO$_2$ pressure for a range of approximately 3.5 decades of pressure. Note that both θ and P are pressure dependent as expected. The solid data points ($p_2 >$ 1 atm) were obtained in The University of Texas laboratories, while the open

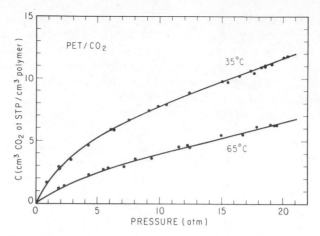

Fig. 1. CO_2 sorption isotherms for poly(ethylene terephthalate).

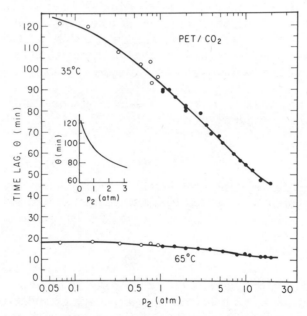

Fig. 2. Effect of upstream CO_2 pressure on diffusion time lag for a 2.0-mil poly(ethylene terephthalate) membrane. Note the logarithmetic scale employed to allow displaying the wide range of upstream CO_2 pressures used. The smoothed 35°C data are plotted on the insert with arithmetic pressure coordinates to show the strong pressure effect on θ near and below atmospheric pressure.

points ($p_2 < 1$ atm) were obtained in the North Carolina State University laboratories using an identical specimen. It is gratifying to see the excellent agreement between the two sets of data obtained using equipment of quite different designs.

DISCUSSION

It is clear from Figure 1 that the amount of sorption is a strongly nonlinear function of pressure and decreases with increasing temperature. There is con-

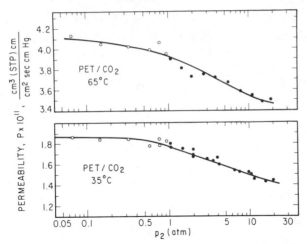

Fig. 3. Effect of upstream CO$_2$ pressure on permeability. Note that on a percentage basis the pressure effect on permeability is larger at 35°C (23% change between 0.07 and 20 atm) than at 65°C (16% change between 0.07 and 20 atm).

siderably less curvature in the isotherm at 65°C than at 35°C. These nonlinear sorption isotherms preclude both the use of Henry's law to describe sorption and the use of the combined set of eqs. (2) and (3) for the experimental transport parameters θ and P.

The results presented in Figure 2 indicate, especially at 35°C, a pronounced effect of p_2 on θ. In fact, these data show no pressure range in which the time lag is reasonably constant. Considerably different values of D would be reported by investigators working at different driving pressures if eq. (3) were casually applied. As the temperature is raised, the magnitude of the time lag decreases as one expects, and the pressure dependence of the time lag is also decreased. For example, at 35°C, θ changes by 63% over the pressure range shown, while at 65°C, this change is only 39%.

The permeability at 65°C is more than a factor of 2 higher than the permeability at 35°C, and the pressure dependence of the permeability is greater at 35°C than 65°C. Although this reduction in pressure effect is less dramatic for the permeability than for the time lag, it is still significant. These observations are gratifyingly consistent with a theory that attributes pressure dependence of θ and P and the nonlinear nature of the sorption isotherm to dual sorption mechanisms which seem to be characteristic of the glassy state.[24] This theory predicts that both θ and P have zero-pressure and high-pressure limits, and Figures 2 and 3 seem to be consistent with this notion. The insert plot on Figure 2 of θ versus pressure on arithmetic coordinates at 35°C shows more vividly the strong pressure dependence between zero and 1 atm.

Presumably, as the temperature approaches the glass transition, the complex relationships responsible for these observed pressure dependences should degenerate into the simple relationships for gases in rubbers given by eqs. (1)–(3). Complete interpretation of these data and additional data spanning the glass transition of PET (about 80°C), in terms of the theoretical models mentioned, is in progress and will be reported in a later paper.

The preceding discussion and data emphasize the value of reporting the pressure at which gas/glassy polymer transport measurements are made.

Moreover, the simple expressions which are adequate to describe sorption and transport of gases in rubbery polymers should not, in general, be used for the more complex case of gases in glassy polymers.

The authors are grateful to the National Science Foundation (The University of Texas) and the Office of Naval Research (North Carolina State University) for financial support of their work.

References

1. V. Stannett, in *Diffusion in Polymers*, J. Crank and G. S. Park, Eds., Academic Press, New York, 1968, Ch. 2.

2. J. Crank and G. S. Park, in *Diffusion in Polymers*, J. Crank and G. S. Park, Eds., Academic Press, New York, 1968, Ch. 1, p. 4.

3. R. M. Barrer, J. A. Barrie, and J. Slater, *J. Polym. Sci.*, **27**, 177 (1958).

4. P. Meares, *J. Amer. Chem. Soc.*, **76**, 3415 (1954).

5. P. Meares, *Trans. Faraday Soc.*, **53**, 101 (1957); *ibid.*, **54**, 40 (1958).

6. H. B. Hopfenberg and V. Stannett, in *The Physics of Glassy Polymers*, R. N. Haward, Ed., Applied Science Publishers, London, 1973, p. 504.

7. A. S. Michaels, W. R. Vieth, and J. A. Barrie, *J. Appl. Phys.*, **34**, 1 and 13 (1963).

8. W. R. Vieth, H. H. Alcalay, and A. V. Frabetti, *J. Appl. Polym. Sci.*, **8**, 2125 (1964).

9. W. R. Vieth and K. J. Sladek, *J. Colloid Sci.*, **20**, 1014 (1965).

10. W. R. Vieth, C. S. Frangoulis, and J. A. Rionda, *J. Colloid Interface Sci.*, **22**, 454 (1966).

11. W. R. Vieth, P. M. Tam, and A. S. Michaels, *J. Colloid Interface Sci.*, **22**, 360 (1966).

12. J. A. Eilenberg and W. R. Vieth, in *Advances in Polymer Science and Engineering*, K. D. Pae, D. R. Morrow, and Y. Chen, Eds., Plenum Press, New York, 1972, p. 145.

13. W. R. Vieth and J. A. Eilenberg, *J. Appl. Polym. Sci.*, **16**, 945 (1972).

14. K. Toi, *J. Polym. Sci., Polym. Phys. Ed.*, **11**, 1892 (1973).

15. P. J. Fenelon, in *Permeability of Plastic Films and Coatings to Gases, Vapors and Liquids*, H. B. Hopfenberg, Ed., Plenum Press, New York, 1974, p. 285.

16. W. R. Vieth and M. A. Amini, in *Permeability of Plastic Films and Coatings to Gases, Vapors and Liquids*, H. B. Hopfenberg, Ed., Plenum Press, New York, 1974, p. 49.

17. A. R. Berens, *ACS Polym. Prepr.*, **15**(2), 197 and 203 (1974).

18. A. R. Berens, *Angew. Makromol. Chem.*, **47**(1), 97 (1975).

19. W. Kollen, paper presented at 80th Nat. Meeting of AIChE, Boston, Mass., Sept. 9, 1975.

20. R. A. Assink, *J. Polym. Sci., Polym. Phys. Ed.*, **13**, 1665 (1975).

21. W. J. Koros and D. R. Paul, *J. Polym. Sci., Polym. Phys. Ed.*, **14**, 1903 (1976).

22. W. J. Koros, D. R. Paul, and A. A. Rocha, *J. Polym. Sci., Polym. Phys. Ed.*, **14**, 687 (1976).

23. D. R. Paul, *J. Polym. Sci. A-2*, **7**, 1811 (1969).

24. D. R. Paul and W. J. Koros, *J. Polym. Sci., Polym. Phys. Ed.*, **14**, 675 (1976).

25. P. J. Fenelon, *Polym. Eng. Sci.*, **13**, 440 (1973).

26. W. J. Koros, Ph.D. dissertation, The University of Texas at Austin, 1977.

27. S. M. Allen, Ph.D. Thesis, North Carolina State University, 1975; S. M. Allen, M. Fujii, V. Stannett, H. B. Hopfenberg, and J. L. Williams, *J. Membrane Sci.*, in press.

Received June 28, 1976
Revised September 14, 1976

JOURNAL OF APPLIED POLYMER SCIENCE VOL. 21, 2905–2912 (1977)

Thermal Degradation of Polymers. XVII. Thermal Analysis of Polyquinazolones and Related Systems

A. GHAFOOR* and R. H. STILL, *Department of Polymer and Fibre Science, UMIST, Manchester, England*

Synopsis

The thermal characterization of a series of polyquinazolones, poly(quinazolone diones), and polybenzoxazinones by thermal analytical techniques (TG, DSC) is described. Comparative thermal stability measurements by dynamic and isothermal TG in air and N_2 are critically discussed. Kinetic studies by isothermal TG in air and nitrogen leading to activation energies are described. The inherent difficulties in comparative thermal stability studies on complex polymer systems are discussed in terms of their structural and compositional variables and their effect on the assessment parameters used.

INTRODUCTION

The polymers studied were prepared as binder materials for tribological application in journal bearings, and this has been reported elsewhere.[1] Poly(quinazoline diones), polyquinazolones, and polybenzoxazinones were chosen for study on the basis of their reported thermal stabilities, ease of preparation, and ability to be fabricated in a prepolymer state.[2-6] The latter was important because it enabled coatings to be prepared by spraying or casting techniques on the inside of a journal bearing bush. Such coatings could then be thermally cyclized to the partial ladder polymer.[1]

This paper reports the thermal characterization of these materials using dynamic and isothermal thermogravimetric analysis (TG) and DSC.

EXPERIMENTAL

Materials

Two polyquinazolinediones, IA and IIA, of generalized repeating structure

where $X = $ —⟨ ⟩—CH_2—⟨ ⟩— in IA and —$(CH_2)_6$— in IIA,

* Present address: Peoples University of Islamabad, Islamabad, Pakistan.

were prepared from prepolymers derived from benzidinedicarboxylic acid (BDC) and diphenylmethane diisocyanate and heethylene diisocyanate as reported previously.[1] A polybenzoxazinone, IIIA, of generalized structure

IIIA

was prepared by cyclization of the prepolymer amido acid

prepared from BDC and isophthaloyl chloride in N-methylpyrrolidone solution. BDC (2.73 g) was suspended in N-methylpyrrolidone (80 ml) containing lithium chloride (0.424 g). This heterogeneous system was blanketed with nitrogen, and isophthaloyl chloride (2.03 g) was added to the stirred solution at such a rate to maintain the reaction medium at 5–2°C with external cooling.

An exothermic reaction took place and the solution became viscous. The solution was heated to 80°–100°C for 20 min and was then added to methanol to precipitate the polymer. A fibrous polymer was obtained which was filtered, washed with water and methanol, and dried at 30°C/2 mm of Hg. Yield, 4.85 g.

ANAL. Found: C, 64.9; H, 3.5; N, 7.0. Calcd for $(C_{22}H_{14}N_2O_6)_n$: C, 65.67; H, 3.51; N, 6.96; O, 23.86%. $[\eta]_0 = 0.38$, determined in concentrated sulfuric acid at 25°C.

DSC analysis of the prepolymer showed it to have a glass transition temperature of 240°C, but no melting endotherm was observed. Studies on a hot-stage polarizing microscope (HSPM) indicated that the sample was slightly birefringent but remained unchanged up to 320°C (the limit of the apparatus used). The DSC trace showed two other features, both endothermic processes. The first, at 250–300°C, involved significantly less energy than the second at 350°C.

Cyclization of the prepolymer amido acid precursor of IIIA was attempted by solvent casting from N-methylpyrrolidone yielding a brittle film after drying at 120°C for 10 min. This film was heated in a nitrogen atmosphere from room temperature to 250°C (10 min) and was maintained at this temperature for 1 hr.

ANAL. Found: C, 64.8; H, 3.7; N, 7.1; Calcd for $(C_{22}H_{10}N_2O_4)_n$: C, 72.13; H, 2.73; N, 7.65; O, 17.49%.

Polyquinazolones IB–IVB of generalized repeating structure

where X = —CH$_2$—(IB), —O— (IIB), —SO$_2$— (IIIB), and —S$_2$— (IVB), were prepared and characterized as previously reported.[1]

The model compounds, 2-methylbenzoxazinone and 2-acetamidobenzanilide, were prepared using known literature methods.[1,7]

The following commercially available high-temperature polymers (Table I) were studied for comparative purposes. The materials were cured where necessary according to the manufacturer's specification.

Thermal-Analysis Studies

TG studies were made on a Stanton thermobalance (Model Mark II) with the furnace programmed for a heating rate of 6°C/min (nominal). A small platinum crucible was used with samples (10 mg). Dynamic experiments were carried out in static air and flowing white spot nitrogen at a flow rate of 200 ml/min with the gas entering at the top of the furnace. Nitrogen was passed over the sample for 30 min before commencement of the heating program to ensure that the tube furnace was free from air. Temperatures are furnace wall temperatures, and buoyancy corrections were applied.

Isothermal studies were made using the following procedure. The furnace was preheated without the sample in position with the required atmosphere passing through the furnace. Prior to operation, the furnace was quickly raised and the crucible placed in position on the rise rod and the furnace lowered and the balance switched on. To prevent air ingress when nitrogen was used as the operating atmosphere, nitrogen was blown down the furnace during this sam-

TABLE I
Commercially Available High-Temperature Polymers

Polymer	Source
Polybenzimidazole (Imidite 2801)	Whittaker Corporation (U.S.A.)
Polybenzoxazole (PB03)	Yorkshire Chemicals
Polyimide (QX-13)	R.A.E., Farnborough
Polyimide (Kerimid 601)	Societe des Usine Chemique
Poly(phenylene sulfide) (RYTON)	Phillips Petroleum (U.K.)
Poly(p-hydroxybenzoic acid) (EKONOL)	Carborundum

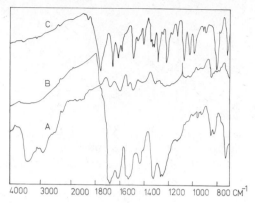

Fig. 1. IR Spectra: A, poly(amido acid) precursor to polybenzoxazinone (IIIA); B, polybenzoxazinone (IIIA); C, 2-methylbenzoxazinone.

ple-loading operation. Nitrogen and air were used in these studies at a flow rate of 200 ml/min.

DSC studies were made on a du Pont 900 thermal analyzer equipped with a DSC cell. The samples ($\simeq 6$ mg) were contained in open aluminum pans, and an empty pan acted as the inert reference material. Studies were made at a heating rate of 20°C/min (nominal).

Hot-Stage Microscopy (HSPM)

Studies were made using a Kofler hot-stage microscope at a similar heating rate to that used in the DSC studies.

Infrared Spectroscopy

Spectra were run on 1% suspensions in potassium bromide discs using a Unicam SP200 spectrophotometer.

DISCUSSION

The preparation and characterization of the precursors to the poly(quinazoline diones) IA and IIA and the polyquinazolones IB–IVB have been reported previously together with their tribological evaluation.[1] The polybenzoxazinone IIIA was unsuitable for tribological studies due to the brittle nature of its films. The preparation of the polyamide acid precursor to the polybenzoxazinone IIIA proceeded smoothly and combustion analysis data and the IR spectra A (Fig. 1) are in accord with the proposed structure and are similar to those reported by Yoda.[5]

The DSC behavior recorded may be ascribed to cyclization (cyclodehydration at 250–300°C) as shown by IR spectroscopy on sample heated to this temperature in the DSC cell (spectrum identical with spectrum B (Fig. 1), followed by degradation at temperatures in excess of 350°C.

The cyclization process yielded polymer IIIA whose combustion analysis data and IR spectrum B (Fig. 1) indicate that cyclization is not complete. The model

TABLE II
PDT and 50% DT Values in Air

Polymer (cyclized)	PDT, °C	50% DT, °C	C.H.T.P.	PDT, °C	50% DT, °C
IA	320	520	1. polybenzimidazole	310	550
IIA	300	494	2. polybenzoxazole	360	550
IIIA	260	492	3. polyimide QX-13	380	580
IB	305	525	4. polyimide (Kerimid)	380	550
IIB	280	520	5. poly(phenylene sulfide)	410	580
IIIB	290	500	6. poly(p-hydroxybenzoic acid)	340	524
IVB	290	525			

TABLE III
W_{30} Values from Isothermal TG in Air

Polymer	IA	IIA	IIIA	IB	IIB	IIIB	IVB
W_{30}	31	61	52	28	31	42	30

compound 2-methylbenzoxazinone has a spectrum C (Fig. 1) similar, but not identical with that of polymer IIIA. Spectrum B (Fig. 1) is, however, in accord with that obtained by Kurihara and Hagiwara,[6] for similar polybenzoxazinones. However, the incomplete combustion analysis figures, the presence of an ash (<0.5%), and the carbonyl absorption band at 1680 cm^{-1} in the cyclized polymer spectrum suggest that uncyclized amide units are present.

Thermal-Analysis Studies

These were made on the cyclized polymers in an attempt to evaluate comparative thermal stabilities. Thermal stability in this context has been assessed by dynamic TG, in terms of the procedural decomposition temperature (PDT), the temperature at which weight loss becomes observable, and the temperature at which 50% decomposition as measured by weight loss had occurred (50% DT).

Isothermal TG studies gave the percentage weight lost after 30 min at 400°C (W_{30}), the time for 50% decomposition (50% D) at various isothermal temperatures; kinetic studies yielded activation energies.

The data obtained from dynamic TG studies were compared with those obtained from the commercial high-temperature polymers (Table II).

The PDT and 50% DT data show that the polymers synthesized in this study had generally lower values than the commercial samples, suggesting inferior thermal stability. Since their application involved fabrication via the soluble precursor stage, this loss in stability was not considered to be sufficiently detrimental to prevent their tribological evaluation.

In order to further characterize these materials, isothermal TG studies were carried out at 400°C in air, which yielded the data presented in Table III. This suggests an order of stability for the A series of polymers of IA > IIIA > IIA, while PDT and 50% DT values suggest that IA > IIA > IIIA and IA > IIA ~ IIIA, respectively.

TABLE IV
Stability Orders for Polyimides

Order	Author	Reference
—O—> —S—> —CH$_2$—	Bower and Frost	8
—O—> —CH$_2$—	Scroog et al.	9
—O—> —CH$_2$—> —SO$_2$—	Nishizaki	10
—S—> —SO$_2$—> —CH$_2$—> —O—	Dine-Hart and Wright	11

Similarly, the B series of polymers also show a different stability order dependent on the mode of assessment used. Thus, 50% DT and W_{30} data indicate that IB ~ IIB ~ IVB > IIIB, while PDT values indicate that IB > IVB ~ IIIB > IIB. Isothermal studies at temperatures between 375° and 450°C indicate that IB > IVB > IIB > IIIB on the basis 50% D values.

This lack of correlation indicates the difficulties inherent in comparative thermal stability studies even within the same work. In this work, the difficulties arise both from the mode of assessment used and the nature of the materials being assessed. Thus, in the A series of polymers, differences in chemical structure should play a major role in determining stability. These, however, may be masked by features such as incomplete cyclization, and the entrainment of monomers and oligomeric materials which affect the assessment parameters to different extents. In the B series, the polymers should have essentially the same repeating structure and differ only in the nature of the hinge grouping X. However, this is an oversimplification; the materials studied are not inherently the same, since they can differ in terms of the extent of cyclization to the quinazolone structure. This can lead to different numbers of potential sites for scission and hence weight loss from within these systems. In addition, the percentage "impurity" level (oligomeric and monomeric species) will also differ.

Such differences may then be reflected in the PDT values obtained where low values may be associated with weight losses due to volatilization of "impurities" from the system. Thus, more realistic values are likely to be obtained from 50% DT and 50% D values which will be less affected by these factors than PDT or W_{30} data.

The thermal oxidative stability of the B series of polymers on the basis of 50% D values should be related to the "hinge group" stability. The order suggested from such data is IB > IVB > IIB > IIIB, that is, —CH$_2$— > —S$_2$— > —O— > —SO$_2$—, assuming that the systems have similar "impurity" levels, degrees of cyclization, and loss of pendent groups.

These results may be compared with published data on a family of polyimides which differ in structure in terms of their hinge groupings. Thus, for systems prepared from similar diamines to those used in this study, the stability orders reported in the literature are as shown in Table IV. The apparent lack of correlation between workers has been discussed[11] and has been ascribed to the different preparative conditions used, the environmental conditions during degradation, and the methods used for assessment.

In view of this, and our comments above, it is not surprising that the results obtained in this study do not correlate unequivocally with the work by other workers (Table IV). Studies on these polymers were also made in nitrogen by

TABLE V
Stability Data from Dynamic TG in Nitrogen

Polymer	IA	IIA	IIIA	IB	IIB	IIIB	IVB
PDT, °C	340	340	325	300	330	320	320
50% DT	576	514	670	a	b	b	700

a Stable char formed after 40% weight loss.
b Stable char formed after 30% weight loss.

TABLE VI
Stability Parameters from Isothermal TG in Nitrogen

Polymer	IA	IIA	IIIA	IB	IIB	IIIB	IVB
W_{30}	28	37	31	32	18	39	27

dynamic and isothermal TG leading to the stability parameters shown in Tables V and VI. These studies suggest a stability order for the A series of IA $\sim$ IIA > IIIA, while 50% DT values suggest IIIA > IA > IIA. For the B series, PDT values suggest essentially a similar order of stability, while 50% DT values suggest IIB > IB $\sim$ IIIB > IVB, that is, —O— > —CH$_2$ $\sim$ SO$_2$ > —S—S—.

The data in Table VI together with 50% D values in the temperature range of 375–450°C suggest for the A series IA > IIIA > IIA, while for the B series, W$_{30}$ and 50% D values suggest IIB > IVB > IB > IIIB, that is, —O— > —S—S— > —CH$_2$— > —SO$_2$—.

The expected order of stability in nitrogen of the "hinge groups" may be predicted in terms of the bond strengths involved in linking the hinge groupings or within the hinge group itself.[12] Thus, —O— > —CH$_2$— > —SO$_2$— > —S—S—. The results are, of course, subject to the limitations discussed previously, but are in general accord with that predicted except for the —S—S— containing system. The anomalous position of this system may arise from crosslinking reactions resulting from scission of the weak disulfide link to give thiyl radicals and their subsequent reactions.

Kinetic Studies

These were made using isothermal TG in air and nitrogen. Weight loss studies in air indicate that at least three phases of weight loss occurred. Thus, a rapid initial weight loss (0–5%) was observed followed by a period of low weight loss which was followed by a period of high rate of weight loss over the rangg of 20–80% decomposition.

In nitrogen, a similar initial rapid weight loss occurred followed by a period of low weight loss (5–20%), which was followed by a region of higher weight loss (20–40%) at which point stabilization occurred. In air and nitrogen, the activation energy data obtained from a plot of $-\log_e K$ versus the reciprocal of the absolute temperature are shown. The initial (E_i) and final E_f) activation energy values were derived from the two processes of weight loss following the 0–5% weight losses due to entrained material. The stability orders obtained for these systems again do not correlate with the previous data.

Thus, for the A series of polymers, IIIA $\sim$ IIA > IA in air from E_f, while IIIA

TABLE VII
Activation Energies in Air and Nitrogen[a]

Polymer	E_i, kcal/mole		E_f, kcal/mole	
	Air	Nitrogen	Air	Nitrogen
IA	21.4	34.0	42.0	52.0
IIA	24.0	39.6	52.0	52.4
IIIA	26.4	54.5	47.7	67.0
IB	27.0	45.3	40.0	61.2
IIB	25.0	32.0	39.2	69.1
IIIB	22.0	29.1	45.1	56.0
IVB	29.0	46.1	47.0	65.6

[a] E_i = Initial activation energy; E_f = final activation energy.

> IIA ~ IA in nitrogen. In the B series, IB ~ IVB > IIB > IIIB from E_f in air, while in nitrogen, E_i yields IVB ~ IB > IIB > IIIB and E_f yields IIB ~ IVB ≫ IB > IIIB.

Thus, the data presented in this paper stress the difficulties associated with comparative thermal stability measurements even within a series of similar polymers showing complex behavior.

The data further confirm the need for caution in comparison of data from different sources and confirm the relevance of standardized reporting procedures for thermal analysis as recommended by the International Confederation for Thermal Analysis (ICTA).[13,14]

One of the authors (A.G.) thanks the S.R.C. for a Research Assistantship.

References

1. A. Ghafoor, J. M. Senior, R. H. Still, and G. H. West, *Polymer,* **15,** 577 (1974).
2. M. Kurihara and N. Yoda, *J. Macromol. Sci.,* **A1** (6), 1069 (1967).
3. M. Kurihara and N. Yoda, *J. Polym. Sci.,* **B-4,** 11 (1966).
4. G. P. de Gaudemaris, B. Sillion, and J. Prove, *Bull. Chem. Soc. Françe,* 171 (1965).
5. N. Yoda, R. Nakanishi, M. Kurihara, Y. Baba, S. Toyama, and K. Ikeda, *Polym. Lett.,* **4,** 551 (1966).
6. M. Kurihara and Y. Hagiwara, *Polym. J.,* **I**(4), 425 (1970).
7. D. T. Zentmeyer and E. C. Wagner, *J. Org. Chem.,* **14,** 967 (1949).
8. W. M. Bower and L. W. Frost, *J. Polym. Sci.,* **A1,** 3135 (1963).
9. C. E. Scroog, S. V. Abramo, C. E. Beer, W. N. Edward, A. L. Endry, and K. L. Oliver, *J. Polym. Sci.,* **A3,** 1375 (1965).
10. S. Nishizaki, *Kagyo Kagaku Zasshi,* **68,** 1756 (1965).
11. R. A. Dine-Hart and W. W. Wright, *Makromol. Chem.,* **153,** 237 (1972).
12. T. L. Cottrell, *The Strengths of Chemical Bonds,* 2nd ed., Butter 13. R. C. Mackenzie, *Talanta,* **16,** 1227 (1967); *ibid.,* **19,** 1079 (1972); *ibid.,* **22,** 101 (1975).
14. H. C. McAdie, *Anal. Chem.,* **39,** 543 (1967); *ibid.,* **44,** 640 (1972); *ibid.,* **46,** 1146 (1974).

Received June 11, 1976
Revised September 15, 1976

JOURNAL OF APPLIED POLYMER SCIENCE   VOL. 21, 2913–2920 (1977)

Irradiation of Poly(vinyl Alcohol) Fibers in the Presence of Chloroform and Carbon Tetrachloride

I. K. VARMA, KAMLESH K. SHARMA, and D. S. VARMA, *Department of Textile Technology, Indian Institute of Technology, Delhi, New Delhi 110029, India*

Synopsis

Radiolysis of poly(vinyl alcohol) fibers (PVA) in the presence of chloroform and carbon tetrachloride was investigated. Decrease in intrinsic viscosity was observed at lower dosages (up to 2.3 megarads); and above this, an increase was noted. The blank samples irradiated under similar conditions showed a continuous decrease in intrinsic viscosity. A discoloration in the samples irradiated in the presence of CCl_4 and $CHCl_3$ was also observed. It is attributed to double bond formation in the backbone. A marginal decrease in the tensile strength of the irradiated fibers was observed. However, the surface characteristics of the fibers did not change on irradiation. The thermogravimetric analysis revealed a better heat resistance in irradiated fibers.

INTRODUCTION

Radiation-induced graft copolymerization of vinyl monomers on poly(vinyl alcohol) fibers has been reported in the literature.[1-11] We were interested in the grafting of methyl methacrylate and related monomers on PVA fibers in the presence of solvents using γ-radiation. A large number of solvents were investigated, and development of a brown color in PVA fibers was observed when chlorinated hydrocarbon solvents such as carbon tetrachloride, chloroform, 1,2-dichloroethane, and methylene chloride were used. A systematic study of the radiolysis of PVA fibers in chloroform and carbon-tetrachloride was, therefore, carried out to investigate the accompanying changes in the properties of the fibers.

EXPERIMENTAL

Poly(vinyl alcohol) fibers were Soxhlet extracted with petroleum ether (40°–60°C) for 24 hr to remove the finishing agents and then dried. The washed fibers were then conditioned for 24 hr at a temperature of 27°C.

Chloroform (B.D.H.), carbon tetrachloride (B.D.H.), methylene chloride (B.D.H.), and 1,2-dichloroethane (B.D.H.) were purified by distillation.

About 0.5 g of the fiber was taken in a test tube and 5 ml of the purified solvent was added. It was then irradiated with γ-radiation at a dose of 252 krad/hr in the presence of air. The fibers were irradiated for six different dosages: 0.5,

2913

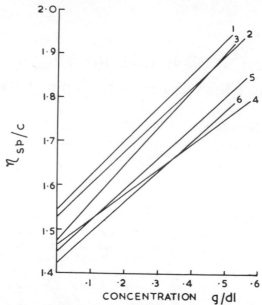

Fig. 1. Intrinsic viscosity evaluation of PVA fibers (PVA-I) (solvent formic acid) irradiated at
0.5 (1), 1.0 (2), 1.5 (3), 2.0 (4), 2.5 (5), and 3.0 (6) megarads.

1.0, 1.5, 2.0, 2.5, and 3.0 megarads.   A sample without solvent was also irradiated
under these dosages to serve as the blank.   After irradiation, the solvent was
removed; fibers were washed and then dried in the vacuum oven at 40°C.

Viscosity was measured with an Ubbelohde suspension level viscometer at
41°C using formic acid (B.D.H. analytical grade) as the solvent.

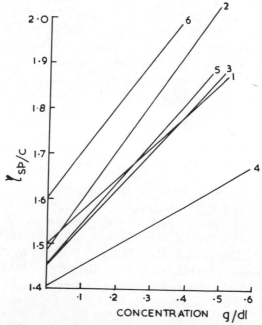

Fig. 2. Intrinsic viscosity evaluation of PVA fibers (PVA-II) (solvent formic acid) irradiated in
the presence of chloroform at 0.5 (1), 1.0 (2), 1.5 (3), 2.0 (4), 2.5 (5), and 3.0 (6) megarads.

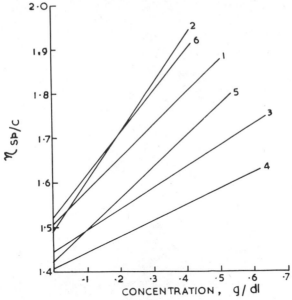

Fig. 3. Intrinsic viscosity evaluation of PVA fibers (PVA-III) (solvent formic acid) irradiated in the presence of carbon tetrachloride at 0.5 (1), 1.0 (2), 1.5 (3), 2.0 (4), 2.5 (5), and 3.0 (6) megarads.

A Stanton HT-D thermogravimetric balance in air was used for thermogravimetric analysis. Fibers were cut into approximately 2–3 mm length, and 20 ± 7 mg of the sample was taken for each analysis. The analysis was carried out in air from room temperature to 500°–600°C. The primary thermograms were obtained by plotting percent residual weight against temperature.

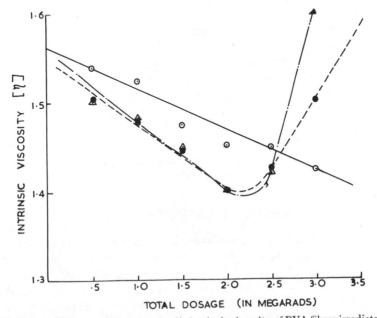

Fig. 4 Plot showing the effect of dosage on the intrinsic viscosity of PVA fibers irradiated as such (⊙) or in the presence of $CHCl_3$ (△) or CCl_4 (●).

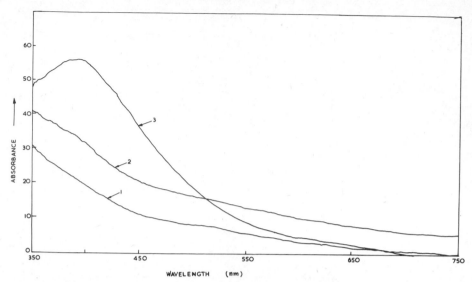

Fig. 5. Visible range spectra (in formic acid) of PVA fibers irradiated in chloroform at 1.0 (1), 2.0 (2), and 3.0 (3) megarads.

The infrared spectra of the fibers in KBr pellets were recorded using a Hilger–Watt spectrophotometer in the range of 4000–700 cm^{-1}.

The visible range spectrum of the fibers in formic acid was recorded using a Beckmann-DK-2A spectrophotometer in the range of 350–750 nm.

The x-ray diffraction photographs were recorded with a Philips Norelco x-ray diffraction unit utilizing the flat film technique. A bundle of parallel fibers was fixed near the collimator. A specimen to film distance of 4 cm was maintained for the entire study. The x-ray equipment was adjusted so as to completely was fixed near the collimator. A specimen to film distance of 4 cm was maintained for the entire study. The x-ray equipment was adjusted so as to completely bathe the bundle of the fibers. The undiffracted beam was so aligned as to fall at the center of the photographic plate. The generator was operated at 30 kV and 22 mA for 3.5 hr. The Joyce–Loebel microdensitometer Mark II with linear and polar tables was used for scanning the x-ray films.

A S4-10 scanning electron microscope (Cambridge Instruments Ltd.) was used to study the surface characteristics at 5 kV.

The breaking load of the fibers was determined using an Instron. The following specifications were used: Gauge length, 5 cm; chart speed, 10 cm/min; jaw speed, 1 cm/min; full scale load, 100 g; number of specimens, 36.

RESULTS AND DISCUSSION

Contradictory results are reported in the literature about the irradiation behavior of PVA. Some authors have indicated that crosslinking takes place on irradiation,[12-14] while others claim a decrease in molecular weight.[15-18] The presence of water in the PVA causes a crosslinking reaction[19] on irradiation.

Figures 1–3 give the viscosity evaluation at different dosages for PVA fibers irradiated in air from 0.5 to 3.0 megarads at a dose rate of 252 krads/hr in the presence of chloroform, carbon tetrachloride, and without solvent.

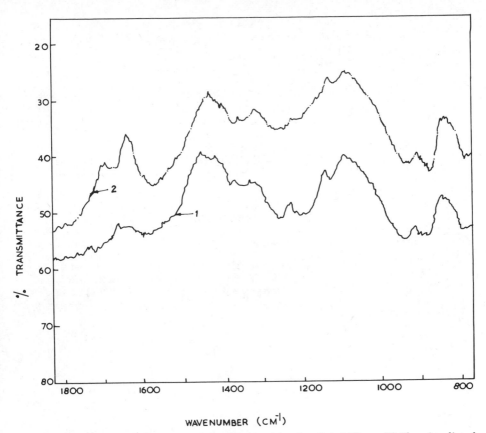

Fig. 6. IR spectra of PVA fibers (in KBr pellets); (1) unirradiated fibers; (2) fibers irradiated at 3.0 megarads in the presence of CCl₄.

Our results indicate a regular decrease in the $[\eta]$ of PVA. In chlorinated solvents, however, an increase is observed at later stages (Fig. 4).

The decrease in $[\eta]$ indicates a chain scission reaction. However, when the dosage was high, an insoluble gel was left and also an increase in viscosity was observed. Thus, crosslinking may become significant at higher dosages.

However, the development of color in the fibers (brownish) indicates some dehydration reaction leading to olefinic bonds in the backbone which may impart color. The visible-range spectra of the various samples were recorded. Poly-(vinyl alcohol) fibers dissolved in formic acid did not show any maxima in the region of 350–750 nm. The maxima at 388 nm were obtained with fibers irradiated in the presence of chloroform (PVA-II) at 3.0 megarads (Fig. 5). For the samples (PVA-II) irradiated for 1.0 and 2.0 megarads, the intensity was less. It was found that the intensity of the color increases with dosage.

The presence of double bonds in the polymer was also indicated by the IR spectra of samples irradiated in carbon tetrachloride (Fig. 6). The spectra of the PVA-III at 3.0 megarads show a sharp and intense peak at 1645 cm⁻¹.

One would obviously conclude that the appearance of the peak at 1645 cm⁻¹ in the IR spectrum is due to extended conjugation which imparted a brown color to the fiber.

Thus, the PVA fibers irradiated in CHCl₃ and CCl₄ undergo not only cross-

TABLE I
Integral Procedural Decomposition Temperature for PVA Fibers

Symbol	Fiber	IPDT, °C
PVA	nonirradiated	378
PVA-I	irradiated without solvent (3.0 megarads)	387
PVA-II	irradiated in the presence of CHCl$_3$ (3.0 megarads)	400
PVA-III	irradiated in the presence of CCl$_4$ (3.0 megarads)	413

TABLE II
Average Breaking Load and Percentage Elongation of PVA Fibers[a]

Fiber	Breaking load, g	% Elongation
PVA	44.5 (21.8)	13.35 (13.4)
PVA-I	43.5 (22.6)	12.20 (13.7)
PVA-III	40.8 (26.3)	12.20 (14.1)

[a] C. V. percent is given in parentheses.

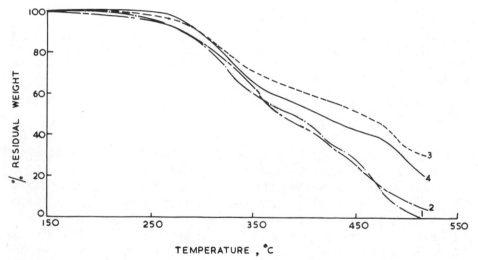

Fig. 7. Primary thermograms of the PVA fibers: (— · — · —) unirradiated fibers; (— · — · —) irradiated at 3.0 megarads; (—) irradiated in CHCl$_3$ at 3.0 megarads; (- - - - -) irradiated in CCl$_4$ at 3.00 megarads.

linking at higher dosage but also elimination reactions leading to conjugated double bond formation in the backbone. Such structures may influence the thermal behavior and tensile properties of the fibers.

The thermal stability of PVA, PVA-I, PVA-II, and PVA-III was examined by primary thermograms (Fig. 7). The integral procedural decomposition temperature (IPDT) values[20] for PVA-II and PVA-III were found to be higher than those of PVA and PVA-I (Table I). Since the IPDT values may be considered to be semiquantitative measures of polymer stability, one can conclude that irradiation of PVA in CHCl$_3$ and CCl$_4$ imparts higher stability to PVA fibers.

The average breaking load and percentage elongation of PVA fibers irradiated with or without solvent is less than that of the nonirradiated fiber (Table II). Decrease in average breaking load was about 9% for PVA fibers irradiated for 3.0 megarads in the presence of carbon tetrachloride.

The scanning electron micrograph of the fibers, however, did not show any change in the surface characteristics. Similarly, no change in x-ray diffraction pattern was observed.

Based on these observations, one can conclude that solvents such as carbon tetrachloride and chloroform which can readily yield free radicals[21-24] help in the discoloration of PVA fibers at high dosages, and also crosslinking is significant. One can write the following mechanism for these reactions:

$$CCl_4 \longrightarrow \cdot Cl + \cdot CCl_3$$
$$CHCl_3 \longrightarrow \cdot CHCl_2 + \cdot Cl$$
$$\cdot CHCl_2 + CHCl_3 \longrightarrow CH_2Cl_2 + \cdot CCl_3$$

$$\text{(double-bond formation)}$$

$$\text{(crosslinking)}$$

$$\text{chain scission}$$

References

1. F. D. Hartley, *J. Polym. Sci.*, **34**, 397 (1959).
2. G. Mine and S. Kaizerman, *J. Polym. Sci.*, **31**, 242 (1958).
3. G. Mine, S. Kaizerman, and E. Rasmussen, *J. Polym. Sci.*, **39** 523 (1959).
4. G. Mine and S. Kaizerman, *Macromole Synthesis* 2, 84 (1966).
5. Y. Ogiwara and M. Uchiyama, *J. Polym. Sci. A-1*, **7**, 1479 (1969).
6. S. Mukhopadhyay, B. C. Mitra, and S. R. Palit, *J. Polym. Sci. A-1*, **7**, 2079 (1969).
7. G. G. Danelyan and R. M. Liushits, *Polym. Sci. U.S.S.R.*, **8**, 1651 (1966).
8. I. Sakurada, T. Okada, and E. Kugo, *Isotopes and Radiation*, 2, 296, 306, 316 (1959).
9. V. A. Kargin, *J. Polym. Sci. C*, **No. 14**, 1601 (1963).
10. G. Odian, R. L. Kruse, and J. H. T. Kho, *J. Polym. Sci. A-1*, **9**, 91 (1971).
11. G. Odian and J. H. T. Kho, *J. Macromol. Sci. Chem.*, **A-4**, 317 (1970).
12. A. Charlesby, *Nucleonics* 12 (6), 18 (1954).
13. M. Matsumoto and A. Danno, *Large Radiation Sources in Industry*, International Atomic Energy Commission, Vienna, 1960, p. 331.
14. I. Sakurada, T. Okada, and S. Kitamira, *Isotopes and Radiation*, 1, 209 (1959).
15. A. Danno, *J. Phys. Soc. Jpn.*, **13**, 609 (1958).
16. A. A. Miller (to General Electric Co.), Br. Pat. 798,146 (1958).
17. S. Okamura, T. Manabe, S. Futami, T. Iwasabi, A. Nakajima, K. Odan, H. Inagaki, and I. Sakurada, in *Proc. 2nd Int. Conf. Peaceful Uses Atomic Energy*, Geneva, Vol. 29, 1958, p. 176.

18. I. Sakurada and S. Matsuzawa, *Kobunshi Kagaku*, **17**, 687, 693 (1960).

19. I. Sakurada, A. Nakajima, and H. Aoki. *Mem. Fac. Eng. Kyoto University*, **21**, 84, 94 (1959).

20. C. D. Doyle, *Anal. Chem.*, **33**, 77 (1961).

21. T. H. Chen, J. U. Wong, and F. J. Johnston, *J. Phys. Chem.*, **64**, 1023 (1960).

22. J. W. Schutte, *J. Amer. Chem. Soc.*, **79**, 4643 (1957).

23. S. Ciborowski and N. Colebourne, *Trans. Faraday Soc.*, **57**, 1123 (1961).

24. H. R. Werner and R. F. Firestone, *J. Phys. Chem.*, **69**, 840 (1965).

Received August 18, 1976
Revised September 21, 1976

JOURNAL OF APPLIED POLYMER SCIENCE   VOL. 21, 2921–2932 (1977)

Graft Polymerization of Triethoxyvinylsilane–Styrene and Triethoxyvinylsilane–Methyl Methacrylate Binary Monomers onto Various Silicates

KIYOSHI HAYAKAWA, KAORU KAWASE, and HIROMI YAMAKITA,

Government Industrial Research Institute, Nagoya, Nagoya, Japan

Synopsis

Triethoxyvinylsilane–styrene and triethoxyvinylsilane–methyl methacrylate binary monomers were polymerized by chemical initiation or by γ-ray irradiation in the presence of silica gel, fire brick, quartz wool, and glass beads. The amount and composition of the polymers grafted to silicates were analyzed by using pyrolysis gas chromatography. When triethoxyvinylsilane alone was subjected to the reaction with silicates, condensation occurred irrespective of the initiating means, and the extent of the reaction was almost proportional to the specific surface area of the silicate. When binary monomer mixture was applied, incorporation of styrene or methyl methacrylate into the grafted polymer was observed whenever a monomer mixture of high styrene or methyl methacrylate content was submitted to the reaction. On each silicate, the relationship between the composition of polymer grafted on it and that of monomer showed a similar pattern in spite of the great difference of the specific surface area. Almost no participation of styrene or methyl methacrylate was observed when the silicate preirradiated in air or under vacuum was heated with the binary monomer mixture. It was concluded that triethoxyvinylsilane reacts with silicates by condensation and that some of the pendent vinyl groups on the silicates are incorporated into the copolymer with styrene or methyl methacrylate.

INTRODUCTION

The grafting of organic polymer onto inorganic macromolecular materials is a fascinating problem not only in view of the widespread field of industrial application, but also because of the fundamental researches. Reactive organosilicon compounds as alkoxyvinylsilanes are regarded to possess the ability to react with silicates and also with vinyl monomers to form copolymers. The pretreatment of glass fibers with such reactive organosilicon compounds is a well-known sizing process to improve the strengths of the glass fiber-reinforced plastics. The formation of chemical bonding as Si—O—Si is generally recognized between the glass surface and such compounds, although other interpretations on the nature of reaction are still seen in the literature.[1] Besides glass fibers, many kinds of silicates were used for similar reactions.[2,3] The reaction of copolymer composed of condensable vinylsilane and ordinary vinyl monomers with silicates could also be added to this category of study.[4]

On the other hand, the polymerization of the vinyl monomers adsorbed on silicic acid and others was well investigated to date mainly in the radiation-

2921

chemical field, and the occurrence of ionic grafting along with that by radical mechanism has been discussed.[5,6,7]

In several fields of investigation, one important problem seemed to be the difficulty of grafting organic polymer effectively enough for practical use on inorganic substances such as silicates. We have intended to graft copolymerize substantial amounts of organic polymers onto inorganic siloxane derivatives by the combination of silanol condensation and addition polymerization. As the reaction of active vinylsilane–vinyl compound binary monomers with silicates directly to form graft copolymer have hardly been studied yet, a few of the common vinyl monomers mixed with triethoxyvinylsilane were polymerized in the presence of silicates by such means as chemical initiation or γ-irradiation, and the polymers inseparable from the silicates were studied for the possible occurrence of grafting reaction between them.

EXPERIMENTAL

Materials

Five silicic compounds including silicic acid and some silicates which widely differed from each other in specific surface areas (called silicates for convenience in the following description) were chosen as the backbone materials: (a) silica gel, 30–60 mesh for gas chromatography (Nishio Kogyo Co. Ltd.); (b) crushed fire brick, 30–60 mesh for gas chromatography (C-22, Yanagimoto Seisakusho Co. Ltd.); (c) glass beads, 210–297 μ in diameter (GB 740K, Tokyo Shibaura Electric Co. Ltd.), washed with concentrated H_2SO_4 and water; (d) quartz wool, 2–4 μ thick (Grade Fine, Nippon Quartz Glass Co. Ltd.); (e) asbestos (Wako Pure Chemical Industries). The silicates, except the glass beads, were used without further purification.

Triethoxyvinylsilane (EVS) was purified by distillation under reduced pressure. Styrene (ST) and methyl methacrylate (MMA) were purified by the ordinary procedures.

Polymerization Initiated by Benzoyl Peroxide (BPO)

The binary monomer mixture of EVS–ST or EVS–MMA, 2.0 to 2.5 ml, containing 0.005 g of BPO per 1 ml mixture, was poured on silicates, 0.3 to 0.5 g, in the glass tube. The glass tubes were sealed off at 10^{-4} mm Hg after thorough degassing with a freeze–thaw cycle, and the mixture was polymerized to the appropriate extent in a thermoregulated water bath. After the polymerization, the reacted silicates were washed with benzene[7] and separated from the solution by glass filters. The silicates in the glass filters were dipped in benzene and thoroughly washed with benzene for a few days, and finally dried *in vacuo* to weigh the unextractable polymer (the organic substance unextractable by this procedure is called the unextractable polymer hereafter).

Polymerization by γ-Irradiation

Both in-source polymerization and postpolymerization were carried out to graft polymerize the binary monomers on silicates. In in-source polymerization, the ampoule was prepared the same way as above without the addition of BPO and was irradiated with γ-rays from a ^{60}Co source at a dose rate of 2×10^4 or 2×10^5 R/hr at 25°C. In postpolymerization, binary monomers were added to the silicates which had been irradiated previously with γ-rays at a dose rate of 1×10^6 R/hr for 107 hr in air at 25°C and sealed under vacuum by the way already described, followed by heating for a given time in the thermoregulated water bath.

In a few cases, the silicates were sealed under 10^{-4} mm Hg into the glass ampoule equipped with a branch having a breakable seal. After irradiation, the other tube containing the monomer mixture was attached to the branch of the irradiated ampoule, and the monomer part was then sealed *in vacuo*. Then the monomer mixture was introduced to the irradiated silicates by breaking the seal between the monomer and the silicate.

Determination of Amount and Composition of Unextractable Polymer

The unextractable polymer supposedly reacted with or grafted onto the silicates should result in an overall increase in weight of the silicates; and actually a weight increase of 15% to 30% was observed for the silica gel subjected to reaction. In the cases of glass beads and fire brick, however, the increase in weight was too small to be measured. Regarding the reacted silica gel, carbon, and hydrogen analyses (by CHN-Corder, Model MT-2, Yanagimoto Seisakusho Co. Ltd.) afforded information on the amount and composition of the unextractable polymer to some extent, although a carbonized part was found to remain in the central domain of silica gel granules after baking of the EVS-containing silica gel for analysis. Nevertheless, this method was completely useless for obtaining information on other silicates owing to extremely low amount of unextractable polymer.

Therefore, the pyrolysis gas chromatography was adopted to determine the amount and composition of the unextractable polymer throughout the experiment. Pyrolysis of the reacted silicates was carried out in a hot tubular reactor, and the degradation products were analyzed with a Hitachi Model K-53 FID gas chromatograph combined with a Perkin–Elmer Printing Integrator 194B.[8]

Figure 1(a) and 1(b) show typical pyrolysis gas chromatograms of silicates containing polymers composed of ST or EVS. The most favorable pyrolysis temperature for both constituents was 650°C. Silicates which contained polymers composed of both ST and EVS developed peaks of both constituents some of which overlapped. Whereas the ST content can be calculated independently from the area of the peak ($t_R = 1.43$) as seen from Figure 1(c), some correction as to the contribution of polyST was inevitable for calculating EVS content from the peak of the lowest retention time ($t_R = 0.21$). The overlapping was more serious in the case of silicates onto which MMA–EVS was grafted, shown in Fig. 1(a′)–1(c′), in spite of the change in optimum experimental conditions.

The extent of grafting was calculated to be 100 times the amount of unextractable polymer obtained from pyrolysis divided by the original weight of silicate, called $G\%$ for brevity.

Characterization of Reacted Silicates

Some of the reacted silica gel was stirred in concentrated hydrofluoric acid for 1 hr to separate the organic polymer from the silicate. After washing once,

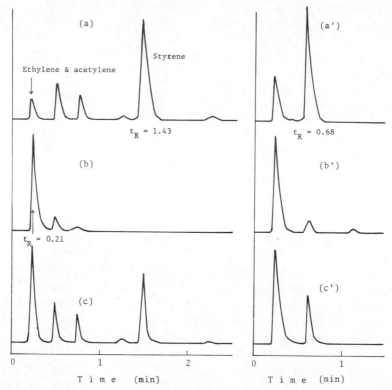

Fig. 1. Typical pyrolysis gas chromatograms of silicates containing various polymers: (a) silicates containing polyST, (b) those containing polyEVS, (c) those containing poly(EVS–ST), (a′) those containing polyMMA, (b′) those containing polyEVS, (c′) those containing poly(EVS–MMA); (a)–(c) 15 sec pyrolysis at 650°C, column temperature, 150°C; (a′)–(c′) 15 sec pyrolysis at 550°C, column temperature, 120°C; column, Apiezon L, 2 m; detector, FID; carrier gas, He.

the treatment was repeated and the remaining moiety washed with water and methanol and dried in a desiccator.

Specific surface areas of silicates were measured by the ordinary B.E.T. method with nitrogen.

Thermogravimetric analysis (TGA) and differential thermal analysis (DTA) of the reacted silicates were performed simultaneously by using a Rigaku Denki TGA-DTA apparatus at a temperature elevation of 5°C/min.

RESULTS

Reaction of Silicates with Triethoxyvinylsilane

While silica gel was treated with EVS in various ways, about 20% by extent of grafting of EVS seemed to react with silica gel independently of the presence of the substance which afforded free radicals, as seen in Table I. In the case of simultaneous irradiation, somewhat higher $G\%$ was observed. As prolonged evacuation of silica gel at 450°C or treatment with H_2SO_4 or NaOH prior to the operation did not bring about any significant improvement in the amount of

TABLE I
Reaction of Silicates with Triethoxyvinylsilane[a]

Silicate	Reaction method	Temp., °C	Reaction time, hr	G% from wt. increase[b]	G% from pyro. GC	G% calcd. from sp. surface area	Remarks
Silica gel (481 m²/g)[c]	heating	46	16	15.4	16.3	28.1	soaked in concd. H_2SO_4
Silica gel (481 m²/g)[c]	heating	63	16	24.7	24.5	28.1	heated for 4 hr at 450°C in vacuo
Silica gel (481 m²/g)[c]	heating	72	16	18.3	26.0	28.1	
Silica gel (481 m²/g)[c]	heating with 0.5% BPO	63	16	19.5	13.0	28.1	
Silica gel (481 m²/g)[c]	simult. irrad.	25	105	34.1	36.1	28.1	2×10^5 R/hr, 10^8 R preirrad. at 25°C in air
Silica gel (preirrad.)	heating	72	17	20.7	22.4	28.1	
Fire brick (6.6 m²/g)[c]	heating with 0.5% BPO	72	17	—	0.28	0.39	
Fire brick (6.6 m²/g)[c]	simult. irrad.	25	105	—	0.78	0.39	2×10^5 R/hr, 10^8 R preirrad. at 25°C in air
Fire brick (preirrad.)	heating	72	17	—	0.28	0.39	
Glass beads [(0.03 m²/g)][c]	heating with 0.5% BPO	72	17	—	0.02	(0.002)	
Glass beads (preirrad.)	heating	72	17	—	0.02	(0.002)	10^8 R preirrad. at 25°C in air

[a] Silicates, 0.5 g; EVS, 2.0 ml.
[b] $G\% = 100 (P - P_0)/P_0$.
[c] Specific surface area.

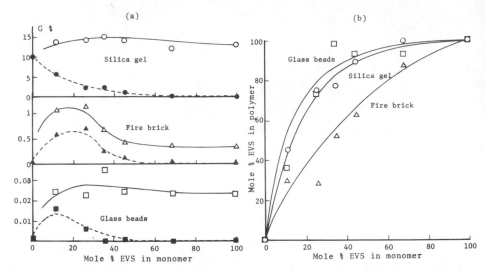

Fig. 2. Reaction of triethoxyvinylsilane–styrene binary monomers with silicates by the initiation of benzoyl peroxide (0.5%). Effect of monomer composition on (a) the amount of the unextractable polymer and on (b) the composition of the unextractable polymer: reaction time, 17 hr at 63°C for silica gel, 17 hr at 72°C for fire brick and glass beads; (a) (O △ □) overall G%; (● ▲ ■) G% of ST monomeric unit in the unextractable polymer.

reacted EVS, the silicates were used in the subsequent experiments without further chemical or heat treatment.

Alternatively, the amount of unextractable polymer appeared to be proportional to the specific surface area of silicates. The calculated G% was shown in Table I, which is the required amount of EVS when the surface of silicate is assumed to be covered monomolecularly with EVS. The coincidence of the amount of unextractable polymer with the calculated one is fairly satisfactory, except for the case of glass beads. The specific surface area of the glass beads was too small to obtain a reliable value by the B.E.T. method.

The overall results show that the main reaction of EVS with silicates is the condensation with the silanol group on the surface of the silicates by releasing ethanol, with the vinyl group left unchanged on the surface. In the simultaneous irradiation method, part of the reacted EVS is possibly polymerized to grafted oligomer.[9]

Reaction of Silicates with EVS–ST or EVS–MMA Binary Monomers by Initiation of BPO

Figure 2(a) shows the overall amount of the unextractable polymer and the content of ST monomeric unit in the unextractable polymer as a function of monomer composition. Although the overall amount of the unextractable polymer was not significantly affected by monomer composition, the incorporation of ST in the unextractable polymer was limited to the case when monomer mixtures of high ST content were adopted.

In spite of the great difference in the amount of the unextractable polymer, the curves in Figure 2(b), indicating the relationship between the composition of the unextractable polymer and that of monomer, showed a similar pattern,

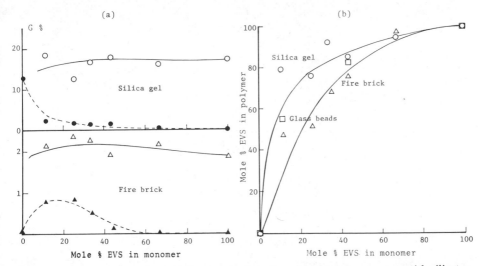

Fig. 3. Reaction of triethoxyvinylsilane–methyl methacrylate binary monomers with silicates by the initiation of benzoyl peroxide (0.5%). Effect of monomer composition on (a) the amount of the unextractable polymer and on (b) the composition of the unextractable polymer: reaction time, 17 hr at 36.5°C; (a) (O △) overall G%; (● ▲) G% of MMA monomeric unit in the unextractable polymer.

and the EVS content in the unextractable polymer was always higher than that in the monomer mixture. The Fineman–Ross plot of the composition did not show a satisfactory linearity, but some data were roughly explained by r_1(ST) = 0.06 and r_2(EVS) = 4.2. However, considering the low polymerizability[10] and copolymerizability of EVS [r_1(ST) = 26, r_2(EVS) = 0, or r_1(MMA) = 37, r_2(EVS) = 0, calculated from the reported Q and e values[11]], the composition of polymer thus obtained from pyrolysis does not coincide with the copolymer composition, and instead the observed reactivity ratio was considered to be the results brought about by overlapping of the separately formed products. In other words, the bulk of EVS independently reacted with the silicate surface and coexisted with a minor amount of the grafted true copolymer. The fact that the by-product polymer recovered from the washing solution was composed mainly of ST supports the above considerations.

Figures 3(a) and 3(b) show the results of the EVS–MMA binary monomer system, corresponding to Figures 2(a) and 2(b). The results seem to be fairly similar to those of the EVS–ST system.

In the TGA and DTA curves of the reacted silica gel, only the endothermic peaks were observable, contrary to the results of Sidorovich et al.[12]

Reaction of Binary Monomers with Silicates Under γ-Ray Irradiation

Figures 4(a) and 4(b) and 5(a) and 5(b) show the amounts of the unextractable polymers and their compositions when the silicates have reacted with binary monomers by the simultaneous irradiation method. The overall feature observed more or less resembled the former cases, though the unextractable polymer was somewhat larger in quantity.

When pure monomer, ST or MMA, was used alone, only a minute amount of

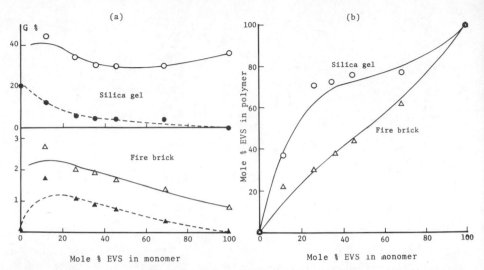

Fig. 4. Reaction of triethoxyvinylsilane–styrene binary monomers with silicates by γ-ray simultaneous irradiation method. Effect of monomer composition on (a) the amount of the unextractable polymer and on (b) the composition of the unextractable polymer: γ-ray irradiation, 105 hr at 2 × 10⁵ R/hr, 25°C; (a) (O △) overall $G\%$; (● ▲) $G\%$ of ST monomeric unit in the unextractable polymer.

the unextractable polymer was detected except for silica gel. Although more investigation is needed to determine whether pure polyST or polyMMA in silica gel was truly grafted or merely occluded, it was confirmed that the merely adsorbed polymer could be removed almost completely by the adopted method of washing in the cases of crushed fire brick and glass beads.

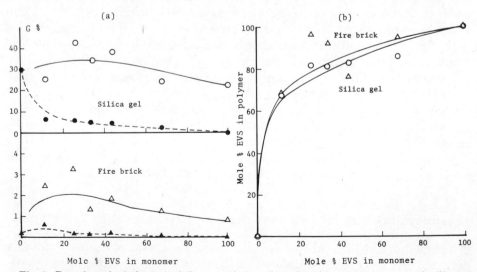

Fig. 5. Reaction of triethoxyvinylsilane–methyl methacrylate binary monomers with silicates by γ-ray simultaneous irradiation method. Effect of monomer composition on (a) the amount of the unextractable polymer and on (b) the composition of the unextractable polymer: γ-ray irradiation, 20 hr at 2 × 10⁴ R/hr, 25°C; (a) (O △) overall $G\%$; (● ▲) $G\%$ of MMA monomeric unit in the unextractable polymer.

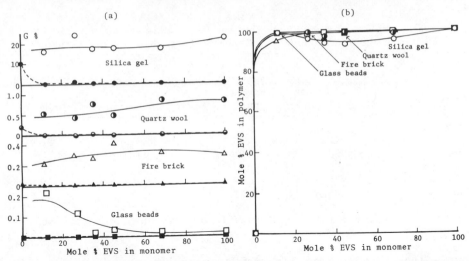

Fig. 6. Reaction of triethoxyvinylsilane–styrene binary monomers with the preirradiated silicates. Effect of monomer composition on (a) the amount of the unextractable polymer and on (b) the composition of the unextractable polymer: preirradiation, 107 hr at 1×10^6 R/hr, 25°C in air; grafting reaction, 17 hr at 72°C; (a) (O ◐ △ □) overall G%; (● ◓ ▲ ■) G% of ST monomeric unit in the unextractable polymer.

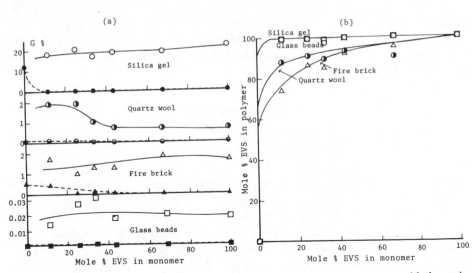

Fig. 7. Reaction of triethoxyvinylsilane–methyl methacrylate binary monomers with the preirradiated silicates. Effect of monomer composition on (a) the amount of the unextractable polymer and on (b) the composition of the unextractable polymer: preirradiation, 107 hr at 1×10^6 R/hr, 25°C in air; grafting reaction, 2 hr at 72°C; (a) (O ◐ △ □) overall G%; (● ◓ ▲ ■) G% of MMA monomeric unit in the unextractable polymer.

Reaction of Binary Monomers with Preirradiated Silicates

The possibility was expected for the preirradiated silicates to initiate the co-polymerization, inasmuch as the polymerization of MMA by the trapped electron on the aluminosilicate[5] and the existence of SiO radical in the irradiated silicates had been reported.[7,13] Figures 6(a) and 6(b) and 7(a) and 7(b) show the results when the silicates preirradiated by γ-rays in air were heated with binary mono-

TABLE II

Reaction of Triethoxyvinylsilane–Styrene and Triethoxyvinylsilane–Methyl Methacrylate Binary Monomers with Silicates Preirradiated Under Vacuum[a]

Silicate	Comonomer of EVS	EVS in monomer mixture, mole %	Overall $G\%$ from pyro. GC	EVS in unextractable polymer, mole %
Silica gel	ST	12.0	19.0	100.0
Asbestos	ST	12.0	3.66	96.9
Fire brick	ST	12.0	0.24	78.0
Quartz wool	ST	12.0	1.03	90.3
Glass beads	ST	12.0	0.0064	100.0
Silica gel	MMA	11.3	28.2	87.6

[a] Preirradiation, 100 hr at 1×10^6 R/hr, 25°C under vacuum; grafting reaction, 17 hr at 72°C.

mers. Table II shows some of the results for the silicates preirradiated under vacuum. The contribution of monomer composition on the amount of the unextractable polymer was rather obscure. The most remarkable feature was that the existence of ST or MMA monomeric unit was hardly if at all observed in the unextractable polymer in the whole range of composition of binary monomers, except for the case when pure ST or MMA was applied, no matter whether the irradiation had been carried out in air or under vacuum. As the preirradiated silicates were thought to have no ability to initiate copolymerization in this reaction condition, the condensation reaction of EVS was regarded as predominant on these preirradiated silicates.

DISCUSSION

It is very difficult to determine whether true grafting was achieved on the silicates. However, as far as experimental observation is concerned, many facts seem to support, though indirectly, the occurrence of true grafting of the concerned copolymer which constitutes part of the unextractable substance on the surface of silicates.

Table III shows the change of the specific surface area before and after the reaction and the change in solubility of the reacted silica gel in hydrofluoric acid. It can be seen that the silica gel which contained only EVS as organic component, including those prepared by preirradiation and heating, retained fairly large specific surface areas and dissolved completely in hydrofluoric acid. On the other hand, when the silica gel contained ST or MMA besides EVS as a constituent of unextractable polymer, the polymer buried the cavities of silica gel completely, and the insoluble silica gel was left behind after treatment with hydrofluoric acid. The remaining silica gel, retaining a glassy form on microscopic observation, did not dissolve in toluene in spite of high ST or MMA monomeric units. When polyST was solely included in silica gel, the reacted silica gel completely dissolved in hydrofluoric acid, leaving polyST as a bulky cluster of granules which freely dissolved in toluene.

When silica gel which had reacted with EVS previously was heated with ST or MMA containing BPO or irradiated in the presence of ST or MMA, the resulting silica gel was found to contain ST or MMA monomeric unit, and the

TABLE III
Specific Surface Area and Solubility of Reacted Silica Gel

Sample	Reaction method	Overall G%	G% of ST or MMA unit	S_S, m²/g	Insoluble fraction in HF, %[a]	Solubility in toluene of HF-insoluble fraction	Remarks
Silica gel (SG)	—	—	—	481	0.0	—	
SG–EVS	Simult. irrad.	23.8	—	187	0.0	—	
SG–EVS–(ST)	Preirrad and heating	15.6	0.0	278	0.0	—	
SG–ST	Heating with BPO	10.1	10.1	≒0	10.9	Soluble	b
SG–EVS–ST	Simult. irrad.	30.0	4.4	≒0	10.8	Insoluble	c
SG–EVS–(MMA)	Preirrad and heating	20.8	0.1	194	0.0	—	
SG–EVS–MMA	Simult. irrad.	34.1	3.8	≒0	9.0	Insoluble	c

[a] Stirred for 1 hr in concentrated HF followed by washing with water. Then stirred another 2 hr in HF and washed with water and methanol and dried in desiccator.

[b] Insoluble part of HF treatment was a cluster of powder-like polymer.

[c] Insoluble part of HF treatment was a glassy substance which resembled the original silica gel.

composition of the unextractable polymer resembled that of the reacted silica gel directly prepared from the binary monomers.

In conclusion, the unextractable polymers in silicates can be regarded as the grafted polymers. The mode of the possible reaction in this system can be explained as follows; (1) the hydrolysis followed by condensation took place between EVS and the silanol group on the surface of the silicates in the presence or possibly in the absence of adsorbed water, and part of EVS may be addition-polymerized with γ-irradiation[9] or condensation-polymerized mutually to oligomers; (2) copolymerization was initiated by BPO or γ-rays, and some of the pendent vinyl groups on the surface of silicates were incorporated in the grafted copolymer (I):

I

and (3) the radicals, if any, on the preirradiated silicates were not active for inducing copolymerization.

References

1. S. Sterman and J. G. Marsden, *Mod. Plast.* **44**, [2] 91, 169 (1967).
2. V. N. Fery, R. Laible, and K. Hamann, *Angew. Makromol. Chem.,* **34**, 81 (1973).
3. C. W. Lentz, *Magazine of Concrete Res.,* **18**, 231 (1966).
4. P. Lagally and P. Argyle, *Ind. Eng. Chem., Prod. Res. Dev.,* **5**, 230 (1966).
5. F. Higashide and Y. Kanazawa, *Kobunshi Kagaku,* **25**, 803 (1968); *Kogyo Kagaku Zasshi,* **73**, 106 (1970).
6. A. Shimizu, K. Hayashi, and S. Okamura, paper presented at the 19th Meeting of The Society of Polymer Science, Japan, Tokyo, 1970, p. 115.
7. K. Fukano and E. Kageyama, *J. Polym. Sci., Polym. Chem. Ed.,* **13**, 1309, 1325, 2103 (1975); *ibid.,* **14**, 23, 275, 1031 (1976).
8. H. Yamakita and K. Hayakawa, *J. Appl. Polym. Sci.,* **13**, 1833 (1969).
9. K. Hayakawa, K. Kawase, H. Yamakita, and S. Inagaki, *J. Polym. Sci. B,* **5**, 1077 (1967).
10. R. Y. Mixer and D. L. Bailey, *J. Polym. Sci.,* **18**, 573 (1955).
11. J. Brandrup and E. H. Immergut, Eds., *Polymer Handbook,* II-141, Interscience, New York, 1966.
12. A. V. Sidorovich, G. S. Buslaev, E. I. Shepurev, N. P. Kharitonov, and V. V. Raglis, *Vysokomol. Soedin. B,* **14**, 749 (1972).
13. N. Sugai, G. Komatsu, and T. Nakagawa, paper presented at the 23rd Meeting of The Society of Polymer Science, Japan, Tokyo, 1974, p. 77.

Received September 9, 1976

JOURNAL OF APPLIED POLYMER SCIENCE   VOL. 21, 2933–2941 (1977)

Master Curves of Viscoelastic Behavior in the Plastic Region of a Solid Polymer

G. TITOMANLIO and G. RIZZO, *Instituto di Ingegneria Chimica,*
Università di Palermo, Italy

Synopsis

Stress relaxation and creep tests following strain ramps were made on Mylar, both above and below the yield stress. The ramp velocity was varied over a 40-fold range. All data exhibit nonlinear viscoelastic behavior. However, those obtained above the yield point, i.e., in the plastic region, could be reduced to single master curves for both the creep and the relaxation tests by means of a simple time shift factor. This factor is inversely proportional to the strain rate existing just prior to the test.

INTRODUCTION

It is well known that most, if not all, polymeric materials are viscoelastic and that, at sufficiently low stresses, the viscoelastic behavior is linear. Linearity implies that the mechanical behavior of the material can be predicted once a few material functions, the viscoelastic functions, have been experimentally determined.

Unfortunately, the linearity breaks down above a certain stress level which, for most polymeric solids, is well below the yield or fracture stress.[1–4] Thus, the design of structurally efficient items where the fracture or yield stress is approached or the analysis of plastic forming techniques where the yield stress is exceeded require a knowledge of the nonlinear viscoelastic behavior of the material.

In the nonlinear region, molecular mobilities and relaxation spectra become dependent upon stress and strain.[5–8] None of the simple rules of linear viscoelasticity apply, including those which allow collecting viscoelastic data taken under different conditions into master curves. It is not excluded, however, that simple rules, albeit different from those of linear viscoelasticity, can be found in the nonlinear region which permit construction of master curves of general use. A contribution in this direction is hopefully given in this paper.

Stress relaxation and creep data taken on Mylar, both above and below the yield stress, will be presented and discussed. The possibility of obtaining master curves will be throughly examined.

EXPERIMENTAL

Constant-velocity stress–strain, constant-force creep, and stress relaxation tests were performed at room temperature (about 25°C) by an Instron tensile

2933

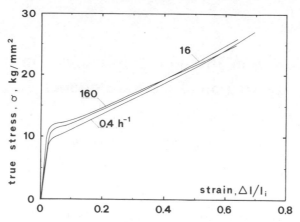

Fig. 1. True stress vs strain in constant velocity extensional tests at different values of initial deformation rate α_i.

testing machine. The material used was poly(ethylene terephthalate) in the form of 10-mil-thick biaxially oriented sheets (Mylar manufactured by du Pont).

The samples had a rectangular shape with a width of 1 cm and were cut all in the same direction from the sheet. The distance between the two Instron jaws at the beginning of each test was 6 cm. Because of the sample shape, a part of the material inside the jaws was effected by the deformation. However, a good reproducibility was found, probably because the jaws were pneumatically driven and the acting pressure was always the same. A large central portion of the test piece was photographically found to deform homogeneously throughout each test, and the deformation Δl_r of a reference zone 3 cm long resulted to a very good approximation proportional to the displacement Δl of the lower jaw. The ratio $\Delta l_r/\Delta l$ was found equal to 0.41. The lower jaw displacement Δl was then used to calculate deformations with respect to an initial equivalent length of the specimen $l_i = 7.3$ cm.

Comparison among tests made with samples of different widths showed that 1 cm was sufficient a width to neglect the hardening effect (due to the cutting of the sample) of the specimen edges.

RESULTS

The experimental results of load versus elongation were converted into true stress σ versus the strain $\Delta l/l_i$ and are reported in Figure 1. In order to convert the load into true stress, the assumption of constant density was made.

The stress–strain curves, reported in Figure 1, differ by the value of the initial deformation rate $\alpha_i = V/l_i$, where V is the velocity of the Instron crosshead. A change of α_i over a 400-fold range produces very small variations of the stress–strain curves. Also, the initial slope of the curves increases by 10% at most by increasing the velocity in the experimental range, approaching a value of about 500 kg/mm^2.

The creep data are reported in Figures 2 and 3. The samples were deformed with a constant velocity up to a fixed value of the force which was then held constant. The subsequent displacement Δl_c of the lower jaw was measured by

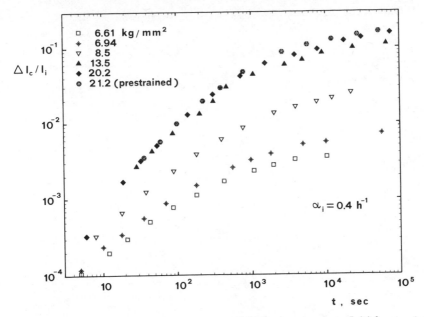

Fig. 2. Creep strain vs time for different values of initial creep stress σ_0. Initial creep stress is reached with constant velocity and initial deformation rate $\alpha_i = 0.4 \text{ h}^{-1}$.

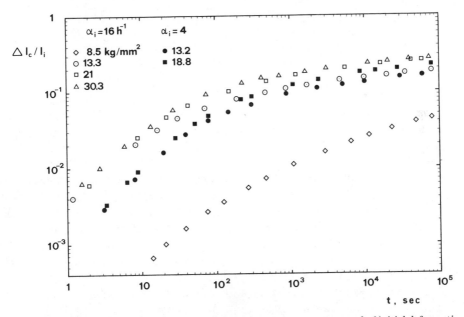

Fig. 3. Creep strain vs time for different values of initial creep stress σ_0 and of initial deformation rate α_i.

a transducer connected to the Instron crosshead. The data are plotted as $\Delta l_c/l_i$ versus time as measured since the force reached the fixed value. In Figure 2, the data refer to a value of α_i equal to 0.4 hr^{-1}. Larger values of α_i (4 and 16 hr^{-1}) are reported in Figure 3. It was not possible to further increase the deformation rate before the creep tests because at larger velocities the Instron cross head had

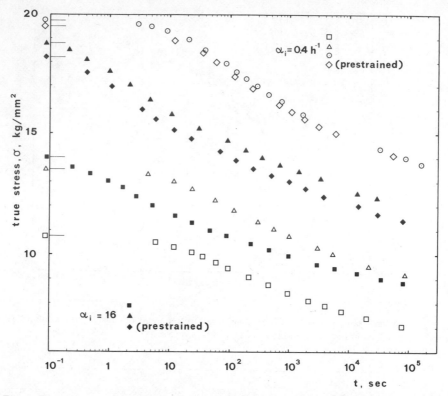

Fig. 4. True stress vs time in relaxation tests after strain ramps with different values of initial deformation rate α_i. The initial stress σ_0, always larger than the yield stress, is indicated by a short horizontal segment.

a small but significant reverse motion after the creep force had been reached. This effect was absent at lower deformation rates within the sensitivity of the transducer system with a recorder full scale equivalent to 1 mm displacement.

The parameter of Figure 2 is the tensile stress σ_0 at the end of the strain ramps which, of course, also represents the initial creep stress. The data of Figure 2 show that, while σ_0 has a large effect on the creep deformation when it is smaller than the yield stress, the creep behavior becomes essentially independent from the stress level provided σ_0 is larger than the yield stress. The latter feature is confirmed by data reported in Figure 3 for other values of α_i. Figures 2 and 3 show also that, when σ_0 exceeds the yield stress, larger values of α_i give rise to faster creep deformations, and at any given time the creep deformation is about directly proportional to the initial deformation rate α_i.

Also the stress relaxation tests were made after constant velocity strain ramps and starting from stresses both larger and smaller than the yield stress. The initial strain rates of the ramps were the same (0.4, 4, and 16 hr^{-1}) as for the creep tests; larger values were avoided for the same reasons. Figures 4 and 5 show that the amount of stress relaxation is large, especially when the initial stress σ_0 is larger than the yield stress. Also, similarly to the behavior observed for the creep tests, at larger values of α_i the stress relaxation occurs more rapidly. This behavior is found consistently for all values of σ_0 provided the yield stress has been

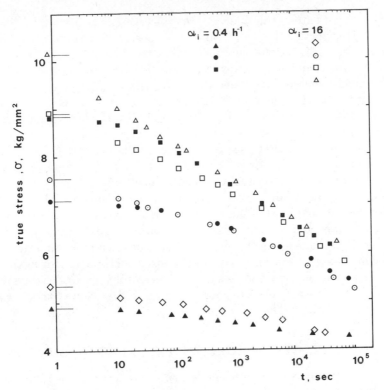

Fig. 5. True stress vs time in relaxation tests after strain ramps with different values of initial deformation rate α_i. For all curves, the initial stress σ_0 is smaller than the yield stress.

exceeded. Below the yield stress (see Fig. 5), the effect of α_i is much less pronounced and tends to disappear by decreasing the value of the initial stress, σ_0.

In Figures 2 and 4 are reported also some data relative to creep and stress relaxation tests made on prestrained samples. These samples were subjected to strain ramps (with the initial deformation rate α_i indicated in the figures) up to a strain $\Delta l/l_i = 0.2$. The motion of the Instron crosshead was then reversed and, after the stress was completely released, the samples were let to recovery for a period of time t_r. The recovery time t_r was varied with the initial deformation rate according to the following rule:

$$t_r \cdot \alpha_i = 4$$

About 35% of the deformation imposed was recovered by the material in all cases. After the recovery, the samples were again elongated with the same cross-head velocity of the previous strain ramp; and, after yielding, when the stress–strain curves of prestrained samples approached that of a virgin sample,[10] stress relaxation and creep tests were performed in the usual manner.

Both the stress relaxation and creep data of these tests are very close to those relative to "normal" tests for equal values of α_i and σ_0. It can thus be stated that the viscoelastic behavior of the material in the plastic region does not seem to depend on the previous deformation history but only on instantaneous values of deformation rate and, to the extent previously shown, of stress level.

Let us further extend this analysis. As the creep deformation at short times is inversely proportional to the "apparent viscosity" of the material defined as the ratio of the stress and the deformation rate, the data of Figures 2 and 3 suggest that (i) the "apparent viscosity" decreases steeply with stress up to the yield stress and has much smaller variations afterward; (ii) the "apparent viscosity" at stresses larger than the yield stress depend upon α_i and to a good approximation seems inversely proportional to it. These preliminary observations are also in good agreement with the stress relaxation data of Figures 4 and 5 provided the "relaxation time" is taken to be proportional to the "viscosity."

Because the amount of stress relaxation after the yield point, and thus the fraction of stress related to viscous elements during elongation, is very large, the fact that the stress–strain curves of Figure 1 show a substantial independence upon the velocity over a 400-fold range confirms that the "apparent viscosity" of the material is nearly inversely proportional to the deformation rate.

We shall now make use of the above observations in a more quantitative form in order to construct master curves of the viscoelastic behavior in the plastic region. We shall assume that relaxation times and viscosity change in a proportional way. We also need to choose in a more precise way the measures of the deformation and of the deformation rate.

SUPERPOSITION RULE IN THE PLASTIC REGION

The classical superposition principle brings creep or stress relaxation data obtained in different situations into unique curves by means of time shift factors. This powerful tool is generally used to account for changes in temperature, and the time shift factor is the inverse of some relaxation time, τ, obviously a function of temperature.

Let us assume that the "viscosity" and the "relaxation time" of the material in the plastic region of an elongational test are proportional to the inverse of the instantaneous deformation rate α. Let us indicate by α_0 the value of α just prior to the start of the viscoelastic tests, either creep or relaxation. The use of a reduced time $\bar{t} = t\alpha_0$ should then gather the stress relaxation and creep data into single curves, at least in the initial time range.

For the creep data, it seems reasonable to assume a measure of the deformation based on the sample length at the begining of the creep itself, l_0, rather than on the "initial" length l_i. Figure 6 reports all creep data (above the yield point) as $\epsilon \equiv \Delta l_c/l_0$ versus $\bar{t}$. It may be observed that a single master curve fits all the data, not only initially, but over the whole time range. It is worth noting that the master curve is obtained in terms of deformation ϵ and not of compliance, unlike the linear viscoelasticity case. However, one might argue that, if the viscous part of the stress could be sorted out, insofar as this stress might well be approximately constant, a compliance based on it would be proportional to the deformation.

Figure 7 reports all relaxation data (above the yield point) as σ/σ_0 versus $\bar{t}$. The fit into a single curve seems slightly less successful because, although curves corresponding to different α_0 values superimpose, some distance is observed between curves differing in the value of σ_0. This is related to the fact that the amount of stress relaxed increases more slowly than the initial stress σ_0. In order to have a good superposition on the complete $\bar{t}$ axis, one should probably refer only to that part of the stress which can relax and thus use the ratio $(\sigma - \sigma_\infty)/(\sigma_0$

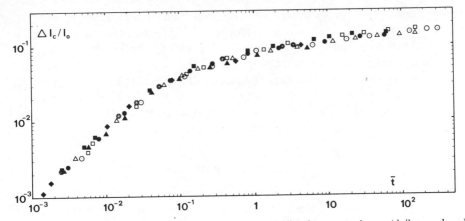

Fig. 6. Master curve for creep tests in plastic region. Modified creep strain $\epsilon = \Delta l_c/l_0$ vs reduced dimensionless time $\bar{t} = t\alpha_0$. Key to symbols same as for Figures 2 and 3.

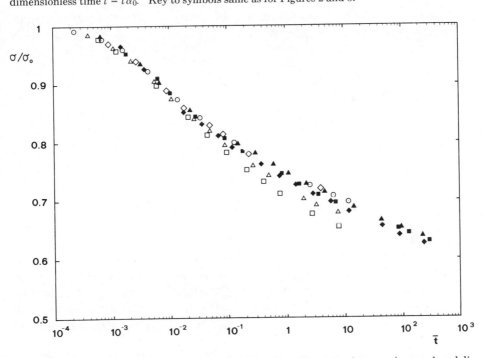

Fig. 7. Master curve for relaxation tests in plastic region. Normalized stress σ/σ_0 vs reduced dimensionless time $\bar{t} = t\alpha_0$. Key same as in Figure 4.

$- \sigma_\infty$), where σ_∞ is the asymptotic value of each stress-relaxation curve. The value of σ_∞ cannot be experimentally determined because of the extremely long times involved. However, if one tentatively assumes that at $\bar{t} = 10$ the material has released 90% of the relaxable stress, σ_∞ can be determined, and the superposition becomes excellent.

CONCLUDING REMARKS

The simple superposition rules which seem to apply in the plastic region are hopefully not restricted to the case of Mylar which was here examined. Some indications of a wider applicability can already be found. In reference 9, the stress relaxation behavior of Lexan (a polycarbonate manufactured by General Electric) was determined, and an inverse dependence of the "relaxation time" upon deformation rate was observed.

It does not seem possible to find simple rules for the intermediate region which goes from the very low stresses, where linear viscoelasticity holds, to the stresses above the yield, where the rules proposed here seem to apply.

In fact, for the case of a creep experiment, following a strain ramp, one can write

$$\epsilon = f(t, \alpha_0, \sigma_0, G, \tau, \text{dimensionless parameters}) \tag{1}$$

where G, τ, and a suitable set of dimensionless parameters identify the material and α_0 and σ_0 uniquely determine the previous deformation history. G and τ are a characteristic modulus and time, respectively, while the dimensionless parameters can be related to the "shape" of the relaxation spectrum. For a given material, the shape of the spectrum is either fixed or a function of the history. Thus, for a given material, one has

$$\epsilon = f\left(\frac{t}{\tau}, \tau\alpha_0, \frac{\sigma_0}{G}\right) \tag{2}$$

or, equivalently,

$$\epsilon = f(t\alpha_0, \tau\alpha_0, \sigma_0/G) \tag{2'}$$

Linear viscoelasticity represents a special case of eq. (2) in the form

$$\epsilon = \frac{\sigma_0}{G} f\left(\frac{t}{\tau}\right) \tag{3}$$

while "plastic" viscoelasticity is represented by a special case of eq. (2'):

$$\epsilon = f(t\alpha_0) \tag{4}$$

The creep data below the yield stress reported in Figure 2, which refers to only one value of the initial deformation rate, cannot be superimposed on each other by means of time shift factors changed arbitrarily with stress. This is true also if the same data are plotted in terms of compliance. It can then be argued that in eq. (2), apart from t/τ, also σ_0/G plays an independent role and more complex than in eq. (3).

As there is certainly an influence of α_0 on the creep behavior (see also Fig. 3), one has to conclude that in the transition region between linear and plastic viscoelasticity, i.e., for most data below the yield stress, all dimensionless groups of eq. (2) seem to play a significant role.

This work was supported by the C.N.R. under Grant CT 75.00290.03.

References

1 I. V. Yannas and A. C. Lunn, *J. Macromol. Sci. Phys.*, **B4**, 603, 620 (1970).
2 I. V. Yannas, N. H. Sung, and A. C. Lunn, *J. Macromol. Sci. Phys.*, **B5**, 487 (1971).
3. I. V. Yannas, *J. Macromol. Sci. Phys.*, **B6**, 91 (1972).
4. H. Bertilsson and J. F. Jansson, *J. Appl. Polym. Sci.*, **19**, 1971 (1975).
5. J. D. Ferry, *Viscoelastic Properties of Polymer*, Wiley, New York, 1970.

6. S. Matsuoka and S. J. Aloisio, *Amer. Phys. Soc. Bull.*, **18**, 3 (1973).

7. J. F. Jansson, *Angew. Makromol. Chem.*, **37**, 27 (1974).

8. I. V. Yannas, A. C. Lunn, and M. J. Doyle, Proc. IUPAC Int. Symp. on Macromolecules, Sec. III, Helsinki, 1972, p. 66.

9. G. Titomanlio, Flow of Solid Polymers, M. Ch.E. Thesis, University of Delaware, 1974.

10. G. Titomanlio, B. E. Anshus, G. Astarita, and A. B. Metzner, *Trans. Soc. Rheol.*, **20**, 527 (1976).

Received June 30, 1976
Revised September 22, 1976

JOURNAL OF APPLIED POLYMER SCIENCE   VOL. 21, 2943–2952 (1977)

Deuteration of Cotton Fibers. II. A Novel Method of Deuteration-Infrared Study of Cellulose in Fiber Form

H. T. LOKHANDE, E. H. DARUWALLA, and M. R. PADHYE,
Department of Chemical Technology, University of Bombay, Matunga, Bombay-400019, India

Synopsis

A new technique enabling the use of cellulosic material in the fiber form during deuteration-infrared studies is reported. A minipress, modified to suit the new technique, is described. Since the material was studied in the fiber form, danger of fiber modification during film formation was avoided. Although the usual KBr pellet technique was utilized for scanning the spectra of the deuterated fibers, preparation of pellet as well as scanning were carried out under fully dry conditions, thus completely avoiding the rehydrogenation of deuterated fibers. The modified minipress containing the pellet forms an airtight assembly allowing repeat scans after any length of time without affecting the quality of the spectra of the deuterated sample.

INTRODUCTION

Elis and Bath[1] were perhaps the first to show the presence of hydrogen bonds in cellulose by infrared spectroscopy using a semitransparent ramie specimen in a mixture of carbon disulfide and carbon tetrachloride. Holliday[2] developed an elaborate process of filament winding in order to overcome some of the serious drawbacks in infrared study of fibrous materials such as scattering, specimen mount, etc. Very little success, however, seems to have been achieved in this direction. Rowen, Hunt, and Plyler[3] used thin films of regenerated cellulose fibers in their infrared studies. Subsequently, a number of workers used this technique to study the cellulose structure by infrared technique or during deuteration-infrared studies.[4–8] However, additional changes in the internal structure of fibers are introduced as a result of solvent action during film formation. Secondly, no commonly available and suitable solvents are to be found for cotton fibers.

There are many solvents that can be used to dissolve cotton fiber to form films. In forming a film, it is obvious that there would be a rearrangement of the H-bonds for such reasons as that the crystal form would be transformed from cellulose I to II. The solvents are difficult to remove, and the cellulose film has a tendency to retain residual solvent. Although the Nujol technique reduces light scattering at adjacent surfaces, it involves considerable grinding of the sample, which is accompanied by serious degradation and structural changes. Apart from this, strong Nujol bands in the region of $-CH_3$ and $>CH_2$ stretching and

2943

Fig. 1. Details of minipress.

deformation[9] vibrations affect the accuracy of measurement in the OH region. The novel direct pressing technique of Zhbankov et al.[10–12] eliminates all the above-mentioned drawbacks, since a mechanically stable semitransparent disk of fibers with flat lustrous surface is used in scanning the spectra. O'Connor, Du'Pre, and McCall[13] successfully employed the KBr disk technique originally reported by Anderson and Woodall[14] for rapid, simple, and reproducible recording of infrared spectra of cotton fibers.

The credit of combining deuteration technique with infrared spectroscopy to characterize the structure of cellulose would have gone to Rowen and Plyler[15] but for the fact that the reported results were not correct, possibly due to defective deuteration technique. Almin,[16] however, successfully combined the two techniques where films of cellulose acetate were employed. Cumberbirch and Spedding[17] extended Zhbankov's direct pressing technique to the deuteration infrared dichroism studies of cellulose fibers in the 3-μ region. Deuteration was carried out after the pressing when splits appeared in the mounted layers during the drying, redeuteration, and redrying stages. Although Fortisan filaments could be studied with certain success, cotton fibers, which were of the order of 15 μ in diameter, however, were found to be too thick to allow accurate measurements of OH stretching bands. Knight et al.[18,19] improved upon Zhbankov's technique by first deuterating a three- to six-fiber-thick layer followed by application of pressure comparable to that used in KBr disk technique. It is reported that the authors encountered the serious error of rehydrogenation of deuterated samples by atmospheric moisture, and every operation carried out under open atmosphere on the deuterated sample was made "as quickly as possible" in order to minimize the sources of error.

The aim of the present investigation was to attempt to overcome some of these difficulties and to develop a method so that the deuteration-infrared technique could be carried out without danger of rehydrogenation of the deuterated cellulose in the fiber form. It was possible to gather more reliable and extended data by using the new technique. Some of the results obtained with the new technique have already been reported.[20]

Fig. 2. Minipress and two modified screws.

Fig. 3. Deuteration assembly.

EXPERIMENTAL

Materials

Fibers. Good-quality Sudanese cotton, ramie, wood pulp in fiber form, and viscose filaments were used in the present work.

Chemicals. Deuterium oxide, 99.5% pure, supplied by Bhabha Atomic Research Centre, Bombay, and spectroscopic-grade KBr supplied by SPEX Industries, Inc., U.S.A., were used in the present work.

Minipress. The Minipress manufactured by Wilks Scientific Corporation, U.S.A., was used (Figs. 1 and 2). Essentially, the minipress is a hollow, stainless steel cylinder with two screws to be screwed up inside the cylinder from both ends. Further modification of the minipress was effected by fabricating a set of brass

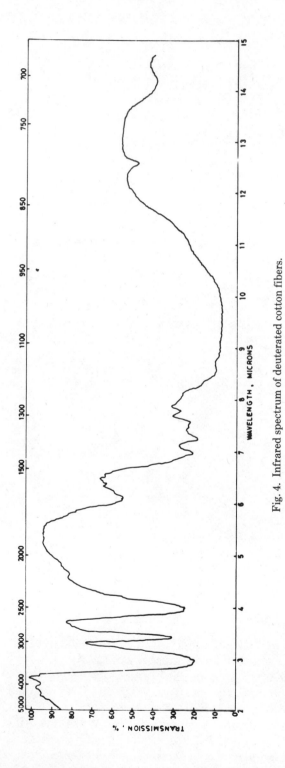

Fig. 4. Infrared spectrum of deuterated cotton fibers.

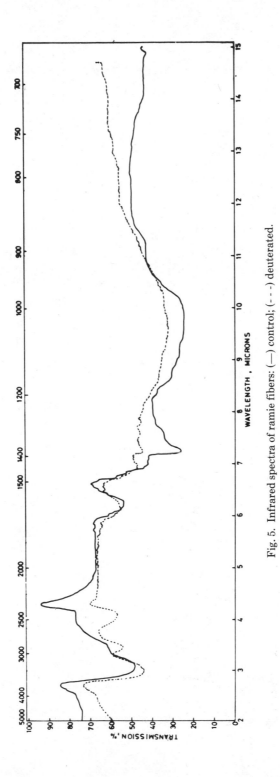

Fig. 5. Infrared spectra of ramie fibers: (—) control; (- -) deuterated.

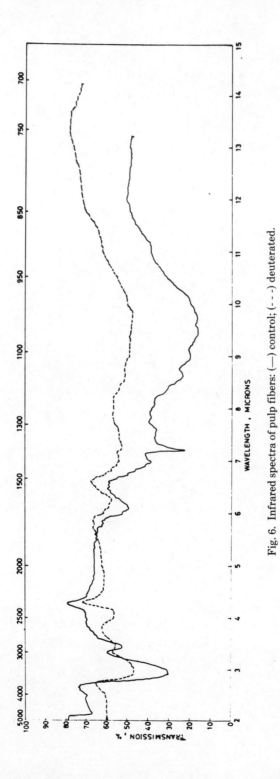

Fig. 6. Infrared spectra of pulp fibers: (—) control; (- - -) deuterated.

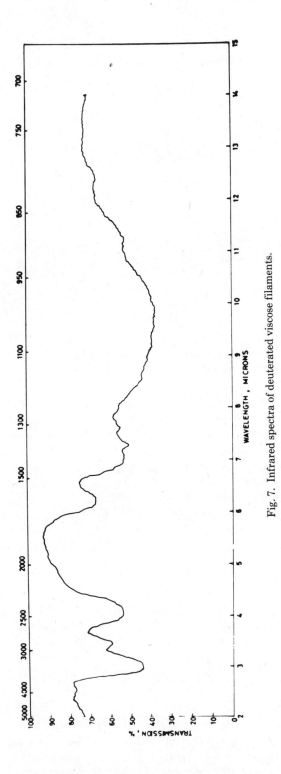

Fig. 7. Infrared spectra of deuterated viscose filaments.

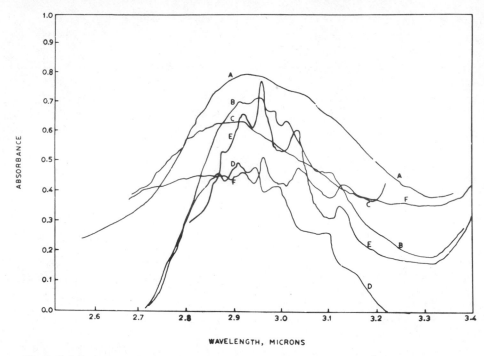

Fig. 8. Infrared spectra in the 3-μ region: (a) Cotton fibers, undeuterated; (b) cotton fibers, deuterated; (c) viscose filaments, undeuterated; (d) viscose filaments, deuterated; (e) ramie fibers, deuterated; (f) pulp fibers, deuterated.

screws exactly similar to the original ones except that they were hollow throughout, with a groove on the top to hold the NaCl plate. The arm of the modified screw was shorter than the original solid screw. The whole assembly was made airtight by using rubber washers at appropriate places.

Dry Box. The dry box was of usual design and was made of cast iron, with a trap door on one side to insert or remove the samples and chemicals, a gas inlet valve, and an arrangement for the application of vacuum on the other side. It was possible to carry out operations inside the dry box in a dry atmosphere created and maintained over sufficiently long periods by the flow of nitrogen gas passing through a drying trap assembly consisting of a sulfuric acid column followed by two towers containing fused calcium chloride (Fig. 3).

Spectrophotometers. A Perkin–Elmer 21 double-beam spectrophotometer was used for recording infrared spectra in the region of 2–12μ. With a view to increasing the dispersion and resolution of the peaks, spectra were recorded on a Beckman DK-2 spectrophotometer in the 3-μ region using appropriate stray light filters.

Methods

Cellulosic fibers were cut to a very fine state of division avoiding any serious changes in the supermolecular structure of the fibers, and were dried over P_2O_5 for 24 hr. Exactly 3 mg of the dried fibers was taken in a clean minibeaker. Exactly 297 mg dry KBr was thoroughly ground in a mortar which was then inserted in the dry box. A bottle containing heavy water (D_2O) and all the components of the modified minipress were also placed inside the dry box. The trapdoor was shut and a flow of dried nitrogen gas started. After ensuring the creation of moisture-free atmosphere inside the dry box, liquid D_2O was added to the cellulosic fibers and allowed to dry. About five to six deuteration-drying cycles followed. Finally, the dried deuterated fibers were added to the previously weighed KBr powder, mixed well, and ground thoroughly.

One of the two stainless steel screws of the minipress was fitted in position, and a small portion of the above mixture was poured into it. The remaining screw was then screwed up and a pellet pressed by adjusting the pressure on the screws at both ends. They were then unscrewed, removed, and the modified set of hollow screws fitted with an airtight assembly containing NaCl plates was introduced into the minipress. This assembly was then removed from the dry box and mounted directly on the infrared spectrophotometer or Beckman DK-2 spectrophotometer for scanning the spectra.

RESULTS AND DISCUSSION

Infared spectra of deuterated cotton, ramie, pulp, and viscose in fiber form obtained by the technique described in this paper are shown in Figures 4–7. A prominent OD peak is seen at 4.1 μ, and the general quality of the spectra is quite good.

To obtain a better resolution of the OH peak in the 3-μ region, spectra of the deuterated cellulosic fiber were recorded on the Beckman DK-2 spectrophotometer from 2.6 to 3.4 μ. The four spectra are given in Figure 8. It may be seen from these results that four well-resolved peaks are obtained for the H-bonded regions in cotton, ramie, pulp fibers, and viscose filaments. The resolution of the four peaks in the 3-μ region for any deuterated cellulosic fibers is better than that obtained previously,[21-23] possibly because of the new infrared-deuteration technique employed in the present investigation which allowed us to study the fibers directly in a moisture-free atmosphere.

The frequencies of the four main bands in case of cotton, ramie, and wood pulp (cellulose I structure) are 3230, 3298, 3350, and 3400 cm^{-1}. For viscose filaments (cellulose II structure), frequencies of the four absorption bands observed are 3230, 3350, 3445, and 3493 cm^{-1}, which correspond well to those observed by Mann and Marrinan[21] using regenerated cellulose in film form.

References

1. J. W. Ellis and J. Bath, *J. Amer. Chem. Soc.*, **62**, 2859 (1940).
2. P. Holliday, *Nature*, **163**, 602 (1949).
3. J. W. Rowen, C. M. Hunt, and E. K. Plyler, *J. Res. Natl. Bur. Stand.*, **39**, 133 (1947).
4. S. D. Dormon and K. M. Rudall, *Disc. Faraday Soc.*, **9**, 251 (1950).
5. L. Brown, P. Holliday, and I. F. Trotter, *J. Chem. Soc.*, 1532 (1951).
6. H. J. Marrinan and J. Mann, *J. Appl. Chem. (London)*, **4**, 204 (1954).
7. H. Sobue and S. Fukuhara, *Kogyo Ksgaku Zasshi*, **63**, 520 (1960); *C.A.*, **56**, 10422 (1962).
8. R. Jeffries, *Polymer*, **4**, 375 (1963).
9. F. H. Forziati and J. W. Rowen, *J. Res. Natl. Bur. Stand.*, **46**, 38 (1951); *C.A.*, **45**, 7872 (1951).
10. R. G. Zhbankov, *Infrared Spectra of Cellulose and Its Derivatives*, Consultants Bureau, New York, 1966, p. 23.
11. R. G. Zhbankov and I. N. Ermolenko, *Izv. Akadem. Nauuk Beluruskui S.S.R., Ser. Fiz.-Tekhn.*, **1**, 15 (1956).

12. R. G. Zhbankov, N. V. Ivanova, and A. Ya. Rozenberg, *Zavodsk. Lab.,* **No. 11,** 1324 (1962).

13. R. T. O'Connor, E. F. Du'Pre, and E. R. McCall, *Anal. Chem.,* **29,** 998 (1957).

14. D. H. Anderson and N. B. Woodall, *Anal. Chem.,* **25,** 1906 (1953).

15. J. W. Rowen and E. K. Plyler, *J. Res. Natl. Bur. Stand.,* **44,** 313 (1950).

16. K. E. Almin, *Sven. Papper.,* **55,** 767 (1952).

17. R. J. E. Cumberbirch and H. Spedding, *J. Appl. Chem. (London),* **12,** 83 (1962).

18. J. A. Knight, M. P. Smoak, R. A. Porter, and W. E. Kirkland, *Text. Res. J.,* **37,** 924 (1967).

19. J. A. Knight, H. Lamar-Hicks, and K. W. Stephens, *Text. Res. J.,* **39,** 324 (1969).

20. H. T. Lokhande, *J. Appl. Polym. Sci.,* **20,** 2313 (1976).

21. J. Mann and H. J. Marrinan, *Trans. Faraday Soc.,* **52,** 481 (1956).

22. J. Mann and H. J. Marrinan, *J. Polym. Sci.,* **32,** 357 (1958).

23. R. J. E. Cumberbirch and R. Jeffries, *J. Appl. Polym. Sci.,* **11,** 2083 (1967).

Received August 20, 1976
Revised September 24, 1976

JOURNAL OF APPLIED POLYMER SCIENCE   VOL. 21, 2953–2961 (1977)

Antiplasticization and Transition to Marked Nonlinear Viscoelasticity in Poly(vinyl Chloride)/ Acrylonitrile–Butadiene Copolymer Blends

GUNNAR BERGMAN, HANS BERTILSSON,* and YOUNG J. SHUR, *Department of Polymer Technology, The Royal Institute of Technology, S-100 44 Stockholm, Sweden*

Synopsis

A series of PVC/NBR blends with varying acrylonitrile (AN) content in the NBR has been studied in uniaxial tension creep tests. The tests have been carried out at 21.5 ± 0.5°C covering creep times from 10 to 1000 sec. NBR with low AN content, having poor compatibility with PVC, gives the blends with higher compliance and increased time dependence of the compliance. A higher AN content in the NBR gives the blends with the opposite properties when the NBR is added in small amounts. NBR with 40 wt-% AN is found to act as an antiplasticizer giving minimal creep compliance when 7 wt-% NBR is added. The antiplasticization reveals a considerably increased stress level at which the transition from approximatively linear to marked nonlinear viscoelasticity occurs and a decreased stress dependence of the creep compliance in the nonlinear viscoelastic range. Since the antiplasticization is also associated with a suppression of the β-transition mechanism, the results provide a demonstration of the importance of β-mechanism in the stress activated processes responsible for the appearance of nonlinear viscoelasticity in solid polymers.

INTRODUCTION

It is common practice to mix existing polymers in such a way that the resulting material has certain properties superior to those of the individual components. In this way, commercially successful high-impact thermoplastics based on brittle poly(vinyl chloride) (PVC) and polystyrene are being produced by addition of a small amount of a rubber.

The most common ways to characterize the materials have been dynamic mechanical investigations, fracture studies, and examinations of the fine structure with electron microscopy. The results from such investigations have given much information concerning the compatibility of the rubber with PVC.

In most polymer blends, incompatibility is thermodynamically true and is mainly evidenced by two damping maxima representing the parent polymers. However, PVC/NBR blends were reported to form a compatible system when the acrylonitrile (AN) content in NBR is larger than 40 wt-%.[1] Many studies have been carried out to characterize the poly(vinyl chloride)/acrylonitrile-butadiene copolymer (PVC/NBR) blends, e.g., dynamic mechanical property,[1–5]

* Present address: Department of Materials Technology, The University of Luleå, S-951 87 Luleå, Sweden.

impact strength,[2,6,7] morphology,[1] and gas transport.[8] However, no available data on the creep property of the blend were reported, although it is of significant importance in engineering applications.

Tensile creep tests on several stress levels over a limited time scale provide a good characterization of the engineering properties as well as a basis for a physical examination of materials.[9] If creep measurements are carried out over many stress levels, the results give information on (a) the transition from the approximatively linear to the marked nonlinear viscoelasticity of the material, and (b) the tendency of increasing the nonlinearity with increasing applied stress.

The present work explores such properties of the PVC/NBR blends as the AN content in the NBR of the blends is varied. The results are discussed with relation to the compatibility of the blends.

MICROSTRUCTURES OF PVC/NBR BLENDS

The morphologic structures of PVC/NBR blends have been examined by Matsuo et al.[1] using contrast electron microscope and the results correlated with dynamic mechanical measurements. The AN content in the NBR was found to significantly affect the compatibility of the blends. NBR with 8 wt-% AN was found to form an incompatible system with PVC, and only slightly smoother phase boundaries were observed as compared to completely incompatible PVC/polybutadiene blends. As the AN level of the NBR was increased to 20 wt-%, there was a continuous rubber network extending throughout the PVC matrix, even in the blends with low rubber content. The rubber particles were also observed to be finer. Dynamic mechanical measurements of this blend showed that the location of the α-transition peak of the rubber phase was not changed with changing rubber content in the blends. However, the corresponding peak for the PVC phase was shifted to lower temperature with increasing rubber content. Such a system, according to Matsuo et al.,[1] is called a semicompatible system and was also observed in PVC/ethylene–vinyl acetate copolymer (EVA) blends with a vinyl acetate content of 65 wt-% and milled at 160°C.[10]

With 30 wt-% AN in the rubber, a fine dispersion of the rubber particles in the PVC matrix appeared together with a continuous rubber network. A relatively compatible system was achieved with 40 wt-% AN in the NBR. Microheterogeneity was still observable, but rubber particles could not be identified, at least not exceeding 100 Å.

In dynamic mechanical measurements of the compatible PVC/NBR blends (AN content 41.6 wt-% in NBR), the α-transition peak of PVC was shifted toward lower temperatures in proportion to the NBR content of the blends. However, the α-transition peak of the NBR was almost lost in the β-transition mechanism of PVC. A slight suppression of the β-transition peak of the PVC in proportion to the NBR content in the blend could be observed. It was also evident that for the blends containing less than 10 wt-% NBR, the dynamic modulus (E') values were larger than those of pure PVC over the temperature range between the α- and β-transitions of PVC. This may be due to the so-called *antiplasticizing effect*. It should be noted that this effect is not visible for the PVC/NBR blends with less than 20 wt-% AN in the NBR. According to the mechanism of the antiplasticizing effect, this would be explained by the mutual interaction between the PVC and NBR.

ANTIPLASTICIZATION

It is well known that small amounts of common low molecular plasticizers, i.e., esters of phthalic acids, added to PVC make the PVC stiffer and slightly more brittle. This phenomenon was interpreted as the antiplasticizing effect of the plasticizers. Jackson and Caldwell[11] have studied the antiplasticizing effect of many substances on polycarbonates and found chlorinated biphenyls to be the most effective. The antiplasticized materials showed an increase in modulus as well as in tensile strength. Jackson and Caldwell have also found that poly-(methyl methacrylate) can be antiplasticized but not polystyrene. Robeson and Faucher[12] have reported that antiplasticization of polycarbonates and polysulfones was signified by the suppression of the β-transition process of the polymers. This was evident from the results that polymers showing an antiplasticizing effect show a decrease in impact strength and that polystyrene, having no pronounced β-transition, showed no antiplasticizing effect. The suppression of the β-transition mechanism as related to antiplasticization was further examined on PVC with small amounts of common phthalic acid ester plasticizers,[13,14] on antiplasticized crosslinked epoxy,[15] and on polycarbonates.[16]

Most of the reports on antiplasticized systems have also shown nonadditivity in specific volumes of the systems.[13,16] The same results were reported for the compatible polymer blends such as PVC/NBR (AN $\geq$ 30%)[8] and PVC/EVA (vinyl acetate = 65 wt-%).[9] Further evidence for antiplasticization in PVC/NBR with high AN content has been reported by Hidemaro[17] who found increased tensile strength, decreased elongation to break in constant strain-rate tensile tests, and the nonadditivity in specific volumes of the blends.

The β-transition in PVC is due to local main-chain movements of a cooperative character.[14] If a polar additive such as an ester-type plasticizer or a polymer having strong polar groups is added to PVC, the interaction will result in secondary bond crosslinks between PVC chains. This will then suppress the β-transition process of the PVC. The specific volume contraction observed when such an antiplasticizing substance is added is evidence of this strong interaction. Further evidence is the reported increase in the second moment (ΔH_2^2) in the NMR absorption line when small amounts of polar plasticizer are added to PVC.[18] Depending on the type of plasticizer, the maximum antiplasticizing effect on PVC seems to be observed at 5–10% plasticizer.

In line with aspects mentioned above, it is very possible that the antiplasticizing effect on PVC due to addition of highly polar NBR (AN = 40%) may take place, at least in the low composition range.

NONLINEAR VISCOELASTICITY

Most polymer materials exhibit an approximatively linear viscoelastic behavior at low strain levels when subjected to an uniaxial tensile stress. At a certain stress level, molecular mechanisms are activated to the extent that the material becomes significantly nonlinear. The appearance of nonlinear viscoelastic behavior in solid polymers has been reviewed by Yannas.[19] The definition of the stress or strain limit of linear viscoelasticity will naturally be arbitrarily chosen. In this work, we use a deviation from linear viscoelasticity exceeding 1% as a criterion for marked nonlinear viscoelasticity. It must be pointed out that for amorphous and crystalline polymers used in engineering applications, the strain limit of linear viscoelasticity lies between 0.005 to 0.01 uniaxial strain. Thus, the strain limit will be quite independent of the kind of definition of strain used.

According to the observed shift in the relaxation time spectrum around the transition to marked nonlinear viscoelasticity, it is proposed that the stress-activated mechanism causing the considerable nonlinearity is of a highly cooperative nature. In a study of the limits of linear viscoelasticity in poly(methyl methacrylate) and poly(ethyl methacrylate), it has been proposed that the appearance of nonlinearity was due to a coupling effect between the α- and β-transition mechanisms.[20] Thus, if the β-transition mechanism of a polymer is suppressed, this will eventually lead to a suppression of the mechanisms responsible to the appearance of nonlinear viscoelasticity. If this is true, the stress limit for the occurrence of marked nonlinear viscoelasticity should be increased by addition of a substance providing an antiplasticizing effect on the polymer.

EXPERIMENTAL

Materials and Specimens

The materials investigated were prepared by physical blending of PVC and NBR at weight ratios of 100/0, 94/4, 93/7, 90/10, and 85/15, using a steam-heated calender mill for 15 min at 160°C, and thereafter by pressing for 10 min at 170°C to a 2-mm-thick sheet.

The PVC powder and the common stabilizing additives used (organic Ba–Cd salts and Pb stearate, totally 3 parts per 100 parts of PVC + NBR) were first milled to a continuous slab. The NBR was then added and milled into the slab.

The PVC used was of suspension grade with $\overline{M}_w$ = 74,000. The NBR samples were of three grades with different AN contents (see Table I).

From the pressed sheets, ordinary dumbbell-shaped specimens were machined out according to SIS 112116 (approximately corresponding to ASTM D638 Type II). Before being subjected to creep measurements, each specimen was annealed 100 hr at 75°C and then cooled very slowly.

Measurements

Uniaxial creep measurements during periods up to 1000 sec were made for the blends at a temperature 21.5° ± 0.5°C. The number of stress levels chosen varied between 10 and 20, depending on the blend. The maximum stress level was chosen so as to give a clear nonlinear response within the experimental time range, approximately 1.2 times the limiting stress of linear viscoelasticity. The creep equipment used and the measurement procedures have been described by Bertilsson et al.[20]

Isochronous stress–strain diagrams were determined from the recorded creep curves by measuring the strain after 10, 100, and 1000 sec. From the diagrams,

TABLE I
Polymers Used in the Blends

Polymers	Commercial name	Manufacturer
PVC	Pevikon S 655	KemaNord AB, Sweden
NBR-1	Hycar 1024 (AN = 21.7%)[a]	B. F. Goodrich Chem. Co., U.S.A.
NBR-2	Hycar 1043 (AN = 29.6%)	B. F. Goodrich Chem. Co., U.S.A.
NBR-3	Hycar 1041 (AN = 41.6%)	B. F. Goodrich Chem. Co., U.S.A.

[a] AN contents determined by Jorgensen et al.[21]

it was possible to determine the extent of the linear viscoelastic range. A best-fit straight line was drawn through the points of the lowest stress levels to origin. The linear viscoelastic limit is defined as the point where the best-fit curve for all stress levels deviates from the straight line by more than 1%.

RESULTS AND DISCUSSION

From the factors discussed in the introduction, it was expected that a variation of AN content in the NBR would give quite different levels of creep compliance. However, differences in the stress dependence of the creep compliance are also quite apparent. In Figure 1, the creep compliance is plotted as a function of creep stress for the blends with 10 wt-% NBR of three different types, respectively.

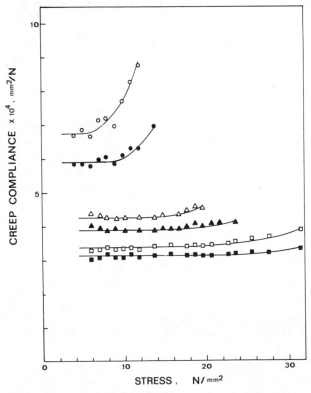

Fig. 1. Creep compliance vs. stress for PVC/NBR blends with NBR content 10 wt-%. PVC/NBR-1: (●) 10 sec; (○) 1000 sec. PVC/NBR-2: (▲) 10 sec; (△) 1000 sec. PVC/NBR-3: (■) 10 sec; (□) 1000 sec.

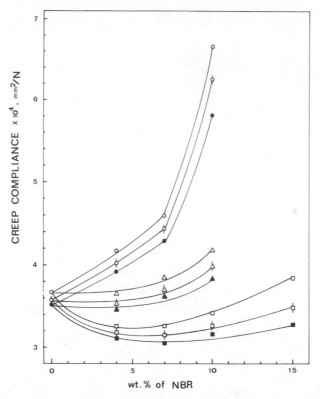

Fig. 2. Creep compliance vs. NBR content in the PVC/NBR blends. PVC/NBR-1: (●) 10 sec; (⌀) 100 sec; (○) 1000 sec. PVC/NBR-2: (▲) 10 sec; (△) 100 sec; (⌂) 1000 sec. PVC/NBR-3: (■) 10 sec; (⌑) 100 sec; (□) 1000 sec.

All the curves are isochronous, and the three samples are each represented by a 10- and a 1000-sec curve. The stress range of the approximatively linear viscoelastic behavior is considerably decreased when the AN content in the NBR is decreased. There is also a marked difference in the expanding deviation from linear theory above the linear limit. Moreover, the time dependence of the linear viscoelastic compliance as well as the nonlinear viscoelastic compliance are more pronounced when the AN content in the NBR is decreased. The PVC/NBR-3 blends, which are most compatible, behave almost the same as the PVC with no additives, with the exception of a slightly lowered compliance level.

Figure 2 shows the creep compliance in the linear viscoelastic range versus NBR content. The antiplasticizing effect in the more compatible blends is evident. The plasticizing effect of NBR-1, with only 21.7% AN, may be operative at very low rubber content in the blends (<4%), although the analysis of the fine structure and the dynamic mechanical damping property classified the PVC/NBR-1 blends as a semicompatible system. With 29.6% AN in NBR, the linear viscoelastic creep properties of the blends seem to be unaffected up to about 5% NBR content. NBR-3 shows a clear antiplasticizing effect. For 1000 sec of creep time, the compliance corresponding to that of pure PVC is attained at 15 wt-% rubber; and for the shorter creep time, it is attained at still higher rubber content because the time dependence of the linear viscoelastic compliance increases with increasing rubber content.

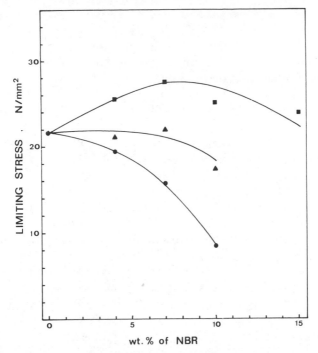

Fig. 3. Limiting stress vs. NBR content in the PVC/NBR blends for 10 sec creep time: (●) PVC/NBR-1; (▲) PVC/NBR-2; (■) PVC/NBR-3.

Figure 3 shows the limiting stress of linear viscoelastic behavior of the blends plotted versus NBR content. The general character of this figure is rather similar to the behavior of the compliance. However, the antiplasticizing effect is more clearly visible. The PVC/NBR-3 blend showed a maximum antiplasticization at about 7% NBR. For PVC/NBR-2 blends, there was some indication of a weak antiplasticizing effect in the composition range up to 7% of the NBR.

The antiplasticizing effect of NBR of PVC was also expected in gas transport results. The rates of permeation and diffusion of He, O_2, N_2, and CO_2 in PVC/NBR blends decreased, but activation energy for diffusion increased with increasing AN content in the NBR.[8] This is due to reduced segmental mobility of the polymer chains because of increased interaction between PVC and NBR with increased AN content.

For a 10-sec creep time, the decrease in the linear viscoelastic creep compliance was about 14%. Under the same conditions, the increase in limiting stress as shown in Figure 3 is about 27%. Since the decrease in compliance is not proportional to the increase in limiting stress, we suspect that the mechanism behind the antiplasticization will also influence the transition to nonlinear viscoelasticity. For clarity, it must be mentioned that the limiting strain is, within the limit of the experimental uncertainty, independent of rubber content up to the concentrations shown in Figure 3. There is an exception, however, for the system PVC/NBR-1, which showed a decrease in strain limit from 0.007 for pure PVC and PVC with 4% rubber content down to 0.005 for 10% rubber content.

The molecular interpretation of the transition from approximatively linear to marked nonlinear viscoelasticity was discussed by Bertilsson et al.[20] They found that the β-mechanism was involved in the linear-to-nonlinear transition.

Segmental motions can be stress activated at temperature far below the T_g, as shown for polycarbonate.[22]   According to Bertilsson et al.,[20] a coupling effect between the α- and β-transition mechanisms (providing conditions for the stress activated process) is responsible for the ostensible nonlinearity.   Thus, it is possible to explain the occurrence of nonlinear viscoelastic responses without any irreversible deformation mechanisms being involved.   All macroscopic deformations reported in this work were fully recoverable.

When the β-transition mechanism of PVC is restrained due to polar interaction with NBR, leading to secondary crosslinks, the coupling mechanism between the α- and β-mechanisms will be restrained in proportion to NBR content.   A higher stress threshold for the appearance of nonlinear viscoelasticity will arise. At higher plasticizer or antiplasticizer contents, the possible sites for the secondary crosslinks will be saturated; and due to the large amount of flexible polymer substance added, the additive will act as a plasticizer.   Thus, we get a maximum in modulus and linear stress limit for the plasticized blend if the system is compatible enough, i.e., the PVC/NBR-3 blend.

One may ask to what extent the crystallinity of the PVC will affect the transition from the linear to nonlinear viscoelasticity and to what extent a plasticizing additive will affect the crystallinity.   Shtarkman et al.[23] have studied composition dependence of the crystallization on the plasticized PVC using small-angle x-ray scattering.   It was found that small amounts of dioctyl phthalate (DOP) (10–15 wt-%) show no effect, but larger amounts could reduce the crystallinity slightly. Pezzin et al.[24] have reported that the β-transition of PVC plasticized by DOP was not affected by changes in crystallinity from 10% to 20%.   This suggested that the rise in stress limit for the linear viscoelastic range is not attributed to an increase in crystallinity.

CONCLUSIONS

1. If NBR has a low AN content, the compatibility of the PVC/NBR blend will be lower and the stress on the PVC phase is comparatively high, leading to nonlinear viscoelastic behavior of the blend at low macroscopic stress levels and to a high deviation from linearity above the linear stress limit.

2. If the AN content in NBR is high (>20%), the compatibility of the PVC/ NBR blend is increased.   Small additions of NBR (<10%) will then act as antiplasticizer.   In the composition range where the antiplasticizing effect has been demonstrated, the stress limit of linear viscoelasticity is increased and the deviation from linearity above the stress limit is relatively small.

3. The relation between the β-transition mechanism and the transition from the approximatively linear to the marked nonlinear viscoelasticity agrees with the explanation of stress-activated nonlinear viscoelasticity proposed earlier.[20]

4. The impact strength of a blend is inversely related to the blend compatibility.[25]   The results show an unfortunate contradiction between the impact strength and the long-term load applicability of PVC blended with NBR.

This investigation is a part of research program on Mechanical Long-Term Properties of Polymers supported by the Swedish Board for Technical Development (STU).   KemaNord AB, Sweden, is thanked for preparing the samples and providing valuable information about them.

References

1. M. Matsuo, C. Nozaki, and Y. Jyo, *Polym. Eng. Sci.*, **9**, 197 (1969).
2. G. A. Zakrzewski, *Polymer*, **14**, 347 (1973).
3. J. W. Horvath, W. A. Wilson, H. S. Lundström, and J. R. Purdon, *Polym. Prepr.*, **8**, 1546 (1967).
4. L. Nielsen, *Mechanical Properties of Polymers*, Reinhold, New York, 1962, p. 173.
5. L. Bohn, *Rubber Chem. Technol.*, **41**, 495 (1968).
6. N. E. Davenport, L. W. Hubbard, and N. R. Pettit, *Br. Plast.*, **32**, 549 (1959).
7. J. Zelinger, E. Sununkova, and V. Heidingsfeld, *Sb. VSCHT Prague*, **9**, 73 (1966).
8. Y. J. Shur and B. Rånby, *J. Appl. Polym. Sci.*, **19**, 2143 (1975).
9. S. Turner, *J. Appl. Polym. Symp.*, **17**, 213 (1971).
10. Y. J. Shur and B. Rånby, *J. Appl. Polym. Sci.*, **19**, 1337 (1975).
11. W. J. Jackson and J. R. Caldwell, *J. Appl. Polym. Sci.*, **11**, 211, 227 (1967).
12. L. M. Robeson and J. A. Faucher, *J. Polym. Sci.*, **B7**, 35 (1969).
13. N. Kinjo and T. Nakagawa, *Polym. J.*, **4**, 143 (1973).
14. G. Pezzin, G. Ajroldi, and C. Garbuglio, *J. Appl. Polym. Sci.*, **11**, 2553 (1967).
15. N. Hata, R. Yamauchi, and J. Kumanotani, *J. Appl. Polym. Sci.*, **17**, 2173 (1973).
16. M. G. Wyzgoski and G. S. Y. Yeh, *Polym. J.*, **4**, 29 (1973).
17. F. Hidemaro, *Aechi-ken Koiyo Shadosho Hokoku*, **5**, 67 (1967).
18. N. A. Novikov, A. S. Shashkov, and F. A. Galil-Ogly, *Polym. Sci. USSR*, **15**, 1198 (1974).
19. I. V. Yannas, *J. Polym. Sci., Macromol. Rev.*, **9**, 163 (1974).
20. H. Bertilsson and J. F. Jansson, *J. Appl. Polym. Sci.*, **19**, 1971 (1975).
21. A. H. Jorgensen, L. A. Chandler, and E. A. Collins, *Rubber Chem. Technol.*, **46**, 1087 (1973).
22. A. C. Lunn and I. V. Yannas, *J. Polym. Sci.-Phys.*, **10**, 2189 (1972).
23. B. P. Shtarkman et al., *Polym. Sci. USSR*, **14**, 1826 (1972).
24. G. Pezzin, G. Ajroldi, T. Casiraghi, C. Garbuglio, and G. Vittadini, *J. Appl. Polym. Sci.*, **16**, 1839 (1972).
25. M. Matsuo, A. Ueda, and Y. Kondo, *Polym. Eng. Sci.*, **10**, 253 (1970).

Received July 1, 1976
Revised September 29, 1976

JOURNAL OF APPLIED POLYMER SCIENCE   VOL. 21, 2963–2978 (1977)

The Weatherability of Polypropylene Monofilaments. Effects of Fiber Production Conditions

D. J. CARLSSON, A. GARTON,* and D. M. WILES, *Division of Chemistry, National Research Council of Canada, Ottawa, Canada K1A OR9*

Synopsis

From a comparison of the photo- and γ-irradiation-initiated oxidations of monofilaments and films, polypropylene oxidation rates and product ratios were found to be independent of sample morphology and orientation. Filament sensitivity to photo-oxidation was, however, drastically affected by extrusion and draw conditions, photosensitivity increasing with increasing draw speed and decreasing draw temperature. Draw effects were minimized by the exclusion of oxygen, indicating that free radicals produced by backbone cleavage during draw react with oxygen to give chromophoric oxidation products. The most important product detectable after drawing was probably the polypropylene hydroperoxide. A phenolic antioxidant reduced hydroperoxide formation, although sufficient hydroperoxide was still produced to accelerate photodegradation as compared with a similarly stabilized undrawn filament. Melt oxidation within the extruder was concluded to be much more important than thermal oxidation of the extruded filament as it cooled on the spinline.

INTRODUCTION

Unstabilized polypropylene (PPH) fibers are known to be very susceptible to sunlight-initiated deterioration.[1] A catastrophic drop in elongation to break, together with a buildup of hydroperoxide and carbonyl oxidation products, has been reported after less than 100 hr of accelerated weathering by xenon arc irradiation in air.[2] Appreciable morphological and structural changes accompany photo-oxidation, with the fibrillar zones being apparently more resistant to photo-oxidative scission than the surrounding nonfibrillar matrix.[3]

The photo-oxidation of PPH films has received extensive study[4] and is believed to be described by reactions (1)–(9). During the early stages of photo-oxidation, initiation to give peroxy radicals $PPO_2\cdot$, reaction (1), is thought to be caused by traces of UV-absorbing impurities (chromophores) such as catalyst residues or oxidation products introduced during processing.[4,5] The nature and concentration of any oxidation products arising from processing must be a major factor in the weatherability of the resulting filament. The major product of photo-oxidation is the tertiary hydroperoxide (PPOOH) which is itself readily photolyzed to give free radicals that can propagate further oxidative chains, reaction (2);

* Research Associate 1975–76.

$$\text{chromophores} \xrightarrow{h\nu/O_2/PPH} PPO_2\cdot \left.\right\} \text{ initiation} \qquad (1)$$

$$PPOOH \xrightarrow{h\nu} PPO\cdot + \cdot OH \xrightarrow{O_2/PPH} 2PPO_2\cdot \qquad (2)$$

$$PPO_2\cdot + PPH \longrightarrow PPOOH + PP\cdot \left.\right\} \text{ propagation} \qquad (3)$$

$$PP\cdot + O_2 \longrightarrow PPO_2\cdot \qquad (4)$$

$$2PPO_2\cdot \longrightarrow PPOOPP + O_2 \qquad \text{termination} \qquad (5)$$

$$2PPO_2\cdot \longrightarrow 2PPO\cdot + O_2 \qquad \text{nontermination} \qquad (6)$$

$$PPO\cdot \begin{cases} \sim CH_2-\overset{\overset{O}{\|}}{C}-CH_2\sim + CH_3\cdot & (7) \\ \sim CH_2-\underset{O}{\overset{CH_3}{C}} + \cdot CH_2\sim & \text{scission reactions} \quad (8) \\ \overset{CH_3}{\underset{\overset{|}{O}\,|\,H}{\sim CH_2-C-CH_2\sim}} + PP\cdot & \text{chain transfer} \quad (9) \end{cases}$$

The hydroperoxide produced during propagation, reaction (3), soon becomes the dominant source of free radicals for further initiation by process (2), and the photo-oxidation accelerates rapidly.[5] Production of free peroxy radicals from any initiator in PPH is, however, a relatively inefficient process because many radical–radical terminations, such as reaction (5), occur within the surrounding polymer cage. In fact, only about one in eight radicals escapes cage combination to take part in propagation reactions.[6] Initially, chain lengths for propagation of free $PPO_2\cdot$ may be 100 or more,[5,6] but this value decreases at higher oxidation levels where high radical concentrations make the termination reaction (5) proportionately more important.

The carbonyl and hydroxyl products result from reactions (7)–(9), involving the macro-alkoxy radicals from reaction (6). These reactions will become more important as photo-oxidation proceeds but do not generally account for more than 15 mole % of the oxidation products and unstabilized PPH films have a fivefold molar excess of PPOOH over >C=O at brittle failure.[4,7] A commercial PPH monofilament has, however, been reported to photo-oxidize to predominantly carbonyl products.[2] It is unclear whether this anomaly results from morphological differences between fibers and films or from the presence of the phenolic stabilizer in the commercial fiber sample.[2]

An objective of the present work was then the clarification of the possible effects of sample morphology on the photo-oxidation mechanism of a series of additive-free, laboratory-extruded PPH monofilaments. A further objective was the determination of the stages of fiber production which are responsible for the photoinitiating oxidation products introduced by the thermal and mechanical processes involved in extrusion and orientation. This was achieved by the systematic variation of the extrusion and drawing conditions.

Industrial practice usually involves the inclusion of a phenolic antioxidant in the molten PPH to minimize melt degradation. The work discussed here was largely carried out without melt antioxidants because these additives cannot be extracted completely from the oriented filaments.[2] However, the usefulness of antioxidants in reducing the oxidation during the various steps of the production processes is also discussed.

EXPERIMENTAL

Monofilament Preparation

Unprocessed, commercial, additive-free, isotactic PPH (Monomer Polymer Labs) was used. Its intrinsic viscosity in decalin at 135°C was found to be 3.2 dl/g, indicating a molecular weight of about 400,000 (Mark–Houwink constants[8] $k = 1.0 \times 10^{-4}$, $a = 0.80$). Extrusion at 220°C with N_2 blanketing of the hopper (see below) was found to cause a 10% drop in intrinsic viscosity for an antioxidant-free melt. The titanium content of the polymer was found by x-ray fluorescence to be 79 ppm. Other PPH samples examined included the commercial 150-μm monofilament used previously (Amtech Inc. Ti content 10 ppm) which contained 0.24 wt-% of octadecyl 3-(3′,5′-di-*tert*-butyl-4′-hydroxyphenyl)propionate[2] and a commercial film (Enjay, 25 μm, Ti content 80 ppm). Both were Soxhlet extracted with acetone for 48 hr and vacuum dried; this procedure gave an additive free film, but did not remove the phenol from the fiber.[2] Samples of the Amtech filament and the unprocessed additive-free polymer were also pressed into films in a nitrogen atmosphere.[7] UV spectroscopy confirmed that the stabilizer in the Amtech polymer could then be removed by acetone Soxhlet extraction. In one sample, 0.1 wt-% 2,4-di-*tert*-butylphenyl(4′-hydroxy-3′5′-di-*tert*-butylbenzoate) (Ciba-Geigy) was compounded with the additive-free polymer before extrusion to investigate its effectiveness as an antioxidant during filament production and as a UV stabilizer after various processing steps.

PPH monofilaments ranging from 50 to 200 μm in diameter were produced using a Maxwell-type screwless extruder (Fig. 1). A commercial laboratory-scale extruder (Custom Scientific Instruments) was used, although the barrel and header were redesigned to improve melt flow and minimize holdup in the barrel. A throughput of about 2 g/min was attained using a 0.125-cm-diameter, single-hole spinneret. Filaments were extruded into air (or nitrogen) and collected at known windup speeds of up to 40 m/min. Spinline tensions (0–5 g) were measured using a damped, top-loading balance (Sartorius 1106) equipped with suitable guides. The hopper used for storage of the polymer was water cooled and could be purged with a continuous flow of nitrogen to minimize degradation. When required, nitrogen blanketing of the spinline was achieved by extruding the filament directly through a narrow cylindrical manifold 60 cm long by 5 cm in diameter in contact with the spinneret face (Fig. 1). A continuous nitrogen flow maintained an atmosphere of <1.5% oxygen as measured by a paramagnetic oxygen analyzer (Taylor Servomex Ltd.). Solidification and cooling then took place virtually entirely in a nitrogen atmosphere. When investigating the effect of the absence of spinline N_2 blanketing, the enhanced cooling of the filament

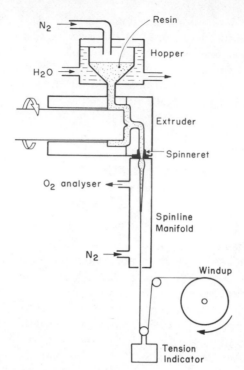

Fig. 1. Laboratory extrusion system. Modified Maxwell extruder, polymer holdup ~4 g.

produced by this continuous nitrogen flow was duplicated by a similar flow of air through the narrow manifold.

Off-line hot drawing normally took place by passage through an air oven at 180°C (30 cm in length), the draw ratio being determined by the relative speeds of the feed and take-up spools. Short lengths of filament (7 cm) were also drawn at known rates on an Instron mechanical tester (Model TTC) at 25°C. Similar samples were drawn under water at temperatures from 25° to 95°C on a Suter horizontal tensile tester, with a fixed draw speed of 12 in./min. Short lengths of filament were also drawn rapidly (~20 in./min) under high vacuum in attempts to eliminate the small amounts of oxidation that appeared to take place on drawing in air.

Photo-oxidation

Single short lengths of filament (4 cm) rigidly mounted on cardboard formers were irradiated in air in an Atlas Weather-Ometer, Model 6000 WR, fitted with a 6000-watt xenon arc lamp and borosilicate inner and outer filters. The Weather-Ometer was run at a constant 30% humidity and a 34°C silver panel temperature.

γ-Initiated Oxidations

Parallel arrays of selected monofilaments, mounted on cardboard frames[2] together with film samples for comaprison purposes, were irradiated in Gammacell 220 (Atomic Energy of Canada Ltd.) cobalt 60 sources at dose rates of 300 and 1000 rads/min. These dose rates are only nominal values because of variations with sample position in the cell. However, within any series at a given dose rate, that dose rate was constant. In the high dose rate cell, the sample compartment reached a temperature of 35°–40°C.

Monofilament Characterization

(i) Infrared (IR) spectra of monofilaments may be obtained by techniques described earlier.[9] Apart from γ-irradiated samples, all spectra reported here were obtained using the "single fiber" technique.[9] Each single monofilament sample was mounted securely on a small cardboard "picture frame" former during irradiation so that IR analysis at each irradiation time could be performed on precisely the same length of the filament. Only a 1-cm length of photo-oxidized fiber is examined by this procedure. The changes in the IR spectrum of PPH on photo-oxidation are well known.[4,7,10] An extinction coefficient of $70M^{-1}cm^{-1}$ was assigned to the 3400 cm^{-1} absorption band, which is largely due to hydroperoxide groups.[10] An average value of $300M^{-1}cm^{-1}$ was assigned to the composite carbonyl absorption centered at 1715 cm^{-1}.[10] Effective sample thicknesses were calculated from the C—H absorption at 2720 cm^{-1} which had been calibrated with a series of film and filament samples of known thickness.

(ii) X-Ray diffraction analysis of rotated single-fiber samples was carried out using Ni-filtered Cu$K\alpha$ radiation from a Philips x-ray source and a modified power camera.[3] The fiber lengths were rotated in a plane at 90° to the incoming x-ray beam to give a diffractogram which depended only on the crystalline/ amorphous content of each fiber. The diffractograms were scanned with a Spex microdensitometer and digitized to permit subsequent data processing.

(iii) The tensile properties of the monofilaments were determined both to characterize the unoxidized filaments and to study the mechanical deterioration produced by photo- and γ-initiated oxidations. The Instron tensile testing machine was used to draw filaments in air at 25°C.

(iv) The total hydroperoxide content of the filaments was determined by a sensitive iodometric method.[5] Filament samples, up to 100 mg, were dissolved in peroxide-free decalin under vacuum by heating briefly (<1 min) to about 140°C and cooling rapidly. The resultant finely divided precipitate was accessible to the reducing medium of sodium iodide in acetic acid/isopropanol, enabling the hydroperoxide content of the whole fiber to be determined. After 5 min of refluxing, the reaction mixture was filtered through a coarse cellulose acetate filter to remove suspended polymer, and the liberated I_3^- determined spectrophotometrically at 360 nm. Separate experiments showed that the filtration process did not change the I_3^- concentration. To determine the extent of photo-oxidation that had occurred on a thin surface layer, whole (undissolved) samples were refluxed in the same manner. The access of the reagents into the hydrophobic monofilament is expected to be restricted to a surface layer a few microns in thickness.[2]

RESULTS

A Comparison of Fiber and Film Oxidative Behavior

Photo-oxidation has been shown to proceed at a rate dependent on the concentrations of UV-absorbing impurities present in the sample.[5] These con-

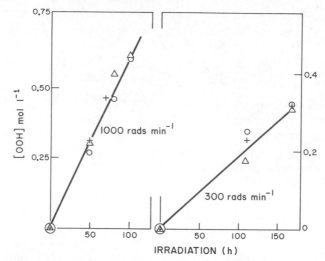

Fig. 2. γ-Initiated oxidation of PPH: (O) undrawn monofilament B4; (+) hot-drawn monofilament B1A; (△) film (Enjay).

centrations may vary appreciably with the processing conditions and so mask any effects of differing morphologies for a series of samples prepared under different processing conditions. Initiation of PPH oxidation by γ-radiation, however, occurs at random throughout the sample because of indiscriminate bond breaking . Propagation and termination reactions are thought to proceed in the same manner in both γ- and UV-initiated oxidations.[4,11]

Figure 2 shows that the γ-initiated oxidative behavior of two additive-free laboratory-extruded filaments (B1A and B4) and the commercial 25-μm film at dose rates of 300 and 1000 rads/min is independent of the nature of the sample. Only the hydroperoxide buildup is shown, but it was found that the carbonyl buildup was similarly independent of the nature of the sample. The yield of carbonyl products was always about 20 mole-% that of hydroperoxide, the proportion increasing slightly at high dose rates.

The structures of the two filaments, B1A and B4, were markedly different: B4 was an undrawn filament with low orientation and residual elongation of 1100%, and B1A was a highly oriented hot-drawn filament with a relatively low residual elongation (160%). The γ-oxidation data for other filaments between these two extremes are listed in Table I. With one exception, all were found to oxidize at very similar rates and to give similar product ratios. The only exception is the commercial filament, which contained an unextractable phenolic stabilizer, and was used previously.[2] This commercial filament yielded much less hydroperoxide than the additive-free filaments, with carbonyl products proportionally more important (Table I). Such behavior persisted even when the filament sample was pressed into a film (Table I). However, the oxidative behavior became identical to those of the additive-free film and fiber samples when the phenolic stabilizer was completely extracted (as shown by UV spectroscopy) from this film by Soxhlet extraction with acetone for 48 hr (Table I). (The resistance to extraction of additives in oriented fibers, as compared to unoriented film, presumably results from the rigid fibrillar structure of the oriented fiber.)

TABLE I
Gamma-Initiated Oxidations

Sample	Crystallinity %	Thickness μm	Initial residual elonga-tion,[c] %	Oxidation product concn., M[a]	
				[OOH]	[$>$C$=$O]
Filament BlA[b]	51	113	160	0.41	0.081
Filament B2A[b]	56	112	380	0.40	0.093
Filament B3A[b]	49	116	500	0.35	0.079
Filament B4[b]	54	114	1100	0.39	0.090
Filament B4[b] (cold drawn 3×)	—	~75	210	0.38	0.063
Amtech 6-mil mono-filament[d]	45	150	80	0.14	0.068
Unextracted Amtech film	—	~70	—	0.11	0.041
Extracted Amtech film[d]	—	~70	—	0.35	0.053
Additive free film[b,d]	—	~70	—	0.42	0.060
Enjay film[d]	~40[e]	25	—	0.43	0.093

[a] From IR data, 60 hr γ-irradiation at 1000 rads/min.

[b] From M.P.L. PPH stock.

[c] Drawn at 200%/min in air at 25°C.

[d] Acetone extracted for 48 hr and vacuum dried.

[e] Calculated from density measurements. Other crystallinities obtained from x-ray data (± 5%).

From the data in Table I and Figure 2, it is obvious that the PPH monofilaments studied here all oxidize in the same manner, which in turn is very similar to that of PPH films. It should, however, be noted that these film and fiber samples, although widely different in degree of orientation and fibrillar content, all have similar x-ray crystallinities (Table I).

All of the filaments studied were below 150 μm in diameter; for diameters above 150 μm, oxidation rates decreased presumably as a result of diffusion-controlled access of O_2 for these thicker fibers.

Variation of Filament Production Conditions

In the absence of morphological effects, the photostability of PPH monofilaments will depend upon the concentration and distribution of UV-absorbing impurities within them. It has often been proposed that oxidation products introduced during processing are a major cause of photo-instability.[4] Production conditions were, therefore, varied to determine precisely at what stage this oxidation occurs and how it may be prevented.

PPH filament resistance to photo-oxidation should ideally be measured by the onset of brittle failure. However, the buildup of OOH and $>$C$=$O products as measured by IR spectroscopy can be correlated with the degradation of mechanical properties and is often used as a convenient nondestructive measure of deterioration. For example, brittle failure of films and fibers usually occurs when ~0.1M —OOH has accumulated. In this paper, [OOH] or [OOH] + [$>$C$=$O] buildup is used as the criterion of photosensitivity. The more UV-

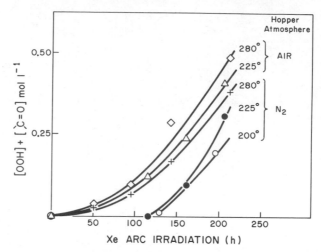

Fig. 3. Effect of extrusion temperature and hopper blanketing on PPH photostability. Filaments all extruded into air.

susceptible the sample, the more rapidly it will reach ~0.1M —OOH. At high conversions (>0.1M), appreciable secondary photolysis and nonuniformity of photo-oxidation complicate photo-oxidations to the extent that rates of product formation at these conversions are difficult to compare.

Up to the brittle failure point of films or filaments, the >C=O component from photo-oxidation accounts for ~10% of the total [OOH] + [>C=O] yield. After this point, the relative proportion of >C=O rises, reaching ~40% of the total product yield at about twice the brittle failure irradiation time.

Extrusion Temperature. Figure 3 shows the photo-oxidative behavior of a series of filaments which had been prepared by extrusion at various temperatures into air. For each extrusion temperature, the photostability was significantly greater for the filament extruded with thorough nitrogen purging of the hopper. For the nitrogen-purged series, the photostability decreased appreciably with increasing header temperature. The remainder of this paper refers to filaments that were all produced with a nitrogen-blanketed hopper and a spinneret temperature of 225°C. Even with apparently identical extrusion conditions, filament photostabilities were not entirely reproducible between different batches, presumably owing to differing amounts of trace oxidation during extrusion.

Nitrogen Blanketing of the Spinline. When molten polypropylene is extruded into air, appreciable oxidation may take place as the sample cools. Several samples were, therefore, extruded into a nitrogen atmosphere (<1.5% oxygen). The filament take-up speed and hence cooling rate was also varied.[12] As is seen in Figure 4, at a fixed extrusion temperature, none of these changes appreciably affected the filament photostability.

Filament Drawing. During the early stages of the investigation, it was observed that the hot-drawn filaments photo-oxidized appreciably faster than their undrawn "parents." This behavior is illustrated in Figure 5, which shows the photo-oxidative behavior of a 120-μm filament drawn 300% through an air oven at 180°C. A reference sample received identical thermal treatment (~8 sec residence time) in a 180°C hot air oven but was not drawn. A more detailed investigation of draw behavior was, therefore, undertaken.

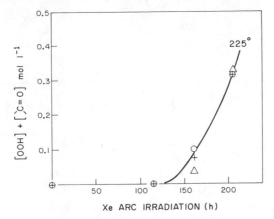

Fig. 4. Effect of windup speed and spinline blanketing on PPH photostability. Extruder header temperature 225°C: (+) extrusion into air, slow windup (20 cm/sec); (O) extrusion into air, fast windup (50 cm/sec); (Δ) extrusion into N₂, medium windup (30 cm/sec).

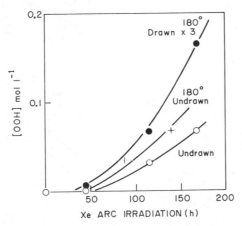

Fig. 5. Effect of hot drawing on PPH photostability: (O) undrawn monofilament; (+) undrawn, but oven treated (8 sec at 180°); (●) drawn ×3 at 180°C, residence time ~8 sec.

For filament samples all drawn 300% at 12 in./min in a water bath at various fixed temperatures, photostability was found to decrease dramatically as the bath temperature was lowered (Fig. 6). Furthermore, for a series of filaments all drawn in air at 25°C on an Instron mechanical tester (Fig. 7), increased drawing speed produced a large decrease in photostability.

To investigate whether the decrease in photostability on drawing was associated with changing fiber structure (fibrillar content, voiding, etc.) produced under different draw conditions or with trace oxidation during the draw, several samples were drawn in the absence of oxygen. The filaments shown in Figure 8 were drawn at similar rates, and so morphological effects such as voiding will be identical. The filaments drawn under vacuum were more stable than the air-drawn filament, but were still slightly less photostable than their undrawn parent. Trace oxidation would be lower for the vacuum-drawn filament since it was preevacuated for 12 hr prior to drawing to reduced O₂ in the polymer and held under high vacuum for 12 hr after drawing to allow for complete decay of any

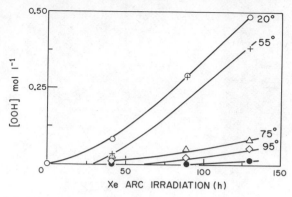

Fig. 6. Effect of drawing temperature on PPH photostability: (●) undrawn monofilament. Filaments drawn 3× at 12 in./min at 20°C (O), 55°C (+), 75°C (△), and 95°C (◇).

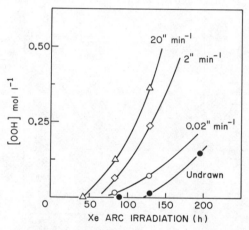

Fig. 7. Effect of draw speed on PPH photostability: (●) undrawn filament. Filaments drawn 3× in air at 25°C with draw speeds of 0.02 in./min (O), 2 in./min (◇), and 20 in./min (△).

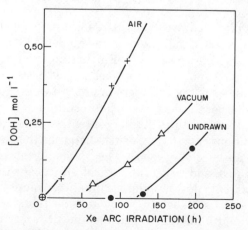

Fig. 8. Effect of drawing atmosphere on PPH photostability. Filaments drawn 3× at ~20 in./min at 25°C in air (+) and under vacuum (△).

radicals before exposure to air. The difference between the vacuum-drawn and the undrawn filaments, therefore, represents either an upper limit of possible morphological effects or the effect of traces of oxygen not completely removed from the filament. The difference between the vacuum-drawn and the air-drawn filaments must then be caused solely by oxidation during the draw step.

Further evidence for the unimportance of morphological effects is provided by the γ-oxidative behavior of a filament cold drawn in air. Such a filament was very susceptible to photo-oxidation (Fig. 8), but on exposure to γ-radiation yielded hydroperoxide levels very similar to those from the other γ-oxidized film and filament samples (Table I). In fact, the widely differing unstabilized samples shown in Table I all have identical γ-oxidation behavior.

The hydroperoxide levels of unirradiated filaments can be determined by iodometric analysis. Laboratory-extruded and commercial filaments contained $<1 \times 10^{-4}M$ hydroperoxide (the detection limit of the technique) before cold drawing, whereas a filament cold drawn in air contained $1.1 \times 10^{-3}M$ hydroperoxide. Such a concentration of extremely photosensitive hydroperoxide chromophores is obviously the origin of the subsequent rapid photo-oxidation. The hydroperoxide buildup from photo-oxidation of the cold-drawn filament followed a half-order dependence when plotted against the irradiation time,[13] with the intercept coinciding with the initial hydroperoxide level. This is consistent with a simple kinetic analysis of the early stages of photo-oxidation, based on the assumption that hydroperoxide photolysis is the dominant source of photoinitiation.[5]

The incorporation of a phenolic stabilizer, 2,4-di-*tert*-butylphenyl(4'-hydroxy-3',5'-di-*tert*-butylbenzoate), into the filament by compounding and extrusion was only partially effective in reducing oxidation during drawing. The hydroperoxide level of a cold-drawn filament was reduced from $\sim 1 \times 10^{-3}M$ (stabilizer free) to $3 \times 10^{-4}M$ (0.1 wt% of the phenol). However, even this level of draw-induced oxidation accelerated the photo-oxidation to such an extent that after 200 hr of irradiation in the xenon arc, the stabilizer had been consumed as evidenced by the loss of its characteristic IR absorbances, and the hydroperoxide level had reached $4 \times 10^{-2}M$. An undrawn filament, also containing 0.1 wt % of this phenol, suffered no observable decrease in stabilizer concentration, and the oxidation product concentration did not reach IR-detectable levels ($<5 \times 10^{-3}M$) within this 200-hr irradiation period.

Photo-oxidative Deterioration of Mechanical Properties

Large decreases in elongation at break were observed for all monofilaments before the oxidation products reached infrared-detectable levels (cf Figs. 5 and 9). In all cases, the load at break dropped less dramatically than the residual elongation. For example, after 40 hr of irradiation, the undrawn filament suffered a 30% loss in load at break while the hot drawn filament remained approximately unaltered.

Hot-drawn samples showed the greatest resistance to deterioration in mechanical properties by γ-irradiation. After 170 hr of γ-irradiation at 300 rads/min, the highly drawn filament B1A (initial elongation 160% at 200%/min) showed the greatest residual elongation of all of the similarly γ-irradiated fiber samples tested (35% at 100%/min).

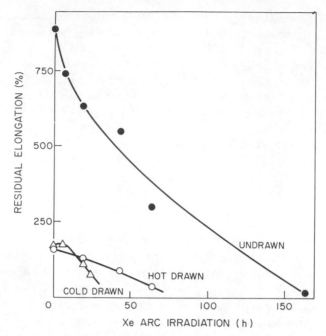

Fig. 9. Effect of photo-oxidation on monofilament residual elongation. Residual elongation to break at 200%/min at 25°C in air: (●) undrawn monofilament; (○) 5× hot-drawn filament at 180°C, residence time ~5 sec; (△) cold-drawn 3× (20 in./min at 25°C.)

DISCUSSION

The Absence of Morphology Dependence

The anomalous behavior reported earlier[2] for the Amtech filament and reproduced here (Table I) is clearly due to the presence of a phenolic stabilizer. However, it is perhaps surprising that little difference was observed in γ-oxidative behavior over such a wide range of films and filaments (Table I, Fig. 2). The orientation process, with its associated conversion from microspherulitic into microfibrillar morphology, might be expected to alter either the amount of polymer penetrated by oxygen, or the overall O_2 permeability of the PPH sample, or possibly the reactivity of the polymer, or a combination of all three. These effects will be discussed separately.

(a) At least during the early stages, γ-initiated oxidation and photo-oxidation are thought to occur solely in the oxygen-permeable, amorphous component of a semicrystalline polymer.[14,15] Sample crystallinities could, therefore, play a part in photostability. Atactic (noncrystalline) polypropylene has, however, been reported to yield only about 15% more hydroperoxide on γ-irradiation than a highly crystalline isotactic sample,[16] and so the magnitude of this effect is likely to be small. Moreover, the samples discussed here have similar overall crystallinities (Table I).

(b) Orientation has been suggested[17] to decrease O_2 permeability of polymers by possibly decreasing the amorphous content at the expense of the largely impermeable crystalline zones, by increasing the tortuosity of the path followed by a diffusant, and by increasing the resistance of amorphous material to molecular motions necessary to provide holes through which a gas molecule might pass. All three effects could reduce the O_2 permeability through highly oriented filaments to such a level that O_2 depletion occurs in the bulk of the oxidizing sample. Below a critical O_2 concentration in the polymer, both the γ- and photo-initiated oxidations must then become oxygen concentration dependent and the oxidation, diffusion controlled. Peterlin[18] has shown that drawn ($>8\times$) polyethylene is two orders of magnitude less permeable to methylene chloride vapor than polyethylene of below $4\times$ draw. However, the data of Connor and Schertz[17] for PPH film indicates only a twofold decrease in O_2 permeability for a large increase in orientation (corresponding to a fivefold increase in tensile strength). Our own data (Table I and Fig. 2) imply that the γ-oxidation is not O_2 diffusion controlled at the highest dose rate used (1000 rads/min) because thin films and relatively thick fibers oxidize at identical rates. Furthermore, the rate of O_2 consumption at 1000 rads/min from Figure 2 is $\sim 1.7 \times 10^{-6} M$/sec, which should lead to only about a 10% reduction in O_2 concentration in the center of 100-μm fibers, assuming a permeability[17] of 1.7×10^{-10} cm^2/sec· (cm Hg). Thus, it would appear that orientation does not cause a drastic decrease in PPH oxygen permeability, perhaps because of the compensating formation of partially permeable crystalline regions as suggested by Vieth and Wuerth[19] or because of microvoid formation opening up the structure.

(c) Different components of the amorphous phase may have differing susceptibilities to photo-oxidation. Previously, it has been argued that highly strained tie molecules may be especially susceptible.[3] However, within the range of samples chosen, this effect is apparently unimportant.

Extrusion Conditions

The data presented in Figures 3 and 4 indicate that under our extrusion conditions, oxidation *within* the extruder is largely responsible for the traces of oxidation products present in the extruded undrawn filaments. A typical filament contained about $1 \times 10^{-4} M$ hydroperoxide, but differences in hydroperoxide levels between filaments could not be reliably determined at this level. The order of photostabilities was, however, consistent with the extent of oxidation anticipated within the extruder. Raising the extruder temperature lowered the photostability, as did omission of hopper blanketing. This behavior is consistent with an earlier study by Burch on PPH extrusion stability.[20] Burch observed that the melt index increased appreciably with increasing extrusion temperature and also when the hopper atmosphere contained $>3\%$ oxygen.

Extrusion into either nitrogen or air had little effect on the filament properties, nor did the enhanced cooling produced by a faster windup rate. Presumably, after the melt emerges from the spinneret, cooling is sufficiently rapid that there is little opportunity for significant oxidation to occur.

Drawing Conditions

It is obvious from Figures 5–9 that drawing, particularly at high rates or low temperatures, reduces photostability. This must be largely due to oxidation occurring during the draw to give chromophores and not morphological or structural changes as is shown in Figure 8 and Table I. Thermal oxidation at high drawing temperatures cannot account for this effect. In fact, thermal treatment alone, without draw, failed to appreciably reduce photostability (Fig.

5). This thermal treatment was more severe than that received during hot drawing, where the filament accelerated out of the oven. The decrease in photostability with *decreasing* draw temperature also indicates that thermally induced oxidation is unimportant.

Oxidation is more likely to result from free radicals produced by bond rupture on drawing the polymer. Radical production by mechanical strain has been directly observed when polymers were crushed at liquid nitrogen temperatures.[21] More recently, strain-induced free radicals have been observed at room temperature, usually by ESR, for a wide range of polymers.[22,23] These radicals will be rapidly scavenged by oxygen, and the resultant peroxy radicals may then initiate oxidation conventionally. Oxidation products produced in this way should be randomly distributed across the fiber cross section and so should be especially effective in initiating further photo-oxidation as compared to the same quantity of radicals in localized zones. The experimentally observed photo-oxidation kinetics of cold-drawn filaments are, in fact, consistent with uniformly distributed —OOH groups from the draw process.[13]

In contrast, the photo-oxidation of PPH films has earlier been shown to occur in a surface layer a few microns thick, reputedly caused by an initial concentration of UV-absorbing impurities in this layer.[7] There is some evidence that the situation is similar in a commercial stabilized PPH monofilament.[2] Concentration of the chromophores and the resulting radicals in a surface layer lead to a reduction in the local kinetic chain length of the propagation reaction as compared to the same number of radicals spread uniformly throughout the total sample volume.

The sensitizing effects of draw at low temperatures and/or high strain rates (Fig. 6 and 7) probably result from the greater radical yield under these conditions as compared to high temperatures and/or low strain rates. The latter conditions will aid interchain slippage and unpleating of folds, rather than backbone fracture to give reactive macro-alkyl radicals.

Photo-oxidative Deterioration of Mechanical Properties

The cold-drawn filament with its high rate of photo-oxidation may be seen to be the most rapidly deteriorating (Fig. 9); however, comparing Figure 5 and Figure 9, it can be seen that for a constant degree of oxidation (e.g., $0.02M$ — OOH), the undrawn filament suffered the greater proportional loss of residual elongation. Highly drawn filaments, which are fibrillar, are therefore more resistant to photo-oxidative deterioration than undrawn filaments (microcrystalline). This behavior is consistent with an earlier study where surface cracking was reported during the photo-oxidation of a commercial filament.[3] Only during the later stages of photo-oxidation, long after the filament had become mechanically useless, did cracking occur in the fibrillar component. In an undrawn filament, no such fibrillar reinforcements are available and crack propagation can occur at low levels of oxidation.

Antioxidants and Processing Oxidation

Oxidation during the various stages of production will be important even for stabilized filaments. Few stabilizers can be completely effective in preventing oxidation during extrusion and drawing, and even a relatively small increase in the oxidation product concentration makes it much harder for any photostabilizer to function effectively because of the increased rate of free-radical production. Clearly, the most effective stabilizers will be those that rapidly scavenge the radicals produced during processing, or those that cleanly decompose the hydroperoxide during storage.[5,24] Many conventional antioxidants such as the hindered phenols will reduce oxidation during the production stages but are poor photostabilizers apparently because they themselves tend to be photolyzed.[24]

This deficiency can obviously be overcome by a combination of an antioxidant and a conventional photostabilizer, such as a nickel chelate. However, the fact that photo-oxidations can be prevented by free-radical scavenging, as can the thermal processes, implies that processing oxidation and photodegradation may be suppressed by the use of light-stable phenolic stabilizers.[5,24]

CONCLUSIONS

1. Over the range of samples tested, films and filaments γ-and photo-oxidize in an identical manner, but the concentration of UV-absorbing impurities responsible for initiating photo-oxidation will vary with the production conditions.

2. Oxidation during extrusion is minimized by removal of oxygen from the polymer feed and a relatively low extruder temperature, whereas nitrogen blanketing of the spinline is found to have little effect.

3. Free-radical production by bond rupture occurs during the draw stage and is most marked at high draw rates and low draw temperatures.

4. Oxidation products resulting from bond breaking during the draw process markedly reduce the photo-oxidative stability of the filament.

5. The formation of UV-absorbing chromophores by oxidation during drawing is reduced by the presence of a phenolic radical scavenger, but not completely suppressed.

6. Chromophore formation during PPH deformation even in the presence of radical scavengers should lead to premature failure of PPH articles at strained points, or points briefly deformed during their lifetime, e.g., knots, tight loops, hinge points, impact zones, etc. This effect will be minimized if the residual elongation in PPH materials is designed to be as low as possible.

References

1. W. R. Hindson, *Text. J. Australia*, **42**, 72 (May 1967).
2. D. J. Carlsson, F. R. S. Clark, and D. M. Wiles, *Text. Res. J.*, **46**, 590 (1976).
3. P. Blais, D. J. Carlsson, F. R. S. Clark, P. Z. Sturgeon, and D. M. Wiles, *Text. Res. J.*, **46**, 641 (1976).
4. D. J. Carlsson and D. M. Wiles, *J. Macromol. Sci., Rev. Macromol. Chem.*, **C14**, 65 (1976).
5. D. J. Carlsson, A. Garton, and D. M. Wiles, *Macromolecules*, **9**, 695 (1976).
6. E. Niki, C. Decker, and F. R. Mayo, *J. Polym. Sci., Polym. Chem. Ed.*, **11**, 2813 (1973).
7. D. J. Carlsson and D. M. Wiles, *Macromolecules*, **4**, 174,179 (1971).
8. H. J. Oswald and E. Turi, *Polym. Eng. Sci.*, **5**, 152 (1965).
9. D. J. Carlsson, F. R. S. Clark, and D. M. Wiles, *Text. Res. J.*, **46**, 318 (1976).
10. D. J. Carlsson and D. M. Wiles, *Macromolecules*, **2**, 587,597 (1969).
11. C. Decker and F. R. Mayo, *J. Polym. Sci., Polym. Chem. Ed.*, **11**, 2847 (1973).
12. J. E. Spruiell and J. L. White, *Polym. Eng. Sci.*, **15**, 660 (1975).

13. D. J. Carlsson, A. Garton, and D. M. Wiles, unpublished results.

14. M. B. Neiman, G. I. Likhtenshtein, Y. S. Konstantinov, N. P. Karpets, and J. G. Urman, *Vysokomol. Soedin.*, **5,** 1706 (1963).

15. T. Seguchi and N. Tomura, *J. Phys. Chem.*, **77,** 40 (1972).

16. C. Decker, F. R. Mayo, and H. Richardson, *J. Polym. Sci., Polym. Chem. Ed.*, **11,** 2879 (1973).

17. W. P. Connor and G. L. Schertz, *SPE Trans.*, 186 (1963).

18. A. Peterlin, *Pure Appl. Chem.*, **39,** 239 (1974).

19. W. Vieth and W. F. Wuerth, *J. Appl. Polym. Sci.*, **13,** 685 (1969).

20. G. M. Burch, *The Chemical Engineer,* 264 (July 1971).

21. S. E. Bresler, S. N. Zhurkov, E. N. Kazebekov, E. M. Saminskii, and E. E. Tomashevskii, *Zhur. Tekh. Fiz.*, **29** 358 (1959).

22. A. Peterlin, *J. Magn. Reson.*, **19,** 83 (1975).

23. M. Sakaguchi, H. Yamakawa, and J. Sohma, *J. Polym. Sci., Polym. Lett. Ed.*, **12,** 193 (1974).

24. D. J. Carlsson and D. M. Wiles, *J. Macromol. Sci., Rev. Macromol. Chem.*, **C14,** 155 (1976).

Received July 22, 1976
Revised September 30, 1976

JOURNAL OF APPLIED POLYMER SCIENCE   VOL. 21, 2979–2990 (1977)

Gel Permeation Chromatography of Ethylene–Propylene Copolymerization Products

TOSHIO OGAWA and TADAMI INABA, *Hirakata Plastics Laboratory, Ube Industries Ltd., Hirakata, Osaka 573, Japan*

Synopsis

A simple method to calculate average molecular weights and D ($\equiv \overline{M}_w/\overline{M}_n$) value from the GPC chromatogram of copolymerization products, especially for ethylene–propylene copolymerization products, was investigated by simulation technique. The method is based on the use of the calibration curve determined by the average ethylene content of the products. In addition to this method, the calibration curve prepared for polypropylene was also applied to determine the D value. Average molecular weights and D values were determined, with small errors, for narrow distribution samples with respect to molecular weight and chemical composition.

INTRODUCTION

Gel permeation chromatography (GPC) is very useful for characterizing high molecular weight materials, especially for the determination of molecular weight distribution of homopolymers. The chromatogram approximately corresponds to the molecular weight distribution curve in shape. In the case of copolymers, however, the GPC chromatogram does not always reflect the molecular weight distribution. We must study profoundly the meaning of GPC chromatogram of copolymers.

Polymer species are separated according to the hydrodynamic volumes of molecules. As put forward by Benoit et al.,[1] when the hydrodynamic volumes of the sample and the standard polymer are the same, the elution volumes are also equal; the molecular weight distribution of the sample can be calculated from its chromatogram by a calibration curve of molecular weight versus elution volume, which is made by the well-characterized polymer standards. However, the hydrodynamic volume of copolymers in solution depends not only on the molecular weight, but also on the comonomer content. Thus, the mixture of the polymer species having a variety of molecular weight and comonomer content is eluted at a given elution count. In this case, the number of the calibration curve cannot, in principle, be fixed by a single one for a given sample, because it must be drawn in accordance with each polymer species. When one intends to obtain statistical values, such as number- and weight-average molecular weights, some assumptions cannot help being involved in the calculation of those values from the chromatogram.

The method proposed by Benoit et al.[2] may be good for this purpose. That is, the molecular weight of polymer eluted at each count is determined by mea-

2980

suring the viscosity of the eluate and applying the universal rule.[1] The error in the molecular weights thus calculated is decreased to some extent. However, the viscosity is averaged over all polymer species eluted at the elution count. Further, a specially designed viscometer accurate to at least 0.01 sec is required, since the eluted polymer solution is considerably diluted. Thus, we studied another simple method for treating the GPC chromatogram. In studies on the determination of the molecular weight distribution, the comonomer content of the products is previously known in the majority of cases. This paper is concerned with the method of treating GPC chromatograms for polymers of known comonomer content.

Our study is limited to ethylene–propylene copolymerization products, which are composed of ethylene–propylene copolymer (EP), polypropylene (PP), and polyethylene (PE) as described in the previous paper.[3] A bivariate normal distribution function and a log-normal one were assumed for the compositional and molecular weight distributions of the copolymer and the molecular weight distribution of the homopolymers, respectively. In the first place, the hypothetical GPC chromatogram of the products was made by using the universal rule proposed by Benoit et al.[1] The statistical values were calculated from the GPC chromatogram by a single calibration curve, which was determined from the ethylene content of the product. The error in these values was discussed in detail.

EXPERIMENTAL

Fractionated copolymers were subjected to the determination of compositional dependence of the relation between molecular weight and intrinsic viscosity. The fractionation experiment by column elution was carried out in the xylene–butyl cellosolve system at 130°C. The fractionation procedure was described in a previous paper.[4] The ethylene content of the fractions was determined by Corish's method,[5] which is based on the ratio of the intensity at 1380 cm^{-1} to that at 1460 cm^{-1} arising from the methyl group and the methyl and methylene groups, respectively, in the infrared spectrum. The intrinsic viscosity of the fractions was determined at 135°C in decalin.

The fractionation experiment for a commercially available high-impact polypropylene was carried out by column elution in the decalin–butyl carbitol system at 165°C.[3] The GPC chromatogram of the polypropylene was measured by using a Shimadzu model-1A, which was mounted with a combination of four columns: $10^6, 10^5, 10^4$, and 10^3 Å permeability crosslinked polystyrene columns. The solvent was o-dichlorobenzene, the operational temperature was 135°C, and the elution rate was 1.0 ml/min. The calibration curve for the sample was prepared based on the method proposed in this paper, after the calibration curve of PP and PE was made from that of polystyrene by applying the universal rule. The details for other experimental conditions were described elsewhere.[5]

CALCULATIONS

Distribution Curve

The calibration curve varying with copolymer composition must be prepared in advance to make or treat the hypothetical GPC chromatogram of copolymers.

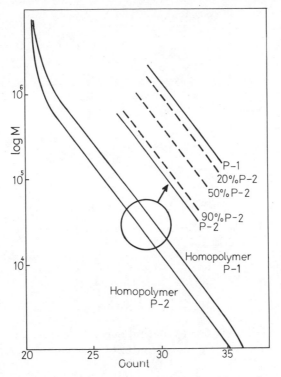

Fig. 1. Schematic calibration curves of homopolymers P-1 and P-2 and copolymers with various comonomer content.

The curve is schematically illustrated in Figure 1. Usually, the calibration curve is located between those of homopolymers composed of each monomer component. The location of the curve can be properly determined by applying the universal rule, which is in the form

$$\log [\eta]M = AV_e + B \tag{1}$$

where $[\eta]$ is the intrinsic viscosity of the copolymer eluted at the elution count V_e; M is the molecular weight; and A and B are constants for a given set of experimental conditions and are independent of copolymer composition. The intrinsic viscosity is a function of molecular weight in the case of homopolymers. This is expressed by the Mark–Houwink equation, $[\eta] = KM^a$ (K and a are constants). Thus, the following calibration curve is derived from eq. (1):

$$\log M = \frac{AV_e}{1 + a} + \frac{B - \log K}{1 + a} \tag{2}$$

In the case of copolymers, however, K and a vary with copolymer composition. No general equations to express them as a function of copolymer composition are present as yet. In practical use, for EP copolymers, an empirical formula must be derived using fractionated copolymers. For choice of formula, it may be pertinent that the intrinsic viscosity of the copolymer $[\eta]_{EP}$ is correlated with those of PP ($\equiv [\eta]_{PP}$) and PE ($\equiv [\eta]_{PE}$), which have the same molecular weight as the corresponding EP copolymer. The following equations were used for this purpose: eq. (3) for PE reported by De La Cuesta[4] and eq. (4) for PP reported by Kinsinger.[5] These were determined in decalin at 135°C (superscript D indicates decalin).

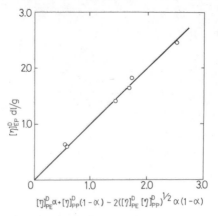

Fig. 2. Empirical relation between intrinsic viscosities of copolymers and homopolymers with same molecular weight as copolymers.

$$[\eta]_{PE}^{D} = 3.9 \times 10^{-4} M^{0.74} \tag{3}$$

$$[\eta]_{PP}^{D} = 1.10 \times 10^{-4} M^{0.80} \tag{4}$$

After a number of trials, we found that $[\eta]_{EP}$ can be expressed by the following equation as a function of comonomer content of the copolymer, $[\eta]_{PE}^{D}$, and $[\eta]_{PP}^{D}$. The result is shown in Figure 2:

$$[\eta]_{EP}^{D} = [\eta]_{PE}^{D}\alpha + [\eta]_{PP}^{D}(1 - \alpha) - 2([\eta]_{PE}^{D}[\eta]_{PP}^{D})^{1/2}\alpha(1 - \alpha) \tag{5}$$

where α is the weight fraction of ethylene of the copolymer. Such a equation may be applicable in o-dichlorobenzene (ODCB) at the same temperature as well, since ODCB is very similar to decalin in solvent properties. $[\eta]_{EP}$ was determined under the conditions corresponding to those of GPC experiment, namely, in ODCB at 135°C. The following Mark–Houwink equations[9] were used for PE and PP:

$$[\eta]_{PE} = 4.9 \times 10^{-4}M^{0.74} \tag{6}$$

$$[\eta]_{PP} = 1.0 \times 10^{-4}M^{0.78} \tag{7}$$

Since the value of a for PE ($\equiv a_{PE}$) was very similar to that for PP ($\equiv a_{PP}$), a for EP ($\equiv a_{EP}$) was assumed that $a_{EP} = (a_{PE}a_{PP})^{1/2}$. K for EP ($\equiv K_{EP}$) was derived from eq. (5) in the form

$$K_{EP} = K_{PE}\alpha + K_{PP}(1 - \alpha) - 2(K_{PE}K_{PP})^{1/2}\alpha(1 - \alpha) \tag{8}$$

Thus, the calibration curve can be drawn to make the hypothetical GPC chromatogram of the copolymer. Further, when the average ethylene content $\bar{\alpha}$ of the copolymer is known, the statistical values can be calculated from the GPC chromatogram by substitution of $\bar{\alpha}$ for α in eq. (8); this is the method presented in this paper.

As described previously, copolymer species having a variety of compositions are included in the fraction obtained at any elution count. The effect of composition on the chromatogram height should be taken into consideration. Generally, the chromatogram height obtained from the refractometer is not only proportional to the instantaneous concentration, but also depends on the copolymer composition. Fortunately, the refractive index increments (dn/dc) for

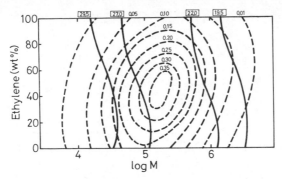

Fig. 3. Relation between molecular characteristics of copolymers and elution counts: numbers in rectangles indicate elution count; (—) copolymers and homopolymers with common elution count; (- - - -) contour lines of molecular weight and compositional distributions. Numbers indicate relative weight.

PE and PP are very similar.[10,11] The chromatogram height of the copolymer was taken as independent of copolymer composition. Further, the chromatogram height was assumed not to be influenced by the molecular weight.

Chromatogram of Products

Distributions with respect to the molecular weight and chemical composition must be assumed to make hypothetical chromatogram for the products. The following distribution function was adopted for the homopolymers according to previous papers:[3,12]

$$W(\ln M) = \frac{1}{\beta_h \sqrt{2\pi}} \exp\left[-\frac{1}{2\beta_h^2} (\ln M - \ln M_0)^2 \right] \qquad (9)$$

where $W(\ln M)$ is the weight distribution function; β_h is the standard deviation for $\ln M$ (usually β_P for PP and β_E for PE instead of β_h); and $\ln M_0$ is the logarithmic peak molecular weight in the log-normal distribution curve (usually $\ln M_P$ for PP and $\ln M_E$ for PE instead of $\ln M_0$). A bivariate normal distribution function was adopted for the distribution of the copolymer:

$$W(\ln M,\alpha) = \frac{1}{2\pi\beta_M\beta_\alpha(1 - \rho^2)^{1/2}} \exp\left\{ -\frac{1}{2(1 - \rho^2)} \right.$$
$$\left. \times \left[\frac{(\ln M - \ln M_{EP})^2}{\beta_M^2} - \frac{2\rho(\ln M - \ln M_{EP})(\alpha - \alpha_0)}{\beta_M\beta_\alpha} + \frac{(\alpha - \alpha_0)^2}{\beta_\alpha^2} \right] \right\} \qquad (10)$$

where $W(\ln M,\alpha)$ is the distribution function for the copolymer; $\ln M$ is the logarithm of molecular weight; α is the ethylene content on a weight basis; $\ln M_{EP}$ is the peak position for the molecular weight distribution; α_0 is the peak position for the compositional distribution; β_M and β_α are the standard deviations for $\ln M$ and α, respectively; and ρ is the correlation coefficient between $\ln M$ and α.

The distribution curve of the homopolymers was divided into 55 increments in simulation. The distribution surface of the copolymer was divided into 5500 increments. Since it is practically impossible to treat these functions in the range from zero to infinity, the distribution range was limited to polymer species eluted from 13.5 to 40.5 count in the GPC chromatogram. Now we defined WPP, WEP, and WPE by

$$WPP = \sum_j f_{PP}(\ln M_j) \tag{11}$$

$$WEP = \sum_j \sum_k f_{EP}(\ln M_j, \alpha_k) \tag{12}$$

$$WPE = \sum_j f_{PE}(\ln M_j) \tag{13}$$

where $f_{PP}(\ln M_j)$, $f_{EP}(\ln M_j, \alpha_k)$, and $f_{PE}(\ln M_j)$ express the weights of jth, (j,k)th and jth increments of PP, EP, and PE components, respectively. The above functions were normalized as follows:

$$WPP + WEP + WPE = 1.0 \tag{14}$$

Obviously, the ratio of PP, EP, and PE is

$$PP:EP:PE = WPP:WEP:WPE \tag{15}$$

In practice, the weight fraction of all copolymer species eluted at a given count V_i is obtained using eq. (10) for given α and $\ln M$, and it can be expressed as $f_{EP}(\ln M_j, \alpha_k)$. Here, the other parameters in eq. (10) were adequately assumed by taking into account the experimental results. In the same manner as with f_{EP}, $f_{PE}(\ln M_j)$ is calculated from eq. (9) after calculation of $\ln M$ at $\alpha = 1.0$ by eq. (8), and $f_{PP}(\ln M_j)$ at $\alpha = 0.0$. Thus, the sum of weight fraction of the polymer species eluted at V_i is given by

$$W(V_i) = \sum_j f_{PP}(\ln M_j)_i + \sum_j \sum_k f_{EP}(\ln M_j, \alpha_k)_i + \sum_j f_{PE}(\ln M_j)_i \tag{16}$$

The hypothetical GPC chromatogram was obtained by calculating $W(V_i)$ for each 2.5-ml increment in elution volume.

The average ethylene content of the original product is given by

$$\bar{\alpha} = \sum_j \sum_k \alpha_{j,k} f_{EP}(\ln M_j, \alpha_k) + WPE \tag{17}$$

TABLE I
Assumed Characteristic Parameters for EP Copolymers

Sample	$\ln M_{EP}$	β_M	α_0	β_α	ρ
EP-1	12.0	1.25	0.435	0.365	0.25
EP-2	12.0	1.25	0.435	0.100	0.25
EP-3	12.0	1.25	0.435	0.600	0.25
EP-4	12.0	1.70	0.435	0.365	0.25
EP-5	12.0	0.80	0.435	0.365	0.25

TABLE II
Calculated Values for EP Copolymers

Sample	Ethylene wt-%	Original			α Calibration			PP Calibration
		$\bar{M}_n \times 10^{-4}$	$\bar{M}_w \times 10^{-4}$	D	$\bar{M}_n \times 10^{-4}$	$\bar{M}_w \times 10^{-4}$	D	D
EP-1	0.468	7.85	35.6	4.54	7.39	40.1	5.43	5.23
EP-2	0.435	7.45	35.5	4.77	7.18	37.2	5.18	4.99
EP-3	0.486	7.95	35.1	4.41	7.55	39.1	5.18	5.00
EP-4	0.468	4.21	64.6	15.4	3.89	73.6	18.9	17.7
EP-5	0.468	12.2	22.6	1.86	11.6	24.9	2.14	2.10

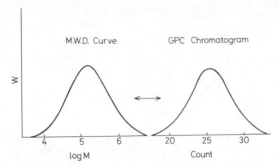

Fig. 4. Molecular weight distribution curve and GPC chromatogram for a EP copolymer.

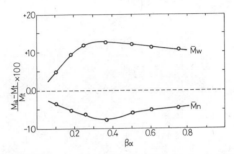

Fig. 5. Error in apparent $\overline{M}_n$, $\overline{M}_w$ as a function of β_α for EP copolymers: M_t, true molecular weight; M_a, apparent molecular weight.

Thus, the apparent average molecular weights of the original products are calculated from the chromatogram obtained above and the calibration curve, which is determined from $\overline{\alpha}$ by using eqs. (8) and (12). When we use the calibration curve exclusive for polypropylene, the calculation is accomplished by setting α = 0 in eq. (8). The so-called true average molecular weights of the original products are calculated from the above f_{PP}, f_{EP}, and f_{PE} by the conventional method.

RESULTS AND DISCUSSION

Polymer Species Eluted at a Given Count

As expressed by eq. (16), various kinds of polymer species are included in a given eluate. In the case of EP copolymers, the polymer species are different in both molecular weight and ethylene content, and their molecular weight and ethylene content were calculated using eqs. (8), (2), and (17). The results is shown in Figure 3; the polymer species having low molecular weight and ethylene content are eluted together with those having high molecular weight and low ethylene content. For example, polypropylene having $M = 10^6$ is eluted together with polyethylene having $M = 3.8 \times 10^5$. However, the shape of the curve on which the polymer species have a common elution count is almost independent of molecular weight and compositional regions, as illustrated by the solid line. In this respect, the elution behavior is different from that of solutional fractionation.[9] Therefore, the statistical values of copolymers obtained from the GPC chromatogram are expected to be less erroneous than those obtained by solutional fractionation.

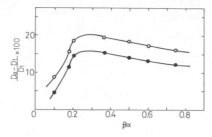

Fig. 6. Error in apparent D value as a function of β_α for EP copolymers: D_t, true D value; D_a, apparent D value.

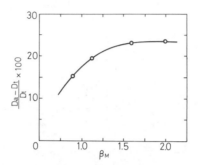

Fig. 7. Error in apparent D value as a function of β_M for EP copolymers.

Pure EP Copolymers

There are many types of copolymerization products. The pure EP copolymer type is the most representative. Characteristic parameters in eqs. (9) and (10) assumed for calculations are shown in Table I. True and apparent molecular weights and their D values were calculated using two kinds of calibration curves: one was obtained from the average ethylene content, eq. (17), of a copolymer sample, i.e., $\bar{\alpha}$ calibration, and the other was that for polypropylene, i.e., PP calibration. The calibration curve prepared for polyethylene was not used for these calculations, because the behavior was expected to be similar to that for PP calibration. The results are shown in Table II and Figures 4–7.

As shown in Figure 4, the GPC chromatogram is very similar in shape to the molecular weight distribution curve. However, the statistical values calculated numerically are sometimes very different from the corresponding true ones. Figure 5 shows that the apparent weight- and number-average molecular weights are larger than the true ones and depend on β_α of the copolymers to some extent. The error, i.e., the deviation from the true values, reaches a maximum at approximately $\beta_\alpha = 0.35$. As shown in Figure 6, a similar behavior is present for D values. Further, it is noticeable that the values obtained by PP calibration are less erroneous rather than those obtained by $\bar{\alpha}$ calibration. So long as we discuss the behavior of D values, the use of the calibration curve exclusive for polypropylene is also preferable to EP copolymers. The effect of molecular weight distribution on the apparent D values (Fig. 7) becomes considerable with increase in β_M, and is almost independent of the apparent D value in the large β_M region. Since ordinarily copolymerized EP copolymers in heptane give 0.35–0.45 for β_α and 1.0–1.5 for β_M,[9] the error in the statistical values is +15–20%, while in fractionated samples it may be within 10%. Thus, the GPC method is definitely useful for characterizing the copolymer fractions having narrow molecular weight and compositional distributions.

PP–PE Blend

This blend belongs to an extreme case among copolymerization products. Its behavior in GPC is important for considering complicated copolymerization products. The molecular weight distribution curve and GPC chromatogram for the blend composed of homopolymers showing broad molecular weight distribution seemingly have a similar shape. However, the result of numerical calculation reveals that this blend has peculiar characteristics in the behavior of apparent $\overline{M}_n$, $\overline{M}_w$, and D values. The results are shown in Tables III and IV and Figures 8–10. Figure 8 demonstrates that the apparent $\overline{M}_n$ and $\overline{M}_w$ largely depend on the difference between two peak molecular weights of component homopolymers. Namely, when the peak position of the PE component is smaller than that of the PP component, the apparent $\overline{M}_n$ is larger than the true one. The apparent $\overline{M}_n$ approaches the true one with an increase of $\overline{M}_n$; and in $M_P > M_E$, this tendency is reversed. On the other hand, the behavior of the apparent $\overline{M}_w$ is completely contrary to that of the apparent $\overline{M}_n$. As shown in Figure 9, the apparent D value coincides with the true one when $M_P \simeq M_E$. The apparent D value is different from the true one when the difference between M_P and M_E is large. Namely, the relation between the true and apparent D values can be classified into two categories; Figure 10 shows this situation schematically.

TABLE III
Characteristic Parameters for Components in PP–PE Blend

Sample	PP		PE		Weight ratios	
	$\ln M_P$	β_P	$\ln M_E$	β_E	PP	PE
PPPE-1	12.0	1.25	9.0	1.25	0.50	0.50
PPPE-2	12.0	1.25	11.0	1.25	0.50	0.50
PPPE-3	12.0	1.25	12.0	1.25	0.50	0.50
PPPE-4	12.0	1.25	13.0	1.25	0.50	0.50
PPPE-5	12.0	1.25	15.0	1.25	0.50	0.50
PPPE-6	12.0	1.25	11.0	1.25	0.70	0.30
PPPE-7	12.0	1.25	11.0	1.25	0.30	0.70

TABLE IV
Calculated Values for PP–PE Blend

Sample	Original			$\overline{\alpha}$ Calibration			PP Calibration
	$\overline{M}_n \times 10^{-4}$	$\overline{M}_w \times 10^{-4}$	D	$\overline{M}_n \times 10^{-4}$	$\overline{M}_w \times 10^{-4}$	D	D
PPPE-1	0.72	18.8	26.2	1.08	15.9	14.7	13.9
PPPE-2	4.03	24.4	6.06	4.95	24.4	4.93	4.75
PPPE-3	7.45	35.5	4.77	7.79	41.0	5.26	5.07
PPPE-4	10.8	65.0	6.00	9.90	84.6	8.55	8.16
PPPE-5	13.8	276	20.0	11.4	395	34.7	32.4
PPPE-6	4.94	28.9	5.84	6.65	33.1	4.97	4.79
PPPE-7	3.40	19.9	5.87	3.66	17.7	4.84	4.67

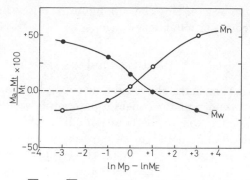

Fig. 8. Error in apparent $\overline{M}_n$ and $\overline{M}_w$ as a function of $(\ln M_P - \ln M_E)$ of PP–PE blend. PP:PE = 50:50 (wt): M_p, peak molecular weight of PP component; M_E, peak molecular weight of PE component.

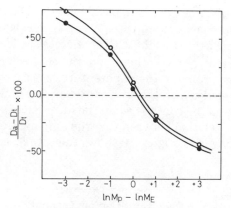

Fig. 9. Error in apparent D value as a function of $(\ln M_P - \ln M_E)$ of PP–PE blend. PP:PE = 50:50 (wt): (—○—) $\overline{\alpha}$ calibration; (—●—) PP calibration.

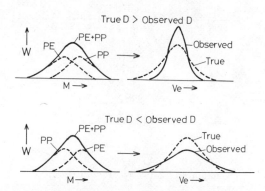

Fig. 10. Schematic representation for relations between peak molecular weights of component homopolymers and apparent D values.

Other Blend Types

PP–EP–PE, PP–EP, and EP–PE blends are classified into the other blend types. We understand the GPC behavior as overlapping that of EP copolymers and PP–PE blend; and, therefore, the behavior is fundamentally the same as shown in Figure 10. Characteristic parameters assumed for calculation are

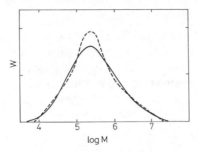

Fig. 11. Calculated and apparent molecular weight distribution curve D for a commercial polymer: (- - - - - -) molecular weight distribution curve obtained from GPC chromatogram, $\overline{M}_n = 1.17 \times 10^5$, $\overline{M}_w = 9.52 \times 10^5$; (—) molecular weight distribution curve calculated based on the column fractionation data. PP:EP = 80:20 (wt), $\overline{M}_n = 9.97 \times 10^4$, $\overline{M}_w = 9.38 \times 10^5$. PP: ln $M_P = 12.0$, $\beta_P = 1.25$; EP: ln $M_{EP} = 13.5$, $\beta_M = 1.25$, $\beta_\alpha = 0.10$, $\alpha_0 = 0.85$, $\rho = 0.25$.

shown in Table V, and the results are shown in Table VI. The error in the calculated values is expected to be within 10% since the average molecular weights of component polymers have similar values. GPC measurement for broad molecular weight distribution polymer leads to large error in D values due to the fluctuation of the baseline of chromatogram, even though we deal with homopolymers.[13] Therefore, the error due to the assumption for the calibration curve is not worthy of mention in the case of these blend types.

Comparison of Simulated Curve with Experimental Curve

The result of solutional fractionation which was performed previously revealed that a commercially available high-impact polypropylene was composed of polypropylene homopolymer and ethylene-rich EP copolymer.[3] The homopolymer content resembled commercial polypropylenes in molecular characteristics, such as molecular weight and its distribution. So, ordinary values for polypropylenes were assumed for β_P and M_P. Appropriate values were also

TABLE V
Characteristic Parameters for Components in PP–EP–PE, PP–EP, and EP–PE Blends

	PP		EP					PE		Weight ratios		
Sample	ln M_P	β_P	ln M_{EP}	β_M	α_0	β_α	ρ	ln M_E	β_E	PP	EP	PE
PEM-1	12.0	1.25	12.0	1.25	0.435	0.365	0.25	11.0	1.25	0.4	0.2	0.4
PEM-2	12.0	1.25	12.0	1.25	0.435	0.365	0.25	11.0	1.25	0.2	0.6	0.2
PEM-3	12.0	1.25	12.0	1.25	0.435	0.365	0.25	—	—	0.6	0.4	0.0
PEM-4	—	—	12.0	1.25	0.435	0.365	0.25	11.0	1.25	0.0	0.4	0.6

TABLE VI
Calculated Values for PP–EP–PE, PP–EP, and EP–PE Blends

Sample	Ethylene wt-%	Original			$\overline{\alpha}$ Calibration			PP Calibration
		$\overline{M}_n \times 10^{-4}$	$\overline{M}_w \times 10^{-4}$	D	$\overline{M}_n \times 10^{-4}$	$\overline{M}_w \times 10^{-4}$	D	D
PEM-1	0.498	4.39	26.3	5.99	5.32	27.4	5.16	4.98
PEM-2	0.483	5.51	30.6	5.56	6.20	33.7	5.43	5.22
PEM-3	0.187	7.50	35.6	4.60	8.70	15.4	5.20	5.01
PEM-4	0.794	3.57	21.1	5.91	3.62	19.4	5.35	5.15

estimated for β_M, M_{EP}, and so on, from viscosity measurement of the EP copolymer component. Thus, we prepared the molecular weight distribution curve from the hypothetical GPC chromatogram. On the other hand, the distribution curve was also obtained from the GPC chromatogram which was determined by experiment. The results are shown in Figure 11. These curves are very much in agreement with each other. Therefore, the results discussed above should be fully taken into consideration when we deal with GPC chromatograms obtained from these copolymerization products.

CONCLUSIONS

A method for treating GPC chromatograms obtained from ethylene–propylene copolymerization products was investigated by simulation technique. The most important problem was how to convert elution count to molecular weight. In this study, the calibration curve to use for this purpose was determined by the average ethylene content of samples. $\overline{M}_n$, $\overline{M}_w$, and D values were obtained for broad distribution copolymers in molecular weight and chemical composition, and these included an error of 15–20%. However, in the case of narrow distribution fractions such as those obtained by solutional fractionation, the error was within 10%. The GPC method is highly useful in this case. In the case of PP–PE blends, the deviation of the apparent values from the true ones became small with decrease in difference between two peak molecular weights. The apparent values are valuable under this special condition. The behaviors for PP–EP–PE, PE–EP, and PP–PE blends are more complicated than for PE–PP blends. The behavior can be fundamentally understood as an overlapping of that of EP copolymer and PP–PE blend. As far as the D values are concerned, the use of the calibration curve for polypropylene as well as the above one is also valuable to the copolymerization products.

The authors wish to thank Dr. S. Tokiura for his encouragement of this study.

References

1. Z. Grubisic, P. Rempp, and H. Benoit, *J. Polym. Sci. B,* **5,** 753 (1967).
2. Z. Grubisic, M. Picot, P. Gramain, and H. Benoit, *J. Appl. Polym. Sci.,* **16,** 2931 (1972).
3. T. Ogawa and T. Inaba, *J. Appl. Polym. Sci.,* **18,** 3345 (1974).
4. T. Ogawa, Y. Suzuki, and T. Inaba, *J. Polym. Sci. A-1,* **10,** 737 (1972).
5. P. J. Corish and M. E. Tunnicliffe, *J. Polym. Sci. C,* **No. 7,** 187 (1964).
6. T. Ogawa, S. Tanaka, and S. Hoshino, *J. Appl. Polym. Sci.,* **16,** 2257 (1972).
7. M. O. De La Cuesta and F. W. Billmeyer, *J. Polym. Sci. A,* **1,** 1721 (1963).
8. J. Kinsinger and R. Hughes, *J. Phys. Chem.,* **63,** 2002 (1959).
9. T. Ogawa, S. Tanaka, and T. Inaba, *J. Appl. Polym. Sci.,* **17,** 319 (1973).
10. R. Chiang, *J. Polym. Sci.,* **28,** 235 (1958).
11. E. E. Drott and R. A. Mendelson, *J. Polym. Sci. B,* **2,** 187 (1964).
12. T. Ogawa and T. Inaba, *J. Polym. Sci., Polym. Phys. Ed.,* **12,** 785 (1974).
13. T. Ogawa and T. Inaba, *J. Appl. Polym. Sci.,* **20,** 2101 (1976).

Received June 25, 1976
Revised October 1, 1976

JOURNAL OF APPLIED POLYMER SCIENCE VOL. 21, 2991–3002 (1977)

The Xanthate Method of Grafting. VI. The Copolymer–Homopolymer Ratio

V. HORNOF,* C. DANEAULT, B. V. KOKTA, and J. L. VALADE, *Groupe de Recherche en Pâtes et Papiers, Département de l'Ingénierie, Université du Québec à Trois-Rivières, Trois-Rivières, Quebec, Canada*

Synopsis

Wood pulp was compolymerized with butyl acrylate as monomer. The xanthate redox method was employed to initiate the reaction. The effect of reaction time and temperature on the relative yield of grafted polymer and homopolymer was investigated. In the lower temperature region (15°–25°C), induction periods ranged from 10 to 30 min. No induction periods were observed at higher temperatures (40° and 60°C). The copolymer/homopolymer ratio was found to depend on both time and temperature. A considerable amount of homopolymer was formed in the initial stage of the reaction. Increased reaction temperature resulted in lower grafting efficiency. Similarly, both graft and homopolymer molecular weights decreased with rising reaction temperature.

INTRODUCTION

Grafting as a technique for the modification of both natural and synthetic polymeric materials has been investigated for a number of years. Cellulose has been one of the most frequently used backbone materials, and corresponding work has resulted in a great number of patents and publications. Several excellent review articles have also been published on the subject.[1–4]

Ideally, the product of a graft copolymerization should contain no homopolymer. The presence of homopolymer in the reaction product usually has a negative effect on its properties. Furthermore, the formation of homopolymer reduces possible copolymer yield, and a costly extraction procedure may be necessary to remove it from the products. Unfortunately, all graft copolymerization methods give rise to some polymer which is not chemically bound to the substrate. Its relative amount depends on different factors such as the type of cellulosic material used, the type of initiator, the type of monomer, as well as on the reaction conditions employed (temperature, concentration of reactants).

The xanthate method of grafting, discovered by Faessinger and Conte,[5] appears to offer considerable advantages over other grafting processes. With pure cellulosic substrates, it has been shown to yield relatively minor amounts of homopolymers.[6,7] When using wood pulps, however, the results vary and are influenced by the residual lignin and hemicellulose. Results published by the

---

* Present address: Department of Chemical Engineering, University of Ottawa, Ottawa, Ontario, Canada, K1N 6N5.

2991

present authors[8] demonstrate that, on the one hand, copolymers almost free of homopolymers could be prepared with bleached Kraft pulps[8] (lignin content ≤0.05%); and, on the other hand, reaction products obtained under the same reaction conditions with mechanical pulp[9] (lignin content = 27%) contained more than 50% homopolymer. Former experiments carried out with a Kraft semibleached pulp[10] (lignin content = 0.8%) gave a clear indication that even the very low amount of lignin present led to a diminished grafting efficiency. However, the amount of homopolymers could be easily reduced in the presence of a higher concentration of hydrogen peroxide as coinitiator. From a more practical point of view, it appears that such a way of increasing grafting efficiency would be too expensive, even after discounting the fact that high concentrations of H_2O_2 considerably reduce the mechanical properties of the pulp. Furthermore, this method of increasing grafting efficiency does not work with high-lignin pulps.[9]

The aim of the present paper is to find out more about the rate of polymer formation in the xanthate grafting system, in particular, as regards the parallel formation of grafted polymer and homopolymer and as regards their respective molecular weights.

EXPERIMENTAL

Materials

Kraft semibleached pulp (lignin content = 0.8%) has been used throughout this work as a grafting substrate. It was supplied by the Consolidated-Bathurst Company, Division Waygamack.

Butyl acrylate (Eastman) was distilled on a column filled with copper rings. The center cut was collected and stored in a refrigerator.

All other reagents used in this work were employed as supplied by the manufacturers.

Copolymerization

The technique of pulp preconditioning as well as the copolymerization conditions have been described in previous papers.[10,11] The degree of xanthation of the pulp was determined by iodometry. The value found was $\gamma = 5.0 \pm 0.4$. All experiments discussed in this article were carried out using conditions as follow: pulp, 4.5 g ± 0.01 g (oven-dry weight of never-dried pulp); monomer (butyl acrylate), 9.00 g; water, 450 ml; surfactant (Tween-40), 0.9 g; H_2O_2, 1.5 g (diluted into 25 ml before adding). The polymerization was terminated by additions of hydroquinone. Excess hydrogen peroxide was destroyed by treating the products with 1% $K_2S_2O_5$ solution.

Extraction

The quantity of homopolymer in the reaction products was determined by a 12-hr Soxhlet extraction of 2–3-g samples of the products with acetone. The calculations concerning the grafting parameters were made considering the loss of pulp during mercerization due to its solubility in NaOH (about 3.5%).

The grafting parameters are defined as follows:

$$\text{total conversion, \%} = (D - B)/C \times 100,$$

$$\text{polymer loading, \%} = (A - B)/B \times 100,$$

$$\text{grafting efficiency, \%} = (A - B)/(D - B) \times 100$$

where A is weight of products after copolymerization and extraction, B is weight of pulp (oven dry, corrected for solubility in NaOH solution), C is weight of monomer charged, and D is weight of products after copolymerization.

Molecular Weights

Grafted Polymer. Grafted poly(butyl acrylate) was isolated by hydrolyzing away the cellulose with 72% sulfuric acid according to the procedure described by Nakamura and co-workers,[12] followed by dissolving the residue in acetone and filtration.

Homopolymer. Poly(butyl acrylate) homopolymer was isolated by shaking dry reaction products with acetone during 3 hr. The clear solution of homopolymer was collected.

In both cases, viscosity was recorded at 25°C in acetone at four different concentrations in Ubbelohde viscometers. Following extrapolation to obtain the intrinsic viscosity $[\eta]$, the corresponding degree of polymerization was calculated according to the expression[12]

$$[\eta] = 5.53 \times 10^{-3} \times P^{0.66}$$

Polymer molecular weight was obtained by multiplying the degree of polymerization P by monomer molecular weight.

RESULTS AND DISCUSSION

While a previous work[10] on the effects of reaction conditions on xanthate grafting used acrylonitrile as monomer, the present work was carried out with butyl acrylate. Preliminary experiments had indicated that copolymerizations with butyl acrylate as monomer resembled closely those with acrylonitrile, with the exception that the reaction rate was considerably higher with the former. This is an important factor: the heterogeneous character of the reaction makes it impossible to withdraw well-defined samples. Therefore, each point on the

TABLE I
Dependence of Grafting on Reaction Time at 15°C

| Sample no. | Time, min | Conversion, % | | | Polymer loading, % | Grafting efficiency, % |
		Homo-polymer	Grafted polymer	Total		
159	5	—	—	0	—	—
158	10	—	—	0	—	—
157	20	—	—	0	—	—
155	30	—	—	0	—	—
185	40	24.6	13.7	38.3	27.1	35.9
153	50	15.0	37.1	52.1	74.3	71.3
161	60	16.5	40.6	57.1	81.1	71.1
160	120	20.3	46.0	66.3	92.0	69.4

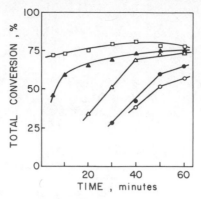

Fig. 1. Total conversion to polymer as a function of reaction time and temperature: (O) 15°C;
(●) 20°C; (△) 25°C; (▲) 40°C; (□) 60°C.

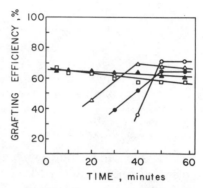

Fig. 2. Grafting efficiency as a function of reaction time and temperature: (O) 15°C; (●) 20°C;
(△) 25°C; (▲) 40°C; (□) 60°C.

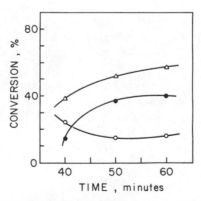

Fig. 3. Copolymer–homopolymer composition of products formed at 15°C: (O) homopolymer;
(●) grafted polymer, (△) total polymer.

conversion curve must be obtained by a separate experiment.   This permits one
to obtain enough sample to determine the copolymer–homopolymer ratio
(grafting efficiency) and to measure the molecular weights.

Experiments were carried out at five different temperatures (15°–60°C), with
reaction times ranging from 5 min to 2 hr.   The data obtained, including total
conversion, conversion to grafted polymer, conversion to homopolymer, polymer
loading, and grafting efficiency, have been compiled in Tables I–V.

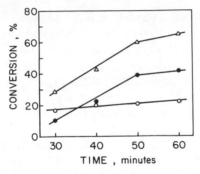

Fig. 4. Copolymer–homopolymer composition of products formed at 20°C: (O) homopolymer; (●) grafted polymer; (△) total polymer.

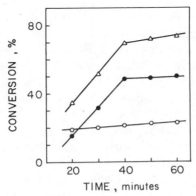

Fig. 5. Copolymer–homopolymer composition of products formed at 25°C: (O) homopolymer; (●) grafted polymer; (△) total polymer.

Figure 1 plots total conversion to polymer as a function of time. The five curves obtained demonstrate the strong effect of temperature on the polymerization. Apart from the normal increase of conversion with rising temperature, the data obtained at the three lower temperatures show rather long induction periods. It is, therefore, clear that it is in particular the initiation reaction which is influenced by reaction temperature. At 60°C, one obtains a very high conversion already at 5 min reaction time, which increases only slightly thereafter.

TABLE II
Dependence of Grafting on Reaction Time at 20°C

Sample no.	Time, min	Conversion, %			Polymer loading, %	Grafting efficiency, %
		Homo-polymer	Grafted polymer	Total		
149	5	—	—	0	—	—
147	10	—	—	0	—	—
148	20	—	—	0	—	—
179	30	17.2	11.1	28.3	22.5	39.1
144	40	20.3	22.1	42.4	44.3	52.2
145	50	21.1	38.9	60.0	77.9	64.9
143	60	23.3	42.1	65.4	84.1	64.3
142	120	20.7	47.0	67.7	93.9	69.4

Similarly at 40°C, the 5-min conversion is quite high (46.4%). Another 15°C drop in temperature, however, gives a system which shows no polymer formation up to 10 min of reaction time. This induction period increases in a regular manner with a further drop in temperature, attaining 20 min and 30 min at 20°C and 15°C, respectively. (The duration of the induction periods is taken as the longest reaction time used which produces no polymer. The true induction periods could be longer by several minutes.) On the other hand, the overall rate of polymerization as estimated from the slopes of the corresponding conversion curves, seems to be much less influenced by the temperature. In all cases, the reaction stops at 60–80% conversion, beyond which polymer formation ceases.

The appearance of induction periods when grafting a vinyl monomer onto wood pulp is not surprising. Previous work[8] involving a series of partially delignified Kraft pulps and acrylonitrile as monomer has indicated the presence of induction periods even with relatively low-lignin pulps (0.6–1.0%). Similar effects have been reported for other grafting systems. During a ceric nitrate-initiated grafting of acrylonitrile with Kraft pulps, Erdelyi[14] observed induction periods which varied from 1 min to 12 min according to the lignin content in the pulp. On the contrary, experiments carried out by Dimov and Pavlov, employing very pure xanthated cellulose (partially hydrolyzed viscose) with acrylonitrile as the monomer and H_2O_2 as the coinitiator, have not shown any induction periods. A similar behavior was reported by Samoylov and co-workers,[15] who investigated grafting initiated by the reaction between the xanthate groups of partially hydrolyzed viscose and pentavalent vanadium (HVO_3).

More important than the total conversion is the percentage of polymer that is truly grafted to the backbone material (grafting efficiency). All grafting techniques produce more or less homopolymer beside the main product. Its relative amount depends on various factors such as the character of the grafting substrate and of the monomer, the nature of the initiating system, etc.

It is indeed true that no grafting system precludes completely the formation of unattached polymer. Considering the example of the [cellulose xanthate/ hydrogen peroxide] initiating system, one observes that ungrafted polymer chains may be started by ·OH radicals:

$$\text{Cell}-\text{O}-\overset{\overset{\text{S}}{\|}}{\text{C}}-\text{S}^- + H_2O_2 \longrightarrow \text{Cell}-\text{O}-\overset{\overset{\text{S}}{\|}}{\text{C}}-\text{S}^{\cdot} + \text{HO}^{\cdot} + \text{HO}^-$$

TABLE III
Dependence of Grafting on Reaction Time at 25°C

| Sample no. | Time, min | Conversion, % | | | Polymer loading, % | Grafting efficiency, % |
		Homo-polymer	Grafted polymer	Total		
91	5	—	—	0	—	—
183	10	—	—	0	—	—
176	20	18.8	15.7	34.5	31.1	45.5
184	30	20.0	31.8	51.8	63.6	61.4
173	40	21.3	48.4	69.7	96.6	69.4
172	50	23.2	49.0	72.2	98.0	67.9
171	60	23.9	49.9	73.8	99.8	67.6
169	120	19.3	56.5	75.8	113.0	74.5

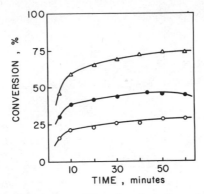

Fig. 6. Copolymer–homopolymer composition of products formed at 40°C: (O) homopolymer; (●) grafted polymer; (△) total polymer.

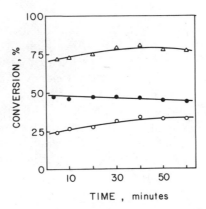

Fig. 7. Copolymer–homopolymer composition of products formed at 60°C: (O) homopolymer; (●) grafted polymer; (△) total polymer.

$$HO\cdot + {}_nM \rightarrow HO-(M)_n.$$

However, growing homopolymer radicals may become copolymers by a recombination with radicals present on the backbone:

$$Cell - O\cdot + \cdot M-(M)_{n-1}-OH \rightarrow Cell-O-(M)_n-OH$$

A mechanism has also been proposed by Gaylord[16] by which graft copolymerization results from termination of growing polymer chains on cellulose by insertion into aldehyde groups.

TABLE IV
Dependence of Grafting on Reaction Time at 40°C

Sample no.	Time, min	Conversion, %			Polymer loading, %	Grafting efficiency, %
		Homo-polymer	Grafted polymer	Total		
132	5	15.9	30.5	46.4	61.0	65.8
131	10	20.7	38.8	59.5	77.5	65.2
130	20	23.1	42.4	65.5	84.8	64.7
128	30	25.6	44.1	69.7	88.2	63.2
129	40	25.9	47.3	73.2	94.4	64.6
127	50	28.4	46.7	75.1	93.3	62.2
126	60	29.4	45.7	75.1	91.4	60.9

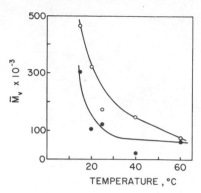

Fig. 8. Homopolymer and graft molecular weight as a function of reaction temperature: (O) homopolymer; (●) grafted polymer; reaction time 60 min.

Previous work[10] has shown that with acrylonitrile as a monomer, the grafting efficiency observed was mostly about 60–70%. Similar results have been obtained with other monomers (styrene, methyl methacrylate, ethyl acrylate). Figure 2 shows the dependence of grafting efficiency on time and temperature in the present system. It is evident that, once again, most grafting efficiency values are situated in the neighborhood of 60%. This relative independence of homopolymer content of the nature of the monomer would indicate that it is rather the character of the backbone material which has the decisive effect on the reaction. Much greater changes in grafting efficiency were observed when using different pulps as substrates.[8,9]

TABLE V
Dependence of Grafting on Reaction Time at 60°C

| Sample no. | Time, min | Conversion, % | | | Polymer loading, % | Grafting efficiency, % |
		Homo-polymer	Grafted polymer	Total		
139	5	24.1	47.9	72.0	95.7	66.5
138	10	26.8	46.3	73.1	92.7	63.4
137	20	27.5	47.3	74.8	94.7	63.3
136	30	31.6	47.7	79.3	95.3	60.2
135	40	34.6	46.7	81.3	93.4	57.5
134	50	33.1	45.0	78.1	89.9	57.6
133	60	33.4	44.3	77.7	88.5	57.0

TABLE VI
Dependence of Polymer Molecular Weight on Reaction Time at 15°C

| Sample no. | Time, min | Intrinsic viscosity $[\eta]$ | | Molecular weight $\overline{M}_v \times 10^{-3}$ | |
		Homo-polymer	Grafted polymer	Homo-polymer	Grafted polymer
185	40	1.630	0.593	707	153
153	50	1.467	0.765	603	225
161	60	1.241	0.936	468	305
160	120	1.022	1.034	348	355

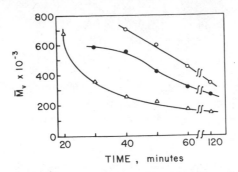

Fig. 9. Homopolymer molecular weight as a function of reaction time and temperature: (O) 15°C; (●) 20°C; (△) 25°C.

The data plotted in Figure 2 also show that, in general, grafting efficiency increases with decreasing temperature. At the three lower temperatures (15°, 20°, and 25°C), grafting efficiency increases with time, especially in the first phases of the reaction. At 40° and 60°C, however, slight decrease in grafting efficiency occurs with increasing reaction time. The behavior of the system is better illustrated in Figures 3–7, which compare the total conversion with the conversion to homopolymer and with the conversion to grafted polymer at each of the five temperatures studied.

Let us discuss these plots in the ascending order of temperature: At 15°C (Fig. 3), the homopolymer content in the product seems to decrease slightly with time, while the increase in total conversion is accounted for wholly by the formation

TABLE VII
Dependence of Polymer Molecular Weight on Reaction Time at 20°C

Sample no.	Time, min	Intrinsic viscosity $[\eta]$		Molecular weight $\overline{M}_v \times 10^{-3}$	
		Homo-polymer	Grafted polymer	Homo-polymer	Grafted polymer
179	30	1.441	0.308	587	57
144	40	1.398	0.659	560	179
145	50	1.158	0.580	421	148
143	60	0.971	0.468	322	107
142	120	0.860	0.376	268	76

TABLE VIII
Dependence of Polymer Molecular Weight on Reaction Time at 25°C

Sample no.	Time, min	Intrinsic viscosity $[\eta]$		Molecular weight $\overline{M}_v \times 10^{-3}$	
		Homo-polymer	Grafted polymer	Homo-polymer	Grafted polymer
176	20	1.588	0.659	680	179
184	30	1.050	0.739	363	213
173	40	0.847	0.695	262	194
172	50	0.768	0.671	226	184
171	60	0.649	0.507	175	121
169	120	0.603	0.419	157	90

of grafted polymer. A similar situation is found at 20°C (Fig. 4) and 25°C (Fig. 5). While the homopolymer content increases slowly up to 60 min of reaction time, it drops again at 120 min (Tables II and III); the bulk of the increase in total conversion is, therefore, once again explained by the formation of grafted polymer. The picture changes at 40°C where both types of polymer show a net increase of an approximately equal magnitude (Fig. 6). Finally, at 60°C (Fig. 7), the amount of copolymer decreases with time while more homopolymer is formed.

The five sets of data discussed in the previous paragraph have one feature in common: the relatively high percentage of homopolymer formed in the beginning of the reaction. It appears that, regardless of whether or not there is an induction period, the first nonzero conversion experiment (40 min at 15°C, 30 min at 20°C, etc.) gives always approximately 20% yield of homopolymer. Under the same conditions, the yield of grafted polymer varies between 11.1% and 47.9%. It is difficult to account for this phenomenon. As a possible explanation, one could conceive of a reaction between hydrogen peroxide and an impurity in the pulp (e.g., residual degraded lignin), which could occur before the onset of the main reaction between hydrogen peroxide and cellulose xanthates and give rise to the formation of homopolymer during the first stages of the process.

The decrease of grafting efficiency with time at the two higher temperatures (40° and 60°C) may be explained by the gradual depletion of xanthate groups available for the initiation reaction. Increased formation of homopolymers in later stages of the reaction at higher temperatures (40° and 50 °C) has also been reported by Dimov and Pavlov. However, greater frequency of chain transfer by monomer could also account for the lower grafting efficiency observed at higher temperatures, especially if this decrease were accompanied by a simultaneous decrease of molecular weight of the polymer formed.

This is clearly the case with the homopolymers, as evidenced by the molecular weight data listed in Tables VI–IX. At 60 min of reaction time, for example, the 15°C molecular weight is 468,000; it decreases gradually to 89,000 at 60°C (Fig. 8). Results obtained with the other reaction times follow a similar pattern. The most probable explanation for this decrease of homopolymer molecular weight with temperature would be an increased rate of chain transfer at higher temperatures.

It has been shown in a previous paper[10] that homopolymer molecular weight

TABLE IX
Molecular Weights at 40° and 60°C

Sample no.	Time, min	Temperature, °C	Intrinsic viscosity [η]		Molecular weight $\overline{M}_v \times 10^{-3}$	
			Homo-polymer	Grafted polymer	Homo-polymer	Grafted polymer
127	50	40	0.613	0.183	160	25
126	60	40	0.569	0.166	144	22
134	50	60	0.273	0.165	47	22
133	60	60	0.414	0.316	89	59

decreased rapidly with reaction time.   This effect is also evident in the present work.   The plots shown in Figure 9 illustrate the abrupt character of this decrease which is the more rapid the higher the temperature.   Because of the complexity of the reaction system, it is difficult to find a satisfactory explanation for this effect.   It is possible that hydrogen peroxide reacts with some components of the pulp producing compounds effective as chain transfer agents.   The concentration of such agents would rise with time, thus reducing molecular weight of the polymers formed.

Molecular weights of the grafted polymer are also listed in Tables VI–IX.   It is evident that they show a much greater variation.   This is believed to be mainly due to the fact that the process of hydrolyzing away cellulose with 72% sulfuric acid also causes some hydrolysis and degradation of the butyl acrylate polymer. Attempts to apply the acetic acid-acetic anhydride method described by Rogovin and co-workers[18] failed, most likely due to a complete transesterification of poly(butyl acrylate) leading to the formation of water-soluble poly(acrylic acid). Nevertheless, Figure 8 shows that at 60 min, molecular weight of copolymerized poly(butyl acrylate) also seems to decrease substantially with increasing reaction temperature.   A similar decrease is also evident at 50 and 120 min of reaction time; experiments stopped at 40 min, and at 30 min they show a certain increase of molecular weight with rising temperature.   At all times, however, graft molecular weight is lower than that of the homopolymer.   A similar effect has been observed in a previous work[10] with acrylonitrile as a monomer; it can be explained by the fact that, unlike the homopolymer, grafted chains grow solely in the vicinity of cellulose (or other pulp components), hence a greater probability of chain transfer to the backbone material will exist.

The molecular weights of grafted poly(butyl acrylate) found in this work are much higher than those observed with polyacrylonitrile.[10,15]   Consequently, the efficiency of modification obtained with the same polymer loading would be lower in the present case.   While an attempt was made to test the papermaking properties of the copolymerized pulps, it was found impossible to disintegrate them sufficiently to make a homogeneous slurry.   Nakamura and co-workers[12] reported that rather extensive crosslinking occurred in the graft copolymerization of cellulose with ethyl acrylate.   This may also be the case in the present work, partly explaining the greater variation of graft molecular weights.

References

1. V. T. Stannett and H. B. Hopfenberg, in *Cellulose and Cellulose Derivatives*, N. Bikales and L. Segal, Eds., Vol. 5, Part 5, Wiley, New York, 1970, pp. 907–936.

2. J. C. Arthur, *Adv. Macromol. Chem.*, **2**, 1 (1970).

3. M. S. Bains, *J. Polym. Sci. C*, **No. 37**, 125 (1972).

4. K. Ward, Jr., *Chemical Modification of Papermaking Fibers*, Marcel Dekker, New York, 1973, pp. 167–215.

5. R. W. Faessinger and J. S. Conte, U.S. Pat. 3,359,224 (Dec. 9, 1967); U.S. Pat. 3,330,787 (July 11, 1967).

6. W. J. Brickman and R. W. Faessinger, *Text. Chem. Color.*, **5**, 38 (1973).

7. K. Dimov and P. Pavlov, *J. Polym. Sci. A-1*, **7**, 2775 (1969).

8. V. Hornof, B. V. Kokta, and J. L. Valade, *J. Appl. Polym. Sci.*, **19**, 1573 (1975).

9. V. Hornof, V. V. Kokta, and J. L. Valade, *J. Appl. Polym. Sci.*, **20**, 1543 (1976).

10. V. Hornof, B. V. Kokta, and J. L. Valade, *J. Appl. Polym. Sci.,* **19,** 545 (1975).

11. B. V. Kokta and J. L. Valade, *Tappi,* **55,** 366 (1972).

12. Y. Nakamura, J. C. Arthur, Jr., M. Negishi, K. Doi, E. Kageyama, and K. Kudo, *J. Appl. Polym. Sci.,* **14,** 929 (1970).

13. J. Brandrup and E. H. Immergut, Eds., *Polymer Handbook,* Interscience, New York, 1967.

14. J. Erdélyi, *Zellstoff Papier,* **8,** 243 (1970).

15. V. I. Samoylov, B. P. Morin, and Z. A. Rogovin, *Faserforsch. Textiltech.,* **22,** 297 (1971).

16. N. Gaylord, *J. Polym. Sci. C,* **37,** 153 (1972).

17. V. Hornof, C. Daneault, B. V. Kokta, and J. L. Valade, to be published.

18. A. A. Gulina, R. M. Livshits, and Z. A. Rogovin, *Vysokomol. Soedin.,* **7**(9), 1529 (1965).

Received June 18, 1976
Revised October 8, 1976

Melt Spinning of Isotactic Polypropylene: Structure Development and Relationship to Mechanical Properties

HARI P. NADELLA, HELEN M. HENSON,* JOSEPH E. SPRUIELL, and
JAMES L. WHITE, *Department of Chemical and Metallurgical
Engineering, The University of Tennessee, Knoxville, Tennessee 37916*

Synopsis

An extensive experimental study of structure development during the melt spinning of polypropylene and in as-spun polypropylene filaments is reported. Five polymers representing different molecular weights and polymerization methods were studied. WAXS, SAXS, and birefringence measurements were used to characterize the structure of the filaments. Spinning through air gives rise to monoclinic crystalline structures and spinning into cold water, the paracrystalline smectic form. Both crystalline and amorphous orientation factors were found to correlate with spinline stress for the different polymers studied. Mechanical properties of as-spun fibers such as modulus, yield strength, tensile strength, and elongation to break also correlate with spinline stress.

INTRODUCTION

Isotactic polypropylene is an important commercial plastic, film, and synthetic fiber. As a fiber, it may exhibit a wide variety of mechanical properties. By suitable processing, it can be used to produce very high modulus and tensile strength fibers[1] or microporous fibers (and films) with large elastic recovery.[2–5] These facts make basic studies of the development of structure and properties of polypropylene fibers as a function of melt-spinning conditions of considerable interest.

The pioneering study of the melt spinning of polypropylene is that of Sheehan and Cole.[1] These authors show that monoclinic polypropylene is produced under normal air quenching conditions, but quenching in cold water produces a paracrystalline smectic structure. Hot drawing of fibers, especially smectic fibers, spun at low take-up velocities yields very high strength fibers. Katayama, Amano, and Nakamura[6] have carried out on-line wide-angle x-ray diffraction and birefringence studies on a spinline and followed the development of crystallinity and orientation. More recently, structure development during melt spinning of polypropylene has been investigated by Fung, Orlando, and Carr,[7] Kitao, Ohya, Furukawa, and Yamashita,[8] Anderson and Carr,[9] Henson and Spruiell,[10] Spruiell and White,[11,12] and Ishizuka and Koyama.[13] Kitao et al. have analyzed the development of orientation in terms of Hermans-Stein-Wilchin-

---

* Present address: Union Carbide Nuclear Division, Oak Ridge, Tennessee 37830.

sky[11,14–17] orientation factors. Spruiell et al.[10–12] have carried out on-line x-ray diffraction and birefringence measurements, quantitatively determined spinline crystallization kinetics, and shown that orientation factors depend upon spinline stress independent of temperature. Polypropylene exhibits unique bimodal orientation when crystallized under stress.[9,10,18] Interpretation of the possible implication and mechanisms of this bimodal orientation have been given by Clark,[19] Anderson and Carr,[9] Spruiell et al.,[10,12] and Clark and Spruiell.[20]

In this paper, we explore the relative behavior of a series of polypropylenes of varying molecular weight and produced by different catalyst systems. This paper continues our studies of structure development during melt spinning.[10–12,21–24] It is also part of an extensive study of the processing of polypropylene in our laboratories which include rheological as well as structure development studies.

EXPERIMENTAL

Materials

Five different polypropylenes with varying levels of molecular weight were studied. Their basic characteristics are summarized in Table I, together with a code naming system. Three of the polymers were highly isotactic Hercules Profax, and two were in the Tennessee Eastman Tenite series. The latter also possess a high level of tacticity, but, perhaps, not quite as high as the Profax polymers. Other possible differences include molecular weight distribution. In the present study, these effects were not fully investigated. A more detailed study of molecular weight distribution effects is underway and will be published at a later date.

The intrinsic viscosities given in Table I were determined at 137°C in decalin and converted to molecular weight using the expression[25]

$$M = ([\eta] \times 10^4)^{1.25} \tag{1}$$

TABLE I.
As-Received Polymer Properties

Manufacturer and commercial code	Melt index, g/min	Our code name	Intrinsic viscosity, dl/g	Weight-average molecular weight	Tacticity
Hercules Profax 6823	0.42	H-0042	3.21 (3.25, 3.30[a])	4.30×10^5	very high
Hercules Profax 6423	6.6	H-0660	2.26	2.77×10^5	very high
Hercules Profax 6323	12.0	H-1200	1.99	2.36×10^5	very high
Tennessee Eastman Tenite 4241	9.00	T-0900	2.01	2.39×10^5	high
Tennessee Eastman Tenite 4221	2.55	T-0255	2.71	3.48×10^5	high

[a] Courtesy of Hercules, Inc.

Melt Spinning

The polypropylenes were melt spun from a Fourné Associates screw extruder and spinning head. The extruder had a 13-mm diameter screw. Constant throughput was maintained by a Zenith gear pump. The spinneret capillary was 0.381 cm long and 0.0762 cm in diameter.

The extrusion temperature was kept constant at 230°C except for H-0660; in this case, filaments were also spun with extrusion temperatures of 200° and 260°C. The polymers, with the exception of H-0042, were extruded at a rate of 2.1 g/min. The H-0042 exhibited extrudate distortion[26,27] under these conditions; to eliminate this, the extrusion rate was reduced to 0.5 g/min. The filaments were normally melt spun through stagnant air at approximately 25°C and were passed around a 3-in. diameter, constant-speed feed roll placed 10 feet from the spinneret. After leaving the feed roll, the filaments were taken up on a Leesona 955 constant-tension winder. Filaments were taken up at speeds of 50, 100, 200, 400, and 550 m/min whenever this was feasible. A Rothschild tensiometer with a 10-g measuring range was used to measure the fiber tension.

In an attempt to produce smectic spun filaments as described by Sheehan and Cole,[1] some H-0660 polymer was spun into a water bath at 9°C placed 9 in. from the spinneret. These filaments were taken up at speeds varying from 25 to 300 m/min.

Wide-Angle X-Ray Diffraction and Crystalline Orientation

Wide-angle x-ray diffraction patterns of the spun filaments were made using a flat plate-type camera and nickel-filtered CuK_α radiation. These patterns were used to determine the crystalline form present and the qualitative features of the orientation.

On-line WAXS measurements on the spinline were made using Rigaku-General Electric rotating-anode generator. This is the apparatus developed by Dees and Spruiell[22] and used by them on high-density polyethylene. Parts of these on-line results for polypropylene have been reported by Spruiell and White.[11,12] The crystalline fraction X was determined from microdensitometer scans made on the WAXS patterns. The relative intensity in the crystalline reflections compared to the amorphous halo was used to compute a crystalline index. The data were normalized by considering density values of X on spun filaments as correct.

Quantitative studies of crystalline orientation were made by measuring the intensity distributions around the Debye rings with a General Electric x-ray diffractometer equipped with a single crystal orienter and an ORTEC counting system. The 040 and 110 monoclinic reflections were measured and used to compute Hermans–Stein crystalline orientation factors.[12,15–17] These factors indicate the orientation of the crystallographic axes with respect to the fiber axis. They are defined in such a way that the orientation factor is unity for a crystallographic axis which is parallel to the fiber axis, equal to −0.5 if the axis is aligned perpendicular to the fiber axis and zero if the axis is distributed randomly. The orientation factors are given by

$$f_j = (\overline{3 \cos^2\phi_{j,z}} - 1)/2 \tag{2}$$

where $\overline{\cos^2\phi_{j,z}}$ is the average value of the cosine squared of the angle between the fiber axis and the j-crystallographic axis ($j = a, b,$ or c). Assuming rotational symmetry about the fiber axis,

$$\overline{\cos^2\phi_{j,z}} = \frac{\int_0^{\pi/2} I_{hkl}(\phi_{j,z}) \cos^2\phi_{j,z} \sin \phi_{j,z} d\phi_{j,z}}{\int_0^{\pi/2} I_{hkl}(\phi_{j,z}) \sin \phi_{j,zd\phi_{j,z}}} \tag{3}$$

where $I_{hkl}(\phi_{j,z})$ is the intensity diffracted from the (hkl) planes which are normal to the j-crystallographic axis.

Using eqs. (2) and (3), the value of f_b was computed from the intensity distribution in the 040 reflection. In monoclinic polypropylenes, the chains are helices whose axes lie along the c-crystallographic axis. There is no convenient set of diffraction planes perpendicular to the c-axis, and the method of Wilchinsky[16,17] was used to compute f_c. He has shown that for monoclinic polypropylene,

$$\overline{\cos^2\phi_{c,z}} = 1 - 1.099 \overline{\cos^2\phi_{110,z}} - 0.901 \overline{\cos^2\phi_{040,z}} \tag{4}$$

where $\cos^2\phi_{110,z}$ and $\cos^2\phi_{040,z}$ are obtained from intensity measurements on the 110 and 040 reflections and eq. (3).

For orthogonal crystal axes,[15]

$$f_a + f_b + f_c = 0 \tag{5}$$

In the case of monoclinic polypropylene, the a-axis is not perpendicular to the c-axis, but it makes an angle of 99.3°. In this case, it is convenient to define an a'-axis which is not a true crystallographic axis but is perpendicular to both the b- and c-crystallographic axes and whose orientation factor can be determined from eq. (5) and the values of f_b and f_c.

Small Angle X-Ray Diffraction

Small-angle x-ray diffraction (SAXS) patterns were obtained on selected fiber samples using a modified Kiessig camera with pinhole collimation. The camera was mounted on a Rigaku-General Electric rotating anode x-ray generator. The patterns were obtained under vacuum conditions, and a custom-made collimator was used. The resolution was about 400 Å.

Density

The crystalline fraction in fibers (determined from WAXS patterns to be monoclinic) were measured in a water–isopropyl alcohol gradient density column at 23.2°C. The column was constructed as described by Tung and Taylor.[29] The samples were allowed approximately 12 hr to seek their level of displacement. Specific volumes $\overline{V}$ were converted to crystalline fraction X through the expression

$$X = \frac{\overline{V}_a - \overline{V}}{\overline{V}_a - \overline{V}_c} \tag{6}$$

where $\overline{V}_c$ and $\overline{V}_a$, the specific volumes of crystalline and amorphous polypropylenes, were obtained from Danusso et al.[30]

Birefringence

The birefringence Δ of the fibers was determined using an Orthoplan polarizing light microscope with a Leitz Berek Compensator. The birefringence of the fiber is the ratio of the measured phase difference to the diameter of the filament. On-line birefringence measurements were made by the same technique with the microscope appropriately mounted so as to observe the running threadline.

Amorphous Orientation

The level of amorphous orientation in the fibers was determined using the theory of Stein and Norris[31] in the manner applied to polypropylene previously by Hoshino et al.[32] and Samuels.[17,33,34] This involves consideration of the relative amorphous and crystalline contributions to the birefringence, calculating the latter and subtracting it out. Specifically, one writes

$$\Delta = f_c X \Delta^0_{\text{cryst}} + f_{\text{amorph}}(1 - X)\Delta^0_{\text{amorph}} + \Delta_{\text{form}} \tag{7}$$

where Δ^0_{cryst} and Δ^0_{amorph} are the intrinsic birefringences of the crystalline and amorphous regions. Δ_{form} is the so-called "form birefringence" [35] and is neglected in the calculations. To calculate f_{amorph}, we use Δ from birefringence measurements, X from density values, and f_c from WAXS measurements. We accept Samuels' results for Δ^0_{cryst} and Δ^0_{amorph}.

Mechanical Properties

The mechanical properties of the melt-spun fibers were measured at room temperature with an Instron tensile tester. Force-versus-elongation curves were obtained at a cross-head speed of 2 in./min using an initial fiber length of 1 in. The tangent modulus, yield strength, tensile strength, and percent elongation to break were measured.

GENERAL SPINNING BEHAVIOR AND STRESS DEVELOPMENT

Certain qualitative features of spinning behavior were apparent. As noted previously, extrudate distortion occurred in the H-0042 at the spinning temperature and flow rate used for all other polymers ($\dot{\gamma}_{w,2.1} \sim 900 \text{ sec}^{-1}$). In order to obtain smooth extrudates, the melt spinning for this specimen was achieved by reducing the flow rate from 2.1 g/min to 0.5 g/min ($\dot{\gamma}_{w,0.5} \sim 210 \text{ sec}^{-1}$).

The Tennessee Eastman polymers could only be spun under limited conditions. With an extrusion temperature of 230°C and an extrusion rate of 2.1 g/min, melt draw ratios V_L/V_0 less than or equal to 62 were achieved. (The polymer grades used in this investigation were not necessarily recommended for fiber spinning by their manufacturers. They were chosen more on the basis of their known differences in behavior than on their ability to be spun.) These polymers exhibited decreasing spinnability with increasing molecular weight.

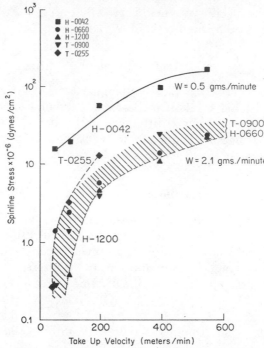

Fig. 1. Effect of take-up velocity on spinline stress of polypropylene fibers. Extrusion temperature is 230°C.

The H-0660 and H-1200 samples could be melt spun at higher take-up speeds and melt draw ratios. Under similar extrusion conditions, samples were spun with $V_L/V_0 = 95$. At the same extrusion rate, higher melt draw ratios could not be examined because of the limitations of our winding apparatus. The H-0042 was drawn down to ratios of 410.

The differences between Hercules and Tennessee Eastman polymers probably could be traced to the fact that the two manufacturers use different catalyst systems in the preparation of the polymers. This may result in differences in tacticity and/or molecular weight distribution. The latter effect may be responsible for the observed differences in spinnability.

The influence of the spinning conditions on the molecular weight of the po-

TABLE II
Characterization of As-Spun Polypropylene Fibers

Sample code	Intrinsic viscosity, dl/g	Weight-average molecular weight	Percent thermal degradation[b]
H-0042	2.50 (2.55[a])	3.14×10^5	27
H-0660	2.24	2.74×10^5	1
H-1200	1.70	1.94×10^5	18
T-0900	1.83	2.13×10^5	11
T-0255	2.33	2.88×10^5	17

[a] Courtesy of Hercules, Inc.
[b] During extrusion.

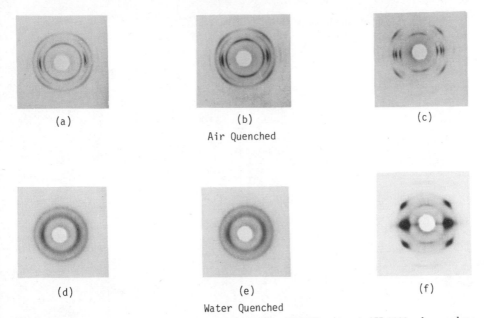

Fig. 2. Effect of take-up velocity and cooling medium on WAXS patterns of H-0660 polypropylene fibers. Extrusion temperature = 230°C. Air quenched: (a) 50 m/min; (b) 200 m/min; (c) 550 m/min. Water quenched: (d) 25 m/min; (e) 100 m/min; (f) 300 m/min.

lypropylenes was assessed from intrinsic viscosity measurements. These results are given in Table II. Degradation due to melt spinning was observed in all the polymers with values ranging from 1% to 27%. The highest degradation (27%) was observed for H-0042, the sample with the highest molecular weight. The molecular weights given in Table II are more significant than those in Table I when considering the structure and properties of the spun filaments.

Figure 1 shows changes of the stress in the spinline with take-up velocity and mass flow rate. The spinline stress was found to increase with the take-up velocity for all the polymers at a specific melt flow rate. The effect of the molecular weight can be observed from the data for samples spun at a melt flow rate of 2.1 g/min. The samples of T-0255 show higher stress levels at a given take-up velocity than the H-1200 samples, and the data on the intermediate molecular weight specimens were scattered between T-0255 and H-1200. Thus, in general, there was a trend toward increasing spinline stress levels with increasing molecular weight. The data also seem to indicate a large effect of melt extrusion rate on the spinline stress. This effect is associated in part with the increased draw-down ratio V_L/V_0 accompanying a decreased extrusion rate through the spinneret and with the increased cooling rate of the smaller diameter filaments. The stress levels in the melt ranged from 0.3×10^6 dynes/cm^2 to 170.0×10^6 dynes/cm^2.

STRUCTURE DEVELOPMENT DURING MELT SPINNING

Qualitative Features

Depending on the threadline cooling rates, the spun filaments of polypropylene were either smectic (paracrystalline) or highly crystalline. The crystalline form

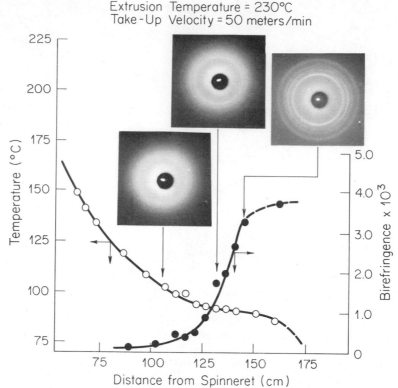

Fig. 3. On-line WAXS patterns, temperature and birefringence profiles for melt-spun H-0660 polypropylene filament.

is the monoclinic α-form. In the present study, it is primarily the highly crystalline monoclinic filaments that were produced. The smectic form occurred only when rapid cooling rates were achieved by quenching the molten threadline into water.

Figure 2 shows WAXS patterns of H-0660 filaments spun either into ambient air or into water at 9°C. The effect of increasing take-up velocity (and spinline stress) is also shown. All filaments were spun with an extrusion temperature of 230°C. It can be seen in Figure 2(a)–2(c) that the samples are highly crystalline and the c-axis orientation is increasing with take-up velocity. For the smectic form in Figure 2(d)–2(f), there is a transformation in crystal structure from an unoriented paracrystalline to highly oriented partially monoclinic type with increasing take-up velocity.

For filaments spun into ambient air, crystallization to the monoclinic form occurs in the threadline. This fact is easily demonstrated with on-line measurements as shown in Figure 3. Here, x-ray patterns made on a running filament at different distances from the spinneret are shown in relation to a temperature and birefringence profile for the same run. A hold in the temperature profile occurs as crystallization begins due to the release of the latent heat of crystallization. During crystallization the birefringence rises rapidly, eventually approaching the birefringence of the as-spun filament.

The effect of spinning temperature on the WAXS pattern is shown in Figure 4 for the H-0660 polymer. Increasing the spinning temperature with other

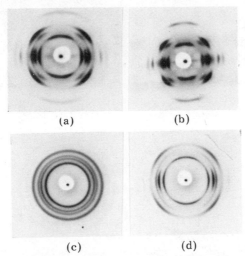

Fig. 4. Variation of the WAXS patterns for H-0660 polymer with extrusion temperature T_E and take-up velocity V_L: (a) $T_E = 200°C$, $V_L = 50$ m/min; (b) $T_E = 200°C$, $V_L = 550$ m/min; (c) $T_E = 260°C$, $V_L = 50$ m/min; (d) $T_E = 260°C$, $V_L = 550$ m/min.

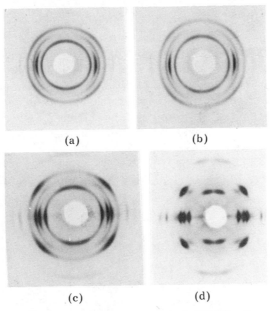

Fig. 5. Effect of molecular weight and extrusion rate on the WAXS patterns of samples spun at 200 m/min. Extrusion temperature is 230°C. Extrusion rate for (a), (b), and (c) is 2.1 g/min: (a) H-1200; (b) T-900; (c) T-0255; (d) H-0042 (extrusion rate is 0.5 g/min).

variables unchanged decreases the viscosity in the upper part of the threadline and results in lower orientation in the spun filament as shown in Figure 4 (compare also to Fig. 2.).

The effect of the molecular weight on the WAXS pattern is illustrated in Figure 5. Comparing the WAXS patterns in Figure 5(a)–5(c) for H-1200, T-900, and T-0255 at a melt extrusion rate of 2.1 g/min and take-up velocity 200 m/min, there seems to be a noticeable decrease in the 110 and 130 arc widths with increasing molecular weight indicating an increase of orientation.

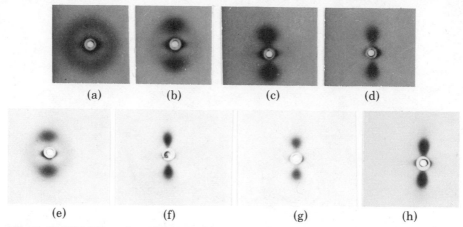

(a)   (b)   (c)   (d)

(e)   (f)   (g)   (h)

Fig. 6. SAXS patterns for melt-spun polypropylene filaments: (a) H-0660, T_E = 260°C, V_L = 50 m/min; (b) H-0660, T_E = 260°C, V_L = 300 m/min; (c) H-0660, T_E = 230°C, V_L = 300 m/min; (d) H-0660, T_E = 230°C, V_L = 550 m/min; (e) T-0255, T_E = 230°C, V_L = 50 m/min; (f) T-0255, T_E = 230°C, V_L = 200 m/min; (g) H-0042, T_E = 230°C, V_L = 50 m/min; (h) H-0042, T_E = 230°C, V_L = 200 m/min.

Comparison of the WAXS pattern for H-0042 sample (Fig. 5) with the other patterns in Figure 5 (spun at same take-up velocity but higher melt extrusion rate) indicates that this H-0042 sample has developed much higher levels of orientation than the other samples. This drastic difference in orientation appears to be a result of a combination of two effects: (1) low extrusion rate and (2) higher molecular weight. The lower extrusion rate results in a lower extrusion velocity through the spinneret capillary and, hence, a higher draw-down ratio (V_L/V_0) for a given take-up velocity. As noted in the previous section, this also leads to higher spinline stresses.

Figure 6 shows the SAXS patterns of various polypropylene filaments spun under a variety of conditions. Under conditions which give rise to low spinline

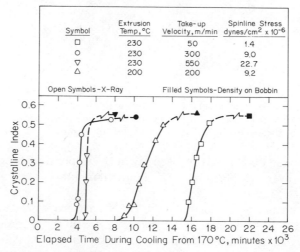

Fig. 7. Crystalline index as a function of residence time in the spinline from analysis of WAXS patterns. Polymer is H-0660 in all cases.

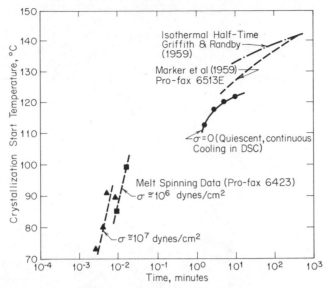

Fig. 8. CCT curve interpretation of crystallization kinetics as a function of cooling rate and stress.

stress such as low take-up velocity and high extrusion temperature, the small-angle pattern exhibits a continuous ring of nearly uniform intensity [Fig. 6(a)]. These are the same conditions which lead to low orientation in the WAXS pattern [Fig. 4(c)]. As the spinning conditions are changed so as to increase the spinline stress, the patterns evolve to definite "two-point" patterns [Fig. 6(b)–6(h)].

On-Line Crystallization Kinetics

Crystallinity levels were obtained from on-line WAXS patterns. These are plotted as a function of spinline residence time in Figure 7. These results generally show an increased rate of crystallization with increased take-up velocity or tension, other things being equal. However, because these are nonisothermal results, it is necessary to separate out the effects of cooling rate, which also increases with take-up velocity, from those due to stress.

These experimental results can be interpreted in terms of "continuous cooling transformation" curves utilized by metallurgists to interpret solid-phase transformations, especially heat treatment of steel.[36] This approach, previously discussed by Spruiell and White,[11,12] is illustrated in Figure 8. Decreased crystallization start temperatures are observed with increased cooling rate. The effect of stress is to shift the CCT curve to shorter times. A comparison is also shown in Figure 8 of the melt-spinning data to the isothermal crystallization data of Griffiths and Randby[37] and Marker et al.[38]

Crystallinity of Spun Fibers

Density measurements for the monoclinic filaments obtained by spinning in air were used to compute the per cent crystallinity in the samples. These measurements indicated crystallinities of order 55 ± 3% for all samples. Careful examination indicated a trend toward increased crystallinity with take-up ve-

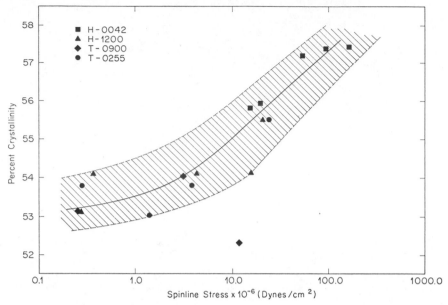

Fig. 9. Crystallinity level of melt-spun fibers as a function of spinline stress.

locity and take-up stress (see Fig. 9). Generally, the Hercules polypropylenes tend to have a slightly higher level of crystallinity than the Tennessee Eastman polymers.

Molecular Orientation

Figure 10 shows Hermans–Stein c-axis crystalline orientation factor (f_c) for the isotactic polypropylenes plotted against the take-up velocity. The orientation factor increases steadily with the take-up velocity. The figure also shows the effect of the molecular weight on the orientation factors. At any given take-up velocity, f_c was found to be higher for higher molecular weight samples. The effect of tacticity, if any, on f_c is not very clear from these results. The large effect of a combination of a higher draw down ratio and high molecular weight is exhibited by the H-0042 filaments. At take-up velocities of 200, 400, and 550 m/min, these filaments show very high values of f_c ($\sim$0.9).

Figure 11 shows crystalline orientation functions plotted versus the spinline stress for the various polypropylenes. Each of the orientation functions f_a, f_b, and f_c falls on a single curve within the experimental accuracy. This shows the importance of the spinline stress on the development of morphology during melt spinning. The value of f_c increases with spinline stress, leveling off at 0.91, which indicates that the c-axes are tending to become more aligned with the fiber axis with increasing stress. The b-axis orientation function (f_b) decreases rapidly reaching a value of -0.48, indicating a near-perpendicular alignment of the b-axes with the fiber axis. The value of $f_{a'}$ decreases slowly at first, but it then decreases rapidly as f_c rises and finally approaches -0.43.

Figure 12 presents the measured birefringence of the filaments as a function of spinline stress. These data were used to obtain the amorphous orientation factors. The amorphous orientation factors were computed from eq. (6) with

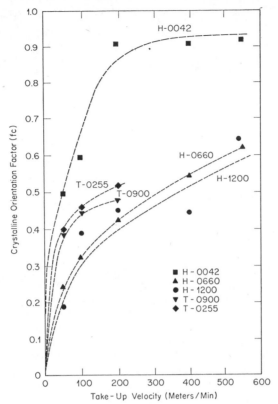

Fig. 10. Hermans–Stein c-axis orientation factor of spun fibers as a function of take-up velocity showing influence of molecular weight.

Δ_{form} taken equal to zero. Although both the crystalline and amorphous orientation factors increase with increasing spinline stress, the orientation developed in the amorphous chains is always much smaller than the orientation in the crystalline regions. The values of the amorphous orientation factors range from slightly less than zero up to about 0.3.

Discussion of Structure Development

The qualitative features of the present study are in general agreement with those of earlier researchers.[1,4–12] The filaments melt spun into water exhibited a paracrystalline, "smectic" structure, while those spun into ambient air were monoclinic. The crystallinity values of the latter samples were of the same order as those obtained by Sheehan and Cole[1] and Samuels.[17,33,34] Orientation increases with take-up velocity and melt draw-down in a way similar to that reported by Kitao et al.,[8] Henson,[10] and Spruiell and White.[11] The variation in the SAXS pattern from a ring pattern at low spinline stresses to a "two point" pattern at high spinning stresses is similar to the behavior reported by Noether and Whitney[4] and Spruiell and White.[11]

In general, the variations in crystalline orientation factors and SAXS patterns are qualitatively similar to those reported for high-density polyethylene.[8,12,21–23] Dees and Spruiell[22] have interpreted these features in the case of polyethylene

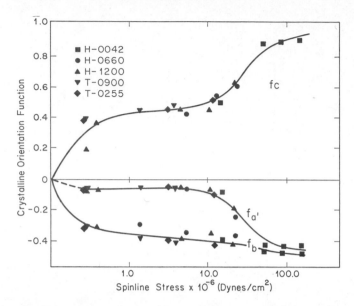

Fig. 11. Hermans–Stein a-, b-, and c-axis orientation factors of spun fibers as a function of spinline stress for five polypropylenes.

to indicate spherulitic morphology at very low spinning stresses which undergoes a transition to a row-nucleated[36] or cylindritic morphology as the spinning stress increases. Spruiell and White[11] have extended this interpretation to the case of polypropylene and the present data are certainly consistent with this general interpretation.

As pointed out by several investigators, polypropylene exhibits a distinctive bimodal orientation of the unit cells when crystallized from the melt under conditions of extensional flow.[9,18–20] Careful examination of the x-ray patterns shown in Figures 2–5 shows that this bimodal orientation occurs in our melt-spun filaments. The bimodal orientation is characterized by one component of the distribution with the c-(chain)axes parallel to the fiber axis and the second component with the c-axes approximately perpendicular to the fiber axis. The former component is here referred to as the c-axis-oriented population, while the latter is referred to as the a'-axis-oriented population. In the case of the H-0660 filaments, we have attempted to assess the relative contribution of these two components to the total orientation by separating the intensity distribution in the 110 reflection into components due to random, a'-axis-oriented, and c-axis-oriented crystals. The results are shown in Figure 13. It is clear that at high spinline stresses the largest proportion of the filament is in the c-axis-oriented population with only about 10–20% of the filament in the a'-axis-oriented population. The presence of the bimodal orientation is thus not likely to invalidate the broad qualitative features of the morphologic structure described in the preceding paragraph. The significance of the a'-axis-oriented component on the morphology of flow-crystallized polypropylene has been considered by Clark and Spruiell[20] and Anderson and Carr.[9] Both conclude that the secondary, or a'-axis-oriented, component consists of very small crystals distributed throughout the sample and probably growing with an epitaxial relationship to the primary, or c-axis-oriented, component.

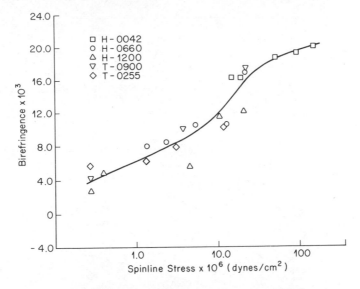

Fig. 12. Birefringence of spun fibers as a function of spinline stress.

A major finding of the present investigation is that the morphology of a broad range of polypropylenes over a range of spinning variables is largely determined by the spinline stress. Figures 9, 11, and 12, 11 in particular, attest to this fact. Spruiell and White[11] have previously published results indicating similar behavior for H-0660 spun at three different temperatures. We may conclude, therefore, that spinning variables such as polymer molecular weight, flow rate, melt temperature, and take-up velocity all affect the morphology of the spun filaments, but the combination of these effects on morphology can be traced to their effect on spinline stress. This result is reasonable if one considers that orientation and birefringence in polymer melts[39–41] and vulcanized rubber[42] are determined by stress and that the orientation of the amorphous phase just as crystallization begins probably determines the crystalline morphology.

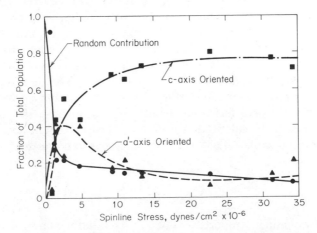

Fig. 13. Relative orientation contributions in H-0660 polypropylene filaments.

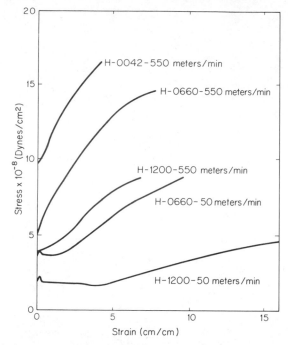

Fig. 14. Typical engineering stress vs strain curves for melt-spun polypropylene fibers.

MECHANICAL PROPERTIES OF SPUN FILAMENTS

Engineering stress (force/initial cross-sectional area)-versus-strain ($\Delta L/L_0$) curves computed from force-versus-elongation data are shown in Figure 14 for typical as-spun filaments. In general, tangent modulus, yield strength, and tensile strength increase with take-up velocity and molecular weight. Elongation to break exhibits the reverse trend. The tensile strength and elongation to break are shown as a function of take-up velocity in Figure 15. The plotted points in this figure and others presented later represent average values from several tests (usually five).

Another observation which can be made from Figure 14 is that filaments spun under low stress conditions exhibited a yield drop and necking elongation, while those spun under higher spinline stresses exhibited less prominent necking.

Figures 16 and 17 show modulus, yield strength, tensile strength, and per cent elongation to break plotted against the spinline stress. For all the samples, the modulus, yield strength, and tensile strength increase while the percent elongation decreases with the spinline stress. It is of interest that the tensile property results from samples of different molecular weights appear to lie within a scatter band which is hardly broader than the expected scatter for the data from a given molecular weight sample. That is, the data appear to be correlated together by the spinline stress.

DISCUSSION

That the mechanical properties may be correlated to the spinline stress evidently results from the fact that the structural features which control the me-

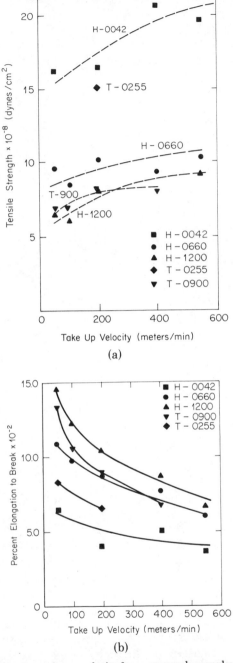

Fig. 15. (a) Tensile strength vs take-up velocity for as-spun polypropylene filaments. (b) Percent elongation to break vs take-up velocity for as-spun polypropylene filaments.

chanical properties are determined by the spinline stress. In the preceding section, it was shown that the molecular orientation and probably other morphologic features of the spun filaments are determined by the spinline stress. We have attempted to establish which features of the morphology are most important in determining the mechanical properties of our spun filaments by

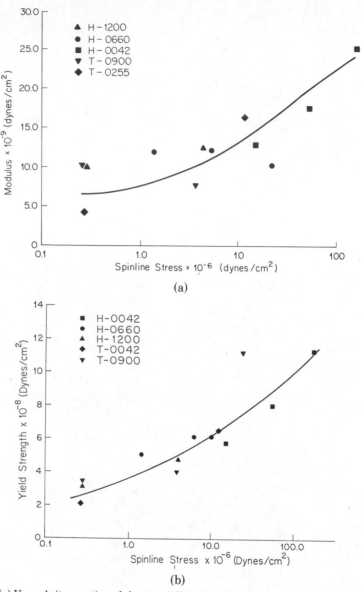

Fig. 16. (a) Young's (tangent) modulus vs spinline stress for polypropylene filaments. (b) Yield strength vs spinline stress for polypropylene filaments.

plotting the properties versus different measurable parameters such as c-axis crystalline orientation factor, amorphous orientation factor, and birefringence (a measure of average orientation). All such parameters correlate the mechanical properties to some degree. The correlation with these structural parameters seemed to produce slightly more scatter than in the case of the spinline stress. Within the range of variables studied, there was little difference between the correlations provided by these various parameters.

The authors would like to thank Hercules, Inc., and Tennessee Eastman for supplying the polymers of this study. Dr. P. Drechsel of Hercules was especially helpful in characterizing samples. This research was supported in part by the National Science Foundation under Grant GK-18897.

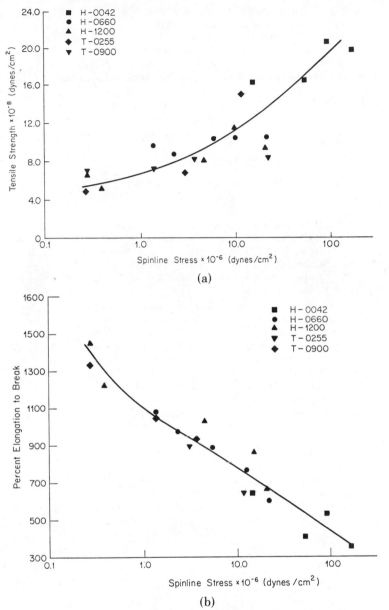

Fig. 17. (a) Tensile strength vs spinline stress for polypropylene filaments. (b) Percent elongation to break vs spinline stress for as-spun polypropylene filaments.

References

1. W. C. Sheehan and T. B. Cole, *J. Appl. Polym. Sci.*, **8**, 2359 (1964).
2. A. J. Herrman, U.S. Pat. 3,256,258 (1966); Br. Pat. 935,809 (1963).
3. E. S. Clark in *Structure and Properties of Polymer Films*, R. W. Lenz and R. S. Stein, Eds., Plenum, New York, 1972.
4. H. D. Noether and W. Whitney, *Kolloid Z. Z. Polym.*, **251**, 991 (1973).
5. B. S. Sprague, *J. Macromol. Sci.-Phys.*, **B8**, 157 (1973).
6. K. Katayama, T. Amano, and K. Nakamura, *Kolloid Z. Z. Polym.*, **226**, 125 (1968).
7. P. Y-F. Fung, E. Orlando, and S. H. Carr, *Polym. Eng. Sci.*, **13**, 295 (1973).

8. T. Kitao, S. Ohya, J. Furukawa, and S. Yamashita, *J. Polym. Sci.*, **11**, 1091 (1973).

9. P. G. Anderson and S. H. Carr, *J. Mater. Sci.*, **10**, 870 (1975).

10. H. M. Henson and J. E. Spruiell, paper presented at Division of Cellulose, Paper and Textile Chemistry, American Chemical Society, Philadelphia, April 1975.

11. J. E. Spruiell and J. L. White, *Polym. Eng. Sci.*, **15**, 660 (1975).

12. J. E. Spruiell and J. L. White, in *Fiber and Yarn Processing*, J. L. White, Ed., *Appl. Polym. Symp.*, **27**, 121 (1975).

13. O. Ishizuka and K. Koyama, *Sen-i-Gakkaishi*, **32**, T-43 (1976).

14. J. J. Hermans, P. H. Hermans, D. Vermeas, and A. Weidinger, *Rec. Trav. Chim. Pays-Bas*, **65**, 427 (1946).

15. R. S. Stein, *J. Polym. Sci.*, **31**, 327 (1958).

16. Z. W. Wilchinsky, *J. Appl. Phys.*, **30**, 792 (1959); *ibid.*, **31**, 1969 (1960); *Adv. X-Ray Anal.*, **6**, 231 (1963).

17. R. J. Samuels, *Structured Polymer Properties*, Wiley-Interscience, New York, 1974.

18. M. Compostella, A. Coen, and F. Bertinotti, *Angew. Chem.*, **74**, 618 (1962).

19. E. S. Clark, *Bull. Amer. Phys. Soc.*, March 1970.

20. E. S. Clark and J. E. Spruiell, *Polym. Eng. Sci.*, **16**, 176 (1976).

21. L. E. Abbott and J. L. White, in *U.S.-Japan Seminar on Polymer Processing and Rheology*, C. D. Bogue, M. Yamamoto, and J. L. White, Eds., *Appl. Polym. Symp.*, **20**, 247 (1973).

22. J. R. Dees and J. E. Spruiell, *J. Appl. Polym. Sci.*, **18**, 1053 (1974).

23. J. L. White, K. C. Dharod, and E. S. Clark, *J. Appl. Polym. Sci.*, **18**, 2539 (1974).

24. V. G. Bankar, J. E. Spruiell, and J. L. White, Melt Spinning of Nylon-6: Structure Development and Mechanical Properties of As-Spun Filaments, University of Tennessee, Polymer Science and Engineering Rep. No. 64, July 1976, *J. Appl. Polym. Sci.* (to appear).

25. R. Chaing, *J. Polym. Sci.*, **28**, 235 (1958).

26. J. P. Tordella, in *Rheology*, Vol. 5, F. R. Eirich, Ed., Academic Press, New York, 1969.

27. J. L. White, in *U.S.-Japan Seminar on Polymer Processing and Rheology*, D. C. Bogue, M. Yamamoto, and J. L. White, Eds., *Appl. Polym. Symp.*, **20**, 155 (1973).

28. G. Natta and P. Corradini, *Nuovo Cimento Suppl.*, **15**, 40 (1960).

29. L. H. Tung and W. C. Taylor, *J. Polym. Sci.*, **21**, 144 (1956).

30. F. Danusso, G. Moraglio, W. Ghiglia, L. Motta, and G. Talamini, *Chim. Ind.*, **41**, 748 (1959).

31. R. S. Stein and F. H. Norris, *J. Polym. Sci.*, **21**, 381 (1956).

32. S. Hoshino, J. Powers, D. G. Legrand, H. Kawai, and R. S. Stein, *J. Polym. Sci.*, **58**, 185 (1962).

33. R. J. Samuels, *J. Polym. Sci. A-2*, **6**, 2021 (1968).

34. R. J. Samuels, *J. Macromol. Sci. Phys.*, **B4**, 701 (1970).

35. M. Born and E. Wolf, *Principles of Optics*, 4th ed., Pergamon, Oxford, 1970.

36. A. Keller and M. Machin, *J. Macromol. Sci. Phy.*, **B1**, 41 (1967).

37. J. H. Griffiths and B. G. Randby, *J. Polym. Sci.*, **38**, 107 (1959).

38. L. Marker, P. M. Hay, G. P. Tilley, R. M. Early, and O. J. Sweeting, *J. Polym. Sci.*, **38**, 33 (1959).

39. W. Philippoff, *J. Appl. Phys.*, **27**, 984 (1956).

40. A. S. Lodge, *Trans. Faraday Soc.*, **52**, 120 (1956).

41. E. B. Adams, J. C. Whitehead, and D. C. Bogue, *A.I.Ch.E.J.*, **11**, 1026 (1965).

42. L. R. G. Treloar, *Physics of Rubber Elasticity*, 2nd ed., Oxford (1958).

Received August 6, 1976
Revised October 14, 1976

JOURNAL OF APPLIED POLYMER SCIENCE   VOL. 21, 3023–3033 (1977)

Cardanol Derivatives as PVC Plasticizers. II. Plasticizer Evaluation

EBERHARD W. NEUSE and JOHANNES D. VAN SCHALKWYK,*

Department of Chemistry, University of the Witwatersrand, Johannesburg, South Africa

Synopsis

A series of cardanol derivatives prepared in a preceding study[1] are evaluated as PVC plasticizers. These include butyl anacardate (3), cyclohexyl anacardate (4), 3-(pentadec-8′-enyl)phenyl acetate (5), 3-(8′,9′-diacetoxypentadecyl)phenyl acetate (6), and 3-(8′-epoxypentadecyl)phenyl acetate (7). The evaluation initially involves compatibility and Brabender plastification testing. The two acetates 6 and 7 as the most promising compounds are selected for further investigation, comprising the determination of tensile properties and thermal stability behavior of compression-molded plasticized PVC sheet material. The extrudability of a plasticized wire coating formulation is also studied. The plasticizing efficiency of both 6 and 7 is on a par with di(2-ethylhexyl) phthalate used as a standard plasticizer. In addition, both acetates show distinct costabilizing efficiency, the epoxyacetate 7 in this respect being superior to the other compounds tested. Cardanol, readily available as a by-product of cashew nut processing, thus may represent a welcome addition to the strained raw material market in the plasticizer field.

INTRODUCTION

Cashew-nut-shell liquid (CNSL), a commercially important by-product of cashew-nut processing, has been the topic of considerable research activity in both the purely scientific and the applied fields. The principal ingredient, constituting some 90% of the liquid, is anacardic acid,[2] a mixture of salicyclic acid derivatives possessing C_{15} hydrocarbon side chains of variable unsaturation as represented by 1. Another, though minor CNSL constituent is cardanol, 2, a mixture of related phenols lacking the carboxylic function.[3] In the commercial cashew nut roasting process, 2 arises from 1 by decarboxylation. The commercial distillation of CNSL, therefore, leads to a product essentially composed of cardanol, which, depending on the thermal history of the shell liquid in the course of both nut processing and distillation, contains the mono-, di-, and triolefinic phenol congeners in considerably varying proportions. While a product obtained under reasonably mild processing conditions generally possesses a high extent of unsaturation typically corresponding to almost two olefinic double bonds per average molecule, an excessively heat-treated cardanol has lost much of its unsaturated character through selective thermal polymerization of the higher unsaturated olefins and may thus well show unsaturation equivalent to little more than one double bond per average molecule.[4]

* Present address: Chemserve Technical Products (Pty) Ltd., Johannesburg, South Africa.

OH

R_1, R_2, R_3, R_4,

1: R = COOH, R_1 = (CH$_2$)$_{14}$—CH$_3$, R_2 = (CH$_2$)$_7$—CH=CH—(CH$_2$)$_5$—CH$_3$,

R_3 = (CH$_2$)$_7$—CH=CH—CH$_2$—CH=CH—(CH$_2$)$_2$—CH$_3$,

R_4 = (CH$_2$)$_7$—CH=CH—CH$_2$—CH=CH—CH$_2$—CH=CH$_2$.

2: R = H, R_1–R_4 as above.

3: R = COO—(CH$_2$)$_3$—CH$_3$, R_1–R_4 as above.

4: R = COO—CH⟨CH$_2$CH$_2$\CH$_2$CH$_2$⟩CH$_2$, R_1–R_4 as above.

CNSL, as well as cardanol itself and some of its derivatives, have over the years found rewarding industrial outlets, notably in the technology of polymeric resins for coating and adhesive applications and in the manufacture of grinding wheel and brake lining materials. These topics have recently been reviewed by Aggarwal[5] and Welgemoed.[6]

With our interest focused on the potential use of cardanol derivatives in the plasticization of poly(vinyl chloride) (PVC), we recently[1] prepared a number of compounds possessing the cardanol molecular skeleton for an evaluation of their plasticizing efficiency. This evaluation study is described in the present account.

RESULTS AND DISCUSSION

The plasticizing efficiency of an additive depends, among other factors, on the presence of suitable polar, polarizable, and nonpolar groups in the molecule.[7-10] Compounds of entirely polar character are unsuitable as plasticizers, and so are compounds with an exclusively nonpolar structure. In either case, the additive's molecules associate with each other rather than with polymer segments and migrate to the surface to form an oily or tacky film. The presence of both polar and nonpolar structural entities in an additive is a minimum requirement of plasticizing behavior. In a plasticizer of this type, exemplified by the adipates or sebacates of 2-ethylhexanol and related alkanols, the ester function as the polar part attaches to a dipole in the polymer, whereas the hydrocarbon groups as the nonpolar portions increase the interchain distances in the polymer bulk and prevent other polymer dipoles from mutual electrostatic interaction, thus acting as shieldingbbarriers betweenppolymer segments. The effect of plasticization with compounds of this type (designated by Leuchs[10] as "shielding" plasticizers) is essentially one of lowering the polymer's glass transition temperature and improving the flexibility at low temperatures, although the price to be paid for this benefit is an increase in the gelling temperature (signifying poorer gelling behavior) and generally a reduced measure of compatibility with the polymer base.

In a second type of plasticizer, represented by di(2-ethylhexyl) phthalate, dinonyl phthalate, and other aromatic esters, a polarizable group constitutes an additional part of the molecule. The presence of such a polarizable entity introduces a hinging effect into the polymer–plasticizer aggregate, as now the polar (ester) and the polarizable (aromatic) groups each may attach to a different polymer dipole, thus connecting the two dipoles via a flexible bridging system in the plasticizer. Representatives of this class of additives, hence, are aptly named "hinging" plasticizers.[10] Generally, enhanced compatibility and improved gelling characteristics (although less pronounced cold flexibility) relative to the first-named plasticizer type are the result of such interplay between both polar and polarizable entities in the compound. It has been recognized that optimal plasticizing efficiency is attained only when the intermolecular bonding forces within the additive arising from these various structural entities are comparable in magnitude with both the secondary bonding forces operative between plasticizer and polymer and the interchain attractive forces within the polymer itself.

The following compounds, previously prepared,[1] were selected for the present plasticizer evaluation study: n-butyl anacardate (3), cyclohexyl anacardate (4), 3-(pentadec-8'-enyl)phenyl acetate (5), 3-(8',9'-diacetoxypentadecyl)phenyl acetate (6), and 3-(8'-epoxypentadecyl)phenyl acetate (7).

In addition to nonpolar aliphatic chains or chain segments, these structures all comprise ester groups and benzene rings comparable in polarity and polarizability with the common phthalates. Compounds 5–7, therefore, should exhibit the gelling and plasticizing behavior characteristic of these hinging-type plasticizers:

OAc

5: $R = (CH_2)_7—CH{=}CH—(CH_2)_5—CH_3$

OAc
|
6: $R = (CH_2)_7—CH—CH—(CH_2)_5—CH_3$
|
OAc

O
/ \
7: $R = (CH_2)_7—CH—CH—(CH_2)_5—CH_3$

The anacardates 3 and 4 both, in addition, possess a phenolic hydroxyl function the polarity of which is generally too high to provide adequate PVC compatibility. Although some diminution in compatibility would, therefore, have to be accepted,* we decided to include the two anacardates in the present evaluation as we were primarily interested in an assessment of the antioxidant effects that could be anticipated to arise from the unprotected phenolic system.[11,12] A somewhat reduced compatibility might also be expected with the monoacetate 5 for lack of an additional polar site within the long hydrocarbon side chain. Aromatic esters with alkyl groups larger than C_{12} generally are unsuitable as primary plasticizers because of excessive paraffinic character. It was, moreover, realized that the olefinic unsaturation in the side chains of 5, contributing to

_____
* Both cardanol and anacardic acid, lacking the additional ester group present in 3 and 4, could be expected to be even less compatible, and indeed the extent of incompatibility observed in a preliminary examination was such that neither product was employed in subsequent investigations.

TABLE I
PVC Test Formulation

Component	Content, parts by weight
PVC resin[a]	57
Plasticizer	40
Stabilizer[b]	2
Lubricant[c]	1

[a] Corvic D 65/6
[b] Interstab M 103 ZF
[c] Loxiol G13

instability in oxidative and UV-radiative environments, would diminish the compound's effectiveness in a PVC blend. On the other hand, the efficacious lubricating properties of long-chain aliphatic esters are well known,[13,14] and we wished to investigate 5 as a plasticizer with additional processing aid characteristics. The acetate 7 was included in this study for reasons of expected co-stabilizing effects exerted by the oxiran ring system as in the common epoxy plasticizers.

Preliminary Screening

In a preliminary small-scale compatibility testing program, a series of 10-g PVC batches of the general formulation given in Table I were made up in which the plasticizer component was varied from 3 through 7. A "blank" formulation containing di(2-ethylhexyl) phthalate (DIOP) as standard plasticizer was included for comparison. The poly(vinyl chloride) resin used was a suspension grade of medium K value (corvic D 65/6); the formulations were stabilized with a barium–cadmium soap (Interstab M 103 ZF, formerly Advastab BC 103 ZF) and were lubricated with a glycerol fatty acid ester (Loxiol G13). The PVC compounds were compression molded at 160°C into flat plate specimens each with dimensions 20 × 30 × 3 mm. The plates were inspected visually. The blank plate containing DIOP, off-white in color and translucent, was flexible and dry in surface appearance, and as expected showed complete plasticizer compatibility. Both the triacetate 6 and the epoxyacetate 7 gave flexible specimens of the same surface appearance, albeit slightly yellow in color, and exhibited the same complete compatibility. No changes in these respects were noticed in the three plates after two months of storage at room temperature. The anacardates 3 and 4, on the other hand, were compatible only to a limited extent and showed a tendency to "sweat out." Accordingly, the yellowish specimens were strongly opaque and, although still flexible, exposed an exudate on the surface which, after several days, formed a thick, oily film. An intermediate behavior was observed with the specimen derived from the monoacetate 5; the yellowish plate, while of dry surface appearance, was slightly stiffer and less transparent than the DIOP specimen.

Although both 3 and 4 in combination (equal parts) with DIOP proved considerably more compatible with the polymer base, the expected antioxidant effects, monitored in a comparative milling test at 170°C in an impinging stream of compressed air, were not sufficiently ostentatious relative to a DIOP formulation to warrant further evaluation.

TABLE II
Brabender Test Results

Plasticizer[a]	τ_{10}[b]	τ_{max}[b]	t_{max},[c] min
DIOP	245	455	1.0
5	92	96	6.2
6	230	590	0.6
7	205	495	0.6

[a] In test formulation as per Table I.
[b] Torque values after 10 min and at maximum, respectively; arbitrary units.
[c] Time to reach τ_{max}.

Brabender Testing

The subsequent testing program, involving compounds 5–7 and, again, DIOP as a standard, was conducted in a Brabender Plastograph operated at 132°C. This instrument allows measurement of the torque exerted by the mixing propellers as the PVC blend is compounded. The torque measured after a reasonable mixing period (arbitrarily set at 10 min in this work) reflects the amount of energy absorbed in the plasticization process, a high torque value indicating a high degree of gelling. Furthermore, the time elapsed to reach maximum torque is a reliable indicator of the rate of plasticizer absorption ("solution") by the polymer resin. The two criteria taken together represent a useful measure of a compound's plasticizing efficiency. The PVC blends employed were of the compositions given in Table I, batch size being limited to 35 g. The results of these Brabender tests are summarized in Table II, which for each formulation lists the torque measured after 10 min of mixing time (τ_{10}), the maximum torque attained (τ_{max}), and the time required to reach maximum torque (t_{max}). The torque values listed are relative instrument readings and, hence, are given in arbitrary units.

The tabulated findings permit the following conclusions: (i) In relation to the DIOP standard, acetate 5 gives low τ_{10} and τ_{max} readings, with t_{max} raised sixfold. This indicates good lubricating characteristics, but rather inferior plasticizing efficiency and suggests discontinuation of testing efforts with that compound. (ii) Both 6 and 7, giving τ_{10} and τ_{max} values in the neighborhood of those resulting from the standard formulation, compare well with DIOP in their gelling characteristics. The maximum torque in both cases actually exceeds that of the DIOP formulation by some 10–30%, whereas the gelling time is reduced by 40%. Although these figures are not necessarily representative, as the limited quantities of compounds available at this stage did not permit repetitive tests, it appears safe to state that both acetates are at least equivalent to the DIOP standard in their gelling behavior. This finding prompted the synthesis of larger quantities of the two compounds 6 and 7 for the mechanical and stability investigations described in the subsequent two sections.

Mechanical Testing

Three formulations according to Table I (100-g batches), containing DIOP, 6, and 7, respectively, were mixed in the Brabender Plastograph for 10 min at 132°C. The blends were compression molded at 160°C to flat sheets of 2-mm thickness. Tensile tests were conducted on specimens cut from the sheets. The results, including tensile strength at break (σ), elongation at break (ϵ), and modulus of elasticity at 100% elongation (E_{100}), are compiled in Table III under the heading "virgin material."

The data show both acetates to be on a par with DIOP in tensile behavior. Compound 6 appears to afford slightly stronger, and 7 slightly weaker, specimens than provided by DIOP, although, again, a larger number of tests will be required to establish any clear trends.

Thermal Stability Testing

The same three formulations as used for the mechanical tests were employed for thermal stability testing. This involved the following three approaches: (i) mechanical testing after controlled heat aging, (ii) differential thermal analysis (DTA), and (iii) color monitoring during controlled heat aging. The required specimens were cut from the compression-molded sheets obtained under the preceding heading.

In the first approach, two sets of tensile specimens were aged at 190°C in air for 30 and 60 min, respectively. Room-temperature tensile tests were performed on these two sets. The results are listed in Table III. It is immediately apparent from the data that the standard formulation suffers a noticeable loss in tensile strength and elongation, and a concomitant increase in modulus, upon exposure to the elevated temperature; this is especially obvious after the 60-min treatment, at which point σ is reduced by 15%, and ϵ by 60%, whereas E_{100} has increased by 112%. In notable contrast, the formulations incorporating 6 and 7 both give virtually unchanged σ and only moderately reduced (24–36% after 60 min) ϵ values, the latter now amounting to almost twice the value measured on the standard; the moduli undergo an increase (after 60 min) by appreciably less than half of that found with DIOP. A clear trend of increasing thermal stability, in terms of strength retention after heat aging, on going from the standard to the two formulations containing 6 and 7 is thus apparent. On comparing 6 with 7, one finds the former slightly superior in this respect.

In the differential thermal analysis approach, bulk samples were subjected to a DTA scan in static air at a heating rate of 8°C/min in a differential thermal

TABLE III
Tensile Properties[a] of PVC Formulations

| Plasticizer[b] | Virgin material | | | Aged for 30 min at 190°C | | | Aged for 60 min at 190°C | | |
	σ,[c] MN m^{-2}	ϵ,[d] %	E_{100},[e] MN m^{-2}	σ,[c] MN m^{-2}	ϵ,[d] %	E_{100},[e] MN m^{-2}	σ,[c] MN m^{-2}	ϵ,[d] %	E_{100},[e] MN m^{-2}
DIOP	14.6	432	3.4	13.5	273	4.9	12.5	174	7.2
6	16.8	445	3.8	17.0	371	4.6	16.6	337	4.9
7	13.5	467	2.9	13.2	365	3.6	13.4	301	4.5

[a] Per Fed. Test Method Std. No. 406, Method 1011, (ASTM D 638); all tests at room temperature. Entries represent averages of five test runs.
[b] Formulations as per Table I.
[c] Tensile strength at break.
[d] Elongation at break.
[e] Modulus of elasticity at 100% elongation.

TABLE IV
Degradation Temperatures[a] of PVC Formulations
Determined by Differential Thermal Analysis[b]

Plasticizer[c]	Degradation temp., °C
DIOP	210
6	255
7	283

[a] Temperature of first major exotherm.
[b] In static air; heating rate 8°C/min.
[c] Formulations as per Table I.

analyzer. The degradation temperatures as determined from the recorded major exotherms are given in Table IV. The figures confirm the superior thermal stability of the formulations plasticized with 6 and 7 relative to DIOP, the epoxidized compound in this respect showing the best performance.

The third approach involved an aging test in which discoloration resulting from HCl elimination and oxidation[15] was monitored as a function of aging time at 190°C. To this end, chips of 2 cm² surface area (one set of 12 for each formulation) were subjected to a heat treatment at 190°C in air, and at specified periods of time, a specimen was removed from each formulation. The experiment was conducted over a period totaling 300 min. A comparison of the colors shown by the chips revealed the expected steady trend of discoloration ranging from a light brown (fawn) in the early stage to a dark reddish-brown and ultimately to a deep black as the heat treatment proceeded.

Significantly, the samples incorporating 6 and 7 displayed discoloration in the sequence stated after heating periods appreciably longer than observed with the DIOP standard samples. Equivalent color hues and associated heating periods for the three formulations are given in Table V. It is seen that the fawn stage is reached after 40 min by the sample containing 7, after 20 min by that containing 6, and after only 10 min by the standard. More conspicuously yet, the dark reddish-brown stage, reflecting a significant extent of dehydrochlorination, is attained by the standard after 30 min, whereas it takes about 2.5 and 4 hr, respectively, for the samples with 6 and 7 to reach the same stage. Finally, the specimens containing DIOP and 6 blackened entirely after about 1.5 and 3.5 hr, respectively, and the one incorporating 7 was not completely black yet at the end of the experiment (6 hr). The epoxyacetate 7, conforming to expectation,

TABLE V
Discoloration of PVC Formulations During Heat Aging Test[a]

Plasticizer[b]	Time period required to reach color stage, min			
	Light brown	Light reddish-brown	Dark reddish-brown	Black
DIOP	10	25	30	90
6	20	80	160	220
7	40	140	250	≫300[c]

[a] Aging test performed at 190°C in air.
[b] Formulations as per Table I.
[c] Sample not completely black after 300 min.

TABLE VI
PVC Wire-Coating Formulation

Component	Content, parts by weight
PVC resin[a]	67
Triacetate 6	28
Stabilizer[b]	4
Lubricant[c]	0.7

[a] Corvic D60/11.
[b] Tribasic lead sulfate.
[c] Spicco CA 103 (calcium stearate).

thus performs best among the three formulations tested, showing a synergistic stabilizing efficiency some 50% higher than demonstrated by the triacetate 6. (It is of interest to compare these results with an earlier study[16] in which the Ba/Cd epoxy combination showed only minor synergism in PVC stabilization. The epoxy plasticizer used in that work, an epoxidized soybean oil, is devoid of the phenyl acetate moiety present in 7, which may thus be implicated as a structural system responsible for some of the synergistic characteristics shown by the cardanol compound.)

On balance, and taking the results of all three types of thermal tests into account, on finds that both acetates are distinctly superior to DIOP in heat stability and strength retention after short-term thermal aging at the high test temperature employed.

Extrusion of Wire-Coating Formulation

An 800-g batch of a typical unpigmented wire-coating PVC formulation plasticized with acetate 6 according to Table VI was granulated and extruded in an effort to establish the behavior of a selected cardanol-type plasticizer under conditions of wire coating and cable sheathing extrusion. A corresponding batch plasticized with DIOP was subsequently extruded on the same machine at identical extruder settings. The extrudate, a continuous tubular profile with nominal 2 mm I.D. and 4 mm O.D., in both cases showed smooth inner and outer

TABLE VII
Tensile Properties[a] of Extruded PVC Wire-Coating Blend

Plasticizer[b]	Tested 48 hr after extrusion[c]		Tested 1 yr after extrusion[d]	
	σ,[e] MN m^{-2}	ϵ,[f] %	σ,[e] MN m^{-2}	ϵ,[f] %
DIOP	20.7	384	21.3	273
6	25.0	438	25.4	313

[a] Per Fed. Test Method Std. No. 406, Method 1011 (ASTM D638), except that specimens were used as cut from extrudate. Entries represent averages of five test runs.
[b] Formulation as per Table VI (same for standard, except with DIOP in lieu of 6).
[c] Conditioned at 23° ± 1°C, 50 ± 4% R.H.
[d] Stored at 20° ± 8°C, 55 ± 20% R.H., and conditioned for 48 hr as in (c), prior to testing.
[e] Tensile strength at break.
[f] Elongation at break.

surfaces. The test material was cream colored, whereas the standard was grayish-white. Tensile properties, determined on the extruded materials immediately and again after one year of storage, are listed in Table VII.

The data show the test formulation to be superior to the standard in both σ and ϵ, although the differences (10–20%) are by no means significant. The long-term stored samples show an ever so slight increase in σ, while a moderate (29%) reduction in ϵ is apparent for both formulations.

Conclusions

The test program discussed reveals a most promising performance of the cardanol derivatives 6 and 7 as PVC plasticizers. In comparison to DIOP as the standard, both compounds incorporated into PVC formulations, while tending to impart a slight yellowish discoloration, exhibit superior plasticizing efficiency and, upon short-term heat treatment at 190°C, show better strength retention, paired with less embrittlement, and higher resistance to degradation. The high-temperature performance indicates costabilizing, and possibly synergistic, effects to be exerted by the two cardanol derivatives, notably the epoxide 7. We must emphasize, however, that the findings here presented are preliminary, and considerably more testing work, including the determination of cold flex properties, electrical, volatility, and migration behavior, water and solvent resistance, milling and injection-molding characteristics, and long-term aging at moderately elevated temperatures (80–100°C), will be required for an adequate plasticizer characterization. It is, furthermore, of interest to study other modifications of the cardanol structure, such as represented by the epoxidized anisole analog of 7 or higher alkanoic ester analogs of 6, which can be expected to possess superior hydrolytic stability. It is intended to include these features in future investigations.

EXPERIMENTAL

PVC Resin. The PVC types, Corvic D65/6 and D60/11, both suspension grades, were commercial resins (African Explosives and Chemical Industries, Ltd.) with Fikentscher K values of about 70 and 65, respectively.

Plasticizers and Other Additives. The anacardates 3 and 4, as well as the acetates 5–7, were obtained in the preceding work.[1] Larger quantities required for Brabender and extrusion testing were synthesized by the known[1] procedures. Di(2-ethylhexyl) phthalate (DIOP) was a commercial product, as were the stabilizers and lubricants used per Tables I and VI.

Small-Scale Compatibility Testing. The general formulation of Table I was employed throughout. The liquid additives (plasticizer, 4.0 g; stabilizer, 0.2 g; lubricant, 0.1 g) were mixed and subsequently homogenized with the PVC resin (5.7 g). Batches so prepared with each of the plasticizers 3–7, as well as with DIOP standard, were compression molded at 160°C in a Carver hydraulic press (cavity dimensions 20 × 30 × 3 mm; platens preheated to 160°C; mold closed at contact pressure) for 5 min at 0.16 MN m^{-2}. Mold and platens were cooled to a room temperature (pressure increased to 0.24 MN m^{-2} during cooldown period) before the specimens were removed. After storing for 48 hr under standard conditions (23° ± 1°C, 50 ± 4% relative humidity), the samples were visually examined as described in the text.

Brabender Testing. Four 35-g batches, incorporating DIOP and compounds 5–7 as plasticizers and formulated as per Table I, were prepared and homogenized as in the small-scale tests except that 3.5-fold quantities of resin and additives were used. The Brabender Plastograph, preheated to 132°C, was charged with a batch, and mixing was started. Both the maximum torque (τ_{max}) and the torque after 10 min of mixing time at the given temperature (τ_{10}) were recorded as arbitrary instrumental readings, and the time (t_{max}) to reach τ_{max} was taken. The data are shown in Table II.

Mechanical Testing. Three 100-g batches, incorporating DIOP and compounds 6 and 7 as plasticizers and formulated as per Table I, were prepared and homogenized as in the preceding tests and were partially gelled by Brabender mixing for 10 min at 132°C. The batches were compression molded to flat sheets of 2-mm thickness in the Carver press under the conditions used in the small-scale compatibility testing. Tensile specimens per Federal Test Method Standard No. 406, Method 1011, Type I, were cut from the sheets. The specimens (set of five for each one of the three formulations) were subjected to tensile tests per cited test method on an Instron testing machine. Tensile strength at break (σ), elongation at break (ϵ), and modulus of elasticity at 100% elongation (E_{100}) were evaluated from the stress–strain curves recorded. The data were averaged over the five runs of each set.

Two more sets, each of five tensile specimens, for each of the three formulations were placed into a circulating-air oven preheated to 190°C and were maintained at that temperature for 30 and 60 min, respectively. Values of σ, ϵ, and E_{100} for the three sets removed after 30 min, as well as for the three corresponding sets removed after 60 min, were taken from the stress–strain curves recorded at room temperature as before and were averaged over the five runs of each set. The averages for both the virgin and the heat-treated samples are compiled in Table III under the proper headings.

Differential Thermal Analysis. An Aminco Thermo Analyzer equipped with platinum/platinum–rhodium thermocouples was employed for the DTA tests conducted over the 25°–400°C temperature range at a heating rate of 8°C/min in static air. The samples used were chips of about 20 mg weight cut from the compression-molded sheets prepared for the mechanical testing. The temperature readings taken from the major exotherm maxima of the thermograms are given as degradation temperatures in Table IV.

Discoloration Tests at 190°C. Rectangular chips of approx. 2 cm² surface area, a total of 12 for each one of the three formulations, were cut from the compression-molded sheets prepared for the mechanical testing. The specimens were placed into a forced-draft oven preheated to 190°C and were removed, one at a time from each formulation, after intervals ranging from 10 min initially to 40 min near the end of the experiment. Discoloration of the chips was assessed visually. The periods of heat aging required for the different formulations to reach four arbitrarily selected color thresholds are recorded in Table V.

Extrusion of Wire-Coating Formulation. A batch consisting of PVC resin (556 g), plasticizer 6 (235 g), stabilizer (33.4 g), and lubricant (5.56 g) according to the formulation of Table VI was thoroughly mixed by hand and was gelled for 12 min on a Bridge laboratory mill at roller temperatures of 140°C (back) and 150°C (front) and a friction ratio of 1:1.15. Disintegration of the gelled and cooled material in a random granulator was followed by extrusion on a single-screw Berstorff extruder (30-mm screw diameter) operated at 50 rpm, head temperature 165°C. A tubular die was employed that permitted extrusion to a hollow round profile with nominal 2-mm I.D., 4-mm O.D. (periodic dimensional checks on the cooled profile revealed an actual wall thickness of 0.85 ± 0.03 mm). A batch identical in all asspects except that it contained DIOP in place of 6 was extruded on the same machine under identical conditions immediately following the first batch, the intermediate charge being marked with a red pigment. Having passed through a room-temperature water bath, the extrudate was collected without tension on a takeup reel and was stored for 48 hr under standard conditions. Samples 10 cm long taken at random from the extrudate (five specimens for each formulation) were checked for dimensions (wall thickness, cross-sectional area) and were subjected to tensile tests on an Instron testing machine. The values of σ and ϵ, averaged over the five runs per formulation, are given in Table VII. The same tests were performed on a portion of the material stored for one year under roof (20° ± 8°C, 55 ± 20% R.H.). The results are listed in the same table.

The authors are indebted to African Explosives & Chemical Industries, Ltd., notably Dr. G. Mears and Mr. W. H. Hofmeyr, for invaluable assistance in the formulation and testing of PVC compounds, and to De Beers Diamond Research Laboratory for cordial cooperation throughout the project. Thanks are also due to the Council for Scientific and Industrial Research for an equipment grant.

References

1. E. W. Neuse and J. D. van Schalkwyk, *S. Afr. J. Sci.,* in press.
2. J. L. Gellerman and H. Schlenk, *Anal. Chem.,* **40,** 739 (1968).
3. W. F. Symes and C. R. Dawson, *J. Amer. Chem. Soc.,* **75,** 4952 (1953).
4. D. Wasserman and C. R. Dawson, *Ind. Eng. Chem.,* **37,** 396 (1945).
5. J. S. Aggarwal, *Paintindia Ann.,* 103 (1967).
6. J. C. Welgemoed, Ph.D. Thesis, Cape Town, 1971.
7. F. Würstlin, *Kolloid-Z.,* **152,** 31 (1957).
8. F. Stühlen and L. Meier, *Kunststoffe,* **62,** 674 (1972).
9. R. Khanna, *J. Oil Col. Chem. Assoc.,* **58,** 16 (1975).
10. O. Leuchs, *Kunststoffe,* **46,** 547 (1956); *ibid.,* **58,** 375 (1968).
11. K. S. Minsker, I. K. Pakhomova, G. I. Burlakova, and L. G. Pakhomov, *Vysokomol. Soedin., A12,* 2307 (1970).
12. H. J. Hageman and C. R. H. I. de Jonge, *Kunststoffe,* **62,** 681 (1972).
13. K. Worschech and K. Wolf, *Kunststoffe,* **61,** 645 (1971).
14. L. F. King and F. Noël, *Polym. Eng. Sci.,* **12,** 112 (1972).
15. A. Gleissner, *Kunststoffe,* **62,** 678 (1972).
16. R. D. Deanin, J. F. Landers, Jr., R. W. Byczko, and I. Linzer, *Polym. Eng. Sci.,* **13,** 35 (1973).

Received July 14, 1976
Revised Sept. 30, 1976

JOURNAL OF APPLIED POLYMER SCIENCE   VOL. 21, 3035–3061 (1977)

The Physical Properties and Morphology of Poly-ε-caprolactone Polymer Blends

DOUGLAS S. HUBBELL and STUART L. COOPER, *Department of Chemical Engineering, University of Wisconsin, Madison, Wisconsin 53706*

Synopsis

The compatibility, morphology, and mechanical properties of poly-ε-caprolactone (PCL) blended with poly(vinyl chloride), nitrocellulose, and cellulose acetate butyrate are described in this study. Methods used in this investigation included differential scanning calorimetry, dynamic mechanical testing, small-angle light scattering, light microscopy and stress–strain testing. Blends of PCL with poly(vinyl chloride) (PVC) are shown to be compatible in all proportions. In the PCL concentration range 40–100%, the PCL crystallizes in the form of negative spherulites. The spherulites were found to be volume filling with as much as 35% PVC. The nitrocellulose blends with PCL exhibited the glass transition behavior of a compatible system over the composition range of 50–100% PCL. At lower PCL concentrations, phase separation was apparent. The PCL crystallinity was present only in the nitrocellulose blends with more than 50% PCL, and it was in the form of rod-like superstructures. Blends of PCL with cellulose acetate butyrate were shown to be phase separated, with one phase having nearly equal proportions of the two polymers. The PCL crystallinity was in the form of negative spherulites and was formed with PCL compositions as low as 50%. Stress–strain results show polycaprolactone to be an effective plasticizer for poly(vinyl chloride) and the cellulose derivatives studied.

INTRODUCTION

A polymer blend is a mixture of two or more different kinds of polymer chains which are not covalently bonded together. This separates blends from block or graft copolymers in which primary bonds link dissimilar chain segments. Compatibility is a relative term used to denote the degree of mixing in a solution, be it for small molecule liquids or for polymer solids. The lack of compatibility between substances leads to phase separation. In blends, macroscale phase separation can lead to a material with very poor mechanical properties due to the presence of large domains which have poor interfacial bonding.

In contrast, a compatible blend exhibits a high degree of mixing and mechanical properties which reflect an average between the constituent polymers. For example, plasticized blends of poly(vinyl chloride)/nitrile rubber combine the low-temperature flexibility and ease of processing of nitrile rubber and the high-temperature permanence and flame retardent properties of poly(vinyl chloride). Another example is blends of poly(phenylene oxide) with styrene copolymers. These blends have the excellent dimensional stability at high temperatures and good electrical properties of poly(phenylene oxide) combined with the lower melt viscosity, shear sensitivity, and cost of polystyrene.[1,2]

Although highly incompatible mixtures of polymers are easy to detect because of their opacity and poor mechanical properties relative to the constituent polymers, complete compatibility is less easily demonstrated. If domains are present, they can often be seen with light or electron microscopes. Completely incompatible polymer films are often opaque, but compatibility is a relative term, and domains may be quite small, resulting in an optically clear specimen. In addition, the index of refraction of the different phases may be similar and allow an incompatible film to be completely clear. Another difficulty is that often the images seen by microscopy are not easily interpreted.

Compatibility may be studied by mutual solvent and light-scattering techniques, which are based on thermodynamic considerations.[3] Moreover, the various methods of determining the glass transition (T_g) of a polymeric material can be applied to blend systems. Normally, compatible systems will exhibit only one T_g located between the T_g's of the constituent polymers. In contrast, an incompatible blend will show the T_g's of the homopolymers. It is now generally accepted that a single intermediate T_g is proof of compatibility even though the sensitivity of the technique may vary. The glass transition can be measured by a variety of methods including thermal analysis, dynamic mechanical testing, changes in refractive index,[4] changes in specific volume on thermal expansion,[5] NMR,[6] and possibly gas chromatography,[7] though it has yet to be used for finding the T_g's in a polymer blend.

BLENDS OF POLYCAPROLACTONE

Koleske and co-workers[8] have blended PCL, and many similar polyesters, with a wide range of polymers and have demonstrated many advantages of the blends over the homopolymers. Their blend systems may be divided into three categories. First, there are blends which have crystalline interactions between the two polymers. For example, a 90/10 blend of polyethylene and PCL exhibits an unaltered glass transition of the polyethylene, which would indicate a thermodynamically incompatible amorphous phase; but the crystalline relaxation maximum for polyethylene occurs at a higher temperature and has a higher magnitude. This phenomenon implies that the PCL restricts the motion of the crystalline polyethylene through some form of interaction.

A second classification of useful blends are those which exhibit the glass transitions of the constituent homopolymers and lack crystalline interactions but still have good mechanical properties. These are said to be mechanically compatible.[9] This behavior indicates that there is some connection between phases, and they differ from compatible systems, which exhibit a single T_g, only in the size of the domains and the extent of the phase separation. Examples of polymers which form mechanically compatible blends with PCL are poly(vinyl acetate), polystyrene, poly(methyl methacrylate),[9] and poly(ϵ-methyl-ϵ-caprolactone).[10]

The third classification are blends which exhibit only one T_g which is intermediate to those of the constituent homopolymers. Polymers that can be blended compatibly with PCL include poly(vinyl chloride), nitrocellulose, phenoxy A (a poly(hydroxy ether) made by Union Carbide), Penton (a chlorinated polyether), styrene–acrylonitrile copolymers, and polyepichlorhydrin.[9]

Blends of Poly-ε-caprolactone and Poly(vinyl Chloride)

Koleske and Lundberg[11] found that PCL/PVC blends were compatible over the full range of compositions. Each blend in the range 10%–90% PVC exhibited only one T_g. Furthermore, it was found that the T_g versus weight fraction plot could be represented quite well by two T_g copolymer equations, the Fox equation,[12]

$$(1/T_{g12}) = (W_1/T_{g1}) + (W_2/T_{g2}) \tag{1}$$

and the Gordon–Taylor equation,[13]

$$T_{g12} = T_{g1} + [kW_2(T_{g2} - T_{g12})W_1] \tag{2}$$

where T_{g12} is the glass transition of the copolymer or blend, T_{g1} and T_{g2} are the glass transitions for homopolymers 1 and 2, W_1 and W_2 are weight fractions, and k is a constant.

They found that the loss modulus (G'') peaks, which represented the T_g's for the blends, when extrapolated to 100% PCL gave a T_g of 202°K even though the quenched T_g for the pure PCL samples was 213°K. This discrepancy was attributed to the influence of crystallinity on the T_g of the PCL homopolymer.

The PCL/PVC blend system was next studied by Ong.[14] All samples were cast from methyl ethyl ketone solutions by evaporating the solvent at room temperature. Ong found that crystallinity was present in blends with up to 70% PVC by weight. The crystallinity had a spherulitic superstructure in all cases, and the spherulites were volume filling with less than 50% PVC. The lamellae, which were investigated by optical and electron microscopy, were found to twist regularly in the blends as they radiated from the centers of the spherulites. In contrast, the pure PCL was found to have irregular twisting of the lamellae. Although the crystallite dimensions were found by x-ray diffraction to decrease with increasing concentrations of PVC, the unit cell dimensions were found not to change with the presence of PVC. Consequently, it was suggested that the PVC molecules were restricted to the interlamellar regions.

Further work on this system was carried out by Khambatta and Stein.[15,16] Their blend samples were cast in dishes at room temperature from solutions of tetrahydrofuran (THF), heated to 70°C, and then slowly cooled. With this sample preparation, samples exhibited somewhat less crystallinity (60% for PCL) than the samples prepared by Ong. As a result of small-angle x-ray scattering (SAXS), they concluded that the amorphous regions in all the blends consisted of two phases. Each phase contained both polymers but in different proportions, and there appeared to be a transition zone between the phases which was about 30 Å thick. The crystalline structure was investigated both by SAXS and small-angle light scattering. They confirmed Ong's findings that the crystallinity was spherulitic and that the spherulites, which become coarser with increasing amounts of PVC, were volume filling until nearly 50% PVC. They postulated that the PCL could not crystallize in high concentrations of PVC because the domain size for the PCL-rich phase became smaller than the size of a critical nucleus.

Blends of Poly-ε-caprolactone and Cellulose Derivatives

Cellulosic derivatives are generally too stiff to be processed without some sort of plasticizer.[17] Since few small molecule plasticizers seem to be effective because of migration and volatilization, polymer blending is potentially quite important to the use of these thermoplastics, especially since polymeric plasticizers migrate very slowly.

Brode and Koleske[9] cast samples of nitrocellulose (NC) (12% nitrogen) blended with PCL from a solvent mixture of isopropanol and n-propyl acetate. As with the PVC/PCL system, they heated the samples above the T_m of PCL and quenched them in liquid nitrogen before proceeding with torsion pendulum experiments. The T_g as indicated by both Q^{-1} and G'' increased steadily with increasing concentrations of NC for the 0–50% NC range.

Stress–strain measurements reveal that the modulus drops and the ability to elongate increases with increasing amount of PCL. Thus, PCL acts as an excellent plasticizer for nitrocellulose. Also, diluting the nitrocellulose with PCL would most likely increase the stability of nitrocellulose to sunlight and heat and thus counteract the main limitations of the material.

Koleske, Whitworth, and Lundberg[8] also blended PCL by various methods with acetylated ethyl cellulose, carboxymethyl cellulose, triacetate cellulose, diacetate cellulose, and cellulose acetate butyrate and found that each cellulosic could form mechanically compatible blends with PCL. For the most part, the PCL proved an effective plasticizer which gave cellulosic blends that were easier to process and more flexible than the pure cellulose esters and ethers.

The objectives of the present study were to analyze polymer blends of poly-ε-caprolactone with poly(vinyl chloride) and with several cellulose derivatives. The research included the determination of compatibility and the characterization of the morphologic, mechanical, and orientation properties of the polycaprolactone blends. The use of differential infrared dichroism for following the dynamic orientation of each component of the compatible amorphous and semicrystalline blends will be reported elsewhere.[18]

EXPERIMENTAL

Materials

The polymer common to all binary blend systems studied here is poly-ε-caprolactone (PCL), which has the repeat unit

$$-\!\!\left[O-(CH_2)_5-\overset{\displaystyle O}{\overset{\displaystyle \|}{C}}\right]_{\!n}\!\!-$$

The PCL used in this study was supplied by Dr. J. V. Koleske of Union Carbide Corporation's Chemicals and Plastics Division and was designated as PCL-700. Other studies on the poly-ε-caprolactone–poly(vinyl chloride) blend system have also used PCL-700.[11,14,16,19] The PCL had been solution polymerized and was in the form of extruded yellow pellets. It is a semicrystalline polymer with a melting point of 61°C.

The polymers blended with PCL were cellulose acetate butyrate, nitrocellulose, and poly(vinyl chloride). All blends are designated in terms of the weight per cent of polymer mixed with PCL. The cellulose acetate butyrate (CAB) had 1.7 butyl and 1.0 acetyl groups per repeat unit and was designated 381-20 by the manufacturer (Tennessee Eastman Company). Although the white CAB powder supplied showed a small amount of crystallinity melting at 168°C, films made from the powder failed to show any sign of a crystalline melting point using differential scanning calorimetry. The nitrocellulose used (supplied by Hercules, Inc.) was designated RS ½ sec. It was furnished as a white powder packed with isopropyl alcohol (30% by weight) because of its flammability. It is reported to be 11.8–12.2% nitrogen, which corresponds to 2.25 ± 0.06 nitro groups per glucose ring. The poly(vinyl chloride) (PVC) used was Union Carbide's QYTQ-387 which was supplied by Koleske and had been used in several other PCL/PVC studies.[11,14,16,43]

Films made of pure CAB, NC, and PVC were all clear. The lack of crystallinity in CAB could be confirmed by thermal analysis, but both PVC and NC degraded below their expected melting points. The NC was assumed to be mostly amorphous. The PVC crystallinity has been estimated to be less than 8% by comparing carbon–chlorine stretching bands in the infrared spectrum.[14] The molecular weights, densities, and solubility parameters for PCL, CAB, NC, and PVC appear in Table I. The solubility parameters have been calculated by the group contribution methods of Small[21] and Hoy.[22]

Sample Preparation

All samples for this study were prepared by spin casting from polymer solutions. In this technique, which has been described elsewhere,[23] a solution of polymers and solvent is forced against the walls of a spinning cylinder. The solvent is evaporated by a slight vacuum and also by heat if desired, with the polymer precipitating onto a sheet of aluminum or paper lining the wall. With this technique, it has been demonstrated that unoriented films with thicknesses as small as 4 μ can be made.

Tetrahydrofuran (THF), which has a solubility parameter of 9.1, was used as the spin-casting solvent. In all sample preparations, the solutions were cast at room temperature. Films for IR work were precipitated from approximately 15 ml of 1% solution; and for samples thicker than 10 μ, portions of 5% solution were added every 15 min to the caster. All samples were dried in a constant stream of air for several hours and then dried for at least four days under vacuum at room temperature. Films thicker than 25 μ were dried for at least one week. After drying, all samples were aged in desiccators at room temperature for at least two weeks. This allows the PCL crystallinity to approach its equilibrium value.[11]

TABLE I
Characterization of Polymers Used

	PCL	PVC	CAB	NC
$\overline{M}_n$	13,000	35,000	77,000	45,000
$\overline{M}_w$	24,000	72,000	—	—
Repeat unit molecular weight	114.145	62.499	323.3	262.6
Density, g/cm³ (20°C)	1.149	1.39	1.15–1.22	1.58–1.65
Solubility parameter—Hoy,[22] (cal/cm³)^{1/2}	9.43	9.47	9.57	9.95
Solubility Parameter—Small,[21] (cal/cm³)^{1/2}	9.34	9.55	8.90	—

a The densities for the amorphous and crystalline PCL are 1.094[44] and 1.187[14], respectively.

The only exception to the above procedure was with some of the samples containing PVC. It was found that in samples dried at room temperature, the glass transitions were depressed somewhat. The amount of depression of the T_g depended on the per cent PVC and the thickness of the film. In pure PVC samples, the T_g was depressed as much as 51°C for a 360-μ sample or as little as 8°C for a 8-μ film. This retention of solvent even at processing temperatures and its effect on PVC properties is well documented.[24,25]

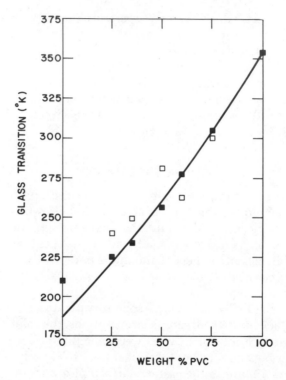

Fig. 1. T_g vs weight percent for (□) PVC/PCL with the Gordon–Taylor equation fit to the (■) quenched data.

It was found that temperatures greater than 80°C were needed to remove the solvent from the PVC samples. Therefore, samples of PVC, PVC blends, and PCL were prepared with 1% Ferro GH-148 liquid thermostabilizer based on the total weight of polymer (Ferro Corporation). These samples were approximately 70 μ thick and were dried under vacuum for 48 hr at room temperature, 48 hr at 105°C, and finally for an additional 60 hr at 48°C. The final drying period was used to help restore the crystallinity lost by melting. These particular samples were annealed at room temperature for an additional two weeks before being used in the DSC and stress–strain measurements. The PVC and 75% PVC samples were somewhat yellowed, but the other samples seemed unaffected in appearance. The dryness of PVC film was confirmed by a DSC measurement of the T_g. For all other experiments, the thin and delicate samples were only dried at room temperature. The amount of solvent in these thin samples was small enough to not seriously affect the results.

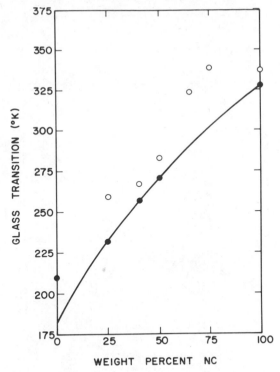

Fig. 2. T_g vs weight percent for (O) NC/PCL with the Gordon–Taylor equation fit to the (●) quenched data.

Mechanical Properties

Mechanical properties of the blend systems were determined by two tensile methods. The first was dynamic mechanical testing at a constant frequency over a wide temperature range. This experiment yields information on dynamic modulus and molecular relaxation processes. Secondly, standard tensile stress–strain tests were performed to measure the modulus, ultimate strength, and elongation at break.

The dynamic elastic modulus E', the loss modulus E'', and the tan δ were measured simultaneously by the Rheovibron dynamic viscoelastomer Model DDV-II (Toyo Measuring Instruments Co., Ltd.). Measurements were made at a frequency of 110 Hz starting from −140°C and heating at 1°–2°C per minute until the samples became too soft to be tested. The readings were taken every 4°–8°C except in transition zones, when the readings were taken every 2°C. The sample chamber was kept dry by a stream of moisture-free nitrogen.

Standard tensile stress–strain experiments were performed at room temperature on an Instron table-model testing machine. All samples were die cut from spin-cast films into standard dumbbell shape (ASTM 412 Type D) with a gauge length of 2.0 in. and a width of 0.126 in. The elongation rate was 0.2 in./min, which is an engineering strain rate of 10%/min. The sample thickness, which was measured with a micrometer, varied from blend to blend (70–100 μ) because samples were made on the basis of weight and not density. The PVC blended films were made somewhat thinner (50–70 μ) to facilitate drying All reported results are the average of three to four runs.

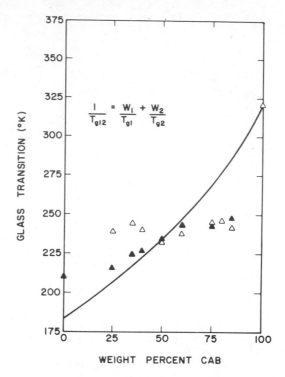

Fig. 3. T_g vs weight percent for ($\triangle$) CAB/PCL with the Fox equation fit to the ($\blacktriangle$) quenched data.

Thermal Studies

Differential scanning calorimetry (DSC) was used to measure heat capacity as a function of temperature. The DSC used in this study was a Perkin–Elmer Model DSC-2. Liquid nitrogen was used as a heat sink, and helium was used as the purge gas. Samples were usually about 30 mg, and a heating rate of 20°/min was used for measuring T_g and T_m. For measuring heats of fusion, the heating rate was 2.5°/min. The heat of fusion peak areas were always greater than 10 in.[2] and were measured with a planimeter. The percent crystallinity was calculated on the basis of a heat of fusion of 32.4 cal/g for PCL, which was found by melting point depression experiments for PCL using ethyl benzoate as diluent.[26] The reference for the heat of fusion calculations was pure indium, which melts with a heat of fusion of 6.80 cal/g.

Morphology Studies

For a complete description of the morphology of a polymer sample, several techniques must be employed because of the different levels of crystalline structure and the limitation of each method. In this research, optical microscopy and small-angle light-scattering were employed to study blend morphology. The small-angle light-scattering apparatus used in this work was a Spectra Physics Model 115 He–Ne continuous-wave gas laser emitting a polarized light beam with a wavelength of 6328 Å. The beam passes through the sample and then through

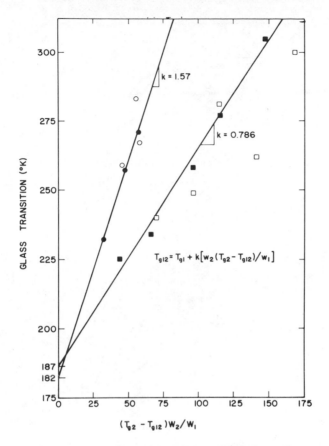

Fig. 4. T_g data for (■) PVC/PCL and (●) NC/PCL blends plotted according to the Gordon–Taylor equation. The lines are fit to the quenched data: (○) NC/PCL; (□) PVC/PCL.

an analyzer, which is a second polarizer. The resulting scattering pattern was recorded on Polaroid Type 52 black and white film. The samples used were approximately 30 μ thick, and the beam intensity was controlled by Wratten gelatine neutral density filters.

The refractive index within a sample can change due to presence of crystalline and amorphous regions, voids, changing anisotrophy, and areas of different orientation. The first two are due to density differences, and the last two are due to orientation differences.[14] SALS was used in this study to determine the nature of the crystalline superstructure and to measure the average radius of the spherulites.[27–30]

All of the optical microscopy was conducted on a Zeiss Universal microscope. Pictures were taken with a 35-mm camera with Ektachrome color film for tungsten lamps. The samples were 5–15 μ thick and were held between glass slides. No heat treatment was used on the samples. The presence of spherulites was indicated by the usual Maltese cross extinction pattern which appears when using crossed polarizers. The sign of spherulites was found by inserting a quartz accessory plate in the path of the light. The extent to which the spherulitic superstructure filled the available volume was qualitatively determined along with the approximate size of the spherulites.

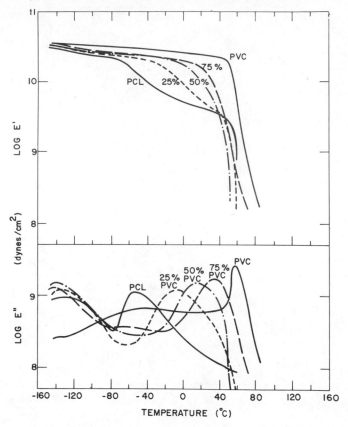

Fig. 5. Temperature dependence of E' and E'' for PVC/PCL.

RESULTS AND DISCUSSION

Thermal Analysis

The DSC glass transitions for each of the three blend systems, PVC/PCL, NC/PCL, and CAB/PCL, are plotted as a function of composition in Figures 1 to 3. These data include the results for samples annealed at room temperature and also for the same samples which have been heated above the melting point of PCL (400°K for NC- and PVC-containing samples and 450°K for CAB mixtures) and then quenched rapidly in the DSC to 150°K.

In random copolymers, there is a high degree of interaction between the different repeat units because they are held together chemically. The glass transition of a random copolymer consequently reflects the composition of the copolymer. Thus, the T_g of random copolymers can usually be represented as a monotonic function of composition by one of the various copolymer equations. Similarly, if blends of polymers are mixed at the segmental level, only one T_g should be evident, and a copolymer equation should be applicable. If a blend system shows only one T_g for a range of composition but these T_g's fail to show a continuous progression from the T_g of one pure component to the T_g of the other, the T_g seen for some of the blends probably represents only one phase in a multiphase system.

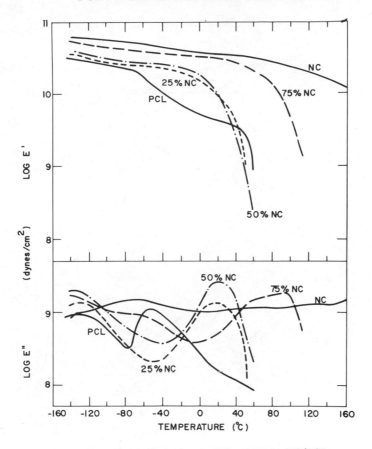

Fig. 6. Temperature dependence of E' and E'' for NC/PCL.

The Gordon–Taylor copolymer equation, eq. (2), has been applied to the T_g data in this study to determine if the blends are single-phase systems or not. For a well-mixed system, the plot of T_g versus $[(T_{g2} - T_{g12})W_2/W_1]$, where W_1 and W_2 are the weight fractions of polymers 1 and 2, respectively, in the amorphous phase, will yield a straight line with a slope of k and an ordinate intercept of T_{g1}.

The T_g's for the PVC/PCL and NC/PCL systems were plotted versus $[(T_{g2} - T_{g12})W_2/W_1]$ in Figure 4. For the quenched samples, W_1 and W_2 are the weight fraction of PCL and PVC or NC, respectively. Straight lines have been fitted by least-squares analysis to these data. For the unquenched samples, W_1 is the weight fraction of PCL in the amorphous phase. The percent crystallinity of PCL was calculated from the DSC heat of fusion measurements. The variable W_2 is the weight fraction of PVC or NC in the amorphous phase assuming that all of the PVC and NC was noncrystalline.

Figure 1 shows that the Gordon–Taylor equation fits the quenched data for the PVC/PCL blends quite well. The thermograms for the blends of 25%, 35%, and 50% PVC display PCL heats of fusion, and consequently, the unquenched T_g's for these samples lie above the curve because the crystallinity reduces the concentration of PCL in the amorphous phase.

The NC/PCL data plotted in Figure 2 present a different situation. Blends

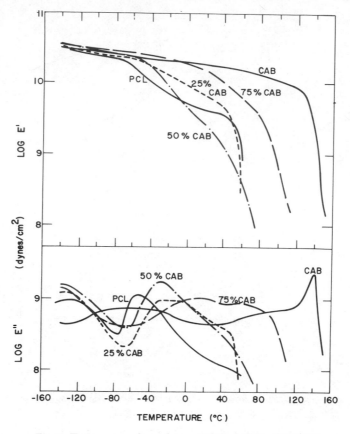

Fig. 7. Temperature dependence of E' and E'' for CAB/PCL.

of 25% and 40% NC showed the opaqueness and a DSC endotherm which indicate the presence of crystallinity. Consequently, melting and quenching produced lower T_g's as expected. Pure nitrocellulose and 50% NC did not show either of these features. Yet, the T_g dropped from 338° to 328°K for NC and from 283° to 271°K for 50% NC after the heating–quenching cycle. Blends of 65% and 75% NC showed high initial T_g's but failed to show any transition after quenching.

The Gordon–Taylor equation fits the quenched points reasonably well for 25%, 40%, and 50% NC. Thus, NC/PCL blends appear to be compatible in the range of 0–50% NC. The unquenched 50% NC does not fit onto the curve even though it did not contain crystalline PCL. Consequently, it would seem that microheterogeneity is present in coarse enough form to allow detection of one of the phases and that the segregation was eliminated by the heating. This trend is continued for 65% and 75% NC. Obviously, large-scale phase separation has produced nearly pure nitrocellulose domains in the 65–75% NC region.

The T_g data for the CAB/PCL blend system are shown in Figure 3. The thermograms for the samples in the range of 0–50% CAB indicate that PCL crystallinity was present. Above 50% CAB, the samples were clear and exhibited no endothermic heats of fusion in the temperature range tested. Cellulosic derivatives often have some crystallinity. As supplied, CAB showed a small amount of crystallinity which melted at 441°K, but none of the spin-cast films which contained CAB exhibited this endotherm. The T_g for pure CAB was measured as 321°K which compares well with a literature value[31] of 323°K; but after heating to 450°K followed by quenching, the thermogram was without transitions.

The quenched T_g's in Figure 3 show a steady increase with increasing amounts of CAB up to 60% CAB, after which the T_g seems to be fairly constant for the 60–85% range. A 91% CAB sample was prepared and tested but showed no transitions. Although the quenched points in the 25–60% CAB range seems to extrapolate to about 200°K, the Gordon–Taylor equation could not fit the data because the Gordon–Taylor plot (not shown) formed a curve rather than a straight line. A Fox equation, eq. (1), curve has been added to Figure 3 as a reference to the expected trend for a compatible system.

A close inspection of Figure 3 shows that for the blends tested, essentially all of the unquenched data and all of the quenched data for samples which were originally noncrystalline fall in the range of 238–248°K, with a somewhat random distribution around an average of 243°K. These results imply that for blends of 25–85% CAB, there are two phases of which one has a fairly constant composition of about 57% CAB judging by the Fox equation. In blends of less than about 50% CAB, the other phase is mostly PCL, and crystallization takes place. Melting followed by quenching forces more PCL into the CAB-rich phase with a lowering of its T_g. Above 50% CAB, the blend has excess CAB, and this excess forms a second amorphous phase which does not usually show a T_g in the DSC experiments.

In addition, the heat capacity change associated with the T_g for samples with more than 50% CAB gets smaller with decreasing concentrations of PCL until it disappears above 85% CAB. Thus, the CAB/PCL blends appear to be only partially compatible. The quenched T_g of the PCL-rich blends rises with increasing concentrations of CAB but does not follow either the Gordon–Taylor

TABLE II
Glass Transition and Secondary Relaxations for
PCL Blend Systems

Blend	Glass transition, °C			Secondary relaxations, °C	
	tan δ	E″	DSC[a]	tan δ	E″
PCL	−41	−56	−63	−125, —	−130, —
25% PVC	8	−4	−33	−132, —	−135, —
50% PVC	50	16	8	−134, —	−132, —
75% PVC	60	36	27	−137, −58	−139, −58
PVC	70	58	83	—, −33	—, −38
25% NC	—	18	−14	−126, —	−130, —
50% NC	—	23	10	−130, —	−138, —
75% NC	52	63, 95	66	−138, −60	−140, −60
NC	88	—	65	—, −60	—, −68
25% CAB	−28, −2	−28, −10	−34	−129, —	−140, —
50% CAB	0	−30	−29	−135, —	−144, —
75% CAB	28	8, 64	−28	−140, —	−140, —
CAB	72	72	48	—, −35	—, −60

[a] The PVC containing samples for the DSC had been annealed and dried at 105°C where as the PVC/PCL samples used in the dynamic mechanical testing had been dried only at room temperature and probably contained a small amount of residual solvent.

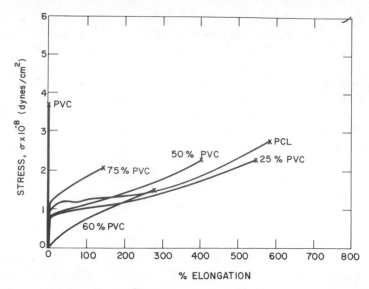

Fig. 8. Stress–strain curves for PVC/PCL at a strain rate of 10%/min.   Crosses indicate the points of failure.

or Fox equation.   At high CAB concentrations, the apparent T_g is essentially constant, which implies that a second, CAB-rich phase forms.

DYNAMIC MECHANICAL TESTING

The dynamic mechanical properties of the PVC/PCL, NC/PCL, and CAB/ PCL blend systems are shown in Figures 5 to 7.   Peak positions for the E'' and tan δ (not shown) curves are summarized in Table II.   Besides the information on the dynamic moduli, these results also give another measure of the glass transition.   Although the T_g's found by this method are somewhat less precise than those found by the DSC, it has been shown[32,33] that mechanical testing can detect segmental motion on a smaller scale than thermal analysis.   Thus, multiple phases may be more easily detected.

In Figure 5, the dynamic mechanical properties for PVC/PCL blends are shown as a function of temperature.   Each homopolymer exhibits two relaxations in the E'' curve.   The higher temperature peak corresponds to a glass transition, while the lower temperature peak may be attributed to a secondary relaxation.[11,14]   In the blends, only one glass transition peak is evident in the E'' curves, though the secondary relaxations of the homopolymers are also evident to some extent.   The sharp declines in the E' and E'' curves for PCL and 25% and 50% PVC in the neighborhood of 50°–60°C can be attributed to the melting of the crystalline PCL.

The dynamic mechanical testing results confirm the capatibility of the PVC/PCL system.   At higher concentrations of PVC, the tan δ and E'' T_g's move progressively to higher temperatures.   The symmetry of all the higher temperature peaks implies that they represent single relaxation phenomena.

The secondary relaxation also seems to shift with blending.   As Koleske and Lundberg noted,[11] the lower-temperature PCL relaxation at −130°C on the E'' curve can be attributed to movement associated with the $(CH_2)_5$ methylene

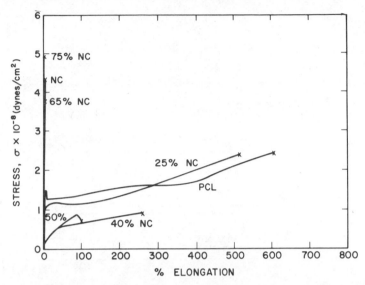

Fig. 9. Stress–strain curves for NC/PCL at a strain rate of 10%/min.

sequence. It has been suggested[34,35] that the movement can be compared to a crankshaft-type rotation around the backbone. As was previously reported,[11] the transition seems to move to lower temperatures upon blending. The broad PVC secondary relaxation at −38°C on the E'' curve also tends to shift to lower temperatures with blending and disappears at high concentrations of PCL.

The dynamic mechanical testing results for NC/PCL blends are presented in Figure 6. The E' curves for 25% and 50% NC seem quite similar, with the samples becoming very soft in the region of the PCL melting point. The 75% NC and 100% NC samples maintain high elastic moduli to much higher temperatures. The E'' curves for the blends show the PCL methylene relaxation at lower temperatures and prominent peaks above 0°C. The NC sample seems to lack a relaxation peak which would correspond to a T_g, but does show a broad peak centered at about −68°C. This peak also appears to be present in the 50% and 75% NC samples.

The lack of an obvious NC T_g peak makes analysis of this blend system somewhat ambiguous. The major transition of the 25% NC blend as shown by the E'' curve is the melting of the PCL at 18°C. The T_g of the amorphous 50% NC blend is in a similar temperature range at 23°C. The symmetry of the E'' peak for the 50% NC blend suggests a compatible blend, since only one relaxation is present.

In the 75% NC blend curve, the interpretation is quite different. The broad relaxation seems to have components at 63° and 95°C. Possibly, the upper component of the E'' relaxation represents the T_g of a nearly pure NC phase. Brode and Koleske[36] measured the NC T_g at 115°C with a torsion pendulum. The peak at 63°C would then represent a second phase containing both NC and PCL.

The secondary relaxation associated with NC seems to be unaffected by the presence of the PCL in 75% NC. Likewise, in 50% NC, this relaxation, which appears as a shoulder on the lower PCL peak in both the E'' and tan δ curves, seems to be in approximately the same position. This peak can be associated

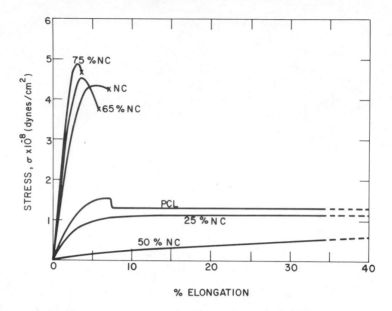

Fig. 10. Stress–strain curves for NC/PCL in the range of 0–40% strain.

with the movement of the six-member anhydroglucose ring.[37]   Its low magnitude
is most likely due to the steric hindrance caused by the nitro groups which are
normally in the equatorial positions.   Their bulkiness prevents the ring from
switching from one chair conformation to the other.

Like the NC/PCL system, the CAB/PCL dynamic mechanical curves lack the
overall symmetry of the compatible PVC/PCL system.   Figure 7 shows that
blends of 25% and 50% CAB have prominent E'' peaks around −20°C, and the
PCL methylene relaxation, near −130°C.   Pure CAB exhibits very broad, low-
magnitude peaks at −60°C and 72°C and a conspicuous peak at 136°C in the
E'' curve.   The 75% CAB blend exhibits a subdued methylene relaxation and
a very broad, double peak in the −20°–80°C range.

For CAB, the low, broad peak at 72°C has been designated the T_g.   The peak
at 136°C on the E'' corresponds to the crystallization and melting of CAB.   For
the blends, the E'' curves indicate that two T_g's are present in each case.   In the
25% CAB blend, the peak corresponding to the T_g seems to be too broad to be
a single phenomena.   In 50% CAB, the peak at −30°C seems to have only one
component, but it lies at a very low temperature.   Possibly a second T_g is hidden
in the long shoulder of the peak.   The 75% CAB clearly has two T_g's which are
56°C apart.   The low-temperature component at 8°C corresponds to the DSC
T_g of −28°C, and the higher temperature peak corresponds to a phase of nearly
pure CAB.   This interpretation is in good agreement with the two-phase model
based on the DSC results.   Thus, CAB/PCL would seem to be a phase-separated
system for 25–75% CAB.

TENSILE PROPERTIES

Typical stress–strain behavior for homopolymers and selected blends in the
range of 25–75% PCL are shown in Figures 8 through 11.   Figures 8, 9, and 11

show the stress–strain curves to failure, while Figure 10 shows the results of
NC/PCL in the range of 0–40% elongation. The stress–strain results are summarized in Table III. The data are averages of three to four runs for ultimate
strength, initial (Young's) modulus, and elongation at failure. Stresses have
been calculated on the basis of the initial cross-sectional area.

As was described previously, the PVC blends used for the stress–strain tests
were made with 1% thermostabilizer and had been dried at 105°C for two days.
A pure PCL sample was given the same thermal treatment. Samples dried at
room temperature were found to elongate to higher strain levels, but the same
trend as a function of composition was evident in the elongation results.

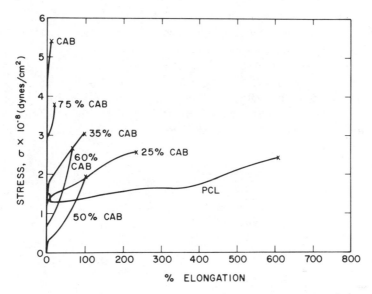

Fig. 11. Stress–strain curves for CAB/PCL at a strain rate of 10%/min.

As Figure 8 and Table III indicate, PCL is a very effective plasticizer for PVC.
The ability to elongate rises quickly with higher concentrations of PCL up to
about 50% PVC. Simultaneously, the modulus and ultimate strength drop
rapidly until 60% PVC. At higher concentrations of PCL, crystallinity is present,
and the samples tend to cold draw.

In Figures 9 and 10, it is evident that the NC/PCL blend system exhibits the
stress–strain behavior of a system which is compatible over a limited range. The
samples in the range of 0–40% NC elongated to over 250%, but the ability to deform drops abruptly between 40% and 65%. The 65% and 75% NC have essentially the same stress–strain behavior as pure NC, which indicates that a nearly
pure, continuous NC phase is present.

Figure 11 shows the stress–strain behavior of the CAB/PCL blend system.
Although thermal and dynamic mechanical testing showed that, most likely,
there is substantial phase separation, the properties shown indicate that PCL
is an effective plasticizer for CAB. The modulus drops, and the ability to
elongate rises with increasing amounts of PCL. As expected, the modulus drops
to a minimum in the sample with the least CAB without having much PCL
crystallinity present (50% CAB).

CRYSTALLINITY STUDIES

Thermal Analysis

Bohn[4] in his 1968 survey of compatible polymer blends found that none of the 13 compatible pairs known to him included a polymer capable of crystallizing. He suggested that the exothermic crystallization process was adverse to the mixing process, and, consequently, compatible blends containing crystallinity would be rare. He supported his contention by citing isomeric pairs of polymers which differ only in configuration and the tendency to crystallize but are incompatible. Examples of these include blends of high- and low-density polyethylene[38] and *cis-* and *trans*-1,4-polybutadiene.[39] The following year, Koleske and Lundberg[11] published the first paper on PVC/PCL blends. Since then, the list of crystalline compatible blends has grown to include PVC/Hytrel (a copolyester),[5] poly(vinyl fluoride)/poly(methyl methacrylate),[40] PVC/poly-ε-caprolactam, poly(ethylene terephthalate)/polycarbonate,[2] and all the PCL-compatible blends.

The degree of PCL crystallinity of the blends used in this study has been calculated from the areas under the heat-of-fusion peaks in the DSC thermograms. The results for the PVC, NC, and CAB blends are shown in Figure 12 as percent

TABLE III
Tensile Properties of PCL Blends

Blend	Elongation, %	Ultimate tensile strength, 10^{-6} dynes/cm^2	Young's modulus, 10^{-8} dynes/cm^2
PCL[a]	443	205	29.9
25% PVC	476	202	33.0
50% PVC	383	227	29.0
60% PVC	273	137	1.29
75% PVC	148	210	61.6
PVC	3.1	307	214
PCL	642	264	50.0
25% NC	510	240	38.5
40% NC	285	84.0	6.80
50% NC	104	67.0	4.47
65% NC	5.7	441[b]	204
75% NC	3.7	497[b]	243
NC	5.9	414[b]	270
PCL	642	264	50.0
25% CAB	243	265	56.8
35% CAB	90.6	300	79.4
40% CAB	44.5	206	87.6
45% CAB	37.4	173	53.5
50% CAB	103.	193	8.01
60% CAB	66.5	261	29.0
75% CAB	25.9	392	134
85% CAB	12.7	270	138
CAB	11.2	548	234

[a] Containing 1% PVC thermostabilizer with same thermal history as the PVC containing samples.

[b] Yield points.

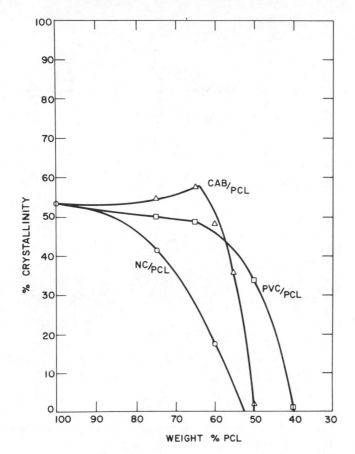

Fig. 12. Degree of PCL crystallinity as a function of composition for PVC/PCL, NC/PCL, and CAB/PCL.

crystalline PCL versus weight percent of the PCL in the blend. Since PCL melts only about 35°C above room temperature, the amount of crystallinity present will increase over a period of weeks or even months with annealing at ambient temperatures. Therefore, data for Figure 12 were obtained from samples which had been aged at least six weeks at room temperature in desiccators.

The data for the PVC/PCL blends are from the samples which were also used for the dynamic mechanical testing. They were aged over four months before the degree of crystallinity was measured. The shape of the PVC/PCL crystallinity curve in Figure 12 is similar to the results of Ong[14] and Khambata,[16] except that they found somewhat higher crystallinities.

The crystallinity data for the nitrocellulose blends were measured for spin-cast films which were used for the stress–strain and dynamic mechanical testing. They were aged six weeks before the DSC work and displayed less crystallinity than the other blends. Possibly over longer periods of time, the crystallinity would rise a few per cent more, but it cannot be expected that the NC/PCL curve on Figure 12 would rise to the levels for the other two blend systems. Even after eight months of aging, a 50% NC sample still did not show a PCL endotherm.

The CAB/PCL blend system differs from the PVC/PCL and NC/PCL systems in the region of high PCL concentration shown in Figure 12 because detectable

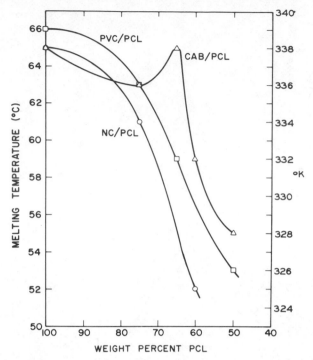

Fig. 13. Melting temperature of PCL as a function of composition for PVC/PCL, NC/PCL, and CAB/PCL.

multiple phases have been shown to be present. The samples which were used for the crystallinity measurements were also used in the stress–strain tests and were aged 11 weeks.

As is seen in Figure 12, there is a noticeable rise in the degree of crystallinity between PCL and 35% CAB, which is followed by a sudden drop to virtually 0% crystallinity at 50% CAB. Lilaonitkul, West, and Cooper[41] have reported that for a phase-separated block copolymer, there is a maximum in crystallinity for one segment as a function of composition which was varied by adjusting the length of the crystallizable segment. They suggested that the amount of crystallinity initially rises with dilution of the crystallizable segment because of incompatibility of the segments and lower viscosity of the system. At higher concentration of the diluting segment, the block lengths of the crystallizable segment become too short for crystallization to take place.

By analogy, incompatibility may enhance the crystallization of a blend component over a limited concentration range. Thus, from 0–35% CAB, incompatibility increases the degree of PCL crystallinity. At higher concentrations of CAB, the constant-composition phase absorbs more of the PCL which would otherwise be in the crystallizable PCL-rich phase. Above 50% CAB, the PCL is drawn into phases with high concentrations of CAB, and crystallization does not take place.

The melting points of the PCL crystalline phase are shown as a function of weight per cent PCL in Figure 13. As PCL is diluted with PVC, NC, and CAB, the DSC melting peak generally shifts to lower temperatures. At the same time, the peak broadens, and the lower temperature tail grows relative to the upper temperature peak.

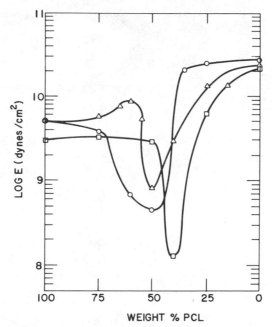

Fig. 14. Young's modulus as a function of composition for (□) PVC/PCL, (○) NC/PCL, and (△) CAB/PCL.

Ong[14] reports that wide-angle x-ray studies show that only one PCL crystalline form is present in all of the crystalline PCL/PVC blends. Thus, he concludes that the drop in melting point T_m indicates decreasing crystalline order and smaller crystallite size.

After melting and quenching, pure PCL showed no signs of recrystallization upon heating at 20°C/min. Nevertheless, the thermogram showed a smaller amount of crystallinity with a T_m of 56°C. This PCL crystallinity had crystallized during the quenching process. All blends of 75% PCL and the 65% PCL blends with PVC and CAB showed exothermic recrystallization peaks above their T_g's. However, the 40% CAB, 40% NC, and 50% PVC blends failed to reform the PCL crystallinity during the reheating in the DSC. The quenched blends which did show recrystallization all had T_m's in the range of 52–54°C.

The rise in the T_m of the CAB/PCL blends correlates to the rise in the degree of crystallinity discussed previously.

Tensile Properties

The effect of crystallinity on the tensile properties of the blends is shown in Figure 14, where Young's modulus as determined by the initial slope of the stress–strain curves has been plotted versus weight percent PCL. The minimum in the curves for the three systems occurs for samples which were highest in PCL content that could not crystallize. With higher PCL concentrations, the PCL crystallinity increases the modulus of the blends.

The modulus for PVC/PCL blends from 0% to 50% PVC was fairly constant because the decline in crystallinity was slow enough that the increasing concentrations of PVC could compensate for the loss in reinforcement. The PCL sample in the PVC/PCL series had been dried at temperatures above the PCL

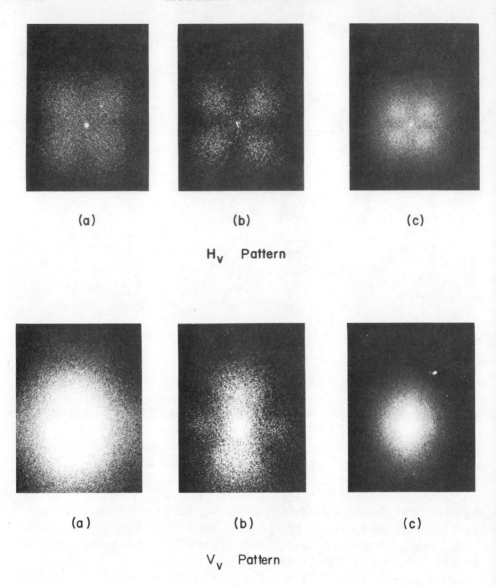

H_V Pattern

V_V Pattern

Fig. 15. Small-angle light-scattering patterns for (a) PCL, (b) 25% CAB, and (c) 35% CAB.

T_m, and the crystallinity was about 5% lower than for PCL dried at room temperature. Consequently, the modulus of the pure PCL was lower than the PCL modulus for the two cellulosic blend systems.

In contrast, the degree of crystallinity in the NC/PCL blends drops more rapidly. Thus, the modulus drops off at higher concentrations of PCL. By similar reasoning the rise in modulus in the CAB/PCL blends between 0% and 40% CAB can be attributed to the PCL crystallinity increases in this region.

At low concentrations of PCL, the constancy of the modulus for the NC/PCL system suggests that a continuous phase of NC is present. The rise in the modulus for the other two systems is much more gradual and implies a higher degree of mixing than is evident in the NC/PCL system.

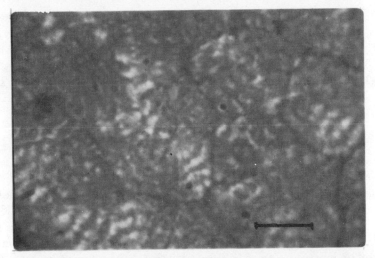

Fig. 16. Cross-polarized light micrographs of 35% PVC. Scale marker is 10 μ.

Morphology Studies

The H_v and V_v scattering patterns for some typical CAB/PCL blends are shown in Figure 15. Similar patterns were obtained with the PVC/PCL system. The scattering patterns show the distinct characteristics for volume-filling negative spherulites. The H_v patterns display the familiar, well-defined, four-leaf clover design with minimum intensities along the meridian and equatorial axes. This symmetry exists for spherulitic superstructures for the chain axes either perpendicular or parallel to radial direction (negative and positive spherulites, respectively). The V_v pattern for these blends are also well defined, with scattering present along both axes but with the larger, more intense lobes along the meridian axis. The vertical symmetry identifies these as negative spherulites, and the good resolution is indicative of volume-filling superstructures with a high degree of ordering.

The scattering patterns for PCL and 35% CAB are somewhat less well defined. The PCL and 35% CAB patterns indicate that negative spherulites are present in both, but the lobes of the H_v patterns are less distinct, and the V_v patterns are almost symmetric. The lack of sharply defined patterns would imply a high degree of disorder was present. It is also possible that the spherulites are not volume filling.

Nitrocellulose blends (25%, 35%, 40% NC) showed H_v and V_v patterns that were essentially radially symmetric (not shown). The maximum intensity was situated in the center of the patterns, and the intensity dropped with increasingly larger scattering angle. These patterns are indicative of randomly distributed crystalline rods which are approximately the size of the wavelength of the laser light.[42]

Ong[14] found that PVC/PCL blends which crystallized from the melt first formed rod-like structures, and then, as the crystallization continued, the scattering patterns of negative spherulites appeared. Furthermore, with SALS and light microscopy, Ong[14] and Khambatta[16] both found that with samples of less than 50% PVC, the PCL crystallinity was volume filling. With 50% or less PCL, regions of pure amorphous material were present.

Since the NC blends showed only rod-like aggregates, it can be inferred that the PCL crystallinity initially goes through the rod-like crystallinity stage. With the PVC and CAB blends, the crystallinity progresses into negative spherulites, but the 25–40% NC blends never get past the initial stage.

The light microscopy studies generally confirmed the SALS studies. Typical cross-polarized micrographs of a 35% PVC blend are shown in Figure 16.

Infrared Spectrum Peak-Position Shifts

If there are acid–base or other attractions between chemical groups on the dissimilar chains, the peak positions of the participating groups should shift to reflect the amount of interaction. In conjunction with infrared dichroism work, the peak positions for the functional groups of the blends of the PVC/PCL and NC/PCL blends were accurately found to the nearest 0.1 cm^{-1} using a Model 180 Perkin–Elmer IR spectrophotometer with the scales expanded as much as possible. The instrument was calibrated with a polystyrene film.

The 635 cm^{-1} and 613 cm^{-1} carbon–chlorine stretching bands of PVC, which represented mostly syndiotactic segments, were found not to shift in blends of 25–91% PVC. Each peak stayed within a 1 cm^{-1} range and showed no signs of splitting.

The nitrocellulose spectrum exhibits an asymmetric carbon–nitro group stretching peak of 1659 cm^{-1} which has a shoulder at about 1652 cm^{-1}. Both constituents stayed within 1 cm^{-1} of their positions in pure NC for blends as dilute as 24% NC. The only change seemed to be that the lower frequency shoulder decreased somewhat in relative intensity with increasing concentrations of PCL which would indicate that blending reduces the small amount of interaction the nitro groups do have with their environment. The carbon–hydroxyl group at about 3440 cm^{-1} was much too broad to accurately determine its shift. This peak could also be influenced by the presence of small amounts of water in the sample.

In contrast, the PCL carbonyl showed significant amounts of shifting for both the PVC/PCL and NC/PCL systems, as is seen in Figure 17. The frequency was essentially constant for the 65–100% PCL region for both sets of blends, but rises abruptly where the crystallinity in both systems drops sharply to zero. The effect of the crystallinity is also demonstrated by measuring the carbonyl peak position of crystalline PCL and its melt. In the molten PCL, the carbonyl can be assumed to be unassociated. The carbonyl frequency rose about 10 cm^{-1} for the following samples when melted:

	C=O frequency, cm^{-1}	
	28°C	75°C
PCL	1725.9	1735.9
25% PVC	1726.3	1734.8
25% NC	1725.7	1735.5

Consequently, the crystalline structure must impose interactions upon the carbonyl.

As the PCL gets further diluted, its frequency tends to decrease. The carbonyl

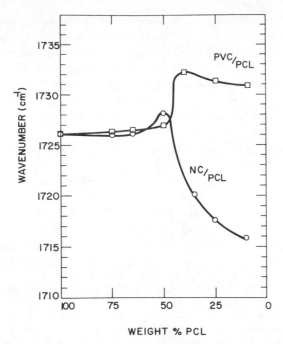

Fig. 17. Carbonyl peak positions as a function of PCL weight percent for PVC/PCL and NC/PCL.

is probably weakly hydrogen bonded to the α-hydrogen of the PVC, and at very high concentrations of PVC, all of the carbonyls will be bonded. Extrapolating the carbonyl position to 0% PCL, it is found that the frequency of 1730.6 cm^{-1} is 5.3 cm^{-1} less than for the pure PCL in the molten state.

The decrease in the carbonyl in the NC blends can also be attributed to hydrogen bonding. It has been shown elsewhere[43] that the hydroxyl groups bond to the ester groups of phthalic acid. The effect on the carbonyl is larger due to the stronger nature of the hydrogen bond. The difference in frequency between molten PCL carbonyl and the extrapolated frequency for 0% PCL in a NC blend (1715.3 cm^{-1}) is 20.6 cm^{-1}. The drop in frequency is especially noticeable in the 50–75% NC region where the hydroxyl to carbonyl ratio changes from 0.33 to 0.98. Infrared work was not done with the CAB/PCL blends because the infrared spectra of the two polymers overlap for the bands of interest.

CONCLUSIONS

Blends of poly-ε-caprolactone (PCL) with poly(vinyl chloride) (PVC) and with several cellulosic derivatives were spin cast from solution. PVC blends with PCL were shown to exhibit only one glass transition temperature (T_g), which, for blends quenched from the melt, could be represented as a function of composition by the Gordon–Taylor T_g equation which is commonly applied to compatible random copolymers.

By a similar criterion, the PCL blends with nitrocellulose (NC) were shown to be compatible for the composition range of 0–50% NC by weight. With higher concentrations of NC, both thermal and mechanical testing indicated that multiple amorphous phases were present, even though the films were clear.

The PCL blends with cellulose acetate butyrate (CAB) were found to exhibit the glass transition behavior of a phase-separated system. Thermal analysis showed that in one phase of the blends, the CAB and PCL were mixed in nearly equal proportions. These conclusions on blend compatibility were generally confirmed by stress–strain measurements for the three blend systems.

The morphology of the PCL crystalline blends was investigated with DSC, small-angle light scattering, and light microscopy. For the PVC blends, PCL crystallinity was found to exist with PVC concentrations as high as 60%. This crystallinity was shown to be in the form of negative spherulites, which were volume filling with up to 35% of the diluting PVC. At higher PVC concentrations, the spherulites decreased in size and were interspersed with amorphous regions.

Stress–strain properties showed a decrease in modulus and increased ductility as the PCL was diluted with the blend polymer. This trend, caused by decreasing PCL crystallinity, is reversed at higher composition levels of the rigid blend component.

The authors wish to thank Dr. J. V. Koleske of the Union Carbide Corporation for supplying samples of polycaprolactone and poly(vinyl chloride). Dr. Robert W. Seymour of the Tennessee Eastman Co. kindly supplied the cellulose acetate butyrate specimen used in this study. Partial support of this research was provided by the Materials and Metallurgy Division of the U.S. Army Research Office and by the donors of the Petroleum Research Fund administered by the American Chemical Society. The authors finally express their appreciation to Mr. Edward M. Sessions who carried out some of the dynamic mechanical testing experiments.

References

1. F. W. Billmeyer, Jr., *Textbook of Polymer Science,* 2nd ed., Wiley, New York, 1962.
2. R. L. Jalbert, in *Modern Plastics Encyclopedia, 1975–1976,* J. Agranoff, Ed., McGraw-Hill, New York, 1975, p. 107.
3. R. Koningsveld, L. A. Kleintjens, and H. M. Schoffeleers, *Pure Appl. Chem.,* **39,** 1 (1974).
4. L. Bohn, *Rubber Chem. Technol.,* **41,** 495 (1968).
5. T. Nishi, T. K. Kwei, and T. T. Wang, *J. Appl. Phys.,* **46,** 4157 (1975).
6. T. K. Kwei, T. Nishi, and R. F. Roberts, *Macromolecules,* **7,** 667 (1974).
7. J. M. Braun, A. Lavoie, and J. E. Guillet, *Macromolecules,* **8,** 311 (1974).
8. J. V. Koleske, C. J. Whitworth, Jr., and R. D. Lundberg, U.S. Pat. 3,892,821 (July 1, 1975).
9. G. L. Brode and J. V. Koleske, *J. Macromol. Sci.-Chem.,* **A6,** 1109 (1972).
10. C. G. Seefried, Jr., and J. V. Koleske, *J. Macromol. Sci.-Phys.,* **B10,** 579 (1974).
11. J. V. Koleske and R. D. Lundberg, *J. Polym. Sci. A-2,* **7,** 795 (1969).
12. T. G. Fox, *Bull. Am. Phys. Soc.,* **2,** 123 (1956).
13. M. Gordon and J. S. Taylor, *J. Appl. Chem.,* **2,** 493 (1952).
14. C. Ong, Ph.D. Thesis, University of Massachusetts, 1973.
15. F. B. Khambatta and R. S. Stein, *Polym. Prepr.,* **15,** 260 (1974).
16. F. B. Khambatta, F. Warner, T. Russell, and R. S. Stein, *J. Polym. Sci.-Phys.,* **14,** 1391 (1976).
17. G. K. Travis, in *Modern Plastics Encyclopedia, 1975–1976,* J. Agranoff, Ed., McGraw-Hill, New York, 1975, p. 16.
18. D. S. Hubbell and S. L. Cooper, *J. Polym. Sci. A-2,* submitted for publication.
19. O. Olabisi, *Macromolecules,* **8,** 316 (1975).
20. *Hercules Nitrocellulose, Chemical and Physical Properties,* Hercules, Inc., 1969.
21. P. A. Small, *J. Appl. Chem.,* **3,** 71 (1953).
22. K. L. Hoy, *Paint Technol.,* **42,** 76 (1970).
23. J. T. Koberstein, S. L. Cooper, and M. Shen, *Rev. Sci. Instrum.,* **46,** 1639 (1975).
24. J. Malac, V. Altmann, and J. Zelinger, *J. Appl. Polym. Sci.,* **14,** 161 (1973).

25. J. Malac, E. Simunkova, and J. Zelinger, *J. Polym. Sci.*, **A-1** (1969).

26. V. Crescenzi, G. Manzini, G. Calzolari, and C. Borri, *Eur. Polym. J.*, **8,** 449 (1972).

27. R. J. Samuels, *J. Polym. Sci. A-2*, **9,** 2165 (1971).

28. R. S. Stein and M. B. Rhodes, *J. Appl. Phys.*, **31,** 1873 (1960).

29. R. S. Stein and P. Wilson, *J. Appl. Phys.*, **33,** 1914 (1962).

30. R. S. Stein, P. Erhardt, J. J. Van Aartsen, S. Clough, and M. Rhodes, *J. Polym. Sci. A-2*, **9,** 295 (1971).

31. W. A. Lee and G. J. Knight, in *Polymer Handbook,* J. Brandrup and E. Immergut, Eds., Wiley-Interscience, New York, 1966, Chap. III, p. 84.

32. J. Stoelting, F. E. Karasz, and W. J. MacKnight, *Polym. Eng. Sci.*, **10,** 133 (1970).

33. W. J. MacKnight, J. Stoelting, and F. E. Karasz, *ACS Adv. Chem. Ser.*, **99,** 29 (1971).

34. T. F. Schatzki, *J. Polym. Sci.*, **57,** 496 (1962).

35. R. F. Boyer, *Rubber Rev.*, **34,** 1303 (1963).

36. A. Nakajima, H. Hamada, and S. Hayashi, *Macromol. Chem.*, **95,** 40 (1966).

37. I. J. Heijboer, *Kolloid-Z.*, **171,** 7 (1960).

38. H. B. Stafford, *J. Appl. Polym. Sci.*, **9,** 729 (1965).

39. Y. Minoura, H. Iino, and T. Tsukasa, *J. Appl. Polym. Sci.*, **9,** 1299 (1965).

40. J. S. Noland, N. Hsu, R. Saxon, and J. M. Schmitt, *ACS Adv. Chem. Ser.*, **99,** 15 (1971).

41. A. Lilaonikul, J. C. West, and S. L. Cooper, *J. Macromol. Sci.-Phys.*, to appear.

42. M. B. Rhodes and R. S. Stein, *J. Polym. Sci. A-2*, **7,** 1939 (1969).

43. B. W. Brodman, M. P. Devine, and M. T. Gurbars, *J. Appl. Polym. Sci.*, **20,** 569 (1976).

44. Union Carbide Bulletin F-42501 *NEW Polycaprolactone Polymers PCL-300 and PCL-700,* 1969.

Received September 20, 1976
Revised November 18, 1976

JOURNAL OF APPLIED POLYMER SCIENCE   VOL. 21, 3063–3075 (1977)

Nonlinear Viscoelastic Behavior of Butadiene–Acrylonitrile Copolymers Filled with Carbon Black*

N. NAKAJIMA, H. H. BOWERMAN, and E. A. COLLINS, *B. F. Goodrich Chemical Company, Technical Center, Avon Lake, Ohio 44012*

Synopsis

Various viscoelastic measurements including dynamic mechanical measurements in tension at 110 Hz from −60° to 160°C, tensile stress relaxation measurements with 100% elongation at 25°, 54°, and 98°C, capillary flow measurements at 70°, 100°, and 125°C, and high-speed tensile stress–strain measurements carried to break at 25°, 56°, and 98°C were performed on four samples of carbon black-filled butadiene–acrylonitrile copolymers. All the data were treated with the same equation for time–temperature conversion. The capillary viscosity–shear rate curves were significantly lower than the complex viscosity–angular frequency curves, indicating "strain softening" with extrusion. The viscosity was estimated from the stress–strain relationship at the yield point. The viscosity as a function of the strain rate is significantly higher than the complex viscosity as a function of angular frequency, indicating "strain hardening" with extension. The strain softening and strain hardening are attributable to the structural changes upon deformation of the carbon black-filled elastomers. With the unfilled elastomers, neither strain softening nor strain hardening were observed in similar measurements.

INTRODUCTION

Viscoelastic analyses of elastomer processing may be performed by investigating the material behavior at small and large deformation and its properties at break. These observations may be made over rates and temperature ranges of processing.[1]

In earlier studies, dynamic mechanical measurement, stress relaxation, stress–strain to break, and steady shear measurements were made on butadiene–acrylonitrile uncompounded raw elastomers. Simple correlation schemes were utilized to cross-correlate the results of these various measurements.[2]

This work involves carbon black-filled compounds of the same copolymers. Cross correlation of the results of the same types of viscoelastic measurements is attempted and the resulting correlation compared to those previously obtained for the unfilled materials. The specific interest is to find differences between the deformation mechanism of filled rubber and that of unfilled rubber, recognizing the fact that the former is a highly structured system whereas the latter is amorphous.

* Presented at International Rubber Conference, Subject No. 3, Physics of Rubber, Tokyo, Japan, October 14–17, 1975.

TABLE I
Butadiene–Acrylonitrile Copolymer Samples

Sample code for filled elastomer	Sample code for raw elastomer	Raw elastomer Hycar[a]	T_g, °C	Mooney (ML-4) at 100°C
1	A	1052-30	−37, −24	35
2	B	1042	−36, −24	78
3	C	1042X82	−34, −24	81
4	D	1002	−28	85

[a] Registered Trademark of B. F. Goodrich Chemical Company.

EXPERIMENTAL

Materials

The raw elastomers used in this study are four butadiene–acrylonitrile copolymers having 33% acrylonitrile content. The glass transition temperature T_g observed by DTA and the Mooney (ML-4) values at 100°C are given in Table I. The carbon black-filled compounds were prepared by dispersing 40 parts carbon black FEF-N550 per 100 parts rubber on a roll mill.

Dynamic Measurements

A Rheovibron (Imass, Inc., Accord, Hingham, Massachusetts 02018) was used in tension at a fixed frequency of 110 Hz over the temperature range of −60°–160°C. For some cases, temperatures to 200°C were used.

Stress Relaxation

An MTS high-speed tensile tester (MTS Division, Research Incorporated, Minneapolis, Minnesota 55424) was used to strain the sample to 100% elongation in less than 0.01 sec. At this elongation, the decay of force was observed as a function of time at temperatures of 25°, 54°, and 98.5°C.

Steady Shear Measurements

An Instron capillary rheometer (Instron Corp., Canton, Massachusetts) was used with a die of 0.050 in. in diameter, 0.990 in. in length, and 90° included angle. The temperatures were 70°, 100°, and 125°C. The shear rate range was 2.9–2900 sec^{-1}. Rabinowitsch's[3] correction and the correction for the entrance energy loss[4] were made to a part of the data.

Stress–Strain Measurements

An MTS high-speed tensile tester was used at drive speeds of 3.16, 31.6 and 344 in./sec (677%, 6,770%, and 72, 800% per sec) at temperatures of 25°, 56°, and 98°C.

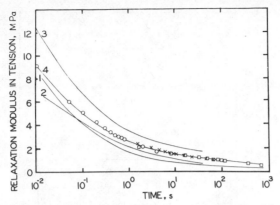

Fig. 1. Stress relaxation curves, reduced to 25°C, of the four carbon black-filled elastomers:
(O) 25°C; (X) 54° → 25°C; (□) 98.5° → 25°C.

RESULTS

Time–Temperature Superpositions

The equation for time–temperature superposition was evaluated from stress relaxation measurements and expressed as[8]

$$\log \alpha_T = C_1(T - T_0)/(C_2 + T - T_0) \tag{1}$$
$$= 5.06(T - T_0)/(94.4 + T - T_0)$$

with T_0 taken as 298°K (25°C). Values of the constants C_1 and C_2 are similar to but somewhat smaller than those for the raw elastomers, i.e., $C_1 = 5.95$ and $C_2 = 109$. Equation (1) will be used with all measurements in this work.

Stress Relaxation

The results of the stress relaxation measurements are converted to those at 25°C and shown in Figure 1 for all four samples. The selected data points are shown with only one sample in order to avoid crowding the figure. The modulus $E(t)$ is expressed as

$$E(t) = [F(t)/A]\alpha(\alpha - 1)^{-1} \tag{2}$$

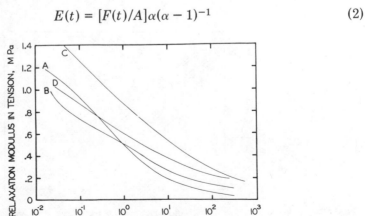

Fig. 2. Stress relaxation curves, reduced to 25°C, of unfilled raw elastomers A, B, C, and D.

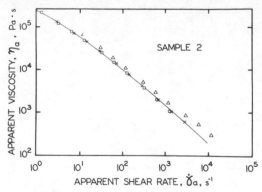

Fig. 3. Steady shear flow curve of carbon black-filled elastomer—test of temperature reduction: (△) 70° → 100°C, (X) 100°C; (□) 125° → 100°C.

where $F(t)$ is the observed force, A is the original cross-sectional area, and α is the extension ratio, i.e., $\alpha = 2$. The term $[F(t)/A]\alpha$ is the stress and $\alpha - 1$ is the strain.

The relative differences of the relaxation behavior of the four samples are very similar to those of the corresponding raw elastomers.[2] For example, in Figure 2, the relative magnitude of the modulus of the raw polymers at times longer than 1 sec was C, the highest, followed by D, B, and A. At times longer than 0.1 sec, the relative magnitude of the modulus of the filled samples were also the same; that is, 3 was the highest, followed by 4, 2, and 1.

Steady Shear Measurements

The viscosity–shear rate relationship of sample 2 is shown in Figure 3, which is the result of time-temperature superposition according to eq. (1). The data at 125°C after reduction to 100°C were in good agreement with the data at 100°C. However, the data of 70°C were not in agreement with those at 100°C. This was the case with all four samples. The reason why the 70°C data did not obey the temperature dependence of eq. (1) is not known at present.

The viscosity–shear rate curves of the four samples are shown in Figure 4.

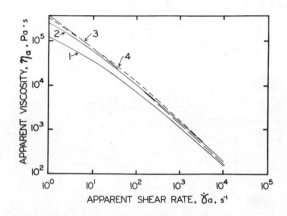

Fig. 4. Steady shear flow curves, reduced to 100°C, of carbon black-filled elastomers.

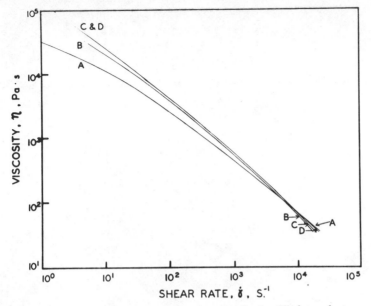

Fig. 5. Steady shear flow curves, reduced to 100°C, of unfilled raw elastomers.

Only the 100° and 125°C data were used. The relative magnitude of viscosities of the four samples are very similar to those of corresponding raw polymers[2,6] (Fig. 5); that is, the viscosities of samples 2, 3, and 4 are very similar, and so are the viscosities of samples B, C, and D. The viscosity of sample 1 is much lower than the rest of the filled samples, and so is the viscosity of A from the rest of the raw polymers.

Figure 6 is a comparison of uncorrected and corrected viscosities of samples 2 and 3. The former are the data shown in Figure 4. The latter are those after Rabinowitsch correction[3] and correction for entrance pressure loss[4] were made. Although the magnitudes of the corrections were large, the relative difference among the two samples remained the same. Therefore, the above comparisons of the behavior between filled and unfilled elastomers (Figs. 4 and 5) are valid.

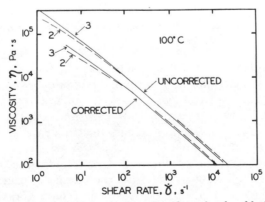

Fig. 6. Magnitude of corrections for steady shear flow data of carbon black-filled elastomers.

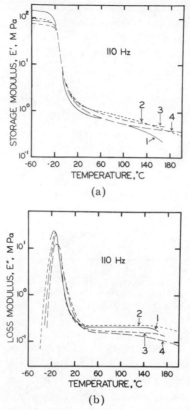

Fig. 7. (a) Storage modulus–temperature curves of carbon black-filled elastomers. (b) Loss modulus–temperature curves of carbon black-filled elastomers.

Dynamic Measurements

The results of the Rheovibron measurements are shown in Figures 7(a) and 7(b), where the observed values of the storage modulus and the loss modulus are plotted against temperature. These samples do not appear very different from each other beyond experimental error. This is very similar to the observation with the raw elastomers,[7] Figures 8(a) and 8(b).

Stress–Strain Measurements (Ultimate Properties)

The ultimate properties obtained by the tensile stress–strain measurements are shown in Figures 9(a) and 9(b), where the stresses at break and the corresponding elongations are plotted separately as functions of the strain rate. The strain rates are expressed as linear elongation rates. All data were reduced to those at 25°C. As in the case of raw elastomers[8] and unfilled vulcanizates,[9] the stresses at break increase with an increase in strain rate [Figs. 9(a) and 9(b)]. However, the fairly large sample-to-sample differences observed with raw elastomers[8] are almost completely removed. The data for the strain at break are excessively scattered [Fig. 9(b)]. Neither the sample-to-sample difference nor the dependence on strain rate can be observed. This is very different from the cases for raw elastomers,[8] Figure 10(b).

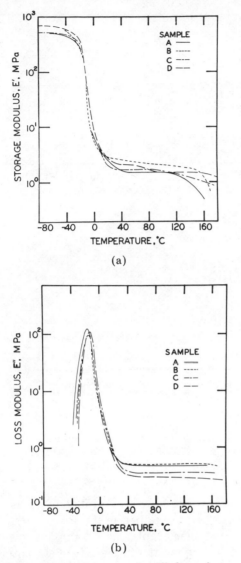

Fig. 8. (a) Storage modulus–temperature curves of unfilled raw elastomers. (b) Loss modulus–temperature curves of unfilled raw elastomers.

DISCUSSION

Viscoelastic behavior of four butadiene–acrylonitrile copolymers filled with carbon black have been examined by four different techniques. Dynamic measurements were made at elongation of less than 1%. Similar to the behavior of unfilled raw elastomers, sample-to-sample difference was not observed in the temperature range of the test. The stress relaxation experiment performed at 100% elongation showed sample-to-sample differences which were very similar to those observed with the corresponding unfilled elastomers. Steady shear measurements also showed sample-to-sample differences very similar to those observed with the unfilled elastomers. On the other hand, sample-to-sample differences are not very significant in the ultimate properties measured by tensile

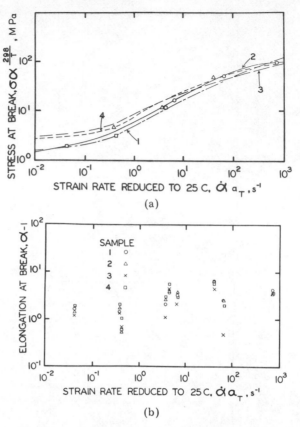

Fig. 9. (a) Stress at break as function of strain rates, reduced to 25°C, of carbon black-filled elastomers: (O) 25°C; (△) 56° → 25°C; (□) 98° → 25°C. (b) Elongation at break as function of strain rates, reduced to 25°C, for carbon black-filled elastomers.

stress–strain tests. This is in contrast to unfilled raw elastomers, where sample-to-sample differences are magnified in this test.

It appears, then, carbon black is playing a dominant role in determining the ultimate properties. The large scatter in the data of elongation at break suggests that the incorporation of carbon black into rubber broadens the distribution of defects, which are probably responsible for determining ultimate properties. On the other hand, failure of unfilled elastomers is known to be significantly influenced by the bulk viscoelastic properties[9]; the question of why the viscoelastic properties of elastomers do not have much influence on ultimate properties of the filled elastomers remains. This question is especially pertinent, when the following facts are recognized: sample-to-sample differences attributable to the elastomer components were seen in the bulk behavior of filled systems such as in stress relaxation and steady shear measurements, but not in the ultimate properties.

Next, the effect of carbon black on the bulk viscoelastic behavior will be examined. A typical approach has been to examine the effect of carbon black concentration on the viscoelastic properties of filled elastomers. Quantitative treatments along this line were based on the analogy of filled rubbers to suspensions consisting of rigid particles dispersed in fluid media.[10,11] However,

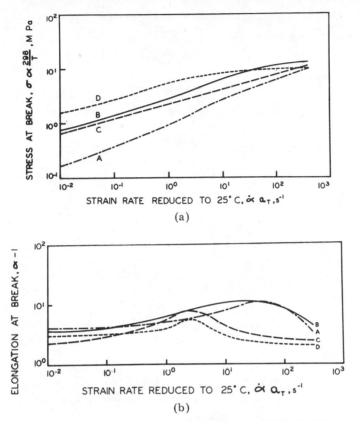

Fig. 10. (a) Stress at break as function of strain rates, reduced to 25°C, of unfilled raw elastomers. (b) Elongation at break as function of strain rates, reduced to 25°C, of unfilled raw elastomers.

this approach is incomplete in that it does not treat the effect of structure introduced by the presence of filler.

In the present work, our interest is to examine the difference in deformational mechanisms between filled and unfilled elastomers. Of particular interest are the three-dimensional structure in the elastomer matrix established by the presence of carbon black, changes in structure with increasing strain, and how such changes are effected in the viscoelastic behavior. This type of investigation was carried out by examining the strain amplitude dependence of the dynamic behavior at fixed frequency and temperature[12] and the shear rate dependence of the viscosity.[13]

In this paper, both strain and strain rate dependences will be examined; dynamic, steady shear, and tensile stress–strain measurements will be used. Interrelations among these three measurements will be investigated to see if there is a unique difference between filled and unfilled elastomers.

The corrected steady shear data of Figure 6 are replotted in Figures 11 and 12 together with the data of the shear complex viscosities calculated from dynamic and tensile stress–strain measurements. The dynamic data were those shown in Figures 7(a) and 7(b). A temperature range of 40°–220°C for sample 2 and 40°–170°C for sample 3 were used. All the data were reduced to 100°C by using eq. (1).

The complex viscosities are significantly higher than the steady shear viscosity

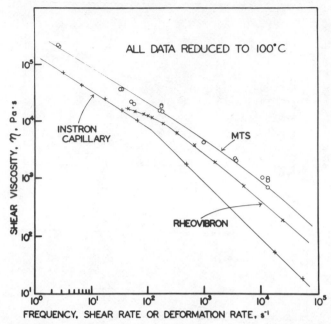

Fig. 11. Viscosities of sample 2 obtained by capillary extrusion, dynamic oscillatory, and tensile stress–strain measurements.

when compared at equal values of angular frequency and shear rate. This is contrary to the results for unfilled elastomers where the two viscosities are in good agreement,[2,6,7] Figures 13 and 14.

The tensile stress–strain data at the yield point were used[2] to calculate

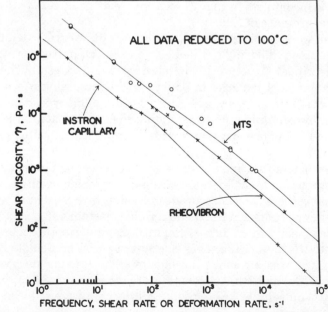

Fig. 12. Viscosities of sample 3 obtained by capillary extrusion, dynamic oscillatory, and tensile stress–strain measurements.

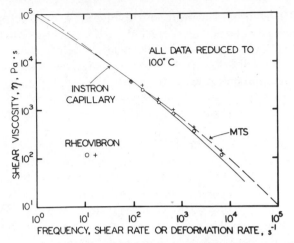

Fig. 13. Viscosities of sample B obtained by capillary extrusion, dynamic oscillatory, and tensile stress–strain measurements.

viscosities η as a function of strain rates $\dot{\gamma}$. The following equations, previously applied to the data of unfilled elastomer, are used:

$$\eta = \frac{1}{3} \left(\frac{\alpha \sigma}{\epsilon} \right) (\alpha t) \tag{3}$$

$$\dot{\gamma} = (\alpha t)^{-1} \tag{4}$$

where σ is the tensile force divided by the cross-sectional area of the unstressed specimen; $\sigma \alpha$ is the tensile stress corrected for the change of the cross-sectional area; α is the extension ratio l/l_0; $\epsilon = \alpha - 1$; t is the observed time; and αt is the reduced time.[14] All data were reduced to 100°C, using eq. (1). The viscosities calculated from the tensile stress–strain data are significantly higher than the complex viscosities from the Rheovibron measurements. This is contrary to the observation for unfilled elastomers, where the two viscosities were in good agreement,[7] Figures 13 and 14.

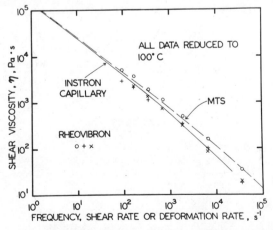

Fig. 14. Viscosities of sample C obtained by capillary extrusion, dynamic oscillatory, and tensile stress–strain measurements.

Because the Rheovibron measurements involve very small deformations, the dynamic data may be regarded as representing the structure with a minimum disturbance. Capillary extrusion involves large deformation and possible structural change as well. Therefore, the difference between the capillary extrusion data and the dynamic data could well be the result of structural changes. The material may be "strain softening" with extrusion. The viscosities calculated from tensile stress–strain behavior are much higher than those from dynamic measurements. The tensile elongation may be altering the material structure resulting in "strain hardening." However, the tendency to harden with increasing strain cannot be detected directly from the shape of stress–strain curves. This interpretation is possible only with reference to the behavior of unfilled elastomers, where corresponding states are found between small and large deformation.[14] Therefore, there is no strain hardening. When the corresponding principle is applied to filled elastomers, the behavior at large deformation does not superpose onto that at small deformation.

It appears that the structure built by the presence of carbon black increasingly jams against elongation until finally the structure yields and, soon afterward, the sample breaks. This mechanism explains why the ultimate properties of filled elastomers are insensitive to the bulk viscoelastic behavior.

Strain softening with extrusion requires further explanation. Although there is no fully satisfactory explanation as to why the steady-state viscosity–shear rate curve and complex viscosity–angular frequency curve are in agreement, such agreements have been observed with unfilled elastomers (Figs. 13 and 14) as well as with many plastic melts. The present argument takes account of this fact.

When carbon black is dispersed in the rubber, the above two curves are not in agreement, but strain softening is observed. The explanation for the softening may be visualized in the following manner. The behavior of material moving from the barrel to the capillary is similar to tensile deformation, where the total elongation corresponds to the reduction of the cross-sectional area.[15] Here, it is 55%, which is far beyond the elongations at break [Fig. 9(b)].

It appears that after passing the yield point and the breakdown of the structure, the compound softens if it is contained in the capillary and kept from breaking. Further investigation is required on the morphologic changes that are manifested by strain hardening and strain softening.

The authors are indebted to Messrs P. R. Kumler, G. Thomas, and R. Schwamberger for the Rheovibron data and to Mr. R. G. Raike for the Instron capillary data. The authors would like to express their appreciation to B. F. Goodrich Chemical Company for permission to publish this work.

References

1. K. Ninomiya, S. Kusamizu, E. Maekawa, and G. Yasuda, *Progress in Polymer Science in Japan*, Vol. 1, M. Imoto and S. Onogi, Eds., Kodansha Ltd., Tokyo, 1971, pp. 377–452.
2. N. Nakajima, H. H. Bowerman, and E. A. Collins, *Rubber Chem. Technol.*, **46**, 417 (1973).
3. B. Rabinowitsch, *Z. Phys. Chem.*, **A145**, 1 (1929).
4. E. B. Bagley, *J. Appl. Phys.*, **28**, 624 (1957).
5. J. D. Ferry, *Viscoelastic Properties of Polymers*, 2nd ed., Wiley, New York, 1970, p. 303.
6. N. Nakajima and E. A. Collins, *Polym. Sci. Eng.*, **14**, 137 (1974).
7. N. Nakajima, E. A. Collins, and P. R. Kumler, *Rubber Chem. Technol.*, **47**, 778 (1974).
8. H. H. Bowerman, E. A. Collins, and N. Nakajima, *Rubber Chem. Technol.*, 307 (1974).

9. T. L. Smith, in *Rheology, Theory and Applications,* Vol. 5, F. R. Eirich, Ed., Academic Press, New York, 1969, pp. 127–221.

10. I. Pliskin and N. Tokita, *J. Appl. Polym. Sci.,* **16,** 473 (1972).

11. J. L. White and J. W. Crowder, *J. Appl. Polym. Sci.,* **18,** 1013 (1974).

12. A. R. Payne and R. E. Whittaker, *Rubber Chem. Technol.,* **44,** 440 (1971).

13. G. V. Vinogradov, A. Ya. Malkin, E. P. Plotnikova, O. Yu. Sabsai, and N. E. Nikolayeva, *Int. J. Polym. Mater.,* **2,** 1 (1972).

14. N. Nakajima, E. A. Collins, and H. H. Bowerman, *Rubber Chem. Technol.,* **47,** 318 (1974).

15. N. Nakajima and M. Shida, *Trans. Soc. Rheol.,* **10** (1), 299 (1966).

Received December 22, 1975
Revised November 17, 1976

JOURNAL OF APPLIED POLYMER SCIENCE   VOL. 21, 3077–3085 (1977)

Studies on the Preparation and Uses of Co-60 Gamma-Ray Irradiated Natural Latex

SUMARNO KARTOWARDOYO, *Balai Penelitian Perkebunan Bogor, Bogor, Indonesia,* and FL. SUNDARDI, *Pusat Penelitian BATAN Pasar-Jum'at, Jakarta, Indonesia*

Synopsis

The properties are described of low-ammonia latex concentrates produced by gamma-ray irradiation (0.5–2.0 Mrad dose) in the presence of carbon tetrachloride or chloroform as sensitizer. Dipping trials with irradiated concentrates and irradiated field latex, for the preparation of condoms and medical gloves, gave products with high ultimate elongation, low modulus, and high permanent set. A change from straight dipping to coagulant dipping and a heat treatment after drying resulted in improved physical properties. A notable feature of products prepared from these materials is their purity, i.e., low content of rubber chemicals. An economic disadvantage, at the present time, is the high initial cost of the irradiation equipment.

Introduction

Organic halogen compounds (carbon tetrachloride or chloroform) were successfully used as sensitizers for the crosslinking of rubber in natural latex concentrates. A dose of 1 Mrad appeared adequate for optimal crosslinking, in the presence of 5% w/w carbon tetrachloride in the latex, as compared with a dose of 10–15 Mrad normally needed in the absence of sensitizer.

Laizier et al.[2] found that the presence of sulfur or certain thio-organic compounds enabled films with low permanent set to be obtained from natural latex concentrates irradiated with doses no higher than 1 Mrad. Puig[3] reported that effective crosslinking of rubber in latex could be achieved with doses of 2.5 Mrad, in the presence of carbon tetrachloride. The physical properties of the films from such latex were considered to be as good as those from vulcanized latex, while the aging properties were better.

Morganstern[4] has also claimed that radiation vulcanization of rubber in latex concentrates can be achieved with a dose of 1 Mrad in the presence of a suitable sensitizer.

Sumarno and Sundardi[5] found that the rate of crosslinking in natural latex concentrates was not significantly affected by the presence of sensitizer when the radiation dose exceeded 4 Mrad. They also showed that crosslinking efficiency (number of crosslinks per 100 eV absorbed) increased with sensitizer concentration until the efficiency reached a maximum value, which was about 10.7 using carbon tetrachloride and about 8.0 using chloroform as sensitizer.

The present paper describes irradiation on both natural latex concentrates

3077

TABLE I

Properties of Natural latex (60% DRC, 0.3% w/w NH$_3$) After Irradiaton, with Chloroform and Carbon Tetrachloride as Sensitzers

Property	Age of Irradiated latex, weeks	0.5 Mrad[a]						1.0 Mrad						2.0 Mrad					
		3.0 phr[b]		7.5 phr		9.0 phr		3.0 phr		7.5 hr		9.0 phr		3.0 phr		7.5 phr		9.0 phr	
		CHCl$_3$	CCl$_4$	CHCl$_3$	CCl$_4$	CHCl$_3$	CCl$_4$	CHCl$_3$	CCl$_4$	CHCl$_3$	CCl$_4$	CHCl$_3$	CCl$_4$	CHCl$_3$	CCl$_4$	CHCl$_3$	CCl$_4$	CHCl$_3$	CCl$_4$
MST, min	1	520	1540	195	400	180	280	375	850	225	480	210	280	400	430	310	410	210	280
	12	739	993	353	843	180	660	1190	1030	250	825	285	560	783	997	366	506	314	393
Viscosity, centipoises	1	48.0	59.1	72.3	72.6	107.4	74.5	63.2	10.7	104.2	88.0	123.4	100.8	60.0	62.0	116.8	110.5	83.5	95.3
	12	54.6	54.7	74.1	76.5	104.8	75.2	58.9	66.2	110.4	99.9	141.7	118.1	56.4	66.0	122.9	290.9	89.9	118.9
KOH Number	1	0.60	0.98	0.62	0.62	0.85	0.82	0.35	—	0.43	—	0.53	—	0.68	0.68	0.61	0.66	0.75	0.85
	12	0.69	0.95	0.88	1.05	1.15	0.92	0.75	0.89	0.96	0.89	0.97	0.88	0.80	0.85	0.78	0.89	0.87	0.83
VFA Number	1	0.10	0.16	0.13	0.09	0.26	0.11	0.04	0.11	0.25	0.15	0.41	0.17	0.17	0.20	0.24	0.07	0.32	0.30
	12	0.07	0.25	0.26	0.17	0.59	0.16	0.19	0.22	0.55	0.30	0.43	0.38	0.18	0.16	0.30	0.16	0.35	0.34

[a] Radiation dose.
[b] Sensitizer content.

TABLE II
Properties of Dried Films from Irradiated Latex (60% DRC, 0.3% w/w NH$_3$, 0.1–0.3% w/w Sulfur)
Using Carbon Tetrachloride (5 phr) as Sensitizer

	1.0 Mrad[a] 0.1%[b]	1.0 Mrad 0.3%	2.0 Mrad 0.1%	2.0 Mrad 0.3%	2.5 Mrad 0.1%	2.5 Mrad 0.3%
Modulus 300%, kg/cm^2	2.2	2.0	2.5	3.0	2.7	3.1
Modulus 500%, kg/cm^2	2.8	2.8	3.4	4.4	4.7	4.7
Tensile Strength, kg/cm^2	110	145	230	220	205	210
Elongation at break, %	1070	1140	1150	1060	1090	1100
Permanent set, %	30	25	12	10	9	9
		After Seven Days of Aging at 70°C in Geer Oven				
Modulus 300%, kg/cm^2	1.2	2.0	1.7	2.0	2.6	2.9
Modulus 500%, kg/cm^2	1.9	2.5	2.8	3.0	3.3	4.1
Tensile strength, kg/cm^2	72	90	160	205	200	250
Elongation at break, %	1100	1080	1110	1150	1150	1160
Permanent set, %	24	20	12	10	10	8

[a] Radiation dose.
[b] Sulfur content.

and field latex, and describes the properties of dried films and dipped goods (medical gloves and condoms) obtained from them.

Experimental

A Co-60 gamma-ray irradiator, "Gamma-Cell No. 220" (made in Canada), with a dose rate of ca. 4.2×10^5 rads/hr was employed. The latex used was from the experimental garden of the BPP Bogor at Ciomas (Bogor) and was preserved and concentrated as required. In these experiments, irradiation was conducted under air (the stoppered bottles were filled up to the neck with latex), and no antioxidant was employed.

The sensitizers carbon tetrachloride and chloroform were employed in the form of 40–50% w/w emulsions in water. Sulfur dispersions (50% w/w) were prepared by ball-milling for 48 hr with 4% w/w Dispersol LR (I.C.I. Ltd.) as dispersing agent.

The KOH number, VFA number, and MST of latex samples were determined in accordance with ASTM procedures,[6] and viscosities were measured with a capillary viscometer as described by Van Gils.[7]

Dried films of latex samples were prepared by spreading the latex on glass plates and drying at ca. 33°C to constant weight.

For the preparation of gloves, the straight dipping method was used with a porcelain former. After preliminary drying at 40°C, the glove was stripped, soaked in water for two to three days, and finally dried in a circulating air oven at 40°C for 2–3 hr unless stated otherwise.

Condoms were made on a glass former using either the straight dipping or coagulant dipping method. In the latter case, the formers were first coated with a coagulant solution consisting of calcium nitrate, ethyl alcohol, and water in the ratios of 1:1:3 by weight. After preliminary drying at 40°–45°C, the condoms were stripped, soaked in water for two to three days and dried in an air oven at 40°C. In some experiments, specified in the text, the condoms were given a final treatment in a steam autoclave at 100°C for 1–2 hr.

TABLE III
Properties of dipped Gloves from Irradiated Latex (Straight-dipping method)

| | 0.3% w/w[a] | | 0.7% w/w[a] | | Commercial medical gloves[d] | |
					A	B
Radiation dose, Mrad	2.5	3.0	3.0	3.0	—	—
Sulfur content, % w/w of latex	0.25	0.25	—	—	—	—
Carbon tetrachloride, phr	5.0	5.0	4.0	5.0	—	—
Modulus 300%, g/cm^2	6.3^b	6.6^c	4.5^c	5.6^c	—	—
Modulus 500%, kg/cm^2	—	—	—	—	10.1	16.0
Modulus 600%, kg/cm^2	11.5	11.5	7.6	8.5	18.5	36.2
Tensile strength, kg/cm^2	135	147	194	176	195	225
Elongation at break, %	1010	930	1000	980	750	710
Permanent set, %	22	22	—	—	5	5

[a] Ammonia content of original latex.
[b] Final heat-treatment given (2–3 hours at 40°C in an air-circulated oven).
[c] No inal heat-teatment iven.
[d] Different commercial gloves purchased in Jakarta.

All measurements of modulus, ultimate elongation, tensile strength, and permanent set were made in accordance with ASTM procedures.[6] The bursting strength of condom samples and the testing for holes were determined by British Standard procedures.[8]

RESULTS

Properties of Irradiated Latices and Films

Table I shows the effect of radiation dose and sensitizer content on the physical properties of latex concentrate stabilized with 0.3% w/w ammonia, using chloroform or carbon tetrachloride as sensitizer.

A main feature of the table is the increase in viscosity and the large reduction in mechanical stability which occurs when the sensitizer content is raised from 3.0 to 9.0 phr. However, with a radiation dose of 2.0 Mrad and 3.0 phr of either chloroform or carbon tetrachloride as sensitizer, the mechanical stability, KOH number, and VFA number of the irradiated latices remain within British Standard specification limits[9] for a period of at least 12 weeks.

TABLE IV
Propertes of condoms Prepared from Irradiated Low-Ammonia (0.3% w/w) Latex Concentrate
(60% DRC) Containing 0.25% W/w Sulfur and 5% w/w Carbon Tetrachloride as Sensitizer
(Straight-Dipping Method)

Radiation dose, Mrad	Modulus 300%, kg/cm^2	Modulus 600%, kg/cm^2	Tensile strength, kg/cm^2	Ultimate elongation, %	Pemanent set, %	Bursting stength, liters of water
2.5	6.7	10.0	176	1000	20	3.95
3.0	7.3	11.1	136	920	19	2.40

If stability proves a problem, it could easily be overcome by the incorporation of stabilizers and/or secondary preservatives where appropriate. In this case, for appreciably longer periods of storage, a higher concentration of ammonia than 0.3% w/w would presumably be necessary to give satisfactory long-term stability.

Table II shows the effect of radiation dose on the properties of dried films of irradiated latices using carbon tetrachloride (5 phr) as sensitizer. In these experiments, small amounts of sulfur were added to the latex before irradiation to determine their effects, if any, on film properties. An increase in the sulfur content from 0.1 phr to 0.3 phr appeared to produce little change in the film properties.

The results of Table II demonstrate the increase in modulus and tensile strength and the decrease in permanent set caused by increasing the radiation dose. Elongation at break shows little change. A radiation dose of at least 2.0 Mrad appears necessary to obtain appreciable crosslinking of the rubber in these experiments. The best heat-aging resistance was obtained at the highest radiation dose employed (2.5 Mrad).

By comparison with conventional sulfur-cured latex films, the films from the irradiated latices are characterized by low modulus, fairly low tensile strength, high elongation at break, and high permanent set.

Dipped Medical Gloves

Table III typifies the properties of dipped medical gloves prepared from irradiated concentrates containing 0.3% or 0.7% w/w ammonia as preservative, and using radiation doses of 2.5–3.0 Mrad with 4.0–5.0 phr carbon tetrachloride as sensitizer. The permanent set figures were unexpectedly high for the radiation doses employed. In comparison with the commercial gloves A or B, gloves from the irradiated latices possessed lower modulus, somewhat lower tensile strength, and appreciably higher elongation at break.

Gloves prepared from the high-ammonia latex with 4.0 phr sensitizer were subjected to 20 sterilizations (½ hr each time) in a steam autoclave at 120°C; 85% of the samples so treated showed no signs of deterioration (a leakage test similar to that applied to condoms was employed).

Condoms from Irradiated Latex Concentrates

Typical properties of the condoms obtained from low-ammonia latex concentrates irradiated in the presence of sulfur, with carbon tetrachloride as sensitizer, are given in Table IV. The products (0.06–0.07 mm thick) were made by the straight-dipping method and were finally heated for 1–2 hr in a steam autoclave at 100°C.

Physical properties were again characterized by low modulus and tensile strength, high ultimate elongation, and high permanent set. The bursting strength of the products approximated the minimum requirement of British Standard 3704,[8] which specifies a figure of 3.0 liters water.

Condoms were also prepared by the same dipping technique from irradiated high-ammonia latex (0.7% NII$_3$, 60% DRC) concentrate, in the absence of sulfur, using a radiation dose of 3 Mrad and 4% w/w carbon tetrachloride as sensitizer.

TABLE V

Effect of Storage on he Viscosity and mst of irradiated Field latex at 30°C (4 phr CCl_4)

Radiation dose, Mrad	Total solids content, %	NH_3 Content, %	3 Weeks		5 Weeks		7 Weeks		9 Weeks		12 weeks		15 Weeks	
			Visc.[a]	M.S.T.[b]	Visc.	M.S.T.	Visc.	M.S.T.	Visc.	M.S.T.	Visc.	M.S.T.	Visc.	M.S.T.
1.0	41.8	0.42	5.2	810	5.3	1620	5.2	>1800	5.3	>1800	5.4	>1800	5.3	>1800
2.0	41.2	0.43	5.4	1350	5.2	>1800	5.3	>1800	5.3	>1800	5.4	>1800	5.5	>1800
3.0	41.3	0.40	5.4	>1800	5.4	>1800	5.2	>1800	5.3	>1800	5.5	>1800	5.4	>1800
4.0	41.6	0.42	5.3	>1800	5.2	>1800	5.4	>1800	5.4	>1800	5.5	>1800	5.4	>1800

[a] Viscosity, in centipoise.
[b] Modified ASTM D 1076 procedure (without dilution, 0 ± 1 g latex, 14000 ± 200 rpm).

TABLE VI

Properties of dipped Films Prepared from Irradiated Field Latex (ca. 30% DRC and 0.6% w/w Ammonia Content) with 5% w/w Carbon Tetrachloride as Sensitizer

Radiation dose, Mrad	Type of film[a]	Modulus 300%, kg/cm^2	Tensile strength, kg/cm^2	Ultimate elongation, %	permanent set, %
1.0	A	9.0	157	908	9.1
	B	3.8	83	1082	12.5
2.0	A	12.4	159	809	8.2
	B	4.5	122	1080	10.7
3.0	A	12.8	194	803	7.1
	B	5.5	112	973	8.7
3.0	A[b]	13.3	250	896	5.8
4.0	A	13.8	164	752	6.1
	B	5.7	98	925	7.5
6.0	A	14.9	147	730	5.2
	B	6.6	87	814	6.5

[a] A = coagulant-dipped film; B = straight-dipped film.
[b] Film finally heated at 100°C for 15 min.

The bursting strength of these products was 3.0–4.0 l. water, and could be further increased by a final heat treatment in a steam autoclave at 100°C for 15–60 min. Still higher bursting strengths (6.0–7.0 l. water) could be achieved by diluting the latex with 10% w/w water before irradiation and using two dips instead of a single dip to obtain the required thickness of product (0.06–0.07 mm). The bursting strengths, considering the smaller size (volume = 80 cm^3, diameter = 2.8 cm), compared well with commercial samples (volume = 150 cm^3, diameter = 3.3 cm, bursting strengths = 4.4–6.0 l. water). No holes were detected in any of the samples when tested in accordance with British Standard 3704.

Dipped Films and Condoms from Irradiated Field Latex

The latex used in this series of experiments was field latex of approximately 30% DRC stabilized with ca. 0.4% w/w ammonia, and irradiated in the presence of ca. 5% w/w carbon tetrachloride as sensitizer. No significant change in the viscosity of the irradiated latex could be detected after 15 weeks of storage, and a high mechanical stability could be maintained (Table V).

Dipped films were prepared with glass formers, using both straight dipping and coagulant dipping techniques. The films were soaked in water for ca. 48 hr and dried at 45°C; where specified, the films were finally heated at 100°C for 15 min. Results are given in Table VI.

The best balance of physical properties appears from Table VI to be achieved with a radiation dose of 3 Mrad. Coagulant-dipped films had considerably higher modulus and tensile strength than those prepared by straight dipping. The effect of a final heat treatment at 100°C on a coagulant-dipped film from latex irradiated with 3 Mrad was to increase tensile strength and ultimate elongation and to reduce the permanent set. Whether or not equally good physical properties could be obtained from irradiated latex concentrates diluted to ca. 30% DRC remains to be established.

TABLE VII

Properties of Condoms Prepared from Irradiated Field Latex (ca. 30% DRC and 0.6% w/w Ammonia Content) by Coagulant Dipping

Radiation dose, Mrad	Time of heating at 100°C, min	Modulus 300%, kg/cm²	Modulus 500%, kg/cm²	Tensile strength, kg/cm²	Ultimate elongation, %	Permanent set, %
1.0	0	9.9	17.6	156.9	904	9.0
	15	12.6	22.2	151.6	852	8.4
	30	11.6	19.5	123.3	838	7.2
2.0	0	12.4	22.2	158.4	810	8.0
	15	13.3	23.4	166.4	820	7.4
	30	13.7	23.6	142.3	852	5.4
3.0	0	13.0	27.5	193.7	802	7.2
	15	14.7	27.8	249.5	896	5.8
	30	13.6	24.9	192.2	860	4.2
4.0	0	15.0	38.6	147.2	730	6.3
	15	18.9	35.4	144.7	720	4.8
	30	18.5	33.5	135.5	666	3.8

With the same irradiated field latex, samples of condoms were prepared on glass formers using the coagulant dipping method. Results are shown in Table VII. In the table, the best balance of physical properties again appears to be obtained at a radiation dose of 3 Mrad. In this case, final heating of the products at 100°C for a period of 15 min increased tensile strength and ultimate elongation, in addition to reducing the permanent set. The bursting strength of these condom samples (thickness ca. 0.10 mm) averaged 7.4 l. water, i.e., considerably higher than the minimum of 3.0 l. required by British Standard 3704.[8]

CONCLUSIONS

1. Irradiated low-ammonia (0.3% w/w) latex concentrates can be prepared, using a radiation dose of 2.0 Mrad and 3.0 phr of either chloroform or carbon tetrachloride as sensitizer, such that the mechanical stability, KOH number, and VFA number remain within British Standard specification limits for a period of at least 12 weeks.

2. Dried films, dipped gloves, and condoms prepared from such irradiated latices are typically of low modulus, fairly low tensile strength, high ultimate elongation, and high permanent set. An increase in modulus and a reduction in permanent set could usually be achieved by increasing the radiation dose.

The bursting strength of condomspprepared from irradiated high-ammonia (0.7% w/w NH_3) latex concentrate could be substantially increased by heating the condoms at 100°C for 15–60 min. Still higher bursting strengths were obtained by diluting the latex with110 water before irradiation.

3. Irradiated field latex containing ca. 0.4% w/w ammonia could be stored for more than three months without significant increase in viscosity; a high mechanical stability could be maintained. The physical properties of condoms prepared from such latices by the coagulant dipping technique could again be improved by a heat treatment at 100°C for 15 min.

4. The absence of conventional rubber compounding ingredients in products prepared from irradiated latex should be advantageous for many medical ap-

plications. An economic disadvantage arises from the high initial cost of the irradiation equipment.

The authors gratefully acknowledge the help of Dr. G. Cockbain (Secretary, International Rubber Research and Development Board, London) in the preparation of this paper and the assistances of Mr. Margo Utomo, Mr. Nurkamari, Miss Budiningsih, Mr. Ibrahim, and Mr. Paino in this work. Thanks are also due the pilot plant and laboratory workers of BPP Bogor and Puslit BATAN Pasar-Jum'at (Jakarta), etc., who also provide their valuable services.

References

1. Y. Minoura and M. Asao, Studies on the gamma-ray irradiation of natural latex. The effects of organic halogen compounds on crosslinking by gamma-ray irradiation, *J. Appl. Polym. Sci.*, **5**, 401 (1961).

2. T. Laizier, M. T. Noel, A. Veber, and M. Pordes, Radiation crosslinking of natural and synthetic elastomers in emulsion or dispersion, in *Proc. Symp. Large Radiation Sources for Industrial Processes, Munich, August 1969,* International Atomic Energy Agency, Vienna, Austria, 1969.

3. J. R. Puig, *Radiation Curing of Natural Rubber Latex,* Soclay, France, C.A.P.R.I., 1970, pp. 6 & 7.

4. K. H. Morganstern, *Int. J. Radiation Eng.,* **1**(1), 87 (1971).

5. S. Kartowardojo and Fl. Sundardi, Studies on the effect of Co-60 gamma-ray irradiation on natural latex, IRRDB Conference, Puncak, 1973.

6. American Society for Testing and Materials, *1967 Book of ASTM Standards, Part 28,* Philadelphia, A.S.T.M., 1967, pp. 1–10, 200–211, 534–548.

7. G. E. Van Gils, *Rec. Trav. Chem.,* **65**, 9 (1964).

8. British Standards Institution, British Standard Specification for Rubber Condoms. B.S. 3704, 1964.

9. British Standards Specification for Centrifuged Ammonia-Preserved Natural Rubber Latices, B.S. 4355, 1968.

Received July 9, 1976
Revised October 27, 1976

JOURNAL OF APPLIED POLYMER SCIENCE VOL. 21, 3087–3097 (1977)

Use of Aldehydes Other Than Formaldehyde in THPOH/Ammonia Flame-Retardant Finishes for Cotton

ARLEN W. FRANK and GEORGE L. DRAKE, JR., *Southern Regional Research Center,* Agricultural Research Service, U.S. Department of Agriculture, New Orleans, Louisiana 70179*

Synopsis

Several aldehydes have been tested as substitutes for the lachrymator formaldehyde in the THPOH/ammonia process. Aldehydes such as acetaldehyde or butyraldehyde promote rapid polymer formation without being incorporated into the finish. Chloral is incorporated to a limited extent, but the finish is sensitive to base. To gain further insight into the polymer-forming process, the reactions of THP and its aldehyde derivatives with ammonia have been investigated in vitro. There is evidence that THP acts as a difunctional reagent, regardless of the aldehyde, forming a linear polymer with a single phosphorus, nitrogen, and oxygen atom in each repeating unit.

INTRODUCTION

The THPOH/ammonia process, one of several developed in recent years for applying flame-retardant finishes to cotton,[1c] consists of padding fabric through a concentrated aqueous solution of tetrakis(hydroxymethyl)phosphonium hydroxide (THPOH), drying to a moisture content of about 10%, and curing with ammonia vapor at room temperature in a closed chamber. The ammonia reacts with the THPOH, depositing a highly insoluble polymer within the fiber.[2,3]

One problem associated with this process is the irritating odor of formaldehyde, a lachrymator, released from the THPOH during padding and drying.[4,5] Methods proposed to overcome this problem include the use of less sodium hydroxide for neutralizing the tetrakis(hydroxymethyl)phosphonium chloride (Thpc) to inhibit formation of formaldehyde[5,6] and the use of sodium sulfite in place of all or part of the sodium hydroxide to tie up the formaldehyde as its bisulfite addition compound.[5,7] These methods have a common disadvantage— formaldehyde is a necessary ingredient in the polymer-forming reaction[8]—and efforts to suppress one inevitably tend to suppress the other. In this paper, we shall explore the possibility of replacing formaldehyde in this process with a different aldehyde.

* A preliminary account of this work was presented at the Southeast-Southwest Combined Regional Meeting, American Chemical Society, New Orleans, La., Dec. 4, 1970.

3087

EXPERIMENTAL

Reagents

Tris(hydroxymethyl)phosphine (THP), analyzing 0.08% CH_2O by the dimedone method,[9] was prepared by passing phosphine through 37% formalin solution, with cadmium chloride as the catalyst, until no more phosphine was absorbed.[10] For this work it was essential that the reaction be complete, for even small amounts of formaldehyde obscured the effect of other aldehydes on THP. Completion of the reaction was signaled by a drop in pH from 9 to 7. THP is deliquescent, but is stable to air for short periods. Its infrared spectrum showed no noticeable increase in P=O absorption after 4 hr of exposure to dry air in a desiccator or to humid air on the refractometer plates, but its refractive index (n_D^{25}, supercooled) dropped from 1.5564 to 1.5491 in 5 min, and to 1.5353 in 4 hr. Prolonged exposure to air should, of course, be avoided.

The aldehydes were reagent-grade products and were used as obtained, except for butyraldehyde, which was redistilled.

Reaction of THP with Aldehydes

A 3.0-g sample of THP, weighed to four decimals and analyzing 16.46 mmole THP by iodometric titration,[11] was treated under nitrogen with acetaldehyde in several portions over a 4-hr period at 0–10°C. The mixture was allowed to warm to room temperature between additions. The THP dissolved slowly, with no noticeable exotherm. After evaporation overnight under a slow nitrogen flow, there remained a colorless oil with a sharp odor. The increase in weight corresponded to 33.72 mmole acetaldehyde, the ratio being 2.05:1 with respect to the THP. The product, Ia, showed weak absorption in the carbonyl region of the infrared, but very strong absorption at 3400 (O—H) and 1010 (C—O) cm^{-1}. Prolonged evacuation of Ia in a vacuum desiccator over phosphorus pentoxide removed half of the acetaldehyde in two days, leaving 16.15 mmole, or 0.92:1 with respect to the THP. This product, Ib, was a colorless oil, n_D^{25} 1.5248, still having a sharp odor and an infrared spectrum similar to that of Ia. The product was soluble in water and ethanol, and insoluble in other common organic solvents. Its titer (as THP) was unchanged, since acetaldehyde does not interfere with the iodometric method used.[11]

Butyraldehyde also formed a 2:1 adduct with THP. In this case, the reaction mixture was heated at reflux for 15 min and then stripped under water pump vacuum for 15 min at 70° to remove the excess aldehyde. The product, II, was a viscous, colorless oil showing very weak absorption at 1700 (C=O) cm^{-1} in the infrared and very strong absorption at 3400 (O—H) and 1010 (C—O) cm^{-1}.

When these reactions were carried out in a glacial acetic acid as reactant and solvent, the THP dissolved at once with an exotherm. The infrared spectra of the phosphonium acetates, $[(HOCH_2)_3PCH(OH)R]OAc$ (R = Me or Pr), showed strong absorption at 3350 (O—H) and 1700 (acetate C=O) cm^{-1}, and the C—O band was shifted to 1040 cm^{-1}.

Reaction of THP and Its Adducts with Ammonia

A solution of THP (2.48 g, 0.02 mole) in 25 ml anhydrous ethanol, contained in a 50-ml flask fitted with a reflux condenser and a gas inlet tube extending under the surface, was purged with nitrogen for 30 min and then treated with ammonia for 15 min. An exothermic reaction set in, and white solids separated all at once. After 5 min, the solids were collected on a filter, rinsed with ethanol, and dried overnight in a vacuum desiccator, leaving 1.24 g (59%) of hard, white solid insoluble in water or any of the common organic solvents. A sample was dried in a drying pistol at 80°/1 mm for analysis (Table I). The N:O:P ratio was 0.75:1.25:1, indicating 75% conversion of the THP to structure III. IR (KBr): 3300 vs (O—H), 2780 s, 1650 m (N—H), 1400 s, 1240 m, 1140 s, 1065 s, 1010 vs (C—O), and 875 m, br cm^{-1}. The presence of the 1650 cm^{-1} N—H deformation band was evidence that the product was not crosslinked like Kasem's product.[12]

A similar reaction with water as the solvent produced some heat owing to solution of the ammonia, but no solids separated until the next day. The product, triturated under water, filtered, and dried, gave an infrared spectrum similar to the above, but with an even stronger N—H deformation band. The N:O:P ratio, based on the analyses (Table I), was 1:1.25:1.

The THP/aldehyde adducts Ib and II, dissolved in a small amount of water and treated with ammonia, both deposited white solids immediately. Purging with nitrogen was unnecessary. The products, triturated under water, filtered, and dried, gave infrared spectra similar to those described above. The N:O:P ratios, based on the analyses (Table I), were 0.9:1:1.4 for the acetaldehyde and 1:1:1 for the butyraldehyde product, the latter providing the best fit to the proposed structure (III).

A solution of THP (2.48 g, 0.02 mole) and chloral (3.31 g, 0.02 mole) in 10 ml water was purged with nitrogen, exposed briefly to ammonia (5 min), purged again, and filtered. The product was triturated under water, filtered, and dried, giving 2.03 g (70.5%) of pale yellow solid. IR (KBr): 3400 vs (O—H), 3250 s, 2900 m, 2800 m, 1640 m (N—H), 1420 m, 1250 m, 1140 m, 1075 s, 1020 m (C—O), 875 m, br, 820 m (C—Cl), and 794 m cm^{-1}.

ANAL. Calcd. for $C_{10}H_{23}Cl_3N_3O_3P_3$: C, 27.76; H, 5.36; Cl, 24.59; N, 9.72; P, 21.48. Found: C, 27.83; H, 5.17, Cl, 23.40; N, 9.02; P, 20.64.

A 0.7725 g portion of this product was hydrolyzed with 25 ml of 1N sodium hydroxide for 1 hr at 60–70°, filtered, rinsed with water and dried, giving 0.4892 g (71.9%) of pale yellow solid. IR (KBr): 3400 vs (O—H), 3250 s, 2900 m, 2800 m, 1650 m (N—H), 1420 m, 1250 m, 1145 vs, 1035 s (C—O), and 865 m, br cm^{-1}.

ANAL. Calcd. for $C_{10}H_{23}N_3NaO_5P_3$: C, 31.50; H, 6.08; Cl, none; N, 11.03; P, 24.37. Found: C, 31.80; H, 6.34; Cl, 0.23; N, 10.84; P, 24.78.

Reaction of Ib with Dimethylamine

A solution of Ib (8.40 g, 0.05 mole) in 15 ml water, contained in a 50-ml flask fitted with a reflux condenser and a gas inlet tube extending under the surface, was purged for 30 min with nitrogen, followed by dimethylamine. Ice cooling was applied as necessary. When the flask was full, the addition was stopped and the contents were stripped on a rotary evaporator. The residue (9.05 g) was distilled under nitrogen, giving 6.55 g (63.9%) tris(dimethylaminomethyl)-phosphine, b$_{0.7}$ 78°–82°, n_D^{25} 1.4790; lit.[13] b$_{0.9}$ 78°–80°, n_D^{25} 1.4795. The identity of the product was confirmed by comparison of its infrared spectrum with that of a sample, b$_{0.4}$ 65°–67°, prepared from Thpc.[14]

TABLE I

Analysis of Polymers Prepared from THP, Ib, or II, and Gaseous Ammonia

Reagent	Solvent	%C	%H	%N	%P
THP	H_2O	35.92	6.98	12.19	27.27
THP	EtOH	34.95	7.26	9.95	29.19
THP, acetaldehyde (Ib)	H_2O	35.75	6.92	10.73	27.17
THP, butyraldehyde (II)	H_2O	34.95	7.16	13.44	29.62
Calcd for C_3H_8NOP (III)		34.29	7.67	13.33	29.48

TABLE II

Effect of Aldehydes on the THP/Ammonia Fabric Treatment

	Undried		Dried 3 min at 85°	Dried 10 min at 85°	Air dried
Aldehyde	% Add-on	O.I.	% Add-on	% Add-on	% Add-on
None					
Conventional	7.6		5.1	0.9	
Rapid quench	0.8		0.8	0	5.3
Delayed quench	1.7				7.5
Formaldehyde					
Rapid quench	14.4	0.327	8.9	0.9	9.5
Delayed quench	15.2	0.321			12.1
Acetaldehyde					
Conventional	12.0	0.319	9.6	1.0	
Rapid quench	3.5		1.8	1.8	5.0
Delayed quench	9.6	0.280			7.6
Butyraldehyde					
Conventional	12.1	0.328	4.1	0.8	
Rapid quench	1.8		0.8	0.8	6.1
Delayed quench	8.4	0.280			13.3
Galactose					
Rapid quench	0		0.9	0	0
Delayed quench	1.6				2.5
Chloral					
Rapid quench	16.0	0.330	9.7	6.2	11.9
Delayed quench	17.0	0.345			18.5
Glyoxal					
Rapid quench	1.7		0.9	1.3	

Fabric Treatments

The fabric used in this work was an 8-oz olive-drab cotton sateen, having an oxygen index[1b] value of 0.198.

In a typical experiment, a 6 × 12 in. fabric swatch was padded, 2 dips and 2 nips, through 50.0 g of solution containing 14.4 g (0.10 mole) 87% THP, 14.7 g (0.1 mole) 30% acetaldehyde, and 0.5 g of a wetting agent (Triton X-100), dried 3 min at 80° in a forced-draft oven, exposed to ammonia for 10 min in an enclosed chamber at room temperature, rinsed 30 min in hot, running tap water, and allowed to air dry. The wet pickup was 63% and the add-on, 9.6% (Table II, column 2).

Variables studied in this work were the aldehyde, the drying time, and the quenching procedure. The data are summarized in Table II.

Analyses

Analysis for phosphorus and chlorine in fabric samples was by x-ray fluorescence,[15] and nitrogen by the Kjeldahl method, after digestion with sulfuric acid. Polymer samples were analyzed by Galbraith Laboratories, Inc., Knoxville, Tenn. Infrared spectra were taken on a Perkin–Elmer 137B instrument with NaCl optics. Measurements of pH were made with a Beckman Zeromatic pH meter equipped with a combination electrode.

RESULTS AND DISCUSSION

Reaction of THP with Aldehydes

When formalin is added to a tertiary phosphine such as triethylphosphine,[16,17] tributylphosphine,[18] or tris(hydroxymethyl)phosphine,[19] the solution becomes alkaline due to formation of the quaternary phosphonium hydroxide:

$$R_3P + CH_2O + H_2O \rightleftharpoons R_3PCH_2OH^+ OH^- \qquad (1)$$

where $R = Et$, Bu, or CH_2OH). The pH of a $0.5M$ THP solution, initially 6.4, rose steadily upon the dropwise addition of 37% formalin solution, reaching 7.4 at the equivalence point and leveling off at 7.9 after a large excess of formalin had been added. Under the same conditions, acetaldehyde (30%) raised the final pH to 7.0, chloral (30%) to 7.2, and glyoxal (40%) to 7.3. The pH of the chloral and glyoxal solutions gradually reverted to 6.5 on standing.*

THP was shaken with full-strength acetaldehyde and allowed to evaporate at room temperature overnight, giving a product having a 2:1 ratio of acetaldehyde to THP. Pumping down in a vacuum desiccator reduced the ratio to 1:1. Both products showed strong O—H absorption and very weak C=O absorption in the infrared. They were evidently the phosphonium hydroxide Ib and its hemiacetal Ia, as shown below:

$$[R_3PCH(CH_3)OH]OH \qquad\qquad [R_3PCH(CH_3)OCHOHCH_3]OH$$
$$Ib \qquad\qquad\qquad\qquad\qquad\qquad Ia$$

Butyraldehyde, heated at reflux with THP and then stripped of excess aldehyde under vacuum at 70°, gave the hemiacetal II, corresponding to Ia.

Upon exposure of Ib or II to gaseous ammonia, a strongly exothermic reaction ensued, and white solids separated within a few minutes. The reaction was faster when the Ib or II was dissolved in a small amount of water before exposure to gaseous ammonia, but no solids separated when the solution was treated with ammonium hydroxide.

THP itself developed neither exotherm nor solids upon exposure to gaseous ammonia, whether or not the THP was dissolved in water, although, after standing overnight, solids separated in both cases. With ethanol as the solvent, an exothermic reaction set in after 15 min, depositing a mass of white solids. These reactions were quite slow compared with the reaction of ammonia with Ib, II, or THPOH.

---

* With full-strength THP and equimolar quantities of the aldehydes, Reuter et al. reported a rise to pH 8.5 with 30% formalin or 10% glyoxal, and to "weakly alkaline" with 30% acetaldehyde.[19] Vullo's observation that THP produced no increase in pH when added to neutral formalin[18] was based on an experiment with an indicator, phenolphthalein, that is not sensitive to pH in this region.

Elemental analyses on the polymers formed in these reactions (Table I) suggest that all four products have the same composition, approaching the empirical formula C_3H_8NOP. The variation in nitrogen content from one product to another reflects the extent of completion of the reaction. The best fit to this empirical formula is a linear polymer (III) containing a single phosphorus, nitrogen, and oxygen atom in each repeating unit*:

$$\left[\begin{array}{c} -CH_2PCH_2NH- \\ | \\ CH_2OH \end{array} \right]_n$$

III

This structure is supported by the infrared spectra, which all show strong, broad absorption in the O—H (and N—H) regions, and strong absorption in the 1010 cm^{-1} region characteristic of C—O stretching in tertiary methylol phosphines. The C—O stretching band appears at 1010 cm^{-1} in THP, at 1040–1050 cm^{-1} in THPO and Thpc[20] and at 1025–1035 cm^{-1} in THP·HgX$_2$ complexes.[9] A shift to higher wavelengths also appears in the IR spectra of the substituted tertiary phosphines RP(CH$_2$OH)$_2$.[9]

An experiment in which Ib was treated with dimethylamine gas instead of ammonia gave a 63.9% yield of tris(dimethylaminomethyl)phosphine, (Me$_2$NCH$_2$)$_3$P, identical to the product obtained from Thpc.[13] If the acetaldehyde had remained and formaldehyde had been released, the product would have been a mixed tertiary phosphine. Clearly, the aldehydes used in the preparation of the quaternary phosphonium hydroxides Ib or II were not present in the amino products, whether monomeric or polymeric.

In contrast, exposure of THP to ammonia in the presence of chloral gave a pale-yellow polymer whose composition approached the empirical formula $C_{10}H_{23}Cl_3N_3O_3P_3$, suggesting a 2:1 copolymer of III and V:

$$\left[\begin{array}{c} -CH_2PCH(CCl_3)NH- \\ | \\ CH_2OH \end{array} \right]_n$$

V

Hydrolysis of this product with 1N sodium hydroxide removed the chlorine, giving a 2:1 copolymer of III and VI:

$$\left[\begin{array}{c} -CH_2PCH(CO_2Na)NH- \\ | \\ CH_2OH \end{array} \right]_n$$

VI

* The THP/ammonia polymer prepared by Kasem et al.[12] also had a 1:1:1 ratio, but its carbon content was high. We ascribe this to formaldehyde crosslinking of the nitrogens on adjacent polymer chains, resulting in a structure IV:

$$\left[\begin{array}{c} CH_2- \\ | \\ -CH_2PCH_2N- \\ | \\ CH_2OH \end{array} \right]_n$$

IV

The absence of N—H absorption in the infrared provides support for this structure.

Consideration of possible mechanisms should provide some insight into the nature of this reaction.

A direct reaction between THP and an amine, shown in eq. (2), probably occurs only when no aldehyde is present. The reaction of formaldehyde-free THP with primary amines such as aniline[14] and with secondary amines such as morpholine[21] or diphenylamine[22] follows this course:

$$(HOCH_2)_3P + 3R_2NH \rightarrow (R_2NCH_2)_3P + 3H_2O \qquad (2)$$

When an aldehyde is present, the reaction can take two paths, depending on which reagent the aldehyde reacts with first. If it reacts with the THP, a reactive intermediate is formed which then reacts with the amine, displacing formaldehyde, eq. (3). The reactive intermediate could be a P-methylol derivative such as the zwitterion[22] $(HOCH_2)_3P^+CH_2O^-$, or an O-methylol derivative such as THP hemiformal.[21] The evidence favors the O-methylol derivative (see Appendix):

$$(HOCH_2)_2PCH_2OCH_2OH + 3R_2NH \rightarrow (R_2NCH_2)_3P + CH_2O + 3H_2O \quad (3)$$

If the aldehyde first reacts with the amine, a reactive intermediate such as R_2NCH_2OH or $CH_2(NR_2)_2$ is formed, which then reacts with the THP to displace formaldehyde, eq. (4):

$$(HOCH_2)_3P + 3R_2NCH_2OH \rightarrow (R_2NCH_2)_3P + CH_2O + 3H_2O \qquad (4)$$

Either mechanism explains the strongly catalytic effect of formaldehyde on the reactions of THP with primary amines such as hexamethylenediamine[8] and with secondary amines such as diphenylamine.[22,23] We favor the third mechanism because it more closely resembles that of the Mannich reaction, where the reaction of the aldehyde with the amine has been found to precede the reaction with the active hydrogen compound.[24]

In the third mechanism, the aldehyde that reacts with the amine should be retained in the product. However, the aldehyde exchange process shown in eq. (5) enables the amine to react with any aldehyde (or hemiacetal) present in the system:

$$(HOCH_2)_3P + RCHO \rightleftharpoons RCHOHP(CH_2OH)_3^+OH^-$$
$$\rightleftharpoons RCHOHP(CH_2OH)_2 + CH_2O \quad (5)$$

Under these circumstances, the amine can (and did) react with the aldehyde bearing the most electron-deficient carbonyl carbon, i.e., formaldehyde in preference to acetaldehyde or butyraldehyde, and chloral in preference to formaldehyde. In practice, the reaction with chloral gave a mixed product, the competition between the aldehydes favoring formaldehyde by 2:1. No doubt, other factors such as steric hindrance or rate of reaction influenced the outcome in this case.

The question of why the reaction stopped at the disubstitution stage (III) when the amine was ammonia remains. We suggest that this reflects the change in state from monomer to polymer, removing the reactants physically from the reaction medium. Polymer III, though less reactive, should still be capable of reacting with formaldehyde, introducing methylene crosslinks without altering the N:O:P ratio, or with ammonia, changing the N:O:P ratio ultimately to 2:0:1.

Fabrics treated with the THPOH/ammonia finish have N:P ratios ranging from 0.75:1 to 1.25:1, depending on the fabric construction,[2,3] the base used to neutralize the Thpc,[6] and other variables. The presence of oxygen in these finishes before oxidation has not been recognized heretofore.

Fabric Treatments

During these experiments, it was discovered that the THP/ammonia polymer could be prepared by mixing equimolar quantities of THP and an aldehyde (formaldehyde, acetaldehyde, butyraldehyde, chloral, etc., but not glyoxal) in water and exposing the solution to gaseous ammonia without isolating the adduct. This technique was adopted for the fabric treatments listed in Table II.

As in the THPOH/ammonia process, the conventional ammonia treatments gave add-ons highly sensitive to drying, falling off rapidly as the moisture content of the padded fabrics decreased.[3] The best results were obtained when the fabrics were cured in the damp state, fresh from the squeeze rolls (column 1). Those which had a 12% add-on appeared to be flameproofed, passing the match test[1a] at an angle of 135° and the oxygen index test[1b] at O.I. values well above 0.26.

To heighten the difference between the aldehydes, the procedure was modified by reducing the ammonia exposure time to 5 min and quenching the fabrics in hot running tap water as soon as they were removed from the ammonia chamber. The immediate quench favored those aldehydes that induced the most rapid polymer formation. Acetaldehyde produced a low add-on, butyraldehyde and glyoxal very little add-on, and galactose no add-on at all. The only aldehydes that showed up well in this experiment were formaldehyde and chloral. Fabric swatches treated with these aldehydes had O.I. values near 0.33, and could not be ignited with a match, even when suspended vertically. As in the conventional treatment, the add-ons fell off as the moisture content of the padded fabrics decreased, all but chloral becoming negligible at the 10-min point (column 3). When the padded fabrics were suspended in the hood for 4 hr and allowed to air dry before exposure to ammonia, all but galactose (including the control) had moderate to good add-ons (column 4).

Since the test appeared to be too severe, the procedure was modified by suspending the test fabrics in the hood *after* the ammonia exposure and allowing them to equilibrate in air before quenching. Acetaldehyde and butyraldehyde showed up somewhat better than in the rapid quench treatment, but only chloral consistently produced add-ons comparable to formaldehyde.

Analyses on the formaldehyde- and chloral-treated fabrics are given in Table III. The N:P atomic ratio varied from 0.70 to 0.96 for the formaldehyde-treated fabrics, and 0.81 to 0.95 for the chloral-treated fabrics. The latter also contained low levels of chlorine, varying in Cl:P atomic ratio from 0.11 to 0.20. Soap-soda boiling[6] stripped the chlorine from the fabric.

CONCLUSIONS

THP reacts with aldehydes in aqueous solution, forming 1:1 and 1:2 adducts formulated as O-adducts (hemiacetals), together with sufficient P-adduct (phosphonium hydroxide) to account for the increase in basicity. The adducts

TABLE III
Analyses of Selected Treated Fabrics

Aldehyde	Undried %P	Undried %N	Dried 3 min at 85° %P	Dried 3 min at 85° %N	Dried 10 min at 85° %P	Dried 10 min at 85° %N	Air dried %P	Air dried %N
Formaldehyde								
Rapid quench	3.82	1.63	3.48	1.27	0.25	0.08	3.44	1.09
Delayed quench	3.72	1.61					3.39	1.18
Chloral								
Rapid quench	3.97 (Cl, 0.60)	1.48	2.81 (Cl, 0.45)	1.03	2.09 (Cl, 0.48)	0.83	3.43 (Cl, 0.70)	1.27
Delayed quench	3.70 (Cl, 0.47)	1.59					3.81 (Cl, 0.74)	1.45

react rapidly with ammonia, forming polymers having a single phosphorus, nitrogen, and oxygen atom in each repeating unit. Similar polymers are obtained with mixtures of THP and the aldehydes and (more slowly) with THP alone. Aldehydes such as acetaldehyde or butyraldehyde, which are less nucleophilic than formaldehyde, are not incorporated in the polymers. These, therefore, have the common structure

$$\left[\begin{array}{c} -CH_2PCH_2NH- \\ | \\ CH_2OH \end{array} \right]_n$$

Chloral, more nucleophilic than formaldehyde, is incorporated to some extent, but the chlorine is sensitive to base.

When applied to cotton sateen by the conventional THPOH/ammonia process, the THP/aldehyde adducts or mixtures produce flameproofed fabrics. Rapid quenching after ammoniation favors those aldehydes that induce the most rapid polymer formation. Under these conditions, only chloral produces results comparable to formaldehyde, but soap-soda boiling strips the chlorine from the fabric.

The structure of THPOH is discussed in the Appendix.

Appendix

The Structure of THPOH

This discussion is presented in an effort to dispel some of the confusion concerning the structure of THPOH. It is our thesis that the properties of THPOH are adequately explained in terms of the equilibrium expression comprising THPOH, THP, formaldehyde, and water, eq. (6), and that the acronym THPOH should be retained because it uniquely describes this reagent.

The acronym was first used in 1963 by Filipescu et al.[25] to describe the product obtained when Thpc is neutralized with lead carbonate or sodium hydroxide, though earlier references to the compound tetrakis(hydroxymethyl)phosphonium hydroxide exist.[19,26-30] Filipescu stated that "the THPOH (tetrakis(hydroxymethyl)phosphonium hydroxide) is believed to exist in equilibrium with tris(hydroxymethyl)phosphine (THP), i.e.,

$$[(HOCH_2)_4P]^+ OH^- \rightleftharpoons (HOCH_2)_3P + CH_2O + H_2O \qquad (6)$$

It was in this sense that the acronym was used in our original papers on the THPOH/ammonia finish.[2,3]

The existence of THPOH as a discrete compound was challenged by Vullo on the grounds that no new phosphonium peak appeared in the ^{31}P nuclear magnetic resonance spectrum of THPOH solution, whether prepared by neutralizing Thpc or by dissolving THP in formalin. New peaks appearing in the tertiary phosphine region near THP were ascribed to the mono-, di-, and trihemiformals of THP.[18]

Titration of Thpc with sodium hydroxide produces a curve with a pH of about 8.8 at the equivalence point, characteristic of a weak acid. Calculation of the acid dissociation constant for the equilibrium

$$(HOCH_2)_4P^+ \rightleftharpoons (HOCH_2)_3P^+CH_2O^- + H^+ \tag{7}$$

gives pK_a values that are not constant, increasing steadily[31] from 4.41 to 5.07. If, however, the zwitterion dissociates further to THP and formaldehyde, the equilibrium changes to the following:

$$(HOCH_2)_4P^+ \rightleftharpoons (HOCH_2)_3P + CH_2O + H^+ \tag{8}$$

The pK_a values must be corrected at each point for the formaldehyde concentration, either by subtracting[31] $\log [CH_2O]$ from the pK_a or by squaring the THP concentration, since the concentrations of THP and CH_2O are equal. The overall dissociation constant, which Fodor called pK_d, is now truly constant[31] at 7.06 ± 0.01.

This argument, coupled with the absence of a suitable peak in the ^{31}P NMR spectrum, eliminates the zwitterion of eq. (7) as a stable component of THPOH solutions (though not, as often invoked,[11,21,31,32] as a transient intermediate).

THP itself is a much weaker base.* Fodor[31] estimated the pK_a for the equilibrium

$$(HOCH_2)_3PH^+ \rightleftharpoons (HOCH_2)_3P + H^+ \tag{9}$$

to be less than 3. Based on displacement experiments, we found THP to be a stronger base than triphenylphosphine (pK_a 2.30), but not as strong as tributylphosphine (pK_a 8.43).[9] The theoretical pK_a, calculated[9] by means of the Taft substituent constant for the hydroxymethyl group, is 3.40.

Clearly, the properties of THPOH solutions are not adequately described by THP, even though the latter may be the major component of the solution. The evidence favors the equilibrium of eq. (6), wherein THP and formaldehyde (or THP hemiformal) are the major components and the phosphonium hydroxide is present in an amount just sufficient to give the solution its feebly basic properties. The concentration of the phosphonium hydroxide is, of course, far too small to be detected by ^{31}P NMR. A parallel can be drawn with ammonium hydroxide, wherein a minute quantity of $NH_4^+OH^-$, formed by hydrolysis of ammonia, accounts for the alkalinity of ammonia solution, even though the latter consists almost entirely of unionized hydrated ammonia.[34]

The extent of hemiformal formation varies with the solvent, amounting to 37% in water, but only 5% in methanol.[18] This is not surprising, since formaldehyde exhibits a greater affinity for alcohols than for water. Hemiacetal formation reflects the extent to which THP, as an alcohol, can compete with the solvent for the excess aldehyde.

The equilibrium of eq. (6) provides a mechanism for the rapid exchange of aldehyde groups. The importance of this aspect has been discussed in the text.

Another consequence of the equilibrium is that the pH of neutral THPOH solutions is concentration dependent. The pH of a $0.01M$ solution is 8.53 and increases by one pH unit for each tenfold increase in concentration. In practical terms, the 40% THPOH solution commonly used as a textile finishing reagent should have a pH of about 11. Obviously, the reagent would decompose before this point was reached.

The authors wish to thank Mr. Biagio Piccolo for the x-ray fluorescence analyses and Mr. John S. Mason for the Kjeldahl nitrogen analyses. Naming of firms or their products in this paper does not imply their endorsement by the U.S. Department of Agriculture.

References

1. W. A. Reeves and G. L. Drake, Jr., *Flame Resistant Cotton*, Merrow, Watford, Herts., England, 1971; (a) pp. 14–16; (b) pp. 19–21; (c) pp. 33–52.

* The pK_a value of 5.5 reported by Grayson[32] was determined by titration of Thpc, and does not, therefore, apply to formaldehyde-free THP. Lucken[33] reported the same value for THP without disclosing how it was obtained.

2. J. V. Beninate, E. K. Boylston, G. L. Drake, Jr., and W. A. Reeves, *Am. Dyest. Rep.*, **57**, 981 (1968).

3. J. V. Beninate, E. K. Boylston, G. L. Drake, Jr., and W. A. Reeves, *Text. Ind.*, **131**(11), 110 (1967).

4. R. J. Berni, D. M. Soignet, J. V. Beninate, and M. W. Pilkington, *Text. Res. J.*, **42**, 576 (1972).

5. T. A. Calamari, S. P. Schreiber, and W. A. Reeves, *Text. Chem. Color.*, **7**, 65 (1975).

6. A. W. Frank and G. L. Drake, Jr., *Text. Res. J.*, **44**, 292 (1974).

7. G. M. Wagner, P. E. Hoch, and I. Gordon (to Hooker Chemical Corp.), U.S. Pat. 3,146,212 (1964); *Chem. Abstr.*, **62**, 4159e (1965).

8. D. J. Daigle and D. J. Donaldson, *J. Appl. Polym. Sci.*, **14**, 248 (1970).

9. A. W. Frank and G. L. Drake, Jr., *J. Org. Chem.*, **36**, 549 (1971).

10. M. Reuter and L. Orthner (to Farbwerke Hoechst A.-G.) U.S. Pat. 3,030,421 (1962).

11. A. W. Frank and G. L. Drake, Jr., *Text. Res. J.*, **43**, 633 (1973).

12. M. A. Kasem, H. R. Richards, and C. C. Walker, *J. Appl. Polym. Sci.*, **15**, 2237 (1971).

13. H. Coates and P. A. T. Hoye (to Albright & Wilson (Mfg.) Ltd.), Ger. Pat. 1,077,214 (1960).

14. A. W. Frank and G. L. Drake, Jr., *J. Org. Chem.*, **37**, 2752 (1972).

15. V. W. Tripp, B. Piccolo, D. Mitcham, and R. T. O'Connor, *Text. Res. J.*, **34**, 773 (1964).

16. J. N. Collie, *J. Chem. Soc.*, **127**, 964 (1925).

17. K. A. Petrov, A. I. Gavrilova, V. M. Nam, and V. P. Chuchkanova, *Zh. Obshch. Khim.*, **32**, 3711 (1962); *Chem. Abstr.*, **58**, 12594h (1963).

18. W. J. Vullo, *J. Org. Chem.*, **33**, 3665 (1968).

19. M. Reuter, L. Orthner, F. Jakob, and E. Wolf (to Farbwerke Hoechst A.-G.) U.S. Pat. 2,937,207 (1960); *Chem. Abstr.*, **54**, 22362a (1960).

20. M. Anteunis, M. Verzele, and G. Dacremont, *Bull. Soc. Chim. Belges*, **74**, 622 (1965).

21. S. E. Ellzey, Jr., W. J. Connick, Jr., G. J. Boudreaux, and H. Klapper, *J. Org. Chem.*, **37**, 3453 (1972).

22. D. J. Daigle, A. B. Pepperman, and W. A. Reeves, *Text. Res. J.*, **41**, 944 (1971).

23. D. J. Daigle, W. A. Reeves, and D. J. Donaldson, *Text. Res. J.*, **40**, 580 (1970).

24. B. B. Thompson, *J. Pharm. Sci.*, **57**, 715 (1968).

25. N. Filipescu, L. M. Kindley, H. E. Podall, and F. A. Serafin, *Can. J. Chem.*, **41**, 821 (1963).

26. Soc. Anon. Manufactures Glaces Produits Chimiques Saint-Gobain, Chauny & Cirey, *Fr. Pat.* 1,011,978 (1952); *Chem. Abstr.*, **51**, 14785g (1957).

27. M. Reuter and L. Orthner (to Farbwerke Hoechst A.-G.) Ger. Pat. 1,041,957 (1958); *Chem. Abstr.*, **55**, 1444b (1961).

28. M. Reuter (to Farbwerke Hoechst A.-G.) Ger. Pat. 1,064,061 (1959); *Chem. Abstr.*, **55**, 11301h (1961).

29. Kh. R. Raver, A. B. Bruker, and L. Z. Soborovskii, *Zh. Obshch. Khim.*, **32**, 588 (1962); *Chem. Abstr.*, **58**, 6857c (1963).

30. Kh. R. Raver, L. Z. Soborovskii, and A. B. Bruker, USSR Pat. 143,395 (1962); *Chem. Abstr.*, **57**, 9882i (1962).

31. L. M. Fodor, A Study of Some Oxidation Reactions of the Tetrakishydroxymethyl Phosphonium Cation, Ph.D. Dissertation, Cornell University, Ithaca, N. Y., 1963.

32. M. Grayson, *J. Am. Chem. Soc.*, **85**, 79 (1963).

33. E. A. C. Lucken, *J. Chem. Soc.*, A 1357 (1966).

34. F. A. Cotton and G. Wilkinson, *Advanced Inorganic Chemistry: A Comprehensive Text*, 2nd ed., Wiley-Interscience, New York, 1966, p. 333.

JOURNAL OF APPLIED POLYMER SCIENCE   VOL. 21, 3093–3103 (1977)

Polymeric Systems for Acoustic Damping. I. Poly(vinyl Chloride)–Segmented Polyether Ester Blends

D. J. HOURSTON and I. D. HUGHES, *Department of Chemistry, University of Lancaster, Bailrigg, Lancaster LA1 4YA, U.K.*

Synopsis

A series of six Hytrel/PVC blends were prepared by solution blending Hytrel in methylene chloride and PVC in tetrahydrofuran. The samples were subsequently prepared in sheet form by hot pressing at 170°C. Physical and mechanical properties of the homopolymers and the blends were investigated. The copolyester homopolymer is a partly crystalline elastomeric material. The level of crystallinity was measured by x-ray diffraction and the sensitivity of this level to heat treatments and quenching determined by DSC. A Morgan pulse propagation meter was used to measure sonic velocity and, indirectly, acoustic impedance of the blends. Dynamic mechanical studies indicated that blends containing 25%–50% by weight of Hytrel were completely compatible in the sense that a single glass transition was observed; but as the Hytrel level was increased to 60% and 65%, a shoulder became apparent on the low-temperature side of the glass transition peak. At 80% Hytrel, two peaks were observed, indicating incompatibility. The glass transition temperatures of these blends were found to decrease linearly with added Hytrel.

INTRODUCTION

This paper is the first of a series of reports on investigations into the use of a variety of polymeric systems as possible acoustic damping materials. The increased awareness of noise as a health hazard is leading to the search for more effective noise attenuation systems. A considerable amount of noise originates in machinery because of the inherently very low damping character of metals. The physical properties of a material which influences its sound insulation performance are stiffness, surface mass, and damping characteristics.[1]

As far as polymers are concerned, it is likely that systems having high damping will not have particularly high moduli. If stiffness becomes an important factor in any given sound insulation application, it is possible to use constrained layer damping[2,3] where the polymeric damping material is trapped between stiff outer skins such as metal sheet. The surface mass of polyyeric damping materials may be enhanced by the incorporation of dense fillers such as barytes or lead, but this will result in a reduction in the maximum level of damping.

This and future work will be concerned primarily with the search for materials exhibiting high damping in the appropriate frequency/temperature range. The acoustic spectrum is generally regarded as extending from 20 Hz to 20 kHz, so it is necessary to have as large and as broad a relaxation dispersion over as much of this frequency range as possible.

The most commonly used damping materials in acoustic and mechanical energy absorption are homopolymers and copolymers[4,5] having a glass transition in the appropriate region. Such damping peaks are generally rather narrow, covering a temperature range of about 30°C for a given frequency in the acoustic range. Polymer blends of varying degrees of compatibility have also been investigated[6,7] and generally lead to a broader loss mechanism than is the case for homopolymers and copolymers alone. Recent work by Sperling and co-workers[8,9] into loss mechanism broadening in interpenetrating polymer network systems has resulted in interesting acoustic damping materials.

In this paper, we are largely concerned with compatible blends of poly(vinyl chloride) (PVC) and a relatively new commercial (du Pont) segmented polyether ester copolymer.[10-13] Nishi, Kwei, and Wang[14] and Kwei and Nishi[15] have reported on certain mechanical properties of this system including the influence of heat treatments.

EXPERIMENTAL

Polymers

Hytrel. This segmented polyether ester (grade 4055) was kindly supplied by the E. I. du Pont de Nemours Company and had been prepared by melt transesterification of dimethyl terephthalate, poly(tetramethylene ether) glycol, and 1,4-butanediol. The product is a random block copolymer of crystallizable tetramethylene terephthalate (4GT), which forms the hard segments, and poly(tetramethylene ether) glycol terephthalate, which forms the soft segments. The structural formula is shown below:

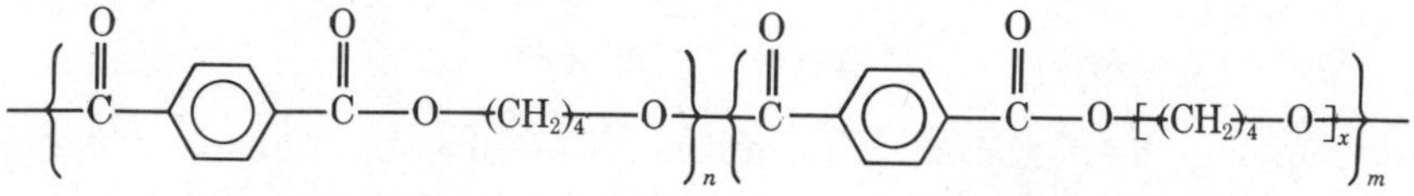

hard segment   soft segment
(4GT)   (PTMEGT)

Poly(vinyl Chloride). A rigid poly(vinyl chloride), Corvic (D60/11), containing no plasticizer was used.

The characterization data for both polymers are shown in Table I.

Preparation of Samples

Six Hytrel/PVC blends were prepared by solution blending where the Hytrel in methylene chloride and the PVC in tetrahydrofuran were mixed and the

TABLE I
Characterization Data for the Poly(vinyl Chloride) and Hytrel Samples
Used in the Preparation of the Blends

	Poly(vinyl chloride)	Hytrel
$\bar{M}_n \times 10^{-3}$	80	30
$\bar{M}_w / \bar{M}_n$ [a]	—	1.56
Density, g/cm³ [b]	1.415	1.152

[a] By GPC.
[b] 23°C.

polymer precipitated by the addition of an excess of methanol. The precipitated blend was centrifuged and then vacuum dried at ambient temperature for two to three days prior to sheeting in a hot press (170°C). These mechanically isotropic sheets had a thickness of 0.5 ± 0.05 mm. The composition of the blends formed were 25:75, 45:55, 50:50, 60:40, 65:35, and 80:20 Hytrel to PVC, respectively.

Measurements

The number-average molecular weights of the homopolymers were measured using a Model 501 Mecrolab membrane osmometer. The Hytrel sample was measured in chloroform and the PVC sample, in tetrahydrofuran. Density measurements were made in a Davenport density gradient column apparatus at 23°C using a carbon tetrachloride–xylene system. The molecular weight distribution of the Hytrel sample was investigated using a Waters GPC apparatus (Model 502).

Crystallinity measurements were made by the wide-angle x-ray diffraction technique using Cu(Kα) radiation. The angular (2θ) range covered was from 7° to 31° with 30-sec intensity readings automatically recorded every 6 min of angle. A Perkin–Elmer differential scanning calorimeter (Model DSC-2) was used at a heating rate of 10°C/min to study the transitions in the Hytrel sample and the effect of thermal treatments on this material.

The reported longitudinal sonic velocity measurements utilized a Morgan pulse propagation meter (Model PPM-5R) which measures the time elapsed in microseconds between the transmission and the subsequent reception of a sound pulse through a known distance in the sheet sample. The dynamic mechanical experiments were conducted using a Rheovibron dynamic viscoelastometer (Model DDV-II). The error involved in determining the glass transition temperature from these data was estimated to be ±1.5°C.

RESULTS AND DISCUSSION

Crystallinity and Thermal Treatments

A number of papers[10,11,13] have described morphological studies of the segmented polyether ester Hytrel. This polymer has been shown to be semicrystalline under certain conditions showing a spherulitic texture with the hard segments (4GT) forming the crystalline phase. Electron microscopy indicates[10] that Hytrel has a two-phase structure consisting of continuous and interpenetrating amorphous and crystalline domains.

In addition to the characterization data shown in Table I, proton NMR was used to estimate the average hard-segment block length. This sample was found to contain 84 mole-% of hard segments having, on average, six 4GT repeat units per block.

Wide-angle x-ray diffraction of the as-received Hytrel lead to scattering intensity-versus-scattering angle (2θ) plots with two peaks (21.5° and 23.5°) and a shoulder at 16.5°. Figure 1 shows a schematic diagram of scattering intensity versus scattering angle from Hytrel. The lower amorphous curve was obtained from a sample held at 200°C for approximately 5 min and then quickly plunged

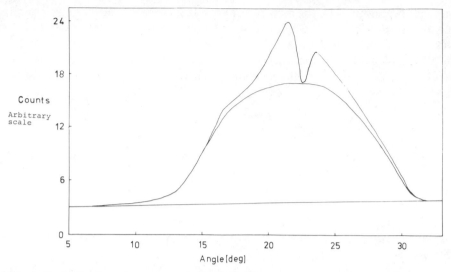

Fig. 1. Scattering intensity vs scattering angle (2θ) diagram for the original Hytrel sample.

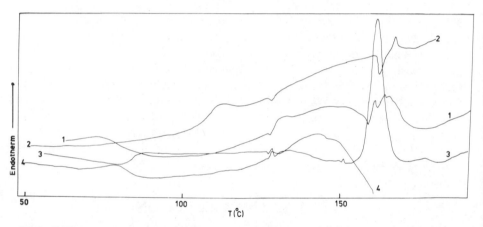

Fig. 2. DSC thermograms of the original and heat-treated Hytrel samples. Curve 1: as received; curve 2: annealed at 100°C for 2 hr; curve 3: annealed at 150°C for 2 hr; curve 4. Sample quenched from 180°C.

into liquid nitrogen and stored there until required. The degree of crystallinity calculated by area measurement was found to be 20%.

Figure 2 shows DSC thermograms of the original Hytrel sample (curve 1), a sample annealed at 100°C for 2 hr (curve 2), a sample annealed at 150°C for 2 hr (curve 3), and a sample which has been heated to 180°C and then quenched in liquid nitrogen (curve 4). Curve 3 shows a hard-segment glass transition at about 80°C, which is in good agreement with a literature value[16] for the 4GT homopolyester. Above this temperature in the as-received sample (curve 1), there is a crystallization exotherm which is absent in curve 2 when the sample had been heated at 100°C for 2 hr prior to the DSC experiment. In the case of curve 3, it is clear that annealing at 150°C for 2 hr results in more or less complete crystallization as there is, again, no evidence of crystallization during the actual DSC experiment. The absence of a hard-segment glass transition in curve 2, but not in curve 3, is thought to be the result of the development of spherulitic structures with interfibrillar amorphous regions at the higher annealing temperature. In the sample annealed at only about 20°C above the hard-segment glass transition temperature, the crystallites are thought to be small but to involve virtually all the hard-segment blocks. There is a small endotherm centered at about 112°C which is thought to be the result of the melting of these small and imperfect crystalline structures. The inflection points in all four thermograms at about 128°C are the result of an instrumental abnormality.

Curves 1 and 2 show a broad endotherm convering the 100°–170°C range which is ascribed to the melting of hard-segment crystalline structures having a wide variety of imperfections. Annealing at 100°C for 2 hr did not appreciably alter the overall level of crystallinity nor did it significantly narrow the melting range. However, annealing at 50°C higher led to a fairly sharp melting point at 162°C. The quenched sample (curve 4) also showed an endotherm, but at a somewhat lower temperature than for the other three curves. It is clear that this sample is also crystallizing during the DSC experiment. In the x-ray diffraction experiments, it was difficult to achieve an amorphous sample and it was necessary to store the sample at low temperature until it was required.

The melting point of the annealed sample (curve 3) was in poor agreement with the reported values of 150°C by Nishi et al.[14] and 185°C by Shen et al.[13] and also differs substantially from the literature value[17] of 232°C for the 4GT homopolyester. The Hytrel samples showed evidence of considerable degradation prior to reaching this temperature.

The thermograms for the blends were very similar to both curve 1 in Figure 2 and to the data published by Nishi et al.[14] for a 50:50 blend.

Sonic Velocity and Dynamic Mechanical Measurements

Table II and Figure 3 present the sonic pulse propagation data for both the homopolymers and for the six blends. The longitudinal sonic velocity (V_L) increases essentially linearly with the weight percent of PVC in the blend up to around 50%. There is then a more rapid increase in V_L with increasing PVC content. It is thought that this increase in slope occurs when PVC becomes a continuous phase. The sample containing 20% by weight of PVC displayed two

TABLE II
Longitudinal Sonic Velocity (V_L) and Acoustic Impedance (Z) Data for
Homopolymers and Blends at 20°C[a]

Composition[b]	V_L, km/sec	$Z \times 10^{-6}$, g/cm^2·sec
100	0.28	0.03
80	0.51	0.06
65	0.68	0.08
60	0.81	0.10
50	0.96	0.12
45	0.92	0.12
25	1.77	0.24
0	1.83	0.26

[a] $Z = \rho \cdot V_L$, where ρ is the density of the polymeric sheet.
[b] Weight percent of Hytrel in the blends.

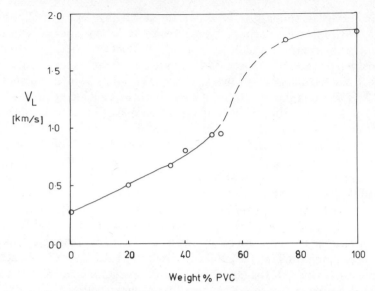

Fig. 3. Longitudinal sonic velocity (V_L) vs weight percent PVC for the homopolymers and the blends.

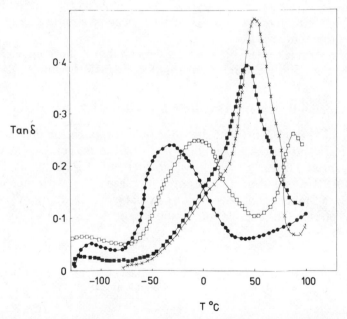

Fig. 4. Plots of tan δ vs temperature for Hytrel (●) and blends containing 80% (□), 65% (■), and 60% (X) Hytrel. The frequency was 110 Hz.

peaks in the tan δ–temperature dispersion (Fig. 4), indicating the presence of both a soft segment/PVC phase and a largely pure PVC phase which at this level of composition will be discontinuous. Nevertheless, this sample lies on the same line (Fig. 3) as the other compatible blends. As this technique utilizes sonic pulses having a wavelength of around 2 cm, it is only sensitive to the blend composition and to the nature of the continuous phase.

The acoustic impedance shows the same trends as V_L when plotted against

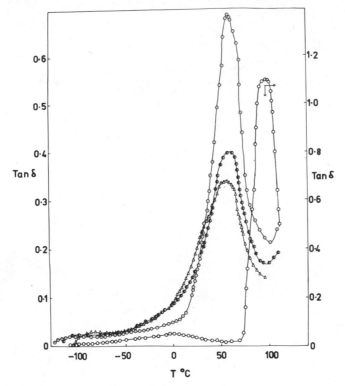

Fig. 5. Plots of tan δ vs temperature for PVC (O) and blends containing 50% (△), 45% (◐), and 25% (◎) Hytrel.   The frequency was 110 Hz.

weight percent PVC.   The acoustic impedance of PVC is very similar to that of polystyrene, which has a reported[18] value of 0.25×10^6 g cm^{-2} s^{-1}.

Figures 4 and 5 show the Rheovibron tan δ–temperature curves for both homopolymers and for all six blends.   All the blends, except the one with 80% Hytrel, show a single glass transition, indicating, at least, a very high level of compatibility.

The Hytrel sample showed two peaks, one at −111°C and the other at −32°C. As it has been shown[13] that the magnitude of the lower temperature transition is dependent on the weight fraction of soft segments, it could be the result of a

TABLE III
Certain Dynamic Mechanical Properties of the Homopolymers and Blends (110 Hz)

Composition[a]	T_g, °C	tan δ_{max}[b]	ΔH, kcal/mole[c]
100	−32	0.24	27.5 (~15)
80	−5, 87	0.25, 0.26	—
65	44	0.40	75
60	49	0.48	55
50	59	0.34	—
45	62	0.40	—
25	63	0.69	125
0	97	1.10	67

[a] Weight percent Hytrel in blends.
[b] Maximum value of tan δ in the glass transition region.
[c] Apparent activation energy.

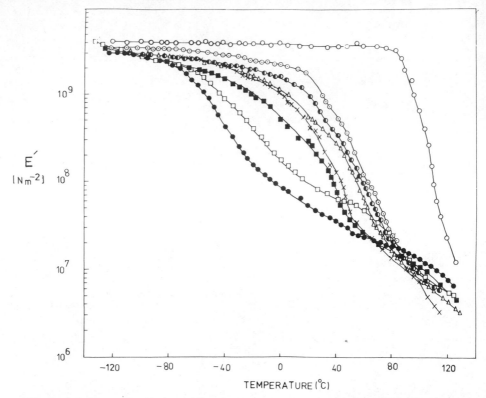

Fig. 6. Plots of dynamic storage modulus (E') vs temperature of PVC (O), Hytrel (●), and blends containing 80% (□), 65% (■), 60% (X), 50% (△), 45% (◔), and 25% (◉) Hytrel. The frequency was 110 Hz.

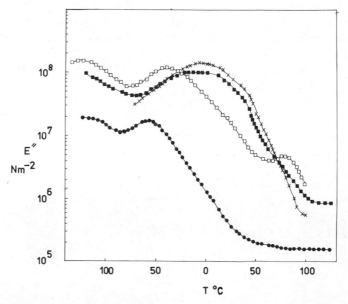

Fig. 7. Plots of dynamic loss modulus (E'') vs temperature for Hytrel (●) and blends containing 80% (□), 65% (■), and 60% (X) Hytrel. The frequency was 110 Hz.

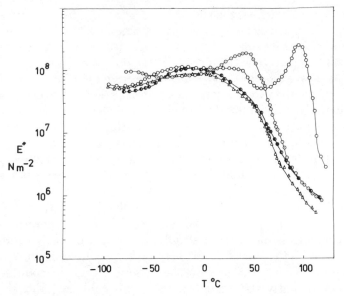

Fig. 8. Plots of dynamic loss modulus (E'') vs temperature for PVC (O) and blends containing 50% (△), 45% (◑), and 25% (◉) Hytrel. The frequency was 110 Hz.

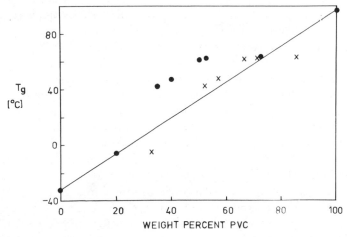

Fig. 9. Glass transition temperatures of the homopolymers and blends (T_g) vs weight percent PVC (●). The symbol (X) refers to the case where only the Hytrel soft segments are considered.

Schatzki-type mechanism involving the $+CH_2)_4O-$ soft-segment group. However, Wetton, and Williams[19] have proposed that the mechanism for this low-temperature relaxation is a damped oscillation of the soft segments about their equilibrium positions. The transition at $-32°C$ is the glass transition of the amorphous soft-segment phase.[13] The PVC homopolymer also showed two transitions. There is a broad minor transition centered at $-1°C$ and the glass transition at $97°C$. These PVC transitions have been discussed by Pezzin et al.[20]

Table III shows that the single glass transitions of all the blends, except the 80% Hytrel blend, moves progressively to lower temperatures with increasing Hytrel content. Tan δ_{max} decreases regularly from a value of 1.10 for PVC to 0.34

for the 50:50 blend. There is then an increase in tan $\delta_{\max}$ for the blend containing 60% Hytrel. Both this blend and the one containing 65% Hytrel show shoulders on the low-temperature side of the curves suggesting the onset of phase separation. This is thought to be the reason for the increase in tan $\delta_{\max}$.

Nishi et al.[14] have reported a very broad transition for a 75% Hytrel/PVC blend and speculate that the two-component transitions are about to be resolved. This is verified in the case of our 80% Hytrel blend (Fig. 4) where there are two distinct loss peaks. They[14] also comment on the fact that the low-temperature PVC transition moves to lower temperatures and decreases in size as the Hytrel level is increased. In this work, this minor transition certainly decreased rapidly with increasing copolyester content, but even at low Hytrel levels it soon became impossible to detect.

Figures 6, 7, and 8 show dynamic storage moduli (E')- and dynamic loss moduli (E'')-versus-temperature plots for all samples. The E'–temperature curves are typical of compatible blends in that only one transition region is discernible, except, of course, in the case of the 80% Hytrel blend where, again, two transition regions occur. This figure also shows the rather high elastic modulus of Hytrel, which is a particularly attractive feature of this rubbery polymer. The E''-against-temperature curves (Figs. 7 and 8) show broad loss peaks for the fully compatible blends.

Table III also shows apparent activation energies for the homopolymer transitions and for those of three of the blends. The activation energies of the Hytrel and PVC glass transitions were 27.5 and 67 kcal/mole, respectively, while that for the low-temperature Hytrel transition was approximately 15 kcal/mole. For the 25% Hytrel blend, the activation energy was 125 kcal/mole, while for the 60% Hytrel blend, the value had dropped to 55 kcal/mole. The onset of incompatibility as shown by the shoulder on the tan δ–temperature peak of the 65% Hytrel blend led to an increased value of 75 kcal/mole for this blend.

Figure 9 shows a plot of the glass transition temperature (T_g) determined from the position of tan $\delta_{\max}$ (110 Hz) versus weight percent PVC. It is clear that there is not a simple linear relation between T_g of all the blends and their compositions. However, only the Hytrel soft segments are thought to be miscible with the PVC as the hard segments form separate crystalline domains. It is reasonable, therefore, only to consider the effect of mixing the Hytrel soft segments with the PVC. This latter plot shows that the glass transitions of compatible blends of PVC and Hytrel can be predicted to a good approximation by eq. (1):

$$T_{g\,\text{blend}} = W_1 T_{g_1} + W_2 T_{g_2} \tag{1}$$

where W_1 and W_2 are the weight fractions and T_{g_1} and T_{g_2} are the glass transition temperatures of the respective components of the blends. This conclusion is in agreement with the findings of Nishi et al.[14]

One of the authors (I.D.H.) wishes to thank the Science Research Council for a Research Studentship.

References

1. W. A. Utley, *Composites*, **6**, 34 (1974).

2. G. L. Ball and I. Salyer, *J. Acoust. Soc. Am.*, **39**, 663 (1966).

3. E. E. Ungar, in *Noise and Vibration Control*, L. L. Beranek, Ed., McGraw-Hill, New York, 1971, Chap. 14.

4. D. J. Williams, *Polymer Science and Engineering,* Prentice-Hall, Englewood Cliffs, N.J., 1971.

5. J. H. Aklonis, W. J. MacKnight, and M. Shen, *Introduction to Polymer Viscoelasticity,* Wiley-Interscience, New York, 1972.

6. H. Mizumachi, *J. Adhesion Soc. Jpn,* **5,** 370 (1969).

7. M. Matsuo, *Jpn Plast.,* **2,** 6 (1968).

8. L. H. Sperling, Tai-Woo Chiu, R. G. Gramlich, and D. A. Thomas, *J. Paint Technol.,* **46,** 47 (1974).

9. J. A. Grates, D. A. Thomas, E. C. Hickey, and L. H. Sperling, *J. Appl. Polym. Sci.,* **19,** 1731 (1975).

10. R. J. Cella, *J. Polym. Sci.,* **C42,** 727 (1973).

11. R. W. Seymour, J. R. Overton, and L. S. Corley, *Macromolecules,* **8,** 331 (1975).

12. M. Brown, *Rubber Ind.,* **9,** 102 (1975).

13. M. Shen, V. Mehra, N. Niinomi, J. T. Koberstein, and S. L. Cooper, *J. Appl. Phys.,* **45,** 4182 (1974).

14. T. Nishi, T. K. Kwei, and T. T. Wang, *J. Appl. Phys.,* **46,** 4157 (1975).

15. T. Nishi and T. K. Kwei, *J. Appl. Polym. Sci.,* **20,** 1331 (1976).

16. *Encyclopaedia of Polymer Science and Technology,* Vol. 11, p. 69.

17. *Encyclopaedia of Polymer Science and Technology,* Vol. 11, p. 71.

18. R. W. B. Stephens, in *Physics of Plastics,* P. D. Ritchie, Ed., Iliffe Books, London, 1965, Chap. 9.

19. R. Wetton and G. Williams, *Trans. Faraday Soc.,* **61,** 2132 (1965).

20. G. Pezzin, G. Ajroldi, T. Casiraghi, C. Garbuglio, and G. Vittadini, *J. Appl. Polym. Sci.,* **16,** 1839 (1972).

Received August 2, 1976
Revised October 26, 1976

Sorption and Diffusion of Water in Glass Ribbon-Reinforced Composites*

B. S. MEHTA, *Plastics Division, Mobil Chemical Company, Canandaigua, New York 14424*, A. T. DiBENEDETTO, *Dept. of Chemical Engineering, University of Connecticut, Storrs, Connecticut*, and J. L. KARDOS, *Dept. of Chemical Engineering, Washington University, St. Louis, Missouri*

Synopsis

The processes of sorption and diffusion of water in anisotropic glass ribbon-reinforced composite films of controlled structural and physical characteristics were investigated in terms of the film properties, e.g., geometry, orientation, and volume fraction of the filler; molding characteristics of the composite film; and the adhesion between the glass ribbon and continuous cellulose acetate matrix. While the diffusion of water through unfilled cellulose acetate film was found to be a simple activated process with very little concentration dependence, the diffusion behavior of glass ribbon-reinforced cellulose acetate was found to be anomalous and concentration dependent.

INTRODUCTION

The long-range mechanical performance of glass-reinforced plastics depends on their stability in varying environmental conditions. There is a particular need for knowledge of the effect of water on these materials. Water, a universally present compound, is capable of diffusing in most materials. Glass-reinforced plastics tend to absorb moisture after extended periods of exposure to high humidity, and this moisture often degrades their mechanical and structural integrity. A knowledge of the mechanism and the rate of diffusion of water in composites thus becomes very important.

The sorption and diffusion of low molecular weight substances such as water by polymers is often sensitive to any change in segment mobility or spatial arrangement of polymer chains. In the case of composite materials, the filler phase incorporated in a matrix material plays an important role in the solution and diffusion processes. Most of the literature concerning diffusion and sorption in heterogenous media deals primarily with crosslinked and crystalline polymers where the crosslinks or crystallites act as the dispersed phase in the continuous amorphous phase. Relatively little work has been reported on diffusion in composite media made by combining two physically different materials.

Nielsen[1] studied the permeability of polymer systems filled with plate-like particles. He developed phenomenological equations to predict the maximum decrease in composite permeability that can be expected for the addition of a filler to a polymer. He extended his analysis to permeability of liquids through

---

* Presented at 31st Annual Conference of the Reinforced Plastics/Composite Institute of the Society of the Plastics Industry, Inc., at Washington, D.C., February 3–6, 1976.

filled polymers when the liquid adsorbs or collects at the filler–polymer interface. Ruhman and Wu[2] have studied the effect of anisotropy on the sorption of benzene vapor in glass–epoxy composite specimens. They also studied the role of internal stresses generated as a result of the dilatation which accompanies the sorption of the organic solvent in a filled system. Very recently, Shen and Springer[3] have studied the absorption and desorption in moisture in Graphite–Fiberite composites under controlled environmental conditions. They developed expressions for the moisture distribution and moisture content as a function of time of one-dimensional homogeneous and composite materials exposed either on one side or on both sides to humid air or to water.

SORPTION AND DIFFUSION IN COMPOSITES

In a composite material with two components A and B, a component A may be in direct contact with component B to produce a two-phase system. Sometimes, there may be an intervening phase between components A and B, thus making it a three-component system. The intervening phase may be deliberately added to improve adhesion, or it may be the result of a chemical reaction between A and B. In the case of poor adhesion, this phase may be air. The simplest case to consider is the case where A and B meet at an interface in the absence of a third phase. Most theoretical studies of the effect of disperse phases on the physical and mechanical properties of composite materials assume perfect adhesion at the interface for simplicity of treatment. This is only a reasonable assumption where such complicating factors as imperfect adhesion leading to the presence of cracks, pores, or small channels, or the presence of impurities at the interface can be neglected. If the composite material is considered to consist of two phases, matrix material and filler, such that these phases can be regarded independent of each other and there is no interaction between matrix and the filler, then the solubility coefficient of the penetrant in the composite system S is given by Barrer:[4]

$$S = S_m \phi_m + S_f \phi_f \tag{1}$$

where ϕ_m and ϕ_f are the volume fractions and S_m and S_f are the solubility coefficients of the matrix and the filler phase, respectively. Equation (1) is an oversimplification of the solution process because it does not account for the adsorption that occurs at the interface. In real situations, the matrix material and filler may not be independent of each other. The matrix material may wet the filler surface and so compete with the vapor for the surface.

When the filler phase is impermeable ($S_f = 0$), eq. (1) becomes

$$S = S_m \phi_m \tag{2}$$

and the solubility equation can be written as

$$C = S_m \phi_m P \tag{3}$$

where C is the concentration of water vapor in the composite and p is the equilibrium pressure. When the adhesion between the filler and the matrix material is not perfect, the existence of holes or microvoids may act as a stable phase. The solution process can in this case be considered to consist of two mechanisms,[5–7] namely, the ordinary dissolution and the hole-filling processes, and can be described quantitatively as follows:

$$C = C_D + C_H = S_m \phi_m P + \frac{C_h' b_p}{1 + b_p} \qquad (4)$$

where ordinary dissolution C_D is represented by the Henry's law term, and the sorption of penetrant into holes, C_H, is represented by the nonlinear Langumuir expression where C_h' is the hole-filling constant and b is the hole affinity constant.

While the diffusion behavior for most of the unfilled polymers can be explained by simple Fickian phenomena were diffusivity is constant and independent of solute concentration, in the case of composites the presence of filler makes the diffusion process more complicated and analysis of the experimental data becomes rather involved.

Diffusion of a gas or vapor in composites can take place by one or more of the following modes: (i) diffusion through the continuous matrix phase, (ii) diffusion through the dispersed and matrix phases, (iii) diffusion through the interfacial region with properties different from the matrix phase, (iv) diffusion through cracks, pores, or small channels present in the composite due to imperfect adhesion or other structural defects.

The presence of impermeable fillers in composites increases the effective length that the diffusing molecules must travel and restricts the effective cross-sectional area for diffusion. It also can reduce the chain mobility of the polymer phase adjacent to the filler surface. For impermeable fillers such as glass ribbons, the diffusion coefficients of composites become very structure sensitive and fluxes may no longer be inversely proportional to the thickness of the composite film. Barrer et al.[8] have shown that for diffusion through composites having impermeable fillers, a simplified equation for diffusion through the composite medium can be written as follows:

$$\frac{\partial c}{\partial t} = \phi_m K D_m \frac{\partial^2 C_m}{\partial x^2} = D_c \frac{\partial^2 c}{dx^2} \qquad (5)$$

where D_m is the diffusivity of the matrix phase, ϕ_m is the volume fraction of the matrix material in the composite film, K is the structure factor for diffusion in the x-direction, and D_c is the diffusivity of the composite film. The structure factor K is a function which describes the reduction of the diffusion coefficient of the composite below the value D_m of the matrix material due to distortion of the path of molecular diffusion around the filler particles dispersed throughout the matrix phase. Equation (5) is applicable only if the composite film is macroscopically isotropic, or, failing that, if the diffusion occurs in only one of the principal directions of the anisotropic composite.

By definition, the concentration of a gas in a composite film is given by

$$C = C_m \phi_m + C_f \phi_f \qquad (6)$$

assuming that there are no cracks or microvoids in the composite. When the filler is impermeable, $C_f = 0$, and eq. (6) is reduced to

$$C = C_m \phi_m \qquad (7)$$

Substituting eq. (7) in eq. (5) yields

$$D_c = K D_m \qquad (8)$$

Nielsen,[1] in his models for the permeability of filled polymer systems, defined the reduction in molecular diffusion path caused by the structure factor K to be inversely proportional to the tortuousity ζ such that $K = 1/\zeta$. The tortuousity ζ is a function of the filler volume fraction, the geometry of the filler particles, and their orientation in the composite. For plate-like particles, e.g., glass ribbons, Nielsen developed the following equation for tortuousity ζ:

$$\zeta = 1 + (W/2t)\,\phi_f \tag{9}$$

where W is the width of the glass ribbon, t is the thickness of the ribbon, and ϕ_f is the filler volume fraction. However, Nielsen pointed out that the actual value of the structure factor would be less than that predicted by eq. (9) because of the variation of concentration of the diffusant perpendicular to the major flux direction (x) as it goes around the filler. Klute[9] and Bixler et al.[10] have proposed that the structure factor actually consists of two impedance factors and can be expressed as

$$K = 1/\zeta\beta \tag{10}$$

where ζ is the tortuousity factor accounting for the increase in diffusion path length caused by the presence of the filler particles and β is a chain immobilization factor which takes into account the reduction in matrix chain segment mobility due to proximity of the filler particles. The chain immobilization factor is greater than 1.0 if there is some interaction between filler and matrix material. If there is no immobilization effect, $\beta = 1$. Mehta et al.[11] applied Nielsen's model for composite permeability to interpret the permeability of nitrogen and oxygen gases in anisotropic composite films made by reinforcing cellulose acetate with glass ribbons. They also found that reduction in composite permeability was more than warranted by tortuousity alone. They explained this further reduction in terms of the size of the influenced matrix phase portion of the unit cell of the composite film.

In this paper, we discuss the application of the above models, eqs. (1)–(10), to explain the diffusion and sorption of water in reinforced anisotropic composites.

EXPERIMENTAL

Materials

For sorption experiments, both unfilled and filled films were prepared by compression molding between two smooth, flat plates. Cast cellulose acetate sheets used for the matrix phase of the composite films were made by XCEL Corporation. The cellulose acetate had 2.5 degrees of substitution and contained about 20%–30% diethyl phathalate plasticizer. The unfilled cellulose acetate films were prepared by laminating several unfilled, cast cellulose acetate sheets and then compression molding the laminate. Making glass ribbon–cellulose acetate composite film is more involved and has been discussed in detail elsewhere.[12,13] First, a sheet of ribbons is formed by cutting prescribed lengths from a tape and placing them in a frame having slots and spaces to align the ribbons so that they are oriented exactly parallel and have a predetermined inter-ribbon spacing. The ribbons are held permanently in the shape of sheets with Scotch tape. The next step involves forming a laminate by laying up alternate sheets of cellulose acetate and ribbons. In the case of composites containing multilayers

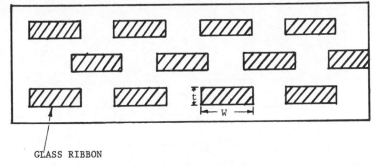

GLASS RIBBON

Fig. 1. Distribution of filler in glass ribbon-reinforced cellulose acetate film.

of glass ribbons, the successive glass layers are arranged so that ribbons in any two consecutive layers are staggered causing the spaces between the ribbons to be always above and below the ribbons in adjacent layers (see Fig. 1). The last step consists of compression molding.

Both unfilled and filled films were made by compression molding for about 15 min at 350°F and 50–100 psi pressure. The compression was always started from room temperature, and the temperature increased gradually with intermittent release of pressure and repressurizing until the desired temperature was reached. The intermittent release of pressure and repressurization helped in pushing out entrapped air bubbles. After the laminate had been heated at the final constant temperature and pressure for about 15 min, the heating was stopped and the film air cooled under pressure to room temperature. This molding cycle ensures complete melting of the matrix so that the glass ribbons are totally embedded, while it at the same time prevents excess flashing and the development of high molded-in stresses. The films were then placed in a desiccator for several days to keep them dry. The details of the films used for sorption experiment are listed in Table I.

Apparatus and Procedure

The experimental setup used for sorption for this investigation is similar in principle to that used by Prager and Long.[14] The apparatus is schematically

TABLE I
Description of Films[a]

Film description		$\langle l \rangle$, mil	ϕ_f, %	No. of filler layers in film
I.D.	Type			
L	Biaxially oriented cast cellulose acetate	20	0	—
M	press molded	43	0	—
N	GRCA	45.4	34.6	4
O	GRCA	21.2	21	1
P	GRCA	18.0	9.15	1
Q	GRCA	18.25	4.70	1

[a] All composite films were made by using glass ribbon 125 mil in width and 5.2 mil thick. GRCA = Glass ribbon/cellulose acetate.

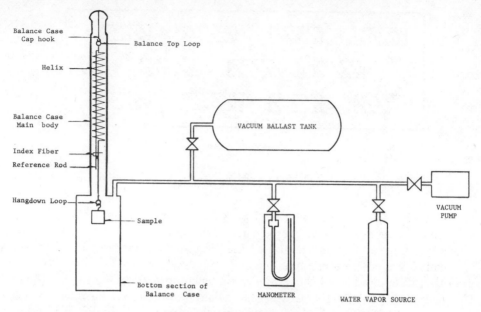

Fig. 2. Sorption cell schematic.

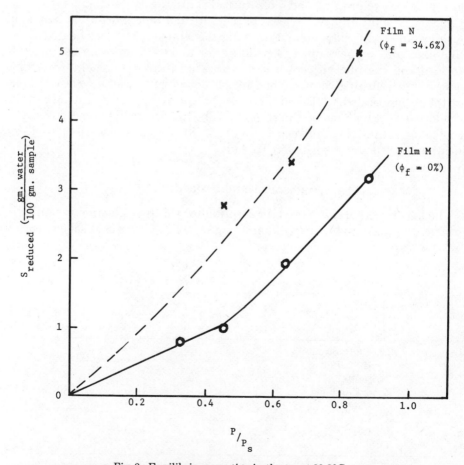

Fig. 3. Equilibrium sorption isotherms at 39.8°C.

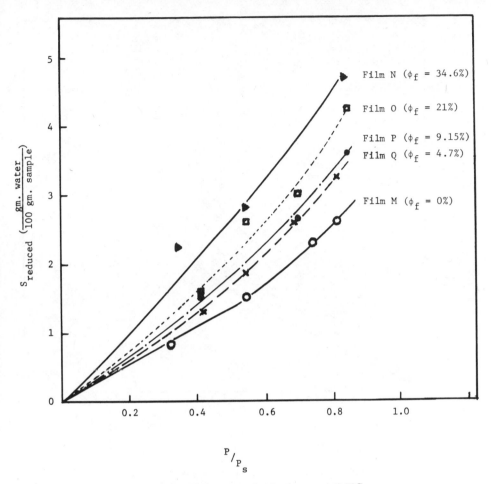

Fig. 4. Equilibrium sorption isotherms at 49.8°C.

shown in Figure 2. In this setup, a specimen of known shape and size is suspended from a sensitive quartz helix spring in an evacuated chamber to keep the specimen in an atmosphere of constant water vapor pressure. The increase in weight of the specimen due to absorption of vapor is then measured as a function of time by observing the extension of the spring using a cathetometer. The quartz spring was obtained from Misco Scientific Co., Berkeley, California. The spring has high tensile strength, negligible coefficient of expansion at all temperatures, and is noncorrosive and practically inert. The cathetometer (obtained from Gaetner Scientific Corporation, Chicago, Illinois) can measure an extension of the spring up to 10 cm and read to within 10^{-4} cm.

In Figure 2, the smaller tank contains liquid water which acts as a supply source for water vapor. The vapor pressure of water is adjusted by control of the temperature of the liquid water, and the relative humidity of the water vapor in the weighing chamber containing the quartz spring and the suspended sample is controlled by a regulating needle valve provided at the outlet of the smaller tank. The bigger tank connected to the weighing chamber acts as a ballast tank and helps keep the water vapor pressure in the chamber constant with a minimum of fluctuation. A vacuum pump is used as the vacuum source for the sys-

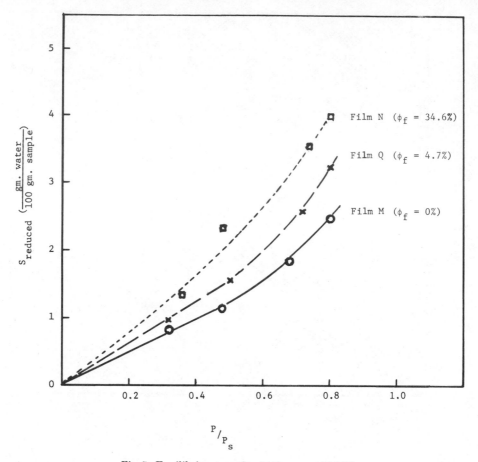

Fig. 5. Equilibrium sorption isotherms at 56.3°C.

tem, and a mercury manometer is used to measure the pressure of the system. The whole sorption system is enclosed in a constant-temperature air bath.

RESULTS AND DISCUSSION

Water sorption data for both unfilled and filled cellulose acetate films were obtained at several temperatures ranging from 39.8 to 64.8 °C and for various relative pressures. The experimental equilibrium sorption isotherms for both unfilled and filled cellulose acetate films are shown in Figures 3–6. While the water uptake by the films is fairly linear at low relative pressures, it increases sharply at high relative pressures. This behavior is very typical of sorption of water in cellulose derivatives and can be interpreted as initial sorption on specific sites followed by some kind of mixing process, e.g., clustering of water molecules in the matrix polymer, possibly in preexisting cavities,[15] and in the case of glass ribbon-reinforced composite films by clustering of water on the surface of hydrophilic glass ribbons also.

The solubility data are sensitive to the mode of preparation of the film. The equilibrium sorption coefficient in the compression-molded film (unfilled) was found to be about 40% lower than the solubility coefficient for a biaxially oriented

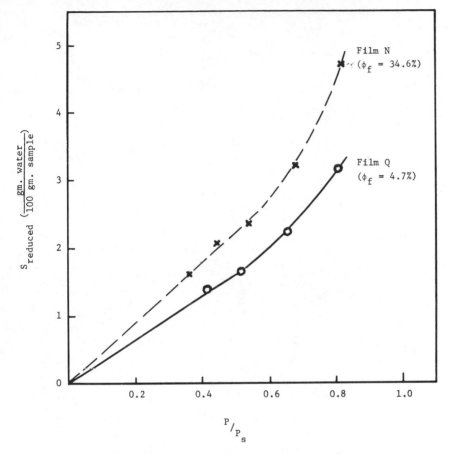

Fig. 6. Equilibrium sorption isotherms at 64.3°C.

cast film. Compression molding the cast film can result in change of its density, orientation, and molecular structure which can affect the solubility coefficient.

To make a reasonable evaluation of the effect of the presence of glass ribbon

TABLE II
Solubility Coefficients for GRCA Films

Film	39.8°C			49.8°C			56.3°C			64.8°C		
	P/P_s	S_{exp}	S_{red}	P/P_s	S_{exp}	S_{red}	P/P_s	S_{exp}	S_{red}	P/P_s	S_{exp}	S_{red}
N	0.454	1.29	2.79	0.348	1.04	2.25	0.360	0.62	1.34	0.364	0.75	1.62
	0.654	1.57	3.40	0.543	1.29	2.79	0.480	1.08	2.34	0.446	0.96	2.08
	0.854	2.31	5.00	0.837	2.18	4.72	0.736	1.64	3.55	0.540	1.09	2.36
							0.800	1.84	3.98	0.679	1.49	3.23
										0.818	2.18	4.72
O				0.413	1.00	1.59						
				0.543	1.64	2.60						
				0.696	1.89	3.00						
				0.848	2.68	4.24						
P				0.413	1.24	1.55						
				0.696	2.11	2.65						
				0.848	2.87	3.60						
Q				0.424	1.17	1.30	0.32	0.88	0.985	0.417	1.26	1.40
				0.543	1.68	1.86	0.504	1.42	1.57	0.513	1.50	1.66
				0.685	2.34	2.59	0.720	2.33	2.58	0.652	2.03	2.25
				0.815	2.93	3.25	0.800	3.01	3.24	0.807	2.86	3.17

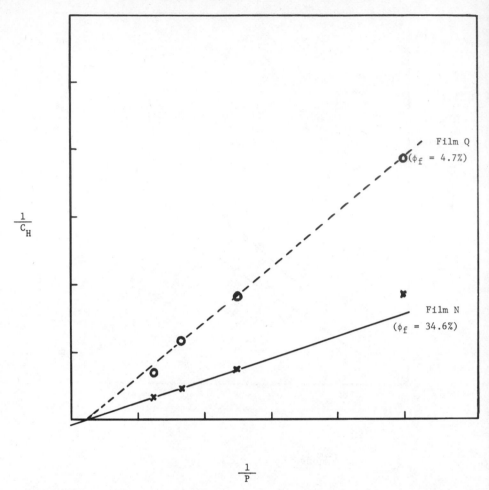

Fig. 7. Langmuir plots for water sorption by hole filling in glass ribbon-reinforced cellulose acetate films at 56.3°C.

in the matrix phase on the overall composite solubility, the experimental solubilities (S_{exp}) were reduced to equilibrium solubility coefficients (S_{red}) based on the weight of the matrix material present in the composite films such that

$$S_{red} = \frac{S_{exp} \times W_c}{W_c - W_f} \qquad (11)$$

where W_c and W_f are the weights of composite film and the filler in the composite film, respectively.

The values of solubility coefficients for glass ribbon–cellulose acetate composites show a consistent increase with filler volume fraction. This could possibly happen for two reasons. First, the glass is very hydrophilic and will have a tendency to absorb water on its surface. The other reason is that during compression molding the solubility characteristics of the film change. The presence of glass ribbon can constrain the free and uniform flow of cellulose acetate in all directions during molding. This could have a twofold effect. Because of the nonuniform flow, wetting may not be complete, and voids can result along the

TABLE III
Sorption and Diffusion Data

Film	Temp., °C	Run no.	p, mm Hg	p/p_s[a]	S, g water vap. 100 g sample	$D_s \times 10^7$, cm²/sec	$D_d \times 10^7$, cm²/sec	$\langle D \rangle = \dfrac{D_s + D_d}{2} \times 10^7$, cm²/sec
L	39.8	S-1	32	0.582	2.89	1.19	1.28	1.24
M	39.8	S-2	18	0.327	0.80	1.45	0.43	0.94
		S-3	25	0.454	0.99	1.87	0.52	1.19
		S-4	35	0.636	1.94	0.98	0.87	0.93
		S-5	48.5	0.882	3.36	0.89	1.18	1.04
	49.8	S-6	30	0.326	0.84	2.22	1.96	2.09
		S-7	50	0.543	1.52	1.88	1.85	1.86
		S-8	68	0.739	2.30	1.88	1.72	1.80
		S-9	75	0.815	2.62	2.00	1.92	1.96
	56.3	S-10	40	0.320	0.93	3.18	3.91	3.05
		S-11	60	0.480	1.15	3.29	2.55	2.92
		S-12	85	0.680	1.85	3.29	2.55	2.92
		S-13	100	0.800	2.48	3.18	2.86	3.02
N	39.8	S-19	25	0.454	1.29	0.86	1.34	1.10
		S-20	36	0.654	1.57	1.49	2.20	1.85
		S-21	47	0.854	2.31	1.33	1.31	1.32
	49.8	S-22	32	0.348	1.04	0.89	2.51	1.70
		S-23	50	0.543	1.29	2.15	1.51	1.83
		S-24	77	0.837	2.18	2.62	2.41	2.51
	56.3	S-25	45	0.360	0.62	3.83	2.36	3.10
		S-26	61	0.488	1.08	3.10	4.00	3.55
		S-27	92	0.736	1.64	3.67	5.35	4.51
N	64.8	S-29	68	0.364	0.75	0.28	1.83	3.06
		S-30	83.5	0.446	0.96	3.91	2.92	3.14
		S-31	101	0.540	1.09	3.91	1.53	2.72
		S-32	127	0.679	1.49	4.21	5.34	4.78
		S-33	153	0.818	2.18	3.00	4.96	3.98
O	49.8	S-34	38	0.413	1.00	2.52	1.85	2.18
		S-35	50	0.543	1.64	1.52	1.83	1.67
		S-36	64	0.696	1.89	2.34	1.50	1.97
		S-37	78	0.848	2.68	1.80	3.30	2.54
P	49.8	S-38	38	0.413	1.24	1.50	1.45	1.48
		S-40	64	0.696	2.11	1.75	2.09	1.92
		S-41	78	0.848	2.87	1.67	0.96	1.31
Q	49.8	S-42	39	0.424	1.17	1.98	1.78	1.88
		S-43	50	0.543	1.68	1.96	1.45	1.70
		S-44	63	0.685	2.34	1.51	1.73	1.61
		S-45	75	0.815	2.93	1.73	1.83	1.78
	56.3	S-46	40	0.32	0.88	2.75	2.00	2.38
		S-47	63	0.504	1.42	2.26	1.87	2.06
		S-48	90	0.720	2.33	2.35	2.39	2.37
		S-49	100	0.800	3.01	2.41	2.19	2.30
	64.8	S-50	78	0.417	1.26	2.95	2.33	2.64
		S-51	96	0.513	1.50	3.45	3.20	3.33
		S-52	122	0.652	2.03	3.50	3.39	3.45
		S-53	151	0.087	2.86	2.89	2.85	2.87

[a] p_s = Saturation vapor pressure at the temperature of the sorption–desorption experiment.

interface which will provide additional sites for absorption of water. Also due to nonuniform flow, the overall characteristics of the matrix phase may be somewhere between those of cast cellulose acetate and the unfilled compression-molded cellulose acetate, but possibly much closer to the latter. Since cast cellulose acetate has a higher solubility, it might contribute to the higher solubility of composites which were evaluated on the basis that the matrix phase behaves only like compression-molded cellulose acetate. The thickness of the water layer adsorbed on the glass surface, calculated on the assumption that adsorption on the glass surface is the only source of water uptake beside the matrix phase, was found to range from 200 to 600 Å for different composite films. A realistic value for the thickness of the water layer could be of the order of 10–20

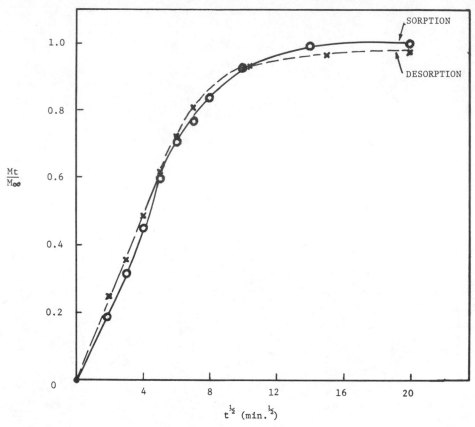

Fig. 8. Sorption–desorption curves for biaxially oriented cast film (20 mil thick; weight of sample 7.433) at 39.8°C and 32 mm Hg of water vapor pressure.

molecular layers of water, which would imply a thickness of the order of approximately 50 Å.   In view of the high value of the calculated thickness of the water layer, it seems reasonable to assume that there are some water-absorbing voids present in the composite system, and clustering seems to be a real phenomenon in composite films.

The clustering of water molecules in the composite films can result if there are microcavities in the matrix phase or if imperfect adhesion between the matrix and filler phase exists along the interface between the glass ribbon and cellulose acetate.   Mehta et al.[9] used a similar composite system to measure diffusion of permeant gases and observed good adhesion between the glass ribbon and cellulose acetate.   However, with water as the diffusant, the cellulose acetate matrix phase has a tendency to swell and this swelling action results in internal compression–extension stresses.[16]   These stresses can cause craze cracking, and water can enter these cracks from which attack then occurs on the glass ribbon bond. A quantitative analysis of the clustering can be made using eq. (4) and Figures 3–6.   The amount of water present as clusters can be determined by subtracting the solubility of the unfilled matrix material (film M) from the reduced solubility of the composite film (films N, O, P and Q) at any given temperature and relative pressure (Figs. 3–6).

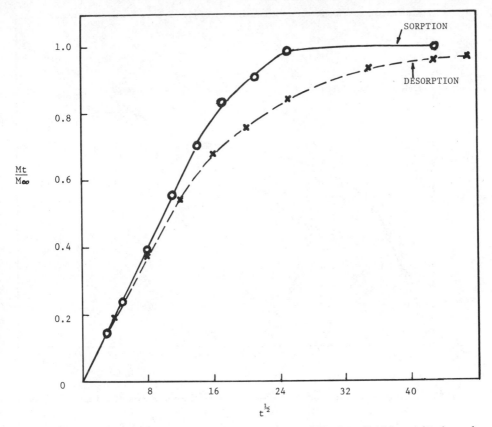

Fig. 9. Sorption–desorption curves for compression-molded film (43 mil thick, weight of sample 8.327 g) at 39.8°C and 35 mm Hg of water vapor pressure.

Such an analysis was done for films N and Q at 56.3°C (Fig. 5), and these data are plotted in Figure 7 according to eq. (4) wherein

$$C_H = \frac{C_h'bp}{1 + bp} \qquad (12)$$

or

$$\frac{1}{C_H} = \frac{1}{C_h'} + \frac{1}{c_h'b} \cdot \frac{1}{P} \qquad (13)$$

The plots of $1/C_H$ versus $1/P$ are straight lines, and the clustering of water in composites can be approximated by the nonlinear Langmuir expression.

The sorption data for both unfilled as well as filled films were obtained by observing the uptake M_t of the diffusant in the film in time t. The uptake data are plotted in terms of reduced uptake $M_t/M\infty$ versus $(t)^{1/2}$, where M_∞ is the equilibrium sorption obtained theoretically after infinite time. The value of D can be deduced from an observation of the initial gradient of the graph of M_t/M_∞ as a function of $(t/l^2)^{1/2}$. Similarly, with suitable interpretation of M_t and M_∞, desorption data can also be used to determine the diffusion coefficient. Since both sorption and desorption data were obtained for a concentration in-

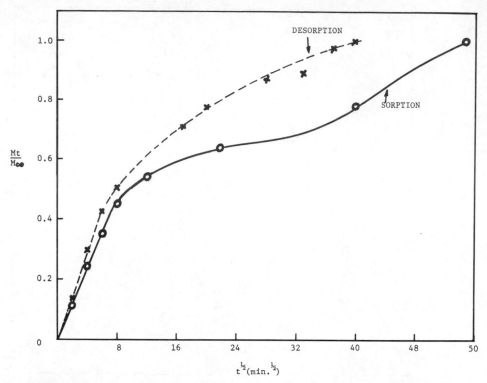

Fig. 10. Sorption–desorption curves for glass ribbon-reinforced plastic film (film N, weight of sample 5 g) at 39.8°C and 36 mm Hg of water vapor pressure.

terval of $0 \rightarrow C_{final}$, the integral diffusion coefficients at the concentration C_f were calculated as follows:

$$D = \frac{1}{C_f} \int_0^{C_f} D dc = \frac{\pi}{32} (K_s{}^2 + K_d{}^2) \tag{14}$$

where K_s and K_d are initial slopes for sorption and desorption, respectively. The diffusion coefficients thus calculated are shown in Table III. Typical sorption–desorption kinetics for the biaxially oriented cast film (film L), compression-molded film (film M), and glass ribbon-reinforced film (film N) are shown in Figures 8–10. While the sorption–desorption curves for the compression-molded film indicated Fickian behavior, the sorption–desorption curves for films L and N showed anomalous behavior. The anomalies are of two types: (a) the sorption curves assume a sigmoidal shape, and (b) desorption becomes faster than sorption. Blackladder et al.[17] explained these anomalies by invoking the effect of internal stress in a film approaching equilibrium from an initially solvent-free state. Sorption of water into initially dry biaxially oriented film and glass-reinforced film will result in an attempt by the outer regions to swell. But the inner matrix phase, especially the portion which is relatively immobilized by adhesion to the glass ribbon, will tend to restrain the increase in volume. This can have a twofold effect. First, swelling of the outer regions of the specimen will cause the core to be stretched. Second, the surface concentration will not immediately reach the true equilibrium value appropriate to unconstrained polymer.

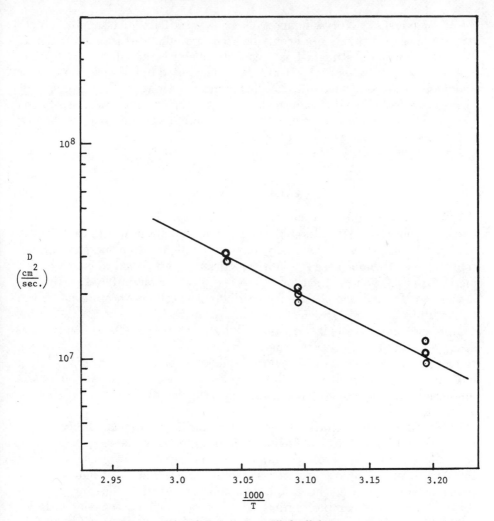

Fig. 11. Water diffusivity in unfilled cellulose acetate.

In the case of compression-molded film, most of the built-in stresses of the cast film were released during molding, and the sorption–desorption kinetics were subject to relatively less internal stress effects. Crank,[14] from his studies of anomalous diffusion, concluded that compression–extension effects caused by internal stresses lead to sigmoidal curves and this effect manifests itself more in the sorption curve than the desorption curve.

The diffusion data for unfilled cellulose acetate film plotted as $\ln D$ versus $1/T$ (Fig. 11) shows a straight-line relationship which is indicative of the exponential activated process described by Fick's law of diffusion. The diffusion data for glass ribbon-reinforced films were very scattered (Table III) and presented irregular trends. Whereas, according to eqs. (8)–(10), the diffusivities for filled films should be far lower than the corresponding diffusivities for the unfilled films due to tortuosity effects and the immobilization effects, they were actually found either equal to or greater than the unfilled systems. Because of significant internal stress effects, sorption–desorption data for filled films become difficult to use for determining diffusion coefficients. However, the initial portions of the M_t/M_∞ versus $t^{1/2}$ curves for most filled films were found to be approximately straight lines, and their slopes could be used to predict diffusion coefficients. The reason for initial straight-line behavior probably is that all composite films had cellulose acetate on both sides of the film exposed to the water vapor, and Fickian behavior is expected for unfilled material. However, as the process of sorption proceeds, the diffusant molecules meet regions close to glass ribbons where polymer segments rearrange themselves more slowly, thus making changes in the time dependence of the diffusion process. This complicates any further analysis of the data.

CONCLUSIONS

1. While the equilibrium solubility coefficients of filled systems should decrease in proportion to the glass ribbon content in view of the impermeable nature of glass ribbons, they were actually found to be higher than those of unfilled cellulose acetate, and these solubility coefficients were found to increase with increase in filler volume fraction. Three explanations are offered for this behavior: (a) The adhesion between glass ribbon and cellulose acetate matrix can fail, resulting in the adsorption of water on hydrophilic glass ribbons. (b) During compression molding of glass ribbon–cellulose acetate film, the solubility characteristics of the cellulose acetate matrix change. (c) The presence of glass ribbon can constrain the free and uniform flow of cellulose acetate in all directions during molding; this may result in incomplete wetting between the filler and matrix phase and can cause voids along the interface, which provide additional sites for absorption of water.

2. The integral diffusion coefficients were calculated from an observation of the initial gradient of the plot of reduced uptake of water by the sample, $(M_t/M\infty$, as a function of $(t/l^2)^{1/2}$ both for unfilled and filled systems. Diffusion of water through unfilled cellulose acetate was found to be a simple Fickian activated process and showed very little concentration dependence. The sorption–desorption kinetics of composite films exhibited non-Fickian behavior with two distinct anomalies: (a) the sorption curves assume a sigmoidal shape, and (b) desorption becomes faster than sorption.

The anomalies are typical of internal stress phenomena which make prediction of diffusivities from sorption kinetics difficult.

This work is part of research conducted by the Monsanto/Washington University Association sponsored by the Advanced Research Projects Agency (ARPA), Department of Defense, and the Office of Naval Research under Contract Number N00014-67-C-0218.

References

1. L. E. Nielsen, *J. Macromol. Sci. (Chem.)*, **A1** (5), (1967).
2. D. S. Ruhman and E. M. Wu, *ACS Polym. Prepr.*, **14**, 475 (1973).
3. C. H. Shen and G. S. Springer, *J. Composite Mater.*, **10**, (January 1976).
4. R. M. Barrer, *Trans. Faraday Soc.*, **35**, 628 (1939).
5. A. S. Michaels and H. J. Bixler, *J. Polym. Sci.*, **L**, 393 (1961).
6. A. S. Michaels, W. R. Vieth, and J. A. Barrie, *J. Appl. Phys.*, **34**, 13 (1963).
7. A. S. Michaels, W. R. Vieth, and J. A. Barrie, *J. Appl. Phys.*, **34**, 13 (1963).
8. R. M. Barrer, J. A. Barrie, and M. G. Rogers, *J. Polym. Sci. A*, **1**, 2565 (1963).
9. C. H. Klute, *J. Appl. Polym. Sci.*, **1**, 340 (1959).

10. H. J. Bixler and A. S. Michaels, *J. Polym. Sci.*, **L**, 393 (1961).

11. B. S. Mehta, A. T. DiBenedetto, and J. L. Kardos, *Int. J. Polym. Mater.*, **3**, 269 (1975).

12. T. B. Lewis, Ribbon Reinforcements in Composite Materials, Reinforced Plastics/Composite Division, The Society of the Plastics Industry, Inc., 25th Annual Technical Conference, 1970.

13. B. S. Mehta, Gaseous Diffusion and Permeation in Fiber-Reinforced Composites, Ph.D. dissertation, Washington University, St. Louis, Mo., 1972.

14. S. Prager, and F. A. Long, *J. Am. Chem. Soc.*, **73**, 4072 (1951).

15. H. Yasuda and V. Stannet, *J. Polym. Sci.*, **57**, 907 (1962).

16. J. Crank, *J. Polym. Sci.*, **11**, 151 (1953).

17. D. A. Blackladder and J. S. Keniry, *J. Appl. Polym. Sci.*, **18**, 699 (1974).

JOURNAL OF APPLIED POLYMER SCIENCE   VOL. 21, 3129–3137 (1977)

The Specific Volume of Poly(4-methylpentene-1) as a Function of Temperature (30°–320°C) and Pressure (0–2000 kg/cm²)

PAUL ZOLLER, *Neu-Technikum Buchs, Kunststofflabor, CH-9470 Buchs, Switzerland*

Synopsis

The dependence of the specific volume of a commercial sample of poly(4-methylpentene-1) (Mitsui TPX, RT-20, abbr. PMP) on temperature (30°–320°C) and pressure (0–2000 kg/cm²) has been determined. Results are reported in tabular form and as approximate fits, making use of the Tait equation. The data show that the crystalline melting transition of this type of PMP is completed at 235°C under zero pressure and gives indication of a glass transition temperature T_g at about 20°C at $p = 0$. Its approximate pressure dependence is given by $dT_g/dp \approx 0.015°C\ kg^{-1}\ cm^2$. The zero pressure results on the melting and glass transitions are in agreement with DTA results. The p-v-T data, quenching experiments, and a determination of the crystalline unit cell (tetragonal, $a = b = 18.70$ Å, $c = 13.54$ Å) confirm earlier work indicating that the room-temperature crystalline specific volume of PMP is greater than the amorphous specific volume. This unusual density behavior persists to a temperature of 50–60°C at $p = 0$ and to temperatures as high as 230–240°C under a pressure of 2000 kg/cm².

INTRODUCTION

Hydrostatic pressure is known to have a profound influence on the physical properties of polymers. Two recent reviews[1,2] have summarized the effects of hydrostatic pressure on the specific volume (equation of state), glass and melting transitions, crystallization, and mechanical properties of polymers. A thorough knowledge of these and other phenomena (e.g., the specific heat, thermal conductivity) at high pressures is necessary for our understanding of polymeric materials, both from the fundamental point of view of the polymer scientist and from the point of view of the plastics engineer, since polymers are almost always processed at high temperatures and pressures, and in use they are often subjected to states of stress possessing a strong hydrostatic component.

One of the most fundamental properties affected by hydrostatic pressure is the specific volume. Although the specific volume is one of the simplest properties to be measured at high pressures and temperatures, relatively little work has been reported using equipment which provides a truly hydrostatic state of stress even for samples in the solid state. The first apparatus to accomplish this was, to our knowledge, that of Parks and Richards,[3] who used it to furnish data on low-density polyethylene (LDPE). Hellwege et al.[4] have described an apparatus capable of pressures to 2000 bar and temperatures to 250°C. It was used to provide data[4] on polystyrene (PS) to 250°C, poly(methyl methacrylate)

3129

(PMMA) to 140°C, poly(vinyl chloride) (PVC) to 100°C, LDPE to 175°C, and high-density polyethylene (HDPE) to 203°C. Heydemann and Guicking[5] reported measurements between −80° and 150°C and pressures to 1000 bar on plasticized PVC and on PMMA. While the pressure in these measurements was truly hydrostatic, the volume changes were calculated from the length changes of a molded sample, thereby assuming the sample to be isotropic. Reliable measurements on a melt do not seem to be possible with this type of apparatus because irreversible length changes (at constant volume) are easily possible in the melt. More recently, Quach and Simha[6] have described equipment capable of very precise p-v-T measurements between 0° and 200°C and pressures to 2000 bar. It has been used to provide data on PS[6] and poly(orthomethylstyrene),[6] isotactic and atactic PMMA,[7] several methacrylates,[8] LDPE,[8] HDPE,[8] and PE of very high molecular weight.[8] We have recently described an apparatus[10] basically similar to the design of Quach and Simha,[6] but having an extended temperature range to at least 380°C (revised upward from the 350°C given in ref. 10) at pressures to 2200 bar. We have already reported data on two polystyrenes.[9,10] This work on poly(4-methylpentene-1) continues the reports on p-v-T properties from our laboratory.

EXPERIMENTAL

Samples

We used a commercial grade of poly(4-methylpentene-1) (PMP), manufactured by Mitsui Petrochemical Industries, Japan, and designated "TPX" RT-20. It is basically an extrusion grade but also used for some injection moldings. In its commercial form, PMP is a light (density ≈ 0.83 g/cm^3), partially crystalline (isotactic) material with a crystalline melting point of about 240°C according to the manufacturer. Despite its crystallinity, it is completely transparent. Pellets were used after they had been thoroughly dried and annealed for about 4 hr at 150°C under a dry N$_2$ atmosphere.

P-v-T Measurements

The apparatus and evaluation procedure for obtaining pressure-volume-temperature (p-v-T) data have been described in detail.[10] The sample (1–2 g) is contained in a rigid sample cell one end of which is closed by a flexible metal bellows. The space in the cell not taken up by the sample is filled with mercury under vacuum. This sample cell is mounted in a pressure vessel, and pressures to 2200 kg/cm^2* are applied with a hand pump using silicon oil as the pressure-transmitting fluid. The pressure is transmitted to the contents of the sample cell by the flexible bellows, which expands until the pressure in the sample cell equals the applied pressure. The displacement of the bellows is measured by a linear variable differential transducer the coil of which is mounted outside the pressure vessel. This displacement can be converted into a volume change of the sample, making use of the cross-sectional area of the bellows and the (known)

---

* We use pressure in units of kg/cm^2 (kilograms-force per cm^2, abbreviated kp/cm^2 in the German literature). Other units may be obtained as follows: 1 kg/cm^2 = 9.80665 × 10^4 N/m^2 = 0.980665 bar = 0.967841 atm = 14.223 psi.

p-v-T properties of the confining mercury. This apparatus is capable of measuring specific volumes of polymers between 30° and 380°C at pressures to 2200 kg/cm^2 with an accuracy of 0.001–0.002 cm^3/g.

Measurements on PMP were performed along 22 isotherms (spaced 10° to 20°C apart) between 30° and 320°C and at pressure increments of 100 kg/cm^2 up to 2000 kg/cm^2. The lowest pressure at which measurements were taken was 100 kg/cm^2. The results quoted for $p = 0$ are therefore extrapolated. This procedure yields more reliable values for the specific volume at $p = 0$, because of some outgassing observed in most polymers at high temperatures.[10]

Determination of Sample Specific Volume

The absolute specific volume of the polymer at one temperature must be known for the evaluation of the data from the p-v-T apparatus.[10] For PMP the room-temperature specific volume is determined as follows: Water and glycerol are mixed until the sample stays suspended in the liquid. The specific volume of this mixture is equal to the specific volume of the sample, and it is determined by weighing an accurately known volume. This procedure is believed to yield the specific volume to ±0.0003 cm^3/g, since a change in liquid density of this magnitude will cause the sample to rise or sink at an easily observable rate.

X-Ray Determination of Crystalline Density

Crystalline reflections from a compression-molded, annealed plate of PMP were scanned in a Philips counter diffractometer. Cu K_α radiation ($\lambda = 1.5418$ Å) was used in conjunction with a Ni filter and pulse-height discriminator. Both the scattering and the divergence slit were set at $1/4$°. The scanning speed was $1/4$°/min. The goniometer scale was calibrated by accurately setting the zero of the scale (to within 0.02°) and by setting the (111) reflection from a silicon calibration sample to an angle $2\theta = 28.47° \pm 0.02°$, corresponding to $d_{111} = 3.1354$ Å.

Differential Thermal Analysis (DTA)

All DTA determinations of the glass transition temperature, the melt temperature range, and the enthalpy of melting were performed on a Mettler TA 2000(B) quantitative thermal analysis system. A dry nitrogen blanket of 15 ml/min was used in all runs.

RESULTS AND DISCUSSION

The specific volume of PMP as a function of pressure and temperature is reported in Table I. The isobars at 0, 500, 1000, 1500, and 2000 kg/cm^2, obtained by crossplotting the appropriate data from Table I, are shown in Figure 1. Individual data points are shown for the 1000 kg/cm^2 isobar in order to indicate the temperatures at which measurements were taken and to give an idea of the scatter in the data.

We first turn the data at zero pressure. The specific volume at 22°C and $p = 0$ is 1.203 cm^3/g. The specific volume-versus-temperature curve at zero

TABLE I
Measured Specific Volumes Versus Temperature and Pressure. Line A Separates Points Belonging to the (Possibly Supercooled) Melt

p (kg/cm²)	TEMP.(°C) 29.0	37.9	49.7	61.1	72.9	83.8	94.6	103.5	115.4	135.1	154.8
0	1.2080	1.2119	1.2182	1.2247	1.2325	1.2377	1.2462	1.2509	1.2595	1.2721	1.2858
100	1.2026	1.2057	1.2120	1.2185	1.2256	1.2308	1.2384	1.2431	1.2502	1.2621	1.2750
200	1.1972	1.1995	1.2058	1.2123	1.2186	1.2238	1.2303	1.2346	1.2417	1.2528	1.2642
300	1.1917	1.1941	1.1996	1.2061	1.2124	1.2169	1.2229	1.2277	1.2340	1.2452	1.2549
400	1.1871	1.1886	1.1942	1.2000	1.2063	1.2107	1.2168	1.2207	1.2271	1.2375	1.2465
500	1.1825	1.1840	1.1892	1.1946	1.2009	1.2046	1.2107	1.2146	1.2202	1.2299	1.2389
600	1.1779	1.1794	1.1842	1.1896	1.1956	1.1992	1.2045	1.2085	1.2141	1.2231	1.2321
700	1.1732	1.1748	1.1792	1.1846	1.1902	1.1939	1.1992	1.2028	1.2084	1.2170	1.2254
800	1.1694	1.1710	1.1750	1.1800	1.1852	1.1894	1.1939	1.1975	1.2027	1.2114	1.2194
900	1.1656	1.1664	1.1704	1.1755	1.1807	1.1840	1.1890	1.1926	1.1974	1.2058	1.2134
1000	1.1618	1.1626	1.1666	1.1709	1.1761	1.1795	1.1844	1.1872	1.1929	1.2006	1.2074
1100	1.1588	1.1596	1.1628	1.1667	1.1720	1.1749	1.1795	1.1827	1.1876	1.1953	1.2022
1200	1.1549	1.1558	1.1586	1.1625	1.1674	1.1704	1.1754	1.1782	1.1831	1.1909	1.1978
1300	1.1519	1.1528	1.1552	1.1588	1.1636	1.1666	1.1713	1.1737	1.1790	1.1865	1.1926
1400	1.1481	1.1489	1.1518	1.1556	1.1599	1.1629	1.1675	1.1700	1.1749	1.1817	1.1883
1500	1.1451	1.1459	1.1484	1.1516	1.1561	1.1584	1.1634	1.1659	1.1704	1.1777	1.1839
1600	1.1420	1.1429	1.1451	1.1482	1.1524	1.1546	1.1593	1.1618	1.1663	1.1733	1.1795
1700	1.1390	1.1399	1.1417	1.1445	1.1486	1.1509	1.1556	1.1581	1.1626	1.1696	1.1751
1800	1.1360	1.1369	1.1387	1.1415	1.1457	1.1479	1.1518	1.1544	1.1585	1.1652	1.1716
1900	1.1334	1.1339	1.1357	1.1385	1.1427	1.1446	1.1485	1.1515	1.1548	1.1616	1.1680
2000	1.1307	1.1309	1.1327	1.1356	1.1398	1.1413	1.1452	1.1470	1.1512	1.1580	1.1636

p (kg/cm²)	TEMP.(°C) 176.5	196.3	206.8	217.7	228.9	A 240.5	250.5	265.9	285.6	303.8	318.9
0	1.3023	1.3209	1.3323	1.3479	1.3675	1.3899	1.4003	1.4137	1.4323	1.4530	1.4738
100	1.2899	1.3061	1.3151	1.3275	1.3454	1.3679	1.3774	1.3881	1.4047	1.4222	1.4397
200	1.2783	1.2921	1.3004	1.3103	1.3258	1.3467	1.3554	1.3673	1.3819	1.3978	1.4129
300	1.2684	1.2806	1.2880	1.2964	1.3095	1.3295	1.3379	1.3485	1.3632	1.3767	1.3902
400	1.2592	1.2706	1.2773	1.2840	1.2955	1.3152	1.3219	1.3326	1.3469	1.3588	1.3707
500	1.2508	1.2615	1.2674	1.2737	1.2840	1.3016	1.3084	1.3183	1.3314	1.3425	1.3536
600	1.2433	1.2532	1.2587	1.2641	1.2724	1.2893	1.2961	1.3052	1.3175	1.3287	1.3390
700	1.2365	1.2456	1.2508	1.2558	1.2633	1.2786	1.2850	1.2937	1.3061	1.3164	1.3260
800	1.2298	1.2381	1.2433	1.2475	1.2550	1.2687	1.2747	1.2835	1.2946	1.3042	1.3138
900	1.2234	1.2314	1.2366	1.2404	1.2467	1.2596	1.2652	1.2732	1.2848	1.2940	1.3024
1000	1.2179	1.2247	1.2299	1.2333	1.2392	1.2513	1.2570	1.2649	1.2753	1.2846	1.2926
1100	1.2119	1.2188	1.2232	1.2274	1.2325	1.2439	1.2487	1.2559	1.2663	1.2756	1.2832
1200	1.2060	1.2137	1.2181	1.2215	1.2259	1.2356	1.2412	1.2484	1.2581	1.2666	1.2746
1300	1.2008	1.2078	1.2122	1.2156	1.2200	1.2289	1.2330	1.2410	1.2511	1.2592	1.2665
1400	1.1965	1.2027	1.2075	1.2105	1.2141	1.2222	1.2271	1.2336	1.2441	1.2518	1.2591
1500	1.1918	1.1976	1.2020	1.2054	1.2090	1.2156	1.2205	1.2269	1.2371	1.2445	1.2518
1600	1.1870	1.1933	1.1970	1.2003	1.2040	1.2101	1.2146	1.2211	1.2305	1.2379	1.2448
1700	1.1835	1.1890	1.1927	1.1952	1.1989	1.2047	1.2088	1.2153	1.2247	1.2313	1.2383
1800	1.1792	1.1847	1.1880	1.1910	1.1938	1.1992	1.2029	1.2095	1.2189	1.2256	1.2322
1900	1.1752	1.1804	1.1841	1.1863	1.1895	1.1937	1.1979	1.2045	1.2131	1.2198	1.2264
2000	1.1713	1.1769	1.1799	1.1824	1.1853	1.1895	1.1924	1.1994	1.2082	1.2141	1.2207

pressure shows a very distinct discontinuity in slope at about 235°C. This is the crystalline melting point of PMP, or, better, the end of the crystalline melting range, since no real discontinuity in specific volume is observed. DTA gives values of 235°–236°C for the end of the melting interval at heating rates of 1°, 5°, and 10°C/min in complete agreement with the p-v-T data. DTA also indi-

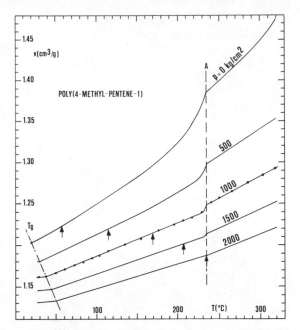

Fig. 1. Selected isobars, spaced 500 kg/cm² apart, in the p-v-T relationship of poly(4-methyl-pentene-1). The line marked T_g gives the approximate dependence of the glass transition temperature on pressure. The line marked A is an isotherm placed through the end of the zero-pressure melting interval. Arrows denote the approximate intersections of the melt isobars with the measured isobars of the sample, i.e., the points in the p-v-T diagram at which crystalline and amorphous regions have the same specific volume.

cates that melting starts at about 170°–180°C. The melting enthalpy is about 5.5–6 cal/g, the uncertainty resulting from different ways of placing the DTA baseline.

If the $p = 0$ isobar of the melt is extrapolated to lower temperatures in order to get an estimate for the amorphous specific volume at room temperature, one gets the unusual result that this extrapolated melt isobar intersects the measured isobar of the sample between 50° and 60°C. If this extrapolation is meaningful, this means that the crystalline specific volume at room temperature is greater than the amorphous specific volume, and it also means that at 50° to 60°C the amorphous and crystalline specific volumes are equal and equal to the specific volume of the sample. This unusual behavior of the specific volume has already been reported on noncommercial PMP samples.[11–13] In order to check this result further, we determined the specific volume of quenched samples. There was a small but definite decrease in specific volume for samples quenched into ice water or liquid nitrogen: annealed samples had a specific volume of 1.203 cm³/g, and the quenched samples gave values between 1.200 and 1.197 cm³/g. The quenched samples still showed very definite x-ray crystallinity. The amorphous specific volume at 22°C therefore must be lower than 1.197 cm³/g.

X-Ray diffraction data were found to be consistent with a tetragonal unit cell with $a = b = 18.70 \pm 0.06$ Å and $c = 13.54 \pm 0.04$ Å. Assuming that the unit cell contains 28 repeat units,[11] the crystalline specific volume is 1.209 ± 0.01 cm³/g, a value which is indeed slightly higher than our sample specific volume. Table II gives the details of the evaluation of the x-ray pattern. Table III compares

TABLE II
Evaluation of X-Ray Diffraction Data of PMP

Obs. angle 2θ	Index	Obs. spac.,[a] Å	Calc. spac.,[a,b] Å
9.50	200	9.31	9.35
12.43	211	7.12	7.12
13.42	220	6.60	6.61
16.37	311	5.41	5.42
16.80	212	5.28	5.26
18.32	321	4.84	4.84
20.65	411	4.30	4.30
21.30	420	4.17	4.18
21.65	322	4.10	4.12

[a] Using λ = 1.5418 Å.
[b] For tetragonal unit cell with $a = b$ = 18.70 Å, c = 13.54 Å.

TABLE III
Structural and Other Data of PMP Samples Used in Different Investigations

Reference	$a = b$, Å	c, Å	Cryst. density, g/cm^3	Sample density, g/cm^3	Melt. point,[a] °C
Natta et al.[14]		13.85		0.831	200–205
Frank et al.[11]	18.66	13.80	0.813	0.847	202–206
Griffith and Ranby[12]			0.828	0.830–0.838	247–250
Litt[13]	18.50	13.76	0.832		
This work	18.70	13.54	0.827	0.831	235–236

[a] Other workers have reported melting points of 228°C[15] and 235°C.[16]

our structural data with that of several laboratory-made samples.[11–14] It is found that our value of a is somewhat larger than that of the other investigations, the value of c somewhat smaller. Note, however, that the samples of the other investigations also showed different melting points. Altogether, we may safely conclude that the crystalline specific volume of this commercial PMP is indeed higher than the amorphous specific volume.

The specific volume $v(0,T)$ at zero pressure can be fitted to polynomials of the form

$$v(0,T) = A_0 + A_1T + A_2T^2 + A_3T^3 + A_4T^4 + \cdots. \tag{1}$$

The following coefficients, obtained by least-squares fitting, reproduce the data in Table I to better than 0.001 cm^3/g over the temperature ranges indicated: For $T <$ 235°C, i.e., for the partially crystalline material, including all of the melting interval, A_0 = 1.2044 cm^3 g^{-1}, A_1 = -1.430×10^{-4} cm^3 g^{-1} °C^{-1}, A_2 = 1.154 $\times$ 10^{-5} cm^3 g^{-1} °C^{-2}, A_3 = -7.315×10^{-8} cm^3 g^{-1} °C^{-3}, and A_4 = 1.705 $\times$ 10^{-10} cm^3 g^{-1} °C^{-4}. For $T >$ 235°C, i.e., for the melt, A_0 = 1.4075 cm^3 g^{-1}, A_1 = -9.095 $\times$ 10^{-4} cm^3 g^{-1} °C^{-1}, and A_2 = 3.497 $\times$ 10^{-6} cm^3 g^{-1} °C^{-2}.

Turning now to the pressure results, we first note that the $p \neq 0$ isobars extrapolated from the melt again intersect the measured isobars of the solid sample. The intersections are marked with an arrow in Figure 1. At these intersections, the crystalline and amorphous specific volumes are again equal (and equal to

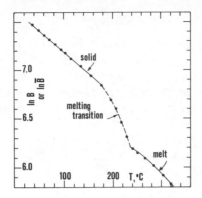

Fig. 2. Temperature dependence of the Tait parameter of PMP. For the solid state and the melting transition, the plot gives ln $\overline{B}$, i.e., the average of the Tait parameter along an isotherm.

the specific volume of the sample), and the points marked with an arrow therefore represent a few isolated points of the p-v-T relations of completely amorphous or completely crystalline PMP. We also note that there is a break in the $p >$ 1000 kg/cm^2 isobars at low temperatures. This break marks the glass transition under pressure.

Extrapolating back to $p = 0$, one obtains a zero-pressure glass transition temperature of about 20°C, in essential agreement with DTA work, which shows a glass transition between 15° and 25°C at a scanning rate of 5°C/min. The approximate pressure dependence of T_g is given by $dT_g/dp \approx 0.015°C/kg/cm^2$. This pressure dependence, while quite uncertain due to the small number of data points below the glass transition line, is much smaller than that found for polystyrene glasses.[4,6,9,10] A pressure dependence of the melting temperature cannot be obtained from these measurements: when the melt is pressurized, no solidification is effected in the time interval required for completion of the measurements along one isotherm (about 10 min). This must be due to the very slow crystallization rate at high temperatures and pressures. All data points to the right of isotherm A placed through the zero-pressure melting point, therefore, belong to the (possibly supercooled) melt.

For mathematical convenience, we have tried to represent our data by a mathematical expression. The so-called Tait equation has been found to yield a good representation of the volume changes along an isotherm for a number of polymers in the glassy state or in the melt.[6,8,9] It is generally written as

$$v(p,T) = v(0,T)\{1 - 0.0894 \ln [1 + p/B(T)]\} \tag{2}$$

where $B(T)$ is the temperature-dependent Tait parameter, and it is determined from each data point along an isotherm, using the zero-pressure specific volume for that isotherm. A value of $B(T)$ independent of pressure indicates that the Tait equation is a good fit to the data. In the solid state of PMP, i.e., up to about 175°C, where melting begins according to the DTA results, and in the melting range itself (175° to 235°C), the Tait parameter is not a constant, but rather increases slowly with pressure (maximum change along an isotherm, about 5%). This observation has also been made on different polyethylenes,[8] which are the only partially crystalline materials studied in terms of the Tait equation. For the melt ($T > 253°C$), the Tait parameter is constant along an isotherm $B(T)$ is usually found to be an exponentially decreasing function of temperature:[8,9]

$$B(T) = B_1 \exp(-B_2 T) \tag{3}$$

In Figure 2, we give a plot of $\ln B$ versus T. Below 235°C, we have plotted $\ln \overline{B}$, i.e., the natural logarithm of the average value of B along each isotherm. It can be seen that the average value of B follows an exponential temperature dependence up to 170° or 180°C, indicating once again that melting starts about here. In the melting range itself, the average value of B drops more steeply until a very distinctive break occurs at 235°C, the end of the melting range. Contrary to expectation, the temperature dependence is not exponential in the melt. A possible explanation for this might be the onset of thermal degradation at 270° or 280°C. The following least-squares fits represent the data in Figure 2:

(a)   Solid state (30°–175°C):

$$\overline{B}(T) = 2087 \exp(-4.533 \times 10^{-3}T)$$

(b)   Melting range (175°–235°):

$$\overline{B}(T) = 1093 + 4.130T - 2.8447 \times 10^{-2}T^2$$

(c)   Melt (235°–320°C):

$$B(T) = 377 + 2.176T - 7.1834 \times 10^{-3}T^2$$

where T is in °C, B and $\overline{B}$ in kg/cm^2. These coefficients substituted into eq. (2), together with the coefficients of the fits for the zero-pressure specific volume given above, reproduce the data of Table I to better than 0.0015 cm^3/g in the melt, to better than 0.003 cm^3/g in the solid state and to better than 0.005 cm^3/g in the melting range.

A comment might be added about the absolute value of $B(T)$ in the melt. The values drop from about 490–340 kg/cm^2 in the temperature range covered, which includes the melt-processing temperature range. These values are considerably lower than those of polystyrene[6,9] or polyethylene[8] in their respective processing ranges, which means that PMP melt, under typical processing conditions, is much more compressible than PS or PE melts. This follows immediately from the fact that the (isothermal) compressibility K may be expressed through the pressure independent Tait parameter B as follows:

$$K(p,T) = -\frac{1}{v}\left(\frac{\partial v}{\partial p}\right)_T = \frac{0.0894}{\{1 - 0.0894 \ln[1 + p/B(T)]\}\cdot[p + B(T)]} \tag{4}$$

In particular at $p = 0$,

$$K(0,T) = \frac{0.0894}{B(T)} \tag{5}$$

The author would like to thank Paul Schawalder for his competent assistance during the course of this work. The material used in this work was donated by Mitsui & Co. Europe GmbH.

References

1. K. D. Pae and S. K. Bhateja, *J. Macromol. Sci.*, **C13**, 1 (1975).
2. S. K. Bhateja and K. D. Pae, *J. Macromol. Sci.*, **C13**, 77 (1975).
3. W. B. Parks and R. B. Richards, *Trans. Faraday Soc.*, **45**, 203 (1949).
4. K. H. Hellwege, W. Knappe, and P. Lehmann, *Kolloid-Z.*, **183**, 110 (1962).
5. P. Heydemann and H. D. Guicking, *Kolloid-Z.*, **193**, 16 (1964).

6. A. Quach and R. Simha, *J. Appl. Phys.*, **42**, 4592 (1971).

7. A. Quach, P. S. Wilson, and R. Simha, *J. Macromol. Sci.*, **B9**, 533 (1974).

8. O. Olabisi and R. Simha, *Macromolecules*, **8**, 206 (1975).

9. P. Zoller, P. Bolli, E. Hersche, and U. Foppa, *Kunststoffe*, **66**, 363 (1976).

10. P. Zoller, P. Bolli, V. Pahud, and H. Ackermann, *Rev. Sci. Instrum.* **47**, 948 (1976).

11. F. C. Frank, A. Keller, and A. O'Connor, *Philos. Mag.*, **4**, 200 (1959).

12. J. H. Griffith and B. G. Rånby, *J. Polym. Sci.*, **44**, 369 (1960).

13. M. Litt, *J. Polym. Sci.*, **A1**, 2219 (1963).

14. G. Natta, P. Pino, G. Mazzanti, P. Corradini, and U. Giannini, *R. C. Accad. Lincei*, **19**, 397 (1955); G. Natta, P. Corradini, and I. W. Bassi, *R. C. Acad. Lincei*, **19**, 405 (1955).

15. K. R. Dunham, J. Vandenberghe, J. W. H. Faber, and L. E. Contois, *J. Polym. Sci.*, **A1**, 751 (1963).

16. F. P. Redding, *J. Polym. Sci.*, **21**, 547 (1956).

Received September 10, 1976

JOURNAL OF APPLIED POLYMER SCIENCE   VOL. 21, 3139–3145 (1977)

Polymerization of Organic Compounds in an Electrodeless Glow Discharge. VIII. Dependence of Plasma Polymerization of Acrylonitrile on Glow Characteristic

H. YASUDA and TOSHIHIRO HIROTSU,* *Polymer Research Laboratory, Chemistry and Life Sciences Division, Research Triangle Institute, Research Triangle Park, North Carolina 27709*

Synopsis

The effects of experimental conditions (i.e., flow rate, pressure, discharge wattage, and glow characteristics) on the plasma polymerization of acrylonitrile were investigated. It was found that the glow characteristic is highly dependent on both flow rate and discharge wattage and that the plasma polymerization depends strongly on the glow characteristic. However, when experimental conditions are selected to maintain a fully developed glow in the tail flame portion of rf discharge, plasma polymerization is independent of discharge wattage and pressure. The polymer deposition rate is linearly proportional to the monomer flow rate. The deviations from this ideal situation are generally attributable to incomplete glow or partial glow under conditions which caused the deviation. The "character" of the glow largely determines the chemistry of the system. Consequently, the properties of polymers formed under different glow characteristics are also different.

INTRODUCTION

In this series of studies on plasma polymerization, we have used the tail flame portion of glow discharge in a relatively simple tube reactor.[1,2] This kind of reactor has a definite advantage in that the accurate flow rate of monomers, which go through the entire volume of the reactor, can be easily measured. In bell-jar-type reactors, on the other hand, the monomer feed-in rate into the reactor does not generally correspond to the monomer flow rate in the plasma region, which is only a small portion of total volume of the apparatus.

In previous studies, 1–3 the discharge power to be used for a monomer was selected so that full glow could be maintained throughout the entire reaction tube at the highest pressure to be used in the experiment. This procedure was chosen based on the observation that the deposition of polymer occurs only on the surface that is exposed to the "glow." Some extent of polymer deposition also occurs onto the surface that is not directly in contact with the "glow;" however, its rate is several orders of magnitude smaller than that in the glow region, and such a polymer deposition is not considered in studies of polymer deposition rate.

Under conditions of full glow in the tail flame portion of an inductively coupled

* Present address: Research Institute for Polymers and Textiles, 4-1 Sawatari, Kanagawa-Ku, Yokohama 22, Japan.

rf discharge, the polymer deposition rates for most organic compounds investigated were found to be nearly independent of discharge power and to be linearly proportional to the monomer flow rate (within a range of experimental conditions).

The importance of the extent of glow was also observed in a study which employed a reaction tube that had a constriction.[4] The apparent intensity of glow in the constriction was much higher than that in the wide portion of the tube, and the deposition rate onto the wall of the smaller-diameter portion (constriction) was found to be higher also. This increase was attributed to the increase of the surface/volume ratio in the constriction, indicating that the polymer deposition rate itself is dependent on the surface/volume ratio. This implies that the deposition rate of polymer in a glow discharge is a system-dependent parameter and not a parameter unique to a monomer. Therefore, a deposition rate observed in a reaction system does not necessarily describe the deposition rates which will be observed in a different reactor.

An important aspect also found in the study[4] was that the increase of the deposition rate in the constriction is not due to the increase in the flow rate. Although the linear velocity increases in the constriction, the total number of monomer molecules passing through the constriction was identical to that in the wider portion of the reactor. This indicates that the characteristics of glow may also be an important factor, although the previous studies[1-3] showed that the deposition rate is nearly independent of the intensity of glow in the full glow region.

In this study, the effect of the glow characteristic was examined at various discharge power values and different flow rates. Acrylonitrile happened to be an ideal monomer for this study since the transition of partial glow to full glow could be observed within convenient ranges of both discharge power and flow rate in the standard reactor used in this series of studies.

EXPERIMENTAL

The flow rate of the monomer was determined by the following method. First, the entire system was evacuated to a pressure of <0.1 μm Hg. Then, without changing the opening of the stopcock which connects to the pump system, a steady-state monomer flow was established by adjusting the metering valve opening, and the pressure of the system was recorded. The stopcock in the downstream side of the reactor was then closed, and the increase in pressure was recorded as a function of time. From the initial rate of pressure increase (dp/dt) and the volume of the reactor V, the flow rate in cm^3(S.T.P.)/min was calculated.

After the determination of flow rate, the system pressure of the steady state was adjusted to 60 μm Hg by controlling the opening of the downstream-side stopcock. It was confirmed that the change in steady-state flow pressure did not cause change in the monomer flow rate within the range of conditions employed in this study.

The extent of glow was examined at each flow rate, simply by observing the glow at a given discharge wattage, while gradually increasing the discharge wattage up to 120 W and then while gradually decreasing it again. The threshold wattage which produces the glow that is fully extended in the entire tube was recorded. Below the threshold value, the flow is weakened and it does not fill

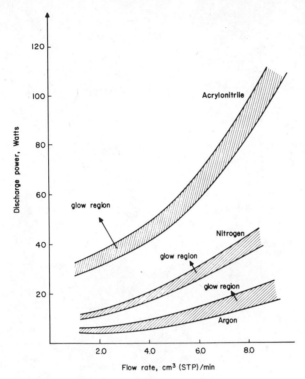

Fig. 1. Dependence of glow on flow rate and discharge power for acrylonitrile, nitrogen, and argon.

the entire volume. The threshold value can be measured only in a rough range; however, it is possible to determine the dependence of glow on the flow rate by using a wide band instead of a line, as shown in Figures 1 and 2.

The polymer deposition rate is determined by measuring the weight increase of small pieces of aluminum foil placed in a fixed position in the reaction tube.

RESULTS AND DISCUSSION

The dependence of glow of acrylonitrile on the flow rate is shown in Figure 1, where the same dependence is compared with nitrogen and argon plasma. With any set of combinations of flow rate and wattage which is located above each line shown by a wide band, the glow covers the entire reaction tube; below the line, the downstream side of the tube is not completely covered by a glow although discharge occurs. The area within a band may be considered as a transient glow region.

Deposition rates were measured under two series of experimental conditions. The wattage dependence was examined at a fixed flow rate of 5.8 cm^3(S.T.P.)/ min. This condition was chosen because it was known that in the full glow region the deposition rate is nearly independent of discharge wattage.[1,2] This condition is shown in Figure 2 by the line AB.

The dependence of deposition rate on flow rate was measured at 60, 100, and 130 W. The line CD in Figure 2 corresponds to the condition at 60 W.

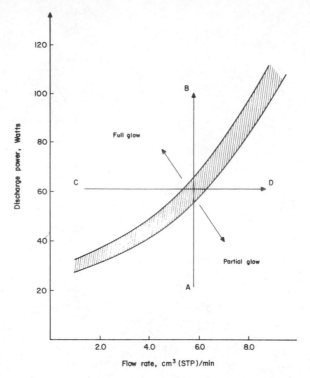

Fig. 2. Influence of glow on experiments: AB, variable discharge power at a fixed flow rate 5.8 cm³(S.T.P.)/min; CD, variable flow rate at a fixed discharge power (60 W).

The wattage dependence is shown in Figure 3, which shows clearly that (1) the apparent dependence of deposition rate on wattage observed at a fixed flow rate (without considering the effect of glow characteristic) may include the effect due to the character of glow, and (2) in fully developed glow the deposition rate is independent of the discharge wattage as previously reported.[1,2]

The flow rate dependence is shown in Figure 4. The results shown in the figure confirm that the deposition rate is proportional to the flow rate, as previously reported.[2] The deviation from this linear dependence on flow rate at higher flow rates is caused by the change from full glow (at low flow rates) to the incomplete glow at higher flow rates as the increase of flow rate crosses the line shown in Figure 2. When the discharge wattage is increased, the increase of flow rate no longer crosses the line within the limits of the experiment, and the deposition rate dependence on flow rate becomes normal.

The properties of polymers that are formed in both the normal glow and weak glow regions are also different. It is observed that the polymer formed in the normal glow region [5.6 cm³(S.T.P.)/min] is brown and insoluble in any solvent, but the polymer formed in the weak glow is light yellow and soluble in polar solvents such as acetone and dimethylformamide.

The dependence of plasma polymerization on the glow characteristic is also reflected in the pressure in the discharge. The system pressure of steady-state flow of the monomer, p_m, changes to a new system pressure of steady-state flow in the discharge, p_g, and the value of $\delta = p_g/p_m$ was taken as an important parameter related to the plasma polymerization.[2,3] In Figure 5, the p_g values are

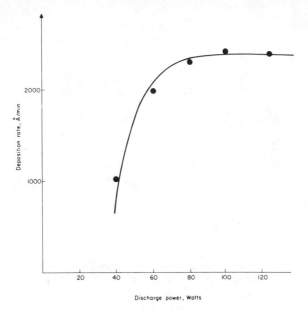

Fig. 3. Dependence of polymer deposition rate on discharge power at a fixed flow rate 5.8 cm³(S.T.P.)/min.

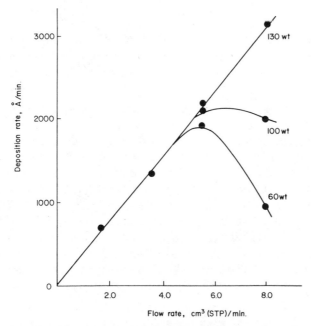

Fig. 4. Dependence of polymer deposition rate on monomer flow rate observed at a fixed discharge power (60 W).

plotted against the discharge wattage for various flow rates.   In this figure, the full glow region is below the line shown by a shaded band.   The results indicate that the value of δ is also dependent on the state of glow but becomes constant (independent of wattage) in the full glow region, although the value of δ itself is dependent on the flow rate.   The fact that δ is independent of wattage in the

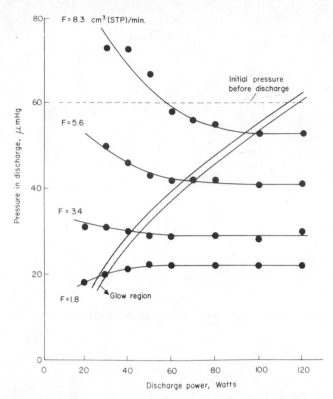

Fig. 5. Dependence of system pressure (of flow) in discharge of acrylonitrile on discharge power at different flow rates.

full glow region is consistent with the wattage-independent deposition rate in this (full glow) region.

The fact that the discharge pressures of acrylonitrile at $F = 8.5$ cm^3(S.T.P.)/min at low discharge powers (see Fig. 5) are above the initial pressure before discharge, p_m, indicates that the mechanism of polymer formation or chemistry involved in the partial glow is different from that in the full glow region. If the partial glow is the same glow as the full glow that occupies only a portion of the reactor, the pressure in the discharge should not increase from the initial pressure (p_m) in the case of acrylonitrile, which has a low δ value.[2] This discussion implies that polymer in the partial glow condition is formed by mechanisms different from those in the full glow region. The difference in properties mentioned above may be reflecting the difference in polymerization mechanisms.

CONCLUSIONS

Results shown in this study indicate that glow characteristic is an important factor to be considered in the study of plasma polymerization. The "character" of the glow largely determines the chemistry of the system. The glow itself is dependent on the combined factor of flow rate of monomer and discharge power. If the flow rate is increased, higher wattage is necessary in some cases to maintain the same glow characteristic. Therefore, the true dependence of polymer deposition rate as well as properties of polymers on operational parameters such as discharge power, flow rate of monomer, and the pressure of the system should be examined without changing the glow characteristic.

Any set of experimental conditions such as that shown by line AB or line CD in Figure 2, which crosses the glow characteristic line, involves an additional change of a parameter "glow characteristic," i.e., from "full glow" to "partial glow" or vice versa. For instance, if the change of glow characteristic is not taken into consideration, we might have reached an erroneous conclusion that the deposition rate of acrylonitrile decreases after passing the maximum as the flow rate increases, based on the experiments carried out at low discharge powers (e.g., 40 W).

The chemistry involved in the partial glow, at least with certain types of monomers, seems to be completely different from that which occurs under full glow conditions. Consequently, the properties of polymers formed in the "full glow" region and in the "incomplete glow" region are also different.

This study is supported in part by the Office of Water Research and Technology, U.S. Department of the Interior, Contract No. 14-30-3301, and by the National Heart and Lung Institute, NIH, U.S. Department of Health, Education and Welfare, Contract No. NIH-NO1-HB-3-2913.

References

1. H. Yasuda and C. E. Lamaze, *J. Appl. Polym. Sci.*, **15**, 2277 (1971).
2. H. Yasuda and C. E. Lamaze, *J. Appl. Polym. Sci.*, **17**, 1519 (1973).
3. H. Yasuda and C. E. Lamaze, *J. Appl. Polym. Sci.*, **17**, 1533 (1973).
4. H. Yasuda and T. Hsu, *J. Appl. Polym. Sci.*, **20**, 1769 (1976).

Received August 3, 1976
Revised September 29, 1976

JOURNAL OF APPLIED POLYMER SCIENCE   VOL. 21, 3147–3152 (1977)

Identification of the Luminescent Species in Low-Density Polyethylene

N. S. ALLEN, J. HOMER, and J. F. McKELLAR, *Department of Chemistry and Applied Chemistry, University of Salford, Salford, M5 4WT, Lancashire, United Kingdom,* and D. G. M. WOOD, *Research Department, I.C.I. Plastics Division Ltd., Welwyn Garden City, Herts., United Kingdom*

Synopsis

The luminescence properties of two low-density polyethylene samples are examined, one prepared using oxygen and the other using a benzoyl-based initiator as catalysts. The fluorescence emission from both samples is assigned to the presence of an impurity, α,β-unsaturated carbonyl of the enone type. The phosphorescence emissions, on the other hand, are different. The phosphorescence emission from the sample prepared using oxygen as an initiator is assigned to the presence of a dienone impurity chromophore, whereas the emission from the sample prepared using a benzoyl-based initiator is assigned to benzoic acid residues.

INTRODUCTION

Luminescence studies of commercial polyolefins have provided valuable information on the nature of light-absorbing chromophores believed to participate in sunlight-induced oxidation.[1–8] The earlier studies[1,2] showed a distinct difference between the phosphorescence emissions from low-density polyethylene and polypropylene samples. In the former case, the emission was attributed to the presence of mixtures of aromatic ketones and/or benzoic acid. Recently, in studies of the photo-oxidation of polypropylene we found no evidence of luminescent impurities other than simple enone and dienone unsaturated carbonyl groups.[4,5,8]

It is well known that organic peroxides, among which are benzoyl-based initiators, may be used in the manufacture of low-density polyethylene[9] and not in polypropylene, and the presence of the residual amounts of these initiators may be responsible for the difference in luminescence between the two polymers. To examine this possibility, we report on the emission properties of two low-density polyethylene samples specially made on a semitechnical scale, one using a typical benzoyl-based initiator and the other, without.

EXPERIMENTAL

Materials

Polyethylene samples, specially prepared using oxygen and *tert*-butylperbenzoate as polymerization initiators, were supplied by I.C.I. (Plastics Division) Ltd. They contained no commercial additives. Polypropylene powder, also

3147

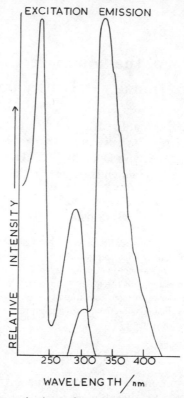

Fig. 1. Fluorescence excitation and emission spectra of polyethylene samples.

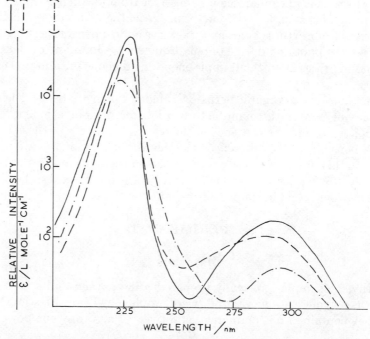

Fig. 2. Comparison of the fluorescence excitation spectra of polyethylene (—) and polypropylene (- - -) with the absorption spectrum of pent-3-ene-2-one in n-hexane (- · · · -).

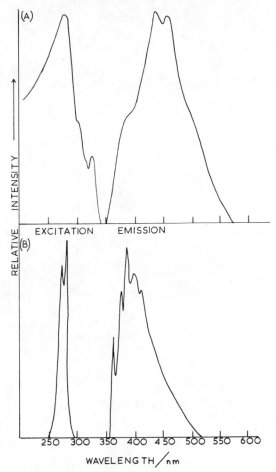

Fig. 3. Phosphorescence excitation and emission spectra of polyethylene chip samples, prepared using oxygen (A) and *tert*-butyl perbenzoate (B) as catalysts. Sample sensitivities were 100 and 3, respectively.

supplied by I.C.I. Ltd. and containing no commercial additives, was vacuum pressed into film (200 μ thick) at 190°C.

The benzoic acid was recrystallized twice from ethanol, and the n-hexane was of spectroscopic quality.

Instrumentation

Ultraviolet absorption spectra were recorded using a Unicam SP800 spectrophotometer.

Fluorescence and phosphorescence spectra were recorded using a corrected double-grating Hitachi Perkin–Elmer MPF-4 spectrofluorometer equipped with two R-446F photomultiplier tubes. Fully corrected excitation spectra were also obtained using the newly developed spectrofluorometer of Cundall et al.[2] (instrumental details to be published). Phosphorescence lifetime measurements were obtained by coupling the sample intensity signal from the fluorometer to a Tetronix DM-64 storage oscilloscope and chopping the exciting light with an electrically controlled shutter.

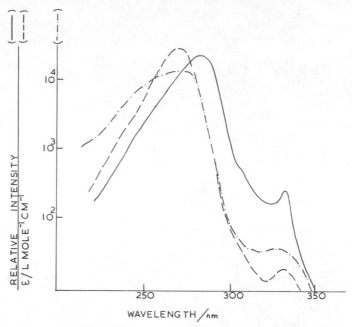

Fig. 4. Comparison of the phosphorescence excitation spectrum of polyethylene, prepared using oxygen as a catalyst (—) and polypropylene (- - -) with the absorption spectrum of *trans,trans,*-hexane-2,4-dienal in *n*-hexane (- · · · -).

RESULTS AND DISCUSSION

Fluorescence Spectra

The fluorescence excitation and emission spectra of both polyethylene samples were identical, and an example is shown in Figure 1. The spectrum is also similar to that obtained earlier for polypropylene[4,5,8] and is attributed to the presence of enone chromophoric impurity groups.

Figure 2 compares the fluorescence excitation spectrum of polyethylene with that of polypropylene and the absorption spectrum of a simple enone (pent-3-ene-2-one).[10] The excitation spectrum does not show the highly structured absorption in the region of 220–260 nm that is exhibited by polynuclear aromatic hydrocarbons.[4,5] Boustead and Charlesby[2] have suggested that a significant proportion of the fluorescence from polyethylene could be due to these species.

Phosphorescence Spectra

In contrast to the fluorescence spectra, the phosphorescence excitation and emission spectra of the polyethylene samples are significantly different and are shown in Figure 3. The phosphorescence emission lifetimes were 2.15 and 2.3 sec for the polyethylene samples prepared using oxygen (A) and *tert*-butyl perbenzoate (B) as initiators. Thus, it is clear from these results that the major phosphorescent chromophoric species in both polymers cannot be the same. In

TABLE I
Phosphorescence Lifetimes and Wave Numbers of Peaks in the Phosphorescence
Emission Spectra of Benzoic Acid and Polyethylene (B)

λ, nm	ν, cm$^{-1} \times 10^2$	$\Delta\nu$, cm$^{-1} \times 10^2$	τ, sec
368	271.7 ⎫		
380	263.2 ⎪		
390	255.8 ⎬ 8.22 ± 0.10		2.30
406	246.3 ⎪		
417	239.8 ⎭		

fact, the phosphorescence spectrum of the polyethylene sample prepared using oxygen is similar to that obtained earlier for polypropylene.[4,5,8] Here, the source of the emission was attributed to the presence of dienone chromophoric impurity groups. The phosphorescence spectrum of the sample prepared with *tert*-butyl perbenzoate, on the other hand, is similar to that of benzoic acid.[2]

Figure 4 compares the phosphorescence excitation spectrum of the former sample (A) with that of polypropylene and the absorption spectrum of a simple dienal (*trans,trans,*-hexa-2,4-dienal).[10] In Table I, we compare the phosphorescence excitation and emission λ_{max} of the latter sample (B) with that of benzoic acid in *n*-hexane. The lifetimes and magnitudes of the vibrational splittings of both emissions are also identical and are also given in Table I. It is evident from these results that the benzoic acid present in the polyethylene samples originates from the polymerization initiator *tert*-butyl perbenzoate.

Finally, the intensity of the phosphorescence emission from the polyethylene sample prepared using *tert*-butylperbenzoate was much greater than that from the sample prepared using only oxygen (Fig. 3). Thus, although the phosphorescence spectrum of the former sample may contain a component due to dienone chromophoric impurity groups, it is evidently overlaid by the much stronger emission from the benzoic acid.

CONCLUSIONS

Our work shows that polyethylene using a benzoyl-based initiator exhibits the presence of strongly phosphorescent benzoic acid residues. When the polymer does not contain the remains of this initiator, it exhibits the phosphorescence emission of dienone impurity units found in polypropylene. Further work in this area of study is in progress.

References

1. A. Charlesby and R. H. Partridge, *Proc. R. Soc. (London)*, **A283**, 312, 329 (1965).
2. I. Boustead and A. Charlesby, *Europ. Polym. J.*, **3**, 459 (1967).
3. N. S. Allen, J. F. McKellar, and G. O. Phillips, *Chem. Ind. (London)*, 300 (1974).
4. N. S. Allen, R. B. Cundall, M. W. Jones, and J. F. McKellar, *Chem. Ind. (London)*, 110 (1975).
5. N. S. Allen, J. Homer, and J. F. McKellar, *Chem. Ind. (London)*, 692 (1976).
6. N. S. Allen, J. F. McKellar, and G. O. Phillips, *J. Polym. Sci., Polym. Lett. Ed.*, **12**, 253 (1974).
7. N. S. Allen, J. Homer, J. F. McKellar, and G. O. Phillips, *Br. Polym. J.*, **7**, 11 (1975)

8. N. S. Allen, J. Homer, and J. F. McKellar, J. Appl. Polym. Sci., to appear.

9. H. F. Mark, in *Encyclopaedia of Polymer Science and Technology,* Vol. 3, 1965, p. 27. Interscience.

10. D. M. S. *U. V. Atlas of Organic Compounds,* Vol. 2, Buttterworth, London, (1966). Directory of Molecular Spectra.

Received October 14, 1976
Revised October 27, 1976

JOURNAL OF APPLIED POLYMER SCIENCE   VOL. 21, 3153–3165 (1977)

Evaluation of Surface-Active Agents by Mechanical Properties of Highly filled Composites

G. PERRAULT and G. DUCHESNE, *Defence Research Establishment, Valcartier, Courcelette, Québec, Canada GOA 1R0*

Synopsis

Mechanical spectroscopy is used to study the behavior under accelerated aging of surface-active additives in highly filled composites using a binder based on an hydroxyl-terminated polybutadiene. First, the mechanical properties of composites containing an amine polyester or an aziridine polyester are compared to those of a composite without any surface-active agents. It is thus confirmed that the aziridine polyester is a better surface-active agent than the amine polyester. The improvement in properties from the aziridine polyester is not affected by accelerated aging at 333°K. It was also established that composites with a mixture of both polyesters showed adequate initial mechanical properties and maintained those properties upon accelerated aging. Various hypotheses are proposed to explain the behavior of surface-active agents.

INTRODUCTION

In a previous article,[1] mechanical spectroscopy was used to evaluate the efficiency of various surface-active additives at the binder–filler interface of highly filled composites. Empirically, the surface agent efficiency was found to be inversely proportional to the height of the mechanical absorption peak at a temperature slightly higher than the glass transition temperature (T_g). This meant that the heights of tan δ and loss modulus (E'') peaks were inversely related to the quality of the solid–binder interface, a good interface being one where it is difficult to create voids.

It was thus suggested to relate the peak heights of tan δ and E'' to differences in void concentrations, ΔC, between composites 1 and 2 by the following equations:

$$\ln \frac{(\tan \delta_1)}{(\tan \delta_2)} = -k \, \Delta C \tag{1}$$

in which k is a constant.

Murayama and Lawton[2] have suggested an equation which predicts a lower tan δ for a composite with perfect adhesion than for an experimental composite composed of tire cord and rubber.

This efficiency criterium is used in this paper to study the behavior of surface-active additives in solid composite propellants. The effects of various experimental parameters on tan δ and E'' were briefly studied as the opportunity

3153

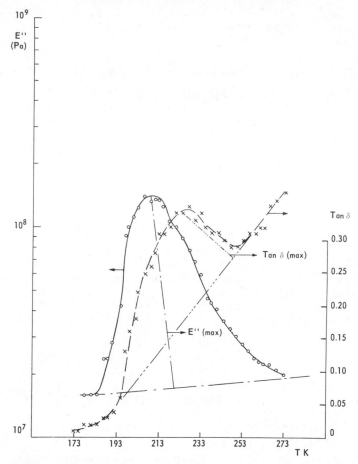

Fig. 1. Mechanical spectrum of sample 1.2 PAZ/0.2 PAM at 110 Hz.

arose from technological requirements, but the emphasis is put on the aging characteristics of composites as shown by the mechanical spectra. In each case, tensile mechanical properties measured on the Instron are discussed in relation to dynamic mechanical properties measured on the Rheovibron instrument.

EXPERIMENTAL

Preparations of composite propellants, measurements of dynamic mechanical properties with the Rheovibron instrument, and determinations of tensile mechanical properties on the Instron have been described.[1] However, in this work, the heights of the mechanical absorption maximum, given in various tables as tan δ(max) and E''(max) for the loss angle (δ) and the loss modulus (E''), respectively, were measured at the maximum perpendicularly to the baseline as shown on Figure 1. The temperature (T) is taken directly at the maximum of the peak.

Aging

For the aging tests on the Instron tensile machine, slabs of propellant in a polyethylene bag are kept in an oven at 60°C without any other control on the environment. After the desired period of time, "dumbbell" samples are punched and lamellae are machined for the Rheovibron trials.

Products

The prepolymer used to obtain the binder of the composites is the α,ω-hydroxypolybutadiene R-45M (HTPB) from Arco Chemical. The curing agent is the dimeric diisocyanate DDI 1410 from General Mills, Inc., and the plasticizer,

TABLE I
Binder Formulations

Sample	HTPB %	HTPB Batch	DDI, %	IDP, %	R
1.2 PAZ/0.2 PAM	63.9	006121	12.1	22.6	0.90
1.2 PAZ/0.2 PAM($-Fe_2O_3$)	63.9	006121	12.1	22.6	0.90
0.9 PAZ/0.3 PAM($-Fe_2O_3$)	64.0	006121	12.1	22.6	0.90
0.9 PAZ/0.2 PAM	62.9	212285	12.1	23.9	0.85
0.9 PAZ/0.2 PAM($344°$K)	62.9	212285	12.1	23.9	0.85
0.9 PAZ/0.2 PAM(Prep)	63.6	006121	11.4	23.9	0.85
0.6 PAZ/0.4 PAM($-Fe_2O_3$)	64.2	006121	12.2	22.6	0.90
0.6 PAZ/0.2 PAM($R = 0.8$)	63.5	212285	11.5	24.2	0.80
0.6 PAZ/0.2 PAM($R = 0.85$)	62.9	212285	12.1	24.2	0.85
0.6 PAZ/0.2 PAM($R = 0.9$)	62.3	212285	12.7	24.2	0.90
0.1 PAZ/0.2 PAM	62.3	212285	12.7	24.7	0.90
2.4 PAZ	63.6	006121	11.4	22.6	0.85
2.4 PAZ ($-Fe_2O_3$)	63.0	006121	12.0	22.6	0.90
0.4 PAM	64.7	006121	12.3	22.6	0.90
0 PAZ/0 PAM	65.0	006121	12.4	22.6	0.90

TABLE II
Influence of PAM or PAZ on Dynamic Mechanical Properties at 110 Hz

Sample	Aging, days	tan δ(max) $T, °K$	tan δ(max) —	E''(max) $T, °K$	E''(max) Pa $\times$ 10^{-8}
0 PAZ/0 PAM	0	230 ± 3	0.12 ± 0.01	220 ± 3	0.8 ± 0.11
	14	230	0.15	217	0.9
	28	236	0.12	216	0.8
	56	233	0.16	221	0.9
0.4 PAM	0	227 ± 1	0.17 ± 0.01	217 ± 1	1.0 ± 0.03
	14	229	0.17	218	1.0
	28	236	0.11	218	0.9
	56	228	0.14	218	0.75
2.4 PAZ($-Fe_2O_3$)	0	233	0.09 ± 0.01	220 ± 1	0.8 ± 0.08
	14	232	0.09	216	0.8
	28	240	0.09	217	0.7
	56	229	0.07	220	0.7

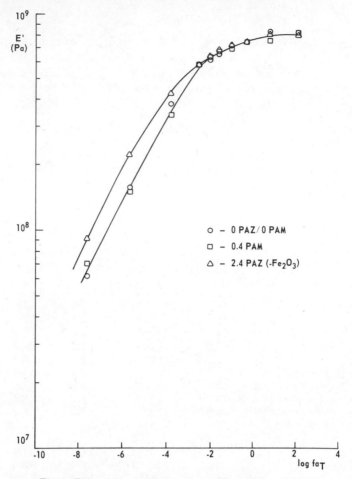

Fig. 2. Effect of surface agents on reduced storage moduli.

isodecyl pelargonate (IDA). Two surface-active agents were studied: one is an aziridine polyester (PAZ) which has been described in a U.S. patent,[3] the other is an amine polyester (PAM) which has been used in previous work.[4]

TABLE III
Influence of PAM or PAZ on Tensile Mechanical Properties at 22.8° C

Sample	Aging, days	σ_m, MPa	ϵ_m, %	E, MPa	ϵ_m/ϵ_r at 227.8° K
0 PAZ/0 PAM	0	0.37	16.5	4.59	7.0/7.5
	14	0.42	16.3	5.66	—
	28	0.40	15.3	5.44	8.5/9.0
	56	0.45	15.0	6.47	7.4/7.4
0.4 PAM	0	0.30	21.4	3.27	33.9/37.3
	14	0.36	22.0	4.56	—
	28	0.33	18.6	4.46	15.8/28.0
	56	0.36	19.5	5.17	9.9/28.3
2.4 PAZ($-Fe_2O_3$)	0	0.79	22.8	8.22	36.2/37.0
	14	0.95	21.0	11.37	—
	28	0.86	17.8	10.42	30.4/31.2
	56	0.95	28.0	11.19	39.6/40.5

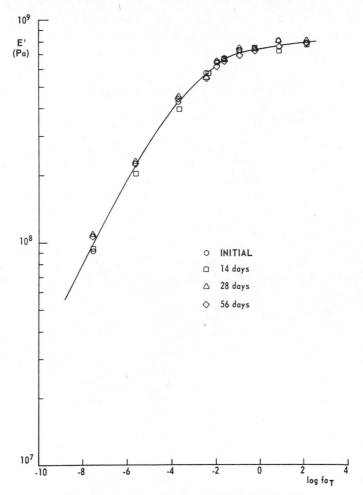

Fig. 3. Aging behavior of sample 2.4 PAZ($-Fe_2O_3$).

Formulations

Since the aim of the work was to study surface agents, all the various composites which were prepared are differentiated by the percentages and nature of surface agents. Thus, composite 1.2 PAZ/0.2 PAM contains 1.2% PAZ and 0.2% PAM in the binder. However, if many composites having the same amount of surface agents have been prepared to study the effect of experiment parameters, the main parameter under study is put inside brackets at the end of the appellation.

All propellants have a solid content of 88%, composed of 69.4% NH_4ClO_4, 18% Al, and 0.6% Fe_2O_3, except composites 1.2 PAZ/0.2 PAM ($-Fe_2O_3$), 0.9 PAZ/0.3 PAM ($-Fe_2O_3$), 0.6 PAZ/0.4 PAM ($-Fe_2O_3$), 2.4% PAZ ($-Fe_2O_3$), 0.4 PAM and the sample without any surface agent (0 PAZ/0 PAM) which are made of 70% NH_4ClO_4 and 18% Al, the absence of Fe_2O_3 being indicated by ($-Fe_2O_3$).

The formulations of the binders are given in Table I. In this table, the amount of surface agent is given only by the sample appelation. All the samples were cured at 60°C to constant hardness, except sample 0.9 PAZ/0.2 PAM which obviously was cured at 71°C. The NCO/OH ratios for each sample are given as R in the last column.

RESULTS AND DISCUSSION

Influence of Surface Agents PAM or PAZ on the Initial Properties of Propellants

Two propellants, 2.4 PAZ($-Fe_2O_3$) and 0.4 PAM, were prepared and compared to a propellant without any surface agent, 0 PAZ/0 PAM.

Mechanical properties measurements on initial samples before aging were done with two different batches of propellants of the same formulation giving a reproducibility of about ±10% on both tan δ(max) and E''(max) (Table II) which is the same as reported previously.[1]

The results of dynamic mechanical properties in Table II confirm that PAZ is a better surface agent than PAM. Indeed, the tan δ(max) and E''(max) values

TABLE IV
Effect of Fe_2O_3 on Dynamic Mechanical Properties

Sample	Aging, days	tan δ(max)		E''(max)	
		T, °K	—	T, °K	Pa × 10^{-8}
1.2 PAZ/0.2 PAM($-Fe_2O_3$)	0	237	0.10	226	0.7
	28	240	0.09	218	0.8
	56	240	0.14	220	0.7
1.2 PAZ/0.2 PAM	0	227	0.14	206	1.2
	28	227	0.20	209	1.5
	56	227	0.18	213	1.5
2.4 PAZ($-Fe_2O_3$)	0	233	0.09	219	0.8
	14	232	0.09	216	0.8
	28	240	0.09	217	0.7
	56	229	0.07	220	0.7
2.4 PAZ	0	230	0.13	209	1.7
	14	227	0.15	209	1.6
	28	227	0.15	211	1.6
	56	233	0.19	209	1.7

TABLE V
Tensile Mechanical Properties of Sample 0.6 PAZ/0.2 PAM at Different R

R	Aging, days	σ_m, MPa	ϵ_m, %	ϵ_m/ϵ_r at 228° K	E, MPa
0.8	0	.32	59	44/92	1.25
	28	.33	58	—	1.11
	56	.34	48	41/82	1.24
0.85	0	.48	55	72/82	2.12
	28	.52	52	—	2.21
	56	.44	30	12/53	2.25
0.9	0	.64	45	53/64	2.93
	28	.68	43	—	2.90
	56	.54	29	19/32	2.59

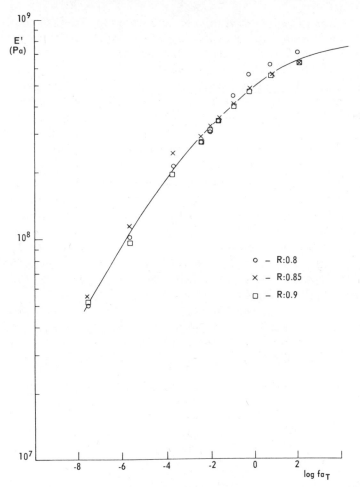

Fig. 4. Reduced storage moduli of sample 0.6 PAZ/0.2 PAM at different R values.

for sample 2.4 PAZ($-$F$_2$O$_3$) are lower than the corresponding ones for both samples 0.4 PAM and 0 PAZ/0 PAM. This conclusion is amply verified by the tensile mechanical properties of Table III for these products. At 22.8°C, for the same strain at maximum stress (ϵ_m), sample 2.4 PAZ($-$Fe$_2$O$_3$) has a maximum stress (σ_m) more than twice as high as samples 0.4 PAM and 0 PAZ/0 PAM.

TABLE VI
Dynamic Mechanical Properties of Samples 0.6 PAZ/0.2 PAM at Different R

R	Aging, days	tan δ(max)		E''(max)	
		T, °K	—	T, °K	Pa $\times$ 10^{-8}
0.8	0	233	0.22	206	1.2
	28	228	0.27	210	1.1
	56	229	0.24	206	1.0
0.85	0	215	0.21	203	1.2
	28	231	0.18	204	1.0
	56	—	0.14	210	1.0
0.9	0	233	0.28	211	0.9
	28	214	0.23	205	1.2
	56	233	0.28	209	1.0

However, the values of tan δ(max) and E''(max) for unaged sample 0 PAZ/0 PAM (Table II) which does not contain any surface agent are lower than those of sample 0.4 PAM, indicating that with freshly prepared composites based on the R-45M/DDI binder, PAM is detrimental to the quality of the solid–binder interface. Again, the tensile mechanical properties (Table III) emphasize the fact that, regarding properties at room temperature, there is nothing to gain by the incorporation of PAM in samples. However, at a temperature of 227.8°K which is just slightly higher than the T_g as measured by dynamic mechanical properties (Table II: $\simeq 218$°K), the composite containing PAM retains its strain while the sample without surface agent shows a dramatic loss of strain capability. These results are an example of the complementary nature of the dynamic and tensile mechanical properties measured on the Rheovibron and the Instron. The Rheovibron works at small elongation (0.3%), whereas the ϵ_m and the strain at rupture (ϵ_r) are obtained at much higher elongation.

Additional information on these surface-active agents can be obtained from the reduced curve of the storage modulus (E') for the same three composites using the WLF shift parameter (Fig. 2). Both reduced curves for samples 0 PAZ/0 PAM and 0.4 PAM are superposable, while the 2.4 PAZ($-Fe_2O_3$) reduced curve is definitely higher. The same trend can be observed from the Young modulus (E) (Table III). This is strong evidence that surface agent PAZ does increase the amount of crosslinking in the matrix or the reinforcement of the matrix by the solid, while PAM does not have any of these effects.

TABLE VII
Effects of Curing temperature on Dynamic Mechanical Properties

Sample	Aging, days	tan δ(max) T, °K	—	E''(max) T, °K	Pa × 10^{-8}
0.9 PAZ/0.2 PAM	0	216	0.20	207	1.7
	14	211	0.21	—	1.9
	28	218	0.23	209	1.6
	56	215	0.23	207	1.6
0.9 PAZ/0.2 PAM (344° K)	0	215	0.23	208	1.9
	14	218	0.22	207	1.9
	28	219	0.20	209	1.8
	56	215	0.18	209	1.1

TABLE VIII
Effect of Curing Temperature on Tensile Mechanical Properties

Sample	Aging, days	σ_m, MPa	ϵ_m, %	ϵ_m/ϵ_r at 228° K
0.9 PAZ/0.2 PAM	0	0.79	37	59/60
	14	0.82	36	—
	28	0.79	36	53/54
	56	0.79	36	49/50
0.9 PAZ/0.2 PAM(344° K)	0	0.75	38	60/62
	14	0.79	37	56/57
	28	0.76	37	51/53
	56	0.76	36	48/49

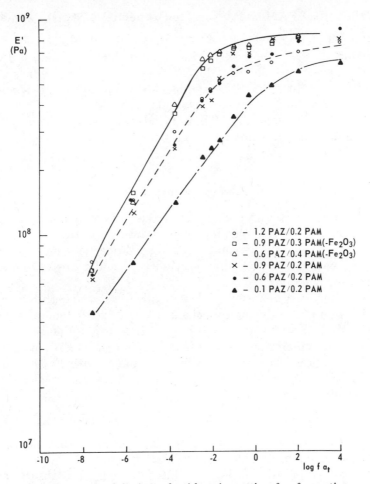

Fig. 5. Reduced storage moduli of sample with various ratios of surface-active agents.

So, in this R-45M HTPB binder, PAZ improves mechanical properties over the whole range of temperature and strains studied. The beneficial effect of PAM is only apparent at low temperature and under strains close to rupture.

TABLE IX
Effect of Prepolymer Batch on Dynamic Mechanical Properties

Sample	Aging, days	tan δ(max)		E''(max)	
		T, °K	—	T, °K	Pa × 10^{-8}
0.9 PAZ/0.2 PAM	0	220	0.23	209	1.9
	14	220	0.22	208	1.9
	28	221	0.20	209	1.8
	56	227	0.18	209	1.1
0.9 PAZ/0.2 PAM(Prep)	0	—	—	—	—
	14	218	0.22	203	1.7
	28	220	0.23	205	1.7
	56	218	0.21	206	1.4

Influence of PAM or PAZ on the Properties of Aged Propellants

For samples 0 PAZ/0 PAM, 0.4 PAM, and 2.4 PAZ($-Fe_2O_3$) aged at 60°C in an oven for 14, 28, and 56 days, the results of both the dynamic and the tensile mechanical properties do not follow any consistent trend (Tables II and III), except for the ϵ_m at 227.8°K of sample 0.4 PAM, which shows a considerable decrease. Accelerated aging does not seem to affect significantly the mechanical properties of those composites. The reduced curves lead to the same conclusion indicating no apparent aging effect. Figure 3 gives the typical reduced curve of sample 2.4 PAZ($-Fe_2O_3$).

Incorporation of Fe_2O_3

For ballistic purposes, it was necessary in the course of this study to incorporate small amounts of Fe_2O_3 in the propellant. This gave us the opportunity to note an effect of Fe_2O_3 on the dynamic mechanical properties which was impossible to foresee even though Fe_2O_3 had previously been demonstrated to intervene on the curing reaction.[5]

Two composites were formulated especially to determine the effect of Fe_2O_3. Table IV summarizes dynamic mechanical properties for samples 1.2 PAZ/0.2 PAM and 2.4 PAZ with and without Fe_2O_3. It is obvious that the incorporation of Fe_2O_3 causes a marked increase of both tan δ(max) and E''(max). If the ratios of the mechanical absorption maxima of samples with Fe_2O_3 over samples without Fe_2O_3 is averaged for composites aged during the same period, the following results are obtained:

$$\tan \delta(max)/\tan \delta(max)(-Fe_2O_3) = 1.8 \pm 0.4$$

and E''(max)/E''(max)($-Fe_2O_3$) = 2.0 ± 0.2. This shows that the incorporation of 0.6% Fe_2O_3 doubles the tan δ and E'' peak heights.

Also, the incorporation of Fe_2O_3 shifts the mechanical absorption peak to higher temperatures by about 10°, an effect which is not noticeable on the T_g as measured by a differential scanning calorimeter. The reduced curves for E' are slightly lower for samples without Fe_2O_3 in the vicinity of the mechanical absorption as expected from the increase of the loss modulus.

However, as can be seen from Table I, it should be noted that samples 1.2 PEZ/0.2 PAM($-Fe_2O_3$) and 1.2 PAZ/0.2 PAM were formulated at the same NCO/OH ratio ($R = 0.9$), while samples 2.4 PAZ and 2.4 PAZ($-Fe_2O_3$) were

TABLE X
Effect of Prepolymer Batch on Tensile Mechanical Properties

Sample	Aging, days	σ_m, MPa	ϵ_m, %	E, MPa	ϵ_m/ϵ_r at 228° K
0.9 PAZ/0.2 PAM	0	0.75	38	3.68	60/62
	14	0.79	37	3.87	57/58
	28	0.76	37	3.75	51/53
	56	0.76	36	4.14	48/49
0.9 PAZ/0.2 PAM(Prep)	0	0.67	39	3.24	61/63
	14	0.70	37	3.59	—
	28	0.72	39	3.47	61/61
	56	0.75	38	3.58	53/55

prepared at NCO/OH ratio of, respectively, 0.85 and 0.9. The problem is to decide whether it is preferable to compare samples with exactly identical formulation or samples which have been empirically optimized around preferred mechanical properties at room temperature of σ_m = 0.6–0.9 MPa and ϵ_m = 40%. As in previous works,[1] it was decided to compare samples with "optimized" formulation which are, in fact typical of products in use. But, as will be described in the following section, samples were formulated at different R values to collect information on the effect of the NCO/OH ratio on the dynamic mechanical properties.

Effect of the NCO/OH Ratio (R)

A variation of R from 0.80 to 0.85 and 0.90 gives large differences in the tensile mechanical properties of three 0.6 PAZ/0.2 PAM samples (Table V). As usual, when R is increased, both E and σ_m increase while ϵ_m decreases. The aging behavior of composites having R = 0.8 and 0.9 was poor after 56 days, as shown by every parameter.

The tan δ(max), E''(max), and T are about equal for all three compounds (Table VI), and it is impossible to establish any relation between the tensile mechanical properties and the dynamic mechanical properties. Even the reduced curves for the three samples before aging do not show any marked differences (Fig. 4), indicating that the increase of R only shifts the dynamic mechanical properties along the time axis as expected for variations in crosslinking.

TABLE XI
Influence of Various PAZ/PAM Ratios on Tensile Mechanical Properties

Sample	Aging, days	σ_m, MPa	ϵ_m, %	ϵ_m/ϵ_r at 228° K	E, MPa
1.2 PAZ/0.2 PAM	0	0.88	30	41/43	6.76
	28	0.89	29	—	6.77
	56	1.00	31	41/42	7.18
0.9 PAZ/0.3 PAM($-Fe_2O_3$)	0	0.74	33	53/54	6.71
	14	0.71	35	—	5.63
	28	0.76	38	58/59	6.01
	56	0.73	37	55/56	6.65
0.6 PAZ/0.4 PAM ($-Fe_2O_3$)	0	0.67	41	59/61	4.86
	14	0.65	39	—	5.21
	28	0.72	40	59/60	5.58
	56	0.68	35	44/56	6.15
0.9 PAZ/0.2 PAM	0	0.79	37	59/60	4.04
	14	0.82	36	—	4.33
	28	0.79	36	53/54	4.10
	56	0.79	36	49/50	4.13
0.6 PAZ/0.2 PAM	0	0.63	38	66/68	3.58
	14	0.75	38	61/62	4.08
	28	0.73	39	63/64	3.85
	56	0.52	38	59/61	2.77
0.1 PAZ/0.2 PAM	0	0.51	23	14/29	3.30
	28	0.52	21	—	3.49
	56	0.56	19	15/20	4.32

Effect of the Curing Temperature

The effect of two curing temperatures, 60° and 71°C, on the dynamic mechanical properties can be seen in Table VII. Only these two temperatures could be studied because of limitations in processing arising from the viscosity and the stability of the various components.

Sample 0.9 PAZ/0.2 PAM cured at 60°C gave tan δ(max) and E''(max) values which were almost stable at different aging period. However, sample 0.9 PAZ/0.2 PAM (344°K) showed a decrease of both values which is especially obvious after 56 days of aging.

The tensile mechanical properties (Table VIII), on the other hand, show identical behavior for both samples, indicating that this change in curing temperature does not have any effect on the mechanical properties.

Effect of Changes in Prepolymer Batch

Dynamic and tensile mechanical properties for two samples having similar formulations, but with two different prepolymer batches, give very close values following a similar trend. The only difference is a slightly better aging behavior of sample 0.9 PAZ/0.2 PAM(Prep) after 56 days at 60°C. The possibilities of reproducing fixed mechanical properties has been proven to be very good.

Effect of Various PAZ/PAM Ratios on Aging

Various samples were formulated to study any possible effect of the PAZ/PAM ratio on the aging behavior of those composites. First, the tensile mechanical

TABLE XII
Influence of Various PAZ/PAM Ratios on Dynamic Mechanical Properties

Sample	Aging, days	tan δ(max)		E''(max)	
		T, °K	—	T, °K	Pa × 10^{-8}
1.2 PAZ/0.2 PAM	0	225	0.14	212	1.2
	28	213	0.20	213	1.5
	56	223	0.18	213	1.5
0.9 PAZ/0.3 PAM($-Fe_2O_3$)	0	229	0.13	219	0.8
	14	235	0.15	217	0.9
	28	235	0.12	222	0.9
	56	241	0.15	222	0.9
0.6 PAZ/0.4 PAM($-Fe_2O_3$)	0	233	0.18	220	0.85
	14	233	0.16	221	0.9
	28	236	0.11	220	0.8
	56	230	0.15	220	0.9
0.9 PAZ/0.2 PAM	0	220	0.23	209	1.9
	14	220	0.22	208	1.9
	28	221	0.20	209	1.8
	56	227	0.18	209	1.1
0.6 PAZ/0.2 PAM	0	219	0.21	206	1.6
	14	220	0.20	209	1.1
	28	215	0.23	209	1.3
	56	218	0.21	207	1.2
0.1 PAZ/0.2 PAM	0	230	0.31	205	1.1

properties in Table XI show that all those composites have satisfactory mechanical properties, excepting sample 0.1 PAZ/0.2 PAM, where all the values are too low indicating the necessity of incorporating sufficient amount of PAZ. All the other samples do not show any definite aging trend.

The summary of dynamic mechanical properties in Table XII leads to the same conclusion that aging does not affect the surface agents using tan δ(max) or E''(max) values. There are some variations that appear to be more or less at random.

The reduced curves show three different sets of curves: a highest one for the two samples without Fe_2O_3, an average one for samples 1.2 PAZ/0.2 PAM, 0.9 PAZ/0.2 PAM, and 0.6 PAZ/0.2 PAM, and a lowest one for sample 0.1 PAZ/0.2 PAM.

All the measurements on the Rheovibrometer were expertly taken by Mr. Yvon Boucher.

References

1. G. Perrault and G. L. Duchesne, *J. Appl. Polym. Sci,* **18,** 1295 (1974).
2. T. Murayama and E. L. Lawton, *J. Appl. Polym. Sci.,* **17,** 669 (1973).
3. H. C. Allen, U.S. Pat. 3,745,074 (1973) and U.S. Pat. 3,762,972 (1974).
4. G. Perrault, *Can. J. Chem.,* **47,** 4515 (1969).
5. G. Perrault, G. L. Duchesne, and M. Tremblay, *Europ. Polym. J.,* **10,** 747 (1974).

Received July 29, 1976
Revised October 14, 1976

JOURNAL OF APPLIED POLYMER SCIENCE   VOL. 21, 3167-3177 (1977)

Polymerization of Organic Compounds in an Electrodeless Glow Discharge. IX. Flow-Rate Dependence of Properties of Plasma Polymers of Acetylene and Acrylonitrile

H. YASUDA and TOSHIHIRO HIROTSU, *Polymer Research Laboratory, Chemistry and Life Sciences Division, Research Triangle Institute, Research Triangle Park, North Carolina 27709*

Synopsis

Properties (free-radical concentration, gas permeabilities, internal stress, and contact angle of water) of plasma polymers of acetylene and of acrylonitrile were investigated as a function of flow rate of monomer in an electrodeless glow discharge. It was found that the monomer flow rate has a strong influence on free-radical concentration, gas permeabilities, and internal stress but little influence on the contact angle of water. The discharge power has little effect on properties when the full glow is maintained in the reactor. Gas permeabilities decrease with increasing concentration of free radicals in plasma polymers.

INTRODUCTION

Although there are numerous reports on the deposition rate of plasma polymerization as a function of some of the operational parameters, relatively little is known about how properties of plasma polymer depend on the operational parameters. This is probably due to the difficulties involved in such a study. First, plasma polymer is formed in a very thin layer which is generally bonded to a substrate that is much thicker than the coating. The characterization of the thin layer in such a composite structure is extremely difficult. Secondly, some of the operational parameters such as flow rate, pressure, and discharge power are system-dependent parameters, and in some cases they have no significant meaning beyond being a means of controlling the process in a particular apparatus.

The dependence of polymer deposition rate on flow rate, for instance, is rather complicated in a bell-jar-type reactor,[1,2] whereas it is generally linearly proportional to the flow rate in a simple tube reactor in the full glow region.[3,4] Therefore, "flow rate" cannot be correlated with the properties of polymer unless the flow pattern is well defined for a system and polymer properties are uniquely related to the flow rate.

There seems to be, however, a common denominator aspect that can be correlated with polymer properties. That is, "better film" is obtained when a polymer film is formed relatively slowly. In the tail flame portion of glow dis-

3167

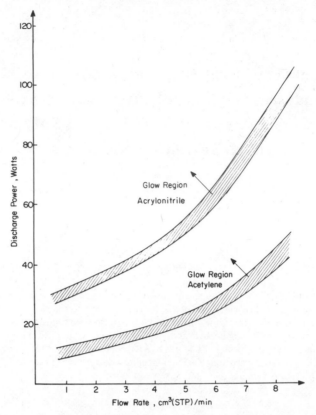

Fig. 1. Dependence of glow on flow rate and discharge power for acrylonitrile and acetylene.

charge used in a series of studies, as reported in the previous report,[4] the flow rate is well defined and the deposition rate is uniquely related to the flow rate. Therefore, the investigation of the flow-rate dependence of polymer seems to be warranted for such a system. A study was carried out using acetylene and acrylonitrile as the monomers. The reasons why those monomers are chosen in this study are as follows: (1) Acrylonitrile and acetylene are monomers which polymerize easily in plasma, which allows us to carry out experiments in wider ranges of conditions. For instance, if a monomer requires a very high discharge power to maintain a full glow, the flow rate cannot be changed much; this will be discussed later. (2) Both monomers yield polymers which have very low characteristic gas permeabilities. Therefore, by depositing plasma polymer onto polyethylene film (which has high gas permeability), the characteristic gas permeability of plasma polymer can be calculated from the overall gas permeability of composite films. If the gas permeability of plasma polymer is not sufficiently low, gas permeabilities of a composite film are controlled mainly by the substrate polymer, which has much larger thickness, and the permeability of a thin deposit cannot be estimated.

EXPERIMENTAL

The flow of a monomer was determined by the measurement of pressure increase rate when the pumping was abruptly stopped in a steady-state flow.

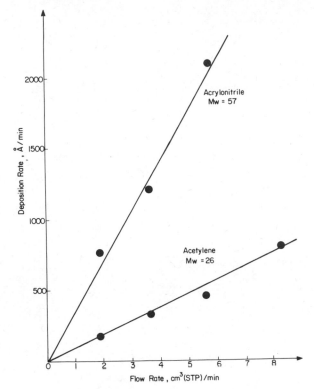

Fig. 2. Dependence of polymer deposition rate on monomer flow rate for acrylonitrile and acetylene.

The detail of the method was described previously.[4] The pressure of the flow
system (before discharge) was adjusted to 60 μm Hg by changing the opening
of a stopcock leading to the vacuum system.

The deposition rate was estimated by weighing the amount of polymer deposit
after a predetermined period of plasma polymerization. The deposition rate
is expressed by thickness growth rate in Å/min, which is calculated from weight
increase, assuming the density of the polymer to be unity. Although the density
of the polymer may be greater than unity, the deposition rate given in Å/min
seems to be adequate enough for the puspose of this study. The deposition rate
in mg/cm^2·min can be obtained by multiplying 10^{-5} by the value of Å/min.

Based on the polymer deposition rate, 1000-Å-thick plasma polymer was deposited onto a low-density polyethylene film. The plasma polymer–polyethylene
composite film was used for the measurement of gas permeabilities (CO_2, O_2,
and N_2), of internal stress, and of contact angle of water.

The internal stress was calculated from the radius of curl formed by a composite film. The internal stress σ in dynes/cm^2 is given by

$$\sigma = \frac{ED^2}{6Rd}$$

when E is the modulus of the substrate polymer ($E = 10^9$ dynes/cm^2 for low-
density polyethylene), D is the thickness of substrate film ($D = 5 \times 10^{-3}$ cm),
R is the radius of the roll into which a composite film curls up, and d is the

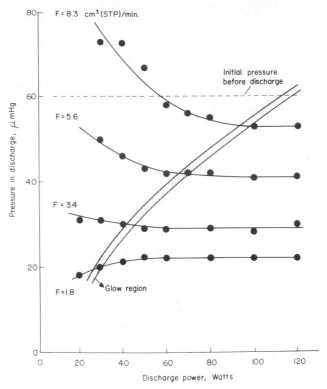

Fig. 3. Dependence of system pressure in discharge of acrylonitrile on discharge power at different flow rates.

thickness of plasma polymer ($d = 10^{-5}$ cm in this study). The details of the method were presented in a previous report.[5]

The permeability of plasma polymer was calculated from the permeability of a composite film which is given by

$$\frac{l}{P} = \frac{l_1}{P_1} + \frac{l_2}{P_2}$$

where P and l are the permeability and thickness, respectively, of a composite film; P_1 and l_1 are the permeability and thickness, respectively, of the substrate polymer; and P_2 and l_2 are the permeability and thickness, respectively, of the plasma polymer. Gas permeabilities were measured by using an isobaric apparatus described previously.[6]

Contact angles of water were measured by a microscope with a goniometer eyepiece by using triple distilled water. Samples for electron spin resonance (ESR) spectroscopy were prepared by depositing a polymer onto a 4-mm-O.D. glass tube according to the method described previously.[7,8]

RESULTS AND DISCUSSION

Acrylonitrile requires higher wattage to maintain the glow than acetylene, as seen in Figure 1, where the threshold discharge power to maintain full glow is plotted against the flow rate. The deposition rates as a function of flow rate are

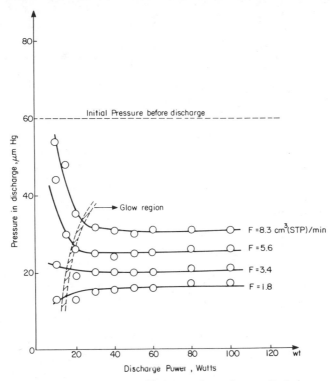

Fig. 4. Dependence of system pressure in discharge of acetylene on discharge power at different flow rates.

shown in Figure 2. The apparent high deposition rate of acrylonitrile compared to that of acetylene is partly due to the difference of molecular weight (i.e., 57 for acrylonitrile and 26 for acetylene). Even after the effect of molecular weight

TABLE I
Characteristics of ESR Spin Signals[a]

Sample	C_s^0, spins/cm^3	Peak width, gauss	Half-life of decay, min Initial	Half-life of decay, min 2nd
Acrylonitrile (100 W)				
$F = 1.8$	8.0×10^{18}	19.0	22	110
$F = 3.4$	4.0×10^{18}	18.5	30	180
$F = 5.6$	1.8×10^{18}	18.0	34	190
$F = 8.3$	1.1×10^{18}	17.0	50	270
Acetylene (45 W)				
$F = 1.8$	1.5×10^{20}	16.5	70	250
$F = 3.4$	1.8×10^{20}	16.0	120	250
$F = 5.6$	3.6×10^{20}	15.0	180	280
$F = 8.3$	4.0×10^{20}	14.0	210	280
Acetylene (100 W)				
$F = 1.8$	2.0×10^{20}	17.5	28	240
$F = 3.4$	2.2×10^{20}	17.0	33	240
$F = 5.6$	2.3×10^{20}	17.0	35	240
$F = 8.3$	3.5×10^{20}	16.0	37	250

[a] F = Flow rate in cm^3(S.T.P.)/min; C_s^0 = initial spin concentration.

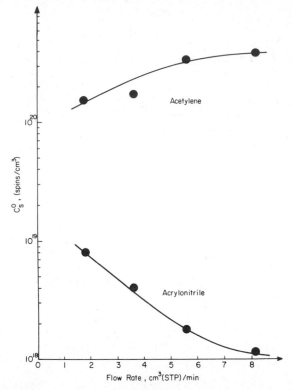

Fig. 5. Dependence of free-radical concentration in plasma polymers of acrylonitrile and acetylene on monomer flow rate (45 W for acetylene and 100 W for acrylonitrile).

is taken into consideration, acrylonitrile has a considerably higher characteristic polymerization rate. The characteristic deposition rate constant k, which is given by

$$\text{deposition rate in } g/cm^2 \cdot \min = k \frac{M \times \text{flow rate in } cm^3(\text{S.T.P.})/\min}{2.24 \times 10^4}$$

where M is the molecular weight of the monomer, represents this difference more clearly.[3]

It is interesting to note that the values of k (i.e., $k = 1.36 \times 10^{-3}$ cm^{-2} for acrylonitrile and $k = 8.12 \times 10^{-4}$ cm^{-2} for acetylene) are roughly proportional to the total number of bonds which easily participate in plasma polymerization (i.e., three for acrylonitrile and two for acetylene). This is in accordance with observation that acrylonitrile polymerizes by utilizing C≡N as well as C=C.[9]

Since plasma polymerization of acetylene allows us to carry out experiments in a wider range of discharge power (>40 watts) without changing glow characteristic, as seen in Figure 1, polymerization was carried out at 100 and 45 watts. No significant difference in deposition rates due to the difference in discharge power was observed. This is in accordance with observations reported previously.[4,10] In Figures 3 and 4, the pressures of steady-state flow in glow discharge are plotted as a function of discharge power for acrylonitrile and for acetylene, respectively. In both cases, results indicate that in the partial glow

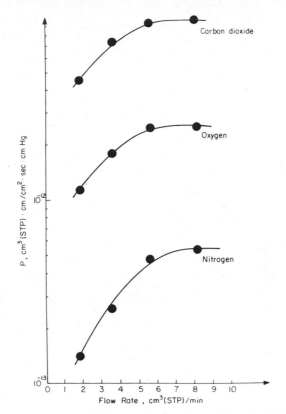

Fig. 6. Dependence of gas permeabilities of plasma polymer of acrylonitrile on monomer flow rate.

region, different chemical reactions occur compared to that in the full glow region. The details of this aspect are discussed in a separate paper.[4] The significance of glow characteristic and the plasma polymerization which is independent of wattage in the full glow region are clearly evident in these results.

Results of ESR study are summarized in Table I. The concentration of trapped free radicals in a plasma polymer is dependent on the flow rate of monomer. As shown in Figure 5, the dependence of free-radical concentration on the monomer flow rate is different for plasma polymerization of acetylene and acrylonitrile. Namely, the concentration of free radicals in plasma polymer of acetylene increases with flow rate, whereas that in plasma polymer of acrylonitrile decreases with increasing flow rate.

A similar discrepancy in the dependence on flow rate is also observed in gas permeabilities. In case of permeabilities, permeability of plasma polymer of acrylonitrile increases with flow rate, as shown in Figure 6, and that of acetylene decreases with increasing flow rate, as shown in Figure 7. Very small differences are observed in gas permeabilities of plasma polymer of acetylene polymerized at 45 and 100 watts, indicating that flow rate has more significant effect than the discharge power on the properties of the polymers.

Although the dependence of gas permeability on the monomer flow rate is opposite in the cases of acetylene and of acrylonitrile, the gas permeabilities

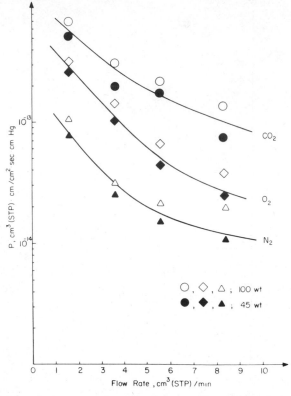

Fig. 7. Dependence of gas permeabilities of plasma polymer of acetylene on monomer flow rate.

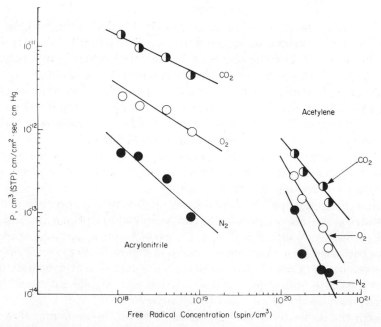

Fig. 8. Correlation between gas permeabilities and free-radical concentration in plasma polymers.

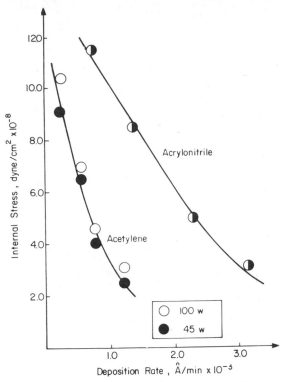

Fig. 9. Dependence of internal stress on the deposition rate.

decrease as the concentration of trapped free radicals increases, as shown in Figure 8. It has been postulated that free radicals in plasma polymers are the consequence of imbalance between the rate of free-radical production by electric discharge and the rate of comsumption mainly due to polymer formation[7,11] rather than creation of free radicals on already formed plasma polymer by UV irradiation. Therefore, it is probable that the monomer which yields a more tightly crosslinked polymer will have also higher numbers of free radicals trapped in the polymer. This trend is clearly seen in Figure 8.

The internal stress in plasma polymer of acrylonitrile and acetylene is highly dependent on the monomer flow rate and decreases with increasing deposition rate in both cases, as shown in Figure 9. Here again, the effect of discharge wattage (acetylene) is insignificant compared to the effect of flow rate. In these plasma polymers, there is no simple correlation between the internal stress and the concentration of free radicals in plasma polymers. Although further investigations are needed for elucidation of the internal stress in plasma polymers, the results clearly indicate that the stress built in a plasma polymer is largely determined by how quickly the polymer is formed.

The contact angles of water on these two kinds of plasma polymers are not sensitive to the flow rate, though a slight decrease in cos θ is observed with increasing flow rate, as shown in Figure 10. This may indicate that by conditions of plasma polymerization. The facts that the internal stress and gas permeabilities are strongly dependent on the flow rate indicate that the flow rate is an important factor to control how these building blocks are assembled in the polymers.

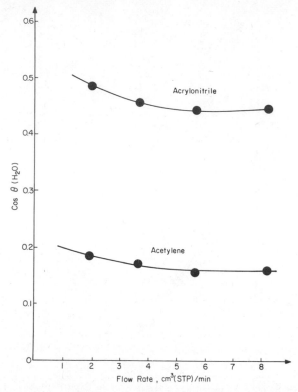

Fig. 10. Dependence of cos θ of contact angle of water on monomer flow rate.

The reason why the effects of flow rate on free-radical concentration and gas permeabilities are different for acetylene and for acrylonitrile is not clear. However, recent studies in progress seems to indicate that acetylene behaves differently from saturated and C=C containing compounds; i.e., results with most other organic compounds follow the trends observed with acrylonitrile.

It has been postulated that overall mechanisms of polymer formation can be represented by repeated stepwise reactions:

Initiation

$$M_i \rightarrow M_i^*$$

Propagation

$$M_i^* + M_k^* \rightarrow M_i - M_k \tag{1}$$

$$M_i^* + M_k \rightarrow M_i - M_k \tag{2}$$

where i and k are numbers of repeating units (i.e., $i = k = 1$ for the monomer) and M^* is a reactive species which can be ion of either charge, an excited molecule, and a free radical.

In the case of acrylonitrile (and many other organic compounds), which requires relatively high discharge power to maintain full glow, the propagation by the reaction of a reactive specie with a monomer, reaction (2), may be favored at high flow rate. In the case of acetylene, on the other hand, which requires very low discharge power to maintain full glow, the propagation by the recombination of two reactive species; reaction (1) may prevail at high flow rate.

If free radicals are the predominant reactive specie, the increase of trapped free radicals in plasma polymer of acetylene with increasing flow rate can be reasonably explained. Namely, the opening of triple bond produces excessive free radicals which cannot be consumed by the coupling reaction.

CONCLUSIONS

In the full glow region of the tail flame of an inductively coupled rf discharge, the flow rate of monomer is the most important factor which influences the properties of plasma polymers of acetylene and of acrylonitrile. It was found that trapped free-radical concentration, internal stress, and gas permeabilities are highly dependent on the monomer flow rate. Gas permeabilities of these two polymers are correlated to the concentration of free radicals, although the flow rate dependences of gas permeabilities and free-radical concentration are opposite in cases of acetylene and acrylonitrile. The internal stress in both plasma polymer decreases with increasing monomer flow rate. No correlation is found between gas permeabilities and the internal stress. The effects of discharge wattage, observed with plasma polymerization of acetylene, on those properties were found to be small. Very small changes in contact angles of water due to the difference in flow rates and discharge wattages were observed.

This study is supported in part by the Office of Water Research and Technology, U.S. Department of the Interior, Contract No. 14-30-3301, and by the National Heart and Lung Institute, NIH, U.S. Department of Health, Education and Welfare, Contract No. NIH-N01-HB-3-2913.

References

1. A. R. Westwood, *Europ. Polym. J.*, **7**, 363 (1971).
2. H. Kobayashi, A. T. Bell, and M. Shen, *Macromolecules*, **7**, 277, 1974.
3. H. Yasuda and C. E. Lamaze, *J. Appl. Polym. Sci.*, **17**, 1519 (1973).
4. H. Yasuda and T. Hirotsu, *J. Appl. Polym. Sci.*, **21**, 3139 (1977).
5. H. Yasuda, T. Hirotsu, and H. G. Olf, *J. Appl. Polym. Sci.*, **21**, 3179 (1977).
6. H. Yasuda and K. Rosengren, *J. Appl. Polym. Sci.*, **14**, 2839 (1970).
7. H. Yasuda, M. O. Bumgarner, H. C. Marsh, and N. Morosoff, *J. Polym. Sci., Polym. Chem. Ed.*, **14**, 195 (1976).
8. H. Yasuda and T. Hsu, *J. Polym. Sci., Polym. Chem. Ed.*, to appear.
9. H. Yasuda, M. O. Bumgarner, and J. J. Hillman, *J. Appl. Polym. Sci.*, **19**, 1403 (1975).
10. H. Yasuda and C. E. Lamaze, *J. Appl. Polym. Sci.*, **15**, 2277 (1971).
11. H. Yasuda, *J. Macromol. Sci.-Chem.*, **A10**(3), 383 (1976).

Received September 28, 1976
Revised October 15, 1976

JOURNAL OF APPLIED POLYMER SCIENCE   VOL. 21, 3179–3184 (1977)

Polymerization of Organic Compounds in an Electrodeless Glow Discharge. X. Internal Stress in Plasma Polymers

H. YASUDA, TOSHIHIRO HIROTSU,* and H. G. OLF, *Polymer Research Laboratory, Research Triangle Institute, Research Triangle Park, North Carolina 27709*

Synopsis

Owing to the unique mechanisms operative in plasma polymerization, a thin layer of plasma polymer deposited on the surface of a substrate shows a tendency to expand, indicating an internal stress in the layer. This stress, σ_s, has been estimated from the observed curling of composite membranes in which the thickness of the plasma coating, d, is much smaller than the thickness of a flexible substrate, D, according to the relation

$$\sigma_s = ED^2/6Rd$$

where R is the radius of the roll into which the composite films curl up and E is the modulus of the substrate polymer. The stress σ_s is found to depend on the kind of monomer used and to be of the order of magnitude 10^8–10^9 dynes/cm^2 with most of the monomers here employed.

INTRODUCTION

When a thick layer (i.e., 1 μm or thicker) of plasma polymer of styrene is deposited on a rigid surface such as a glass plate, the layer of plasma polymer tends to buckle and crack.[1] This phenomenon was thought to be due to absorption of moisture from the atmosphere and consequent swelling of the layer.[1] More recently, it has been observed that a composite film consisting of a thin layer of plasma polymer deposited on a flexible polymeric substrate such as polyethylene often shows a marked tendency to bend and to curl up. This curling is observed even during plasma polymerization. It may be attributed to an internal stress arising in the plasma layer during polymerization.

In all cases of curling observed in such composite membranes, the direction of bending was such that the membrane was convex toward the side of the layer. This is the situation schematically indicated in Figure 1. This sense of bending is in marked contrast to that expected if the layer were deposited by conventional polymerization. As is well known, conventional polymerization proceeds, with

---

* Present address: Research Institute for Polymers and Textiles, 4-1 Sawatari, Kanagawa-Ku, Yokohama 221, Japan.

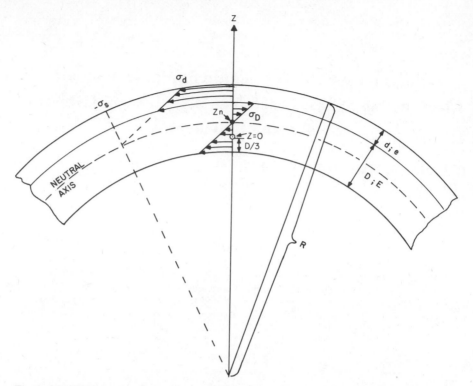

Fig. 1. Model of a composite membrane, bending because of a stress σ_s in the thin layer deposited by plasma polymerization onto a flexible polymeric substrate. Layer and substrate have thicknesses d and D and Young's moduli e and E, respectively.

very few exceptions, under volume decrease: the specific volume of the polymer is smaller than that of the (liquid) monomer. A thin film of liquid monomer polymerized on top of a flexible substrate would contract and cause bending concave toward the side of the layer, i.e., in the direction opposite to that obtained with plasma polymerization.

We conclude that the internal stress in the plasma-polymerized layer is an expansive one. The origin of this stress is largely a matter of speculation, but the following intuitive picture may provide a useful rationalization. Reactive species—such as ions of either charge, excited molecules, and free radicals—are continuously formed in the plasma and impinge onto the already laid-down plasma polymer,[2] which contains a great number of radicals also.[3] These highly reactive species, in attaching themselves to the polymer, are imagined to become frequently wedged between existing polymer chain segments. This wedging effect is thought to give rise to the observed expansive stress.

In this study, an attempt is made to estimate the internal stress, which builds up in the plasma polymer, from the extent of curling of composite films prepared by depositing a layer of plasma polymer on low-density polyethylene film.

CALCULATION OF INTERNAL STRESS

Our purpose is to derive a relationship between the radius of curvature of the curling membrane and the stress causing it.

Figure 1 represents the model on which the calculation will be based. The substrate has thickness D and Young's modulus E; the plasma-polymerized layer has, correspondingly, d and e. If the substrate were constrained to its original shape, a "swelling stress," σ_s, would develop in the plasma-deposited layer. This stress exerts a bending moment which is partly relieved when the membrane is allowed to bend. Bending creates reactive stresses in the substrate, and equilibrium will be reached when the moment of the stresses in d is opposite and equal to the moment of the stresses in D,

$$M_d + M_D = 0$$

where the moments are those with respect to the neutral axis (see Fig. 1). A second equilibrium condition is that the stress integrated over the cross section perpendicular to the neutral axis must be zero, as no external force is applied. These two equilibrium conditions are sufficient to calculate the location of the neutral axis and to derive the desired relationship between the swelling stress σ_s and the radius of curvature of the composite membrane. This is done first for the general case where d can assume any value and subsequently for the special case that d is small compared with D.

General Case

For purposes of calculation, we assume a coordinate axis z perpendicular to the membrane and put the origin, $z = 0$, at a distance $D/3$ from the bottom of the composite membrane (Fig. 1).

The strain ϵ is assumed to vary linearly with distance from the neutral axis:

$$\epsilon = k(z - z_n)$$

where k, a constant which determines the strain, will be dependent on σ_s and where z_n is the coordinate of the neutral axis. The stress in d will be given by

$$\sigma_d = -\sigma_s + ek(z - z_n)$$

and in D by

$$\sigma_D = Ek(z - z_n)$$

Since the membranes are thin compared to their lateral dimensions, shear stresses may be ignored. Application of the two mentioned equilibrium conditions yields the dependence of the strain constant k on stress and the material constants and the location of the neutral axis z_n:

$$k = \frac{\sigma_s d}{[(ED^2/6)(1 + 4ed/ED + 3ed^2/ED^2) - (ED + ed)z_n]} \tag{1}$$

$$z_n = (d/6)\{1 - (d/D) + [d^2/D(D + d)](E - e)/E\} \tag{2}$$

The radius R of the roll into which the membrane curls up (Fig. 1) is given by

$$R = (1/k) + \Delta \tag{3}$$

where $\Delta = (2D/3) + d - z_n$ is the distance of the neutral axis from the upper surface of the membrane.

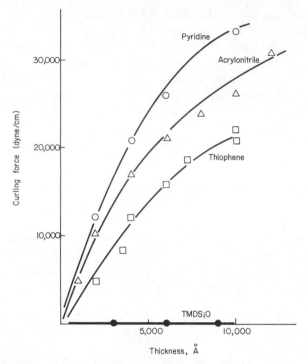

Fig. 2. Curling force $\sigma_s d$, which is the product of the internal stress (σ_s) and the thickness (d) of the plasma-deposited layer, is plotted vs d. The three curves correspond to layers obtained by plasma polymerization of the indicated monomers.

Special Case $d \ll D$

In all the membranes used, the plasma-polymerized layer has a thickness d very much smaller than D, the thickness of the substrate. As d approaches zero, z_n also becomes zero, eq. (2).

If it is assumed that $d \ll D$ and that e and E are of the same order of magnitude, we get from eq. (2)

$$z_n \simeq d/6$$

and from eq. (1)

$$k \simeq 6\sigma_s d/(ED^2)$$

With all our membranes, D is always less than 1% of R, so $D \ll R$ and, a fortiori, $\Delta \ll R$. Hence, we have according to eq. (3)

$$R \simeq 1/k \simeq ED^2/(6\sigma_s d)$$

This yields the desired estimate of σ_s from a measurement of R:

$$\sigma_s = ED^2/(6Rd) \tag{4}$$

At a given radius of curvature R, the stress σ_s is directly proportional to Young's modulus of the substrate and to the square of its thickness, and inversely proportional to the thickness d of the plasma polymer layer.

EXPERIMENTAL

Preparation of Composite Films

A strip (1 cm × 8 cm) of low-density polyethylene film ($D = 5 \times 10^{-3}$ cm, $E = 10^9$ dynes/cm^2) was used as the substrate. A plasma coating was deposited on this film by the usual method, which was described elsewhere.[1] The coating thickness was estimated from the known deposition rate of each polymer. Most strips curled in the course of the coating; therefore, in order to prevent curling and to obtain a uniform coating, the strip was supported on a stiff film (Mylar A) by means of aluminum foil fixed at both ends.

Measurement of the Radius of Curled Films

After polymerization, the strip was taken off from the supporting film, and the uncoated portion (under the aluminum foil) was cut off. The film was kept in air at room temperature for approximately 24 hr before the measurement of curling was taken. The radius of the curled film was measured by a caliper with a vernier scale.

RESULTS AND DISCUSSION

The force per unit width of film which causes curling is given by the product of stress σ_s and layer thickness d, i.e., $\sigma_s d$. This curling force was measured with plasma coatings of different thicknesses and with different monomers. The results, appearing in Figure 2, show that the curling force in a layer of plasma polymer increases with increasing layer thickness.

At small values of the layer thickness, the curling force $\sigma_s d$ increases linearly

TABLE I
Internal Stress of Plasma Polymer (thickness = 4000 Å;
reaction conditions: 30 μm Hg monomer pressure and 80W power)

Monomer	Structure	σ_s, dynes/cm^2
Thiophene		2.7×10^8
Pyridine		5.2×10^8
Acrylonitrile	$CH_2{=}CH{-}C{\equiv}N$	4.3×10^8
Furan		7.0×10^8
Styrene	$CH_2{=}CH$	4.3×10^8
Acetylene	$CH{\equiv}CH$	3.8×10^8
2-Methyloxazoline	CH_3	0
Tetramethyldisiloxane	$H{-}\underset{Me}{\overset{Me}{Si}}{-}O{-}\underset{Me}{\overset{Me}{Si}}{-}H$	0

with d; this means that σ_s is independent of layer thickness and is a material constant. The curling force tends to deviate from this linear dependence on d at a greater coating thickness; the stress σ_s decreases with increasing thickness of the layer. This seems to be related to cracking of the layer, which has been observed to occur in relatively thick layers and will certainly relieve a part of the internal stress. Figure 2 indicates that a meaningful value of σ_s can be determined from eq. (4) if the coating thickness is limited to values of 4000 Å or less.

Although only one kind of substrate polymer of a given thickness was used in this study, it is clear that the method can be adapted to cover a wide range of internal stress by suitable changes of thickness and modulus of the substrate.

The values of internal stress measured at 4000 Å coating thickness for some plasma polymers are listed in Table I. All plasma polymer coatings were prepared under an arbitrarily chosen set of conditions. The results may, therefore, not be unique as the internal stress may also depend on the conditions of plasma polymerization. The possibility of such a dependence is being studied further.

The data in Table I show that most monomers give layers having internal stress in the range of 10^8–10^9 dynes/cm^2. The two monomers 2-methyloxazoline and tetramethyldisiloxane, however, gave layers with no observable bending and, hence, zero internal stress.

The detailed characterization of the structure and properties of plasma-polymerized layers is difficult and lags far behind their technologic exploitation. Accordingly, it is not possible at present to interpret the significance of the results in Table I in terms of polymerization mechanisms or structure of the layer. The purpose of this communication is to show that an expansive stress of considerable magnitude exists in certain plasma-deposited polymeric layers and to propose the simple method employed here for the measurement of that stress. It is hoped that this approach will contribute to the further study and understanding of the structure and properties of these layers.

This study was supported in part by the National Heart and Lung Institute, NIH, U.S. Department of Health, Education and Welfare, Contract No. NIH-N01-HB-3-2913, and by the Office of Water Research and Technology, U.S. Department of the Interior, Contract No. 14-30-3301.

References

1. H. Yasuda, *Appl. Polym. Symp.*, **No. 22,** 241 (1973).

2. H. Yasuda and T. Hsu, *J. Polym. Sci., Polym. Chem. Ed.,* to appear.

3. H. Yasuda, M. O. Bumgarner, H. C. Marsh, and N. Morosoff, *J. Polym. Sci., Polym. Chem. Ed.,* **14,** 195 (1976).

Received August 20, 1976
Revised October 26, 1976

Poly(fluoroalkoxyphosphazenes)—Versatile Seal Materials

JOHN C. VICIC and KENNARD A. REYNARD, *Horizons Incorporated, Division of Horizons Research Incorporated, Cleveland, Ohio 44122*

Synopsis

Poly(fluoroalkoxyphosphazene) fluoroelastomers are members of a new family of polymers based on a phosphorous–nitrogen backbone. Physical property evaluation tests have demonstrated that these fluoroelastomers possess excellent stress–strain properties, low-temperature flexibility, thermal stability, and resistance to a variety of demanding environments including synthetic lubricants, hydrocarbon fuels, and aqueous caustics. Their service temperature range is about −60°–200°C. Poly(fluoroalkoxyphosphazene) fluoroelastomers have shown the capability to function in severe dynamic applications; i.e., lip seals ($1\frac{7}{8}$ in. I.D.) performed for >1000 hr at 5500 rpm in MIL L-7808G lubricant at 115°C. Also, O-ring seals successfully completed a 1000-hr dynamic qualification test over a temperature range of −54°–163°C in a rod seal test apparatus. These elastomers can be used for seals, O-rings, gaskets, diaphragms, hose, and protective coatings.

INTRODUCTION

Extreme service applications for fluoroelastomers have grown steadily as a result of new developments in military and civilian requirements. These applications demand strong, solvent-resistant materials which are capable of service over wide temperature extremes in a variety of fluids and air.

Poly(fluoroalkoxyphosphazene) elastomers, developed by Horizons Incorporated, have demonstrated the potential to meet the requirements of new and existing extreme service applications. Poly(fluoroalkoxyphosphazene) elastomers are members of the polyphosphazenes, a series of polymers based on an alternating phosphorous–nitrogen backbone. Peroxide-cured poly(fluoroalkoxyphosphazenes) display excellent fluid resistance, good mechanical properties, low-temperature flexibility, and thermal stability. Their service temperature range is −60° to about 200°C.

The technology and commercial development of poly(fluoroalkoxyphosphazene) elastomers have been licensed to the Firestone Tire and Rubber Company. These polymers are now being marketed in pilot plant quantities under the trade name phosphonitrilic fluoroelastomers and the trademark PNF.

EXPERIMENTAL

Synthesis. Synthesis of the poly(fluoroalkoxyphosphazene) elastomers used in our studies followed procedures described previously.[1,2]

3185

Compounding. Compounding of poly(fluoroalkoxyphosphazene) elastomers was carried out in an Atlantic Research Helicone Mixer Model 2CV, a C. W. Brabender Prep. Center Mixer Model C.E. 0.6, and on a P. E. Albert 6 × 12 in. two-roll rubber mill. Test specimens were compression molded and vulcanized under pressure in a heated, hydraulically operated press. Process and vulcanization conditions varied according to compound characteristics.

Physical Testing. Test procedures for characterization and evaluation of poly(fluoroalkoxyphosphazene) elastomer vulcanizates were as follows: (1) ASTM D-3196T, Tentative Method of Tension Testing Solid Urethane and Other Rubbers; (2) ASTM D-573, Accelerated Aging of Vulcanized Rubber by the Oven Method (ASTM D-3196T tensile specimens were used for stress–strain determinations); (3) ASTM D-471, Change in Properties of Elastomeric Vulcanizates Resulting from Immersion in Liquids (ASTM D-3196T tensile specimens were used for stress–strain determinations); (4) ASTM D-3137, Hydrolytic Stability of Elastomeric Vulcanizates (a test temperature of 100°C was used instead of the 85°C specified) (ASTM D-3196T tensile specimens were used for stress–strain determinations); (5) ASTM D-1053, Measuring Low-Temperature Stiffening of Rubber and Rubber-like Materials by Means of a Torsional Wire Apparatus; (6) ASTM D-395, Compression Set of Vulcanized Rubber.

RESULTS AND DISCUSSION

Many essentially chloride-free elastomeric or plastic poly(fluoroalkoxyphosphazenes) have been prepared following the reaction sequence shown[3] by eqs. (1) and (2):

$$(Cl_2PN)_3 \underset{250°C, \text{ vac.}}{\rightleftharpoons} [Cl_2PN]_n \qquad (1)$$

$$[Cl_2PN]_n + 2n\,NaOR \xrightarrow{\text{solvent}} [(RO)_2PN]_n + 2n\,NaCl \qquad (2)$$

Only polyphosphazene derivatives which contain CF_3CH_2O- and $HCF_2C_3F_6CH_2O$- substituents will be discussed in this paper because polymers which contain these groups are being commercialized at the present time. The physical and chemical characteristics of a copolymer are determined by the side chains and their relative proportions in the final polymer.

Representative properties for an uncured $[(CF_3CH_2O)_2PN-(HCF_2C_3F_6CH_2O)_2PN]_n$ copolymer or a

$$[(CF_3CH_2O)_x PN-(HCF_2C_3F_6CH_2O)_y PN-(RO)_z PN]_n$$

terpolymer, where $x \cong y$, x and $y \gg z$, and the sum of x, y, and z is equal to 6, are shown in Table I. For convenience, the terpolymer is simply referred to as a $[(CF_3CH_2O)_2PN-(HCF_2C_3F_6CH_2O)_2PN]_n$ terpolymer. The fluoroelastomer is a soft gum with good green strength and little or no cold flow. The T_g is quite low (−67°C). Weight-average molecular weight is usually in the millions, and polydispersity ranges[4] from 3 to about 20. Specific gravity of the polymer is 1.72.

Horizons Incorporated has conducted a fairly extensive compounding effort with $[CF_3CH_2O)_2PN-(HCF_2C_3F_6CH_2O)_2PN]_n$ copolymers and terpolymers (small amount of cure site) to evaluate these elastomers as replacements for

TABLE I
Typical Properties for $[(CF_3CH_2O)_2PN-(HCF_2C_3F_6CH_2O)_2PN]_n$ Elastomers

Physical state	elastomer
Glass transition temperature	−67°C (DTA)
Initial decomposition point in air, by TGA, 2.5°C/min	325°C
$[\eta]$ at 30°C (in acetone)	2.0–5.0 dl/g
Soluble in	ethanol, acetonitrile, Freon TA
Insoluble in	hexane, benzene, Freon E-2
Chemical and oxygen resistance	excellent

TABLE II
Typical Range of Physical Properties for
$[(CF_3CH_2O)_2PN-(HCF_2C_3F_6CH_2O)_2PN]_n$ Elastomer Vulcanizates

100% Modulus	1.4–10.5 MPa
Tensile strength	7.0–17.5 MPa
Elongation	100–350%
Hardness, Shore A	40–90
Compression set, 70 hr/150°C	20–50%
Tear strength	5.3–53 kN/m

existing materials used in extreme service lip seal, O-ring, and gasket applications.[5-9] An assortment of fillers and curatives were studied, and the properties in Table II are typical of the wide range possible.

Typical $[(CF_3CH_2O)_2PN-(HCF_2C_3F_6CH_2O)_2PN]_n$ elastomer formulations consist of three major components: fillers (reinforcing or extender types); a high-activity magnesium oxide (Elastomag 170) for efficient cure and enhanced thermal stability; and a peroxide curative. Auxiliary ingredients such as silanes, coagents, stabilizers, and process aids have all found use in compounds for specialized applications.

The best vulcanizate properties are obtained with fillers which have a neutral or basic pH. Filler loadings range from 10 to 100 parts per hundred rubber. Silane-treated silica fillers, either fumed (Tullanox 500) or precipitated (Quso WR82), and silane-treated clays (Nulock 321L, Burgess KE) are the fillers of choice for good mechanical properties and thermal stability. Carbon black fillers produce excellent vulcanizate properties, but they are limited in long-term service in the 135°–150°C range.

Peroxide curatives such as dicumyl peroxide, 2,5-dimethyl-2,5-di-*tert*-butylperoxyhexane and α,α-bis(*tert*-butylperoxy)diisopropylbenzene have been utilized successfully for effective cure and enhanced thermal stability. Peroxide concentrations of 0.2–2 parts per hundred by weight of rubber have been used for $[(CF_3CH_2O)_2PN-(HCF_2C_3F_6CH_2O)_2PN]_n$ terpolymers. Copolymers generally require higher peroxide levels. Sulfur cures have been accomplished with some terpolymers, but they are not recommended when thermal stability is a prerequisite.[10] Compounded stocks can be processed on conventional rubber process equipment.

Low-temperature flexibility of $[(CF_3CH_2O)_2PN-(HCF_2C_3F_6CH_2O)_2PN]_n$ vulcanizates compares favorably with other commercial fluoroelastomers, as shown by the Gehman subzero flexibility data depicted in Figure 1. The

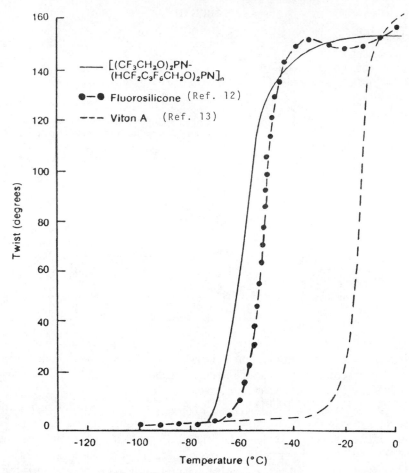

Fig. 1. Comparison of low-temperature Gehman properties of extreme service fluoroelastomers.

$[(CF_3CH_2O)_3PN-(HCF_2C_3F_6CH_2O)_2PN]_n$ vulcanizates have low-temperature flexibility superior to that of fluorocarbon rubbers and comparable to, or better than, that of fluorosilicone rubbers.

The $[(CF_3CH_2O)_2PN-(HCF_2C_3F_6CH_2O)_2PN]_n$ vulcanizates possess good thermal stability. Isothermal aging data for lip seal materials, shown in Table III, indicate lifetimes of about 500 hr at 177°C and 200 hr at 200°C. Tensile strength decreases gradually with exposure time, but thermal history has only minor detrimental effects on moduli, hardness, or elongation. Compression set remains quite low after exposure to these temperatures. Comparable vulcanizates can be expected to be serviceable in excess of 1000 hr at 150°C. Preliminary results[11] with a stabilizer, zinc 8-hydroxyquinolate, are extremely promising and suggest that this stabilizer may further improve thermal stability of the vulcanizates when used with appropriate fillers.

Fluid resistance of $[(CF_3CH_2O)_2PN-(HCF_2C_3F_6CH_2O)_2PN]_n$ polymers in general is good to excellent. Immersion studies for seal formulations in several lubricants and a hydraulic fluid are presented in Tables IV and V. The test vulcanizate displayed excellent retention of stress–strain properties, low volume swell, and hardness change after more the 1000 hr of immersion at 125°C in MIL

TABLE III
Thermal Stability in Air of $[(CF_3CH_2O)_2PN-(HCF_2C_3F_6CH_2O)_2PN]_n$ Vulcanizates

	0 hr	72 hr	144 hr	240 hr	504 hr
At 177°C					
50% Modulus, MPa	3.5	3.6	3.7	3.5	3.5
100% Modulus, MPa	9.9	—	—	—	—
Tensile strength, MPa	10.2	9.6	9.3	8.6	8.7
Elongation, %	105	95	85	90	95
Hardness, Shore A	70	—	—	—	73
Compression set, %					
70 hr/150°C in air	23				
70 hr/177°C in air	46				

	0 hr	24 hr	68 hr
At 200°C			
Tensile strength, MPa	10.2	7.7	4.9
Elongation, %	70	70	50
Hardness, Shore A	83	81	83
Compression set, %			
22 hr/150°C in air	26		
22 hr/200°C in air	49		

TABLE IV
Lubricant Compatibility of a $[(CF_3CH_2O)_2PN-(HCF_2C_3F_6CH_2O)_2PN]_n$ Vulcanizate

	125°C			150°C	
	0 hr	504 hr	1008 hr	72 hr	168 hr
MIL-7808G[a]					
50% Modulus, MPa	3.1	2.6	2.2	2.8	2.8
100% Modulus, MPa	9.7	8.9	7.4	8.9	8.4
Tensile strength, MPa	11.3	9.3	8.3	9.8	8.4
Elongation, %	110	105	115	115	100
Hardness, Shore A	77	70	71	72	69
Volume change, %	—	+9.9	+11.3	+9.2	+14.0
Compression set, %					
70 hr/150°C in air	21				
MIL L-23699[a]					
50% Modulus, MPa	3.1	3.1	2.8	3.0	3.0
100% Modulus, MPa	9.7	9.3	8.1	9.4	9.1
Tensile strength, MPa	11.3	10.0	9.5	10.0	9.7
Elongation, %	110	110	120	110	110
Hardness, Shore A	77	73	73	74	74
Volume change, %	—	+5.2	+6.0	+3.0	+4.4
Compression set, %					
70 hr/150°C in air	21				

[a] Commercial synthetic ester lubricants.

L-7808G and MIL L-23699 lubricants. The same vulcanizate also held up well at 150°C for the time period tested.

As shown in Table V, operational lifetime for a vulcanizate in MIL H-83282 flame-retardant hydraulic fluid should be about 500 hr at 177°C. Further improvements in the solvent resistance and thermal stability of the base elastomers or improved compounding may significantly extend lifetimes and increase service temperatures.

TABLE V
Hydraulic Fluid Compatibility of a
$[(CF_3CH_2O)_2PN-(HCF_2C_3F_6CH_2O)_2PN]_n$ Vulcanizate

	0 hr	168 hr	336 hr	504 hr
MIL H-83282[a] at 177°C				
50% Modulus, MPa	3.5	3.2	2.6	2.9
100% Modulus, MPa	9.9	—	—	—
Tensile strength, MPa	10.2	8.4	7.2	6.3
Elongation, %	105	90	90	95
Hardness, Shore A	70	—	—	—
Compression set, %				
70 hr/150°C in air	23			
70 hr/177°C in air	46			

[a] Commercial synthetic hydrocarbon fluid.

TABLE VI
Resistance of a $[(CF_3CH_2O)_2PN-(HCF_2C_3F_6CH_2O)_2PN]_n$ Vulcanizate to Jet Fuel

	0 hr	24 hr	120 hr	312 hr	Retention, %
JP-4 at 115°C					
Tensile strength, MPa	11.4	10.5	9.4	7.9	69.3
Elongation, %	80	75	75	75	93.8
Hardness, Shore A	80	77	75	72	90.0
Fluorosilicone tensile retention[13]					
72 hr/115°C, 45%					

Hydrocarbon fluids have a limited effect on $[(CF_3CH_2O)_2PN-(HCF_2C_3F_6CH_2O)_2PN]_n$ vulcanizates, as would be expected of an elastomer with high fluorine content. Volume swell in the ASTM fuels is minimal, with the most pronounced swell observed in Fuel C, which has a high aromatic content and is the most polar of the fuels. Resistance of

$$[(CF_3CH_2O)_2PN-(HCF_2C_3F_6CH_2O)_2PN]_n$$

vulcanizates to military jet fuel also is impressive, as shown in Table VI. Compare the vulcanizate's tensile retention after 312 hr at 115°C in JP-4 with a fluorosilicone after 72 hr immersion. Similar results have been obtained in JP-5, JP-7, and A-1 jet fuels.

Seals, gaskets, and coatings often are exposed to high humidity conditions. Therefore, they must be hydrolytically stable to remain functional. After nearly 900 hr at 100°C and 100% relative humidity, the vulcanizate shown in Table VII retained almost 85% of its original tensile properties.

The $[(CF_3CH_2O)_2PN-(HCF_2C_3F_6CH_2O)_2PN]_n$ elastomers also are stable to aqueous alkali at temperature, as shown in Table VIII. Dilute acids have only minor effect on vulcanizate properties; however, strong mineral acids and glacial acetic acid cause loss in physical properties. Further work in the area is planned because compounding variables may have a role in acid resistance.

Poly(fluoroalkoxyphosphazene) elastomers have demonstrated the capability to function in severe dynamic applications. For example, lip seals ($1\frac{7}{8}$ in. I.D.) performed for over 1000 hr at 5500 rpm in MIL L-7808G lubricant at 115°C.[5,9]

TABLE VII
Hydrolytic Stability of a Typical
$[(CF_3CH_2O)_2PN–(HCF_2C_3F_6CH_2O)_2PN]_n$ Vulcanizate at
$100°C$ and 100% Relative Humidity

	0 hr	168 hr	384 hr	888 hr
100% Modulus, MPa	10.1	8.6	8.8	6.1
Tensile strength, MPa	12.1	12.2	11.6	10.1
Elongation, %	115	135	135	145
Hardness, Shore A	55	69	70	70

TABLE VIII
Alkali Resistance of a $[(CF_3CH_2O)_2PN–(HCF_2C_3F_6CH_2O)_2PN]_n$ Vulcanizate[a]

	0 hr	24 hr	120 hr
Tensile strength, MPa	12.1	8.7	8.3
Elongation, %	120	110	110
Hardness, Shore A	60	60	61

[a] 30 wt-% aqueous KOH at $93°C$.

O-Ring seals based on $[(CF_3CH_2O)_2PN–(HCF_2C_3F_6CH_2O)_2PN]_n$ terpolymer withstood 1000 hr of dynamic qualification testing in a rod seal test apparatus over a temperature range of $-54°–163°C$ and pressure up to 21 MPa. Upon completion of the test, the seals remained soft and flexible. Newer seal compounds based on $[(CF_3CH_2O)_2PN–(HCF_2C_3F_6CH_2O)_2PN]_n$ terpolymer are expected to perform for 1000 hr in air or fluids at $-60°–177°C$ with intermittent service at $200°C$ possible. Additional dynamic tests with these new compounds are contemplated.

In summary, poly(fluoroalkoxyphosphazene) elastomers are a unique class of polymers capable of extreme service use. Their novel preparative route only requires a single polymerization step after which a variety of different polymer types can be prepared. Copolymers and terpolymers are readily prepared, and polymer properties can be tailored by proper choice of substituents. Vulcanizates possess a combination of low-temperature flexibility, thermal stability, good mechanical properties, petrol-oil and lubricant compatibility, and resistance to chemical attack and hydrolysis. These elastomers can be used for seals, O-rings, gaskets, diaphragms, hose, and protective coatings—in general, any application that requires a versatile, extreme-service elastomer.

The authors wish to express their gratitude to the U.S. Army and U.S. Navy for their support of this research. O-Ring dynamic tests were conducted by the Air Force Materials Laboratory, Elastomers and Coatings Branch, Wright-Patterson Air Force Base, Dayton, Ohio.

References

1. K. A. Reynard and S. H. Rose, *Synthesis of New Low Temperature Petroleum Resistant Elastomers*, Horizons Inc., Cleveland, Ohio, Contract DAAG 46-70-C-0075, AMMRC CR 70-26, Dec. 1970, AD 720 215.

2. S. H. Rose, K. A. Reynard, and J. R. Cable, *Synthesis of New Low Temperature Petroleum Resistant Elastomers*, Horizons Inc., Cleveland, Ohio, Contract DAAG 46-69-C-0076, AMMRC CR 70-1, January 1970, AD 704 332.

3. H. R. Allcock, *Phosphorus–Nitrogen Compounds*, Academic Press, New York, 1972.

4. G. S. Kyker and T. A. Antkowiak, *Rubber Chem. Technol.*, **47,** 32 (1974).

5. K. A. Reynard, R. W. Sicka, J. C. Vicic, and S. H. Rose, *Development of Thermally Stable Poly(fluoroalkoxyphosphazene) Transmission Seals for the UH-1 Helicopter,* Horizons Inc., Cleveland, Ohio, Contract DAAG 46-72-C-0073, AMMRC CTR 73-41, Sept. 1973, AD 773 652WM.

6. K. A. Reynard, R. W. Sicka, J. C. Vicic, and S. H. Rose, *Elastomers for Service with Engine Lubricants and Hydraulic Fluids,* Horizons Inc., Cleveland, Ohio, NAVAIR Contract N00019-72-C-0419, June 1973, AD 762 800.

7. K. A. Reynard, R. W. Sicka, J. C. Vicic, and S. H. Rose *Elastomers for Service with Engine Lubricants and Hydraulic Fluids,* Horizons Inc., Cleveland, Ohio, NAVAIR Contract N00019-73-OC-0406, Mar. 1974, AD 781 715.

8. J. C. Vicic and K. A. Reynard, *Poly(fluoroalkoxyphosphazene) Lip Seal Materials,* Horizons Inc., Cleveland, Ohio, Contract DAAG 46-74-C-0056, AMMRC-CTR 75-26, Oct. 1975, AD A021 001.

9. R. E. Singler, K. A. Reynard, R. W. Sicka, J. C. Vicic, and S. H. Rose, *Polyphosphazene Fluoroelastomers for Aircraft Seal Applications,* 19th National SAMPE Symposium, California, Apr. 1974.

10. P. E. Gatza and P. Touchet, *Polyphosphazene Fluoroelastomers for Fuel Service under Arctic Conditions,* presented at Technology Assessment and Planning Conference, Phosphazenes and Phosphazene High Polymers, AMMRC, May 1975.

11. G. S. Kyker, U.S. Pat. 3,867,341 (February 18, 1975).

12. O. R. Pierce, *Appl. Polym. Symp.* **No. 14,** 7 (1969).

13. A. Wilson, *Measurement of Rubber Elasticity at Low Temperature Using a Twist Recovery Apparatus,* AMMRC Tech. Rep. 66-4-CM, 1966.

14. Dow Corning Product Bulletin 17-167, Dow Corning Corporation, Midland, Michigan, 1972.

Received August 16, 1976
Revised September 23, 1976

JOURNAL OF APPLIED POLYMER SCIENCE   VOL. 21 3193–3209 (1977)

A Comparison of the Physical Properties of Radiation and Sulfur-Cured Poly(Butadiene–co–Styrene)

G. G. A. BÖHM, M. DETRANO, D. S. PEARSON, and D. R. CARTER,

Firestone Tire & Rubber Company, Akron, Ohio 44317

Synopsis

The physical properties of radiation- and sulfur-cured poly(butadiene–co–styrene)-based stocks were compared. It was found that the measured lower ultimate strength of radiation-cured stocks is in part attributable to the difference in the glass transition temperatures of the stocks cured by the two methods (an increase in T_g is caused by sulfur curing). Another factor contributing to the difference in performance is the apparent nonuniform crosslink density distribution in radiation-cured stocks containing carbon black filler. A higher crosslink density in the immediate vicinity of carbon black particles was postulated based on a to-be-expected distribution of secondary electron energy at interfaces with an appreciable change in density between neighboring phases. The invoked difference in network topology, supported by solvent swelling measurements on sulfur- and radiation-crosslinked vulcanizates can explain not only the slightly lower ultimate strength of radiation-cured stocks but also the superior fatigue and crack propagation performance measured for these vulcanizates. Finally, theoretical arguments were presented to explain the inferred large strength deficiency of radiation-cured rubbers reported by other investigators on the basis of chain scissions encountered during radiation crosslinking.

INTRODUCTION

The voluminous literature on the irradiation of rubbers which has been published over the last 30 years has made little mention of the physical properties of vulcanizates cured by this method. The data reported infer that the strength of radiation-cured rubbers, and particularly of natural rubber, is appreciably lower than that of rubber stocks cured with sulfur–accelerator curing systems. The ability of polysulfide linkages to dissipate localized stresses was invoked to rationalize these findings. However, recently published data on polybutadiene, poly(butadiene–co–styrene), poly(butadiene–co–acrylonitrile), and ethylene–propylene copolymers[1] have shown that the tensile strength of radiation-cured gum and carbon black-filled vulcanizates is about equal to that of their conventionally cured counterparts. It is believed that the earlier observed findings can be attributed to cure-retarding impurities or compound ingredients present in the rubber or added to the stock during compounding. Such chemicals increase the dose requirement for cure and consequently result in the occurrence of a greater number of unavoidable side reactions such as scissions. Moreover, degradation of the rubber by ozone generated by the radiation source may have been a contributing factor, particularly since many of the earlier experiments were carried out with gamma rays, in which case a prolonged exposure of the sample in the ozone-rich environment was required. The results of these earlier investigations have recently been summarized in a review article.[2]

It is the objective of this work to expand on the most recent studies by a more detailed investigation of the dynamic physical properties of poly(butadiene–co–styrene) rubber.

EXPERIMENTAL

Sample Preparation

Solution-polymerized poly(butadiene–co–styrene), made and sold by Firestone under the trade name Stereon 700 (M_n = 1.2 × 10^5, M_w/M_n = 2), was used throughout this study. The compositions of the compounds prepared from it are listed in Table I. The stocks were made by blending the elastomer, filler, and curatives in a Brabender Plasticorder, followed by additional mixing on a two-roll mill. The samples were subsequently molded and heat cured at 418°K for 30 min in an electric press. To facilitate the removal of the rubber samples from the mold, they were sandwiched between two 1.25 × 10^{-2}-cm-thick Mylar sheets.

Radiation vulcanization was effected by passing the Mylar-covered samples, placed on a horizontal conveyor belt, through a scanned electron beam 61 cm. wide and oscillating at 60 Hz. In those cases where irradiation was to be carried out at elevated temperatures, a special environmental cell was used which permitted exposure of the samples in an inert gas atmosphere. The energy of the electrons produced by a Dynamitron accelerator and the sample thickness were chosen in such a way that only the initial, almost linear part of the depth–dose distribution function was utilized in the irradiation of the samples. By a two-side exposure of the samples under these conditions, it was possible to achieve an almost uniform dose distribution throughout the plaques. This was confirmed by dose measurements on a multilayer composite phantom comprised of alternating layers of rubber stock and dosimeter tapes. Dosimetry measurements were performed using the bleaching of blue cellophane, the rate of which had been previously calibrated by calorimetry. The average dose rate used in the experiments was 1 Mrad/sec.

Physical Measurements

Stress–strain properties were measured in triplicate on an Instron tester using ring samples with an inside diameter of 1.57 cm which were cut from slabs approximately 0.2 cm thick. A testing speed of 5 cm/min was employed.

The dependence of the torsion modulus on temperature was determined with the help of a Tinius Olson tester using samples 0.63 × 5.0 × 0.2 cm in size. The entire probe assembly was dipped into a liquid nitrogen–ethanol mixture which permitted cooling of the rubber samples to temperatures well below the glass transition temperature T_g. Raising the temperature with the aid of an electric heater, measurements were then made at intervals of 3°K. A stirrer was used to ensure a uniform temperature profile across the rubber sample.

Flex life and crack propagation measurements were carried out with a Monsanto fatigue-to-failure tester in constant strain mode. Dumbbell-shaped

TABLE I
Compound Recipes for Sulfur- and Radiation-Cured Stocks

	S_1	S_2	S_3	S_4	R_1–R_6
Masterbatch[a]	156	156	156	156	156
Sulfur	1.4	1.6	1.75	1.9	—
Santocure NS	0.8	0.9	1.0	1.1	—
p-Dichlorobenzene	—	—	—	—	2

[a] Masterbatch: Stereon 700, 100 phr; ISAF, 50 phr; ZnO, 3 phr; stearic acid, 2 phr; Santoflex 13, 1 phr.

samples (7.6 cm long, 0.15 cm thick), with a beaded edge for slip-free clamping, were used for the flexing experiments. After mounting, the samples were precycled to 10^4 cycles using the strain amplitude selected for the experiment. The permanent set developed was subsequently taken up by an adjustment of the sample holder position. A similar correction was performed every 10^5 cycles. During the test, the probe was subjected for a quarter of each cycle to an increasing strain at constant acceleration which was released during the second quarter cycle. The sample was then held at zero strain for half a cycle to allow recovery to the original unstrained length. The number of cycles to failure were recorded automatically.

Similarly shaped but 20-cm-wide samples were used for crack propagation measurements. Special holders were fabricated for the mounting of these wide samples in the Monsanto tester. Following precycling and permanent set adjustment in the manner described above, a 5-cm-long horizontal cut starting from one side was introduced along an imaginary center line of the sample. The position of the crack tip was marked and the increasing cut length was measured as a function of the number of cycles.

Solvent Swelling Measurements

The volume fraction of rubber in swollen gum or carbon black-filled rubber, V_r, was determined by swelling the cured samples in the solvent of choice at room temperature for approximately 70 hr. During this time period, the solvent was changed after the first day. The samples were then weighed and subsequently dried in vacuo until a constant weight was achieved. Finally, V_r data were calculated using the dry weight to correct for the loss of sol.

A differential thermal analyzer made by du Pont, Model #900, was employed for the determination of glass transition temperatures.

RESULTS

Physical Strength

The stress at break of radiation- and sulfur-cured carbon black-reinforced poly(butadiene–co–styrene) vulcanizates is compared in Figure 1. Here as well as in many of the other graphs, the 300% modulus was selected as a measure of crosslink density since an almost linear relationship between it and dose has been noted for the carbon black-filled rubber compounds of this study. Aside from

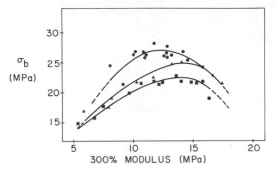

Fig. 1. Stress at break measured at test temperatures indicated in parenthesis: (■) radiation (297°K); (▲) radiation (292°K); (●) sulfur (297°K).

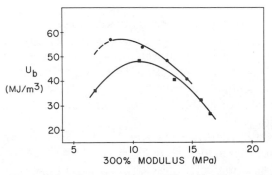

Fig. 2. Energy at break measured at 292°K: (■) radiation; (●) sulfur.

the curves representing measurements carried out at 297°K, data are shown for radiation-cured samples tested at 292°K. This seemed important since an about 5°K higher glass transition temperature has been measured for the sulfur-cured vulcanizates. This additional curve thus allows strength comparisons to be made at equal $T - T_g$. The graph shows a similar dependence of the stress at break on crosslink density for both types of networks; however, a shift of the tensile strength maximum toward higher moduli values can be noted for the radiation-cured rubbers. This shift is not observed when the stress-at-break data are plotted against V_r, the volume fraction of rubber in the toluene-swollen vulcanizate. The maxima then occur at $V_r = 0.215$.

A 16% lower tensile strength maximum is observed for the radiation-cured samples, which is reduced to 8% when the testing is done at equal $T - T_g$. This somewhat reduced tensile strength should also manifest itself in a lower energy to break, U_b, and hysteresis at break, H_b, which is shown in Figures 2 and 3. U_b was determined by measuring the area under the stress–strain curve. To measure H_b, a sample was extended to within a few per cent of the breaking stress and then retracted to zero stress at the same strain rate. Graphic integration of the area bounded by the extension and retraction curve yielded the hysteresis at break. As anticipated, we notice a lower energy to break for the radiation-cured samples. It is interesting to note, however, that the interdependence of hysteresis and energy to break first noted by Harwood and Payne[3] is preserved in this case with the data for both types of networks lying on the same curve. The fact that this relationship holds not only for a vulcanizate of given crosslink

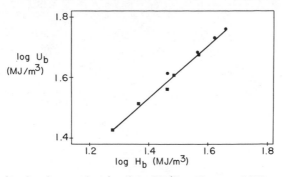

Fig. 3. Energy at break vs hysteresis at break for BD/S copolymers of different crosslink densities measured at 292°K: (■) radiation; (●) sulfur.

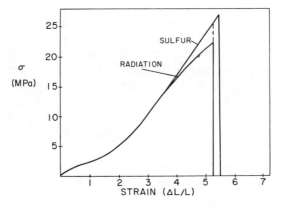

Fig. 4. Stress–strain curves of radiation- and sulfur-cured BD/S copolymers with identical 300% modulus.

density tested at different temperatures and strain rates as reported in the literature but also for rubbers with different types and distributions of crosslinks defines the broad universality of this concept. The equation might thus also apply to composites, heterogeneous in crosslink density, carbon-black concentration, or type, etc.

The lower energy to break of radiation-cured samples is, however, only partially attributable to a lower ultimate tensile strength. This can be gleaned from Figure 4, which compares the general shape of the stress–strain curves for the two types of vulcanizates cured to the same 300% modulus value. The curves are about identical up to $\lambda = 3$, above which a gradual divergence is notable. The sulfur-cured vulcanizate shows continued strain hardening which has often been ascribed to a nonaffine deformation of the network. In contrast, the stress–strain curve of the rubber cured by radiation exhibits a gradually decreasing slope followed by a break of the sample at a lower strain level. For the case depicted in Figure 4, it can be calculated that approximately 30% of the higher E_B measured for sulfur-cured vulcanizates is attributable to the divergence in the stress–strain curves, the remaining 70% is due to higher elongation-at-break values. While the actual difference in E_B varies with the degree of cure obtained in the rubbers (Fig. 2), the contribution of these two factors remains about the same.

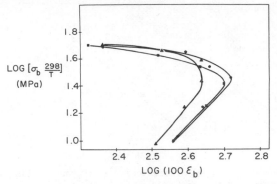

LOG [$\sigma_b \frac{298}{T}$]
(MPa)

LOG (100 $\mathcal{E}_b$)

Fig. 5. Rupture data (failure envelopes) for radiation- and sulfur-cured BD/S copolymers: (●) sulfur; (▲) radiation [V_r(rad) = V_r(sulfur)]; (■) radiation [300% M(rad) = 300% M(sulfur)].

The above referred-to divergence of the stress–strain curves at high extensions does not occur with gum vulcanizates. There, the characteristic sharp upturn of the curves on approach of the extensibility limit is noted for both radiation as well as sulfur-cured rubbers, suggesting that the phenomenon is associated with the presence during radiation cure of carbon black filler.

A more general dependence of ultimate tensile properties on crosslink density and other network characteristics can be gleaned from an examination of the failure envelopes. Provided time–temperature superposition is applicable, it has been shown by Smith[4] that failure data obtained at different temperatures and strain rates superimpose on a plot of log σ_b (T_0/T) versus log ϵ_b ($\epsilon_b = \lambda_b - 1$) and yield a master curve called the failure envelope. Figure 5 shows such a plot for a sulfur-cured sample and two radiation-cured rubber vulcanizates, one having an equal 300% modulus, the other showing an equal volume fraction of rubber (swollen in toluene at 292°K) compared to the sulfur-cured stock. As will be shown later, the expected equal correlation of modulus and volume swelling of the vulcanizate in a solvent does not hold true for these two vulcanizates, and, consequently, both conditions (300% modulus = const., V_r = const.) are used as somewhat arbitrary points of reference. The points on the failure envelope were determined by measuring the ultimate strength σ_b and strain at break ϵ_b for the polymers in a stress–strain experiment at a constant strain rate of 5 cm/min but at different temperatures. As can be seen, a considerable lower maximum extensibility is observed for the radiation-cured rubbers when compared at $V_r = 0.232$. This trend holds true for a broad range of V_r values (Fig. 6). A lower maximum extensibility of radiation-cured rubbers is also noted for vulcanizates of equal modulus, yet the difference in $(\lambda_b)_{max}$ values is much smaller than in the case of V_r = const.

Fatigue Failure

The results of flex life measurements carried out at 292°K in the constant strain mode are shown in Figure 7. There, the number of cycles to failure are plotted as a function of the energy of deformation expended during each flex cycle. The results of measurements carried out at different strain amplitudes as well as with compounds cured to different crosslink densities are all included in this graph.

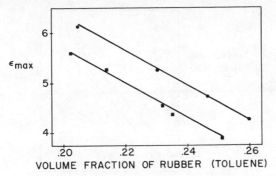

Fig. 6. Maximum extensibility for radiation- and sulfur-cured BD/S copolymers: (●) sulfur; (■) radiation.

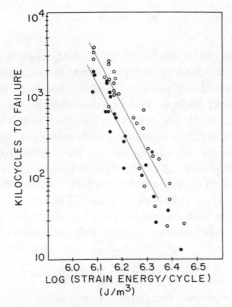

Fig. 7. Fatigue failure data obtained under cyclic test conditions at 292°K: (●) sulfur; (O) radiation.

A considerable degree of scatter of the data points can be observed, which is to be expected from such a measurement. It was determined, however, that considerable separation of the 95% confidence domains determined for the two sets of data points exists. The two straight lines fitted through the data points below $W = 2.2 \times 10^6$ Jm^{-3} using the least-squares method indicate that the radiation-cured stocks have an about two times greater flex life. At high energies per cycle, the data fall below the straight-line approximation of the low energy-per-cycle data. This trend has been observed before[5] and has been interpreted by a gradual transition from rough to smooth cut growth as W_0 approaches a value at which tearing occurs catastrophically. The observed greater flex life of radiation vulcanizates could be due to either a smaller rate of crack initiation or to a slower crack propagation. The former might not be totally unexpected since different molding and curing conditions were used. The sulfur-cured stocks were vulcanized under pressure at 418°K, whereas only atmospheric pressure

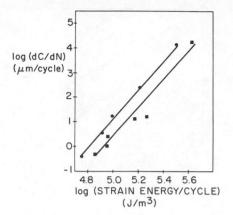

Fig. 8. Cut growth data obtained in pure shear under cyclic test conditions at 292°K. The 300% modulus of the samples was 9.5 MPa: (●) sulfur; (■) radiation.

was acting on the molded samples during radiation cure at 292°K. Density measurements carried out on both types of compounds prior to and after vulcanization did not reveal any porosity in the cured samples and only a minor densification was noted, such as would be expected by the crosslinking.

To clarify the contribution of the two mechanisms to the observed flex life differences, crack propagation measurements were performed at 292°K in the constant strain mode on samples cured to a 300% modulus of 9.3 MPa. The results are shown in Figure 8. A reduced crack propagation rate is noted for the radiation-cured stocks, the magnitude of which is somewhat larger than what would be anticipated from the flex-life data of Figure 7. Theory predicts that the slope of the fatigue-to-failure and crack propagation curves (Figs. 7 and 8) be equal. Our data yield values of 5.8 and 6.0, respectively.

Glass Transition Temperature

Changes in glass transition temperature are associated with a vulcanization of rubber compounds. Figure 9 shows data obtained on three carbon-black-filled stocks: one cured with sulfur, the other two, by irradiation at 292° and 418°K, respectively. Doses and sulfur levels were adjusted such that an equal modulus of 7.6 MPa was obtained for the three samples. The inflection points on the torsion modulus–temperature curves were taken as a measure of the glass transition temperature. Figure 9 reveals a 6°K higher glass transition temperature for the sulfur-cured stock when compared to the sample which was radiation crosslinked at 292°K. In the case of irradiation at 418°K, the temperature used for sulfur curing, an about 1°K lower T_g was noted. No attempt was made to interpret this small difference as it might be within the error of the experiment. DTA data of gum and filled compounds (Table II) show a similar trend. Here again, we find an increase in T_g of 4°K on sulfur curing, in contrast to no T_g change associated with a radiation cure. The latter observation is in line with theoretical predictions one can make assuming a chemical crosslink density in the irradiated sample of $M_c \geq 5000$. The fact that somewhat different ΔT_g values were determined from DTA and torsion modulus data is not surprising, since the measurement of the glass transition temperature is sensitively de-

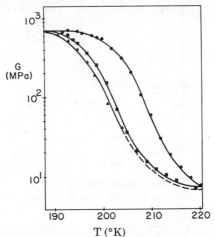

Fig. 9. Shear modulus measured in torsion for samples cured at temperatures indicated in parenthesis: (■) radiation (292°K); (▲) radiation (418°K); (●) sulfur (418°K).

pendent on the tool and on sulfur curing thus suggests that aside from the formation of $C—S_n—C$ crosslinks, other products such as vicinal polysulfide crosslinks, cyclic sulfides, and pendent sulfur-containing groups are generated which represent a considerable modification of the polymer backbone and thus cause an increase in the glass transition temperature. Such reactions have already been reported in the literature.[6]

Network Topology

In an effort to discover any differences which might exist in network topology between radiation- and sulfur-crosslinked rubbers, swelling experiments were conducted on both gum- as well as carbon black-filled vulcanizates. The work of Flory[7] suggests a simple relationship between crosslink density or the elastic modulus of a given polymer and equilibrium swelling, with the polymer solvent interaction coefficient as the only adjustable parameter. One would expect, therefore, the data points for the radiation and sulfur-cured stocks to fall on a single curve. This, however, has not been found in our experiments. The results obtained, illustrated in form of the dependence of V_r, the volume fraction of rubber in the solvent-swollen vulcanizate on the 300% modulus, are shown in Figures 10 and 11. A similar plot is obtained if the force of retraction at $\lambda = 3$ (equilibrium modulus) is used instead of the dynamic 300% modulus. For any given V_r value, one observes a higher 300% modulus for radiation-cured, filled samples (Fig. 10) regardless of whether they were irradiated at 292° or at 418°K.

TABLE II
T_g (DTA) Changes in BD/S Copolymers (Stereon 700) on Curing

Gum and compound (50 phr ISAF)	T_g, °K
Uncured	195
Radiation (cured at 292°K)	195
Radiation (cured at 418°K)	194
Sulfur (1.4 phr S, cured at 418°K)	199

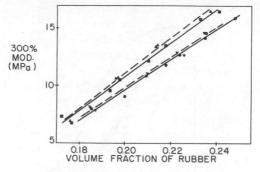

Fig. 10. Swelling of carbon-black-filled vulcanizates in toluene and tetrahydrofuran (THF) at 292°K: (■) radiation (toluene); (▲) radiation (THF); (●) sulfur (toluene); (▼) sulfur (THF).

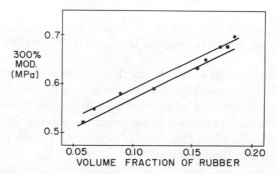

Fig. 11. Swelling of gum vulcanizates in toluene at 292°K: (■) radiation; (●) sulfur.

This difference in strength, which varied somewhat with the degree of cross-linking (12% at $V_r = 0.235$ for toluene), was noted in samples swollen either with toluene or with tetrahydrofuran (THF). The latter polar solvent was used to elucidate the possible contribution of the relatively polar sulfur, present only in the heat-cured sample, to the observed differences in swelling behavior. As can be gathered from Figure 10, the curves for THF and toluene can be super-imposed by a parallel shift as would be expected from the difference in poly-mer–solvent interaction parameters. The difference in modulus at any V_r value, however, has not diminished with the use of THF.

Identical measurements carried out on gum rubbers yield quite different re-sults (Fig. 11). Here, the moduli values (V_r = const.) of the radiation- and sul-fur-cured samples are identical within the error of the experiment. This finding is in line with the predictions of the Flory–Rehner equation and eliminates the possibility that the modulus difference seen in Figure 10 is attributable to a change in solvent–polymer interaction coefficient caused by the presence of sulfur in one sample. The evidence rather suggests that in contrast to gum vulcanizates, radiation- and sulfur-cured stocks containing carbon black filler have a different network topology.

DISCUSSION

The findings of earlier investigations (summarized in ref. 2) all indicate a considerably lower ultimate strength for radiation-cured poly(butadiene–co–styrene). The reported strength deficiency relative to their sulfur-cured counterparts of 30% and more, we believe, can in part be attributed to main chain scissions generated simultaneously with crosslinking. The total number of scissions induced during radiation vulcanization, $[S]$, depends on their yield per unit dose, $G(S)$, and on the total dose R required for cure: $[S] = G(S)R$. Irradiation of the BD/styrene rubbers in air, the presence of certain chemicals, and higher irradiation temperature all raise $G(S)$. The cure dose, in turn, that is, the dose required to obtain a certain modulus in the vulcanizate, is increased by a number of crosslink-retarding chemicals present, particularly in emulsion-polymerized rubbers, and by additives such as antioxidants, processing aids, oil, etc., added to the stock during compounding.

The effect of main chain scissions on the physical properties of cured vulcanizates can be understood in terms of the reduction in molecular weight of the elastomer and the associated increase in the chain end contribution. If a certain modulus is to be achieved in a vulcanizate regardless of whether or not scission is occurring during crosslinking, the increase in chain ends (chains which have no load-bearing capability) has to be compensated by an increase in the number of chemical crosslinks. The associated decrease in the average molecular weight of an elastically active strand and its effect on failure properties such as energy to break can be estimated as follows.

The tensile modulus E can be calculated according to Langley[8]:

$$E = 3g\nu RT \tag{1}$$

where

$$\nu = (q\rho/M_0)W_g T_e^{1/2} + 2\epsilon T_e \tag{2}$$

where ν is the concentration of elastically effective strands, q is the fraction of repeat units joined to another unit by an intermolecular crosslink, W_g is the gel weight fraction, ϵ is the effective concentration of potential entanglements, and T_e is the entanglement trapping probability.

For crosslinking by radiation, $q = q_0 R$, where q_0 is the number of crosslinked units produced per unit dose. Moreover, $T_e^{1/2} = (1 - W_s^{1/2})^2$ for $M_w^0/M_n^0 = 2$. Equation (2) can then be rewritten as follows:

$$\nu = \frac{(q_0 R)}{(M_0)}(1 - W_s)(1 - W_s^{1/2})^2 + 2\epsilon(1 - W_s^{1/2})^4 \tag{3}$$

The sol weight fraction W_s remaining in a vulcanizate following simultaneous crosslinking and scission is, according to Saito,[9]

$$W_s + W_s^{1/2} = \frac{1}{q_0 R P_n} + \frac{p_0}{q_0} \tag{4}$$

where

$$\frac{p_0}{q_0} = \frac{1G(S)}{2G(X)}$$

Equations (3) and (4) can be combined to eliminate $q_0 R$:

$$p_0/q_0 = (W_s + W_s^{1/2}) - \frac{1}{M_0 P_n}\frac{(1 - W_s)\cdot(1 - W_s^{1/2})^2}{[\nu - 2\epsilon(1 - W_s^{1/2})^4]} \tag{5}$$

If the vulcanizates are to be compared at equal modulus, then ν = const. W_s

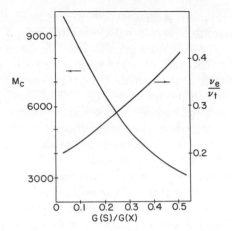

Fig. 12. Effect of $G(S)/G(X)$ encountered during radiation vulcanization on the average molecular weight between elastically effective chemical crosslinks (M_c) and on the chain-end contribution (ν_{end}/ν_{tot}) for samples having identical tensile moduli; $M_n{}^0 = 10^5$, $M_w/M_n = 2$, ν(effective) $= 3 \times 10^{-4}$ moles/cm^3.

can then be calculated as function of p_0/q_0. From this, we can determine the chain end contribution

$$V_e/V_t = 1 - (1 - W_s{}^{1/2})^2 \tag{6}$$

(the number of structural units in chain ends per total number of structural units) and the average molecular weight per elastically active strand

$$M_c = \frac{(1 - W_s{}^{1/2})^2}{\nu - 2\epsilon(1 - W_s{}^{1/2})^4} \tag{7}$$

V_e/V_t and M_c were calculated for a polybutadiene of $M_n = 10^5$ and $M_w/M_n = 2$. A density of elastically effective strands and entanglements of $\nu = 3 \times 10^4$ and $\epsilon = 1.7 \times 10^{-4}$ moles/cc, respectively, were chosen. The results shown in Figure 12 indicate a considerable effect of chain scissions on the chain-end contribution and on M_c, respectively. To estimate the effect of a reduction in M_c on failure properties, one can make use of the relationship between M_c and the maximum extensibility of a rubber network. Assuming an affine deformation of the network $\lambda_m(\infty)$, the maximum extension ratio that would be attainable if rupture did not occur should be proportional to $M_c{}^{1/2}$. However, experiments by Smith[10] have shown that the maximum observable extension ratio $(\lambda_b)_{max} < \lambda_m(\infty)$ is proportional to $M_c{}^{0.75}$. This empirical relationship, together with the data of Figure 12, clearly illustrate that an increase in $G(S)/G(X)$ encountered during vulcanization will result in a marked decrease in $(\lambda_b)_{max}$ which, in turn, will cause lower failure properties such as tensile strength, energy to break, etc. The earlier reported low physical properties of radiation cured rubbers ($G(S)/G(X)$ values of 0.15 were measured for irradiation *in vacuo* and much higher values must be anticipated for exposure in air) can thus be explained. A more detailed discussion of the effect of scission on the failure properties of vulcanizates is in preparation.[11]

Let us now return to the findings of this study. The results of our work indicate a difference in ultimate strength of 16% which reduces to 8% when the samples are tested at equal $T - T_g$. In a separate experiment not reported here, we have found that only a negligible amount of scission occurred during the radiation curing of the samples used for this analysis. This was done by sol-gel analysis and subsequent interpretation of a Charlesby–Pinner plot[12] which yields $G(S)/G(X)$, the ratio of the G values for scission to crosslinking. Having excluded the possibility of degradation occurring on radiation curing, we conclude that the remaining 8% discrepancy in ultimate strength must relate to an inherent difference of the networks formed during vulcanization.

The greater strength of sulfur-cured samples has been often attributed to the invoked ability of polysulfide crosslinks to break and re-form under stress, a process which was neither anticipated to occur nor observed for carbon–carbon crosslinks generated by peroxide or radiation vulcanization. However, stress relaxation experiments performed by Tobolsky and Lyons[13] have shown no evidence for a mechanical lability of the weak S_n crosslinks at room temperature. In a more direct approach, Lal[14] was able to demonstrate that polysulfide crosslinks are not essential for attaining high tensile strength in natural rubber vulcanizates. This was accomplished by measurements on samples in which the polysulfide linkages were converted to mono- and disulfide crosslinks by reaction with triphenyl phosphine. This evidence placed considerable doubt on the validity of the crosslink slipping mechanism. The greater physical strength of sulfur-cured stocks may, in part, be attributable to an internally relaxed network formed by the thermal lability of the sulfur crosslinks at vulcanization temperatures. In line with this reasoning, C–C crosslinks formed by irradiation can permanently entrap stresses and strains introduced in the sample through prior molding, etc. These, one could argue, might result in a lower ultimate strength of the vulcanizate. An irradiation cure of the rubber stocks at a temperature such as is used for a sulfur cure would at least in part simulate the state of a stress-free vulcanizate. Experiments carried out under these conditions showed a considerable rate of scission occurring which itself caused a decrease in stress at break and thus interfered with the proving of the above hypothesis. Other factors, such as differences in the distribution of network chains, could also contribute to the measured lower physical strength of radiation-cured rubbers. This aspect will be discussed later in conjunction with solvent swelling data.

Contrary to the performance of the vulcanizates at strains near the maximum extensibility, the irradiated samples exhibit a greater fatigue life when undergoing cyclic deformation at small to moderate strains. The crack growth data of Figure 8 attribute the superior performance on flexing to a slower crack propagation rate. Andrews et al.[15] have shown that the number of stress cycles required for an original flaw to grow from a length C_0 to C_1 can be expressed as

$$\Delta N = ([n - 1]Bk^n W_0^n)^{-1} \{C_0^{1/n-1} - C_1^{1/n-1}\} \qquad (8)$$

where W_0 is the stored energy density at a distance away from the crack; k is a slowly varying function of the strain; and B and n are constants. The number of cycles to failure can then be calculated by assuming that $C_1 \gg C_0$:

$$N_f = A W_0^{-n} \qquad \text{with} \qquad A = ([n - 1]Bk^n C_0^{n-1})^{-1} \qquad (9)$$

The data of Figure 7 conform to this relationship with $n = 5.8$ and A(radiation)/A(sulfur) = 2.05. Additional information can be gained from the cut growth data of Figure 8, which can be adequately represented by eq. (10):

$$dC/dN = BT^n \tag{10}$$

For the sample geometry chosen, the tearing energy T is equal to $W_0 l$, where l is the height of the unstrained test piece. Our data yield $n = 6$ and B(sulfur)/ B(radiation)~4.

Since $A(R)/A(S) < B(S)/B(R)$, it must be concluded that the difference in flex life measured for the two vulcanizates can only in part be attributed to a difference in the dynamic cut growth constants B. Unfortunately, the data of this study cannot provide any further detail on possible variances of either C_0 or k which one would have to assume in line with eqs. (9) and (10). However, an observation which might bear on this question is that the crack surface of the irradiated stock is somewhat rougher than that of the sulfur-cured vulcanizate which could imply a larger C_0 for the former network.

The surprising and most informative result of this study is presented in the swelling data of Figures 10 and 11. They indicate a different modulus–V_r relationship for radiation- and sulfur-cured vulcanizates and attribute these variances to the presence of carbon black. The latter observation, as well as the fact that similar data are obtained for stocks irradiated at 292° and 418°K (omitted in Figs. 10 and 11), eliminate the possibility that styrene–rich domains entrapped by room-temperature irradiation of the random copolymer are responsible for these findings.

Also ruled out can be the contribution of a slight crosslink density gradient one might expect in the sulfur-cured sample due to the heat conduction-controlled advance of the cure front. This can be concluded from Figure 10, which shows a linear dependence of modulus on V_r over a considerable crosslink density (modulus) range. A near independence of the $M = f(V_r)$ relationship on crosslink density distribution was also confirmed experimentally using radiation-cured samples in which a crosslink density gradient across the sample thickness was introduced by variations in the energy of the electron beam used for the exposure.

An interpretation of the data is, however, possible if one considers the somewhat complex deposition of energy by ionizing radiation in a heterogeneous matrix such as is represented by the elastomer–carbon black dispersion. When a high-energy electron such as generated by the radiation source used in this study traverses a polymer, a large number of secondary electrons are produced along its track. These lower-energy electrons are responsible for essentially all the physical and chemical effects induced by the radiation act. They dissipate their energy of several hundred eV by interaction with the molecules of the surrounding matrix. Ions, excited species, and radicals are produced, some of which then cause the formation of a chemical crosslink.[16] The region of influence of a secondary electron approximated by a sphere with the point of its creation as center increases with the energy of the electrons and decreases with the density of the surrounding material. A range of 100 Å in water has been estimated[17] for an electron energy of 300 eV, and a similar travel distance should be encountered in polymers of unit density. The number of secondary electrons produced per volume element is proportional to the density of the polymer.

We can now apply this information to describe the energy dissipation of

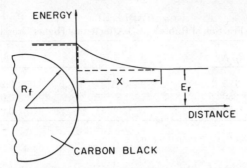

Fig. 13. Schematic of energy deposition near a carbon-black–rubber interface on irradiation of carbon-black-filled elastomer: (—) with energy transfer; (- - -) without energy transfer.

electrons for a carbon-black-filled elastomer. Figure 13 shows the energy deposited as a function of the distance away from the center of a carbon black particle schematically depicted as a sphere. The dotted line represents the situation in which either an equal or no energy exchange at all takes place across the carbon black (cb)–rubber (r) interface. The ratio of the energies depositied in the carbon black and the rubber matrix, $E_{cb}/E_r = 1.8$, is equal to the density ratio ρ_{cb}/ρ_r for the two materials. However, the greater number of electrons generated in the carbon black will cause more energy to be moved across the phase boundary into the rubber matrix than will be returned to the carbon black. This energy transfer across the phase boundary will, of course, only be effected by secondary electrons generated in the two materials near the interface. The thickness x of rubber around each carbon-black particle in which an energy $E > E_r$ is deposited by energy transfer is governed by the maximum penetration into the rubber of electrons produced in the surface region of the carbon-black particle. Based on the estimated range of secondary electrons in polymeric materials, one can reason that x should be smaller than 50 Å. The actual energy distribution is thus expected to follow the solid line. Moreover, since the number of crosslinks produced per volume element of rubber is proportional to the energy deposited in it, we must expect that an increased crosslink density will be encountered in the immediate vicinity of carbon black particles. The volume fraction ϕ_r' of rubber affected by a higher crosslinking can be calculated using eq. (11):

$$\phi_r' = \frac{\phi_f}{\phi_r}\left\{\frac{(R_f + x)^3}{R_f{}^3} - 1\right\} \tag{11}$$

$$\phi_r = 1 - \phi_f \qquad \phi_r = \phi_r' + \phi_r''$$

where R_f is the radius of the filler (carbon black) particle, ϕ_f is the volume fraction of filler, ϕ_r is the total volume fraction of rubber, ϕ_r'' is the volume fraction of rubber unaffected by this process, and x is the thickness of the above referred-to rubber layer surrounding the carbon black particle. The ϕ_r' values calculated for rubber stocks containing filler particles of different size are listed in Table III. As can be gathered, ϕ_r' is large for small particles and high filler levels such as are used in our study.

The effect of this nonuniform crosslink density in the rubber phase to be expected with radiation crosslinking on the physical properties of vulcanizates can only be qualitatively assessed. Let us for this purpose compare two hypothetical

TABLE III
Volume Fraction of Rubber (ϕ_r') Affected by Higher Crosslinking[a]

R_f, Å	ϕ_r'
125	0.205
250	0.093
1250	0.017

[a] Assumption: $X = 25$ Å, $\phi_f = 0.22$ (50 phr).

ISAF black-filled rubber vulcanizates having equal modulus: one, labeled A, with a uniform crosslink distribution throughout the rubber matrix, and another, B, possessing a distribution similar to the one described for radiation-cured vulcanizates. We would, first of all, expect that V_r(A) would be larger than V_r(B). This should be the case since the modulus of ISAF-reinforced rubber exhibits à steep dependence on crosslink density. Moreover, the modulus increase should be particularly sensitive to crosslinks formed in the vicinity of carbon black particles as this region is mainly responsible for the reinforcement in strength of vulcanizates by carbon black fillers. Consequently, fewer crosslinks in the bulk of the rubber matrix should be required in case B to achieve a 300% modulus M(A) = M(B), and hence sample B should swell more than sample A. It might be worth adding that one should not expect the swelling to be much affected by an increase in the density of crosslinks near the carbon-black surface. As shown by Kraus,[18] swelling of rubber in this region is already much restricted, and thus a further immobilization of the network there should be of little consequence. Secondly, the higher chemical crosslink density near the carbon-black particle should result in a lower hysteresis at break and a reduced $(\lambda_b)_{max}$ for case B. Both of the above predictions have been observed in our investigation. Finally, it is reasonable to assume that the cut growth rate encountered in sample B is smaller than in A because of the smaller crosslink density predicted for the bulk of the former sample. One would expect the tortuous path taken by a slowly growing crack around the filler particles to be mainly influenced by the viscoelastic response of the bulk of the rubber matrix and to a lesser degree by the regions around carbon black particles. A detailed assessment of the contribution that the more crosslinked regions of B make to the cut growth rate measured for the composite cannot be made at present. The greater flex life of radiation-cured stock is, however, worth noting. It suggests that composites of the type predicted to exist in radiation-cured, filled rubber vulcanizates be more extensively explored.

The authors are much indebted to Messrs. J. Wilson, D. Diehl, and E. Galloway for the irradiation of the samples and for much of the sample preparation and testing work. Also appreciated are the helpful discussions with Mr. Weissert, Dr. Avgeropoulos, and Dr. Tveekrem. Finally, the authors wish to thank Dr. G. Alliger for his continued support of these investigations and The Firestone Tire & Rubber Company, Inc., for permission to publish this work.

References

1. D. S. Pearson and G. G. A. Böhm, Rubber Chem. Technol. **45**, 193 (1972).
2. G. G. A. Böhm, in *The Radiation Chemistry of Macromolecules*, Vol. II, M. Dole, Ed., Academic Press, New York, 1973, Chap. 12.

3. J. A. C. Harwood and A. R. Payne, *J. Appl. Polym. Sci.*, **12**, 889 (1968).

4. T. L. Smith, *J. Polym. Sci. A*, **1**, 3597 (1963).

5. G. J. Lake and P. B. Lindley, *J. Polym. Sci.*, **8**, 707 (1964).

6. L. Bateman, C. G. Moore, M. Porter, and B. Saville, in *The Chemistry and Physics of Rubber-like Substances*, L. Bateman, Ed., Wiley, New York, 1963, Chap. 15.

7. P. J. Flory and J. Rehner, Jr., *J. Chem. Phys.*, **11**, 512 (1943).

8. N. R. Langley, *Macromolecules*, **1**, 348 (1968).

9. O. Saito, in *The Radiation Chemistry of Macromolecules*, Vol. I, M. Dole, Ed., Academic Press, New York, 1973, Chap. 11.

10. T. L. Smith, in *Rheology, Theory and Applications*, Vol. 5, F. R. Eirich, Ed., Academic Press, New York, 1969, Chap. 4.

11. G. G. A. Böhm, in preparation.

12. A. Charlesby and S. H. Pinner, *Proc. R. Sci.*, **A249**, 367 (1959).

13. A. V. Tobolsky and P. L. Lyons, *J. Polym. Sci. A2*, **6**, 1561 (1968).

14. J. Lal, *Rubber Chem. Technol.*, **43**, 664 (1970).

15. E. H. Andrews and B. J. Walker, Proc. R. Soc., **A325**, 57 (1971).

16. G. G. A. Böhm, *J. Polym. Sci. A2*, **14**, 437 (1976).

17. D. E. Lea, *Actions of Radiation on Living Cells*, 2nd ed., Cambridge, 1956.

18. G. Kraus, *J. Appl. Polym. Sci.*, **7**, 861 (1963).

Received August 5, 1976
Revised November 8, 1976

JOURNAL OF APPLIED POLYMER SCIENCE   VOL. 21, 3211–3222 (1977)

Bound Rubber and "Crepe Hardening" in Silicone Rubber

PETR VONDRÁČEK and MIROSLAV SCHÄTZ, *Department of Polymers, Prague Institute of Chemical Technology, 166 28 Prague 6, Czechoslovakia*

Synopsis

Some recent results of the research aimed to correlate properties of filled silicone rubber compounds with surface properties of fumed silica fillers are reported. It is shown that the specific interaction between silica surface silanol groups and the siloxane chain of silicone rubber plays the main role in "crepe hardening" and bound rubber formation in compounds. The silanol coverage of silica determines the tightness of polymer–filler network in bound rubber. The experimental data fit Meissner's theory of bound rubber quite well. Remilling of "crepe hardened" compounds was also studied, and the structure of the remilled compounds is proposed. The activation energy of bound rubber formation on mixing was found to be 16.8 kJ/mole; this suggests that physical rather than chemical processes are involved in the interaction between silica and silicone rubber.

INTRODUCTION

The reinforcement of rubbers by fillers depends on several factors: particle size, structure, and filler loading, all determining the polymer–filler contact area available for mutual interaction. The degree of surface interaction activity is the last, but not the least, factor influencing the reinforcement of rubbers. This factor is determined by the physical and chemical nature of both filler surface and elastomer matrix.

.This paper is concerned with the problem of determining a correlation between properties of fumed silica fillers and their interaction with silicone rubber. Silicone rubber possesses very poor mechanical properties when unfilled. It must be reinforced by active silica filler for technical application.

"CREPE HARDENING" AND BOUND RUBBER IN SILICONE RUBBER COMPOUNDS

The best reinforcing action of fumed silica in silicone rubber is accompanied by technologically undesirable hardening of uncured compounds on storage. The time-dependent "crepe hardening" accompanied by extensive bound rubber formation is one of the characteristics of the fumed silica–silicone rubber system.

3211

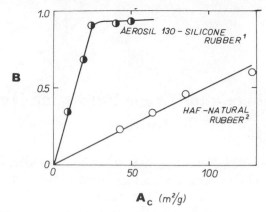

Fig. 1. Bound rubber content B as a function of polymer–filler contact area A_c after prolonged storing (approx. 2000 hr) at 25°C.

The "crepe hardened" compounds crumble when put on a roll mill and become again processable only on prolonged milling.

Figure 1 shows the bound rubber content formed in fumed silica-filled silicone rubber after prolonged storage[1] at 25°C and in natural rubber filled with carbon black[2] as a function of the polymer–filler contact area. The results (Fig. 1) demonstrate that the surface interaction activity of fumed silica is much greater than the activity of carbon black in hydrocarbon rubber. This indicates a much more extensive bonding between silica and silicone rubber.

The enormous surface interaction activity of fumed silica in silicone rubber seems to be responsible for "crepe hardening." The surface activity of silica is determined by its surface chemistry,[3–5] which seems to be a very complex subject.[6–8] However, the main feature of the silica surface is that a great number of strongly protonized[9] silanol (hydroxyl) groups are present, which should be capable of specific interaction with siloxanes.[10,11,12]

Typical groups which can occur on the fumed silica surface[13] are sketched in Figure 2. The presence of silanol groups on the silica surface make the attachment of various other groups possible, and the surface activity of silica can be modified in this way.[13,14]

Our previous work[4,5] on silicone rubber–silica system showed "crepe hardening" as a time- and temperature-dependent process closely connected with bound rubber formation. We have also studied the influence of storing temperature (up to 135°C) on silica surface activity in silicone rubber and evaluated the activation energy of "crepe hardening" and bound rubber formation on storage as being approximately 42 kJ/mole (10 kcal/mole).

EXPERIMENTAL

Compounds were prepared from methylvinylsiloxane rubber Lukopren G 1000, made by VCHZ Synthesia, Kolin, Czechoslovakia, of viscosity-average molecular weight 500,000.

Various silicas differing from each other by their surface nature (Table I), were incorporated in silicone rubber on a laboratory two-roll mill in about 30 min. Properties of these compounds were studied on storage after mixing at various storing temperatures.

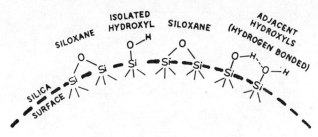

Fig. 2. Chemical groups on the surface of fumed silica.[13]

The plasticity of compounds was measured by the penetrometric method,[15] based on the principle of forcing the conical indentor (weight 135 g, apex angle 30°) into a sheet of the material to be examined for a fixed time of 5 sec. The plasticity values are expressed as a penetration degree (°P), i.e., the indentor penetration of 0.1 mm into the sheet examined at 25°C. Samples stored at higher temperatures were left to cool to room temperature before determining their plasticity.

Bound rubber content and its equilibrium swelling in benzene were determined on samples stored at different temperatures for various periods. Samples of compounds approximately 0.2 g in weight were immersed in benzene (approx. 50 ml) for at least six days with a twice-a-day exchange of fresh solvent. Swollen samples of extracted compounds were weighed, dried first at room temperature and then overnight at 80°C, and weighed again. The bound rubber content B is expressed as the percentage of the original silicone rubber found to be insoluble in benzene.

TABLE I
Typical Properties of Silica Filler Used

Filler	Manufacturer	Surface area, m^2/g	Surface treated with	Surface silanol coverage, $SiOH/nm^2$
Aerosil 130	Degussa	80	untreated	3[a]
Aerosil R 972	Degussa	130	dimethyl-dichloro-silane	0.75[a]
Aerosil 200	Degussa	200	untreated	3[a]
HDK N 20 S	Wacker-Chemie	200	untreated	1.3[b]
HDK H 20/1	Wacker-Chemie	174	trimethyl-chloro-silane	0.92[b]
HDK H 20/2	Wacker-Chemie	174	trimethyl-chloro-silane	0.41[b]
HDK H 20/3	Wacker-Chemie	174	trimethyl-chloro-silane	0.59[b]

[a] From reference 18.

[b] Calculated from the titration data of Dr. Stohr, Experimental products provided by Dr. Stohr of Wacker-Chemie, Zweigbetrieb Kempten.

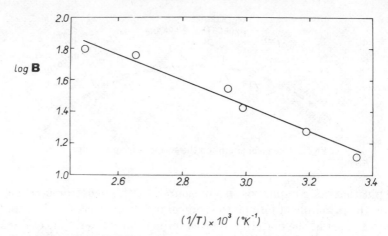

Fig. 3. Logarithm of bound rubber content B as a function of reciprocal absolute temperature of mixing 40 phr of fumed silica into silicone rubber in Plastograph Brabender.

The "crepe hardened" compounds were remilled on a laboratory two-roll mill for the time necessary to obtain processable and homogeneous compounds. The remilled compounds were shelf aged again, and their properties were studied during storage at 25°C.

The Brabender Plastograph was used for mixing compounds at different temperatures. The filler was incorporated into preheated polymer within 10 min, and the mixture was then mixed for an additional 10 min at a given temperature. After mixing in the heated Plastograph chamber, the compound was homogenized on a two-roll mill at room temperature for the next 5 min. The samples for bound rubber determination were then cut off and immersed in benzene for six days with a twice-a-day exchange of solvent.

RESULTS AND DISCUSSION

Activation Energy of "Crepe Hardening" and Bound Rubber Formation

Southwart[16,17] derived from bound rubber data in fumed silica filled silicone rubber an activation energy of approximately 84 kJ/mole (20 kcal/mole) immediately after mixing but of only 42 kJ/mole (10 kcal/mole) in samples after prolonged storage. Therefore, he proposed chemical polymer–filler interaction during the mixing stage and immediately after mixing; prolonged storage might be controlled by diffusion.

To verify this suggestion, we studied bound rubber formation during mixing at different temperatures in silicone rubber containing 40 phr fumed silica having a surface area of 200 m^2/g (Aerosil 200) in a heated chamber of the Brabender Plastograph.

Results of the bound rubber measurements in compounds mixed at a temperature range of 25°–130°C are given in Figure 3, where the logarithm of bound rubber content is plotted against the reciprocal absolute temperature of mixing. The activation energy of bound rubber formation on mixing was calculated from

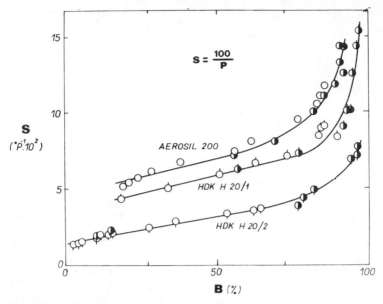

Fig. 4. Stiffness S as a function of bound rubber content B in silicone rubber containing 40 phr of 200 m²/g type fumed silicas differing in surface treatment. Compounds stored at 25°C (O) and 135°C (◑) after mixing.

the slope as being 16.8 kJ/mole (4 kcal/mole). This value suggests physical rather than chemical interaction and probably hydrogen bonding between surface silanol groups of silica and polysiloxane chains, as proposed by Chahal,[14] Nelson and Ionina,[12] Boonstra et al.,[13] and the authors of this paper.[1,4,5]

The higher value of activation energy of bound rubber formation and "crepe hardening" in silicone rubber filled with fumed silica at longer storing time[1,4,5,16,17] might be taken as evidence for polymer–filler interaction controlled by diffusion except at very short storage time, as proposed by Southwart.[16,17]

But generally, the silica–silicone rubber interaction in unvulcanized compounds appears to be of a physical nature.

Effect of Silica Silanol Coverage on "Crepe Hardening" and Bound Rubber Formation

To investigate the effect of silica silanol inactivation on the behavior of the silica in silicone rubber, compounds filled with silicas differing by degree in their surface modification (Table I) were studied on storage after mixing.

Figure 4 shows stiffness S as a function of bound rubber content B in compounds containing 40 phr of fillers having a comparable surface area of approximately 200 m²/g. The stiffness S is defined as a reciprocal plasticity P measured penetrometrically. The stiffness should be proportional to the modulus. It is shown in Figure 4 that compound stiffness increases with bound rubber content during storage. The polymer–filler crosslinks are formed in compounds on storage, and the number of the polymer–filler crosslinks increases with increasing bound rubber content forming a pseudovulcanized structure, which is indicated by an increase in stiffness.

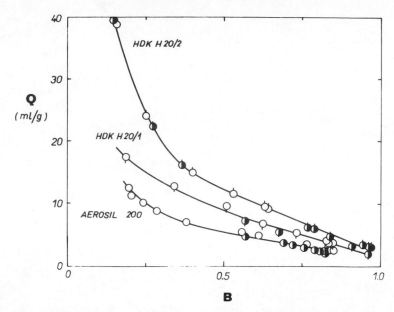

Fig. 5. Bound rubber swell Q as a function of bound rubber content B in silicone rubber containing 40 phr of 200 m²/g type fumed silicas differing in surface treatment. Compounds stored at 25°C (O) and 135°C (◑) after mixing.

After prolonged storing when the filler surface is practically saturated by the polymer, the content of the insoluble bound rubber can change only slightly. The unreacted free silanol groups might react with polymer chains already bound to the filler surface and cause, in this way, additional crosslinking of bound rubber and tightening of the formed rubber gel. This is manifested by the great increase in hardening at a relatively small change in bound rubber content.

Figure 5 shows the equilibrium swell Q of bound rubber in benzene as a function of bound rubber content B in the same compounds as in Figure 4. These results obtained at a practically constant polymer–filler contact area in compounds suggest a different topological nature of bound rubber gel depending on the surface nature of silica filler. It is clear that the untreated silica surface with high silanol concentration (Aerosil 200) results in a more tightly held network capable of less swelling as compared to the treated silica surface. The lower the silanol concentration, the looser the polymer–filler network is, contributing less to the compound stiffness.

The compound stiffness is plotted in Figure 6 as a function of volume fraction of rubber in the equilibrium swollen bound rubber v_r. There is a linear dependence of compound stiffness on the bound rubber swelling. Therefore, one can see that the compound stiffness is proportional to the crosslink density of bound rubber formed through polymer–filler interaction in the silicone rubber compound on mixing and storing. It seems that the storing temperature has no substantial influence on the bound rubber nature and its contribution to compound stiffness. The results suggest that "crosslink density" of bound rubber is determined by the concentration of free silanols at a constant polymer–filler contact area available.

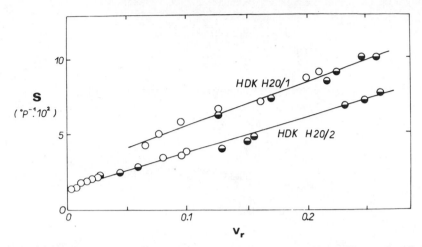

Fig. 6. Stiffness S of silicone rubber compounds containing 40 phr of 200 m²/g type fumed silicas differing by the level of surface treatment as a function of v_r. Compounds stored at 25°C (O) and 135°C (◓) after mixing.

Correlation with Meissner's Theory of Bound Rubber

Meissner's theory of bound rubber[2] treats the effect as random adsorption of structural units of polymer on reactive sites which are assumed to exist on the surface of filler particles. For the simplest system of filled monodisperse polymer, this theory predicts the linear dependence of "adsorption index" γ on logarithm U (free "unbound" rubber, $U = 1 - B$).

The "adsorption index" γ can be taken as a "crosslinking index" proportional to the crosslink density and also to the modulus G. When one takes the stiffness S as a measure of the modulus, nearly linear dependence of the stiffness on log U can be expected. Our experimental data plotted in Figure 7 fit quite well the predicted linear dependence up to high bound rubber content in compounds containing fillers with different silanol group content. The slope of the experimental dependences of S on $-\log U$ is proportional to the silanol coverage of silica fillers. This indicates again a near correlation between the silica silanol coverage and the "structuring" or "crosslinking" action of the silica in silicone rubber.

Effect of Silanol Coverage and Storage Temperature on Silica Surface Activity

This is also clearly demonstrated by results in Figure 8, where bound rubber content B, stiffness S, and swell Q are plotted as a function of free silanol group concentration in compounds containing 40 phr of fumed silica fillers after one week of storing at 25°C. The surface treatment of silica (see Table I) results in a lower interaction level between elastomer and silica surface.

The remarkable part of the experimental data is the effect of storing temperature on the surface activity measured by bound rubber. In Figure 9, the specific bound rubber content b (steady-state bound rubber content in grams per 100 m² of the polymer–filler contact area), defined in our previous work[4,5]

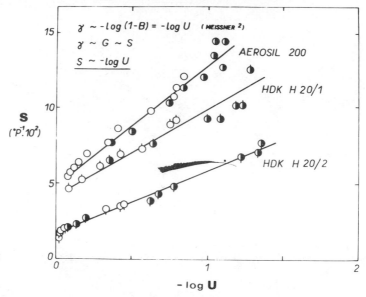

Fig. 7. Stiffness S of compounds containing 40 phr of 200 m²/g type fumed silicas differing in surface treatment as a function of −log U (unbound rubber). Compounds stored at 25°C (○) and 135°C (◑) after mixing.

as a measure of the filler surface activity, is plotted as a function of silanol coverage in compounds having a polymer–filler contact area of approximately 80 m²/g. The bound rubber values were measured after 2800 hr of storing at 25°C (lower curve) and 135°C (upper curve).

The silica surface activity is not influenced by the silanol coverage at 135°C, where all the samples show their maximum surface interaction activity. On the other hand, the surface activity of treated silicas at 25°C decreases with decreasing surface silanol concentration. The elevated storing temperature renders the treated silica surface as active as the untreated one, probably because of unreacted free silanol groups remaining on the silica surface after its modification.

The free silanol groups are sterically hindered at a lower temperature, thus not contributing to the interaction with silicone rubber. However, the sterically hindered silanol groups seem to contribute to hydrogen bonding with siloxane groups of polymer at higher temperatures, when the possibility of removing the treating groups by thermal scission is excluded due to the constant activation energy of the bound rubber formation.[1]

The surface interaction activity of untreated silica reaches its maximum value at a storage temperature of 25°C. At higher storage temperatures, this value remains unaffected. This has been ascribed to the increased probability of approaching polymer chains and surface silanol groups necessary for the hydrogen bond formation. Increased mobility and straightening of polysiloxane chains occur at higher temperatures.[1,4,5] The diffusion rate is also higher at higher temperatures. This effect is more pronounced in compounds with small total silanol concentration.

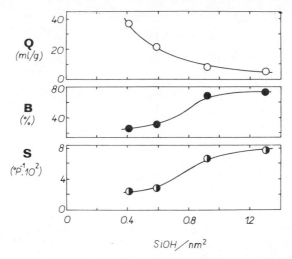

Fig. 8. Stiffness S, bound rubber content B, and its swell Q as a function of silanol coverage in silicone rubber containing 40 phr of 200 m²/g type fumed silica differing in surface treatment level. Compounds stored one week at 25°C.

Effect of Remilling "Crepe Hardened" Compounds

Very few results have been published on the effect of remilling of "crepe hardened" silicone rubber compounds filled with fumed silica.

Table II lists properties obtained in compounds containing 40 phr of treated and untreated fumed silicas, respectively, after prolonged shelf aging (approx. 1000 hr) at 25° and 135°C followed by remilling the "crepe hardened" compounds on a two-roll mill. The favorable effect of surface modification at 25°C, which vanishes at higher storage temperatures, is again clearly evident. The remilling time of a compound containing treated silica stored at 25°C is reduced to about one half the value for the untreated filler. The heated compounds of silicone rubber with treated silica filler behave in the same way as compounds filled with the untreated material.

The remilling of "crepe hardened" compounds results in a rather dramatic increase in compound plasticity accompanied by a relatively small decrease in bound rubber content (Fig. 10). In Figure 10 are plotted results obtained in compounds with 40 phr of Aerosil 130 and Aerosil R 972 (Table I) during prolonged storing (approx. 1000 hr) at various temperatures after mixing. These results are compared with the data obtained during prolonged storage of remilled compounds at 25°C (the field of points between dotted curves).

The bound rubber gel is much looser in remilled compounds than in compounds after mixing as shown in Figure 11, where the swell Q is plotted as a function of bound rubber content for compounds stored after mixing and remilling, respectively. A crosslinked structure of a continuous polymer–filler network can be assumed in compounds stored after mixing, their structure and tightness depending on the surface silanol concentration. The remilling of "crepe hardened" compounds rearranges the structure of bound rubber gel so that there is no remarkable difference in the character of the gel due to variations in silica surface which has been found in compounds after mixing.

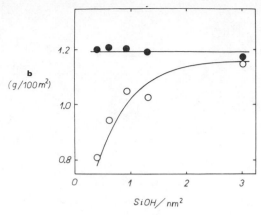

Fig. 9. Specific bound rubber content b as a function of silanol coverage of fumed silica and a storing temperature in compounds with polymer–filler contact area of 80 m²/g polymer, stored for 2800 hr at 25°C (O) (blank points) and (●) 135°C (full points).

The possibility of mechanical destruction of polysiloxane on remilling was verified by the prolonged remilling of the unfilled silicone rubber vulcanizate containing 89% of gel. This vulcanizate was prepared by adding 0.05 phr of 50% paste of dicumyl peroxide in silicone oil (Perkadox PDS-50) to silicone rubber and vulcanizing the mixture at 125°C for 15 min under pressure. The gel content was reduced by milling for 1 hr to 78%, which is nearly the same reduction as occurred in "crepe hardened" filled compounds on remilling (Table II). The behavior on the mill of both systems is very similar, and the gel is macroscopically incoherent, contrary to the coherent gel in compounds and the unfilled vulcanizate before milling.

The authors ascertained from the results that the remilling of "crepe hardened" compounds results in mechanical destruction of polymer–filler bridging. The partially destroyed polymer–filler network, due to polysiloxane mechanical scission, is regenerated on additional storage.

TABLE II

Properties of Compounds Containing 40 phr of Aerosil Fillers After Prolonged Storing Approx. (1000 hr) at Various Temperatures and After Remilling[a]

Filler	Storing temperature, °C	Bound rubber, %	Stiffness, 100/°P	Swelling in benzene, ml/g	Time of remilling, min
Aerosil 130	25	93 (79)	8.3 (2.5)	3.0 (7.6)	50
(untreated)	80	94 (82)	8.3 (2.2)	2.8 (9.5)	60
	135	93 (79)	8.3 (2.2)	2.6 (9.7)	50
Aerosil R 972	25	87 (77)	5.9 (2.1)	4.5 (10.8)	25
(dimethyldi-	80	96 (85)	7.7 (2.0)	2.9 (9.9)	60
chlorosilane treated)	135	97 (79)	9.1 (2.2)	2.6 (9.3)	70
Unfilled vulcanizate[b]	—	89 (78)	—	—	60

[a] The data in brackets are obtained in remilled compounds.

[b] Conditions of vulcanization: 0.05 phr Perkadox PDS 50, 125°C/15 min, under pressure.

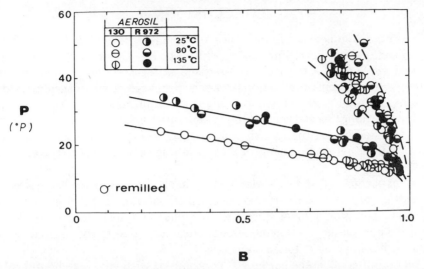

Fig. 10. Penetrometrical plasticity P as a function of bound rubber content B in silicone rubber containing 40 phr of Aerosil 130 (untreated) and Aerosil R 972 (treated) silicas. Compounds stored at various temperatures after mixing, then remilled and stored again at 25°C.

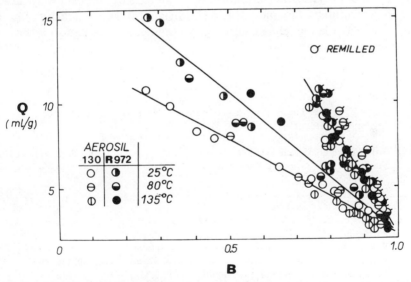

Fig. 11. Bound rubber swell Q as a function of bound rubber content B in silicone rubber containing 40 phr of Aerosil 130 (untreated) and Aerosil R 972 (treated) silicas. Compounds stored at various temperatures after mixing, then remilled and stored again at 25°C.

The structure of remilled compounds seems to consist of incompletely remilled regions, freely connected by polymer chains, the number of which has been decreased by mechanical destruction. These regions cause a relatively high bound rubber content in the remilled compounds, whereas the much reduced stiffness and increased swelling are due to the decreased number of polymer chains connecting the gel regions with each other throughout the compound.

CONCLUSIONS

The interaction between fumed silica, of various surface silanol concentration, and silicone rubber has been investigated. The results indicate that the interaction is much more extensive in comparison with carbon black–organic rubber systems. The specific interaction between silica surface silanol groups and the siloxane chain by hydrogen bonding plays the main role in "crepe hardening" and bound rubber formation in fumed silica filled silicone rubber. The surface treatment decreasing the free silanol coverage results in a more loosely held polymer–filler network, capable of more swelling as compared to the untreated silica.

The experimantal data fit Meissner's theory of bound rubber quite well, suggesting that the filler particles function as polyfunctional crosslinks. The chemical interaction between silica filler and silicone rubber seems to be excluded in "crepe hardening" and bound rubber formation due to the negligible value of the activation energy found on mixing.

The remilling of "crepe hardened" compounds with very high bound rubber content results in a great increase in the compound plasticity and swelling, accompanied by a relatively small change in bound rubber content. This effect is interpreted through the existence of incompletely remilled regions, freely connected by a decreased number of polymer bridgings, due to the mechanical destruction of polysiloxane on remilling. There is no important difference in behavior of remilled compounds during additional storage. The topology of the remilled silica-filled silicone compounds seems not to depend on the surface properties of the silica filler.

References

1. P. Vondráček, CSc. Thesis, Institute of Chemical Technology, Prague, 1973.
2. B. Meissner, *J. Appl. Polym. Sci.*, **18**, 2483 (1974).
3. L. E. St. Pierre and R. S. Chahal, *J. Polym. Sci.*, **C30**, 429 (1970).
4. P. Vondráček and M. Schätz, *Sci. Pap. Inst. Chem. Technol.* (Prague), **C24**, 77 (1976).
5. P. Vondráček and M. Schätz, *Proceedings of the International Rubber Conference, "Rubber '73"*, Paper A12, Prague, 1973.
6. J. A. Hockey, *Chem. Ind. (London)*, **9**, 57 (1965).
7. H. P. Boehm, *Angew. Chem.*, **78**, 617 (1966).
8. H. P. Boehm, *Adv. Catal.* **16**, 225 (1966).
9. M. R. Basila, *J. Chem. Phys.*, **35**, 1151 (1961).
10. A. V. Kiselev and V. I. Lygin, *J. Surface Sci.*, **2**, 236 (1964).
11. A. V. Kiselev, G. A. Galkin, and V. I. Lygin, *Trans. Faraday Soc.*, **60**, 431 (1964).
12. K. V. Nelson and N. V. Ionina, *Vysokomol. Soedin.*, **A14**, 573 (1972).
13. B. B. Boonstra, H. Cochrane, and E. M. Dannenberg, Presented at the International Rubber Conference, Munich, 1974.
14. R. S. Chahal, Ph.D. dissertation, McGill University, Montreal, 1968.
15. M. Schätz and K. Švehla, *Sci. Pap. Inst. Chem. Technol. (Prague)*, **C10**, 5 (1966).
16. D. W. Southwart, Ph,.D. dissertation, Loughborough University of Technology, Loughborough, 1974.
17. D. W. Southwart, Precision Rubber Division, Dunlop Ltd., Shepshed Loughborough, personal communication, 1974.
18. Degussa, Aerosil—Manufacture, Properties and Application, Frankfurt M., 1974.

Received August 5, 1976

JOURNAL OF APPLIED POLYMER SCIENCE   VOL. 21, 3223–3235 (1977)

Effects of Number-Average Molecular Weight of Liquid Hydroxyl-Terminated Polybutadiene on Physical Properties of the Elastomer

KATSUHIRO ONO, HIDETOSHI SHIMADA, and TOSHIHIDE NISHIMURA, *Idemitsu Petrochemical Co., Ltd., Tokyo 100, Japan,* SHINZO YAMASHITA, *Department of Chemistry, Faculty of Polytechnic Sciences, Kyoto Institute of Technology, Kyoto 606, Japan,* HIROSHI OKAMOTO, *Department of Applied Chemistry, Aichi Institute of Technology, Toyota 470-03, Japan,* and YUJI MINOURA, *Department of Chemistry, Research Institute for Atomic Energy, Osaka City University, Osaka 558, Japan*

Synopsis

The relationships between the molecular weight of liquid hydroxyl-terminated polybutadiene (HTPB) and the physical properties of the elastomers were investigated. HTPB having various molecular weights were cured with 4,4′-diphenylmethane diisocyanate (MDI) by the one-shot method and the physical properties of these elastomers obtained were measured. The tensile strength, modulus, tear resistance, and hardness decreased with increase in the molecular weight of HTPB, and this phenomenon was remarkable in the low molecular weight HTPB (below about 3000). On the other hand, the ultimate elongation increased linearly with increase in the molecular weight of HTPB. The effects of incorporating a short-chain diol, N,N-bis(2-hydroxypropyl)aniline, on the physical properties of the elastomers are also discussed.

INTRODUCTION

Liquid hydroxyl-terminated polybutadiene (HTPB) can be crosslinked with chain extension by the reaction of the terminal hydroxyl groups with a variety of diisocyanates and yield vulcanizates comparable to those from conventional butadiene rubbers.[1-6] Although the properties of elastomers of HTPB vary widely depending on the physical properties of liquid polymers such as molecular weight, molecular weight distribution, functionality, degree of branching, and microstructure,[7] very little in the way of experimental results has yet been reported.

In this paper, the relationships between the number-average molecular weight $(\overline{M}_n)$ of HTPB and the physical properties of the elastomers are discussed. For this purpose, the elastomers were prepared by the one-step reaction of HTPB $(\overline{M}_n$ of about 1000–8000) with 4,4′-diphenylmethane diisocyanate (MDI). The effects of $\overline{M}_n$ of HTPB on the properties such as tensile strength, modulus, ultimate elongation, and hardness were investigated. At the same time, the

3223

change in the properties of the elastomers of HTPB compounded with a short-chain diol known as reinforcing agent was also studied with respect to $\overline{M}_n$ of HTPB.

EXPERIMENTAL

Materials

Liquid hydroxyl-terminated polybutadiene (HTPB) having a molecular weight of about 1000–8000 was prepared on a laboratory scale according to the patents[8] and used for the preparation of the elastomers by a one-step reaction with diisocyanate (MDI) (hereinafter referred to one-shot elastomers). Poly bd R-45HT and R-45M from ARCO Chemical Co. were also used for comparison. The physical properties of prepared HTPB and commercial R-45HT and R-45M are illustrated in Table I.

4,4′-Diphenylmethane diisocyanate (MDI) as curing agent and N,N-bis(2-hydroxypropyl)aniline (HPA) from Upjohn Co. as reinforcing agent were used without further purification. Solvents and other reagents were also used without further purification.

Vulcanization

The one-shot elastomers were obtained using MDI as vulcanizing agent and di-n-butyltin dilaurate (DBTDL) as catalyst. The vulcanization of HTPB was carried out by compression molding at 120°C for 60 min.

Measurements

Physical Properties of Liquid Polybutadiene. The molecular weight measurement was carried out with a vapor pressure osmometer (Knauer Co.) using benzene as the solvent. Molecular weight distribution was measured by high-speed liquid chromatography (HLC-802 Toyo Soda Co.) and gel-permeation chromatography (GPC-1AR Shimadzu Co.). Measurement of the microstructure was carried out by the infrared method of Morero.[9] The hydroxyl content was determined by the analytical procedure[10] suggested by ARCO Chemical Co., and the H_2O content was determined according to the Carl Fisher method. Bulk viscosity was measured with a B-type viscometer at 30°C.

Properties of One-Shot Elastomers. Dumbbell-shaped specimens for measuring tensile strength, modulus, and elongation and B-type specimens for tear resistance testing (0.5-mm thick, respectively) were die cut from the elastomer sheets which were stored at room temperature for one week. The physical properties were measured at room temperature using an IS-500 Autograph (Shimadzu Co.) at a strain rate of 500 mm/min.

Swelling was measured as follows: specimens of the elastomers (20 × 20 × 0.5 mm) were weighed and then immersed in benzene. After 72 hr at room temperature, the specimens were wiped with filter paper, weighed again, and then exposed for 72 hr in the atmosphere. Benzene was removed, by placing the specimens under vacuum for 24 hr, and the samples were reweighed. The differences between the weights after benzene removal and the initial weight

TABLE I

Chemical Structure and Molecular Weight of Liquid Hydroxyl-Terminated Polybutadiene

HTPB mol. wt[a]	Hydroxyl content, meq/g	$\bar{A}_n$[b]	$\bar{A}_w$[b]	$\bar{A}_w/\bar{A}_n$	Functionality	Bulk viscosity (30°C) poises	Microstructure, %[d]			H2O content, wt-%
							Cis	Trans	Vinyl	
350	1.69	87	160	1.83	2.28	24	15.7	58.7	25.5	0.05
530	1.44	94	219	2.32	2.20	42	15.4	57.0	27.6	0.07
740	1.35	113	238	2.11	2.35	47	16.0	59.2	24.8	0.05
2220	0.99	135	232	1.72	2.20	39	15.0	57.8	27.2	0.05
2310	0.98	—	—	—	2.26	37	16.6	58.3	25.1	0.05
2460	0.86	150	256	1.71	2.12	42	14.2	58.1	27.6	0.05
2550[e]	0.85	136[c]	315[c]	2.31[c]	2.17	54	15.6	57.9	26.4	—
2690	0.72	—	—	—	1.94	63	15.6	57.4	26.9	0.05
2810[f]	0.70	—	—	—	1.95	53	—	—	—	—
3710	0.55	—	—	—	2.04	131	15.6	57.5	26.8	0.05
4210	0.49	—	—	—	2.06	—	—	—	—	—
5500	0.28	—	—	—	1.60	—	—	—	—	—
8040	0.25	371	770	2.08	2.01	891	16.1	58.7	25.3	0.08

[a] Number-average molecular weight determined by vapor pressure osmometer using benzene as solvent.

[b] Number- and weight-average chain length determined by high-speed liquid chromatograph (HLC-802 Toyo Soda Co.).

[c] Determined by gel permeation chromatography (GPC-1AR Shimadzu Co.).

[d] Obtained by the infrared method of Morero.[9]

[e] Commercial Poly bd R-45HT from ARCO Chemical Co.

[f] Commercial Poly bd R-45M from ARCO Chemical Co.

of the samples were regarded as the amount of sol. The sol fraction was determined as

$$S = [(W - W_A)/W] \times 100$$

and the swelling ratio $1/V_R$ was expressed by the equation

$$1/V_R = 1 + [(W_B/W_A - 1)\rho_2]/\rho_1$$

where W is the initial weight, W_A is the weight after removing benzene, W_B is
the weight of the swollen sample, ρ_1 is the density of benzene, and ρ_2 is the density
of the sample after removing benzene.

RESULTS AND DISCUSSION

Physical Properties of Liquid Polybutadiene

Some of the data on the structure of polybutadiene obtained by radical polymerization were reviewed by Condon[11] and Richardson.[12] An important conclusion was that a trans-1,4 structure was energetically more favorable than
cis-1,4 and vinyl structures because of the low energy requirement for trans-1,4
addition. The microstructure of HTPB was investigated using the infrared
method of Morero.[9] The key bands for cis-1,4, trans-1,4, and vinyl structures
of HTPB gave very good agreement with those proposed by Morero. As shown
in Table I, the microstructures of all HTPB were almost the same, and the
trans-1,4 structure was most predominantly consistent with the conclusion of
Condon[11] and Richardson.[12] The content of the vinyl structure was about 27%
and hence smaller than that of conventional polybutadiene obtained by ionic
polymerization. This may lead to a higher performance of the elastomers at low
temperature.[13] In fact, the higher performance at low temperature of cured
HTPB has been verified.[14] As can be seen from Table I, the ratio of weight-
average chain length to number-average chain length, $\overline{A}_w/\overline{A}_n$, ranging from 1.71
to 2.32, is independent of the $\overline{M}_n$ of HTPB. It may be easily understood that
the molecular weight distribution of HTPB is relatively narrow and close to a
Gaussian distribution.

The functionality F_n of HTPB is shown by eq (1):

$$F_n = \frac{\overline{M}_n}{\text{equivalent weight}} \tag{1}$$

Hence, eq. (2) is derived from eq. (1) using the relation that the equivalent weight
is the reciprocal of the hydroxyl content per gram of polymer:

$$\text{hydroxyl content} = F_n \times (1/\overline{M}_n) \tag{2}$$

Figure 1 shows the relationship between $1/\overline{M}_n$ and the hydroxyl content of
HTPB; and from the slope, F_n is found to be 2.2. This value is slightly greater
than 2.0, which is consistent with the results reported by other investigators.[15–18]
Therefore, it was suggested that these HTPB molecules have little branching.

The relationship between $\overline{M}_n$ and the bulk viscosity of HTPB measured with
a B-type viscometer is linear (Fig. 2). Expressed in formula form, the experimental equation is

$$\log \eta = 1.16 + 0.22 \times 10^{-3}\overline{M}_n \tag{3}$$

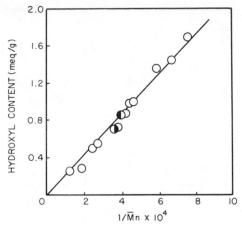

Fig. 1. Relationship between hydroxyl content and number-average molecular weight of liquid hydroxyl-terminated polybutadiene: (◐) commercial Poly bd R-45HT; (◑) commercial Poly bd R-45M.

where η is the bulk viscosity at 30°C. This result may be taken to indicate that the structures (especially microstructures), functionalities, and molecular weight distributions of all HTPB are essentially equal. The relation obtained in this work is similar to that of broad-distribution hydroxyl-terminated polybutadiene.[19]

Effects of Number-Average Molecular Weight of Liquid Polybutadiene on Mechanical Properties of Elastomers

It has been considered that mechanical properties of the elastomers based on liquid polymers may be varied widely depending on the physical properties of prepolymers such as molecular weight, molecular weight distribution, func-

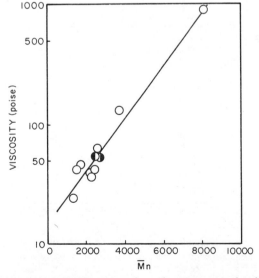

Fig. 2. Relationship between bulk viscosity and number-average molecular weight of hydroxyl-terminated polybutadiene (B-type viscometer, 30°C): (●) commercial Poly bd R-45HT and R-45M.

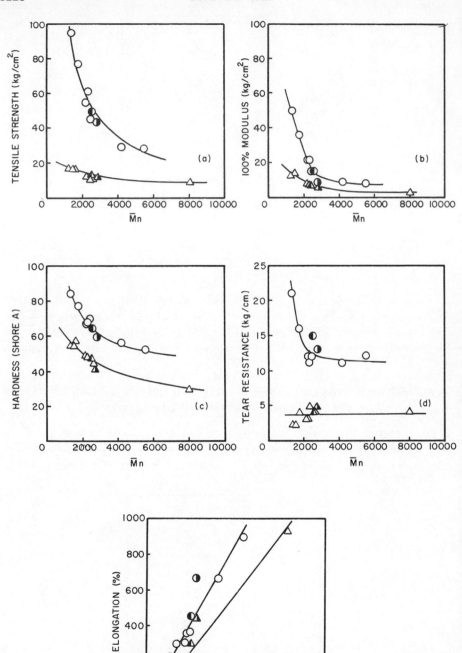

Fig. 3. Effect of number-average molecular weight of hydroxyl-terminated polybutadiene on mechanical properties of elastomers obtained by one-shot method: (△,▲,▲) elastomers obtained by one-shot method, NCO/OH = 1.0; (○,◐,◑) one-shot elastomers reinforced by short-chain diol N,N-bis(2-hydroxylpropyl)aniline (HPA), HTPB/HPA = 1.0, NCO/OH = 1.0; (◐,▲) commercial Poly bd R-45HT; (◑,▲) commercial Poly bd R-45M. Vulcanizing agent, 4,4′-diphenylmethane diisocyanate; catalyst, di-n-butyltin dilaurate.

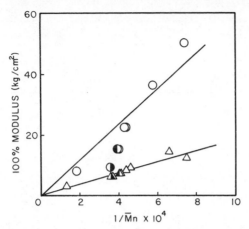

Fig. 4. Relationship between 100% modulus of elastomers obtained by one-shot method and $1/\overline{M}_n$ of liquid hydroxyl-terminated polybutadiene: ($\triangle,\blacktriangle,\blacktriangle$) elastomers obtained by one-shot method, NCO/OH = 1.0; ($\bigcirc,\mathbf{O},\mathbf{O}$) one-shot elastomers reinforced by short-chain diol N,N-bis(2-hydroxy-propyl)aniline (HPA), HTPB/HPA = 1.0, NCO/OH = 1.0; ($\mathbf{O},\blacktriangle$) commercial Poly bd r-45HT; ($\mathbf{O},\blacktriangle$) commercial Poly bd R-45M.

tionality, degree of branching, microstructure, etc.[7] Tables II and III show the mechanical properties of the elastomers prepared by the reaction of HTPB and MDI, and the effect of the added short-chain diol in relation to $\overline{M}_n$ of HTPB. These results are shown in Figure 3. As is illustrated in Figure 3(a), tensile strength of the one-shot elastomer decreased with increase in $\overline{M}_n$ of HTPB, and this phenomenon was most pronounced below $\overline{M}_n$ of about 3000. The 100% modulus, hardness, and tear resistance illustrated in Figures 3(b)–3(d), respectively, decreased with increase in $\overline{M}_n$ in a manner similar to tensile strength. On the other hand, ultimate elongation of one-shot elastomers [Fig. 3(e)] increased linearly with increase in $\overline{M}_n$ of HTPB.

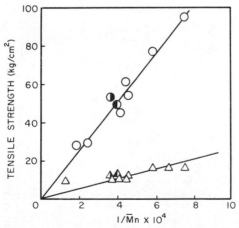

Fig. 5. Relationship between tensile strength of elastomers obtained by one-shot method and $1/\overline{M}_n$ of liquid hydroxyl-terminated polybutadiene: ($\triangle,\blacktriangle,\blacktriangle$) elastomers obtained by one-shot method, NCO/OH = 1.0; ($\bigcirc,\mathbf{O},\mathbf{O}$) one-shot elastomers reinforced by short-chain diol N,N-bis(2-hydroxypropyl)aniline (HPA), HTPB/HPA = 1.0, NCO/OH = 1.0; ($\mathbf{O},\blacktriangle$) commercial Poly bd R-45HT; ($\mathbf{O},\blacktriangle$) commercial Poly bd R-45M.

TABLE II

Mechanical Properties of Elastomers from HTPB, HPA, and MDI by One-Shot Method[a]

HTPB mol. wt	Grams HPA per 100 g HTPB	Grams MDI per (100 g HTPB + HPA)(g)	Tensile strength, kg/cm²	Elongation, %	Modulus, kg/cm²			Tear resistance, kg/cm	Hardness	
					100%	200%	300%		Shore A	Shore D
1350	16.7	42.3	95	220	50	85	—	21	84	28
1740	13.3	33.8	77	290	36	54	—	16	77	28
2220	9.8	24.8	54	300	22	37	54	12	67	21
2310	9.7	24.5	61	350	22	36	50	11	68	21
2460	8.5	21.5	45	360	15	24	36	12	70	18
2550[b]	8.4	21.3	49	450	15	22	30	15	64	19
2810[c]	6.9	17.5	53	660	9	12	15	13	59	15
4210	3.6	9.0	29	660	9	11	14	11	56	15
5500	2.7	7.0	28	890	8	9	11	12	52	14

[a] HTPB = liquid hydroxyl-terminated polybutadiene; HPA = N,N-bis(2-hydroxylpropyl)aniline (from Upjohn Co.); MDI = 4,4-diphenylmethane diisocyanate. HTPB/HPA = 1.0; NCO/OH = 1.0; cure cycle, 60 min at 120°C; catalyst, di-n-butyltin dilaurate (0.05 phr).
[b] Commercial Poly bd R-45HT from ARCO Chemical Co.
[c] Commercial Poly bd R-45M from ARCO Chemical Co.

TABLE III
Mechanical Properties of Elastomers from HPTB and MDI by One-Shot Method[a]

HTPB mol. wt	Grams MDI per 100 g HTPB	Tensile strength, kg/cm²	Elongation, %	Modulus, kg/cm²			Tear resistance, kg/cm	Hardness	
				100%	200%	300%		Shore A	Shore D
1350	21.1	16	120	12	—	—	2	54	17
1530	18.0	16	100	14	—	—	2	54	17
2220	12.4	12	160	9	—	—	3	49	13
2310	12.3	10	170	8	—	—	3	48	13
2460	10.8	10	220	7	9	—	5	47	12
2550[b]	10.6	13	290	7	10	—	4	47	13
2810[c]	8.8	12	430	6	8	10	5	41	11
8040	3.1	9	920	3	4	5	4	29	8

[a] HTPB = Liquid hydroxyl-terminated polybutadiene; MDI = 4,4'-diphenylmethane diisocyanate. NCO/OH = 1.0; cure cycle, 60 min at 120°C; catalyst, di-n-butyltin dilaurate (0.05 phr).
[b] Commercial Poly bd R-45HT from ARCO Chemical Co.
[c] Commercial Poly bd R-45M from ARCO Chemical Co.

According to Flory,[20] the retractive force per unit initial cross-sectional area at the rubbery state is described as

$$\sigma = \nu RT(\alpha - 1/\alpha^2)(1 - 2\overline{M}_c/M) \tag{4}$$

where σ is retractive force per unit initial cross-sectional area, ν is the concentration of crosslinked units, R is the gas constant, T is absolute temperature, α is a relative length given by l/l_0 (l_0 is the initial length and l is the tensile length), $\overline{M}_c$ is the number-average molecular weight of the network chain, and M is the molecular weight of the primary molecules. Yamashita[7] predicts that when the liquid rubbers, which have a functional group on each terminal, are cured with trifunctional vulcanizing agents, M in eq. (4) becomes infinite, and therefore σ is proportional to ν. The value of ν is inversely proportional to $\overline{M}_c$ according to the following equation:[21]

$$\nu = \rho/\overline{M}_c \tag{5}$$

where ρ is density. For one-shot elastomers based on HTPB, it can be easily predicted that σ is inversely proportional to $\overline{M}_c$. Hence, σ is given by eq. (6) by postulating that $\overline{M}_n$ of HTPB is proportional to $\overline{M}_c$:

$$\sigma = A/\overline{M}_n \tag{6}$$

where A is constant.

Figure 4 is a plot of 100% modulus versus reciprocal number-average molecular weight of HTPB. An approximately linear relationship can be observed between them. This result is satisfactorily consistent with eq. (6).

A plot of tensile strength versus reciprocal $\overline{M}_n$ of HTPB is shown in Figure 5. The tensile strength is inversely proportional to $\overline{M}_n$ in a manner similar to 100% modulus. Equation (7) was therefore obtained:

$$T_B = B/\overline{M}_n \tag{7}$$

where B is constant.

From these results, it can be inferred that the tensile strength and 100% modulus of the elastomers will be dependent on $\overline{M}_c$ and ν.

Apart from the usual butadiene rubbers, the elastomers prepared with HTPB have, however, urethane linkage in their main chains. We must consider the effect of urethane groups on the properties of the elastomers. In one-shot elastomers obtained under the condition of NCO/OH = 1.0, the reaction forming urethane linkage may be most favorable compared to the reactions producing allophanate and biuret linkages. The concentration of urethane linkage increases with decreasing $\overline{M}_n$ of HTPB, followed by an increase in intermolecular hydrogen-bonding sites[22] which leads to the growth of pseudo-crosslinks. Because of the reasons mentioned above, tensile strength, 100% modulus, and hardness will increase with a decrease in $\overline{M}_n$ of HTPB. This consideration fully explains the results of Figures 3(a)–3(d).

Effect of Number-Average Molecular Weight on Swelling of the Elastomers

The effect of $\overline{M}_n$ of HTPB on the physical properties of the one-shot elastomers is also illustrated in the results of swelling measurements using benzene.

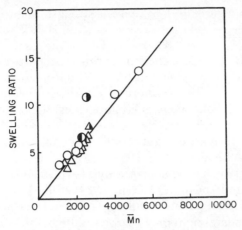

Fig. 6. Relationship between swelling ratio of elastomers obtained by one-shot method and $\overline{M}_n$ of liquid hydroxyl-terminated polybutadiene: (△,▲,▲) elastomers obtained by one-shot method, NCO/OH = 1.0; (○,◐,◑) one-shot elastomers reinforced by short-chain diol N,N-bis(2-hydroxy-propyl)aniline (HPA), HTPB/HPA = 1.0, NCO/OH = 1.0; (◐,▲) commercial Poly bd R-45HT; (◑,▲) commercial Poly bd R-45M.

The swelling ratio Q linearly increased as $\overline{M}_n$ increased (Fig. 6). This result will also be explained by taking into account the urethane group content of the elastomers.

The experimental relation between Q and ν was given by Lorenz[23] as follows;

$$Q \propto 1/\nu \qquad (8)$$

From eq. (5) and the assumption that $\overline{M}_c$ is proportional to $\overline{M}_n$ of HTPB, relation (9) is obtained:

$$Q \propto \overline{M}_n \qquad (9)$$

At this point, it should be noted that ν is proportional to the concentration of urethane linkage in the HTPB-based elastomer.

On the other hand, sol fraction equalled approximately 10% in any of the elastomers. Because of the relatively high sol fraction of the elastomers, it seems that unre unreacted HTPB will exist to some extent in these elastomers. Hence, complete vulcanization will lead to improvement of the mechanical properties of the elastomers. From the description mentioned above and the result of Figure 6, it can be easily seen that the urethane group content will greatly affect the physical properties of the one-shot elastomers.

Reinforcement of Elastomers by Short-Chain Diol

The reinforcement by short-chain diol in urethane chemistry is well known. N,N-Bis(2-hydroxypropyl)aniline (HPA) was used as reinforcing agent. Ryan[4] has investigated the reinforcing effect of HPA on commercial Poly bd R-45M and concluded that when the amount of HPA used as a modifier was increased (Poly bd R-45M/HPA ratio from 1 to 0.5), the properties of the elastomer were greatly improved. In this work, HPA was mixed at a HTPB/HPA ratio of 1.0.

As can be seen from Figures 3(a)–(d), tensile strength, 100% modulus, hardness, and tear resistance decreased with increase in $\overline{M}_n$ of HTPB, and the phenomenon was marked below $\overline{M}_n$ of about 3000 as well as for the elastomers without HPA. By incorporating HPA into the elastomers, these properties increased over the wide range of HTPB $\overline{M}_n$ and, therefore, the diol appears to impart the reinforcing effect to the elastomers. This reinforcing effect was obvious in low molecular weight HTPB (below about 3000). Ultimate elongation of one-shot elastomers reinforced by HPA, however, linearly increased as $\overline{M}_n$ of HTPB increased. The effect of the diol on ultimate elongation was observed in accordance with other properties of the elastomers.

The reinforcement by short-chain diol may be explained by taking into account an increase in the urethane linkage from HTPB with MDI and that from HPA with MDI. Hence, the remarkable reinforcing effect of the diol on the elastomers at HTPB low molecular weight may be due to a higher urethane group content according to the higher volume of the diol under the constant condition where the HTPB/HPA ratio equals 1.0. On the other hand, in the case of the reinforcement by short-chain diols, it should also be considered an auxiliary effect based on the stiffness of the elastomer backbone by the aromatic ring of short-chain diols (in the case of aromatic ones), except for the urethane linkage.

Conclusions

1. Tensile strength, 100% modulus, hardness, and tear resistance of one-shot elastomers based on HTPB decreased with increase in HTPB $\overline{M}_n$. The phenomenon was pronounced with low molecular weight HTPB (below about 3000). On the other hand, the ultimate elongation increased linearly with $\overline{M}_n$.

2. The relationship between 100% modulus (σ) or tensile strength (T_B) and $\overline{M}_n$ of HTPB could be explained using Flory's equation. The σ or T_B was expressed by the following equation:

$$\sigma \text{ or } T_B = A/\overline{M}_n$$

where A is constant.

3. The effects of $\overline{M}_n$ of HTPB on the physical properties of one-shot elastomers based on HTPB may be interpreted by considering the concentration of the crosslinked chains and the urethane group content of the elastomers.

4. The effects of the short-chain diol (HPA) on the one-shot elastomers should take into account the stiffness of the backbone of the elastomers by the aromatic ring (from HPA) and a succession of the urethane linkage from HPA and MDI, namely, the hard segment.

This work is part of Studies on Liquid Polymers undertaken by the Research Group of Polymer Chemistry and Technology, Japan.

References

1. Idemitsu Petrochemical Co. Technical Report BD-2 Poly bd liquid Rubber (May, 1973) and ARCO Chemical Co., Product Bulletin BD-1 (March, 1974), BD-2 (March, 1974) and BD-3 (October, 1974).

2. P. W. Ryan, *Br. Polym. J.*, **3,** 145 (1971).

3. P. W. Ryan, *Rubber World*, **163**(4), 47 (1971).

4. P. W. Ryan, *J. Elastoplastics*, **3**, 57 (1971).

5. J. A. Verdol, P. W. Ryan, D. J. Carrow, and K. L. Kund, *Rubber Age* **7**, 57 (1966).

6. J. A. Verdol, P. W. Ryan, D. J. Carrow, and K. L. Kund, *Rubber Age* **8**, 62 (1966).

7. Shinzo Yamashita, *Kobunshi no Bunshi-setsukei*, Part 3, p. 114–147, (1972) Baifukan.

8. U.S. Pat., 3652520. Atlantic Richfield Co., U.S. Pat., 3652520 (March 28, 1972). O. W. Burke, Jr., J. A. Kizer, and P. Davis, U.S. Pat., 3673168 (June 27, 1972).

9. D. Morero, A. Santanbrogio, L. Porri, and F. Clampelli, *Chem. Ind.,* **41**, 758 (1959).

10. ARCO Chemical Co., Analytical Procedure II-20, based on
    (1) ASTM E-222-65T, Part 31,
    (2) Scott's *Standard Methods of Chemical Analysis*, Vol. 2, p. 2197,
    (3) *Anal. Chem.*, **31**, (11), 1809 (1959).

11. K. E. Condon, *J. Polym. Sci.,* **11**, 139 (1953).

12. W. S. Richardson, *J. Polym. Sci.,* **13**, 229 (1954).

13. R. F. Hoffman and R. H. Gobran, *Rubber Chem. Technol.,* **46**, 139 (1973).

14. K. Ono and T. Nishimura, *J. Soc. Rubber Ind. Jpn.* (Nippon Gomu Kyokai-shi), 48(5), 263 (1975).

15. C. H. Bamford, A. D. Jenkins, and R. P. Wayne, *Trans. Faraday Soc.,* **56**, 935 (1960).

16. W. H. Stubbs, C. R. Gore, and C. S. Marvel, *J. Polym. Sci. A-1*, **4**, 1898 (1966).

17. S. F. Reed, *J. Polym. Sci. A-1*, **9**, 214 (1971).

18. S. F. Reed, *J. Polym. Sci. A-1*, **10**, 649 (1972).

19. D. M. French, *Rubber Chem. Technol.,* **42**, 71 (1969).

20. P. J. Flory, *Ind. Eng. Chem.,* **38**, 417 (1946).

21. S. Yamashita, *Chemistry*, **26**, 804 (1971).

22. Y. Yamaguchi, T. Yokoyama, and T. Tanaka, *J. Chem. Soc. Jpn., Ind. Chem. Sec.* (*Kogyo Kagaku Zasshi*), **73**, 1531 (1970).

23. O. Lorenz and C. R. Parks, *J. Polym. Sci.,* **50**, 299 (1961).

Received August 18, 1976

Randomly Branched Styrene/Divinylbenzene Copolymers. I. Preparation, Molecular Weight Characterization, and GPC Analysis

M. R. AMBLER and D. McINTYRE, *Institute of Polymer Science, The University of Akron, Akron, Ohio 44325*

Synopsis

A series of randomly branched copolymers of styrene and divinylbenzene were prepared using a benzoyl peroxide-initiated free-radical bulk polymerization at 78°C. DVB contents were varied from 0.01% to 2%. Two samples were polymerized with 0.4% DVB to different conversions: series 9A at 6% conversion and series 9B at 15% conversion (just short of the gelation point). Both samples were fractionated and the fractions characterized by ultracentrifugation, light scattering, osmometry, viscometry, and gel permeation chromatography. The data indicated that the fractions were not of narrow MWD and that the breadth of the MWD of the fractions from series 9B were greater than those of 9A. GPC calibration curves of M, $[\eta]$, and $M[\eta]$ were generated for both 9A and 9B fractions by employing curve-fitting techniques to the GPC data. For all of the fractions 9B, the molecular weight calibration provided accurate values of $\overline{M}_z$, $\overline{M}_w$, and $\overline{M}_n$, suggesting that no serious peak spreading had occurred in the GPC experiments. The universal calibration parameter $M[\eta]$ for the 9A fractions agreed with that of linear polystyrene, while that of the high-conversion series 9B did not. It will be shown in a later paper that series 9B is highly branched, while 9A is lightly branched. Consequently, it is recommended that any GPC analysis of branching units make an allowance for the deviation of highly branched polymers from the linear $M[\eta]$ calibration curve.

INTRODUCTION

There are several ways of preparing branched polymers. Branched structure is always possible during polymerization if chain transfer to polymer occurs. Diene monomers also are subject to branching during their polymerization because of the residual double bonds in the chain. But branching which occurs in this fashion is largely uncontrollable. Branched polymers can be synthesized. Star and graft polymers are two branched structures which can be synthesized by anionic and cationic polymerization techniques. Polymerization of monomers with high functionality (and also copolymerization with multifunctional monomers) is also possible, either through polycondensation reactions or by free-radical polymerizations. The latter approach has been used successfully by several authors to prepare highly branched polymers. Thurmond and Zimm[1] copolymerized difunctional styrene (Sty) and tetrafunctional divinylbenzene (DVB) using free-radical polymerization to prepare a highly branched structure. The nature of the branching is such that a spherically shaped molecule should be formed since there is a large amount of DVB and consequently a high branch density.

3237

The possibility of analyzing the amount of branching in a polymer sample from gel permeation chromatography (GPC) has been known for some time.[2-11] However, the central point in any such analysis is the calibration curve to be used for such an analysis. In this paper, an experimental GPC calibration curve was obtained for randomly branched polymers. In particular, polystyrene/divinylbenzene copolymers were synthesized at different conversions. Fractions were then obtained over a large molecular weight range. The fractions were then characterized by molecular weight and intrinsic viscosity measurements.

The GPC calibration curves were then determined for M, $[\eta]$, and $[\eta]M$ as a function of elution volume for the branched fractions. It is demonstrated that none of the above functions lies on the same calibration curve as that obtained for linear polystyrene so that more attention must be given to the general behavior of branched versus linear polymers in their elution characteristics. It is further shown that only with extensive branching is there an appreciable error in using the common calibration curve based on linear polymers.

EXPERIMENTAL

Solvents

All solvents used in this study were dried and purified by distillation over finely ground calcium hydride. Nitrogen gas, dried by passage through 1-ft column of Drierite, was bubbled into the enclosed system through a fine capillary tube. The first 100 ml of distilled solvent was discarded. The center cut was collected in a 4-l. flask and stored.

The styrene and divinylbenzene monomers used in the polymerization studies were ACS reagent grade and practical grade, respectively.

Monomers

Just prior to its use, styrene was purified by bubbling nitrogen gas through it for 1 hr to remove dissolved oxygen. No attempt was made to remove inhibitor. Divinylbenzene was used as received from MCB, with no attempt to remove either dissolved oxygen or inhibitor. Impurity levels of DVB were checked by gas chromatography. It was found that the monomer as received is, as reported by the manufacturer and by Thurmond and Zimm,[1] of the order of 35% m-divinylbenzene, 16% p-divinylbenzene, 30% m-ethylvinylbenzene, and 13% p-ethylvinylbenzene.

Poly(divinylbenzene) is reported by MCB to be insoluble in its monomer; therefore, clarity of the monomer was used to check for polymer. Mixing the styrene with an excess of methanol will precipitate any dissolved polystyrene, and this test was used to check for polystyrene. Both monomers were found free of dissolved polymer.

Polymer Standards

The linear polystyrene samples used in this study were all of narrow molecular weight distribution. They were obtained from several sources, including samples prepared and characterized in these laboratories,[12] samples from Waters Asso-

TABLE I
Standard Polystyrene Samples

Sample no.	Ref.	M_w, g/mole	M_n, g/mole	$[\eta]$[c]
D-I-1-1	12	9,600,000	—	14.4[d]
LJF-9	12	4,500,000	—	8.267
11b	PCC	4,000	—	—
7b	PCC	37,000	—	—
61970	WA	2,610,000	1,990,000	4.733
25167	WA	867,000	773,000	2.234
41984	WA	200,000	193,000	0.726
25170	WA	33,000	36,000	0.232
25171	WA	10,000	9,600	—
25168	WA	20,800	20,000	—
NBS 705	NBS	179,000[a] 190,000[b]	171,000	—
NBS 706	NBS	257,800[a] 288,100[b]	—	—

[a] Light scattering.
[b] Analytical ultracentrifuge.
[c] dl/g; THF at 30°C.
[d] Reference 12.

ciates (WA), Framingham, Mass., the National Bureau of Standards (NBS), Washington, D.C., and Pressure Chemical Company, Pittsburgh, Pennsylvania (PCC). The identification and molecular weights are given in Table I.

Ultracentrifugation

All sedimentation-equilibrium experiments were performed with a Beckman Model "E" analytical ultracentrifuge using either an AN-J four-place equilibrium rotor or an AN-F four-place rotor. The RTIC unit was calibrated with a mercury thermometer. The Rayleigh interferometric system was used for all sedimentation-equilibrium runs.

Initial concentrations were based on the volumetrically determined concentrations. Multicell runs were made with interference and/or Schlieren cells having +0.6°, 0.0°, and −0.6° wedge centerpieces. FC 43 oil was used to lift the solutions off the bottom of the cells so that the fringes could be properly read.

The sedimentation-equilibrium molecular weights were determined in cyclohexane. Values of 0.928 for $\bar{v}$, 0.764 for ρ, and 0.1705 for dn/dc were used based upon linear polystyrene.[12]

The following equations were used to determine the weight- and z-average apparent molecular weights, $M_{w,app}$ and $M_{z,app}$, respectively:

$$M_{w,app} = \frac{2RT}{(1 - \bar{v})\omega^2} \cdot \frac{1}{(r_b^2 - r_m^2)} \cdot \frac{(C_b - C_m)}{C_0} \tag{1}$$

$$M_{z,app} = \frac{M_{w_b}C_b - M_{w_m}C_m}{C_b - C_m} \tag{2}$$

where R is the gas constant, $\bar{v}$ is the partial specific volume of solute, ρ is the solvent density, ω is the velocity in radian/sec, r is the distance from axis of rotation in cm (b = cell bottom and m = cell meniscus), T is the absolute temperature, and $(C_b - C_m)$ is the change in concentration in fringe numbers. M_{w_b} is equal to the weight-average molecular weight at the cell bottom and M_{w_m} is equal to the weight-average molecular weight at the cell meniscus.

Since most of the experimental runs were made at several degrees above the ideal temperature, all true $\overline{M}_w$ and $\overline{M}_z$ values were obtained by extrapolating the apparent values to zero concentration according to the method and following the equation given by Fujita[13]:

$$\frac{1}{M_{w,\text{app}}} = \frac{1}{M_w} + 2A_2\overline{c} \qquad (3)$$

$$\overline{c} = \frac{C_b + C_m}{2} \qquad (4)$$

where A_2 is the second virial coefficient and $\overline{c}$ is close to the original concentration. Correspondingly, $1/M_{z,\text{app}}$ is plotted versus $\overline{c}$ (g/cc) to obtain $\overline{M}_z$ at $c = 0$.

A second correction was occasionally needed. Ideally, in order to apply extrapolations like eq. (3), all apparent molecular weights must be determined such that the variable $[(1 - v)\omega^2 (r_b{}^2 - r_m{}^2)]/2RT$ is constant.

Light Scattering and Clarification of Solutions

A Phoenix low-angle light-scattering photometer had been modified extensively to include very low angles of observation.[12] This light-scattering photometer has the capability of measuring from 140° to 15° of observation angle. Secondary concentrations were prepared by volumetric dilution of a master solution. Samples were filtered through 0.2-μ membrane filters into the specially designed scattering cells equipped with dust traps. Optical cleaning was accomplished by centrifugation. The samples were centrifuged for 2 hr at 4000 rpm in a Sorvall SS-4 centrifuge equipped with a type HB-4 high-speed swinging bucket rotor. Solvents were centrifuged at 4000 rpm for a minimum of 8 hr. A specially constructed oven around the centrifuge allowed the handling of solutions above room temperature.

The standard Sofica light scattering photometer was employed for the lower molecular weight samples and was used over an angular range of 30°–150°. Clarification by repeated slow filtration of solutions through 0.2-μ filter membranes was followed by a visual check for dust in the instrument using the natural light of the mercury lamp viewed at low angles.

Differential Refractometry

A Brice–Phoenix differential refractometer was used with a constant temperature circulator maintaining control to ±0.2°C. The calibration constants in two solvents of differing refractive index, toluene and cyclohexane, were determined with polystyrene standard NBS 705 at 30°C. The values of dn/dc for cyclohexane at various temperatures were taken from the work of (O'Mara and McIntyre.[14] For THF, the value of dn/dc for all of the branched samples was determined to be 0.1963. There was no variation in dn/dc with either branching or molecular weight. The measured value is close to that reported by Jordan[15] for linear polystyrene, 0.1926.

Absolute Scattering Values

The scattering standard used in all cases was benzene. Its Rayleigh ratio for unpolarized light of 5461 Å wavelength and 23°C was taken to be[16] 1.58×10^{-5}. The Rayleigh ratio R_0 increases with temperature, and the equation of Carr and Zimm[17] was used for calculating the Rayleigh ratio at different temperatures:

$$R_{90,2} = R_{90,1} \frac{(T_2 n_2{}^2)}{(T_1 n_1{}^2)} \tag{5}$$

where the subscript 1 refers to the temperature given with the reported R_{90} value (23°C) and subscript 2 refers to the calculated value at another temperature, T_2.

The method of Zimm[18] was used to determine $\overline{M}_w$, $\langle S^2 \rangle_z$, and A_2; $\overline{M}_w$ is the weight-average molecular weight, $\langle S^2 \rangle_z$ is the z-average mean-square radius of gyration, and A_2 is the second virial coefficient. (c/I_c) was plotted versus $\sin^2(\theta/C) + KC$, where K is an arbitrary constant, to give two limiting curves for zero concentration and zero angle.

Osmometry

The Mechrolab Model 502 membrane osmometer was used with toluene solutions for all except one sample that was used with tetrahydrofuran (THF) solutions. Temperatures were controlled at 35°C for the toluene experiments and at 24°C for the THF experiment. Gel cellophane 600-D-type membranes were used for the most part because of their tight porosity (10,000 molecular weight diffusion limit). Solutions were prepared as previously discussed. The osmotic height was measured for the solvent on both sides of the membrane first, then for each concentration, and again for solvent on both sides to ensure that the same readings were obtained and no diffusion or other problems had occurred. All data were linearly extrapolated to zero concentration.

Variable-Shear Capillary Viscometer

A Cannon–Ubbelohde variable-shear dilution viscometer was used to determine the intrinsic viscosity at low shear rates. Typical shear rates for organic solvents range from 300 to 3000 sec^{-1}. In no case was there a shear-rate dependence.

Gel Permeation Chromatography

A Waters Associates Ana-Prep gel permeation chromatograph (GPC) was used with THF at 40°C. The following set of 4-ft Styragel columns was used: one 7 $\times 10^5$ to 5×10^6 Å; one 1.5×10^5 to 7×10^5 Å; one 1.5×10^4 to 5×10^4 A; two 5×10^3 to 1.5×10^4 Å; and one 2000 to 5000 Å. The size designations are those given by Waters Associates. This particular column sequence had a plate count of 700 ppf using a 5-sec injection of o-dichlorobenzene. The solvent was THF at 40°C at a flow rate of 1 ml/min.

The standard differential refractometer detector was coupled with the Waters differential UV detector set at 254 mμ wavelength, providing dual detector capability. This arrangement was necessary in order to use the GPC at the low

TABLE II
Initial Sty/DVB Polymerization Batches

Bottle no.	% BP[a]	% DVB[b]	Temp., °C	Gelation time, hr
1	0.125	0.0125	76	16
2	0.120	0.0100	76	19
3	0.125	0.0617	76	14
4	0.126	0.2690	76	12
5	0.120	1.22	78	5
6	0.100	2.12	78	5

[a] BP = Benzoyl peroxide.
[b] DVB monomer as received.

concentrations required to eliminate corrections for concentration effects (0.05% for the linear polystyrene samples and 0.10% for the branched polystyrene samples). Samples were prepared on a weight/volume basis and filtered using 1-μ Millipore filter membranes. Full-loop injections were used both in generating the calibration curves and also in analyzing chromatograms as a function of elution volume. The above column set was found to be adequate in resolving all but the very high molecular weight ($> 10^6$) polystyrene samples.

Polymerization and Fractionation

A polymerization scheme similar to that of Thurmond and Zimm[1] was used, where PSty/DVB copolymer was synthesized by a free-radical bulk polymerization. In this work the inhibitors were not removed from the monomers prior to the polymerization.

The first series of polymerizations were designed to determine the relationship between DVB content and the time to visible gelation at 78°C. Table II lists the pertinent data for the batches run. The increase of gelation time from 5 hr to 19 hr as the DVB content decreased from 2% to 0.01% is in the expected direction. However, the 16-hr gelation time (obtained from the final calibration line) at 78°C and 0.06% DVB was faster than that observed by Thurmond and Zimm, who found 16 hr of gelation time at 67°C and 0.08% DVB content. This was undoubtedly due to the higher polymerization temperature.

Next, the polymerization rate was studied as a function of DVB content. Four batches were polymerized to predetermined total reaction times and stopped. The results are listed in Table III. Series 9, 1% DVB monomer charge, was found

TABLE III
Conversion Versus Polymerization Time

Bottle no.	Time, hr	% BP	% DVB[a]	Temp, °C	% Conversion
7	9	0.125	0.010	81	55.1
8	6	0.127	0.105	78	33.3
9A	2	0.125	0.988	78	5.7
9B	4	0.125	0.988	78	15.2

[a] Monomer as received.

to have a 15% conversion at the gel point. This value is consistent with the result of Malinsky,[19] who found 13%–14% conversion at gelation at 70°C.

For the low conversion, high DVB series 9A and 9B, percent conversion was plotted versus polymerization time and extrapolated to a time intercept of 48 min. This is the induction period for this polymerization. Undoubtedly, this high induction period is due to the inhibitors in the monomers. Straight lines were drawn through each of the remaining data points and the time intercept point. The slopes of these three lines, representing the polymerization rates, were plotted versus DVB content; and it was found that as DVB content increased from 0.01% to 1%, the polymerization rate decreased from 6.7%/hr to 4.7%/hr. These numbers may not be absolutely correct since they are based on the assumption that the 48-min induction period is constant for all DVB levels. But even if the induction period decreases as the DVB content decreases, the polymerization rate will still decrease as the DVB content increases. These results are not expected since Flory[20] and Malinsky[19] report that DVB is appreciably more reactive than styrene. However, the reduction in polymerization rate found here is probably due to the fact that DVB had 1200 ppm t-butylcatechol inhibitor while styrene had only 100 ppm t-butylcatechol. Thus, an increase in DVB causes an increased inhibition of the polymerization by reducing initiator concentration and reducing the rate of polymerization.

These three batches (7, 8, and 9) also served as a study of branching as a function of conversion. From each bottle, half (called A) was removed when polymerization had proceeded halfway toward its gel point time. The other half (called B) was allowed to polymerize to just short of the gel point. Of these six samples, the two of highest DVB content, batch 9, were selected for fractionation. The solution properties of the fractions were subsequently measured and considered to be typical randomly branched polymers. Series 9 was selected because of the relatively high branching. It contained 0.4% active DVB as compared to less than 0.1% DVB in the Thurmond and Zimm work[1] and 0.02% DVB in the GPC study of Tung.[21] Therefore, these polymers should be more highly branched than polymers in the previous studies and therefore more representative of highly branched commercial polymers.

All samples were checked for macrogel content by filtering 0.1% THF solutions through 1-μ filters (Millipore) and measuring the loss in concentration. None had any measurable macrogel. Checks for microgel were made in the course of making light-scattering measurements. Only the highest molecular weight fraction of the high-conversion polystyrene showed a sharp downward trend at 15°C, indicating the presence of a small amount of microgel.

The purified samples 9A and 9B were fractionated using a solution-precipitation technique. Approximately 1.5 g sample was dissolved in 150 ml benzene in a beaker and titrated dropwise with methanol to the point of heavy turbidity, heated to the point of clarity, and allowed to slowly recool to room temperature. The dispersion was added to 50-ml stainless steel tubes designed to fit the Sorvall Model SS-4 centrifuge and centrifuged at 5000 rpm for 1 min. The supernatant was poured back into the beaker for further fractionation. The swollen polymer phase in the centrifuge tubes was dissolved in benzene, collected, and dried. In this fashion, several crude fractions were prepared. One crude fraction, 9B2, was refractionated in the same manner into two subfractions, 9B2-1 and 9B2-2.

RESULTS AND DISCUSSION

Molecular Weight Characterization

Six fractions were selected for characterization studies to allow the widest possible spread in both branching and molecular weight. These are listed in Table IV. Three fractions are from the low conversion series (A): 9A1, 9A3, and 9A5. Three fractions are from the high conversion series (B): 9B2-1, 9B2-2, and 9B3.

All of the molecular weight results ($\overline{M}_z$, $\overline{M}_w$, $\overline{M}_n$) are compiled in Table V. Good agreement in $\overline{M}_w$ is found for the three samples for which $\overline{M}_w$ was determined both by sedimentation equilibrium (UC) and light scattering (LS) techniques. $\overline{M}_n$ is from osmotic pressure measurements (OP).

The fractions from the highly branched series 9B are broader in molecular weight distribution than those of the lightly branched series 9A. This reflects the increased complexity of the polymer as the molecular weight and conversion increases. There undoubtedly exists in a system like this not only a distribution with respect to molecular weight, but also a distribution with respect to branching. These contribute in different ways to the entropic and enthalpic

TABLE IV
Branched Polystyrene Fractions Characterized

Low conversion series	High conversion series
9A1	9B2-1
9A3	9B2-2
9A5	9B3

TABLE V
Summary of Molecular Weight Data for Branched Polystyrenes

Fraction	$\overline{M}_z$ (UC)	$\overline{M}_w$ (UC)	$\overline{M}_w$ (LS)	$\overline{M}_n$ (OP)	$[\eta]$*
9A5	139,000	88,200	88,400	67,000	0.456
9A3	595,000	400,000	407,000	206,000	0.977
9A1	—	—	572,000	348,000	1.305
9B3	352,000	210,000	228,000	127,000	0.714
9B2-2	—	—	2,230,000	322,000	1.202
9B-1	—	—	5,240,000	681,000	2.109

*THF at 30°C

TABLE VI
Results from Final Curve-Fitted Calibration Curves

Fraction	$[\eta]$ (dl/gm)	$\overline{M}_z$ (gm/mole)	$\overline{M}_w$ (gm/mole)	$\overline{M}_n$ (gm/mole)
9A5	0.45	121,000	90,100	66,100
9A3	1.01	614,000	372,000	223,000
9A1	1.29	954,000	614,000	328,000
9B3	0.71	361,000	212,000	140,000
9B2-2	1.34	11,500,000	2,010,000	326,000
9B2-1	2.13	15,000,000	5,280,000	920,000

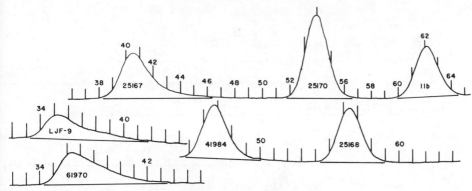

Fig. 1. GPC curves of linear polystyrene standards in Ana-Prep GPC (refractive index vs elution volume counts; sample numbers underneath curve).

variables that govern fractionation by fractional precipitation. This effect has to be recognized in the later GPC analysis. Also contributing to the observed distribution differences is the overall higher molecular weights of the 9B series fractions.

The molecular weight data indicate that the branched fractions are not monodisperse. In order to study the effect of branching on the solution properties, it is necessary to correct for these polydispersities. To do this, the GPC data were used to provide a quantitative picture of the molecular weight distri-

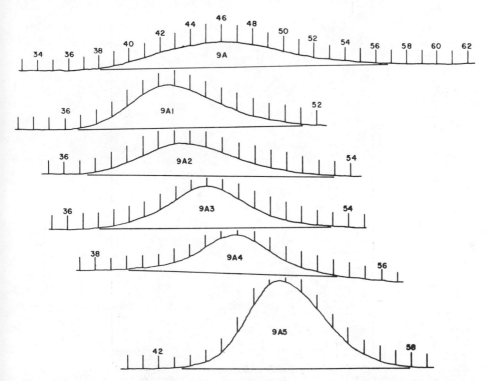

Fig. 2. GPC curves of 9A branched series in Ana-Prep GPC (refractive index vs elution volume counts; sample numbers underneath curve).

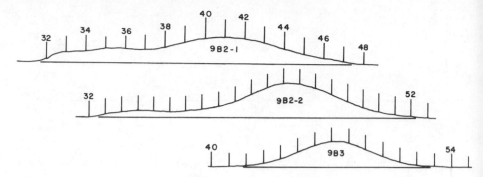

Fig. 3. GPC curves of 9B branched series (refractive index vs elution volume counts; sample numbers underneath curve).

butions. Having previously determined the necessary characterization data on these fractions, calibration of the GPC was done using curve fitting techniques. The basic assumption made was that branching in a whole polymer is a single-valued function. With this assumption, the fractions of one branched series should obey one common calibration curve. An underlying assumption in this approach is, of course, that the chromatogram represents an accurate picture of the molecular size distribution and therefore molecular weight.

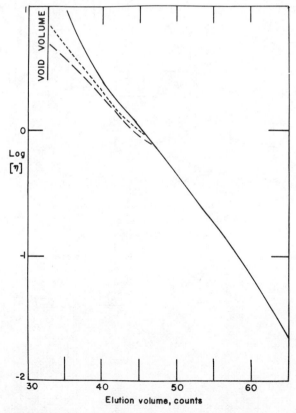

Fig. 4. Final curve-fitted intrinsic viscosity calibration curves for polystyrene in Ana-Prep GPC: (—) linear; (– –) 9B series. (- - -) 9A series.

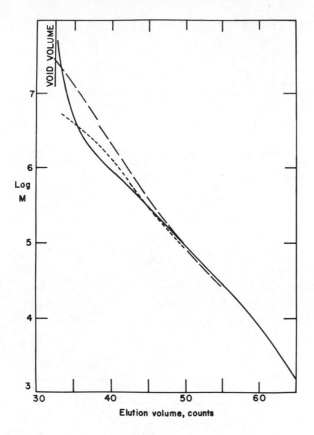

Fig. 5. Final curve-fitted molecular weight calibration curves for branched polystyrene in Ana-Prep GPC: (—) linear; (– –) 9B series; (- - -) 9A series.

The curve fitting analyses were done by using the following equations:

$$M_z = \frac{\Sigma w_i M_i{}^2}{\Sigma w_i M_i} \tag{6}$$

$$M_w = \Sigma w_i M_i \tag{7}$$

$$M_n = \frac{1}{\Sigma w_i / M_i} \tag{8}$$

$$[\eta] = \Sigma w_i [\eta]_i \tag{9}$$

The weight fraction data were obtained from the GPC curve in the normal manner, and the $\overline{M}_w$ and $[\eta]$ data were taken from the characterization values shown in Table V. The procedure was to (1) develop a molecular weight calibration curve using $\overline{M}_w$ values for the fractions, (2) develop an $[\eta]$ calibration curve using $[\eta]$ data, and (3) develop an $\langle S^2 \rangle$ calibration curve using the $\langle S^2 \rangle_z$ data for the fractions. All the characterized fractions were used because they eluted at different volumes yet overlapped in volume to define all the elution volume regions of the calibration curve.

The GPC curves of the linear standards and the two branched series (A and B) are shown in Figures 1–3, respectively. Included for reference are the GPC

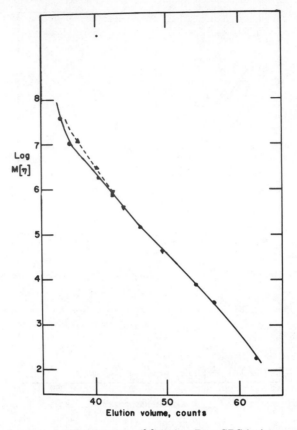

Fig. 6. Curve fitted universal calibration curve ([η]) in Ana-Prep GPC (points represent experimental data; lines are curve-fitted data): (●) PSty; (▼) series A; (▲) series B.

curves of the fractions not characterized.   Whole sample 9B could not be ana-lyzed because plugging of the column occurred when it was injected into the GPC apparatus.   Sample 9B1 also plugged the GPC.   This was undoubtedly due to a small amount of the microgel present in the polymerized sample and discussed earlier.

A comparison of the GPC curve-fitted results of Table VI to the character-ization data of Table V reveals good agreement in all parameters.   No corrections for peak dispersion were required to develop a precise calibration curve over the entire molecular weight range.   Even though the molecular weight calibration curve was developed using only $\overline{M}_w$ data, the final results for $\overline{M}_z$ and $\overline{M}_n$ agreed quite well with the characterization data.   This fortified the original assumption that the chromatogram represented the actual molecular weight distribution. This suggests that for samples of broad molecular weight distribution, peak dispersion is not a problem.   However, it must be recognized that just because the calibration curves for the branched series coincides with that of the linear species, especially at low molecular weight, the structure is not necessarily the same.   This aspect of the results will be discussed later.

Some justification of the curve-fitting approach should be made.   In order to apply curve-fitting to the data, it is assumed that (1) the elution volume is a single-valued function of each of the two parameters M and [η], (2) the same chromatogram is an expression of the two different parameters, (3) there are no double-valued positions along the elution volume space, and (4) both parameters are monotonically decreasing functions. Additionally the solution properties of the polymers in the GPC columns are assumed to be at "infinite dilution." An independent study of the concentraion dependence of both branched series had shown that "infinite dilution" was a good approximation in the GPC analysis.

The final GPC calibration curves derived from the preceding analysis of $[\eta]$, M, and $[\eta]M$ are shown in Figures 4–6. In each case, the calibration curve obtained for linear polystyrene is also shown as a solid curve. It is evident from Figure 4 that for a given $[\eta]$ value, branched samples elute from the GPC sooner than linear polymers, and the deviation from linear polystyrene increases as branching increases from the low-conversion (lightly branched) series 9A to the high-conversion (highly branched) series 9B. Further, at low elution volumes, the rise in $[\eta]$ is less rapid for the branched samples than for the linear samples.

In Figure 5, for a given molecular weight (MW), branched samples elute from the GPC later than linear polymers. Both the $[\eta]$ and MW relations to elution volume for branched polymers show an increasing deviation from the linear polystyrene as branching increases; however, the deviation is in opposite directions. Both deviations are related to the flattening out of the $[\eta]$–M plot for branched polymers.

Some comments regarding the universal calibration parameter $M[\eta]$ shown in Figure 6 must be made. It is obvious that the $M[\eta]$ calibration for the lightly branched series 9A agrees well with that of linear polystyrene, while the corresponding $M[\eta]$ plot for the highly branched series 9B deviates from the linear line. An explanation of this effect involves an extensive analysis of the GPC separation mechanism itself. This will be dwelt on in the succeeding papers. Any GPC analysis of branching must make allowance for the deviation from the linear calibration curve. If there is a significant amount of high-conversion branched polymer in the sample, the error in molecular weights could be as high as a factor of 2. Many commercial samples would have to be corrected by this factor. An analysis of Pannell's GPC data[2] on grafted polystyrene indicates that the deviation in the ln $[\eta]M$ plot even in these samples approaches the factor of 2.

In general, no GPC analysis is better than the calibration curve. In this study the overlap of fractions was required to validate the simplest interpretation of the data, namely that the deviation from the unversal calibration is due to increasing branching. It is always possible to adduce a more ad hoc hypothesis that the deviation is due to adventitious combination of errors. However, it was felt that a better understanding of the deviations from the universal calibration for branched polymers was necessary in order to generalize this observation and apply it to other variants of macromolecular structure. To this end, an extensive study of the solution properties of these branched polymers was undertaken to determine actual sizes and their relation to the mechanism of the GPC separation process.

References

1. C. D. Thurmond and B. H. Zimm, *J. Polym. Sci.*, **8**, 477 (1952).
2. J. Pannell, *Polymer*, **13**, 277 (1972).
3. M. Kurata, M. Abe, M. Iwama, and M. Matsushima, *Polym. J.*, **3**, 729 (1972).

4. M. R. Ambler, R. D. Mate, and J. R. Purdon, *J. Polym. Sci., Polym. Chem. Ed.*, **12,** 1759 (1974).

5. M. R. Ambler, R. D. Mate, and J. R. Purdon, *J. Polym. Sci., Polym. Chem. Ed.*, **12,** 1771 (1974).

6. E. E. Drott and R. A. Mendelson, *J. Polym. Sci. A-2*, **8,** 1361 (1970).

7. E. E. Drott and R. A. Mendelson, *J. Polym. Sci. A-2*, **8,** 1373 (1970).

8. G. Kraus and C. J. Stacey, *J. Polym. Sci. A-2*, **10,** 657 (1972).

9. M. Kurata, H. Okamoto, M. Iwama, M. Abe, and T. Homma, *Polym. J.*, **3,** 739 (1972).

10. A. R. Shultz, *Eur. Polym. J.*, **6,** 69 (1970).

11. L. Westerman and J. C. Clark, *J. Polym. Sci., Polym. Chem. Ed.*, **11,** 559 (1973).

12. E. L. Slagowski, Doctoral Thesis, University of Akron, Akron, Ohio, 1972.

13. H. Fujita, *Mathematical Theory of Sedimentation Analysis*, Academic Press, New York, 1962.

14. J. H. O'Mara and D. McIntyre, *J. Phys. Chem.*, **63,** 1435 (1959).

15. E. F. Jordan, Jr., *J. Polym. Sci. A-1*, **6,** 2209 (1968).

16. H. Utiyama, in *Light Scattering From Polymer Solutions*, M. B. Huglin, Ed., Academic Press, London, 1972, p. 78.

17. C. I. Carr and B. H. Zimm, *J. Chem. Phys.*, **18,** 1616 (1950).

18. B. H. Zimm, *J. Chem. Phys.*, **16,** 1093, 1099 (1948).

19. J. Malinsky, J. Kapban, and K. Dusck, *J. Macromol. Sci., Chem.*, **A5,** 1071 (1971).

20. P. J. Flory, Principles of Polymer Chemistry", Cornell, Ithaca, N.Y., 1953, p. 391.

21. L. H. Tung, *J. Polym. Sci. A-2*, **7,** 47 (1969).

Received January 30, 1976

JOURNAL OF APPLIED POLYMER SCIENCE   VOL. 21, 3251–3260 (1977)

Shear Creep Recovery Behavior of IUPAC Low-Density Polyethylenes

PAWAN K. AGARWAL and DONALD J. PLAZEK, *Department of Metallurgical and Materials Engineering, University of Pittsburgh, Pittsburgh, Pennsylvania 15261*

Synopsis

Shear creep and creep recovery measurements were carried out on three low-density polyethylenes that were the object of extended investigations of the International Union of Pure and Applied Chemistry Working Party on the Structure and Properties of Commercial Polymers. The measurements were carried out in torsion at 130° and 153°C using a frictionless apparatus with a magnetic levitation bearing. The three samples were found to be experimentally the same at short deformation times and at high shear rates. Larger nonlinear recoverable compliances were exhibited by one of the samples, which is suspected of containing a high molecular weight tail, possibly microgel, at long times and low creep stresses.

INTRODUCTION

In 1967, the International Union of Pure and Applied Chemistry (IUPAC) Working Party on Structure and Properties of Commercial Polymers initiated studies on the rheological properties of three low-density polyethylene (LDPE) samples which were similar in their chemical characterization and in their melt-flow behavior but which exhibited differences in processing and end-use properties. The culmination of these cooperative studies is the Working Party report which was prepared by Dr. Joachim Meissner. He presented this extensive report[1] at the IUPAC International Symposium on Macromolecules, Madrid, September 15–20, 1974.

The samples studied are designated A, B, and C. The principal practical differences cited are critical film drawdown speeds and the optical properties of blown film. Samples B and C can be drawn almost twice as fast as A. B and C are also close to one another optically and exhibit less haze due to surface roughness than does A. Their gel permeation chromatography (GPC) curves are nearly identical, and their flow curves, i.e., viscosity–shear rate curves, are virtually identical. Number-average molecular weights M_n are reported to be the same ($\sim 2 \times 10^4$), but light scattering results indicate that the weight-average molecular weight M_w of sample A ($> 10^6$) is higher than that of B (6×10^5) and C ($8-9 \times 10^5$). This difference is believed to be due to a small high molecular weight tail in A, probably microgel.

Viscosity, dynamic mechanical property, and stress relaxation measurements yielded results which differed very little. Among the most convincing differences

3251

found in the characterization measurements were those seen in the extrusion viscometry end effects and extrudate swell, where sample A showed larger effects than B and C, which again were similar. Some results that showed differences between samples, such as the conditions for the onset of melt fracture, have to be questioned because of the contradictory trends reported by different participating laboratories.

It was noted that when differences were observed between the samples, they appeared consistently to be more exaggerated at lower rates of shear; see, for example, the tensile stress–strain curves presented for different rates of strain.

Having heard the Working Party Report, we expressed an interest in the materials, and we consequently were kindly supplied with samples by Dr. Meissner. We had previously become convinced that creep recovery in the terminal region of response was among the most sensitive material properties if not the most sensitive to variations of the molecular weight distribution. It, therefore, seemed reasonable that if small differences in the molecular weight distributions were responsible for the observed processing differences, then the recoverable creep compliances should also be significantly affected. The viscoelastic response of the three LDPEs had already been shown by various members of the Working Party to be indistinguishable at times out to about 100 sec. We obviously had to look at the response at substantially longer times.

EXPERIMENTAL

Measurements of torsional creep and recovery on disc-shaped samples were carried out at 130° and 153°C in a frictionless creep apparatus[2] *in vacuo* (ca. 5 microns Hg). The three IUPAC samples A, B, and C are commercial-grade low-density (0.92_0 g/cm^3) polyethylenes which were manufactured by BASF, Ludwigshafen am Rhein, Germany. In addition to measurements made on the IUPAC samples, we are reporting results obtained on a hydrogenated narrow-distribution anionically polymerized polybutadiene, HPB, which was kindly supplied to us by Professor William W. Graessley. Molecular weights obtained for this material, before and after hydrogenation, from intrinsic viscosities were both 33,000 (measurements made by Mr. Gregory Smith at Northwestern University). The heterogeneity indices, M_w/M_n, before and after hydrogenation were 1.05 (GPC, corrected for diffusion spreading) and 1.27 (GPC, not corrected), respectively. The melting point was found to be 111° ± 2°C, and the density (quenched from the melt) was 0.913 g/cm^3 at 25°C. The low density and melting point are due to the short-chain branching resulting from the vinyl content of the parent PBD (19 vinyl groups/1000 backbone carbon atoms). Residual unsaturation was less than one double bond per 1000 carbon atoms.

RESULTS

Initial measurements of the recoverable shear compliance $J_r(t)$, cm^2/dyne, were found to be nonreproducible at times greater than 100 sec. Since our measurements had to extend over lengthy periods of time, days instead of minutes, it was reasonable to be wary of thermal degradation. To decrease and hopefully eliminate degradation and its measurable effects, 0.1% by weight of

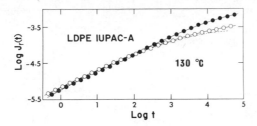

Fig. 1. Logarithmic plot of recoverable compliance $J_r(t)$, cm²/dyne, vs time, sec, for the IUPAC-A sample showing the effect of thermal degradation on the recovery of this sample. Open circles indicate the recovery after 4 hr of creep ($\eta = 1.15 \times 10^6$ poises); filled circles represent the recovery after 65 hr of creep ($\eta = 1.60 \times 10^6$ poises). Maximum stress in the sample in both cases is 285 dynes/cm². Dashed curve is the estimated recovery curve at this stress level of the thermally stabilized sample.

Santonox antioxidant, 4,4-thiobis(6-t-butyl-m-cresol) (recommended and generously supplied to us by Dr. Robert Mendelson of Monsanto), was added to the samples in toluene solutions. The toluene was subsequently stripped off in a rotary vacuum evaporator. The resulting samples gave no indication of any degradation for periods as long as a week at temperatures between 130° and 150°C *in vacuo*. The onset of measurable degradation was not pursued further. Although thermal degradation was effectively eliminated the measurements of the recoverable strain per unit stress clearly indicated a remaining lack of uniqueness which was shown to reflect that the recovery response was strongly nonlinear at times greater than 100 sec at 130°C.

In the linear range of viscoelastic response, the ratio of the shear strain, which is monotonically increasing with the time after loading in creep, to the fixed applied stress is a unique characterizing curve, the shear creep compliance $J(t)$, cm²/dyne:

$$\frac{\gamma(t)}{\sigma_0} = J(t) = J_g + J_d \, \psi(t) + \frac{t}{\eta} \tag{1}$$

where J_g is the glassy recoverable contribution to the total deformation (ca. 1 $\times 10^{-10}$ cm²/dyne) which is independent of time during the usual periods of measurement. The normalizing constant, the retarded steady-state recoverable compliance J_d, is often, as it is in this study, more than $10^4 J_g$. The recoverable creep compliance function $\psi(t)$ ranges from 0 to 1 as t, the time, goes from 0 to infinity. The permanent strain per unit stress accumulates linearly in time with a coefficient which is the reciprocal of the limiting low rate of shear viscosity η. The usually referred to steady-state recoverable compliance J_e is equal to $J_g + J_d$. Recoverable compliance $J_r(t)$ ($= J(t) - t/\eta$) curves depicting the response of sample A, as received at 130°C, are shown logarithmically as a function of the logarithm of time (sec) in Figure 1. The compliance points represented by the open circles were obtained following a period of 4 hr of creep. A viscosity of 1.2 $\times 10^6$ poises was calculated from the creep terminal velocity. At the beginning of the recovery, the residence time of the sample at 130°C was 35 hr. Since recoverable deformation continued to accumulate at recovery times greater than that of the time of creep, it was apparent that steady-state creep deformation, defined by $\psi(t) = 1$, had not been attained.

The recoverable strain at recovery times approaching or greater than the time

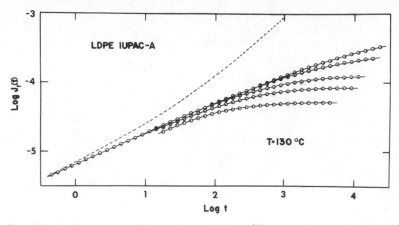

Fig. 2. Logarithmic plot of recoverable compliance $J_r(t)$, cm^2/dyne, vs. time, sec, for the IUPAC-A sample at various stress levels: $\ominus - \sigma_{max} = 60$ dynes/cm^2, $\odot - 187$ dynes/cm^2, $\odot$ 1256 dynes/cm^2; $\odot$ 3602 dynes/cm^2; $\ominus$ 14691 dynes/cm^2. Dashed line is the creep curve at the lowest stress level. All curves at 130.0°C.

of creep must be less than that reflecting the characteristic recovery curve. For the curve in Figure 1, the stress at the cylindrical surface of the samples, σ_{max}, was 285 dynes/cm^2. In an attempt to reach steady state, a creep run extending for 65 hr was made. The ensuing recovery is depicted by the filled-in circles in Figure 1. The viscosity deduced just preceding the recovery (total residence time at 130°C $\sim$ 110 hr) was 1.6×10^6 poises. A later determination (160 hr residence time) revealed a substantially higher viscosity of 1.7×10^7 poises. The increasing viscosity reflects the thermal degradation that was occurring. The response of a stabilized sample is represented by the dashed line which shows that both $J_r(t)$ curves for the unstabilized material were enhanced at long times by the thermal degradation. Crosslinking clearly dominated chain scission.

The results obtained at 130°C on stabilized IUPAC sample A are summarized in Figure 2 where recovery curves are shown which were obtained following creep curves that approached 10^5 sec in duration. The different curves represent recoveries where the σ_{max} levels ranged from a low of 60 dynes/cm^2 (top curves, highest compliance at long times) to a high of 14,700 dynes/cm^2 (bottom curve, lowest compliance at long times).

The stress levels for the intermediate curves along with viscosity values are given in Table I. At the highest stress level, the speed of response of our recording system was being pushed. It is, therefore, reasonable to assume that the recovery starting point is in doubt and that all of the recovery curves are merged into one at times less than 10 sec. This fanning pattern is the most common form of nonlinear response of polymer melts encountered.[3,4,5] The characteristics appear to be threefold: (1) the departure from short-time linear behavior occurs at a critical strain level; (2) the compliance level decreases with increasing stress; (3) the time to attain steady state diminishes with increasing stress. Note that the $J_r(t)$ curves for Sample A following the creep runs with the lowest stresses do not reach their long-time limiting levels. The dashed line represents the total creep compliance curve obtained at the lowest level of σ_{max}.

In Figure 3, the creep compliance of sample A at 130°C is compared with the

TABLE I
Characterizing Parameters of the IUPAC Polyethylenes[a]

| σ_{max} | IUPAC-A | | | IUPAC-B | | IUPAC-C | |
	$\log \eta$	$\log J_e$	$\log J_r (10^4)$	$\log \eta$	$\log J_e$	$\log \eta$	$\log J_e$
60	6.114		−3.57	6.164	−3.79[b]	6.140	−3.89
187	6.114		−3.685	6.164	−3.84	6.140	−3.90
1260	6.072	−3.900[b]		6.146	−3.96	6.127	−3.98
3600	6.045	−4.065		6.107	−4.06	6.107	−4.12
14700	5.825	−4.290		5.865	−4.23	5.869	−4.27

[a] All measurements at $T = 130°C$. Units: σ, dyne/cm^2; η, poises; J_e, cm^{2}dyne.
[b] J_e obtained by reasonable extrapolation. HPB data: $\log \eta = 3.501$ (130°C); $\log \eta = 3.663$ (115°C); $\log J_e = -5.840$.

response observed at 153°C ($\sigma_{max} = 60$ dynes/cm^2 for both). The dashed lines represent the permanent deformation t/η terms in eq. (1). The dotted line is t/η at 130°C and $\sigma_{max} = 14,700$ dynes/cm^2. The change in level reflects a factor of 2 decrease in η as a function of σ_{max}.

The corresponding $J_r(t)$ curves for sample A at 130° and 153°C are shown in Figure 4, where the upper branch at each temperature was obtained at $\sigma_{max} = 60$ dynes/cm^2 and the lower branch at $\sigma_{max} = 1260$ dynes/cm^2. Note that superposition, by a time-scale shift, of the $J_r(t)$ curves measured at different temperatures and at the same stress level is indicated. This is in accord with similar results obtained on a polystyrene sample in the nonlinear range of response.[3] Since the viscosity in the experimental range of stresses does not show a large variation, the observation that J_e is independent of the temperature at a given stress level is compatible with the proposition that J_e is an intrinsic function of the rate of shear $\dot{\gamma}$.[6] The curves should more properly be identified as $J(t,\dot{\gamma})$ to explicitly indicate the nonlinearity observed at long times at most of the stress levels.

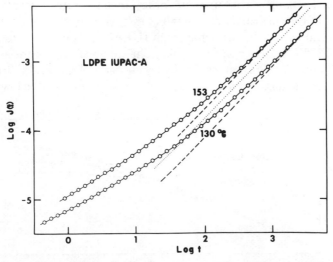

Fig. 3. Logarithmic plot of creep compliance vs. time at indicated temperatures. In both cases, the dash line is the viscous contribution to the creep compliance at the lowest stress level, 60 dynes/cm^2. The dotted line is the viscous contribution to the creep at 130°C at the maximum stress level studied, which is 14,700 dynes/cm^2.

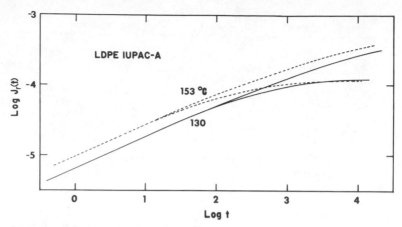

Fig. 4. Logarithmic plot of recoverable compliance vs time at 153°C (represented by dash lines) and at 130° represented by solid lines. In each case, top line corresponds $\sigma_{max} = 60.0$ dynes/cm^2, and the bottom line corresponds to $\sigma_{max} = 1256$ dynes/cm^2.

In addition, we have to qualify the presentation of our results by noting that the compliances have all been calculated as if they were in the linear range of response. The correction for the rate of shear dependence of the viscosity for our circular parallel plate geometry (twisting a right circular cylinder) is available.[7] This is analogous to the Weissenberg correction for tube flow.[8] However, the corresponding expressions for a viscoelastic deformation do not exist. Assuming that the corresponding corrections are of the same magnitude as those indicated by the viscosity correction expressions, our slight intrusion into the nonlinear range should result in errors that are of the same level of our usual experimental uncertainty, i.e., several per cent. The maximum possible correction indicated by the above cited expression[7] is 25%. This obtains when the viscosity is inversely proportional to the rate of shear. This dependence is strictly speaking approachable[9,10] but unachievable, since the rate of shear $\dot{\gamma}$ would be independent of the shearing stress; $\sigma = \eta(\dot{\gamma})\dot{\gamma} = (K/\dot{\gamma})\dot{\gamma} = K = $ a constant.

The recoverable compliance behavior of IUPAC sample C, low-density polyethylene at 130°C, is shown in Figure 5. The range of σ_{max} is the same as was applied to sample A. The values for $J_r(t,\dot{\gamma})$ for samples A and C are the same within about 5% at short times and/or at high stress levels. At the lowest stresses

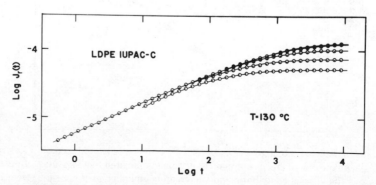

Fig. 5. Logarithmic plot of recoverable compliance vs. time for the IUPAC-C sample at 130°C. Pip directions correspond to applied creep stresses as indicated in Figure 2.

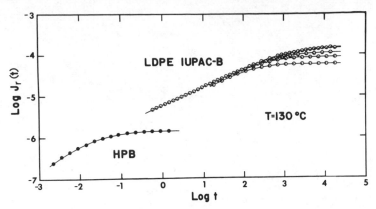

Fig. 6. Logarithmic plot of recoverable compliance vs. time of IUPAC-B and the hydrogenated polybutadiene (HPB) sample. Pip directions correspond to the stress levels indicated in Figure 2.

at long times, $J_r(t,\dot{\gamma})$ of A is more than twice as big as that of C. The qualitative difference that should be noted is that steady state was attained at all stress levels for C and that for $\sigma_{max} < 200$ dynes/cm^2, the $J_r(t,\dot{\gamma})$ values for C are the same indicating that the response was linear at all times.

The results for sample B, shown in Figure 6, for all intents and purposes are the same as those for C. All the curves for B are within about 10% of the corresponding curves for C at long times and within about 3% at short times. The recoverable compliance of the hydrogenated polybutadiene, HPB, is also shown in Figure 6. Its response was found to be linear over the entire accessible range of creep shear stresses, which ranged up to $\sigma_{max} = 59,000$ dynes/cm^2. The persistent linear response, the level of J_e, and the relatively short time to reach steady-state behavior are all indicative of a very narrow molecular weight distribution. To obtain the limited amount of transient response displayed before steady state was reached, a special detector system was employed. The position of a light lever which was reflected off of a mirror on the creep instrument rotor was detected with a Schottky barrier photocell Model PIN-LSC/2 (United Detector Technology, Santa Monica, California), and the output, which was a measure of the angular deformation, was displayed and photographed on a storage oscilloscope Model 564 B (Tektronix, Beaverton, Oregon 97005).

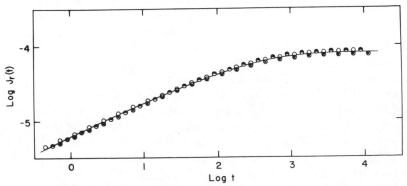

Fig. 7. Logarithmic plot of recoverable compliances for (O) IUPAC-A, (◓) B, and (⊗) C as a function of time; $\sigma_{max} = 3600$ dynes/cm^2.

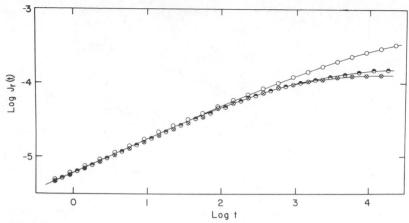

Fig. 8. Logarithmic plot of recoverable compliances for IUPAC-A, B, and C. Symbols as indicated in Figure 7; σ_{max} = 60 dynes/cm^2.

Use of the fast-responding photocell and the oscilloscope made it possible to obtain recovery measurements at times as short as 2 msec. The limiting factor was the moment of inertia of the instrument rotor and not the detection system.

The HPB sample clearly reached steady-state deformation in less than a second at 130°C. It is interesting to note that the J_e value obtained for this special narrow molecular weight distribution linear polyethylene, 1.45 × 10^{-6} cm^2/dyne, is quantitatively close to the high molecular weight limiting values obtained on all the polymers measured with the exception of polybutadiene.[11] Values for poly(dimethylsiloxane), poly(vinyl acetate), poly(α-methylstyrene), cis-1,4-polyisoprene, compiled by Graessley,[11] and polystyrene[3] and polyisobutylene[12] are all within 25% of 1.25 × 10^{-6} cm^2/dyne. At present, there is no known reason for such a universality.

In Figures 7 and 8, the recoverable creep compliances of the IUPAC polyethylenes are compared. In Figure 7, the $J_r(t)$ curves obtained, where σ_{max} = 3600 dynes/cm^2, for three materials are presented. At this relatively high shearing stress, no significant differences in the response curves can be seen. At the lowest stress level, σ_{max} = 60 dynes/cm^2, however, it can be seen in Figure 8 that beyond 100 sec, IUPAC polyethylenes B and C approach steady-state response (attained in approximately 4 hr), while A diverges from the common curve toward ever increasing values. It looks as if J_e (σ_{max} = 60 dynes/cm^2) for A might be about 2 × 10^{-3} cm^2/dyne, which would make it three to four times higher than the values for B and C. At still lower stress levels or strain rates, the trend indicates even larger differences.

These differences can clearly be seen in terms of the steady-state response as a function of the maximum rate of shear present in the specimens, $\dot{\gamma}_{max}$. Figure 9 includes logarithmic plots of $J_e(\dot{\gamma})$ as a function of log $\dot{\gamma}_{max}$. The filled-in circles represent the recoverable compliance values for A attained at 10^4 sec. Since steady state was not achieved for sample A, these values constitute minimum limits. The values shown for sample B were decreased 12% to emphasize the similarity of the steady-state behavior of B and C.

The viscosity values obtained on A and C are also presented logarithmically in Figure 9 as a function of log $\dot{\gamma}_{max}$. They illustrate another characteristic

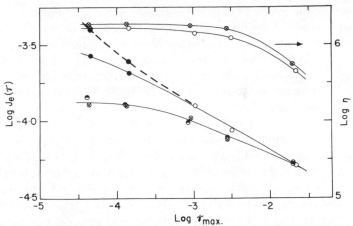

Fig. 9. Logarithmic plots of steady-state recoverable compliances of IUPAC A, B, and C as a function of the maximum strain rate in the samples. Viscosities of A and C also presented. Symbols as in Figure 7, except for the lower filled points (solid line) which represent J_r, 10^4 sec, for IUPA-A and therefore are minimum limits for J_e. The upper filled points (dashed line) are extrapolated estimates of the true steady-state levels.

feature which has been observed previously,[3,13] and that is: severe nonlinear behavior of $J_r(t,\dot{\gamma})$ can be encountered at shear rates that are several decades slower than those at which the initial departure of the viscosity from its limiting low rate of shear value can be seen.

DISCUSSION AND CONCLUSIONS

The three IUPAC low-density polyethylenes A, B, and C have been found to display the same viscoelastic response within experimental uncertainty at short times (low strains) and high stresses. Sample A, which is suspected of containing a microgel component, deviates from a common recoverable compliance curve toward higher compliances at relative long times (>100 sec at 130°C) and low creep stresses. At the lowest creep stresses, $\sigma_{max} = 60$ dynes/cm², linear steady-state deformation was achieved with samples B and C, but A remained nonlinear at long times and did not reach a steady-state deformation in 10^5 sec of creep.

These results, although in agreement with the elongational deformation results shown in Meissner's report, contradict conventional wisdom which, over the past several decades, has maintained that linear viscoelastic behavior, measured at low stresses and at long times, is not pertinent to the processing of commercial polymers where nonlinear responses at short times and high stresses are believed to be the appropriate descriptors. In part, we now realize that at *low strains*, linear behavior usually obtains at all ordinary stress levels and that nonlinear response appears to enter with the passage of time when a critical strain is achieved.[3,4,14] Apparently, in the case of sample A, the microgel particles interact with one another to a far lesser degree when the strain and the strain rate are sufficiently high and their contribution to the support of applied tractions diminishes. In the same way, the effect of molecular weight heterogeneity is diminished at long times of deformation at high rates of shear.[3,13] The rate of disentangling of high molecular weight species must be enhanced relative to the rate of entangling by the shearing field.

In noting that the effects seen in the elongational measurements are paralleled by the phenomena we have observed in shear, we wish to claim that there exists no evidence to indicate that there are any rheological phenomena that occur in elongation (save that which is uniquely caused or related to dilation arising from the tension) that are not paralleled in shear. Until such evidence is obtained, it seems to be unnecessary to resort to the far more difficult and less accurate elongational measurements. Varied claims have been made for the strain rate dependence of the elongational viscosity: increases, decreases, and no change are all reported. While we assume that the viscosity being referred is the steady-state parameter that is a measure of permanent deformation, there appears to be an increasing number of investigators that report what is being called the "stressing viscosity," which is defined as the time-dependent stress divided by the imposed constant rate of strain. This certainly is a legitimate definition just so long as it is recognized that this parameter is a viscoelastic function and that the long-time limiting value is the commonly referred to viscosity. Limiting values of viscoelastic functions are often elusive and difficult to establish; for example, we have found that constancy only has meaning on a logarithmic time scale. If a measured strain is "constant" for an hour after a day of creep, the constancy must persist for two or three days before it can be considered effectively constant.

Many high polymers at the temperatures of interest take hours, days, or even weeks to reach steady-state deformation. When appraising results obtained in elongation, we ask ourselves the question: Can a polymer filament be extended at a high strain rate for hours, days, or weeks? If the time to reach steady state in shear, where the duration of the deformation process is usually no problem, is established, confidence in the achievement of steady-state deformation in elongation could be enhanced. Comparison of existing data on similar materials made in both modes, shear and elongation, indicate that the terminal relaxation times are close to one another.

This work was carried out under the principal support of the National Science Foundation under Engineering Division Grant GK 43292. This paper was presented by P. K. Agarwal in partial fulfillment of the requirements for the degree of Doctor of Philosophy in Materials Engineering, University of Pittsburgh, 1975.

References

1. J. Meissner, *Pure Appl. Chem.*, **42**, 553 (1975).
2. D. J. Plazek, *J. Polym. Sci. A-2*, **6**, 621 (1968).
3. D. J. Plazek and V. M. O'Rourke, *J. Polym. Sci. A-2*, **9**, 209 (1971).
4. C. P. Wong and G. C. Berry, *ACS Polym. Prepr.*, **15**, 126 (1974).
5. R. A. Stratton and A. F. Butcher, *J. Polym. Sci. A-2*, **9**, 1703 (1971); *J. Polym. Sci., Polym. Phys. Ed.*, **11**, 1747 (1973).
6. H. Markovitz, *J. Polym. Sci., Symp.*, **50**, 431 (1975).
7. B. D. Coleman, H. Markovitz, and W. Noll, *Viscometric Flows of Non-Newtonian Fluids*, Springer-Verlag, Berlin, 1966.
8. B. Rabinowitsch, *Z. Phys. Chem.*, **A145**, 1 (1929).
9. F. E. Helders and J. D. Ferry, *J. Phys. Chem.*, **60**, 1536 (1956).
10. C. P. Wong and G. C. Berry, *ACS Polym. Prepr.*, **17**, 413 (1976).
11. W. W. Graessley, *Adv. Polym. Sci.*, **16**, 60 (1974).
12. D. J. Plazek and N. Raghupathi, unpublished results.
13. G. C. Berry, private communication.
14. D. J. Plazek, W. Dannhauser, and J. D. Ferry, *J. Colloid Sci.*, **16**, 101 (1961).

Received August 16, 1976
Revised November 18, 1976

JOURNAL OF APPLIED POLYMER SCIENCE   VOL. 21, 3261–3267 (1977)

The Molecular Weight Average Obtained by Combining Quasielastic Light-Scattering and Intrinsic Viscosity Measurements

M. E. MCDONNELL and A. M. JAMIESON, *Department of Macromolecular Science, Case Western Reserve University, Cleveland, Ohio 44106*

Synopsis

For "monodisperse," randomly coiled macromolecules, we find that the molecular weight, intrinsic viscosity, and diffusion coefficient are accurately related by

$$[\eta]M_{D,\eta} = 3.0 \times 10^{-27}(D_t^0\eta_0/T)^{-3}(\text{erg}/^\circ\text{K})^3/\text{g}$$

This equation holds for denatured proteins in $6M$ GuHCl(aq) as well as for narrow polystyrene fractions in tetrahydrofuran. For a Schulz distribution of molecular weights, the weight measured from combining diffusion and viscosity data is closely approximated by

$$M_{D,\eta} = M_w^{0.425}M_z^{0.575}$$

These equations are verified with measurements of wide molecular distributions of polystyrene in toluene and data from the literature. These relations provide a rapid, nondestructive method to determine a well-specified molecular weight average of small quantities of polymers in a wide diversity of solvents using quasielastic light scattering techniques to evaluate polymer diffusion coefficients.

INTRODUCTION

With the development of simple, rapid, but accurate procedures for measuring polymer diffusion coefficients in solution using quasielastic laser light-scattering techniques,[1] a reexamination of the usefulness of the Mandelkern–Flory (MF) method[2] for molecular weight determination from a combination of diffusion and viscosity measurements becomes a worthwhile proposition. For many of the novel polymers currently being synthesized, which often have complex chemical composition and are soluble only in unconventional solvents, the MF theory offers a possible easy route to molecular weight determination. However, synthetic polymers are invariably polydisperse, and one must address the question of how variability in molecular weight distribution affects the molecular weight determined by the MF method. More specifically, can one accurately define a particular molecular weight average measured from diffusion and viscosity analysis that is insensitive to the polymer–solvent system or degree of polydispersity? An approach to this problem is discussed in the following paper.

3261

The method is tested using polystyrene samples of different polydispersities which were independently characterized.

BACKGROUND

According to Flory's treatment of the solution hydrodynamics of flexible polymer coils,[3] the intrinsic viscosity is related to the radius of gyration of the polymer by the equation

$$M[\eta] = 6^{3/2}\Phi_0\alpha_\eta^3\langle R_g{}^2\rangle^{3/2} \tag{1}$$

where Φ_0 is a constant which depends on the hydrodynamic model, α_η is the polymer chain expansion parameter as measured by intrinsic viscosity, and $\langle R_g{}^2\rangle$ is the mean-square radius of gyration. Similarly, the translational diffusion coefficient at zero concentration may be written

$$D_t^0 = \frac{kT}{f_0} = \frac{kT}{6^{1/2}P_0\eta_0\alpha_f\langle R_g{}^2\rangle^{1/2}} \tag{2}$$

where P_0 is a frictional constant, η_0 is the solvent viscosity, and α_f is the expansion parameter obtained in a frictional coefficient measurement. According to subsequent modifications of the Flory theory, α_η and α_f are not quite identical.[4] Combination of these equations leads to the Mandelkern-Flory equation[2]

$$M[\eta] = \Phi_0(P_0)^{-3}(\alpha_\eta/\alpha_f)^3 k^3(D_t^0\eta_0/T)^{-3} \tag{3}$$

Application of this expression to molecular weight determination is based on the premise that the parameter

$$\beta = \frac{\Phi_0{}^{1/3}\alpha_\eta}{P_0\alpha_f(100)^{1/3}} \tag{4}$$

is insensitive to polymer–solvent interaction. The earliest experimental evidence that eq. (4) is indeed insensitive to these parameters was given by Vallet.[5]

THE MF EQUATION IN POLYDISPERSE SYSTEMS

To apply eq. (3) to molecular weight determination for most synthetic polymers, we must consider the effect of polydispersity on intrinsic viscosity and diffusion coefficient measurements. As is well known, v1] defines a viscosity-average molecular weight M_η through the Mark–Houwink equation which depends on the polymer–solvent interaction:

$$[\eta] = K_\eta M_\eta{}^a \tag{5}$$

A similar relation can be defined for the diffusion coefficient:

$$D_t^0 = K_D M_D{}^{-b} \tag{6}$$

where $3b = a + 1$. However, the problem of suitably defining a diffusion coefficient average from the experimental optical mixing spectrum must be solved. By suitable spectral analysis procedures,[6] it is possible to obtain a z-average diffusion coefficient $(D_t^0)_z$ and parameters related to the breadth and shape of the molecular weight distribution. To obtain the latter requires light scattering data of high precision.[7] The z-average diffusion coefficient cannot be related to a well-defined molecular weight average in any simple way unless one assumes a specific functional form for the distribution of molecular weights.

The Schulz distribution function is a unimodal distribution formula with two adjustable parameters which successfully describes the molecular weight distributions obtained in a variety of condensation and addition polymerizations[8] as well as in certain fractionation by precipitation procedures.[8] The Schulz function defines the concentration $C(M)dM$ of molecules with molecular weight in the range M to $M + dM$ by

$$C(M)dM = y^{h+1}M^h e^{-yM}dM/\Gamma(h+1)$$

where the adjustable parameters h and y are related through the number- and weight-average molecular weights: $M_n = h/y$, and $M_w/M_n = (h+1)/h$. Using this distribution, Ford et al. showed[9] that it is possible to relate the z-average diffusion coefficient to a diffusion-average molecular weight M_D:

$$M_D = \frac{1}{y}\left[\frac{\Gamma(h+2)}{\Gamma(h+2-b)}\right]^{1/b} \tag{7}$$

where y and h are parameters used in defining the Schulz distribution and b is the exponent in eq. (6). Similarly, one may write

$$M_\eta = \frac{1}{y}\frac{\Gamma(h+1+a)}{\Gamma(h+1)} \tag{8}$$

Rewriting eq. (2) for polydisperse samples in terms of the constants of eqs. (5) and (6) gives

$$M_{D,\eta}[\eta] = 100\beta^3 k^3 (D_t^0\eta_0/T)^{-3}g^{-1} = K_\eta K_D{}^3/D_t^{03} \tag{9}$$

where

$$M_{D,\eta} = M_D{}^{a+1}/M_\eta{}^a$$

For a Schulz distribution eqs. (7) and (8) indicate

$$M_{D,\eta} = \frac{1}{y}\frac{\Gamma(h+1)}{\Gamma(h+3b)}\frac{\Gamma(h+2)}{\Gamma(h+2-b)} \tag{10}$$

An alternative way of deriving eq. (10) is implicit in the analysis of Johnsen[10] who used the Schulz function to evaluate polydispersity corrections to $[\eta]$ and $(D_t^0)_z$ which would enable correct comparison of hydrodynamic radii deduced by either quantity when working with polydisperse samples.

Before we can apply eq. (9) to molecular weight determination of unknown polymers, two steps are necessary. We must first determine the hypothetically system-insensitive constant of proportionality β by an experimental route. Secondly, it would be a significant advantage to find a numerical approximation for eq. (10) that is simply and directly related to conventional molecular weight averages (rather than the Schulz parameters h and y), is accurate over a wide range of polydispersities, and at the same time is insensitive to the nature of polymer–solvent interactions reflected in the parameter b.

To determine the β value of eq. (4), two substantially different relatively monodisperse systems were used. Data for globular proteins denatured in $6M$ guanidine hydrochloride and $0.1M$ mercaptoethanol at 25°C and for polystyrene samples with 1.06 polydispersity in tetrahydrofuran at 30°C were analyzed.

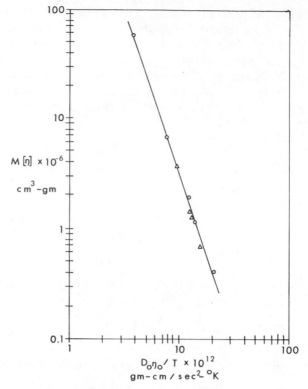

Fig. 1. Product $M[\eta]$ as a function $D_t^0 \eta_0 / T$. The straight line shows the best fit to a cubic relation between the two quantities. The slope of the line implies $\beta = 2.3 \times 10^6$.

These measurements have been discussed previously.[11,12] Each infinite dilution diffusion coefficient is extrapolated from diffusion coefficients at four or five different concentrations at or below 10 mg/ml. The total light scattered was constant to within 1%, and a total of 1024 400-point frequency spectra were collected for each sample in less than 3 min.

The data from the two relatively monodisperse systems are displayed in Figure 1. The line gives the best least-squares fit to the data according to eq. (9). This line implies that $\beta = (2.27 \pm 0.09) \times 10^6$, which is significantly below theoretically predicted results for flexible coils of 2.7×10^6. The low value of β, in fact, is consistent with predicted values for solid spherical particles; but since each homologous series of polymers follow eq. (6) with a value of b between 0.5 and 0.6, obviously a solid spherical model is not satisfactory either.[11,12]

The accuracy with which eq. (9) predicts molecular weight depends on the accuracy in measurements of D_t^0 and $[\eta]$. We have determined that the accuracy of our D_t^0 measurements are 3%, of the solvent viscosity, 0.5%, and of the intrinsic viscosity, 2%. This leads to a 13% instrumental uncertainty in our molecular weight determinations. Using the accuracies cited by some workers,[7] we conclude that state-of-the-art equipment could decrease the overall instrumental uncertainty to 3%.

In earlier work,[11] we calculated the variation of $M_{D,\eta}/[(M_w M_z)^{1/2}]$ as a function of b and h. In order to define a more system-insensitive numerical approximation to $M_{D,\eta}$, applicable to wide polydispersity, we set the geometric mean

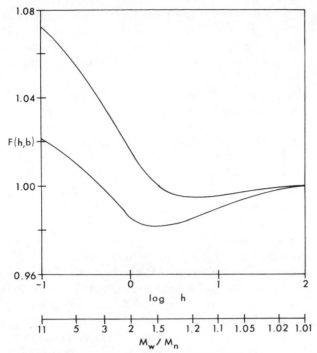

Fig. 2. For a Schulz distribution, $F(h,b) = M_{D,\eta}/M_w^{0.425}M_z^{0.575}$ is shown as a function of width parameter h or polydispersity M_w/M_n. The upper curve corresponds to $b = 0.6$ and the lower one, to $b = 0.5$.

of $M_{D,\eta}$ for the extreme b values and polydispersity of 2 equal to the weighted average of M_w and M_z:

$$b = 0.5 \qquad b = 0.6$$
$$\frac{[M_{D,\eta}|h = 1.0 M_{D,\eta}|h = 1.0]^{1/2}}{M_w{}^m M_z{}^{1-m}} = 1 \qquad (11)$$

and find $m = 0.425$. In Figure 2, $M_{D,\eta}/M_w{}^m M_z{}^{1-m}$ is plotted for $0.5 < b < 0.6$ and $0.1 < h < 100$. The upper limit of the range corresponds to $b = 0.5$. Note that the deviation of $M_{D,\eta}$ from the respective average $M_w^{0.425}M_z^{0.575}$ is never more than 7%, even for values of polydispersity as large as 11.

We, therefore, conclude from the above that the appropriate form of the MF equation for molecular weight determination in polydisperse systems is

$$M_{D,\eta}[\eta] = 3.0 \times 10^{-27}(D_t^0 \eta_0/T)^{-3}(\text{erg}/°\text{K})^3/\text{g} \qquad (12)$$

with

$$M_{D,\eta} \approx M_w^{0.425}M_z^{0.575} \qquad (13)$$

RESULTS

To test the usefulness of eqs. (12) and (13), we studied two broad molecular weight determinations of polystyrene dissolved in toluene at 25°C and also analyzed the data of Johnsen[10] for a polydisperse polystyrene sample at 25°C in four different solvents made up of ethyl acetate and ethanol. The two samples we measured were provided by the Dow Chemical Company and had been characterized by analytical gel permeation chromatography to indicate polydispersities (M_w/M_n) of 2.5 and 4.6. Intrinsic viscosity measurements were made by Lenora A. Griffin while a participant in the N.S.F. Student Science Training Program EPP 75-05603.

Since the above discussion depends on z-average diffusion coefficients which are evaluated by spectral analysis in the high-frequency limit,[9] the spectrum was fitted from the first to the twelfth half-width.[11,12] Using these values to extrapolate to D_t^0, the $M_{D,\eta}$ values determined for the two samples by eq. (12) are 3.43×10^5 and 4.16×10^5. The values of $M_w{}^{0.425}M_z{}^{0.575}$ computed for the two samples from the reported GPC molecular weight averages using eq. (13) agree with these results to within 4% on the sample with polydispersity of 2.5 and to within 10% on the sample with a polydispersity of 4.6. Both these comparisons are within our experimental uncertainty.

Johnsen[10] studied a polystyrene sample approximating a Schulz distribution with 1.46 polydispersity in ethyl acetate–ethanol solutions ranging from 0% to 10.66% in ethanol. It is concluded that β varies by 15% over this range in solvent composition; however, on the basis of the large uncertainties associated with the presented diffusion coefficients extrapolated to zero concentration, this conclusion does not seem definitively established. If we interpret Johnsen's data using eq. (12), the apparent molecular weight varies between 3.40×10^5 and 2.25×10^5, the mean being 2.74×10^5. In only one system were the data of sufficient quality to have four diffusion constants within 5% of their best straight-line fit. This measurement produces a molecular weight average of 2.50×10^5. The values of h and y for the sample studied by Johnsen[10] lead to a molecular weight determination of $M_w{}^{0.425}M_z{}^{0.575} = 2.64 \times 10^5$. In the systems studied, the agreement between the predictions of eqs. (12) and (13) is within the uncertainty limits consistent with a 7% uncertainty in diffusion coefficient. Judging from the quality of the concentration extrapolations, this degree of uncertainty cannot be excluded.

DISCUSSION AND CONCLUSIONS

We have proposed that application of the MF method combining a z-average D_t^0 and $[\eta]$ determines a molecular weight average which closely approximates that deduced by eq. (13), irrespective of polymer–solvent combination. Data are presented for solutions of polydisperse polystyrenes in toluene which support this contention. Our arguments, however, are based on the two assumptions that the polymer has a unimodal molecular weight distribution and that individual macromolecules approximate spherical symmetry. In addition, to establish the universal reliability of eq. (13), it would be advantageous to study other polymer–solvent combinations which include bimodal distributions. A particularly fruitful group of systems for the implementation of the procedure described above are the block copolymers in dilute solution recently discussed by Wang.[13]

Quasielastic laser light scattering permits rapid determination of the diffusion coefficient. Current developments in the determination of intrinsic viscosity from single concentration measurements[14] suggest that intrinsic viscosity can be measured with equal speed. The result is that from two rapid measurements the molecular weight can be quickly calculated for an unknown polymer–solvent combination. If more information, such as a Mark–Houwink relation, is known, it is in addition possible to deduce a measure of polydispersity. However, we have previously proposed more accurate methods for evaluating molecular weight averages and polydispersity parameters in these systems.[12]

References

1. A. M. Jamieson and A. R. Maret, *Chem. Soc. Rev. (London)*, **2**, 325 (1973).
2. L. Mandelkern and P. J. Flory, *J. Chem. Phys.* **20**, 212 (1952).
3. P. J. Flory, *Principles of Polymer Chemistry*, Cornell University Press, Ithaca, N.Y., 1953, Chap. XIV.
4. H. Yamakawa, *Modern Theory of Polymer Solutions*, Harper and Row, New York, 1971.
5. G. Vallet, *J. Chim. Phys.*, **47**, 649 (1950).
6. D. E. Koppel, *J. Chem. Phys.*, **57**, 4816 (1972).
7. J. C. Brown, P. N. Pusey, and R. Dietz, *J. Chem. Phys.*, **62**, 1136 (1975).
8. F. W. Billmeyer and W. H. Stockmayer, *J. Polym. Sci.*, **5**, 121 (1950).
9. N. C. Ford, Jr., R. Gabler, and F. E. Karasz, *Adv. Chem. Ser.*, **125**, 25 (1973).
10. R. M. Johnsen, *Chem. Scripta*, **2**, 31 (1972).
11. M. E. McDonnell and A. M. Jamieson, *Biopolymers*, **15**, 1283 (1976).
12. M. E. McDonnell and A. M. Jamieson, *J. Macro. Sci.-Phys.*, **B13**, 67 (1977).
13. F. W. Wang, *Macromolecules* **9**, 97 (1976).
14. A. Rudin and R. A. Wagner, *J. Appl. Polym. Sci.*, **19**, 3361 (1975).

Received July 29, 1976
Revised September 29, 1976

Preparation of Asymmetric PTFE Membranes and Their Application in Water Purification by Hyperfiltration

FERNANDO VIGO, ALDO BOTTINO, STELIO MUNARI, and GUSTAVO CAPANNELLI, *Institute of Industrial Chemistry, University of Genoa, Genoa, Italy*

Synopsis

Asymmetric PTFE membranes suitable for purifying and separation by reverse osmosis also in aggressive conditions of the feed were prepared. A technique has been set up in order to obtain the necessary porous supports, using sintering of PTFE emulsions in the presence of salts. The pore distribution, hydraulic permeability, and shape by microscopic observation were investigated. Asymmetric membranes were then prepared by deposition of these porous supports onto dense thin PTFE films. Their properties were checked in a reverse osmosis plant with NaCl, saccharose, chromium, nickel, copper, detergents, and oil emulsions.

INTRODUCTION

As previously reported,[1-5] the possibility has been verified of obtaining, via radiation grafting, PTFE membranes suitable for purification and desalination by reverse osmosis.

These membranes showed good performances, associated perhaps with their basic polymeric film structure.[6] The mean value for a 9-μ-thick (nominal) membrane was 90% rejection of sodium chloride with a permeability of about 100 l./m²d at 70 atm pressure. Such performance, even if interesting, is not unusual in comparison with the results obtained with other commercially available membranes.[7-9] However these membranes are endowed with exceptional chemical, physical, and biological stability, typical of the basic PTFE film, which would permit their use in very severe conditions of pH, temperature, and bacterial concentration. It would allow, in practice, a great saving in the management of plants operating, for example, hyperfiltration in purifying waste water or concentrating acid mining effluents or galvanic industries waste, by permitting a notable reduction in the plant running costs through less membrane replacement. It should be remembered, in fact, that in certain cases, as in whey concentration, recent estimates[10] indicate membrane replacement as 30% of the total cost.

It must also be remembered that the successful application of hyperfiltration depends, especially in the case of ecological problems, on the capacity that relatively small plants have to treat comparatively large daily volumes. From this point of view, the performances obtained by our membranes did not seem to us satisfactory, considering that the above-mentioned permeability values are obtained only with 9-μ membranes and thus creating handling difficulties.

It was preferred, therefore, to attempt to synthesize asymmetric films made from a high-selectivity thin layer supported by a porous layer of the same material, the purpose of which is to make the membrane resistant and manageable.

This paper will then deal with the preparation of asymmetric PTFE membranes and with the practical performances obtainable. Attention will be given to the setting up of the porous supports which themselves represent, in our opinion, a remarkable result, in relation to the application these films could have even in fields other than hyperfiltration.

PART I. POROUS SUPPORTS

EXPERIMENTAL

Preparation of PTFE Films

It has been verified by electron microscopy[11] that the structure of PTFE films obtainable by sintering from aqueous suspension[12–14] consists of dendritic fibrillar aggregates of the polymer particles present in the emulsion used.

In the same way it was established[6] that films obtained from emulsions composed of particles of different size or of different aggregation gave membranes with different physicochemical properties. On the basis of this observation, we were able to obtain highly permeable membranes exploiting sinterized films from special emulsions and with special techniques.

Unfortunately, the commercial PTFE films available are unable to give us such a variety of properties and we had to prepare them from aqueous PTFE suspensions kindly supplied by Montedison S.p.A.—Spinetta Marengo Plant.

In our research we have concerned ourselves with studying the best conditions both to obtain a thin, homogeneous film, without most of the defects one normally meets in commercial products, and to prepare porous films with different degrees of porosity.

Preparation of Porous Films

Porous PTFE films are commercially available under several trade names and for several uses and are obtained with different techniques.[15–17] None of these, as far as has been possible to ascertain, is made up from PTFE only, but all contain different minor components which, in our case, would have added to the obtained support a dimensional stability different from that of the real membrane and would have influenced the result of the radiation grafting process.[5,18]

Therefore, it was decided to induce a coagulation of the suspension so as to obtain, with subsequent sintering, a film with particles formed by aggregation of numerous, much smaller particles (0.2–0.3 μ) originally present in the suspension. According to this, the films so obtained should exhibit interspaces between one particle and the other, and thus exhibit "macropores." We had already verified, as mentioned above, that films obtained from suspensions of particles with different diameter showed different permeability characteristics.[6]

Since, however, the change in performance of the membranes obtainable from these films has not been found to be sufficiently wide, we thought that the presence of salts in the suspension would enable us to modify more substantially the performance of the films. The basis for this choice was the following: (1) the dissolved salts can influence the aggregation of the suspension; (2) during the film preparation, the water evaporates leaving salts crystals, and after removal of the salts by soaking, empty spaces remain in the film.

Salts were chosen on the basis of their solubility in the emulsion, their chemical stability, their melting point, and, above all, their crystal morphology. The last because the sintering requires a preliminary transition during which the suspension is spread out on a chromium-plated steel plate, and there, water is evaporated before the sintering or "baking."

As feedstock, a PTFE emulsion with these characteristics was employed: Trade name, Algoflon D 60. Composition, PTFE 16%; Triton X100[3] %; perfluoro-octanoic acid 0.3%; water to 100%. Particle size, 0.2–0.3 μ.

A large number of salts were examined, but in this study we will limit ourselves to describing the effect of three: NaCl, NaF, and $BaCl_2 \cdot 2H_2O$.

The properties of the three salts are given in Table I. In Figure 1 are reproduced the microphotographs of the crystals as they precipitate from the mother liquor of the suspension (mixture of water, Triton X100, and perfluoro-octanoic acid).

Since crystal size and particle aggregation rate are affected by temperature, we took care to check as carefully as possible the conditions of the preliminary drying process. This was achieved with a fan set to blow, tangentially to the surface of the emulsion, a jet of air at an adjustable temperature to bring about drying of the film in 10 sec. Likewise, the coating (at constant rate) and baking (sintering) conditions were controlled. The values of the essential parameters were as follows: Salt concentration, variable up to 30% ($BaCl_2$) max conc. Coating rate, 0.004 m/sec. Drying temperature, 85–120 and 170°C. Sintering rate, 10 min. Sintering temperature, 400°C.

Immediately after sintering, the film was quenched in distilled water at 20°C. Then, another coating process was set up, and so on, up to the required thickness. The quenching process had the aim both to lock the polymer in a state of minimum crystallinity in order to obtain a higher rate of radiochemical grafting[18]

TABLE I Melting points and Water Solubilities of the Salts

Salt	Melting point, °C	Water solubility, g/100 cc
NaCl	801	35.7
NaF	988	4.22
$BaCl_2 \cdot 2H_2O$	962	58.7

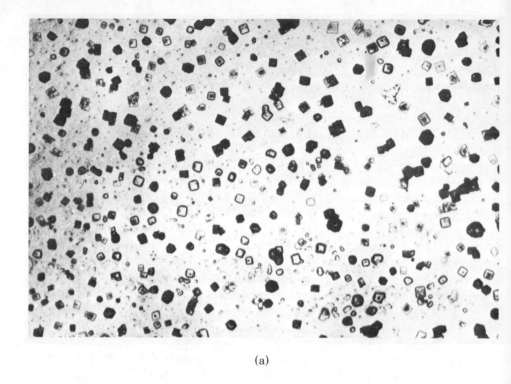

(a)

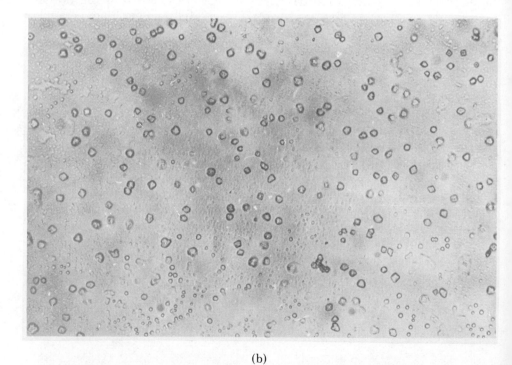

(b)

Fig. 1. Microphotograph of salt crystals as they precipitate from dispersant solution of the emulsion.

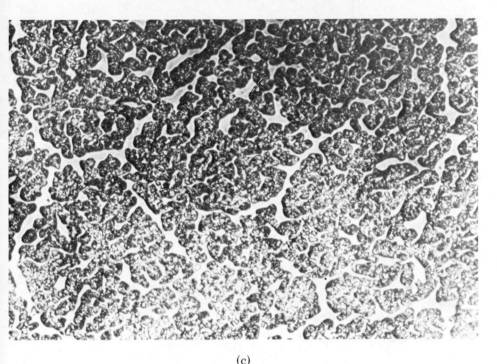

(c)

Fig. 1 (*continued*)

and to extract the salt from inside the pores.

After this treatment, in fact, the salt concentration that had reached 60 wt % in the dried film had a mean value of 3% (after just one water soaking).

As far as thickness is concerned, it was checked during the preparation with the number of successive layers of emulsion, but it was noted that according to the type and concentration of the salt, the final result varied as is shown in Figure 2(a) and 2(b).

This fact was taken into account in preparing films. The film was then removed from the plate, its thickness was measured followed by qualitative porosity control by a gas diffusion method, and transformed into a hydrophilic support by radiation grafting.

Porosimetry and Microscope Observation

A very important aspect to evaluate the film performances is undoubtedly its porosity ratio or the pore diameters ratio of the porous film. For this purpose, a Carlo Erba porosity meter, Type AG 60, was used. A known amount (approx. 0.5 g) of cut porous film, carefully dried, was introduced into the dilatometer ampoule. The ampoule was then filled under vacuum with distilled mercury and assembled into the test circuit, which essentially is composed of an autoclave capable of reaching 1000 atm, connected to a mobile contact controlling the mercury level in the capillary bonded to the sample holder ampoule.

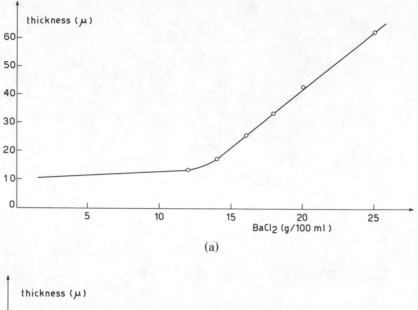

(a)

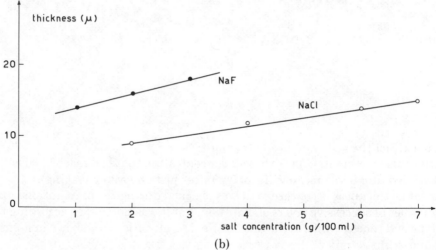

(b)

Fig. 2. (a) and (b) Film thickness vs salt concentration in the emulsion.

The movement of mercury as a result of the pressure is converted in terms of volume of filled pores, while the pressure at which this movement takes place is related to the mean pore diameter.   It is, therefore, possible to measure varying pressures from 0 to 1000 atm and volume fractions in agreement with pore diameters from 75 to 75.000 Å.   A blank is needed to give the volume decrease due both to mercury compressibility and to PTFE itself.

A high-resolution optical microscope was used for the observations on salt crystals on the surface and on film sections.

Support Preparation

Earlier,[1,2] the high hydrophilicity of the membrane produced by our technique was pointed out.   This hydrophilicity is coupled to a high possibility of dimen-

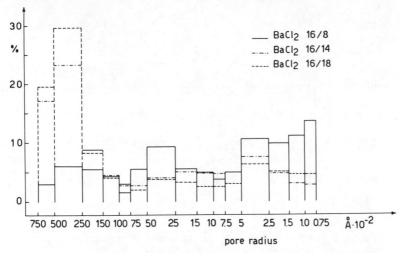

Fig. 3. Porosity ratio in films obtained from three different BaCl₂ concentrations.

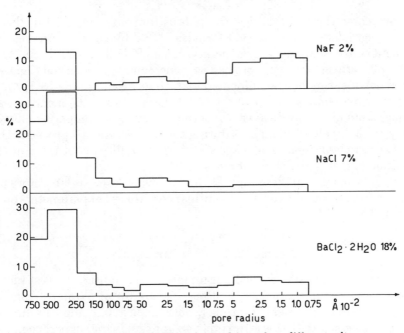

Fig. 4. Porosity ratio in films obtained from three different salts.

sional changes both depending on the moisture content and on the interaction which the ionic groups present in the membrane can have with the wetting brine. It follows that to have a suitable support for such a membrane, it must be able to follow membrane dimensional changes and show the same physicochemical properties; otherwise, creeping and incoherency between membrane and support can be expected.

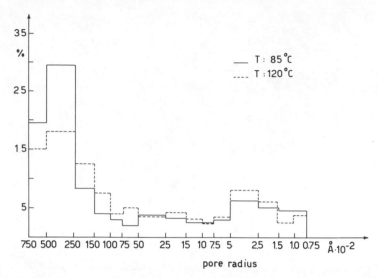

Fig. 5. Porosity ratio in films obtained from two different drying temperatures.

To overcome these difficulties, the porous film was subjected to the same grafting treatment necessary to transform the PTFE film into membranes. This treatment consists, briefly, of grafting styrene on PTFE by γ-radiation[19]. The amount of grafted styrene is expressed as % increment of the initial film weight. Grafted polymer can then be sulfonated to introduce ionic groups (SO_3^{2-}). The supports have themselves some of the typical properties of the membranes (ion exchange), but obviously do not show permselectivity or semipermeability, nor do they repel dissolved substances during the reverse osmosis process. On the other hand, they present an average water permeability about three orders of magnitude higher than the membranes.

Tests carried out with these supports in our reverse osmosis laboratory plant[3] had, therefore, the aim to control the influence of different parameters on their permeability.

Permeability Measurements

Permeability tests were carried out under these conditions: Test material, distilled water. Temperature, 25°C. Pressure, 30–70 atm. Water stream values through support, expressed in l./m²·day, were taken at 0, 1, and 2 hr during the test. In some cases, the test was run up to 48 hr to study the support compaction, but, normally, the plotted stream values are always those taken at 1 hr.

TABLE II Crystallizable Compounds Classification

Group	Specifications
A	Sublimation without decomposition
B	Sublimation and decomposition
C	Neither sublimation nor decomposition
D	No sublimation but decomposition

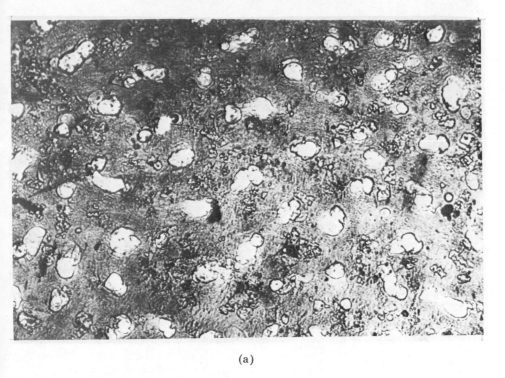

(a)

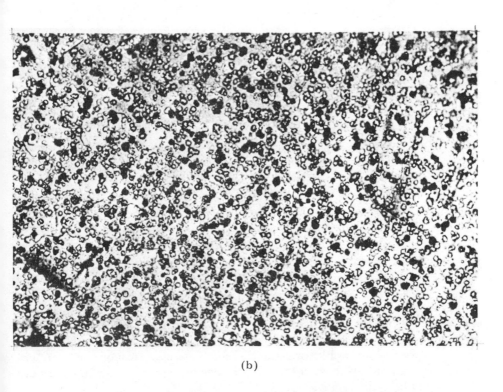

(b)

Fig. 6. Microphotographs of the surface of films obtained with three different salts.

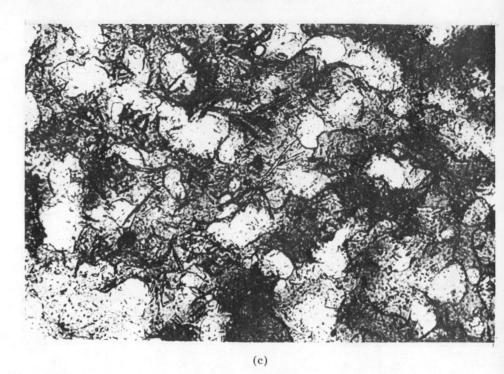

(c)

Fig. 6 (*continued*)

RESULTS AND DISCUSSION

Influence of Type and Concentration of the Salt and Drying Temperature on Pore Size

The prepared porous films were subjected to porosimetry, and the more representative results will be reported in the following figures.

Figures 3 and 4 present the influence of the salt concentration on pore size distribution. The last is influenced not only by the salt nature but also by its concentration. Further measurements done varying the film thickness did not show any relevant effect on the distribution, and an increase in film thickness apparently will decrease only the permeability. In order to control the effects of the crystallization rate and thus of the size of salt crystals and their influence on diameter and number of pores, some of the films were prepared and dried at different temperatures. These experiments we carried out using emulsions with $BaCl_2$, and the films obtained were subjected to porosimetry; results are reported in Figure 5.

It is important to remember that the preparation of the porous film was carried out with these leading criteria: (a) to control the coagulation of the emulsion with some agent operating in the liquid phase; (b) availability in the solid phase of some agent which would prevent the complete sintering of the particles. Moreover, these agents must not modify the chemical properties of the film and they should be easily removable.

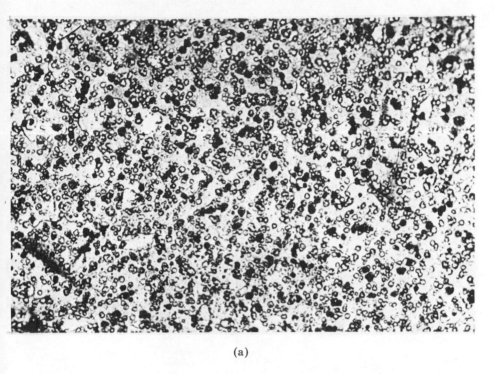

(a)

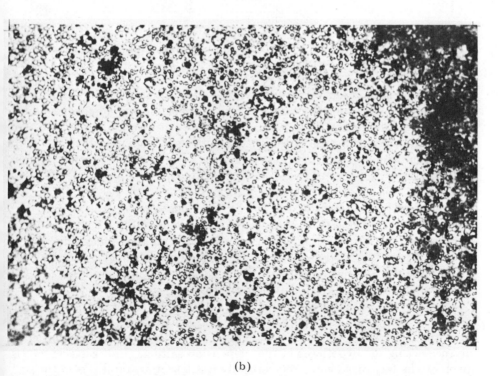

(b)

Fig. 7. Microphotographs of the surface of films obtained from 2% NaF at different drying temperatures.

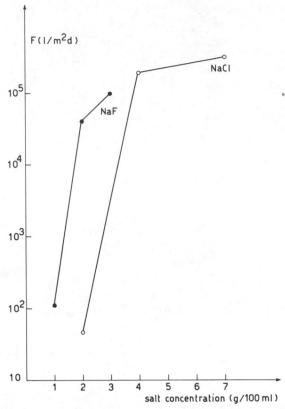

Fig. 8. Hydraulic permeability of the supports (at 30 atm) vs NaCl and NaF concentrations.

At the beginning, tests carried out with various typical coagulants gave only (HCl, acetone, etc.) defective films without appreciable and homogeneous porosity. The explanation for this behavior is based, in our opinion, on the high temperature needed for the sintering, which takes it to an initial melting with the possibility of occlusion of the eventual pores due to polymer softening. On the other hand, good results were obtained with compounds capable to be entrapped into the polymeric matrix.

Compounds able to form definite crystalline solids were used, divided into the groups shown in Table II, in connection with the operating conditions (high temperature) to which they had to be subjected during the film baking. Compounds of type A (i.e., NH_4Cl) and B (i.e., oxalic acid) did not give valuable results, while the best results were obtained with type C compounds (i.e., NaCl) and partially with type D (i.e., $Ca(ClO_4)_2$). The experiments previously reported were carried out on the basis of this classification. Moreover, the results of the microscope observation support as probable cause of pore formation the precipitation of crystals of solid particles stable up to 400°C in the polymer body, not neglecting the hypothesis of the suspension salting. Indirect evidence is given by the fact that some salts (certainly $BaCl_2$) act as stabilizers of the suspension[20] because of the presence of a nonionic surfactant (Triton X100). Consequently, the pores in these films must have an average diameter similar to that of the crystals, and further evidence is given both from the comparison

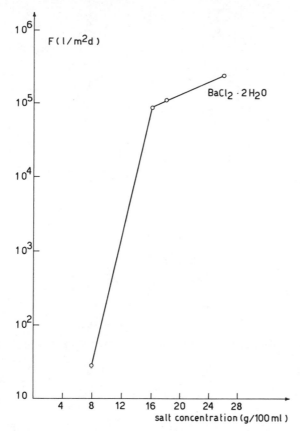

Fig. 9. Hydraulic permeability of the supports (at 30 atm) vs $BaCl_2 \cdot 2H_2O$ concentration.

of the porosity ratio with diameter ratio of the crystals and from the microscope observations.   Therefore, the experimental results can be explained as follows.

(a) **Effect of Salt Concentration.**   The porosity ratios in Figure 3 show that an increase in salt concentration leads to an increase in large-diameter pores. This behavior can be explained keeping in mind the influence of salt concentration on the crystal growth; this leads, moreover, to a prediction of the existence of a certain concentration value at which the most crystalline structures will produce "closed cell" pores and then nonporous films.   Permeability measurements will confirm this hypothesis.

(b) **Effect of Nature of Salt.**   Differences among pore distributions obtainable with three different salts (Fig. 4) do not allow us to draw strictly quantitative relationships for the above-mentioned reasons, but allow us to draw the hypothesis that the pore "shape" is strictly related to that of the crystals.   By "shape" we mean not only the crystal size, but even and above all its morphology, which, in the case of $BaCl_2$, has been considered above as the leading factor responsible for the unusual increase in porosity with film thickness.

(c) **Effect of Drying Temperature.**   Comparison of the pore distributions (Fig. 5) shows that the number of thin pores increases as the temperature increases.   As is well known, the crystal formation induced by rapid flashing off

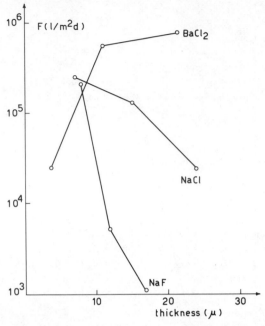

Fig. 10. Hydraulic permeability of the supports (at 30 atm) obtained from different salts vs thickness.

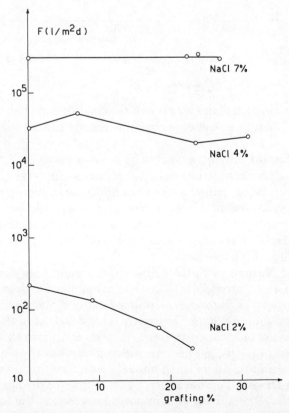

Fig. 11. Hydraulic permeability of the supports (at 30 atm) obtained from NaCl vs % graft.

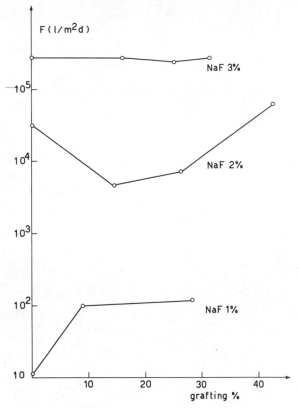

Fig. 12. Hydraulic permeability of the supports (at 30 atm) obtained from NaF vs % graft.

of the solvent generates small crystals and therefore produces pores with small diameters.

It must, nevertheless, be pointed out that if the solvent evaporates at an eccessive rate, i.e., close to the boiling point, the pores are wider and more irregular (this result has been obtained in the case of $BaCl_2$ emulsion dried at 170°C); this is due to the mechanical effect of small vapor bubbles which prevent a regular deposition of the formed crystals.

It is also noteworthy that the salts are very easily extracted from the polymeric matrix, as has been confirmed by chemical tests.

Microscope Investigation on Film Surfaces

Three films obtained from emulsions containing, respectively, NaCl, NaF, and $BaCl_2$ were scanned by the optical microscope, and the microphotographs were compared with those of the isolated crystals (Fig. 1).

The surfaces appear different (Fig. 6) depending upon the salt employed and furthermore the particle aggregates partly resemble the morphology and the sizes of the salt crystals.

The microscope investigation has also clearly shown the influence of drying temperature on the pore size, as can be clearly seen by comparing the photos in Figure 7.

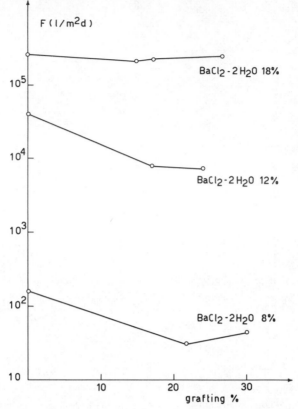

Fig. 13. Hydraulic permeability of the supports (at 30 atm) obtained from BaCl$_2$·2H$_2$O vs graft.

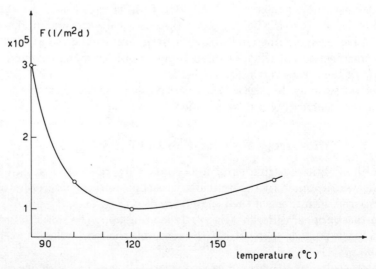

Fig. 14. Hydraulic permeability of the supports (at 30 atm) obtained from BaCl$_2$·2H$_2$O vs drying temperature.

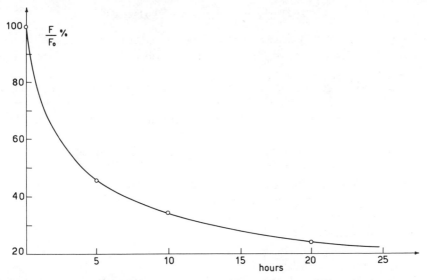

Fig. 15. Hydraulic permeability of the supports (at 30 atm) obtained from $BaCl_2 \cdot 2H_2O$ vs testing time.

Influence of Salt Concentration on Permeability

Figures 8 and 9 report the permeability versus NaCl, NaF, and $BaCl_2$ concentration, respectively, in the initial emulsion, related to films with a thickness of 10 microns and 20% grafted styrene. The curves give a clear confirmation of the existence of a salt critical concentration below which a structure with open pores cannot exist.

Influence of Thickness on Permeability

In Figure 10, permeabilities with NaCl, NaF, and $BaCl_2$ are plotted versus support thickness. The values are related to supports prepared with constant salt concentrations in the emulsion and with a grafting of 20%.

We note that, in the case of NaCl and NaF, an increase in film thickness causes a sharp decrease in permeability, and this is obviously related to the pore size. As can be observed from the slope of the curves, this effect is higher for NaF, which produces very fine crystals, while for NaCl (larger crystals, Fig. 1) it is necessary to reach thicknesses three times larger in order to have the same permeability decrease.

In the case of $BaCl_2$, the permeability, instead of decreasing, increases with film thickness. This behavior can be related to the peculiar structure of pores derived from $BaCl_2$ dendritic crystal precipitation. In our opinion, successive layers of emulsion cannot form a homogeneous film, owing both to deep irregularities in the substrate and to the thermal treatment necessary to "bake" the film.

Influence of Styrene Grafting

In Figures 11–13 the values of hydraulic permeability at 30 atm of 10-μ-thick films obtained from three different concentrations of salt (NaCl, NaF, BaCl$_2$) are reported.

The plotted curves can be interpreted if we analyze the change of the porous film structure after grafting and sulfonation. As reported elsewhere,[18] the styrene grafting begins at the PTFE surface; but for high yields (up to 30%), the inner body of the polymer is grafted and behaves like the polystyrene.

It follows that, because of the sulfonation of the grafted polymer, we are dealing with a film practically made from highly hydrophilic poly(styrensulfonic acid) (PSSA). For low grafting yields, the hydrophilic groups are hold in a stiff matrix and the cross section of the pores is controlled; if the grafting yield increases, the whole body collapses with a loss of the initial stiffness and an increase in permeability, as in the case of a wetted sheet of paper. For this reason the permeability passes through a minimum value increasing the grafting, as more clearly seen from Figure 11 (NaF).

This trend is less sensitive the higher the concentration of the salt added to the emulsion. The simplest explanation consists, in our opinion, of the fact that a higher concentration of dissolved salt can cause not only a higher number of crystals but also a higher number of large crystals and, therefore, of large pores. In these conditions (due easier diffusion of the monomer), the grafting, from the beginning, proceeds into the body of the film and induces a structure relaxation, and the permeability increases.

TABLE III R.O. Asymmetric Membranes Performances (NaCl 0.2 H)

Membrane no.	Thickness, microns	% Graft	Flux, l./m² · day	% Rejection
150	28	18.6	32	88
294	32	31	66	84
323	40	32	53	87
328	54	35	68	86
378	45	37	60	86
379	45	32	74	86
380	45	32	50	85
381	45	32	53	90
382	50	38	67	86

TABLE IV R.O. Asymmetric Membranes Performances (Saccharose 0.2%)

Membrane no.	Thickness, microns	% Graft	Flux, l./m² · day	% Rejection
292	32	30	70	99
293	32	32	80	80
294	32	31	58	99
323	40	32	53	90
327	51	36	62	95
329	23	37	85	90
331	30	33	67	95
332	30	31	55	90

Influence of Drying Temperature

In Figure 14, permeability values are plotted versus drying temperature of the emulsion. The curve is referred to supports obtained with $BaCl_2$ (this salt was normally used for the preparation of asymmetric membranes, but it is reasonable to extend the results to films obtained with other salts.

Influence of Compaction

In Figure 15, the permeability versus testing time is plotted at 30 atm for a support obtained from 18% $BaCl_2$. This behavior, similar for all supports, is related both to the plastic properties of the PTFE film and to its spongy structure. Practically, the support, after 24 hr of testing, looses 80% of its permeability.

This fact does not influence its usefulness for the preparation of asymmetric membranes as the mean permeability of the supports is about 10^5 l./m²·day; the 20% of this value is enough not to interfere with the flow properties of the thin film.

PART II. ASYMMETRIC MEMBRANES

EXPERIMENTAL

Preparation of Asymmetric Membranes

The asymmetric membranes were obtained by deposition of porous layers on a 6–8 μ-compact, thin film previously prepared. The depositions of the porous layers were carried out without detaching the dense film from the plate. To obtain the support, emulsions containing $BaCl_2$ (16% PTFE–18% $BaCl_2$·$2H_2O$) were employed, chosen on the basis of the previous porosimetry and permeability measurements.

The technique employed for the preparation of the porous support was exactly the same as described in part I: constant, too, were coating, baking, and quenching conditions. The only change, introduced on the basis of the results

TABLE V

R.O. Asymmetric Membranes Performances (With Various Kind of Industrial Effluents)

Feed	Membrane no.	Thickness, microns	Flux, l./m² · day	% Rejection
2% NiSO₄	326	54	45	98
	327	54	40	94
CrO₃ 150 mg/l.	326	54	42	94
	327	54	40	97.5
0.5% Cu tartrate	326	54	60	99.4
	327	54	21	99.5
1% Oil emulsion	326	54	35	99.2
	327	54	26.5	99.9
Anionic detergents, 20 ppm	326	54	30	99
	327	54	35	97

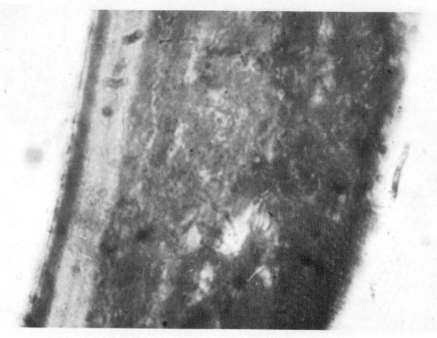

Fig. 16. Microphotograph of a section of asymmetric membrane.

obtained from experimental tests, was the drying temperature which was set up at 120°C to obtain a porous support more homogeneous and with small pore size.

The asymmetric film was easily detached from the plate; its thickness was measured (the thickness data reported in following tables are always referred to this stage of the membrane preparation). After a control of the absence of defects, the film was grafted with styrene and sulfonated, obtaining, in this way, the asymmetric membranes whose performances in reverse osmosis depend only on the thin layer of support. Performances were tested in the apparatus already used in the characterization of the porous films.

RESULTS AND DISCUSSION

Performances of the Membranes

All membranes, which differed only in the thickness of the porous layer, were subjected to reverse osmosis tests for the following purposes: (1) ascertain the asymmetric nature of the membrane; (2) ascertain the independence of membrane permeability from support thickness; and (3) verify the possibility to apply this type of membrane to the problems of industrial water desalination, concentration, and purification.

In Tables III and IV, the results obtained for 0.2M NaCl solution and saccharose (2 g/l.) are reported.

Some tests were carried out with industrial effluents; the results are reported in Table V.

The presence of a porous layer on the membranes so obtained appears not only from the microphotographic examination, as is shown in Figure 16, but also from the performances. If we compare the flux between these membranes and those prepared from a dense film and previously reported[3] for the same thickness, we obtain a ratio ranging from 6 to 8.

In spite of these good results, we were unable to obtain, using this technique, the main goal for which the study was undertaken. Indeed, at the beginning, we hoped to prepare membranes formed with very thin layers of dense film (say, 1–3 μ) able to supply relatively high fluxes and easily manageable for added support.

Several experimental difficulties prevented us from being successful. The most important, in our opinion, are the following: (1) Under our experimental conditions, it was quite impossible to obtain homogeneous dense film of the required thickness (without defects). (2) Also, if the film is obtained, it does not bear up under the baking cycles necessary to prepare the support. (3) The crystals formed in the support may alter the thin layer.

CONCLUSIONS

On the basis of the results obtained, we believe we have reached substantially two aims:

1. A new technique suitable to provide porous PTFE films which can be used not only as support for the thin membranes, but can be applied in other fields. A better control of the porosity is necessary, and it would involve a systematic study of the crystalline nucleation rate under the conditions which occur during the drying of the polymer suspensions.

2. New asymmetric PTFE membranes. This material, being not appreciably soluble in common solvents or chemical agents, on the one hand requires a relatively complicated preparative technique and, on the other, promises exceptional characteristics of stability and life.

It must be pointed out that, in spite of the heterogeneous nature of the matrix, the radiation grafting takes place homogeneously, at least under our experimental conditions, in spite of the different porosity of the membrane layers.

References

1. S. Munari, F. Vigo, G. Tealdo, and C. Rossi, *J. Appl. Polym. Sci.,* **II**, 1563 (1967).
2. S. Munari, F. Vigo, C. Rossi, and G. Tealdo, *Ricerca Scientifica,* **No. 7–8,** 642 (1967).
3. S. Munari, C. Rossi, and F. Vigo, *Quaderni de La Ricerca Scientifica,* **No. 49,** 99 (1968).
4. S. Munari, Communication to the 4th Int. Congr. Radiation Research, Evian, France, June 28–July 4, 1970.
5. G. Canepa, S. Munari, C. Rossi, and F. Vigo, *Desalination,* **13,** 159 (1975).
6. S. Munari, F. Vigo, M. Nicchia, and P. Canepa, *J. Appl. Polym. Sci.,* **21,** 243 (1976).
7. S. Loeb and S. Sourirajan, *Adv. Chem. Ser.,* **38,** 1117 (1962).
8. R. L. Riley, J. D. Gardner, and U. Merten, *Science,* **143,** 801 (1964).
9. R. L. Riley, J. D. Gardner, and U. Merten, *Desalination,* **1,** 30 (1966).
10. F. Besik, *Canad. Food Ind.,* 32 (July 1971).
11. A. Battaglioli, Industrial Chemistry Degree Thesis, University of Genoa, 1971/1972.
12. H. Brown and G. H. Crawford, *The Science and Technology of Polymer Films—Florocarbons Polymer,* O. J. Sweeting, Ed., Interscience, 1971.

13. J. F. Lontz and W. B. Happoldt, Jr., *Ind. Eng. Chem.,* **44,** 1800 (1952).

14. O. Loercher, R. Steffen, and A. Consolati (to Farbwerke Hoechst A. G.), S. African Pat. No. 6,806,378 (March 24, 1969).

15. Simimoto Ent. Ind. (ASS) Fr. Application 2,222,200 (Oct. 18, 1974).

16. W. G. Grot (to du Pont de Nemours), Ger. Offen. 2,129,470 (Dec. 23, 1971).

17. R. Roberts (to du Pont de Nemours), Fr. I. 367,819 (July 24, 1964).

18. C. Rossi, S. Munari, and G. Tealdo, *Chim. Ind.,* **45,** 1444 (1963).

19. H. Battaerd and W. Tregear, *Graft Copolymers,* Wiley, New York, 1967.

20. M. Doscher, G. E. Myers, and D. C. Atkins, Jr., *J. Colloid Sci.,* **6,** 223 (1951).

21. P. Canepa, S. Munari, M. Nicchia, and F. Vigo, *Chim. Ind.,* **56,** 535 (1974).

22. A. Golomb, *Plating,* **57,** 1001 (1970); *ibid.,* **59,** 316 (1972).

23. A. Golomb, *Plating,* **60,** (5), 482 (May 1973).

24. H. R. Hank and S. Sourirajan, *J. Water Pollution Control Fed.,* **44,** 1372 (1972).

Received September 1, 1976

JOURNAL OF APPLIED POLYMER SCIENCE   VOL. 21, 3291–3309 (1977)

Mechanical Anisotropy in Injection-Molded Polypropylene

MITSUYOSHI FUJIYAMA and HIROSHI AWAYA, *Research and Development Division, Tokuyama Soda Co., Ltd., Tokuyama-shi, Yamaguchi-ken, Japan,* and SHUKICHI KIMURA, *Plastic Division, Tokuyama Soda Co., Ltd., Tokuyama-shi, Yamaguchi-ken, Japan*

Synopsis

By use of a mod with a film gate, two straight polypropylenes (PP) with different melt flow index (*MFI*) and a glass fiber-reinforced polypropylene (FRPP) were injection molded at various temperatures into square plates with orientational anisotropy. The anisotropies of tensile property, tensile impact strength, and flexural property were studied on the molded sample cut mainly in the machine direction (MD), 45°-direction (45°), and transverse direction (TD). Both the orders of the yield strength and tensile impact strength of the FRPP, and those of the necking stress and tensile impact strength of the straight PP, were MD >45° >TD, which are reasonable tendencies. The orders of the yield strength and flexural modulus of the straight PP were MD > TD > 45°, which suggests the presence of shear deformation between the lamellae in the skin layer. The variation of the flexural modulus with the angle to the MD fitted well to Hearmon's equation. Generally, for straight PP, the anisotropy of various properties increased as the *MFI* and cylinder temperature became lower, or as the skin layer became thicker. For the FRPP, the anisotropy increased as the cylinder temperature became higher, or as the degree of the orientation of glass fibers became higher.

INTRODUCTION

Since polymer melt crystallizes under high shear stress, molecular chain orientation occurs on injection molding. Accordingly, the properties of the processed article may be affected by its direction, namely, by anisotropy. Many studies have been done on the mechanical anisotropies of oriented films.[1–15] However, studies on the mechanical anisotropies of injection-molded articles are few.[16–18] This may be due to the orientational inhomogeneity in injection-molded articles. According to Ballman et al.,[16] as the degree of the orientation of injection-molded polystyrene increases, the tensile strength, elongation, and Izod impact strength in the MD increase and those in the TD slightly decrease. Ogorkiewicz et al.[17] injection molded polypropylene into wide-bottom trays, cut the specimens in various directions, measured the variations of tensile and shear moduli with angle, and found that their variations fitted well to Hearmon's equation.[19] Krebs[18] measured the variations of the tensile yield strength and ultimate elongation of an injection-molded low-pressure polyethylene with angle, and found that the yield strength was the lowest and the ultimate elongation was the highest in the 45°-direction.

In the previous paper,[20] we showed that an injection-molded PP showed a clear two-phase structure of skin and core when its cross section was observed with a polarized microscope; and we estimated the higher-order structures of the skin

3291

and core layers by means of wide-angle x-ray diffraction, small-angle x-ray scattering, melting behavior, density, dynamic viscoelasticity, and tensile test. In the skin layer, the c-axis highly oriented parallel to the MD, and the plane of the lamellar structure of about 160 Å in thickness was normal to the MD. The density was about 0.907 g/cm^3, which was nearly equal to that of the core layer. Although the major part of crystallites melted in the same temperature range as that of the core layer, there was about 5.3% of a high-temperature melting structure ($T_m = 182°C$). The dynamic tensile modulus E' in the MD decreased more slowly with increasing temperature than that of the core layer, and held high in the range of ca. 30°C, just above the temperature at which E' of the core layer suddenly dropped. The tensile yield strength in the MD was about 1.5 times higher than that of the core layer. In general, PP melt crystallizes under high shear stress on injection molding. From these experimental results, it was concluded that the skin layer was composed of, or contained, a so-called "shish kebab" structure which was in parallel to the MD and was imbedded in a row structure. The core layer was composed of spherulites.

In other papers,[21,22] we studied the effect of molecular weight and molding conditions on the mechanical properties of injection-molded PP's through the skin/core morphology. The thickness of the skin layer increased with decreases in cylinder temperature, injection speed, and MFI. It was practically not affected by injection pressure and mold temperature. The tensile yield strength, necking stress, tensile modulus, flexural modulus, flexural strength, mold shrinkage, and annealing shrinkage increased with decreasing cylinder temperature and were in linear relationships with the thickness of the skin layer, regardless of the MFI.

However, only one direction was studied in previous papers[21,22] (flow direction = orientation direction). When we are to evaluate the strength, rigidity, shrinkage, and other properties of actually processed articles, we need to study the properties of all directions. Thus, in this investigation we studied the anisotropies of injection-molded PP. Since the molecular orientation of the injection-molded PP is concentrated in the skin layer, we chose the thickness of the skin layer as an internal structure parameter as in the previous papers[21,22] and discuss the experimental results from the viewpoint of the skin/core morphology. Although the thickness of the skin layer was influenced by the kind of resin and processing conditions, it was most influenced by the MFI and cylinder temperature.[21] Then, in this work, we studied the latter two factors. Furthermore, since the orientation of glass fibers as well as molecular chains participated in the properties of FRPP, it was also studied. The properties studied here were all mechanical ones, namely, tensile yield strength, necking stress, tensile impact strength, flexural modulus, and flexural strength. The directions studied were generally the MD, 45°-direction, and TD for all samples, and 22.5°- and 67.5°-directions were also added in some cases.

EXPERIMENTAL

Materials

The resins used in this study were three commercial isotactic polypropylenes: L (low-MFI straight PP, MFI = 1.6 dg/min); H (high-MFI straight PP, MFI = 8.2 dg/min); and G (FRPP, glass fiber content = 20 wt-%), which were manufactured by Tokuyama Soda Co., Ltd.

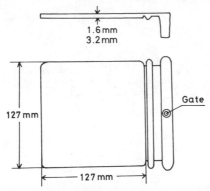

Fig. 1. Shape of mold cavity.

Molding

To obtain specimens of uniform anisotropy, square plates were injection-molded by use of a mold with a film gate.   The shape of the mold cavity is shown in Figure 1.   Injection molding was carried out with a Toshiba IS 200A-Type

TABLE I
Injection-Molding Conditions[a]

Plate thickness, mm	Sample	Cylinder temperature, °C				Injection pressure, kg/cm²
		FZ	CZ	MZ	AD	
1.6	L	180	170	190	170	860
		180	200	220	200	680
		180	230	250	230	480
		180	260	280	260	460
	H	180	170	190	170	460
		180	200	220	200	400
		180	230	250	230	350
		180	260	280	260	350
	C	180	170	190	170	570
		180	200	220	200	460
		180	230	250	230	370
		180	260	280	260	350
3.2	L	180	180	190	180	450
		180	200	220	200	400
		180	230	250	230	350
		180	260	280	260	350
	H	180	180	190	180	400
		180	200	220	200	400
		180	230	250	230	350
		180	260	280	260	350
	G	180	180	190	180	400
		180	200	220	200	420
		180	230	250	230	350
		180	260	280	260	350

[a] FZ = feed zone; CZ = compression zone; MZ = metering zone; AD = adaptor. Mold temperature: 40°C, cooling time; 30 sec; injection speed; max.

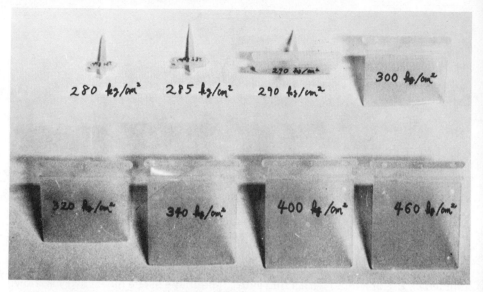

Fig. 2. Short-shot test; 3.2 mm^t plate, L sample molded at 250°C.

20-ounce reciprocating-screw injection-molding machine. The molding conditions are shown in Table I. The cylinder temperature was measured at the metering zone (MZ). To obtain fine articles, the injection pressure was changed since the short-shots occurred when low-*MFI* resins were molded at low cylinder temperatures, and the flashes occurred when high-*MFI* resins were molded at high cylinder temperatures. We have already confirmed that the injection pressure has little effect on the thickness of the skin layer and mechanical properties.[21]

To confirm whether the specimen of uniform anisotropy was actually obtained by the mold cavity, a short-shot injection-molding test was carried out. The results are shown in Figure 2. Below the injection pressure of 285 kg/cm^2, resins enter into only the sprue and runner. They do not enter into the cavity until the injection pressure reaches 290 kg/cm^2. Flow length increases with increase in injection pressure. Above an injection pressure of 400 kg/cm^2, the cavity is completely filled with resins. The short-shot test indicates that the resins flow uniformly from the film gate. This suggests that the orientation state is also uniform. The isotropic specimens were obtained by compression molding at 215°C under a pressure of 100 kg/cm^2 for 10 min, followed by cooling with water.

Measurements

Thickness of Skin Layer. The injection-molded plate was cut about 0.1 mm thick in the TD, and was observed by a universal projecter (Olympus UT350) under cross-Nikols with a magnification of 50×. A clear skin/core morphology was observed. Since the thickness of the skin layer was not uniform, the center area was used as representative area.

Tensile Property (JIS K6758-1968). To obtain specimens for tensile tests, square plates 1.6-mm thick were cut at the center in the MD, 45°-direction, and TD with a JIS Type-3 dumbbell cutter. For the L sample molded at 250°C and the G sample molded at 220°C, the 22.5°- and 67.5°-directions were also added

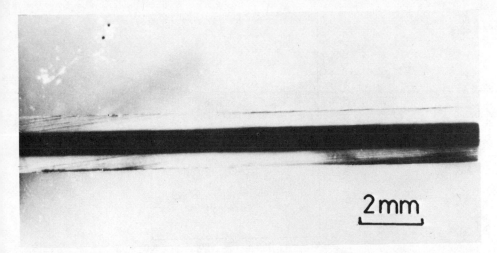

Fig. 3. Example of polarized micrograph of the cross section of injection-molded PP. L Sample molded at 250°C.

to the above directions. The tensile properties were measured with a Shimazu Autograph IS-5000 Type at 23°C. The chuck distance was 6 cm; the mark-line distance, 1 cm; and the tensile speed, 20 mm/min. The average value of three samples was adopted.

Tensile Impact Strength (ASTM 1961 Part 9). To obtain the specimens for tensile impact strength (*TIS*), square plates 1.6-mm thick were cut at the center in the MD, 45°-direction, and TD with a *TIS* dumbbell cutter. The *TIS* was measured at 23°C. The average value of six samples was adopted.

Flexural Property (ASTM D790). To obtain the specimens for flexural tests, square plates 3.2-mm thick were cut at the center in the MD, 45°-direction, and TD with a saw. For the L sample molded at 190°C and the G sample molded at 220°C, the 22.5°- and 67.5°-directions were also added to the above directions. The flexural properties were measured with a Shimazu Autograph IS-5000 Type at 23°C. Span length L was 5 cm, and bending speed was 10 mm/min. Flexural modulus E and flexural strength FS were calculated by eqs. (1) and (2), respectively:

$$E = \frac{PL^3}{4\delta bh^3} \tag{1}$$

$$FS = \frac{3P_Y L}{2bh^2} \tag{2}$$

where P is load, P_Y is yielding load, δ is flexion amount, and b and h are, respectively, width and thickness of the specimen.

RESULTS AND DISCUSSION

ThicKness of Skin Layer

An example of the polarized micrograph of the cross section of an injection-molded PP is shown in Figure 3; since it was printed by a quick copier, darkness is inverted. A clear two-phase structure with skin (outer bright portion) and core (inner dark portion) is observed.

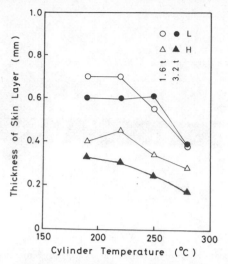

Fig. 4. Effect of cylinder temperature on thickness of the skin layers.

The effect of cylinder temperature on the thickness of the skin layer is shown in Figure 4. Although the thickness of the skin layer generally decreases with increase in cylinder temperature, there are exceptional cases where the thickness of the skin layer does not change, or even increases, with increase in cylinder temperature. This is probably so because the injection pressure is reduced when the cylinder temperature is raised as shown in Table I. On pressure-controlling-type injection molding, the thickness of the skin layer increases as the injection pressure decreases.[21] Since the injection moldings in this work were carried out under pressure slightly higher than the short-shot pressure, they were possibly controlled by pressure in contrast to the previous work.[21]

No skin layer was observed in the G sample.

Tensile Property

Yield Strength. The effect of cylinder temperature on the yield strengths in various directions for the L, H, and G samples is shown in Figure 5(a)–5(c), respectively. The variations of the yield strengths of the L sample molded at 250°C and the G sample molded at 220°C with the angle to the MD are shown in Figures 6 and 7, respectively. While the yield strength of the G sample decreases gradually from the MD to the TD, those of the L sample and H sample are MD ≫ TD > 45°; the 45°-direction is the lowest. This fact is worth noting.

When the tensile stress σ is applied to the specimen as shown in the upper part of Figure 8, the normal stress σ_N and shear stress τ, both of which act in the plane whose angle is $(90° - \theta)$ against σ, are represented by eqs. (3) and (4), respectively:

$$\sigma_N = \sigma \cos^2 \theta \tag{3}$$

$$\tau = \sigma \sin \theta \cos \theta \tag{4}$$

The variations of σ_N and τ with θ are shown in the lower part of Figure 8. The shear stress τ shows a maximum at $\theta = 45°$ with a value of $\sigma/2$.

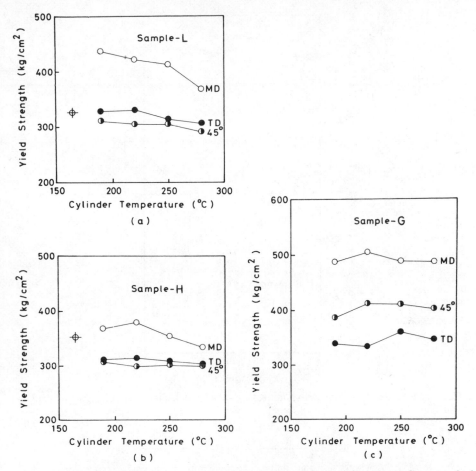

Fig. 5. Effect of cylinder temperatures on yield strengths in various directions. Cross-marked points are for compression-molded materials: (a) L sample; (b) H sample; (c) G sample.

The orientation direction of the molecular chains and lamellae in the skin layer of the MD-, 45°-, and TD-specimens are shown in Figure 9. (It was shown in the previous paper[20] that the lamellae in the skin layer were perpendicular to the MD.) Since the orientation directions of the molecular chains and/or lamellae in the skin layer of the 45°-specimen coincide with the 45°-direction at which the shear stress τ is maximum, the 45°-specimen is under the state where slips between the oriented molecular chains or lamellae most easily occur. However, it is difficult to elucidate the yield phenomenon in terms of intermolecular deformation, which pulls apart the van der Waals bonds, since it is observed under considerably large deformation. It is rather reasonable to elucidate it by interlamellar deformation. On interlamellar deformation, it might be easier to make the lamellae slip by shear stress than to pull them apart by tensile stress. Both facts, that the 45°-direction is under the state where the shear deformation most easily occurs and that the shear deformation can be done with a weak force due to the higher-order structure of injection-molded PP, indicate that the yield strength in the 45°-direction is the lowest.

Ward et al.[8] showed that the modulus of an anisotropic polyethylene sheet

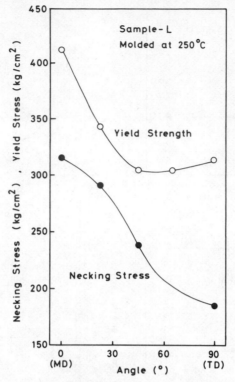

Fig. 6. Variations of yield strength and necking stress with angle to the MD; L sample molded at 250°C.

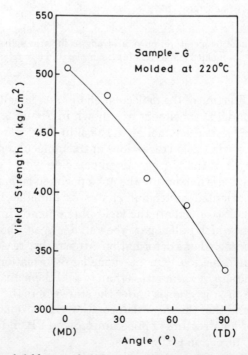

Fig. 7. Variation of yield strength with angle to the MD; G sample molded at 220°C.

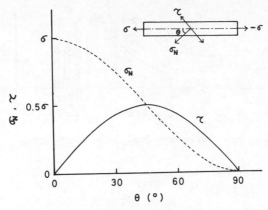

Fig. 8. Variations of normal stress σ_N and shear stress τ with angle θ.

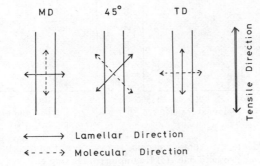

→ Lamellar Direction

←- - - -→ Molecular Direction

Fig. 9. Orientation directions of molecular chains and lamellae in the individual specimen.

was the lowest at 45°-direction and elucidated it with the concept of interlamellar shear deformation.

On the assumption that the yield of the skin layer originates in the interdirections are schematically drawn in Figure 10. In the MD, the interlamellar materials (amorphous chains) are elongated by tensile stress. In the 45°-direction, the lamellae slip past each other by shear stress; and in the TD, by tensile stress. Furthermore, at the center of the injection-molded PP, there is not only a skin layer but also a core layer composed of spherulites. The yield of the core layer may be ascribed to the overlapping of spherulite and interspherulite deformations.

The order of the yield strength of the G sample (FRPP) is reasonably MD > 45° > TD. It is assumed that the yield strength of the FRPP is rather governed by the glass fiber orientation than by the molecular orientation or the higher order structure of base resin. The fact that the order of the yield strength of the FRPP is 45° > TD, in contrast to the straight PP, suggests that the yield does not occur by shear stress but by tensile stress in all cases in the FRPP.

The yield strengths in the MD, 45°-direction, and TD of the straight PP increase with the decrease in cylinder temperature. Consequently, all the directions become strong if the MD is strengthened. Such tendency has been observed also for T-die film.[15] For such resins as polyethylene and polystyrene, the TD is weakened when the MD is strengthened by molecular orientation.[16] Such tendency for the orientation-crystallized polypropylene is ascribed to a

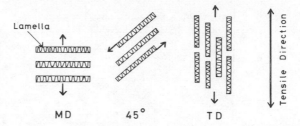

Fig. 10. Elementary processes of yield phenomena in various directions.

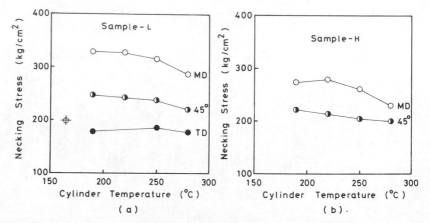

Fig. 11. Effect of cylinder temperatures on necking stresses in various directions. Cross-marked point is for compression-molded material: (a) L sample; (b) H sample.

"woven structure."[20,23] However, the previous results[20] and the fact that the yield strength in the MD is far higher than that in the TD suggest that the woven structure is mainly composed of the warp, and the woof component is very small. The order of the dependence of the yield strength on cylinder temperature is MD ≫ TD > 45°, which is in accordance with the order of the yield strength of the skin layer (*vide infra*). The yield strength of the G sample is practically independent of cylinder temperature. It is assumed that the reduction of the yield strength which originates in the decrease of the molecular chain orientation caused by the increase in cylinder temperature and the reduction in yield strength caused by the decrease in injection pressure[21] may balance the increase in yield strength which originates in the increase in glass fiber orientation caused by the increase in cylinder temperature.

Necking Stress. The effect of cylinder temperature on necking stress in various directions for the L and H samples is shown in Figure 11(a) and (b), respectively. The variation of the necking stress of the L sample molded at 250°C with the angle to the MD is shown in Figure 6. The L sample molded at 220°C in the TD ruptured soon after the yield point and did not show necking. Since one of the three specimens showed necking for the L sample molded at 190°C in the TD, its value was adopted. The H sample in the TD and the G sample in all directions ruptured soon after the yield points and did not show necking. For the L sample, the der of the necking stress is 9 or MD > 45° > compression-molded > TD. This is reasonable, for the difficulty of the unfolding of the lamellae is in this order, as shown in Figure 12. According to the theory of Kasai

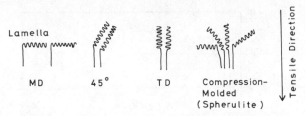

Fig. 12. Unfolding of the lamellae in the skin layer of an injection-molded article in various directions and in a compression-molded one.

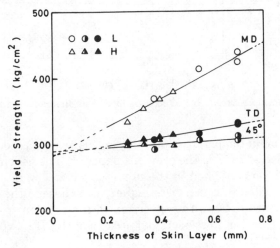

Fig. 13. Relationship between yield strengths in various directions and thickness of the skin layer.

et al.,[24] since the molecular unfolding occurs after the lamellae change to elongation direction, the lamellae must rotate by 90° and 45° in the MD- and 45°-specimens, respectively. On the other hand, they need not rotate in the TD specimen. Consequently, the order of difficulty of the necking is MD > 45° > TD, and hence the necking stress is also in the same order.

The necking stress, just like the thickness of the skin layers, tends to decrease with increasing cylinder temperature. From this fact, a certain relationship between the necking stress and the thickness of the skin layer (*vide infra*) is expected.

Relations Between Tensile Properties and Thickness of Skin Layer. The relation between the yield strength or necking stress and the thickness of the skin layer is shown in Figures 13 and 14. The yield strengths and necking stresses in all directions correlate linearly with the thickness of the skin layer, having positive slopes, regardless of the *MFI* of the resins. By extrapolating the thickness of the skin layer to 0.8 mm and zero, the values for the various tensile properties of the skin and core layers were obtained, as shown in Table II. The yield strengths of the skin and core layers obtained from the injection-molded dumbbell (one-directional specimen) in the previous paper[22] were, respectively, 450 kg/cm² and 260 kg/cm², agreeing perfectly with those in the MD in Table II. However, the yield strength of the core layer obtained here is slightly higher than that in the previous paper.[22] This is probably so because the specimen

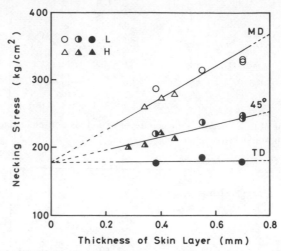

Fig. 14. Relationship between necking stresses in various directions and thickness of the skin layer.

molded at the mold temperature of 40°C in this work was cooled more slowly than that molded at 13°C in the previous paper.[22] The necking stresses of the skin and core layers obtained in the previous paper[22] were, respectively, 390 kg/cm² and 200 kg/cm², which were higher than those in the MD in Table II. This is probably so because the specimen in the previous paper, the ASTM dumbbell, had a higher cross-sectional area than the JIS Type-3 dumbbell in this work.

For the tensile strength, it is advantageous to injection mold the skin layer as thick as possible since the yield strength of the skin layer is higher than that of the core layer in all directions, as shown in Table II. Since the skin layer of the 45°-specimen had a strong possibility to yield by shear deformation as mentioned above, we tried to calculate the shear yield strength of the skin layer from the tensile yield strength of the skin layer of the 45°-specimen. As shown in Figure 8, when the tensile stress σ is applied to the specimen, the shear stress on the plane at 45° is $\sigma/2$. Namely, the shear yield strength of the skin layer is one half of the tensile yield strength of the skin layer of the 45°-specimen. The shear yield strength of the skin layer, calculated in this way, is 155 kg/cm². The shear yield strength of the skin layer corresponds to the interlamellar slipping yield strength, and the tensile yield strength in the MD of the skin layer corresponds to the interlamellar pulling-apart yield strength. The former is about one third of the latter.

TABLE II
Values of the Various Tensile Properties of Skin and Core Layers

Tensile property	Layer	MD	45°	TD
Yield strength, kg/cm²	skin	452	309	334
	core	282	290	284
Necking stress, kg/cm²	skin	368	254	180
	core	176	176	176

Tensile Impact Strength (TIS)

The effect of the cylinder temperatures on the *TIS* values in various directions for the L, H, and G samples is shown in Figure 15(a)–15(c), respectively. For all the samples, the order of the *TIS* is MD > 45° > TD. Since the *TIS* is proportional to the integral of the tensile stress at high-speed tensile deformation (about 3 m/sec) from zero to rupture elongation, i.e., the area of the stress–strain curve at high speed elongation, the *TIS* shows a low value when the stress is high but the elongation is low. Since the skin layer occupies a considerably wide part in the injection-molded PP and the lamellae in the skin layer are arranged as shown in Figure 10, the order of the ease of stress propagation is MD > 45° > TD. Further, since the difference in the ease of the stress propagation is magnified at the high-speed deformation, the elongation at high speed should also be in the same order. Furthermore, since the order of the stress is MD > 45° > TD, the order of the multiplied value of the stress by the elongation should be MD > 45° > TD, and, consequently, the *TIS* is also in the same order.

The *TIS* of the L sample shows a notable maximum at 250°C in the MD and 45°-direction and a small maximum at the same temperature in the TD. The *TIS* values of the H and G samples are practically independent of the cylinder temperature. Since the thickness of the skin layer decreases gradually with increasing cylinder temperature, the *TIS* is almost independent of the thickness of the skin layer, and the structural factor which governs the *TIS* is not obvious. However, as clearly observed on the L sample in the usual cylinder temperature range, the *TIS* values of an injection-molded PP in all directions become higher when the *TIS* in one direction becomes higher. This is in contrast to the injection-molded polystyrene.[16] Thus, so far as the impact strength is concerned, it is better to mold the MD as tough as possible on injection molding PP.

For the resins studied here, the order of the *TIS* is L sample≫ H sample > G sample in the MD and 45°-direction, and G sample >L sample ≈ H sample in the TD. When an injection-molded article fractures by impact, the strength depends on the impact direction. If the impact is added mainly in the MD, the order of the strength will be L sample ≫H sample > G SAMPLE/ If the impact is added mainly in the TD, the order will be G sample > L sample ≈ H sample. Although the impact direction is not known in most cases, a fracture should occur along the impact direction when the impact energy in a certain direction exceeds the impact strength in the direction. If the impact strengths in the TD of two materials are equal, the one which has higher impact strength in the MD and/or 45°-direction will have higher total impact strength. For example, the L sample, which has nearly equal *TIS* as the H sample in the TD and has higher *TIS* than the H sample in the MD and 45°-direction, will have higher total impact strength.

Finally, we will compare the *TIS* of the injection-molded PP with that of the compression-molded PP, which is regarded as an isotropic sample. As for the *TIS*, the compression-molded material is situated between °C for the L sample. Also it is situated between the MD and 45°-direction of the injection-molded material molded at 250°C for the H sample.

Since the compression-molded material is isotropic, it shows same impact strength in any direction. If an isotropic article is obtained by injection molding, the *TIS* will be the same as that of the compression-molded article in any direction. (Strictly speaking, they are not exactly the same since cooling conditions

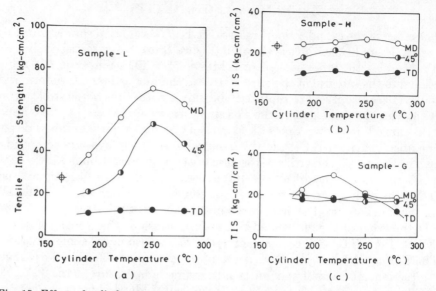

Fig. 15. Effect of cylinder temperatures on tensile impact strengths in various directions. Cross-marked points are for compression-molded materials: (a) L sample; (b) H sample; (c) G sample.

differ.) Consequently, in comparison with the usual anisotropic injection-molded article, the isotropic one may have higher impact strength in the TD though it may have lower impact strength in the MD and 45°-direction. In other words, it cannot be essential that the isotropic injection-molded article has higher impact strength than the usual anisotropic one. However, it seems to be safe to adopt the isotropic one since its impact strength in the TD is higher. For the injection-molded PP, as shown in Figure 15(a) and 15(b), it might be better to mold the MD as tough as possible, since the impact strength in the TD tends to increase with increase of the impact strength in the MD.

Flexural Property

Flexural Modulus. The effect of the cylinder temperatures on the flexural moduli in various directions for the L, H, and G samples is shown in Figure 16(a)–16(c), respectively. The order of the flexural moduli of the straight PP's is MD > TD > 45°; the 45°-direction is the lowest, as in the case of the tensile yield strength. This fact can be elucidated by the shear deformation in the skin layer, as in the case of the tensile yield strength.

The order of the flexural modulus of the FRPP is reasonably MD ≫ 45° > TD. The flexural modulus of the FRPP might be governed mainly by the orientation of glass fibers rather than by the molecular orientation or the higher order structure of base resin.

The flexural moduli of the straight PP's decrease in the MD and TD and slightly increase in the 45°-direction with increase in cylinder temperature. Since the flexural modulus in the 45°-direction decreases slightly with increase in cylinder temperature, it is of advantage to injection mold the straight PP's so that the skin layer is as thick as possible when the cylinder temperature is as low as possible. The flexural moduli of the G sample vary irregularly and in-

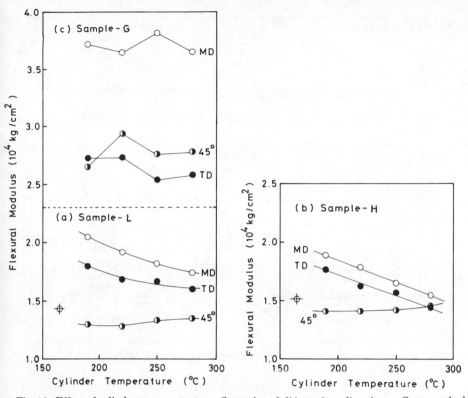

Fig. 16. Effect of cylinder temperatures on flexural moduli in various directions. Cross-marked points are for compression-molded materials: (a) L sample; (b) H sample; (c) G sample.

dependently with cylinder temperature. The reduction of the flexural modulus which originates in the decrease of the molecular orientation caused by the increase in cylinder temperature and the reduction of the flexural modulus caused by the decrease in injection pressure may balance the increase of the flexural modulus which originates in the increase in glass fiber orientation caused by the increase in cylinder temperature.

In comparison with the compression-molded PP, which is regarded as an isotropic sample, the flexural modulus of the injection-molded PP is slightly lower in the 45°-direction.

Finally, flexural moduli of the resins will be compared with one another. As for the flexural moduli of the L sample and the H sample, both being stlatter is higher in the 45°-direction. This is probably so because the L sample possesses a thicker skin layer than the H sample. The skin layer shows higher flexural modulus in the MD and TD and a lower one in the 45°-direction than the core layer (*vide infra*). As for the flexural moduli of the straight PP and FRPP, the latter is higher than the former in all directions. The discrepancy is most noticeable in the MD.

Flexural Strength. The effect of the cylinder temperatures on the flexural strengths in various directions for the L, H, and G samples is shown in Figure 17(a)–17(c), respectively. The order of the flexural strengths of the straight PP's is TD ≳ MD ≫ 45°; the 45°-direction is by far lowest. The fact that the flexural

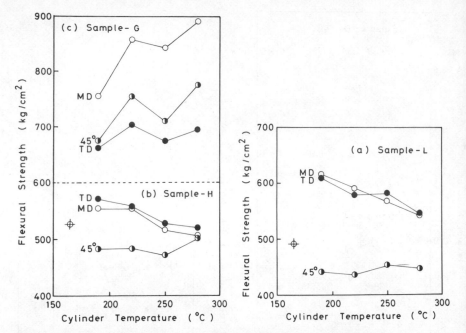

Fig. 17. Effect of cylinder temperatures on flexural strengths in various directions. Cross-marked points are for compression-molded materials: (a) L sample; (b) H sample; (c) G sample.

strength is the lowest in the 45°-direction is ascribed to the shear deformation in the skin layer as in the case of the tensile yield strength. The reason why the flexural strength in the MD is nearly equal to that in the TD and is by far the lowest in the 45°-direction is not known.

The flexural strength decreases with increase in cylinder temperature in the MD and TD, and is almost independent of the cylinder temperature or slightly increases with increase in cylinder temperature in the 45°-direction. Since the thickness of the skin layer decreases with increase in cylinder temperature, as shown in Figure 4, it is assumed that the flexural strength of the skin layer is higher than that of the core layer in the MD and TD, and the latter is higher in the 45°-direction. The details will be discussed later.

The flexural strength in the 45°-direction of the injection-molded sample is lower than that of the compression-molded one. This may be explained by the fact that the flexural strength in the 45°-direction of the skin layer is lower than that of the core layer, which is composed of spherulites as in the compression-molded one.

As for the flexural strengths of the L sample and the H sample, the former is higher than the latter in the MD and TD, while the latter is higher in the 45°-direction. This is because the L sample possesses a thicker skin layer than the H sample.

The order of the flexural strength of the G sample is MD > 45° > TD, which is a reasonable tendency, as in the case of the tensile yield strength. The flexural strength of the G sample increases with increase in cylinder temperature, which is probably because the orientation of glass fibers increases with increase in cylinder temperature. The flexural strength of the G sample varies irregularly with cylinder temperature. This is due to the variation of the injection pressure.

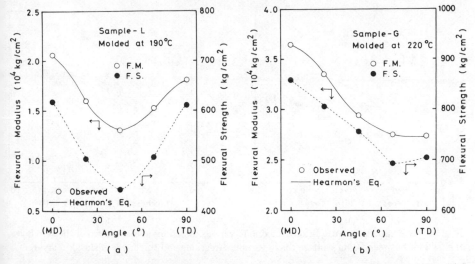

Fig. 18. Variations of flexural moduli and flexural strengths with the angle to the MD: (a) L sample molded at 190°C; (b) G sample molded at 220°C.

Variations of Flexural Modulus and Flexural Strength with Angle

The variations of the flexural moduli and flexural strengths of the L sample and the G sample with the angle to the MD are shown in Figure 18(a) and 18(b) respectively. The flexural modulus and flexural strength show a similar tendency together. Both the flexural modulus and flexural strength of the L sample show minima in the 45°-direction, while those of the G sample gradually decrease in a reverse S-shape with increase in the angle.

According to Hearmon,[19] the tensile modulus E_θ, at arbitrary angle θ, of the material of uniform anisotropy can be calculated from the tensile moduli E_0, E_{45}, and E_{90} in the 0°-, 45°- and 90°-directions through eq. (5):

$$\frac{1}{E_\theta} = \frac{\cos^4\theta}{E_0} + \frac{\sin^4\theta}{E_{90}} + \left(\frac{4}{E_{45}} - \frac{1}{E_0} - \frac{1}{E_{90}}\right) \sin^2\theta \cos^2\theta \tag{5}$$

Although it may not be proper to apply eq. (5) to an injection-molded article since it gets a skin/core morphology and/or the orientation of glass fibers is not uniform in the FRPP, we try to apply eq. (5) to the injection-molded PP. The variations of E_θ values with θ, calculated by eq. (5) for the L sample molded at 190°C and G sample molded at 220°C, are shown by solid lines in Figure 18(a) and 18(b), respectively. The calculated values fit fairly well with experimental ones. Since in the injection-molded article (like the injection-molded plate with the film gate as in this work) anisotropy is regarded uniform in the lengthwise direction, while it is not uniform thicknesswise, eq. (5) seems to be meaningful.

Relations Between Flexural Modulus or Flexural Strength and Thickness of the Skin Layer. The relations between the flexural moduli in various directions and the thickness of the skin layer are shown in Figure 19(a). The flexural modulus increases with increase in thickness of the skin layer in the MD and TD, and it decreases with increase in the thickness of the skin layer in the 45°-direction. This fact indicates that the flexural modulus of the skin layer is higher than that of the core layer in the MD and TD, while the latter is

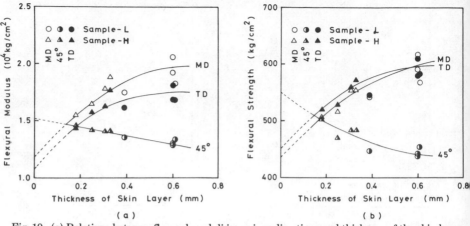

Fig. 19. (a) Relations between flexural moduli in various directions and thickness of the skin layer. (b) Relations between flexural strengths in various directions and thickness of the skin layer.

higher in the 45°-direction. The flexural modulus of the core layer, which is obtained by extrapolating the thickness of the skin layer to zero, is different among in the MD, 45°-direction, and TD. The reason for this discrepancy is not obvious. Since in the 45°-direction the relation between the flexural modulus and the thickness of the skin layer is linear and the scattering of the points is small, extrapolation can be carried out with considerably high precision. The flexural modulus of the core layer, obtained in this way, is ca. 15000 kg/cm^2, which is nearly equal to that of the compression-molded specimen [cf. Fig. 16(a) and 16(b)]. On the contrary, since in the MD and TD the points scatter considerably, extrapolation is inaccurate.

The relations between the flexural strengths in various directions and the thickness of the skin layer are shown in Figure 19(b). As the flexural modulus, the flexural strength increases with increase in the thickness of the skin layer in the MD and TD and decreases with increase in the thickness of the skin layer in the 45°-direction. These facts indicate that the flexural strength of the skin layer is higher than that of the core layer in the MD and TD and the latter is higher in the 45°-direction. This is in contrast to the fact that the tensile yield strength of the skin layer is higher than that of the core layer also in the 45°-direction, though the reason is not obvious.

CONCLUSIONS

The anisotropies of the tensile property, tensile impact strength, and flexural property of injection-molded PP were studied. The results are summarized in Table III.

TABLE III
Anisotropies of Tensile Property, Tensile Impact Strength, and Flexural Property

Property	Straight PP	FRPP
Yield strength	MD ≫ TD > 45°	MD > 45° > TD
Necking stress	MD > 45° > TD	—
Tensile impact strength	MD > 45° > TD	MD > 45° > TD
Flexural modulus	MD > TD > 45°	MD ≫ 45° > TD
Flexural strength	TD ≳ MD ≫ 45°	MD > 45° > TD

The orders of the yield strength, tensile impact strength, flexural modulus, and flexural strength of the FRPP were MD > 45° > TD, which were reasonable tendencies. On the other hand, the orders of the yield strength and flexural modulus of the straight PP were MD > TD > 45°; the 45°-direction was the lowest. This seems to be due to the shear deformation between the lamellae in the skin layer. The order of the necking stress of the straight PP was MD > 45° > TD. This is probably so because the lamellae in the skin layer are perpendicular to the MD. The unfolding of the lamellae becomes difficult in the same order. Regardless of the *MFI* of the resin, the yield strengths and necking stresses in various directions were respectively in a linear relationship with the thickness of the skin layer, having positive slopes and the same zero intercepts. The variation of the flexural modulus with the angle to the MD fitted well to Hearmon's equation. The degree of the anisotropies of various properties for the straight PP generally became higher as the *MFI* and cylinder temperature became lower, or as the skin layer became thicker. On the other hand, for the FRPP, it generally became higher as the cylinder temperature became higher, or as the degree of the orientation of glass fibers became higher.

The authors would like to thank the Tokuyama Soda Co., Ltd., for permission to publish this paper.

References

1. Y. Ito, *Kobunshi Kagaku*, 18, 220 (1961).
2. G. Rauman and D. W. Saunders, *Proc. Phys. Soc. (London)*, 77, 1028 (1961).
3. G. Rauman, *Brit. J. Appl. Phys.*, 14, 795 (1963).
4. V. S. Kim and A. N. Levin, *Sov. Plast.*, 3, 52 (1966).
5. M. Takayanagi, K. Imada, and T. Kajiyama, *J. Polym. Sci. C, no. 15*, 263 (1966).
6. V. B. Gupta and I. M. Ward, *J. Macromol. Sci., Phys.*, B1, 373 (1967).
7. V. B. Gupta, A. Keller, and I. M. Ward, *J. Macromol. Sci., Phys.*, B2, 139 (1968).
8. V. B. Gupta and I. M. Ward, *J. Macromol. Sci., Phys.*, B2, 89 (1968).
9. Z. H. Stachurski and I. M. Ward, *J. Polym. Sci. A-2*, 6, 1083 (1968).
10. Z. H. Stachurski and I. M. Ward, *J. Polym. Sci. A-2*, 6, 1817 (1968).
11. Z. H. Stachurski and I. M. Ward, *J. Macromol. Sci., Phys.*, B3, 445 (1968).
12. W. W. Darlington and D. W. Saunders, *J. Macromol. Sci. Phys.*, B5, 207 (1971).
13. G. R. Davies, A. J. Owen, I. M. Ward, and V. B. Gupta, *J. Macromol. Sci., Phys.*, B6, 215 (1972).
14. A. J. Owen and I. M. Ward, *J. Macromol. Sci., Phys.*, B7, 279 (1973).
15. H. Awaya and T. Isobe, *Kobunshi Kagaku*, 29, 196 (1972).
16. G. B. Jackson and R. L. Ballman, *SPE J.*, 1147 (Oct. 1960).
17. R. M. Ogorkiewicz and G. W. Wiedmann, *Plastics & Polymers*, 337 (Dec. 1971).
18. J. Krebs, *Kunststoffe*, 60, 185 (1970).
19. R. F. S. Hearmon, *An Introduction to Applied Anisotropic Elasticity*, Oxford University Press, London, 1961.
20. M. Fujiyama, *Kobunshi Ronbunshu*, 32, 411 (1975).
21. M. Fujiyama and S. Kimura, *Kobunshi Ronbunshu*, 32, 581 (1975).
22. M. Fujiyama and S. Kimura, *Kobunshi Ronbunshu*, 32, 591 (1975).
23. M. Kojima, *Kobunshi Kagaku*, 25, 276 (1968).
24. N. Kasai, S. Fujiwara, S. Morioka, H. Kurose, M. Kakudo, and T. Watase, *Kogyo Kagaku Zasshi*, 64, 55 (1961).

Received November 10, 1975
Revised October 15, 1976

JOURNAL OF APPLIED POLYMER SCIENCE   VOL. 21, 3311–3318 (1977)

The Entanglement Plateau in the Dynamic Modulus of Rubbery Styrene–Diene Block Copolymers. Significance to Pressure-Sensitive Adhesive Formulations

G. KRAUS and K. W. ROLLMANN, *Phillips Petroleum Company, Bartlesville, Oklahoma 74004*

Synopsis

Styrene–diene (butadiene or isoprene) block copolymers of the SDS or $(SD)_x$ type exhibit a plateau in the dynamic storage modulus located between the glass transitions of the polydiene and polystyrene domains. When the polydiene is the continuous phase, the height of this plateau can be estimated with good success from the entanglement spacing molecular weight of the polydiene and the filler effect of the polystyrene domains. The effect of introduction of a center block-compatible diluent can also be calculated, although the simple procedure used here tends to underestimate the plasticizer effect, particularly at high diluent concentration. Nevertheless, the calculation furnishes a useful criterion of compatibility of the polydiene center blocks and low molecular weight resins used commonly as tackifiers in pressure-sensitive adhesives. Center block compatibility is essential for the development of tack in these compositions.

INTRODUCTION

The dynamic storage modulus of high molecular weight SDS block polymers (S = styrene, D = butadiene or isoprene) exhibits a plateau region between the two domain glass transitions. The height of this plateau is governed mainly by the connectivity of the glassy polystyrene domains. However, when the polystyrene domains are spherical, which is usually the case when the styrene content does not exceed 20% by weight, the plateau modulus may be expected to be determined by the density of the entanglement network of the rubbery center blocks, augmented by the reinforcing effect of the polystyrene domains. It is shown that this is true not only for the pure block polymers, but also for their blends with center block-compatible diluents. The latter case has important implications in the use of these polymers in pressure-sensitive adhesives.

THEORETICAL CONSIDERATIONS

The quasiequilibrium shear modulus of an entanglement network is given by application of the theory of rubber elasticity as

$$G_{eN}^0 = (\rho/M_e)RT \tag{1}$$

3311

where ρ is the density, M_e is the entanglement spacing molecular weight, and R and T have their usual meaning. High molecular weight homopolymers and random copolymers exhibit a plateau in the (isothermal) G'-versus-frequency curve at the level of G_{eN}^0. In dynamic data at fixed frequency and varying temperature, this plateau is also discernible, at least as an inflection point which occurs *near* the minimum in $\tan \delta$. In block polymers, there is additional reason for selecting G' at the minimum in $\tan \delta$ to compare with G_{eN}^0—it is the point on the curve least affected by the two domain glass transitions and represents the closest approach to a quasiequilibrium state. However, before a valid comparison can be made it is necessary to introduce the filler effect. As shown by Holden,[1] for spherical polystyrene domains the Guth and Gold[2] equation should apply, hence,

$$G_{eN}^0 = (\rho/M_e)RT(1 + 2.5c + 14.1c^2) \cong G'(\tan \delta_{min}) \qquad (2)$$

where c is the filler (polystyrene) volume fraction and T is now the temperature at the minimum in $\tan \delta$.

The effect of a diluent on the entanglement plateau modulus is to reduce it by v_2^2, the square of the volume fraction of polymer.[3] Thus, if all the diluent is assumed to enter the rubber phase of the block polymer,

$$G'(\tan \delta_{min}) \cong v_2^2 (\rho/M_e)RT(1 + 2.5c + 14.1c^2) \qquad (3)$$

Note that v_2 is the volume fraction of polymer in the rubbery phase alone, while c is the volume fraction of polystyrene in the entire composition. Also, ρ/M_e is the entanglement density in the *undiluted* rubber. Values of M_e for the homopolymers are given by Ferry[3] as follows: polybutadiene, 1900; polyisoprene, 5750. We assume that these values apply also to long sequences of butadiene and isoprene units in block polymers.

The block copolymers used in this study were products of alkyllithium polymerization and were either of the linear (SDS) or of the radial multichain (SD$\rightarrow$)$_x$ type. In the latter, the functionality of the central branch point was approximately 4. The presence of a single crosslink per molecule has no discernible influence on the entanglement network, and its effect was neglected.

EXPERIMENTAL

Polymer characterization data are given in Table I. Molecular weights were determined by gel permeation chromatography using universal calibration and do, where applicable, take into account long-chain branching.

Commercial polymeric resins of low molecular weight, commonly used in formulation of pressure-sensitive adhesives, were used as diluents. Diluent concentration was varied from 43% to 56% by weight. Resins investigated are shown in Table II.

Films approximately 0.05 cm thick were compression molded at 153°C between silicone release paper. From these, small (0.318 × 0.318 cm) test pieces were cut for determination of the complex dynamic moduli. The latter were measured with a Vibron Model DDV-II viscoelastometer (Toyo Instrument Co., Tokyo, Japan) at 35 Hz in the shear mode.

For electron microscopy, ultrathin sections were prepared by cryomicrotomy and stained by the osmium tetroxide technique of Kato.[4] They were then examined under a Philips EM 300 transmission electron microscope.

TABLE I
Polymer Characterization Data

No.	Diene	Styrene, %	Structure[a]	$M_w/1000$	$M_n/1000$
1[b]	Isoprene	0	L	1963	626
2	Isoprene	15	L	130	83
3	Isoprene	15	R	314	217
4	Butadiene	0	R	223	173
5	Butadiene	0	R	298	228
6	Butadiene	10	R	199	157
7	Butadiene	20	R	103	87
8	Butadiene	20	R	149	120
9	Butadiene	20	R	204	163
10	Butadiene	20	R	314	241

[a] L = Linear; R = radial.
[b] cis-Polyisoprene.

Pressure-sensitive tack was measured on 0.003–0.005-cm-thick films using a Polyken Probe Tack Tester. The probe material was No. 304 stainless steel. Contact time was 1 sec, contact pressure, 10 kPa, and probe separation rate, 1 cm/sec. Test results given are averages of five specimens.

RESULTS

Figure 1 shows the storage modulus and loss tangent of polymer 9, a butadiene–styrene block polymer of 20% styrene content, as a function of temperature. The plot is typical of the data obtained for all block polymers of this study. Note the pronounced plateau in G', extending from about $-20°-+60°C$, and the minimum in tan δ locating the approximate center of the plateau. Data for the same polymer blended in equal weights with the rosin ester diluent (resin A) are shown in Figure 2. The effect of the diluent is to shift the low-temperature maximum in tan δ from $-82°$ to $-12°C$ and to lower the value of G' at temperatures exceeding $-8°C$. There no longer exists a real plateau, only a region of diminished slope. Whereas with the pure polymer the definition of the "plateau modulus" by the minimum in tan δ is not critical to the evaluation of G_{eN}^0, it is so with the diluted polymer and introduces an element of uncertainty.

For the undiluted homopolymers, there is very good agreement between G' (tan δ_{min}) and G_{eN}^0 calculated from eq. (1):

	$T(\tan \delta_{min})$, °C	$G'(\tan \delta_{min}) \times 10^{-6}$, dyn/cm²	G_{eN}^0 (calc.) $\times 10^{-6}$, dyn/cm²
Polybutadiene (#4)	-40	11.0	9.1
Polyisoprene (#1)	24	3.9	3.9

Figure 3 shows a comparison of $G'(\tan \delta_{min})$ calculated by the appropriate equation, (1), (2), or (3), with experimental values. Satisfactory agreement is obtained also for the block polymers, but for compositions containing large amounts of diluent, the calculation overestimates the "plateau" modulus by a factor of roughly 1.5.

TABLE II
Resins Investigated

Resin	Trade Name	Type	Source
A	Foral 85	Rosin ester	Hercules, Inc.
B	Wingtack 95	Polyterpene	Goodyear Chemical Co.
C	Super Sta-Tac 80	Polyolefin	Reichold Chemical Co.
D	Zonarez 7085	Polydipentene	Arizona Chemical Co.
E	Zonarez B-85	Poly(β-pinene)	Arizona Chemical Co.
F	Picco Alpha 115	Poly(α-pinene)	Hercules, Inc.
G	Resin 18-240	Poly(α-methylstyrene)	Amoco Chemical Co.
H	Cumar LX-509	Coumarone-indene	Neville Chemical Co.

Electron-microscopic examination showed spherical polystyrene domains in all the block polymers. Not all the block polymer/diluent mixtures were examined, but those that were and for which data are displayed in Figure 3 likewise exhibited spherical morphology.

DISCUSSION

For the homopolymers $G'(\tan \delta_{min})$ not only shows good formal agreement with the calculated G_{eN}^0, but the frequency and temperature of measurement is easily shown to place the data squarely into the entanglement plateau region for these rubbers as determined by Ferry and associates.[5,6] The success of eq. (2) for the pure block polymers (unflagged points in Fig. 3) thus supports the contention that the height of the plateau in G' is governed by the entanglement network of the center blocks augmented by the filler effect of the spherical polystyrene domains. It also supports the assumption that normal (homopolymer) entanglement spacings prevail in the polydiene continuum of the block polymers.

There are several reasons why the calculation for the diluted block polymers provides less satisfactory agreement. The entanglement region of viscoelastic response is not as well defined, and the procedure for locating its center by the minimum in $\tan \delta$ is only an approximation. Also, this minimum is shifted toward higher temperature, where the segmental motions of the polystyrene blocks may no longer be frozen in, particularly in the interphase region between the matrix and the polystyrene domains. The effect of this would be a decrease in the observed storage modulus. Finally, the $v_2{}^2$ relation, eq. (3), for the diluent effect has not been extensively tested experimentally and may well be an oversimplification. Consequently, the prediction of $G'(\tan \delta_{min})$ to within $3/2$ of the observed value without the use of adjustable parameters must be regarded as a successful confirmation of the basic ideas underlying the extremely simple theory. Moreover, the calculation can serve as a simple practical test for compatibility of a diluent with the diene portion of block polymers of the present type and has important implications in their use in adhesives.

When a polymeric diluent of $T_g \gg T_g$ (polydiene) is polystyrene-compatible or is incompatible with either phase of the block polymer, the result must be an increase in G' in the plateau region—not only can there be no plasticization of the rubbery matrix, but the effective total filler content is increased.

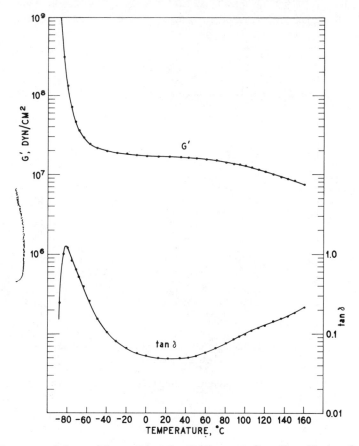

Fig. 1. Storage modulus and loss tangent for 20/80 styrene/butadiene block polymer (polymer 9).

It has been shown[7] that effective tackifying resins in rubber-based adhesives are those that raise T_g and plasticize the rubber at higher temperatures in the manner shown in Figures 1 and 2. Indeed, every mixture shown in Figure 3 (flagged points) was an effective pressure-sensitive adhesive. On the other hand, resin B was not an effective tackifier for butadiene–styrene block polymers and was shown to be incompatible with both phases[8]; $G'(\tan \delta_{\min})$ for polymer 9 containing 43% of this resin was 7.02×10^7 dyn/cm^2, well in excess of the value of the pure block polymer.

The ratio of the experimental value of $G'(\tan \delta_{\min})$ to that calculated by eq. (3) appears to be a remarkably accurate criterion for polydiene center block compatibility of a resin and, together with the shift in T_g, for effectiveness as a tackifier. Some illustrative examples are shown in Table III. In every case where $G'_{\text{obs}}G'_{\text{calc}} > 1$, little or no tack is observed. Resin E in the butadiene–styrene block copolymer seems to be an example of partial compatibility as judged by the large shift in T_g, together with the modestly large G' ratio. Nevertheless, its tack value is low.

The success of the G' ratio as criterion of tackifier effectiveness appears to be founded in the following. First, the stainless steel substrate (probe) is a high-energy surface, while the adhesives are nonpolar or at best very weakly polar

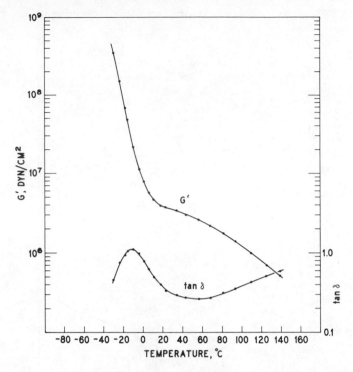

Fig. 2. Storage modulus and loss tangent for 50/50 blend of polymer 9 with resin A.

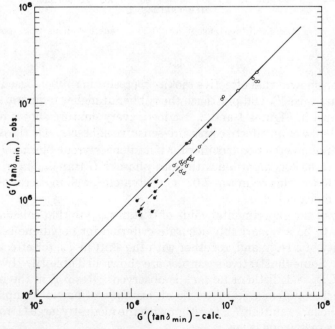

Fig. 3. Storage modulus at the minimum in the loss tangent. Open circles: Polybutadiene and butadiene–styrene block polymers. Closed circles: Polyisoprene and isoprene–styrene block polymers. Flagged circles denote mixtures with center block-compatible polymeric diluents of low molecular weight.

TABLE III
$G'(\tan \delta_{min})$ and Pressure-Sensitive Tack

Block polymer	Resin	%	G'_{obs}/G'_{calc} (at $\tan \delta_{min}$)	$\Delta T_g{}^a$, °C	Probe tack,[b] g
Butadiene–styrene (#10)	A	50	0.65	69	1240
Butadiene–styrene (#9)	A	50	0.65	70	1050
Butadiene–styrene (#9)	A	43	0.69	55	850
Butadiene–styrene (#9)	B	43	15.6	18	0
Butadiene–styrene (#9)	C	50	0.71	76	1270
Butadiene–styrene (#9)	D	50	0.53	76	930
Butadiene–styrene (#9)	E	50	3.5	61	32
Butadiene–styrene (#9)	F	50	0.61	98	1310
Butadiene–styrene (#9)	G	50	15.2	27	26
Butadiene–styrene (#9)	H	43	15.0	16	0
Isoprene–styrene (#3)	A	43	0.85	36	920
Isoprene–styrene (#3)	B	43	0.68	42	1090
Isoprene–styrene (#3)	C	50	0.84	51	1420
Isoprene–styrene (#3)	D	50	0.59	54	1430
Isoprene–styrene (#3)	E	50	0.58	56	1502
Isoprene–styrene (#3)	F	50	0.68	72	1560
Isoprene–styrene (#3)	G	50	7.4	16	110
Isoprene–styrene (#3)	H	43	67	2	0

[a] ΔT_g = shift in maximum in $\tan \delta$.
[b] Polyken tack tester, 25°C, 1 sec dwell time, 1 cm/sec probe withdrawal rate.

compositions of relatively low free surface energy. They undoubtedly spread on the substrate, and the thermodynamic work of adhesion would not be expected to vary widely from one example to another. Consequently the probe tack value is governed mainly by the rheological properties of the adhesive layer.

As Dahlquist[9] has shown, a necessary requirement of tack is the establishment of extensive (preferably full) molecular contact with the microscopically rough substrate surface, which generally will be assured if the 1-sec compressive creep compliance is ca. 10^{-7} cm²/dyne or more. This is equivalent to a shear compliance of $J(1) \geqq 3 \times 10^{-7}$ cm²/dyne for rubbery materials on Poisson's ratio 1/2. According to Riande and Markovitz,[10]

$$|J(t)| \cong |J^*(\omega)| \qquad \omega = 1/t \qquad (4)$$

where $|J^*(\omega)|$ is the absolute magnitude of the complex dynamic shear compliance. If $\tan \delta$ is not large (say, $\leqq 0.35$),

$$|J^*(\omega)| \cong 1/G'(\omega) \qquad (5)$$

is a good approximation. For 35 Hz, $\omega = 220$ rad/sec and $t = 0.0045$ sec, so that

$$J(1) > J(.0045) \cong 1/G'(35 \text{ Hz}) \qquad (6)$$

At 25°C, the requirement that $J(1) \geqq 3 \times 10^{-7}$ cm²/dyne will be met conservatively if

$$G'(35 \text{ Hz}) \leqq 3.3 \times 10^6 \text{ dynes/cm}^2 \qquad (7)$$

The adhesive compositions of Figure 3 generally fulfill this condition at the minimum in $\tan \delta$. However, since G' is relatively flat at the minimum in tan

δ, $G'(\tan \delta_{min}) \approx G'(25°C)$, and the adhesive will not be seriously contact-limited in the 25°C probe tack test.

The second requirement of a tackifier, that it raise T_g, has to do with the value of the force measured on withdrawal of the probe once full contact has been established. Since the prevailing strain rate is rather high, the viscoelastic behavior of the adhesive on a shorter time scale (than the 1-sec dwell time for establishment of full contact) becomes important.[7,9] A high loss modulus reflecting ability to dissipate strain energy is required. On isochronal plots like Figures 1 and 2, shorter response times are represented by lower temperatures. Obviously, a large upward shift in T_g moves the adhesive into a region of greater modulus and increased mechanical losses.

This discussion not only furnishes a rationale for the observation of Table III, but also makes clear the limitations of the G' ratio as a criterion of tackification. It is based specifically on the condition of temperature and time of the probe tack test. The extent to which it can be applied to tack measured under other conditions may be expected to depend on how far these deviate from the present ones.

The authors are indebted to O. L. Marrs for the preparation of the adhesive formulations and for the measurements of adhesive tack.

References

1. G. Holden, in *Block and Graft Polymerization*, R. J. Ceresa, Ed., Wiley, New York, 1973, Chap. 6.

2. E. Guth and O. Gold, *Phys. Rev.*, **53**, 322 (1938).

3. J. D. Ferry, *Viscoelastic Properties of Polymers*, 2nd ed., Wiley, New York, 1970.

4. K. Kato, *Polym. Eng. Sci.*, **7**, 38 (1967).

5. R. H. Valentine, J. D. Ferry, T. Homma, and K. Ninomiya, *J. Polym. Sci. A-2*, **6**, 479 (1968).

6. R. A. Dickie and J. D. Ferry, *J. Phys. Chem.*, **70**, 2594 (1966).

7. M. Sherriff, R. W. Knibbs, and P. G. Langley, *J. Appl. Polym. Sci.*, **17**, 3423 (1973).

8. G. Kraus, F. B. Jones, O. L. Marrs, and K. W. Rollmann, *J. Adhesion*, **8**, 235 (1977).

9. C. A. Dahlquist, in *Treatise on Adhesion and Adhesives*, R. L. Patrick, Ed., Marcel Dekker, New York, 1969, p. 219.

10. E. Riande and H. Markovitz, *J. Polym. Sci., Phys. Ed.*, **13**, 947 (1975).

Received September 21, 1976
Revised October 19, 1976

JOURNAL OF APPLIED POLYMER SCIENCE   VOL. 21, 3319–3329 (1977)

Gel Permeation Chromatography of Polyethylene. I. Calibration

A. BARLOW, L. WILD, and R. RANGANATH, *U.S. Industrial Chemicals Co., Cincinnati, Ohio 45237*

Synopsis

An accurate GPC calibration is essential if computer techniques are to be utilized in obtaining the molecular weight distribution and degree of long-chain branching from an intrinsic viscosity and GPC trace of a polymer. The use of the National Bureau of Standards Linear Polyethylene Standard Reference Material, SRM 1475, to calibrate GPC is described. Employing this calibration, the Mark–Houwink relationship for linear polyethylene in 1,2,4-trichlorobenzene was established utilizing narrow molecular weight fractions derived through fractionation of SRM 1475 and other polymers. This Mark–Houwink equation was subsequently employed for the evaluation of high molecular weight fractions which were then used to extend the GPC calibration to the high molecular weight region not covered by SRM 1475. An iterative technique was used to obtain coincidence of the measured intrinsic viscosity and the viscosity calculated from the GPC data. The accuracy of the GPC calibration was demonstrated by obtaining coincidence of the measured and calculated viscosity of high and low molecular weight polymers of both narrow and broad polydispersity.

INTRODUCTION

Gel permeation chromatography (GPC) is probably the most powerful single analytical tool for polymer evaluation available to the polymer chemist. The description of the molecular weight distribution (MWD) derived through the GPC technique for a wide range of polymer types has given valuable insight into the nature of the polymerization process, influence of production variables, and control of end-use properties. The increasing routine use of GPC for resin analysis has borne many fruits, particularly through more sophisticated methods of data handling.[1,2] However, the GPC process itself only provides a separation of the various molecular species according to their size, and then it is necessary to calibrate each system to provide MWD data. The inability, in practice, to provide consistent and reliable MWD data from instrument to instrument and from time to time is a source of increasing frustration as more detailed use of data is undertaken.

Over the past decade, we have applied the GPC method to analysis of all types of polyethylene products.[3–6] A major part of the effort in developing the technique has been directed toward establishing an effective calibration procedure. An approach has evolved which it is believed will yield the needed consistent and reliable MWD data from any instrument or system of columns providing good molecular separation over the range of molecular weight of interest. The method

3319

involves an initial detailed calibration using the National Bureau of Standards Linear Polyethylene Standard Reference Material, SRM 1475, to cover the low to medium molecular weight region (10^3 to 7×10^5), with high molecular weight fractionated samples to extend the calibration into the higher molecular weight region. A broad-MWD secondary standard is then established and used in routine calibration experiments. Details of the method are given below.

EXPERIMENTAL

Materials

In addition to the NBS material, two other linear polymers were also employed in the calibration procedure. From past experience, the latter were known to have broad polydispersities and exhibited a complete absence of long-chain branching.

Two low molecular weight hydrocarbons, dotriacontane ($C_{32}H_{66}$) and tetratetracontane ($C_{44}H_{90}$), having molecular weights of 450 and 618, respectively, were purchased as pure compounds from CHEM SAMP CO (4692 Kenny Road, Columbus, Ohio 43220).

The solvent used throughout all the measurements described in this paper was distilled 1,2,4-trichlorobenzene (TCB). For both convenience and economy, all the TCB solvent is recycled by distilling it under vacuum.

Solution Viscosity

Solution viscosities were measured at 140°C in modified Ubbelohde viscometers; automatic timing devices accurate to 0.01 sec were used to measure the solvent and solution flow times. The polymer was dissolved in TCB, a 0.1% solution being employed to determine the inherent viscosity. It was found, for the linear polyethylene fractions, that below 1.2 dl/g inherent and intrinsic viscosity values are indistinguishable. Above this value, Martin's single point determination technique[7] was employed to calculate the intrinsic viscosity. It was determined that the constant to be used in Martin's method applied to linear polyethylene in TCB at 140°C is 0.294.

Fractionation

The three linear polymers were fractionated using both the gradient elution column technique[3] and the preparative GPC procedure.[8] In utilizing the gradient elution method, polymer (10 g) was loaded on the Chromosorb-P column packing by cooling from hot xylene solution. A continuous exponential solvent gradient was employed at 115°C with 70:30 and 20:80 mixtures of xylene and ethylene glycol monoethyl ether as solvent and nonsolvent, respectively. Aliquots, 400 ml each, of the column effluent were collected and the polymer was precipitated in acetone, filtered, and dried.

The preparative GPC was equipped with three Waters preparative-scale GPC columns packed with Styragel having porosities of (a) mixed $10^2/10^3$ Å, (b) 10^4 Å, and (c) 10^5 Å. The unit was operated at 105°C using xylene as solvent at a flow rate of 40 ml/min. The maximum sample size was 1 g, i.e., 100 cc of a 1%

solution.   Normally, 100-ml aliquots of the column eluent were collected, the polymer precipitated with acetone, and the fractions recovered using a Millipore filter.

GPC analysis of fractions obtained from the two preparative techniques indicated that the gradient elution technique provided the narrower-MWD fractions in the medium-low molecular weight region.   Preparative GPC proved more effective in providing narrow-MWD fractions in the high molecular weight region.

Gel Permeation Chromatography

Gel permeation chromatography data were obtained using a modified Waters Model 200 GPC instrument equipped with an automatic sample injection system and digital curve translator.   Measurements were made using four Styragel packed columns having porosities of 10^4 Å, 10^4 Å, 10^5 Å, and 10^6 Å arranged in order of increasing porosity.   Trichlorobenzene at 140°C was used as the solvent; the flow rate was 1 ml/min.

Two minor modifications were made to the basic GPC unit.   In order to improve the baseline stability, i.e., long-term drift, the block holding the two photodetector cells was cooled with thermostated water and maintained at a constant 55°C temperature.   This also reduced the baseline noise.

The second modification was made to improve the temperature control of the siphon oven.   Measurements had shown a 40°C temperature differential existed between the top and bottom of the siphon oven at 135°C; therefore, a recirculating fan was installed.   It was calculated, and shown by experiment, that a 5°C change in siphon temperature would cause a 1% change in retention volume.   Consequently, the heating system was changed so that the temperature was controlled through a thermistor detector.   This resulted in a marked improvement in elution volume reproducibility.

Derivation of Mark-Houwink Relationships

The linear polyethylene SRM 1475 was fractionated by both the gradient elution technique and preparative GPC in order to provide well-defined, sharp fractions.   The solution viscosity of the fractions was measured as described above; the solution was then withdrawn from the viscometer and injected into the GPC.   The GPC data for the fractions were analyzed using a calibration based on the MWD provided with SRM 1475 as outlined below.   The weight-average molecular weight of each fraction was plotted as a function of intrinsic viscosity.   Using these data, the Mark–Houwink coefficients were determined and substituted in the GPC computer program.   The data for the fractions were subsequently recomputed to give the viscosity-average molecular weights using the summation

$$M_v = \left(\sum_{i=1}^{\infty} w_i M_i{}^\alpha \right)^{1/\alpha}$$

and

$$[\eta] = K M_v{}^\alpha$$

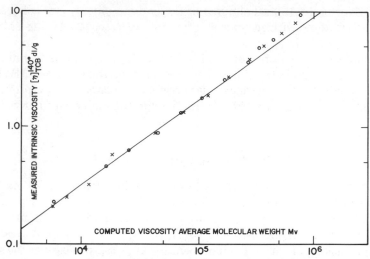

Fig. 1. Mark–Houwink relationship for polyethylene in TCB at 140°C. Also divergence shown by high molecular weight fractions caused by incorrect extrapolation of the initial GPC calibration: (—) Mark–Houwink equation; (○) polymer A; (×) polymer B.

These molecular weights (M_v) were then plotted against the measured viscosities in order to obtain a better estimate of the Mark–Houwink coefficients. This procedure was repeated until no further change occurred in the coefficients, at which time there was also good agreement between the measured and calculated viscosities. The final equation, illustrated in Figure 1, was determined as

$$[\eta] = 3.95\times10^{-4} \ M_v^{0.726}$$

This is in excellent agreement with the relationship of Wagner et al.[9] for polyethylene in TCB at 135°C, which was determined as part of the derivation of the MWD for SRM 1475. The coefficients of the Mark-Houwink equation established by Otocka[10] and Whitehouse[11] in TCB at 135° and 130°C, respectively (Table I), also are in good agreement with the above equation.

CALIBRATION PROCEDURES

A gel permeation chromatograph may be calibrated utilizing either a well-characterized whole polymer having a broad molecular weight distribution or a series of equally well-characterized sharp fractions. In our opinion, the former is preferred since it provides a continuous calibration which may be rapidly ap-

TABLE I
Mark–Houwink Coefficients Determined for Linear Polyethylene
in 1,2,4-Trichlorobenzene[a]

Reference	$K \times 10^4$	α
Wagner[9]	3.92	0.725
Otocka[10]	5.1	0.706
Whitehouse[11]	4.95	0.715
This work	3.95	0.726

[a] $[\eta]$ Expressed in dl/g.

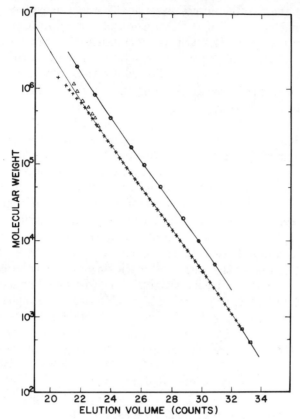

Fig. 2. Molecular weight calibration curves for polystyrene and polyethylene indicating discrepancies which may occur through incorrect extrapolation of the PE curve: (□) low molecular weight compounds; (×) NBS calibration points; (△) high molecular weight fractions (M_v); (—) corrected curve (polyethylene); (○) polystyrene standards.

plied and minimizes effects due to axial dispersion and band broadening. Unfortunately, such a broad-MWD standard is not available for polyethylene, and we have combined both methods to obtain a satisfactory calibration utilizing SRM 1475 at the lower molecular weights and fractions at the higher ranges.

Initial Calibration

The initial calibration of the GPC was achieved using the linear polyethylene SRM 1475 which is of known MWD. This was accomplished in the following manner. At least six samples of the polymer, 0.25% concentration, were injected into the GPC and the output was tabulated in the form of elution volume, i.e., count number (C), versus integrated weight percent (I_x). A reading of the differential refractive index (polymer solution concentration, i.e., GPC trace) was taken at every 0.2 counts. The integration was performed using the Schulz–Dinglinger equation

$$I_x = \sum h_n + \tfrac{1}{2} h_{n+1}$$

Since there were slight variations in the integrated weight at each reading, the averages of the readings were tabulated at each count interval. The information

provided by NBS, i.e., integral weight per cent (I_x) versus molecular weight (M), was then employed to obtain the initial elution volume (C)-versus-molecular weight (M) calibration for the GPC. The large number of points thus obtained are used to compute an equation for the calibration curve. In general, a third-degree polynomial has been found to give the best fit, i.e.,

$$\log M = A_0 + A_1 C + A_2 C^2 + A_3 C^3$$

where M = molecular weight; A_0, A_1, A_2, and A_3 are constants; and C is count number. Since the NBS material has a narrow polydispersity, the calibration covers only the 700 to 10^6 molecular weight range (Fig. 2); and, in our opinion, due to uncertainty about the extremes, only the 10^3 to 7×10^5 range is usable. Although too narrow for most commercial polymers, the calibration spans a sufficient breadth of molecular weight to enable us to derive the Mark–Houwink equation as described above and provides an excellent starting point for an extended calibration.

Extension of Calibration

The sample SRM 1475 covers only a narrow range of molecular weights and is therefore limited in its usefulness. In the low molecular weight region, the calibration is readily improved through use of the linear hydrocarbons dotritriacontane and tetratetracontane. The main problem is extending the calibration at the high molecular weight end while continuing to maintain the accuracy of the initial calibration over the whole molecular weight range. A purely mathematical extension of the calibration equation is not desirable since it is heavily influenced by any slight discrepancy in the high molecular weight data points of the initial calibration and uncertainty as to the shape of the curve.

The use of sharp high molecular weight fractions to provide count versus molecular weight again places a great deal of reliance on single points. It also demands independent methods of measuring the molecular weight of the fractions, e.g., osmometry and/or light scattering with all their attendant problems.

TABLE II
Molecular Weight Data for Linear Polymer A Fractions

Fraction	M_n × 10^{-4}	M_w × 10^{-4}	R	M_v × 10^{-4}	Viscosity, dl/g Calcd.	Viscosity, dl/g Measured
8	54.1	105.1	1.95	97.8	8.79	9.51
10	28.7	54.8	1.91	50.7	5.46	5.76
11	21.5	40.4	1.88	37.2	4.36	4.84
12	18.1	31.1	1.72	28.9	3.63	3.64
14	10.7	18.5	1.73	17.1	2.48	2.59
16	6.93	11.6	1.67	10.7	1.76	1.76
18	4.61	7.52	1.63	6.93	1.29	1.30
20	3.01	4.79	1.59	4.44	0.93	0.87
22	1.72	2.67	1.55	2.50	0.61	0.61
24	1.07	1.76	1.64	1.62	0.45	0.45
28	0.32	0.63	1.94	0.57	0.21	0.24
Whole polymer	1.58	11.79	7.45	8.97	1.55	1.53

A combination of the two techniques was finally adopted which, in essence, provides continuous coverage of the extension of the calibration curve with multiple checks of the accuracy. This is accomplished by calculating the viscosity-average molecular weight for each fraction from the intrinsic viscosity and computing it from the GPC data. The calibration curve is then adjusted to obtain coincidence of the two values for all the fractions. The method is described in detail in the following.

The preparative GPC was employed to fractionate two different linear homopolymers, designated A and B, which contain a significant amount of high molecular weight material; that is, more than 10% of the material has a molecular weight $>10^6$. Each resin was fractionated once only, and the fractions were precipitated, dried, and weighed. The integral viscosity distribution curves showed that both fractionations were successful. A number of high molecular weight fractions were obtained in each case. The same solutions at 0.1% concentration, used for the viscosity measurements, were subsequently analyzed by GPC, and the computed viscosity-average molecular weight of the fractions was plotted as a function of the measured intrinsic viscosity (Fig. 1).

It can be seen that, as the molecular weights of the fractions increase, the points diverge from the Mark–Houwink relationship, exhibiting lower molecular weight values. All the lower molecular weight fractions (<300,000) have GPC curves which fall within the limits of the NBS standard calibration. As the portion of the GPC curve which is covered by the extrapolated region of the calibration curve increases, the deviation from the Mark–Houwink relationship also increases, showing that the extrapolated calibration curve is in error and underestimates the molecular weight of the samples. This assumes that the linear Mark–Houwink relationship as derived above is realistic.

The calibration was therefore corrected in the following manner. The viscosity-average molecular weight of the fraction was calculated from its intrinsic viscosity using the Mark-Houwink equation. The viscosity-average count number was determined from the GPC data for the fractions. The C_v–M_v points for all the high molecular weight fractions were then calculated from the initial calibration curve (Fig. 2). Utilizing these points to extend the calibration curve

TABLE III
Molecular Weight Data for Fractions of Linear Polymer B

Fraction	M_n $\times 10^{-4}$	M_w $\times 10^{-4}$	R	M_v $\times 10^{-4}$	Viscosity, dl/g Calcd.	Viscosity, dl/g Measured
9	48.9	93.3	1.91	86.7	8.05	8.07
13	34.0	67.5	1.98	62.1	6.33	6.48
14	22.0	45.2	2.06	41.6	4.73	5.02
16	17.1	32.5	1.90	29.9	3.72	3.79
18	10.8	20.7	1.92	18.8	2.66	2.71
20	7.4	13.4	1.81	12.2	1.94	1.86
22	4.8	8.0	1.69	7.4	1.35	1.33
24	2.8	4.6	1.64	4.3	0.91	0.87
30	0.73	1.29	1.77	1.18	0.36	0.32
32	0.46	0.83	1.83	0.76	0.26	0.25
Whole polymer	1.84	14.83	8.07	11.09	1.81	1.70

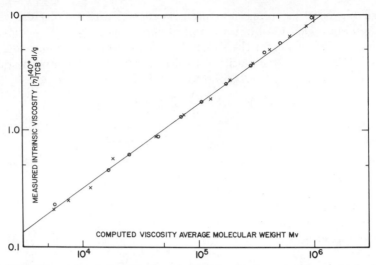

Fig. 3. Mark–Houwink relationship for polyethylene showing coincidence obtained for high molecular weight fractions using the correct extrapolation of the GPC calibration curve: (—) Mark–Houwink equation; (O) polymer A; (X) polymer B.

resulted in an overestimation of the molecular weight of the fractions. In order to counterbalance this tendency, the calibration curve was recalculated including the molecular weights derived using the original calibration curve which corresponded to the viscosity-average count numbers. This procedure was repeated three or four times until no further improvement in the measured and calculated data was obtained. The calibration curve thus derived by the computer is shown in Figure 2. This calibration was checked by analyzing the fractions obtained from linear polymers A and B and comparing the Mark-Houwink relationship thus obtained with that obtained using the NBS fractions. The final results are shown in Tables II and III and plotted in Figure 3.

It can be seen that, with the exception of the very highest molecular weight fraction, the measured and calculated viscosity values for the fractions and whole polymers are within acceptable limits. The changes in the molecular weight averages calculated for the NBS standard caused by the modification of the upper part of the calibration curve are insignificant and within experimental error (Table IV).

The calibration curve thus established covered the molecular weight range of 2×10^2 to 10^7, i.e., the range of most interest in the polyethylene area. As a

TABLE IV
Effect of Correcting GPC Calibration at High Molecular Weight
End on Molecular Weight Data of NBS Standard SRM 1475

Original calibration			Corrected calibration		
M_n $\times 10^{-4}$	M_w $\times 10^{-4}$	R	M_n $\times 10^{-4}$	M_w $\times 10^{-4}$	R
1.72	5.43	3.16	1.73	5.47	3.16
1.74	5.26	3.02	1.75	5.28	3.01
1.73	5.46	3.15	1.74	5.49	3.15

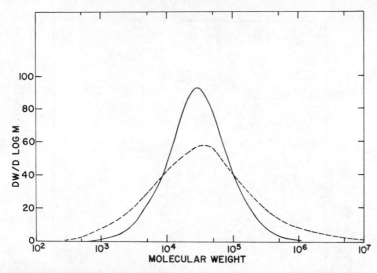

Fig. 4. Comparison of MWD curves for SRM 1475 (—) and Marlex 6009 (- - -).

further check on the accuracy of the calibration, six whole polymers of linear polyethylene varying in molecular weight and polydispersity were examined through solution viscosity and GPC measurements. The results, Table V, showing the excellent agreement between the measured and calculated solution viscosities, confirmed the accuracy of both the calibration and the experimental technique.

Secondary Standard

The calibration curve, which covers a wide molecular weight range, was utilized to establish a secondary calibration standard. The secondary standard enables the calibration to be rapidly checked over the whole molecular weight range on a routine basis and provides a means for calibrating new column systems. The criteria for selecting this polymer were that it was a linear polyethylene, had a broad MWD, i.e., covers the minimum and maximum elution volumes observed for high pressure polyethylenes, and preferably has a symmetric MWD. The polymer Marlex 6009 fulfills these requirements, as is shown in Figure 4 where the MWD curve is compared with that for SRM 1475. To establish Marlex 6009 as the secondary standard, it was subjected to GPC analysisaat least six times,

TABLE V
Comparison of Calculated and Measured Solution Viscosities for Linear Polyethylene

Resin	M_n $\times 10^{-4}$	M_w $\times 10^{-4}$	R	Viscosity, dl/g	
				Calcd.	Measured
R	0.97	3.89	4.01	0.75	0.78
S	1.29	6.58	5.11	1.02	1.01
T	1.52	9.93	6.53	1.33	1.26
U	1.62	13.08	8.07	1.62	1.68
V	1.75	18.92	10.81	2.09	2.05
W	0.89	21.16	23.78	2.23	2.34

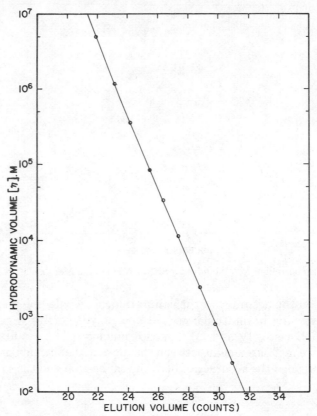

Fig. 5. Universal GPC calibration curve illustrating coincidence of the polyethylene and polystyrene data: calculated universal calibration (PE data) (—); polystyrene data points (O).

and the integral weight (I_x)-versus-molecular weight data were averaged at each elution volume (0.2 count) interval.

Universal Calibration

The universal calibration hypothesis proposed by Benoit[12] has shown itself to be most useful in enabling the GPC calibration established for one polymer to be converted to that for a different polymer system. Its greatest value to us, however, is in enabling one to determine realistic molecular weight data for long-chain branched materials such as low-density polyethylene.[4-6] The classical methods of establishing the structural parameters, i.e., molecular weight and long-chain branch index, would inevitably be more time consuming and probably less accurate.

The universal calibration is readily established by combining the Mark–Houwink equation for the polymer–solvent system employed in the GPC with the molecular weight calibration equation of the instrument as shown:
GPC Calibration

$$\log M = A_0 + A_1 C + A_2 C^2 + A_3 C^3$$

Mark–Houwink equation

$$\log [\eta] = \log K + \alpha \log M$$

Universal calibration equation

$$\log [\eta M] = \log K + (1 + \alpha)(A_0 + A_1 C + A_2 C^2 + A_3 C^3)$$

Briefly, the universal calibration hypothesis states that the molecules are separated during GPC on the basis of hydrodynamic volume. As can be seen in Figure 2, the molecular weight calibration curves for polyethylene and polystyrene are quite separate, but coincidence of the hydrodynamic volume $(M\eta)$- -versus-elution volume curves for these two polymers (Fig. 5) clearly confirms the accuracy of the concept. The Mark–Houwink coefficients for polystyrene in TCB at 140°C were determined as $K = 1.90 \times 10^{-4}$ and $\alpha = 0.655$, which are in close agreement with Otocka's values.[10]

CONCLUSIONS

The data obtained in developing a reliable GPC calibration technique has led to the following conclusions:

(a) The NBS standard reference material SRM 1475 provides a most satisfactory method of calibrating the GPC for the molecular weight range of 10^3 to 7×10^5.

(b) The calibration may be accurately extended at the high molecular weight end by using suitable fractions and obtaining coincidence of the viscosity-average molecular weights calculated through viscosity measurements and computed from the GPC data for the fractions. This assumes accurate Mark–Houwink coefficients.

(c) A linear polyethylene having a symmetric broad molecular weight distribution provides a useful secondary standard capable of rapidly and routinely verifying the accuracy of a calibration over a wide molecular weight range or calibrating new column sets.

(d) The equations for the GPC calibration and Mark–Houwink relationship are readily combined to provide the universal calibration for the GPC equipment. This allows one to calibrate the GPC for polymers for which it is difficult to obtain standards. Most importantly, it provides a means for analyzing long chain-branched polymers such as low-density polyethylene and obtaining realistic values for the molecular weight averages and long-chain branch index.

References

1. A. Ram and J. Miltz, *J. Appl. Polym. Sci.*, **15**, 2639 (1971).
2. E. E. Drott and R. A. Mendelson, *J. Polym. Sci. A-2*, **8**, 1361 (1970).
3. P. M. Kamath and L. Wild, 22nd ANTEC of SPE 1966, SPE Technical Papers 12, 1966, p. XVII-6.
4. L. Wild and R. Guliana, *J. Polym. Sci. A-2*, **5**, 1087 (1967).
5. L. Wild, R. Ranganath, and T. Ryle, *J. Polym. Sci. A-2*, **9**, 2137 (1971).
6. L. Wild, R. Ranganath, and A. Barlow, *J. Appl. Polym. Sci.*, **21**, 3331 (1977).
7. J. H. Elliot, K. H. orowitz and T. Hoodock, *J. Appl. Polym. Sci.*, **14**, 2947 (1970).
8. A. Barlow, L. Wild, and T. Roberts, *J. Chromatogr.*, **55**, 155 (1971).
9. H. L. Wagner and C. A. J. Hoeve, *J. Polym. Sci., Polym. Phys. Ed.*, **11**, 1189 (1973).
10. E. P. Otocka, R. J. Roe, N. Y. Hellman, and P. M. Muglia, *Macromolecules*, **4**, 507 (1971).
11. B. A. Whitehouse, *Macromolecules*, **4**, 463 (1971).
12. Z. Grubisic, H. Benoit, and P. Rempp, *J. Polym. Sci.*, **5B**, 753 (1967).

Received September 22, 1976
Revised October 19, 1976

JOURNAL OF APPLIED POLYMER SCIENCE   VOL. 21, 3331–3343 (1977)

Gel Permeation Chromatography of Polyethylene. II. Rapid Evaluation of Long-Chain Branching and Molecular Weight Distribution

L. WILD, R. RANGANATH, and A. BARLOW, *U.S. Industrial Chemicals Co., Cincinnati, Ohio 45237*

Synopsis

A comparison is made of two methods by which one may derive molecular weight distribution and degree of long-chain branching using only the measured solution viscosity of a branched polyethylene whole polymer and its GPC trace. These are (a) Drott and Mendelson method and (b) Ram and Miltz procedure. In each case, the purpose of the method is to devise a means by which one may establish a relationship between solution viscosity and molecular weight for use in conjunction with the GPC universal calibration relationship of Benoit et al. The effectiveness of these theoretical approaches is evaluated by comparison with the true D and degree of long-chain branching data obtained using our complete iterative analysis method. Such a detailed comparison using low, moderate, and highly branched resins leads to a conclusion that both the techniques provide very good MWD and branching data and, further, that they may be considered interchangeable for most resins. For highly branched resins, the Ram and Miltz method, which is slightly more sensitive to the presence of a high degree of long-chain branching, is preferred. In practice, the Drott and Mendelson method has the advantage of using less computer time and providing a direct measure of degree of long-chain branching, and thus is likely to be used most frequently.

INTRODUCTION

Over the past few years, gel permeation chromatography (GPC) has established itself as the most powerful analytical tool available to the polymer chemist. This technique provides the cornerstone of our polyethylene structure studies and has been used extensively, with considerable attention being paid to both the practical operation of the instrument and the details of data analysis. Some aspects of this work have been reported previously,[1,2] particularly concerning the importance of effective GPC calibration.

Through GPC, one obtains a molecular separation based on size (hydrodynamic volume), and the resultant separation is displayed on a chart as a weight distribution, which may be converted to a molecular weight distribution by a suitable calibration method. In the analysis of low-density polyethylenes, the nature of the separation (by size) presents both a distinct problem and an opportunity. This is because almost all low-density polyethylenes exhibit long-chain branches which exert a strong influence on molecular size. Thus, the weight distribution provided by GPC is influenced by both long-chain branching and molecular weight, making molecular weight calibration very difficult. The

3331

dual dependence of GPC separation on molecular weight and LCB does, however, provide the opportunity for obtaining information as to the degree of LCB present in a particular resin as well as its molecular weight and molecular weight distribution (MWD).

The means by which one might resolve the problem of separating out the two effects due to molecular weight and LCB was provided by Benoit et al.[4] He demonstrated that the GPC elution volume can be related to a hydrodynamic volume parameter $M[\eta]$, i.e., GPC calibration in terms of $[\eta]M$ applies to all polymer systems and provides a universal calibration for a particular instrument. When applied to a branched polymer like polyethylene, if one knows the solution viscosity of the molecular species eluting at any particular point, one may simply determine its molecular weight, allowing one to construct a MWD curve. Further, a knowledge of the actual solution viscosity in relation to the solution viscosity which would be exhibited by a linear species of the same molecular weight provides a measure of the degree of LCB.[5]

The great potential of the GPC technique for the analysis of branched polyethylenes can thus be appreciated, for it is only through a knowledge of both MWD and degree of LCB that one can hope to understand the complex behavior of these materials. Because of this, considerable effort has been expended in these and other laboratories to establish practical methods of applying the universal calibration concept of Benoit to the GPC analysis of polyethylenes.

The calibration of the GPC in terms of $[\eta]M$, i.e., establishing a universal calibration, is readily achieved using *linear* polymer standards because the relationship between solution viscosity and molecular weight is normally well defined and known in terms of the Mark–Houwink equation $[\eta] = KM^\alpha$. The problem in the analysis of branched polymers finally becomes the problem of determining the value of the solution viscosity at each molecular weight level for the material being analyzed.

Several approaches are possible and have been tried for establishing the solution viscosity–molecular weight relationship for a particular branched resin. They break down into two categories, one involving the measurement of the viscosity values at differing molecular weight levels,[1,6,7] and the second approach attempting to establish a theoretical relationship between solution viscosity and molecular weight which may be quantified by reference to the measured solution viscosity of the unknown whole polymer.[8,9,10] The former approach presents considerable practical difficulty, while the problems associated with the latter type of method are those concerning the effectiveness of the theoretical definition of the solution viscosity–molecular weight relationship for real branched resins.

The uncertainties possible when using any of the theoretical approaches dictated that our initial application of the universal calibration concept be through a method using direct solution viscosity measurement of the various molecular weight species from a parent resin. The technique involves an initial preparative fractionation, followed by GPC and solution viscosity determinations on the resulting fractions, from which one may derive the molecular weight of each of the fractions and allow the direct construction of a molecular weight calibration curve for the parent resin. The calculations have been computerized with the inclusion of an iterative section in the program to correct for the polydispersity of the fractions. The details have been reported earlier,[1] and this has become known as our standard iterative analysis method for the derivation of molecular weights, molecular weight distribution, and degree of LCB. The results are unambiguous but the method is time consuming and needs considerable experimental equipment.

In the studies described below, an attempt is made to evaluate the effectiveness of the more rapid methods of Ram and Miltz (R & M) and Drott and Mendelson (D & M) in providing realistic MWD and degree of LCB data.

THEORETICAL RELATIONSHIPS BETWEEN SOLUTION VISCOSITY AND MOLECULAR WEIGHT FOR BRANCHED POLYMERS

As indicated in the Introduction, in the absence of a means of directly determining the solution viscosity of the various molecular weight branched species in a resin, one must find a means of defining the relationship between solution viscosity and molecular weight for any particular resin in order to use the universal calibration. Such a definition has been attempted using two different approaches. One involves the use of a theoretical relationship between degree of LCB and solution viscosity from which one may derive the solution viscosity–molecular weight relationship. This method has been described by Drott and Mendelson[8] and by Shida and Cote.[9] The second method[10] makes no assumption as to the relationship between degree of LCB and solution viscosity and molecular weight value. Both choose the numerical values of their expressions by an iteration procedure using the conditions that the final computed solution viscosity of the whole polymer equals the experimentally measured value.

The two approaches are outlined in the following paragraphs.

Ram and Miltz Procedure

For linear polyethylenes, the solution viscosity–molecular weight relationship is expressed by the Mark–Houwink equation $[\eta]_{lin} = KM^{\alpha}$, where K and α are constants for a given solvent at a particular temperature. No such simple relationship is possible for the long chain-branched polyethylenes.

An approach to a derivation of the solution viscosity–molecular weight relationship for branched polyethylenes has been suggested by Ram and Miltz. In their method, the formulation of a Mark–Houwink-type relationship for a branched polymer is assumed to be described by a polynomial expression as in

$$\ln [\eta] = \ln K + \alpha \ln M + b \ln^2 M + c \ln^3 M$$

where α and K have the same significance and values that qualify for a linear polymer. The parameters b and c for each branched polyethylene under consideration are varied in such a way that the computed solution viscosity of the whole polymer equals the measured value. With the aid of this expression the GPC data for the branched LDPE is interpreted to determine its molecular weight distribution.

The method takes advantage of the experience and information gathered in the past on the branched polyethylenes of varying degrees of long-chain branching. It has been observed that the different long chain-branched polyethylenes all behave as linear polyethylenes below the molecular weight level of 5×10^3 and up to this threshold value (say, M_0) can be represented by the simple Mark–Houwink relationship:

$$\ln [\eta]_{TCB}{}^{140} = \ln K + \alpha \ln M \qquad \text{for } M < M_0 = 5 \times 10^3$$

where $K = 3.95 \times 10^{-4}$ and $\alpha = 0.726$. Above this molecular weight level, the solution viscosity–molecular weight relationship is expressed by the polynomial referred to earlier, viz.,

$$\ln [\eta] = \ln K + \alpha \ln M + b \ln^2 M + c \ln^3 M \qquad \text{for } M \geqslant M_0 = 5 \times 10^3$$

The GPC data of the whole polymer are handled with the aid of this polynomial expression for solution viscosity based on the fact that this viscosity is made up of the contributions from each species, and thus

$$[\eta]_{\text{total}} = \Sigma W_i [\eta]_i$$

In applying this to the GPC curve, we have the weight fraction of species i,

$$W_i = h_i / \Sigma h_i$$

where h_i is the height of the GPC curve at the corresponding count number (elution volume).

The specific Mark–Houwink relationship is

$$[\eta]_i = K M_i{}^{(\alpha + b \ln M_i + c \ln^2 M_i)} \qquad \text{for } M_i \geqslant M_0$$

i.e.,

$$[\eta]_i M_i = K M_i{}^{(1 + \alpha + b \ln M_i + c \ln^2 M_i)} \qquad \text{for } M_i \geqslant M_0$$

The left-hand side of this expression is the molecular size of the species according to which it is separated in gel permeation and directly corresponds to the count number C_i at which it appears. Applying the universal calibration, it is now possible to use the crude chromatogram and the measured value of the solution viscosity of the whole polymer (both at the same temperature and in the same solvent) to obtain the best values of b and c by trial and error. In turn, the above viscosity–molecular weight relations yield the complete molecular weight data.

Drott and Mendelson Procedure

This method, developed for characterizing long-chain branching and molecular weight distribution of branched whole polymers from GPC and intrinsic viscosity measurements, is an iterative computer program where the branching index λ, defined as the ratio

$$\frac{\text{number of branch points in the molecule}}{\text{molecular weight}}$$

is varied until the solution viscosity calculated using GPC data matches with the experimentally measured viscosity of the whole polymer. Using this value of λ, the raw GPC curve is interpreted to calculate the MWD for the whole polymer.

The basic equations and assumptions used in the LCB calculations are

(a) In the GPC, the universal calibration assumption, viz., that the separation of molecules is controlled by their hydrodynamic volume, holds good for both linear and branched polyethylenes. That is,

$$[\eta]_{lin}M_{lin} = [\eta]_{br}M_{br}$$

(b) The viscosity ratio is

$$[\eta]_{br}/[\eta]_{lin} = g^{1/2}$$

where g is a function related to the number of branch points in a molecule. The specific function derived by Zimm and Stockmayer[11] for a trifunctional branch point with reference to a polydisperse polymer is

$$\langle g_3 \rangle = \frac{6}{\lambda M} \left[1/2 \left(\frac{2 + \lambda M}{\lambda M} \right)^{1/2} \ln \left(\frac{(2 + \lambda M)^{1/2} + (\lambda M)^{1/2}}{(2 + \lambda M)^{1/2} - (\lambda M)^{1/2}} \right) -1 \right]$$

(c) The intrinsic viscosity of a branched whole polymer can be calculated from

$$[\eta]_{br} = \Sigma W_i[\eta]_{br_i} = K\Sigma W_i M_i^\alpha \cdot [g(\lambda M_i)]^{1/2}$$

where K and α are Mark–Houwink constants and λ is the branching index defined earlier.

(d) The branching index λ is assumed to be independent of molecular weight for a given polymer. That is, λ is a constant for the whole spectrum of molecular weights that go to make up the whole polymer.

In the computer program, λ is varied until calculated and measured viscosities are in good agreement. To calculate the intrinsic viscosity, the branched calibration curve corresponding to the assumed value of λ must be obtained first. This is achieved through the use of the two functions

$$[\eta]_{br_i} = f(\lambda M_i)$$

and

$$[\eta]_{br_i}M_i = f(C)$$

which is the universal calibration where C is the elution volume.

Essentially, this leads to the branched calibration curve

$$C = f(M)$$

with which the GPC curve is interpreted to yield the molecular weight distribution of the whole polymer.

EXPERIMENTAL

The only experimental data needed for the evaluation of MWD and degree of LCB by either of the above procedures are the measured solution viscosity, GPC trace, and calibration equation for the GPC columns in use.

Solution Viscosity

Theoretically, intrinsic viscosity, $[\eta]$, should be used in the above calculations, but in practice, inherent viscosity,

$$\{\eta\} = \frac{\ln \eta_{rel}}{\text{concn.}}$$

is used and considered equivalent to $[\eta]$ for the relatively low-viscosity branched whole polymers. Determination of $\{\eta\}$ is carried out in a 0.15% solution in TCB at 140°C, and the same solution is injected into the GPC. The accuracy of the solution viscosity value is important and so samples are usually run in duplicate and an automatic timer is now used for improved timing accuracy.

GPC Calibration

The GPC column systems are not permanent and may vary in their operational characteristics over a period of time, finally needing replacement. It is therefore essential to devise a reliable and effective calibration procedure if one is to derive a long-range reproducibility comparable with that obtainable in successive runs. Initial calibration of the GPC is established using National Bureau of Standards SRM 1475 linear polyethylene whole polymer standard and high molecular weight linear polyethylene fractions from preparative fractionation of broad-MWD resins. The details of the technique are given in the previous paper.[3] Routine calibration is achieved directly using a secondary standard, a broad-MWD, homogenized linear polyethylene, with known MWD as derived as part of the initial calibration experiment.[3] The universal calibration is derived mathematically by combining the Mark–Houwink relationship for PE in TCB at 140°C,

$$[\eta] = 3.95 \times 10^{-4} \, M_v{}^{0.726}$$

with the linear polyethylene calibration equation. This is also outlined in the previous paper.[3]

RESULTS AND DISCUSSION

Both the Ram and Miltz (R & M) and the Drott and Mendelson (D & M) methods of evaluating the raw GPC data were readily translated into appropriate computer programs. Each program incorporates a systematic search procedure in which changing values of b and c in the case of the R & M and λ in the D & M method were entered into the program loop. The set of values produces an initial calibration curve (count vs. molecular weight) in conjunction with the universal calibration from which an MWD is computed. This, in turn, is transposed into a viscosity distribution using the viscosity–molecular weight relationship from which the calibration curve was first obtained and an average value for $[\eta]$ is calculated. A binary search procedure is used, which is terminated when $[\eta]$-computed $= [\eta]$measured within less than 1%. The MWD data from this final loop are typed out, the MWD curve plotted out, and the various molecular weight

TABLE I
Description of Resins

	MI	Density	Resin type
SRM 1476	1.2	0.931	tubular reactor, low conversion resin: low degree of LCB
LDPE A	2.8	0.924	autoclave reactor, high conversion resin: high degree of LCB

TABLE II
Comparison of MWD Data for SRM 1476 Computed by Differing Methods

Technique	$M_n \times 10^{-4}$	$M_w \times 10^{-4}$	R	$[\eta]_{meas}$	$[\eta]_{comp}$	g'
Complete iterative analysis	2.19	8.47	3.87	0.85	1.33	0.64
Ram and Miltz	2.10	8.32	3.97	0.85	1.30	0.65
Drott and Mendelson	2.09	8.39	3.99	0.85	1.31	0.65

averages are calculated, together with a computed value for the solution viscosity that a linear polyethylene of the same MWD would exhibit ($[\eta]_{lin}$). The ratio of measured viscosity to the linear viscosity is called g' (i.e., $g' = [\eta]_{br}/[\eta]_{lin}$), and this is taken as a measure of the degree of LCB. As the degree of branching increases, the measured $[\eta]_{br}$ deviates further from the linear polyethylene value $[\eta]_{lin}$ and g' becomes smaller.

As indicated in the Introduction, the objective of the present studies is to determine whether either the R & M or D & M methods provide MWD data which are more realistic than those derived using a linear polyethylene calibration with correction for branching. Further, we would like to establish to what extent the rapid methods produce data equivalent to that derived completely experimentally using our complete iterative analysis. To provide a direct test of the rapid method, it was decided to compare the actual data produced for two test resins (Table I). The first, SRM 1476, was chosen as a simple resin with a relatively low level of branching and a narrow, symmetric MWD. The second, LDPE A, has been included as an example of a resin with a high degree of branching and a broad irregularly shaped MWD. This LDPE A sample is one in which the molecular weight dependence of branching is expected to be difficult to define by any simple relationship. This material should, therefore, provide a good test of the effectiveness of the two rapid analytic methods.

The complete iterative analysis technique was undertaken on both LDPE A and SRM 1476 to provide comparison data. More than usual care was taken to assure that the experimental data were accurate, and all fractions derived from the gradient elution fractionation were included in the analysis. The resulting data represent the best we can do with our complete iterative analysis method, and the molecular weight and MWD data should approximate very closely the true values. These data are listed in Tables II and III, where they are compared with those derived using the R & M and D & M methods. In addition, data were obtained for LDPE using a calibration derived using SRM 1476, with MWD determined by the iterative analysis method, as the GPC standard.

TABLE III
Comparison of MWD Data for LDPE A Computed by Differing Methods

Technique	$M_n \times 10^{-4}$	$M_w \times 10^{-4}$	R	$[\eta]_{meas}$	$[\eta]_{comp}$	g'
Complete iterative analysis	1.85	34.7	18.8	0.88	3.12	0.31
SRM 1476 Standard	1.69	19.1	11.3	0.88	2.16	0.45
Ram and Miltz	1.85	37.5	20.2	0.88	3.20	0.28
Drott and Mendelson	1.95	33.1	17.0	0.88	3.04	0.29

TABLE IV

MWD and Branching Data for a Series of LDPE Resins Computed by Differing Methods

Resin	Iterative analysis				R & M method				D & M method				
	$M_n \times 10^{-4}$	$M_w \times 10^{-4}$	R	g'	$M_n \times 10^{-4}$	$M_w \times 10^{-4}$	R	g'	$M_n \times 10^{-4}$	$M_w \times 10^{-4}$	R	g'	$\lambda \times 10^4$
SRM 1476	2.19	8.47	3.87	0.64	2.10	8.32	3.97	0.65	2.09	8.39	3.99	0.65	0.25
LDPE I	2.01	11.9	5.92	0.52	2.03	11.0	5.43	0.54	2.04	11.1	5.42	0.54	0.63
LDPE II	2.41	11.8	4.98	0.50	2.22	11.4	5.12	0.53	2.25	11.4	5.07	0.53	0.73
LDPE III	1.98	6.89	3.48	0.69	1.88	7.57	4.02	0.65	1.88	7.61	4.04	0.65	0.50
LDPE IV	2.53	15.1	5.97	0.50	2.40	17.5	7.32	0.46	2.42	17.5	7.23	0.46	0.69
LDPE V	2.06	18.0	9.0	0.38	1.82	18.1	9.93	0.38	1.86	17.6	9.42	0.39	1.09
LDPE A	1.85	34.7	18.8	0.31	1.85	37.5	20.2	0.28	1.95	33.1	17.0	0.29	1.14

Complete Iterative Method Versus SRM 1476 Standard

The SRM 1476 branched polyethylene standard MWD data were determined experimentally using the complete iterative method, and so the same data apply to both methods of analysis. Good agreement would be expected when applying the two methods of evaluation to any resin with a relatively low level of LCB. In the case of application to a highly branched resin like LDPE A, however, the use of the SRM 1476 standard calibration should considerably underestimate the level of LCB and hence the breadth of MWD. The data in Table II indicate that this is indeed the case and confirm that the use of the SRM 1476 calibration standard is not a good method for evaluating GPC data for highly branched resins.

Ram and Miltz Versus Drott and Mendelson Method

The R & M method was proposed as a possible improvement over the D & M method inasmuch as it is not confined by the assumption of constant degree of LCB, λ, as a function of molecular weight. It is of interest to see if the former method is significantly better in practice. When applied to the low degree of LCB resin, SRM 1476, it is clear from the data in Table II that both methods lead to essentially the same answer. Surprisingly, the same is true in the case of the highly branched resin, LDPE A, with the only significant difference being noted in the value of the weight-average molecular weight M_w. It is observed that the R & M method results in a slightly higher M_w value than does the D & M method (see Table III).

The tendency for R & M to give higher M_w values has been confirmed with other types of resin, but essentially it only occurs at high levels of LCB. In general, however, it is clear that both methods provide essentially the same MWD data. It is obvious also that either method is an improvement over the use of the SRM 1476, as both are sensitive to the differing levels of LCB present in the differing resins.

R & M and D & M Methods Versus Complete Iterative Analysis Method

The final test of any rapid method is a check on how close the computed MWD and degree of LCB data are to actual data. In the present instance, we assume that our complete iterative analysis successfully approximates the true molecular weight values, and so a comparison has been made of the data from the complete analysis with those derived by the R & M and D & M methods. The data are compared in Tables II and III for SRM 1476 and LDPE A and in Table IV for a short series of differing resin types.

The results for LDPE A prove extremely encouraging, as can be seen in Table III. Both R & M and D & M methods give average molecular weight data which are in excellent agreement with those derived by the complete iterative method. The ability of both R & M and D & M methods to provide data which are very close to those produced by the complete iterative method is further illustrated by the data in Table IV. Here, the degree of LCB as indicated by g' is in good agreement among the three sets of data. Also, the λ values computed by the D & M method and shown in the last column of Table IV are, as one would expect, consistent with the variation of g'. Increasing λ corresponds to decreasing g'.

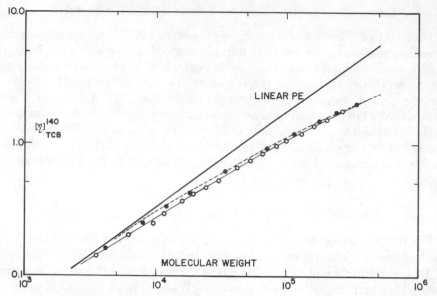

Fig. 1. Comparison of $[\eta]$-M relationship for SRM 1476: (- - -) R & M; (●) D & M; (O) iterative.

The results so far presented suggest that either the R & M or D & M technique may be used to provide realistic MWD and degree of LCB data for most branched polyethylenes. However, the D & M method, in particular, has been criticized[9] from the point of view that its basic assumption (that the degree of LCB, λ, is constant as a function of molecular weight) is not always true in practice. To provide a more detailed comparison of the methods which may throw some light on this question, data have been expressed in terms of the solution viscosity-

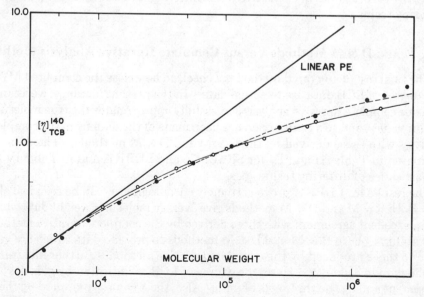

Fig. 2. Comparison of $[\eta]$-M relationship for LDPE A: (- - -) R & M; (●) D & M; (O) iterative.

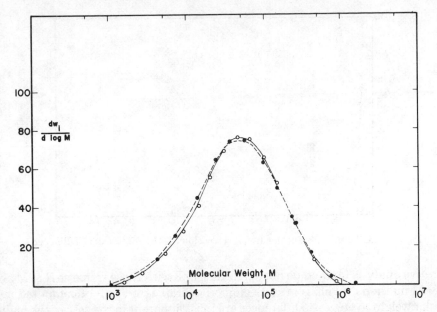

Fig. 3. Comparison of MWD curves for SRM 1476:   (- - -) R & M; (●) D & M; (○) iterative.

molecular weight relationships (Figs. 1 and 2) and complete MWD curves (Figs. 3 and 4).

From the solution viscosity–molecular weight relationships, particularly those given in Figure 2, one is led to conclude the following:

(i) The data computed by both the R & M and D & M methods are practically identical.   This is surprising in light of the quite different assumptions associated with the two methods.

(ii) The solution viscosity–molecular weight relationships obtained from the

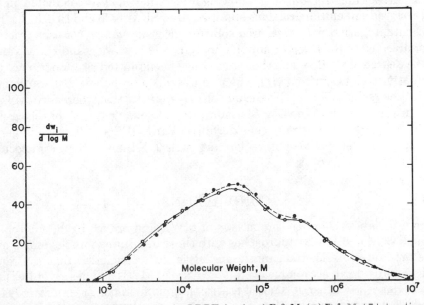

Fig. 4. Comparison of MWD curves for LDPE A.   (- - -) R & M; (●) D & M; (○) iterative.

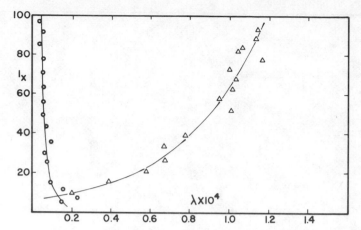

Fig. 5. Distribution of branching frequency within SRM 1476 (○) and LDPE A (△).

iterative analysis method do not agree very well with those from the R & M and D & M methods. This is in spite of good overall agreement of computed molecular weight averages. Differences are most apparent in the case of the highly branched resin LDPE A, in the higher molecular weight regions.

This latter observation is consistent with the view that in the case of LDPE A, the relative degree of LCB (g' or λ) increases with increase in molecular weight. This, in turn, suggests that, although reasonable values for average molecular weight and degree of LCB are forthcoming from the rapid evaluation methods, they give no direct indication of the specific nature (i.e., degree of LCB) of the individual polymer species present in the whole polymer. This should not be surprising in light of the small amount of informational input to the computer when making the molecular weight calculations.

The inability of the D & M method to describe the individual polymer species can be further illustrated by the following interesting analysis conducted on the series of gradient elution fractions obtained from SRM 1476 and LDPE A. The GPC data, together with measured solution viscosity values, for each fraction were subjected to the D & M computer analysis. This provides individual values for the degree of LCB, λ, and those data have been plotted as a function of the cumulative weight per cent (I_x), which represents a branching distribution for each of the resins (Fig. 5). The results clearly indicate that whereas SRM 1476 conforms quite well to the D & M assumption of constancy of λ, in the case of LDPE A λ is observed to vary considerably. For LDPE A, λ is much larger in the higher molecular weight region (at high I_x) than at lower molecular weights.

CONCLUSIONS

From the above detailed comparison of MWD and branching data obtained by the R & M and D & M approaches with those determined by the more complete method of Wild, Ranganath, and Ryle, it is concluded that the rapid methods provide an acceptable overall measure of MWD and degree of LCB for polyethylenes. Further, it is noted that both rapid methods give essentially the same computed data, and thus one would prefer the Drott and Mendelson method over that of Ram and Miltz on the basis of the reduced computer time needed for the former method. A value of λ is also obtained directly as an average degree of LCB by the D & M method, which is an additional convenience. For routine analysis of branched polyethylene resins, the D & M method is preferable to the complete iterative analysis method, not only on the basis of the reduced time and effort needed, but also because the experimental simplicity of the D & M approach leads to extremely reliable and reproducible data. This, of course, assumes that the GPC calibration is properly derived and monitored. However, wherever it is the intent to pursue detailed branching structure studies for polyethylenes, the more detailed methods of analysis are essential as it is clear that the D & M assumption of constancy of λ within any particular resin is not true for many polyethylene types.

References

1. L. Wild, R. Ranganath, and T. Ryle, *J. Polym. Sci.,* **9A-2,** 2137 (1971).
2. L. Wild and R. Guliana, *J. Polym. Sci. A-2,* **5,** 1087 (1967).
3. A. Barlow, L. Wild, and R. Ranganath, *J. Appl. Polym. Sci.,* **21,** 3319 (1977).
4. Z. Grubisic, H. Benoit, and P. Rempp, *J. Polym. Sci.,* **5B,** 753 (1967).
5. B. H. Zimm and R. W. Kilb, *J. Polym. Sci.,* **37,** 19 (1959).
6. G. Kraus and C. Stacy, *J. Polym. Sci.,* **10A-2,** 657 (1972).
7. D. Goedhart and A. Opschoor, *J. Polym. Sci.,* **8A-2,** 1227 (1970).
8. E. E. Drott and R. A. Mendelson, *J. Polym. Sci.,* **8A-2,** 1361 (1970).
9. J. Cote and M. Shida, *J. Polym. Sci.,* **9A-2,** 421 (1971).
10. A. Ram and J. Miltz, *J. Appl. Polym. Sci.,* **15,** 2639 (1971).
11. B. H. Zimm and W. H. Stockmayer, *J. Chem. Phys.,* **17,** 130 (1949).

Received September 22, 1976
Revised October 19, 1976

JOURNAL OF APPLIED POLYMER SCIENCE   VOL. 21, 3345–3354 (1977)

Influence of Processing Parameters and Molecular Weight on the Mechanical Properties of PVC

D. M. SHINOZAKI, *Department of Mechanical Engineering, University of Manitoba, Winnipeg, Manitoba, Canada*, and K. WOO, J. VLACHOPOULOS, and A. HAMIELEC, *Department of Chemical Engineering, McMaster University, Hamilton, Ontario, Canada*

Synopsis

The role of a variety of processing parameters in determining the mechanical properties of solid PVC has been examined. Annealing pretreatment has been shown to increase both the yield stress and the modulus. It was found that the density of the material similarly increased as the annealing progressed, and when the density reached a limiting value, the yield stress and modulus also reached a limiting value. The molecular weight of the resin, as measured by its intrinsic viscosity, also affected the various mechanical properties measured. However, the yield stress increased while the modulus decreased as the molecular weight increased. This unusual behavior was thought to be a secondary effect. Finally, the addition of increasing amounts of stabilizer to the PVC resin resulted in an increase in modulus and a decrease in yield stress. This was consistent with a model for plastic deformation in which the stabilizer acted as small hard particles. The activation strain volume did not change with different concentrations of stabilizer, further supporting a model for a two-phase structure.

INTRODUCTION

Processing and Mechanical Properties

There has been increasing interest recently in the detailed deformation mechanisms in glassy polymers.[1-3] The accurate measurement of mechanical properties such as yield stress and modulus has, therefore, become important. In many cases, commercially obtained sheet material has been used for these measurements. However, the role of processing parameters in affecting the mechanical behavior of these materials has not always been reported. Parameters such as molecular weight, annealing pretreatment, and additive content may have a significant effect on the mechanical behavior. In careful studies related to deformation mechanisms, it is necessary to compare the processing parameters when comparing mechanical behavior.

Stabilization Behavior of PVC

Poly(vinyl chloride) (PVC) is one of the most important commercial plastics in use. It is chemically one of the least stable of the common polymers, and commercially obtained specimens must contain some additives needed to sta-

3345

bilize the molecules. The use of additives of many different types is common in plastics, but very little information has been presented about the role of these additives in their mechanical behavior. Various commercially obtained materials which have been used by investigators in the past have not necessarily contained the same additives. Studies of yield point and mechanisms of flow in glassy polymers, particularly where PVC is concerned, may be influenced by the type and quantity of heat stabilizer used.

PVC is subject to degradation by heat at temperatures above about 100°C. The stabilizer usually falls into one of several groups of compounds. For example, commonly used ones are (1) inorganic metal salts, (2) metallic soaps and salts of organic acid, (3) metal complexes, and (4) organotin compounds. The chemical reactions by which these compounds stabilize the plastic are not known with certainty.[4] However, it is generally agreed that the barium–cadmium salt complexes used in these studies serve three main functions. First, they react with the hydrogen chloride produced by the thermal degradation process. Secondly, they react with PVC molecules at points of deviation from the idealized structure to reduce the number of positions on the molecule where decomposition might easily initiate. Finally, they react with the molecule to interfere with the "zipper-like" decomposition of the molecule. It has been shown that the barium–cadmium complex does attach itself to the PVC molecules after milling.

The modification of the molecular architecture in this way is expected to affect the mechanical behavior of the solid plastic.

Molecular Weight

Molecular weight is one of the important parameters in processing polymers. Changes in molecular weight have a direct effect on the mechanical properties of the solid polymer.[5] However, the greatest changes in deformation behavior with molecular weight occur at low molecular weights, and the relatively minor changes at higher molecular weights typical of commercial PVC resins have not been examined previously. In addition, the combined influence of stabilizer content and molecular weight has not been studied.

Annealing

In processing polymers, annealing pretreatment has a significant influence on the mechanical behavior of the final solid.[6] Parameters such as yield stress and modulus are affected strongly by the temperature and time of annealing. This is generally well known in that mechanical studies of glassy polymers usually are preceded by some kind of annealing. The purpose behind this heat treatment is to standardize the initial "structure" of the polymer to eliminate this "structural" variable. The quantitative relationship between these mechanical parameters and the annealing pretreatment has never been elucidated in PVC.

EXPERIMENTAL

PVC resin was obtained from Esso Chemical Canada Limited. Four different grades with nominal intrinsic viscosities of 0.63, 0.86, 1.00, and 1.19 (dl/g, cyclohexanone at 30°C) were tested. Stearic acid was used as a lubricant, and Mark

99 as a stabilizer (a high-efficiency barium–cadmium complex solid). The stabilizer is manufactured by Argus Chemical Corporation of Brooklyn, New York.

The premix of resin, stabilizer, and lubricant was blended in a heated mortar and pestle at a temperature of about 85°C. The blended premix was compounded in a miniature mixing/injection molding machine. Specimens suitable for a standard tensile test were injection molded from the same machine at temperatures which were adjusted according to the melt viscosity of the material. The specimens were approximately $3/4$ in. long with a $5/16$ in. gauge length which was $1/16$ in. in diameter.

A series of specimens was annealed at 110°C for various times (5, 10, 20, 60, and 180 min). These were mechanically tested, and the parameters of interest were measured as a function of annealing time. In addition, the density was measured. From this, a consistent thermal pretreatment was derived for the subsequent test.[5]

The stabilizer content range which was tested was 2–6 parts per hundred resin by weight (phr). The lower limit was fixed by the minimum amount necessary for thermal stabilization. The upper limit was fixed by the difficulty encountered in processing higher concentrations.

The stearic acid lubricant concentration was 0.54 phr for all specimens. For each sample of given stabilizer content, five tensile specimens were molded and tested. The variation in yield stress over the five specimens at the same strain rate was less than 1%. All tests were performed at room temperature, 23° ± 2°C.

EXPERIMENTAL RESULTS

Annealing Pretreatment

As expected, the various parameters of interest changed in the early stages of annealing but reached a saturation value after some time of annealing (about 20 min at 110°C). Figures 1–3 show the change in tensile yield stress, tensile modulus, and elongation at fracture as a function of annealing time. The density of the material also shows dependence on annealing time (Fig. 4). After about 20 min, the density has increased by about 1.7%. All specimens contained 4.5 phr Mach 99 stabilizer. The results show that 20 min of annealing at 110°C should be sufficient to standardize the specimen microstructure for the subsequent tests.

In general, it is expected that annealing will affect the mechanical properties of glassy polymers. The thermomechanical processing of the polymer specimen introduces internal stresses into the material which are a result of the inhomogeneous structure. The subsequent annealing will relax the internal stresses, effectively removing some local inhomogeneities in the structure, regions of low density, or high defect concentration. The reduction in density of the specimen suggests this may occur over the first 20 min of annealing at 110°C. The removal of some of the inhomogeneities or regions of high defect concentration will affect the mechanical properties.[5] In general, it is expected that the regions of highest defect concentration will anneal out first, since the driving force is highest. These are the regions which would yield first according to either of the recently pos-

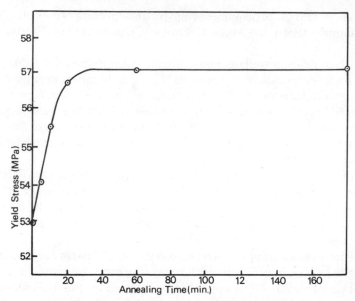

Fig. 1. Variation of tensile yield stress as a function of annealing time at 110°C. Stabilizer content 4.5 phr Mark 99.

tulated models for glassy flow.[4,5] Hence, the removal of these regions on annealing would result in an increase in yield stress and also in an increase in tensile modulus. The simultaneous saturation of density and these mechanical parameters are therefore consistent with both Argon's and Sternstein's views on plastic flow mechanisms.

Molecular Weight Dependence of Properties

Increases in nominal intrinsic viscosity (η) result in measurable changes in mechanical properties. The yield stress increases and the modulus decreases (Figs. 5 and 6). Changes in stabilizer content shifted each of the curves, but the shape of the curves remained similar.

There have been relatively few studies of the influence of molecular weight upon the mechanical properties of glassy polymers.[5] Both modulus and yield stress change only slightly with molecular weight at those values of molecular weight typical of commercially obtainable polymers. These relationships between the mechanical parameters and molecular weight appear to depend upon the type of polymer examined.

The changes in yield stress seen in PVC in these experiments amount to a negligible amount (approximately 4%), in agreement with the small changes seen in other polymers. However, the tensile modulus decreases with increasing molecular weight by a significant amount (approximately 15%). In most polymers, the modulus varies with molecular weight only at very low molecular weights.[6] The tensile moduli of polystyrene, poly(dichlorostyrene), and poly-(methyl methacrylate) (PMMA) have been shown to be almost independent of molecular weight at typically high molecular weights. Polycarbonate may show a slight decrease in modulus as molecular weight increases, while the modulus of PMMA increases slightly with log $\overline{M}_V$. In a study of plasticized PVC,[7] Young's modulus was constant for $\overline{M}_w > 5 \times 10^4$, and it decreased rapidly when $\overline{M}_w$ was reduced below this value.

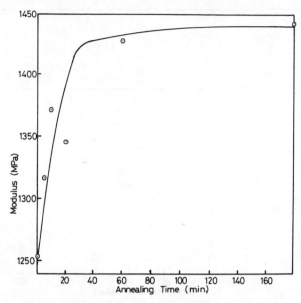

Fig. 2. Variation of tensile modulus as a function of annealing time at 110°C. Stabilizer content 4.5 phr Mark 99.

As $\overline{M}_w$ increases, it is expected that the modulus should increase if it changes at all. The decreasing modulus can be best rationalized as a secondary effect. This may arise from a number of causes, one of which is the degree of syndiotacticity in the molecules. If this varies with $\overline{M}_w$ as a result of the polymerization conditions, then the degree of crystallinity in the PVC also changes. The modulus is then the composite modulus of a two-phase material, depending on $\overline{M}_w$ only indirectly as the syndiotacticity varies.

The final parameter of interest is the nominal ultimate tensile strength (UTS), which is the maximum load reached in the tensile test, divided by the initial cross-sectional area. The change in the nominal UTS is to be expected. The

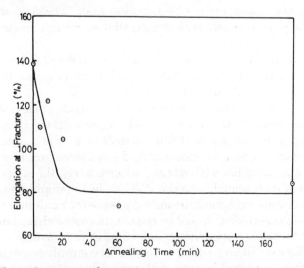

Fig. 3. Elongation at fracture as a function of annealing time at 110°C. Stabilizer content 4.5 phr Mark 99.

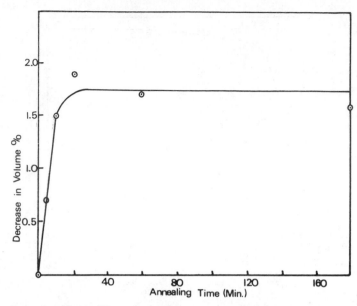

Fig. 4. Change in specific volume with annealing time.

higher $\overline{M}_w$ material will have a higher elongation to fracture, which implies a larger strain hardening capacity. In amorphous polymers, one work hardening mechanism is orientation hardening. The greater the elongation which a given specimen can withstand, the greater the degree of orientation in that specimen before failure. Hence, the higher $\overline{M}_w$ specimens will elongate further and be more highly oriented on a molecular scale. The UTS is, therefore, higher in these specimens.

Stabilizer Content

Figures 7 and 8 show the effect of changes in stabilizer content on the tensile yield stress and tensile modulus. The data presented here are for PVC resin with a nominal intrinsic viscosity of $\eta = 0.63$ and $\eta = 1.00$. The yield stress decreases and the modulus increases with increasing stabilizer content over a range of strain rates.

There are two distinct effects which might be expected from the addition of a nonpolymeric substance such as a barium–cadmium complex. It depends upon the distribution of the additive on a molecular scale.

If the stabilizer is distributed through the compounded plastic on a molecular scale and attaches itself chemically to the PVC molecule,[7,8] then the stabilizer molecule would primarily act to stiffen the molecule. The stabilizer molecules would act as branches, and the modulus and yield stress would simultaneously increase with increasing branch content. Alternatively, the effect of the greater concentration of such branches to the PVC molecule would be to increase the free volume and therefore simultaneously decrease the modulus and yield stress. In any case, the general effect would be the simultaneous change in modulus and yield stress in the same sense, either increasing or decreasing.

If the stabilizer is distributed in the form of second-phase particles in a PVC matrix, the effect expected is quite different. The dispersion of small, hard particles in the PVC matrix would result in an increase in modulus of the com-

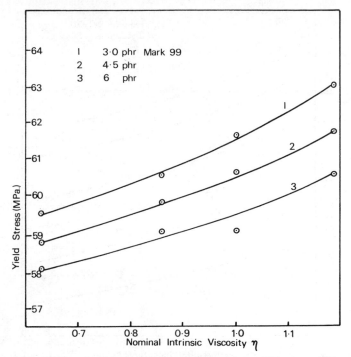

Fig. 5. Change in yield stress with nominal intrinsic viscosity at different stabilizer contents.

posite material with increasing concentration of second-phase particles. However, the yield stress will decrease. According to models for deformation in glassy polymers,[1,2] both dilatational and shear mechanisms of flow are initiated at points of stress concentration. Structurally, these are not clearly defined but

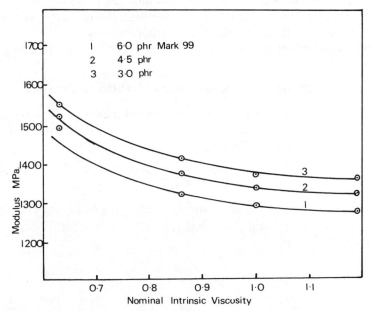

Fig. 6. Change in tensile modulus with nominal intrinsic viscosity at different stabilizer contents.

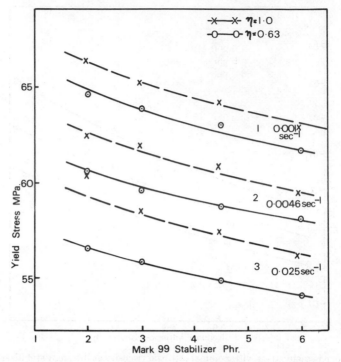

Fig. 7. Effect of stabilizer content on tensile yield stress at different strain rates for two different viscosity resins.

obviously refer to any local inhomogeneities in density or stiffness. The presence of a dispersed second-phase results in local inhomogeneities which act as stress concentrators. Such local stress concentrations are necessary to activate the local shear processes which form the microcavities, the precursor to the crazes.[2] The changes in modulus and yield stress with increasing stabilizer content are, therefore, consistent with the stabilizer acting as a dispersed second phase.

Deformation Mechanisms and Stabilizer Content

The influence of stabilizers on the mechanical properties can be examined directly by measuring the activation parameters of plastic flow. If we assume an activated rate process for flow,[9] the strain rate of the form

$$\dot{\epsilon} = \dot{\epsilon}_c \exp\left(-\frac{\Delta F}{\kappa T}\right)$$

where $\dot{\epsilon}_c \equiv$ fastest attainable strain rate, $\Delta F \equiv$ standard free energy of activation, $\kappa =$ Boltzmann constant, and $T =$ temperature, where the tensile strain volume of activation is given by

$$\Omega_\sigma = -\left(\frac{\partial \Delta F}{\partial \sigma}\right)_{T,P}$$

$$= \kappa T \left(\frac{\partial \ln \dot{\epsilon}}{\partial \sigma}\right)_{T,P}$$

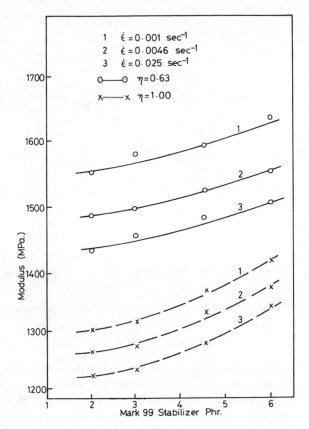

Fig. 8. Effect of stabilizer content on tensile modulus at different strain rates for two different viscosity resins.

The term Ω_σ is the strain volume of the reaction, or the local additional tensile strain produced in an activation process, integrated through the specimen.[9] This remains constant over the range of strain rates used (Fig. 9).

However, for increasing molecular weight (increasing viscosity η), the tensile strain volume of activation increases. This suggests that the molecular size has a direct influence on the yielding process—larger molecules require a larger activation strain volume. In addition, stabilizer content changes do not affect the activation process. The implication is that changes in stabilizer content do not substantially affect the flow process in yielding. If the primary role of the stabilizer were to attach itself to the polymer molecule and thereby affect the yielding process, then different concentrations of stabilizer should affect the activation volume for yielding. Since they do not, the role of stabilizer additives in affecting the yielding process is more likely that of second-phase particles.

The changes in yield stress, modulus, and tensile strain volume of activation are, therefore, consistent with a model that distributes stabilizer as a second-phase particle in the PVC matrix.

For PVC with nominal intrinsic viscosity of $\eta = 1.00$, the tensile strain activation volume is approximately $\Omega_\sigma = 1.8 \times 10^{-21}$ cm^3, while for $\eta = 0.63$, $\Omega_\sigma = 1.5 \times 10^{-21}$ cm^3. These agree approximately with the typical values reported by Li.[9]

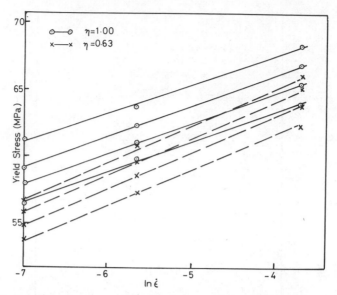

Fig. 9. Effect of strain rate on yield stress for two different viscosity resins.

CONCLUSIONS

It is clear that processing parameters such as molecular weight, thermal pretreatment, and additive content play a significant role in determining the mechanical behavior of glassy polymers such as PVC. In any discussion of mechanical properties, it is important that the material used in tests be prepared in a consistent manner which takes such factors into account. In particular, it is expected than an examination of deformation mechanisms would be affected by these variables.

The authors would like to thank Dr. J. Changfoot of Esso Chemical Canada who kindly provided material and advice in these experiments. The mechanical tests were performed in the Metallurgy Department of McMaster University using facilities generously provided by Professor David Embury.

References

1. S. S. Sternstein and F. A. Myers, *The Solid State of Polymers*, P. H. Geil, E. Baer, and Y. Wada, Eds., Marcel Dekker, New York, 1974, p. 539.

2. A. S. Argon, *ibid.*, p. 573.

3. A. N. Gent, *ibid.*, p. 597.

4. J. V. Koleski and L. H. Wartman, *Poly(vinyl Chloride)*, Gordon and Breach, New York, 1969.

5. J. R. Martin, J. F. Johnson, and A. R. Cooper, *J. Macromol. Sci. Rev., Macromol. Chem.*, **C8**, 57 (1972).

6. T. E. Brady and G. S. Y. Yeh, *J. Appl. Phys.*, **42**, 4622 (1971).

7. A. H. Frye and R. W. Horst, *J. Polym. Sci.*, **45**, 1 (1960).

8. A. H. Frye and R. W. Horst, *J. Polym. Sci.*, **40**, 419 1959.

9. J. C. M. Li, C. A. Pampillo, and L. A. Davis, *Deformation and Fracture of High Polymers*, H. H. Kausch, J. A. Hassell, and R. I. Jaffee, Eds., Plenum Press, New York, 1973, p. 239.

Received July 30, 1976
Revised October 21, 1976

JOURNAL OF APPLIED POLYMER SCIENCE   VOL. 21, 3355–3365 (1977)

Benzoyl Peroxide-Induced Graft Polymerization of 2-Methyl-5-Vinylpyridine Onto Polyester/Wool Blend

S. H. ABDEL-FATTAH, S. E. SHALABY, E. A. ALLAM, and A. HEBEISH, *Textile Research Division, National Research Center, Cairo, Egypt*

Synopsis

Graft polymerization of 2-methyl-5-vinylpyridine (MVP) onto polyester/wool blended fabric was carried out using benzoyl peroxide as initiator. The graft polymerization reaction was conducted under a variety of conditions. The graft yield increased by increasing benzoyl peroxide concentration from 0.559 mmole/l. to 1.657 mmole/l. Further increase in benzoyl peroxide concentration (i.e., up to 2.795 mmole/l.) decreased grafting. Increasing the MVP concentration from 4% to 10% caused a significant enhancement in grafting. The same held true for raising the polymerization temperature within the range of 65°–85°C. The grafting reaction proceeded initially at a fast rate and decreased with time to a slower rate. The grafted samples showed improved dyeability toward acid dye, increased density, and decreased moisture regain as compared with the untreated blend. Furthermore, a tentative mechanism for initiation of grafting was suggested.

INTRODUCTION

Chemical modification of wool via grafting polymerization can be achieved through either physical or chemical activation of wool.[1-3] Subjecting wool to high-energy radiation[3-8] or low-energy radiation in the presence and absence of sensitizers[6,9-14] produces wool macroradicals which are capable of initiating grafting. Similar wool radicals can be brought about by the action of redox systems,[15-19] ceric ion,[20,21] periodate ion,[22] acetonyl(acetonato) copper(II)–trichloroacetic acid complex,[23-27] potassium permanganate,[28,29] benzoyl peroxide,[30] dimethylaniline–benzyl chloride mixture,[31] thiourea in acid medium,[32] and other redox system such as Fe^{3+}–thiourea,[33] di-*tertiary*-butyl peroxide–thiourea,[34] and hydrogen peroxide–thiourea.[35] Creation of free radicals on the wool backbone through chain transfer has also been possible.[36]

Though much of these studies have been devoted to the kinetics of grafting, yet a substantial amount of information about the physicomechanical properties as well as dyeability of the grafted wool is available.[1-3,6,37] Relatively little information, however, is available regarding the kinetics of polymerization and the modification effect on polyester, i.e., poly(ethylene terephthalate), though investigations on high-energy and ultraviolet radiation of this material have been carried out in the presence and absence of vinyl monomers.[38-47] Chemical methods have also been used to initiate vinyl graft polymerization onto polyester.[48-56] It should be emphasized that in both the radiation and chemical methods of grafting, the homopolymer of the vinyl monomer is to be expected, but often can be suppressed by suitable additives.[57-60] An improvement in dyeability elevation of melting point, and accentuation of antistatic properties of polyester could be achieved by grafting the latter with acrylic acid.[61] Polyester copolymerized with 2-vinylpyridine could also be dyed with acid dyes.[62]

The aim of the present work was to study the graft polymerization of MVP on polyester/wool blended fabric. The polymerization was initiated by benzoyl peroxide in aqueous medium. Variation in properties such as moisture regain, density, and dyeability of the grafted blend were evaluated.

EXPERIMENTAL

Materials

Merino wool fibers were purified by Soxhlet extraction with acetone for 24 hr, followed by washing with cold, distilled water and air drying.

Poly(ethylene terephthalate) fibers and fabrics, kindly supplied by Hoechst, 1.2 den/40 mm (cotton type), were purified by Soxhlet extraction with methanol for 24 hr, followed by washing with cold, distilled water and air drying.

Wool fabric and polyester/wool blended fabric (50:50), kindly supplied by Misr El-Mehala El-Kobra Company, were purified by a mild scouring treatment with Lissapol NX (Ciba) for 30 min at 50°C followed by washing for 30 min with cold, distilled water and air drying.

2-Methyl-5-vinyl pyridine (MVP) was pure-grade chemical and freshly distilled (75°C/13 mm Hg) before use.

Benzoyl peroxide was freshly prepared according to the method of Vanino and Herzer.[63] Kiton Fast Red B1 (Ciba), C.I., 17045, was used.

Grafting Procedure

Graft copolymerization was carried out under atmospheric oxygen in a 100-ml stoppered Erlenmeyer flask. The sample (0.5 g) was introduced into a 50-ml aqueous solution containing the monomer and the emulsifying agent (Emulsogen GG-Hoechst). The flask was immediately stoppered and placed in a thermostated water bath for a certain period till the required temperature was reached, and the initiator was then added. The reaction was allowed to proceed for different periods of time. The sample was washed with distilled water and Soxhlet extracted with methyl alcohol and dried. Extraction with alcohol and drying was repeated to constant weight. The graft yield was calculated on the basis of constant dry weight, determined by storing the substrate over phosphorus pentoxide at room temperature.

% graft yield

$$= \frac{\text{dry weight of grafted sample} - \text{dry weight of original sample}}{\text{dry weight of original sample}} \times 100$$

RESULTS AND DISCUSSION

The effect of initiator and monomer concentration and reaction time on the graft yield was investigated to discover the optimal conditions for grafting. Presented below are the results obtained along with appropriate discussion.

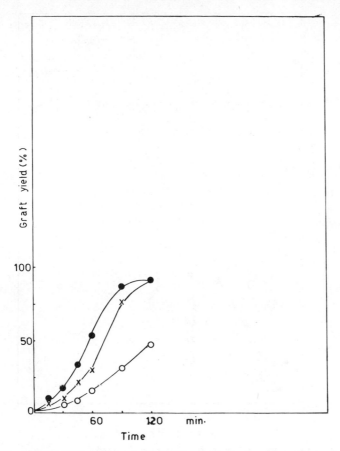

Fig. 1. Effect of benzoyl peroxide concentration on the rate of grafting. Benzoyl peroxide concentration: (O) 0.559 mmole/l.; (X) 1.657 mmole/l.; (●) 2.795 mmole/l.; reaction medium, 10% MVP, temperature 75°C, material-to-liquor ratio, 1:100.

Effect of Initiator Concentration

Figure 1 shows the effect of benzoyl peroxide concentration on the graft yield. As is evident, the graft yield increases with increasing benzoyl peroxide concentration up to 1.657 mmole/l. Further increase in benzoyl peroxide concentration lowers grafting significantly. The initial slow rates of grafting at lower benzoyl peroxide concentration could be attributed to oxygen inhibition, whereas the higher graft yield obtained upon increasing the benzoyl peroxide concentration is direct evidence that the benzoyl peroxide free radical participates in the initiation of the graft. On the other hand, depression of grafting when using higher benzoyl peroxide concentrations provides evidence that benzoyl peroxide radicals may be involved in the termination reaction similar to other initiating system.[54] However, it is possible that when the concentration of benzoyl peroxide was increased beyond the maximum amount, homopolymerization rate increased, and therefore there was a decrease in the graft yield. Indeed, a tremendous amount of homopolymer formation was observed upon use of higher amounts of benzoyl peroxide.

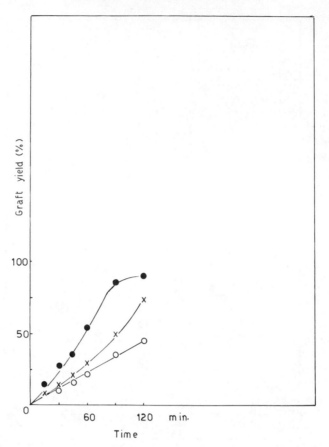

Fig. 2. Graft yield as a function of MVP concentration. MVP concentration: (○) 4%; (X) 6%; (●) 10%; benzoyl peroxide concentration, 1.675 mmole/l.; temperature, 75°C, material-to-liquor ratio, 1:100.

Effect of Monomer Concentration

The effect of MVP concentration on the graft yield was evaluated in a series of polymerizations in which three monomer concentrations, viz., 4%, 6%, and 10%, were used. Results are shown in Figure 2. It is clear that increasing the monomer concentration from 4% to 6% causes an outstanding enhancement in the graft yield, particularly when the grafting reaction is allowed to proceed for longer periods. The same holds true for 10% monomer concentration, but the polymerization levels off with time.

Effects of Temperature

Figure 3 shows that increasing the polymerization temperature from 65°C to 75°C enhances the rate of grafting significantly. Further enhancement in the grafting rate could be achieved by raising the temperature to 85°C. Raising the polymerization temperature would be expected to cause (a) creation of more active species, i.e., free radicals, in the reaction medium due to faster decomposition rate of benzoyl peroxide; (b) enhancement of the swellability of the blend; (c) increasing the anisotropic swelling of the wool component in the blend with

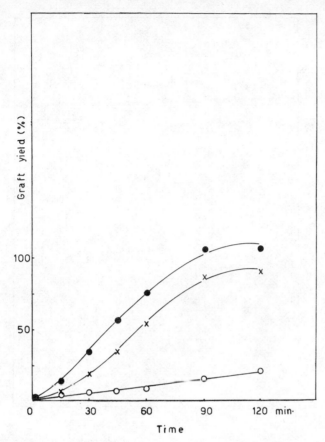

Fig. 3. Effect of temperature on grafting: (O) 65°C; (X) 75°C; (●) 85°C. MVP concentration 10%, benzoyl peroxide concentration, 1.657 mmole/l.; material-to-liquor ratio, 1:100.

resulting scission of the side linkages to bring about additional free radicals on the wool backbone; (d) increased mobility of the monomer molecules; (e) higher rate of monomer diffusion from the reaction medium to the blend; (f) possible reaction between the growing homopolymer chain with the substrate and/or the substrate macroradicals; (g) enhancement in the rate of initiation and propagation of the graft. The net effect of these factors is certainly increased grafting.

Based on the results of Figure 3, the apparent activation energy was calculated. For this purpose, we used an Arrhenius equation by plotting $\log R_p$ versus $1/T$ (Fig. 4). The apparent energy of activation calculated from the slope of the line is about 5.5 kcal/mole, which is of the same order as that obtained for the usual redox polymerization.[64,65]

Effect of Reaction Time

The effect of reaction time on the graft yield may be realized from Figures 1, 2, and 3. Increase in reaction time is accompanied by a significant enhancement in the graft yield. However, at higher temperatures, the enhancement in the latter caused by the initial periods of the reaction is much greater than that

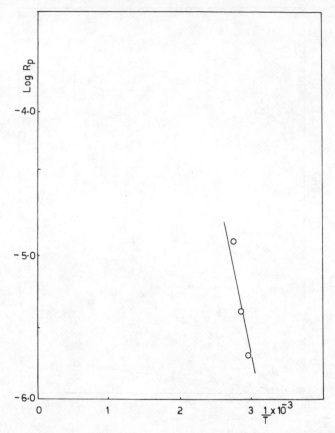

Fig. 4. Logarithm of initial rate of graft polymerization R_p of MVP vs $1/T$:   MVP concentration, 10%; benzoyl peroxide concentration, 1.657 mmole/l.; material-to-liquor ratio, 1:100.

brought about by prolonging duration during the later stages of polymerization. That is, the grafting reaction proceeds initially at a fast rate and decreases with time to a slower rate.   This could be associated with depletion in monomer and initiator concentrations as well as reduction in the available active centers on the substrate (blend) backbone as the reaction proceeds.

Tentative Mechanism for Initiation of Grafting

In the foregoing section, it has been shown that considerable graft formation occurred on polyester/wool blended fabric when MVP was polymerized in the presence of this blend.   That grafting took place on both components of the blend is clearly shown in Figure 5, where fibers and fabrics of 100% polyester and 100% wool proved to be amenable for grafting.   However, wool is much more susceptible to grafting than polyester.   This is rather expected, since wool contains many possible centers for free-radical formation such as thiol, amine, hydroxyl, etc.   Beside this, wool acquires an open structure and good swelling properties which facilates diffusion of both monomer and initiator.   In contrast, polyester is highly crystalline, markedly hydrophobic and contains only few types of centers for free-radical formation.

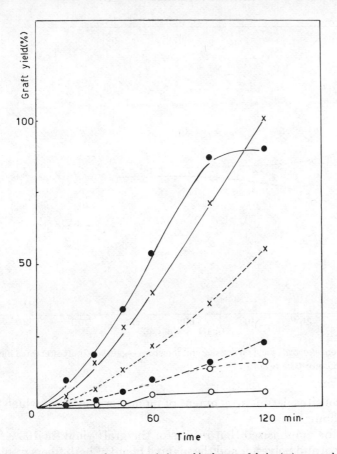

Fig. 5. Grafting onto various substrates: (O) wool/polyester fabric; (●) manual blend of wool and polyester fibers; (X) wool fabric; (X) wool fibers; (O) polyester fabric; (O) polyester fiber; MVP concentration, 10%; benzoyl peroxide, 1.657 mmole/l.; temperature, 75°C; material-to-liquor ratio, 1:100.

Hence, introduction of free radicals into wool may be accomplished by (a) direct hydrogen abstraction from the wool molecules by the primary free-radical species ($C_6H_5COO\cdot$) brought about by decomposition of benzoyl peroxide or by the secondary free-radical species ($C_6H_5\cdot$) caused by decomposition of the primary radical species, and (b) homolytic scission of the disulfide bonds through anisotropic swelling of wool at higher temperature used and/or under the influence of the initiator employed. Addition of the wool radical to the double bond of the monomer results in a covalent bond between wool and monomer, with creation of a free radical on this monomer which is capable of propagating a chain by subsequent addition of monomer molecules.

In case of polyesters, active centers seem to be created by either direct hydrogen abstraction or by oxidizing the polymer to hydroperoxide at several points along the chain in a random manner. The hydroperoxide decomposes into the active form at high temperature to produce ultimately macroradicals one of which may be represented as

$$CO \quad C_6H_4-CO-O-\overset{\cdot}{C}II-CII_2-$$

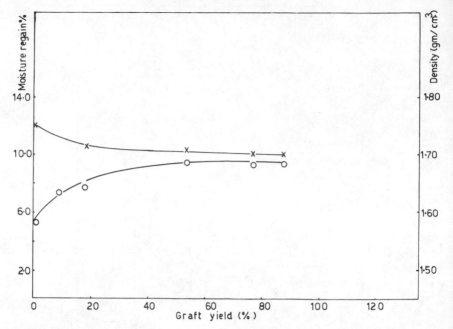

Fig. 6. Influence of graft yield on density and moisture regain % of polyester/wool blended fabric:
(O) density; (X) moisture regain %.

These radical sites permit attachment of monomer molecules which may grow
into short chains.

It should be emphasized that results of the graft yield for 100% fibers and
fabrics of wool and polyester and the manual blend of both fibers would not give
a means to show to what extent each component contributes to the graft yield
on the polyester/wool blended fabric (Fig. 5), since the substrates used have
different histories as well as different constructions with respect to fabrics. But
the data justify the aim which they were designed for. That is, wool and polyester
can be graft copolymerized with MVP by benzoyl peroxide under the conditions
used in this investigation.

Properties of the Grafted Blend

Polyester/wool fabrics of varying graft add-on of MVP were prepared and
evaluated for moisture regain, density, and dyeability.

Moisture Regain. Moisture regain of the grafted fabrics was determined
by allowing the samples to attain equilibrium moisture at 25°C and 65% relative
humidity. Figure 6 shows the moisture regain versus graft yield. At a graft yield
of ca. 20%, the moisture regain decreases from 12% to 10.5%. Increasing the graft
yield up to 90% causes only little further decrease in the moisture regain. The
decrease in moisture regain is unequivocally due to the introduction of hydrophobic poly(methylvinylpyridine) into the substrate. Beside blocking some of
the water sorptive sites, particularly in the wool component, the polymer produces a hydrophobic environment inside the blend. The point that increasing
the graft yield does not have a significant effect on moisture regain suggest either
(a) that the graft yield represents few polymer chains with high molecular weight

TABLE I
Dye Exhaustion by Polyester/Wool Blended Fabric
During Dyeing with Acid Dye Kiton Fast Red BL (CiBA)

Graft yield, %	% Exhaustion after								
	0 min	5 min	10 min	15 min	20 min	30 min	40 min	50 min	60 min
0	0	22.3	45.5	58.3	70.9	77.5	89.1	93.1	96.4
8.1	0	62.5	71.6	81.1	89.5	94.6	100	100	100
15.2	0	65.2	73.5	81.8	90.9	95.5	100	100	100
21.5	0	67.4	74.8	83.3	92.3	96.4	100	100	100
45.7	0	70.2	76.3	84.7	93.1	96.8	100	100	100
57.7	0	73.8	77.8	86.2	94.2	99.0	100	100	100

or (b) that grafting of higher levels brings about the opening of the substrate to an extent that outweighs the shift toward hydrophobic nature.

Density. The density of the samples was determined by a density gradient column. The liquids used to prepare the gradient column were xylene (density = 0.886) and carbon tetrachloride (density = 1.595). Figure 6 shows the effect of grafting on the density of the blended fabrics. Obviously, the density of the fabric increases with increasing the graft yield up to ca. 50%. Therefore, increasing the graft yield has no significant effect on the density. The increase in density could be associated with location of the graft polymer within the noncrystalline regions of the fiber, thus filling the voids present in the amorphous regions.

Dyeability. The grafted blended fabrics were dyed with the acid dye Kiton Fast Red B1(CIBA), C.I.17045, at 100°C using a material-to-liquor ratio of 1:100. The dyeing bath was prepared so as to give 5% shade in the presence of acetic acid (3%) and Glauber salt (3%). Dyeing was carried out for different lengths of time varying from 5 to 60 min. It was observed that the depth of shade of the grafted and the untreated fabrics increases with increasing duration of dyeing. However, the grafted fabrics showed higher depth of shade than the untreated fabric, though the depth of shade was independent of the magnitude of grafting. The loss in concentration of the dye bath was determined colorimetrically, and the amount of the dye on the fiber was calculated. The results are shown in Table I. The results agree with the observation of increasing depth of shade with increasing duration of dyeing as well as the point that the grafted samples acquire higher depth of shade than the untreated fabric.

References

1. C. S. Whewell, *Text. Progr.* **2**(3), 1 (1970).
2. L. C. Watt, *J. Macromol. Sci.*, **C-5**, 175 (1970).
3. H. L. Needles, L. J. Sarfeld, and D. M. Dowhamiuk, *Text. Res. J.*, **42**, 558 (1975).
4. K. Arai, M. Negishi, S. Komine, and K. Takeda, *J. Appl. Polym. Symp.*, **18**, 545 (1971).
5. J. L. Williams and V. Stannett, *Text. Res. J.*, **38**, 1065 (1968).
6. A. Hebeish and A. Bendak, *Teintex*, **10**, 719 (1971).
7. N. S. Batty and J. I. Guthrie, *Polymer*, **16**, 43 (1975).
8. N. S. Batty and J. I. Guthrie, Abstracts of the 5th International Wool Conference, Aachen, September 2–11, 1975, p. 341.
9. H. L. Needles, *Text. Res. J.*, **40**, 579 (1970).
10. H. L. Needles, *Text. Res. J.*, **40**, 860 (1970).

11. H. L. Needles and L. J. Sarfeld, *Appl. Polym. Symp.*, **18**, 569 (1971).

12. H. L. Needles, *J. Appl. Polym. Sci.*, **15**, 2559 (1971).

13. H. L. Needles and W. L. Wasley, *Text. Res. J.*, **39**, 97 (1969).

14. H. L. Needles and K. V. Alger, Abstracts of the 5th International Wool Conference, Aachen, September 2–11, 1975, p. 316.

15. D. S. Varma and R. K. Sarkar, *Text. Res. J.*, **41**, 610 (1971).

16. A. J. Mckinson, *J. Appl. Polym. Sci.*, **14**, 3033 (1970).

17. M. Negishi, K. Arai, and S. Okada, *J. Polym. Sci.*, **11**, 115 (1967).

18. L. Valentine, *J. Text. Inst.*, **46**, T270 (1965).

19. K. Arai, H. Tabei, and T. Ohnuma, Abstracts of the 5th International Wool Conference, Aachen, September 2–11, 1975, p. 339.

20. A. Kantouch, A. Hebeish, and A. Bendak, *Eur. Polym. J.*, **7**, 153 (1971).

21. A. Bendak, A. Kantouch, and A. Hebeish, *Kolor. Ert.*, **13**, 106 (1971).

22. A. Kantouch, A. Hebeish, and A. Bendak, *Text. Res. J.*, **42**, 7 (1972).

23. A. Hebeish, A. Bendak, and A. Kantouch, *J. Appl. Polym. Sci.*, **15**, 2733 (1971).

24. W. S. Simpson and W. Van Pelt, *J. Text. Inst.*, **58**, T316 (1967).

25. W. S. Simpson, *J. Appl. Polym. Sci.*, **15**, 967 (1971).

26. W. S. Simpson, *Appl. Polym. Symp.*, **18**, 585 (1971).

27. D. B. Early and W. S. Simpson, Abstracts of the 5th International Wool Conference, Aachen, September 2–11, 1975, p. 330.

28. A. Kantouch, S. H. Abdel-Fattah, and A. Hebeish, *Polym. J.*, **3**, 675 (1972).

29. S. H. Abdel-Fattah, A. Kantouch, and A. Hebeish, *J. Chem. (Egypt)*, **17**(4), 311 (1974).

30. K. Arai, S. Komine, and M. Negishi, *J. Polym. Sci. A-1*, **8**, 917 (1970).

31. A. Bendak, M. I. Khalil, M. H. El-Rafie, and A. Hebeish, *J. Appl. Polym. Sci.*, **19**, 335 (1975).

32. A. Hebeish, S. H. Abdel-Fattah, and M. H. El-Rafie, *J. Appl. Polym. Sci.*, **20**, 3449 (1976).

33. A. Hebeish, S. H. Abdel-Fattah, and A. Bendak, *Angew. Makromol. Chem.*, **37**, 11 (1974).

34. A. Bendak, S. H. Abdel-Fattah, and A. Hebeish, *Angew. Makromol. Chem.*, **43**, 11 (1975).

35. A. Hebeish and A. Bendak, *J. Appl. Polym. Sci.*, **18**, 1305 (1974).

36. A. Bendak and A. Hebeish, *J. Appl. Polym. Sci.*, **17**, 1953 (1973).

37. H. L. Needles and L. J. Sarfeld, *Text. Res. J.*, **44**, 147 (1974).

38. J. C. Berigton and D. E. Eaves, *Nature*, **178**, 1112 (1956).

39. N. Geacintov, S. Stannett, and E. W. Abrahamson, *Makromol. Chem.*, **36**, 52 (196)1

40. A. A. Armostrung and H. A. Rutherford, *Text. Res. J.*, **33**, 264 (1963).

41. V. T. Stannett, J. L. Williams, and G. S. P. Verma; *Polym. Prepr. Amer. Chem. Soc., Div. Polym. Chem.*, **12**(2), 504 (1971); *Chem. Abstr.*, **78**, 160782 (1973).

42. K. Ishigure, K. Yoshida, and V. T. Stannett, *J. Macromol. Sci. Chem.*, **7**(4), 813 (1973); *Chem. Abstr.*, **78**, 136954 (1973).

43. V. Stannet, D. K. Woods, L. G. Roldon, S. B. Sello, and C. V. Stevens, *Text. Res. J.*, **43**, 205 (1973).

44. I. Vlagiu and V. Stannet, *Rev. Roum. Chem.*, **17**(1–2), 379 (1972); *Chem. Abstr.*, **76**, 155370 (1973).

45. I. Sakurada, Y. Ikada, and T. Kawahara, *J. Polym. Sci. A-1*, **11**, 2329 (1973).

46. D. Campbell, K. Arai, and D. T. Turner, *J. Polym. Sci.*, **A-4**, 2597 (1966).

47. P. D. Kale and H. T. Lakhands, *J. Appl. Polym. Sci.*, **19**, 461 (1975).

48. V. V. Korshak, K. K. Mozgova, N. A. Shkolina, B. N. Kaorostylev, O. Ya. Lipovetskaya, and A. P. Zasechkina, *Vysokomol. Soedin.*, **4**, 1469 (1962); *Chem. Abstr.*, **59**, 4104 (1963).

49. V. V. Korshak, K. K. Mozgova, and S. P. Krukovskii, *Plasticheskie Massy*, **6**, 9 (1959); *Chem. Abstr.*, **54**, 14755 (1960).

50. V. V. Korshak, K. K. Mozgova, and M. A. Shkolina, *Vysokomol. Soedin.*, **1**, 1604 (1959); *Chem. Abstr.*, **54**, 14755 (1960).

51. P. V. Kozlov, M. M. Iovleva, and N. A. Plate, *Vysokomol. Soedin.*, **1**, 1100 (1959); *Chem. Abstr.*, **55**, 6025 (1961).

52. P. V. Kozlova, M. M. Lovleva, A. Kh. Khakimova, and A. Zenin, *Vysokomol. Soedin*, **2**, 1575 (1960); *Chem. Abstr.*, **55**, 19323 (1961).

53. K. Suzuki, I. Kido, and Tanabe, *Seni Gakkaishi*, **28**(9), 343 (1972); *Chem. Abstr.*, **77**, 165878 (1972).

54. S. E. Shalaby, E. A. Allam, N. Y. Aboy Zeid, and A. A. Bayazid, *J. Appl. Polym. Sci.*, to appear.

55. I. Sakurada, Y. Sakaguchi, and Y. Sakai, *Sen'i Gakkaishi*, **21**, 136 (1965).

56. I. Sakurada, Y. Ikada, and I. Kawahara, *J. Polym. Sci. A-1*, **11**, 2329 (1973).

57. J. C. Bonnefis and Y. R. Puig, *J. Appl. Polym. Sci.*, **15**, 553 (1971).

58. K. N. Rao, M. H. Rao, P. N. Moorthy, and A. Charlsby, *J. Polym. Sci. B*, **10**, 893 (1972).

59. I. M. Trivedi, P. C. Mehta, K. N. Rao, and M. H. Rao, *J. Appl. Polym. Sci.*, **19**, 1 (1975).

60. T. Okada, Y. Shimano, and I. Sakurada, *Nippon Genshiryoku Kenkyusho Ghusa Hokuku, J.A.E.R.I.*, **5028**, 35 (1972).

61. D. Tanner, (to E. I. du Pont de Nemours & Co., Inc.) Jpn. Pat. 38-10342 *Chemical After-treatment of Textiles*, H. Mark, R. S. Wooding, and S. M. Atlas, Eds., Wiley-Interscience, New York, 1971, p. 258.

62. I. Sakurada and T. Okada, U.S. Pat. 3,649,494 (March 14, 1972); *Chem. Abstr.*, **77**, 7183 (1972).

63. L. Vanino and F. Herzer, *Arch. Pharm.*, **253**, 426 (1915).

64. Y. Tabata, H. Kitano, and H. Sabue, *J. Polym. Sci.*, **A-2**, 3639 (1964).

65. M. Negishi and K. Arai, *J. Appl. Polym. Sci.*, **9**, 3465 (1965).

Received June 22, 1976
Revised October 22, 1976

JOURNAL OF APPLIED POLYMER SCIENCE   VOL. 21, 3367–3379 (1977)

Change of Viscoelastic Properties of Epoxy Resin in the Curing Process

KATSUHITO SUZUKI and YASUSHI MIYANO, *Hitachi Research Laboratory, Hitachi Limited, Hitachi, Japan,* and TAKESHI KUNIO, *Faculty of Engineering, Keiougijuku University, Yokohama, Japan*

Synopsis

This paper is concerned with the relation between the time and temperature dependences of the flexural properties and the curing conditions for the bisphenol A-type epoxy resin with acid anhydride hardener. Relaxation moduli of epoxy resin, prepared at several curing temperatures and times, were measured in the temperature range from $T_g - 70°C$ to T_g. The master curves of relaxation modulus for the epoxy resin could be constructed, using their thermorheological simple properties. The time–temperature shift factors of the epoxy resin could be approximately expressed by the Arrhenius equation with the activation energy 59.4 kcal/mole. independent of its curing conditions. The curing time and temperature were equivalent, that is, the short curing time at high temperature corresponded to the long curing time at low temperature. The curing time–temperature shift factor could be approximately expressed by the Arrhenius equation with the activation energy 21.3 kcal/mole, which was higher than the activation energy 14.2 kcal/mole obtained in the measurements of gel times. The increase in the values shows that the temperature dependences of reaction rates increase with progressing gelation.

INTRODUCTION

The viscoelastic behavior of amorphous polymers has been widely studied, and it has become well known that their mechanical properties are governed by the time–temperature reduced law, and that the temperature dependence of the time–temperature shift factor can be expressed by a WLF equation.[1] The authors measured the stress–strain relation of unsaturated polyester resins and found that at high crosslinking densities, the temperature dependence of the time–temperature shift factor could be expressed by an Arrhenius equation,[2] but at low crosslinking densities it could be expressed by a WLF equation.[3] The relationship between polymer structure and viscoelastic behavior, thus, has been made considerably clear.

On the other hand, very little is known about the change of the viscoelastic properties of unsaturated polyester, epoxy, and other thermosetting resins in the curing process. The purpose of the present investigation is to shed light on the time and temperature dependences of mechanical properties of the epoxy resins having different curing degrees prepared at various curing temperatures and times. When a liquid epoxy resin is cured, its viscosity starts to rise at the gel point, and the resin eventually becomes a viscoelastic solid after going through the rubber state. In this study, the process of change to the rubber state was measured by means of a Culastometer, and with regard to the viscoelastic solid,

3367

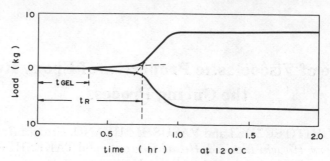

Fig. 1. Load–time curve obtained by Culastometer.

the relaxation moduli at various temperatures were measured by the flexural constant strain test.

As a result, it was revealed that the time-temperature reduced law held in this case and that the time-temperature shift factor did not depend on curing conditions of the resin and could be expressed by the same Arrhenius equation, and also that the curing time and curing temperature were equivalent.

EXPERIMENTAL

The epoxy resin was Dow Chemical DER 332; this is a diglycidyl ether of bisphenol A with a molecular weight of approximately 350. The crosslinking agent used in the curing reactions was Hitachi Chemical methyl himic anhydride (MHAcP). The catalyst was Shikoku Chemical 2-ethyl-4-methylimidazol (2E4MZ). These materials were mixed at proportions of 100 g DER 332, 103.6 g MHAcP, and 1 g 2E4MZ. Mole ratio of epoxy group/acid anhydride was 1/1.

Measurement of Gel Time and Rubber Time

Gel time t_{Gel} and rubber time t_R were measured with Japan Synthetic Rubber Culastometer II[4,5] for the samples weighing 2 g and at 0.25° torsional angle, in the temperature range from 100° to 150°C. From the load–time curve shown in Figure 1, the time when the load started rising and the time it later rose suddenly were taken, respectively, as t_{Gel} and t_R, and their relationships with curing temperature were investigated.

Measurement of Relaxation Modulus

Preparation of Test Pieces. Originally, it was planned to prepare the test pieces at 100°–150°C, the same curing temperature as in the Culastometer, but the resin was heated by the curing reaction heat and could not be kept at constant temperature. Therefore, first the resin was precured for 6 hr at 80°C, where very little heat generation at curing was observed, and then cured at 100°–150°C. First, the precuring was performed by pouring liquid resin into a mold of 130 × 140 × 5 mm inside dimensions held at 80°C in an air oven for 6 hr. This 6 hr for precuring is equivalent to twice the estimated gel time at 80°C. The precured

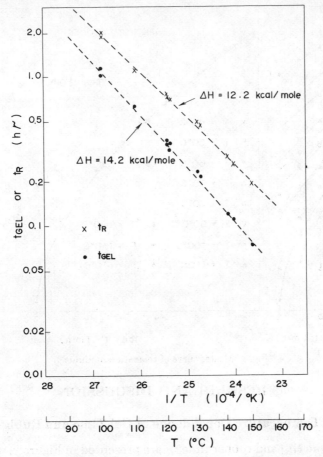

Fig. 2. Arrhenius plot of gel time t_{Gel} and rubber time t_R.

resin plate was then cured for the specified time by inserting it between two steel plates previously maintained at 100°–150°C in an air oven.

By temperature measurements with a thermocouple buried in the precured resin plate, it was confirmed that the resin temperature rose to 150°C within 6 min and that no particular heat generation occurred thereafter. Curing time was taken at 2–16 times the t_R at each curing temperature. From the resin plate thus prepared, test pieces 10 mm wide, 130 mm long, and 5 mm thick were taken and subjected to measurement of relaxation modulus.

Measurement of Relaxation Modulus. Relaxation modulus was measured in a three-point flexural test at a constant strain rate,[6] with an Autograph IS-20T (a product of Shimazu Seisakusho Ltd.). The temperature dependence of the relaxation modulus was measured in the temperature range from $T_g - 70°C$ to T_g, below the curing temperature. A deformation speed of 5 mm/min, for a span of 100 mm, was taken as standard. For test pieces of the lowest or highest curing degree, that is, for those cured at 100°C·4 hr and 150°C·2.56 hr, the time dependence of relaxation modulus was examined in greater detail by varying the deformation speed from 0.05, 0.5, 5, to 50 mm/min.

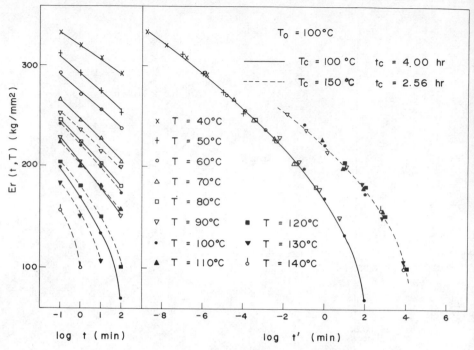

Fig. 3. Master curve of relaxation modulus.

RESULTS AND DISCUSSION

Curing Temperature Dependence of Gel Time and Rubber Time

The gel time t_{Gel} and rubber time t_R are presented in Figure 2, which shows that both t_{Gel} and t_R, within the curing temperature range of 100°–150°C, can be expressed by the Arrhenius equation.

$$\log \frac{t_1}{t_2} = \frac{\Delta H}{2.303R} \left(\frac{1}{T_1} - \frac{1}{T_2} \right) \tag{1}$$

where $t = t_{Gel}$ or t_R, in hr, ΔH = activation energy, in kcal/mole, R = gas constant, 1.69×10^{-3} kcal/deg °C·mole, and T = curing temperature, in °K.

Also from Figure 2, the activation energy ΔH of reaction was calculated to be 14.2 kcal/mole for t_{Gel} and 12.2 kcal/mole for t_R. These values agree approximately with 14 kcal/mole activation energy obtained by Tanaka et al. from measurements of gel time, chemical composition, and viscosity, with regard to a bisphenol A-type epoxy resin and acid anhydride hardener.[7] Also with various combinations of other epoxy resins and hardeners, the activation energy required for the curing reaction is reported to be 8–17 kcal/mole.[8] Therefore, the results obtained here seem to be reasonable.

Relationship of Relaxation Modulus to Curing Temperature and Curing Time

In Figure 3, the experimental relaxation curves for samples cured at 100 °C·4 hr and 150°C·2.56 hr are shown on the left, and the master curves at the reference

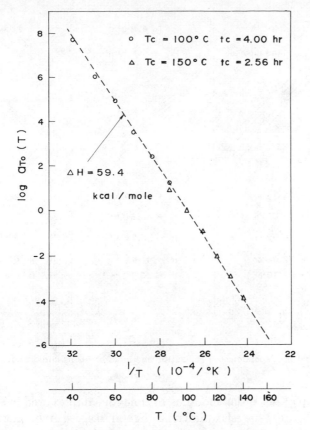

Fig. 4. Arrhenius plot of shift factor $a_{T_0}(T)$

temperature $T_0 = 100°C$ are shown on the right. For both samples, smooth superimposed curves were obtained, and the time–temperature reduced law held. The relationship between temperature and time–temperature shift factor $a_{T_0}(T)$ is shown in Figure 4. The $a_{T_0}(T)$ for samples prepared at 100°C·4 hr and 150°C·2.56 hr agreed with each other and could be expressed by an Arrhenius equation irrespective of curing conditions. The activation energy was calculated to be 59.4 kcal/mole, which approximated the value obtained with unsaturated polyester resins.[3]

Figure 5 shows the relationship between temperature and relaxation modulus at time $t = 1$ min for samples prepared for various curing times at curing temperatures of 100°, 120°, and 150°C. It is seen that relaxation modulus increases as curing time lengthens.

Figure 6 shows the relationship of temperature and relaxation modulus at $t = 1$ min for samples prepared at 100°–150°C curing temperature and a curing time twice the t_R. It is seen that in the lower temperature region, the relaxation moduli agree with each other regardless of curing conditions but that in the higher temperature region, the relaxation moduli are higher for samples with higher curing temperatures.

Figure 7 shows the relationship between time and relaxation modulus at reference temperature $T_0 = 100°C$ for samples used in Figure 5. It is seen that the longer the curing time, the higher the relaxation modulus. Figure 8 indicates

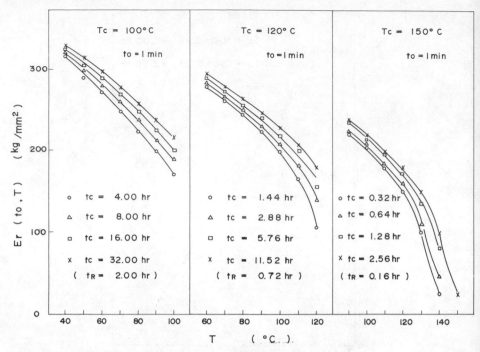

Fig. 5. Temperature dependence of relaxation modulus of resins cured under several conditions.

the relationship of relaxation modulus to time for samples used in Figure 6. As in the case of Figure 6, the relaxation moduli tend to agree in the short time region regardless of curing conditions, but in the long time region, they become higher for samples with higher curing temperatures.

As mentioned above, the time and temperature dependences of relaxation modulus have been made clear for samples prepared at various curing temperatures and times. Using relaxation modulus as a yardstick, the correlation between curing temperature and time will be discussed, so as to find, for example, the length of curing time at 150°C that corresponds to 4 hr at 100°C.

In Figure 3, the master curves for two samples prepared under different curing conditions are somewhat different and cannot be superposed by shifting along the horizontal axis. This presumably suggests that the form of a master curve differs depending on the combination of curing temperature and time, and consequently that curing temperature and time must be considered separately. Therefore, on the relaxation modulus–time curve with curing time as the parameter as shown in Figure 7, the point at which the 100°C·4 hr cured sample shows a relaxation modulus of 200 kg/mm^2 was taken as a reference, and it was attempted to superpose, by shifting along the horizontal axis, the points of other samples where they show a relaxation modulus of 200 kg/mm^2. The quantity of shift here is $(\log t' - \log t'_0) = \log t'/t'_0 = \log Cd$, where Cd means the curing degree of each sample against the 100°C·4 hr cured sample as the reference, and it is the relaxation time–curing time shift factor.

Figure 9 indicates the relationship between curing degree C_d and curing time. The point A corresponds to the value of 100°C·4 hr cured sample as the reference.

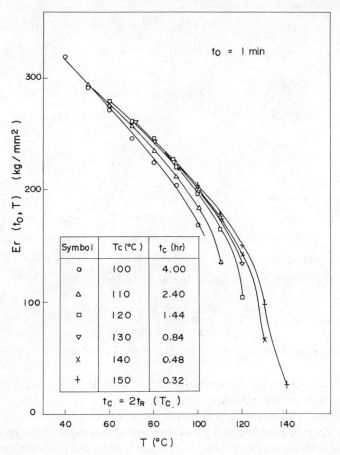

Fig. 6. Temperature dependence of relaxation modulus of resins cured under several conditions.

In Figure 9, the samples cured at 110°, 130°, and 140°C have only one C_d point respectively, because they were prepared under one curing condition.

To standardize the data of Figure 9, an attempt to superpose them by shifting along the horizontal axis was made. This operation corresponds to a conversion of curing time to temperature, which means that the state of a sample cured at a high temperature for a short time corresponds to that of a sample cured at a low temperature for a long time. In other words, the time–temperature reduced law recognized for the viscoelastic phenomena is extended to the reduction of time and temperature in chemical reactions.

Figure 10 presents a C_d master curve where 100°C curing temperature is used as the reference. The relationship between temperature and curing time–temperature shift factor $b_{T_0}(T)$ used in drawing this master curve is shown in Figure 11. It could be expressed by an Arrhenius equation with activation energy 21.3 kcal/mole.

Figure 11 also gives the $a_{T_0}(T)$ and the $c_{T_0}(T)$, obtained from time–temperature reduction of relaxation modulus and from gel time at 100°C as the reference, respectively. In Figure 11, the 21.3 kcal/mole activation energy obtained

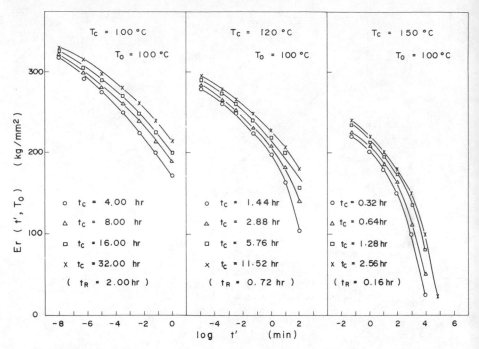

Fig. 7. Time dependence of relaxation modulus of resins cured under several conditions.

from the curing degree lies between the 14.2 kcal/mole from the gel time and the 59.4 kcal/mole from the relaxation modulus.

As mentioned above, it has been made clear that the activation energy based on the relaxation process below T_g was constant irrespective of curing conditions, and that the activation energy of curing reaction obtained from the curing degree with relaxation modulus as the yardstick was larger than the value obtained from the gel time. These results will be discussed in relation to other physical values.

Table I gives the specific volume, T_g, heat distortion temperature HDT, and infrared absorbance of the samples used for the measurement of the relaxation modulus. These values were measured in order to estimate the curing states of samples from characteristics other than mechanical properties.

First, the degree of chemical reaction in the resin will be discussed in terms of epoxy group content. In the 80°C·6 hr precuring, about 80% of the epoxy groups have undergone reaction. At the subsequent 100°–150°C curing, the degree of reaction rises to a maximum of 90%. This means that, as far as epoxy group content is concerned, there is not much difference among the resins with various curing degrees used in the present study. This, presumably, is why the activation energy based on the relaxation process below T_g was constant irrespective of the curing conditions of the samples.

Next, specific volume at 23°C will be discussed. After the precuring at 80°C·6 hr, the specific volume has decreased by 3.3%, but after the subsequent 100°–150°C curing, the value has increased. In the 150°C·2.56 hr cured sample, the specific volume has increased by 0.9% over that of the 80°C·6 hr precured sample.

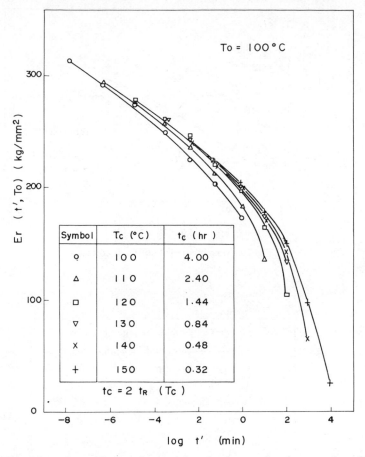

Fig. 8. Time dependence of relaxation modulus of resins cured under several conditions.

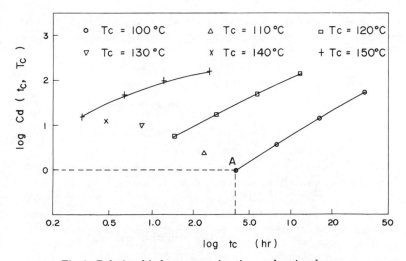

Fig. 9. Relationship between curing time and curing degree.

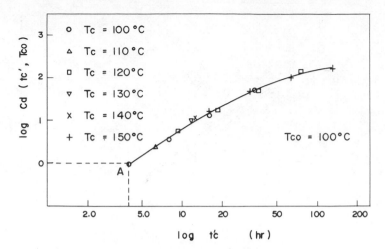

Fig. 10. Master curve of curing degree.

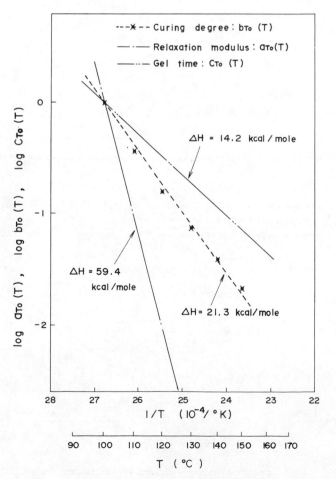

Fig. 11. Arrhenius plot of shift factor.

TABLE I
Properties of the Samples

Sample		Specific volume at 23°C, cc/g	T_g, °C	HDT,[a] °C	Infrared absorbance epoxide at 915 cm^{-1}	phenyl at 1500 cm^{-1}
No.	Cure schedule, °C/hr					
1	non cure	0.8358	—	—		1.41
2	80/6	0.8084	78	72		0.30
3–1	80/6 + 100/4	0.8136	112	109		0.26
3–2	80/6 + 100/8	0.8137	119	114		0.25
3–3	80/6 + 100/16	0.8142	123	119		0.24
3–4	80/6 + 100/32	0.8143	125	120		0.23
4	80/6 + 110/2.4	0.8145	123	118		—
5–1	80/6 + 120/1.44	0.8153	128	120		—
5–2	80/6 + 120/2.88	0.8155	129	126		—
5–3	80/6 + 120/5.76	0.8160	131	129		—
5–4	80/6 + 120/11.52	0.8168	136	135		0.20
6	80/6 + 130/0.84	0.8166	136	125		—
7	80/6 + 140/0.48	0.8169	136	130		—
8–1	80/6 + 150/0.32	0.8179	135	130		0.18
8–2	80/6 + 150/0.64	0.8183	143	137		0.17
8–3	80/6 + 150/1.28	0.8183	150	143		0.14
8–4	80/6 + 150/2.56	0.8198	155	151		0.14

[a] Heat distortion temperature; ASTM D-648-55T, fiber stress 18.56 kg/cm^2.

Meanwhile, both T_g and HDT rose with an increase in curing time, and sometimes there were cases when T_g was higher than curing temperature. From these facts, it may be deduced that, in the sample epoxy resins used, about 50% of the epoxy groups reacted to form a crosslinked structure and reduce the volume, before reaching the gel point, but in the reaction thereafter, the volume slightly increased while the crosslinking density increased. Thus, after the gel point, the molecular movement presumably was impeded by the increase in viscosity, and the temperature dependence of the reaction velocity had changed so that presumably the activation energy after the gel point obtained from the curing degree was larger than that obtained from the gel time.

The activation energy based on the relaxation process and that obtained from the curing degree are fundamentally different, because the former is based on molecular movement and the latter on chemical reaction. In the latter case, however, the reaction should also take place after the reactive points approach each other. From the viewpoint of molecular mobility, therefore, the activation energy due to the relaxation process is also related to reaction. This point requires further investigation.

CONCLUSIONS

With a system consisting of a bisphenol A-type epoxy resin and an acid anhydride hardener, the gel times and relaxation moduli of samples prepared at various curing times and temperatures were examined. The results are summarized as follows:

(1) Activation energy of reaction obtained from gel time was 14.2 kcal/mole, which was close to similar values reported in the literature.

(2) For relaxation moduli of samples of different crosslinking densities prepared under various curing conditions, the time–temperature reduced law held within the temperature range from $T_g - 70°C$ to T_g. The time–temperature shift factor was not dependent on curing conditions and could be approximated by an Arrhenius equation with an activation energy of 59.4 kcal/mole.

(3) As a yardstick of curing degree of cured resin, a relaxation time–curing time shift factor C_d was introduced from a relaxation modulus–time curve with curing time as the parameter; and further, the curing temperature–curing time shift factor was obtained from a C_d–curing time curve with curing temperature as the parameter. With this, it was shown that curing temperature and curing time could be reduced.

(4) It was found that curing temperature–curing time shift factor in paragraph (3) above could be approximated by an Arrhenius equation with an activation energy of 21.3 kcal/mole. This value represented the activation energy of curing reaction after gelation, when relaxation modulus was used as a yardstick. The value was larger than that obtained from the gel time in paragraph (1) above. This is presumably because, with progress of the reaction, viscosity rises and molecular movement is impeded, and thus reaction velocity becomes more dependent on temperature.

The authors wish to express their sincere gratitude to Dr. N. Shito, Hatachi Research Laboratory, Hitachi, Ltd., for his valuable advice and suggestions, and also to Mr. N. Shibata at the same laboratory for his cooperation in the experiments.

References

1. J. D. Ferry, *Viscoelastic Properties of Polymers*, Wiley, New York, 1961, p. 215.
2. M. Kitoh, Y. Miyano, and K. Suzuki, *Kobunshi Ronbunshu*, **32**, 55 (1975).
3. M. Kitoh and K Suzuki, *Kobunshi Ronbunshu*, **32**, 147 (1975).
4. Japan Synthetic Rubber Co., Ltd., *Jpn. Plast.*, **7**, 46 (1973).
5. M. Umeno, *Goseijushi*, **17**, 8 (1971).
6. M. L. Williams, *A.I.A.A. J.*, **2**, 785 (1964).
7. Y. Tanaka and H. Kakiuchi, *J. Appl. Polym. Sci.*, **7**, 1063 (1963).
8. W. G. Potter, *Epoxide Resins*, Plastics Institute, London, 1970, p. 56.

Received September 10, 1976
Revised October 22, 1976

JOURNAL OF APPLIED POLYMER SCIENCE   VOL. 21, 3381–3405 (1977)

Heterogeneous Network Polymers. IV. Dynamic Mechanical Properties—Composition—Phase Structure Relationships

TETSUO MORI, KATSUMI OGAWA, and TAKEHIDE TANAKA,
*Department of Materials Science and Technology, Kyushu University,
Fukuoka, Japan 812*

Synopsis

Heterogeneous network polymers were prepared from poly(D-glutamic acid) (PGA) and poly(oxyethylene glycol) (PEG). The content of PGA was systematically varied: 30%, 40%, 50%, 60%, 65%, and 70% by weight. The molecular weights of the crosslinking PEG were 300, 600, 900, and 1800. The plots of the dynamic mechanical tan δ peak temperatures, the PGA interhelical distances (x-rays) and the densities against PGA contents showed a distinct break between 50% and 60%. The photographs under polarizing microscope also indicated an occurrence of phase inversion in the above content region. PGA containing small amounts of PEG and PEG containing small amounts of PGA were found to constitute the continuous phases, respectively, above and below the phase inversion region, while a well-mixed phase is always the dispersed phase. The glass transition was ascribed to the micro-Brownian motions of PGA, PEG, and PEG above and below the phase inversion region, respectively.

INTRODUCTION

Many commercially important plastics and rubbers are prepared by the methods of polymer blends, block, or graft copolymerization. These materials are endowed with more desirable properties by combination of the properties of each component polymer. In general, the component polymers are incompatible with each other, one of them being a hard-component polymer and the other, a soft-component polymer. It is well known that the properties of these materials depend on the glass transition temperatures of the component homopolymers, the composition, the domain structure resulting from incompatibility, the synthetic conditions (temperature, concentration, solvent, and the rate of evaporation of the solvent), etc.[1–6]

We have been interested in the preparation and the physical properties of heterogeneous network polymers which are composed of different polymeric chains. We chose synthetic polypeptides and polyethers as hard- and soft-component polymers, respectively. Synthetic polypeptides in the solid state exhibit characteristic properties as they can retain various secondary structure such as α-helix, β-form, and random coil owing to the intra- and intermolecular hydrogen bonds. Polyethers have been widely used as a soft component in polyurethane elastomers.

3381

In the previous papers,[7-9] we showed that poly(ϵ-N-carbobenzoxy-L-lysine) and poly(L-glutamic acid) can be crosslinked with isocyanate-terminated polyethers and poly(oxyethylene glycol), respectively, and we discussed mainly the relation between the glass transition temperature and the composition. It was found that the dynamic mechanical properties of heterogeneous network polymers were greatly influenced by several factors such as the relative content of a polypeptide and a polyether, the compatibility of the polypeptide with the polyether, the crosslink density, and the concentration of free carboxyl groups. As mentioned above, however, the physical properties of this type of polymers may also be greatly influenced by the domain structure.

In this paper, we describe the dynamic mechanical properties—composition–domain structure relationships based on dynamic mechanical measurements, infrared spectra, wide-angle x-ray diffraction patterns, and polarizing microscopy. In the present work, we chose poly(glutamic acid) (PGA) and poly(oxyethylene glycol) (PEG) as hard- and soft-component polymers, respectively. The heterogeneous network polymers were synthesized by esterification of carboxyl groups in PGA with the hydroxyl groups in PEG in the absence of catalysts. A series of the heterogeneous network polymers have been prepared by systematically varying the PGA content and the molecular weight of PEG.

EXPERIMENTAL

Materials

Poly(D-glutamic acid) (PGA) prepared by saponification of poly(γ-methyl D-glutamate) had a molecular weight in the range of 42,000–46,000. The extent of hydrolysis determined by quantitative analysis of methoxy groups (Zeisel method) was 97%–99%.

Poly(oxyethylene glycol) (PEG) had number-average molecular weights of 330, 570, 880, and 1830, which will be designated as PEG300, PEG600, PEG900, and PEG1800, respectively. Heterogeneous network polymers with systematically varied PGA content as 30%, 40%, 50%, 60%, 65%, 70% by weight were synthesized. For example, 2.00 g PGA was dissolved in 21 ml N,N-dimethylformamide (DMF) at 100°C. Then, 1.32 g PEG was added and dissolved. The clear solution was poured onto a mold coated with fluoride varnishes. The mold was placed in an airtight metal box and heated in an oven for two to three days at 100°C. The box was then opened to allow DMF to evaporate slowly—it usually took three to four more days until DMF was completely gone. For convenience, we hereafter use the designation PGA-PEG300 (60/40) to represent a heterogeneous network polymer made of PGA and PEG300 at 60 and 40 wt %, respectively. At least two films of network polymers having the same composition were synthesized to check the reproducibility of the properties except for PGA-PEG1800 (70/30), for which we could prepare only once.

Apparatus and Procedures

Dynamic mechanical measurements were made with a Model DDV-IIC Rheovibron at 110 Hz in the temperature range of −120°–200°C. The temperature was raised at a rate of 1.5–2°C/min.

TABLE I
Reaction of PGA with TEGME

PGA-TEGME no.	$1/K^a$	Found,[b] %			Calcd.,[b] %			$\rho,^c$ %
		C	H	N	C	H	N	
1	1.0	49.79	6.61	8.33	49.79	6.55	8.29	24.9
2	2.0	50.65	6.91	7.33	50.65	6.88	7.51	35.8
3	5.0	51.00	7.06	7.10	51.00	7.00	7.23	40.3

[a] K = [—COOH]/[—OH], mole ratio of carboxyl groups in PGA to hydroxyl groups in original reaction mixtures.
[b] Elemental analysis.
[c] Degree of esterification reaction calculated by carbon content.

Wide-angle x-ray diffraction patterns were obtained with a Rigaku Denki Type D-3F x-ray generator. Nickel-filtered CuK_α radiation was used at 35 kV and 15 mA.

A Nikon polarizing optical microscope Type POH was used to observe the domain structure or optical anisotropy. Micrographs of cross sections of thin specimens approximately 50 microns thick, sectioned with the use of a razor blade, were taken.

Infrared absorption spectra of the network polymers were measured on a Perkin-Elmer Model 567 spectrophotometer using a multiple internal reflection (MIR) accessory.

Swelling measurements were made as follows. Samples of about 0.15 g were allowed to swell in DMF for seven days at 25°C. Then, the swollen samples were weighed and dried to constant weights at 100°C. Swelling ratio q and gel percent g were determined from equations

$$q = 1 + (W_a - W_b)d_p/W_a d_s$$

and

$$g = W_b/W \times 100$$

where W is the weight of the unswollen network polymer, W_a is the weight of the swollen gel, W_b is the weight of the dry gel, d_p is the density of the network polymer, and d_s is the density of the solvent.

RESULTS AND DISCUSSION

Reaction of PGA with Triethylene Glycol Monoethyl Ether (TEGME)

To confirm that the curing process of the heterogeneous network polymers is effected by the esterification of the γ-carboxyl groups of PGA with the hydroxyl groups of PEG, the following model experiments were undertaken. PGA was allowed to react with the monofunctional TEGME in DMF; the reaction conditions were the same as those under which the heterogeneous network polymers were synthesized. Yellow translucent films (abbreviated PGA-TEGME) were obtained after complete evaporation of DMF and unreacted TEGME; evaporation of a substantial portion of TEGME could not be avoided because its boiling point is 248°C.

In Table I are shown the mole ratios of the hydroxyl group in TEGME to the

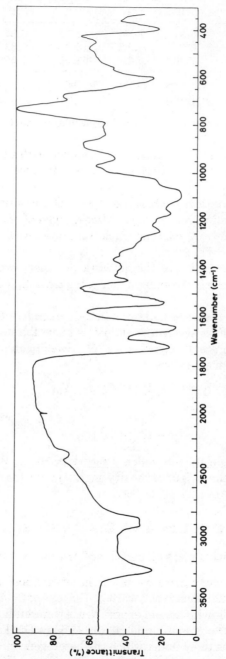

Fig. 1. Infrared spectrum of PGA-TEGME (no. 3) measured by multiple internal reflection method.

carboxyl group in PGA in the original reaction mixtures and the elemental analyses of the films that were extracted with DMF at room temperature for seven days. From the observed carbon contents, the degrees of esterification, ρ, were calculated under the assumption that the incorporation of TEGME into PGA as unextractable was effected exclusively by the esterification of γ-carboxyl groups of PGA. From those ρ values, the elemental analyses for H and N were back-calculated. The agreement between the found and the calculated values appears to verify the above assumption and the effectiveness of the extraction of the unreacted polyethers with DMF at room temperature.

In Table I, the larger $1/K$ became the more TEGME remained in contact with PGA during the course of reaction even if the evaporation of TEGME had to be taken into account. The fact that the larger $1/K$ gave rise to the considerably increased degree of esterification suggests that eventually nearly quantitative esterification might be accomplished with a completely unvolatile polyether glycol.

Figure 1 shows the infrared spectrum of PGA-TEGME (no. 3) measured by a multiple internal reflection (MIR) method. The amide I, II, and V bands appear at 1645, 1540, and 600 cm^{-1}, respectively. These bands are characteristic of polypeptide chains which exist in α-helix conformation. A strong band at around 1090 cm^{-1} arises from the C—O—C stretching vibration of TEGME.

Characterization of Heterogeneous Network Polymers

Table II shows the mole ratio K of the carboxyl groups in PGA to the hydroxyl groups in PEG in the reaction mixtures, the density d, the gel percent g, the

TABLE II
Characterization of Heterogeneous Network Polymers

	K[a]	d,[b] g/cm³	g,[c] %	q[d]	$\nu \times 10^3$,[e] mole/g	$C \times 10^3$,[f] mole/g
PGA-PEG300(40/60)	0.85	1.283–1.303	91.5–92.4	1.70–1.74	3.4	0
PGA-PEG300(50/50)	1.28	1.276–1.296	93.0–96.4	1.62–1.63	2.9	1.1
PGA-PEG300(60/40)	1.90	1.306–1.308	96.7–99.0	1.61–1.88	2.3	2.3
PGA-PEG300(65/35)	2.38	1.310–1.322	98.5–99.7	1.68–1.73	2.1	2.9
PGA-PEG300(70/30)	2.98	1.326–1.339	98.6–99.5	1.88–1.92	1.8	3.6
PGA-PEG600(30/70)	0.95	1.283–1.285	76.3–77.6	2.26–2.33	2.3	0.7
PGA-PEG600(40/60)	1.47	1.278–1.300	78.2–91.8	1.72–2.56	2.0	1.3
PGA-PEG600(50/50)	2.21	1.278–1.305	89.3–96.2	1.84–2.19	1.7	2.3
PGA-PEG600(60/40)	3.31	1.304–1.309	97.4–99.4	1.97–2.05	1.4	3.3
PGA-PEG600(65/35)	4.10	1.314–1.323	97.3–99.8	1.99–2.34	1.2	3.8
PGA-PEG600(70/30)	5.16	1.336–1.346	98.5–99.3	2.27–2.51	1.0	4.4
PGA-PEG900(30/70)	1.46	1.271–1.287	74.5–75.6	2.34	1.4	1.3
PGA-PEG900(40/60)	2.28	1.281–1.300	80.1–94.7	1.89–2.33	1.3	1.8
PGA-PEG900(50/50)	3.41	1.287–1.304	82.3–94.8	2.15–2.79	1.1	2.9
PGA-PEG900(60/40)	5.11	1.308–1.310	96.9–98.8	2.20–2.34	0.88	3.8
PGA-PEG900(65/35)	6.33	1.317–1.325	97.6–99.3	2.25–2.70	0.78	4.3
PGA-PEG900(70/30)	7.96	1.318–1.338	97.4–99.0	2.46–2.80	0.66	4.8
PGA-PEG1800(50/50)	7.09	1.282	91.4–94.8	2.60	0.51	3.4
PGA-PEG1800(70/30)	16.6	1.308	94.8	3.43	0.30	5.2

[a] K = [—COOH]/[—OH], mole ratio of carboxyl groups in PGA to hydroxyl groups in PEG in reaction mixtures.

[b] Density, measured by a floation method using carbon tetrachloride and cyclohexane at 25°C.

[c] Gel per cent, in DMF at 25°C.

[d] Swelling ratio, in DMF at 25°C.

[e] Crosslink density.

[f] Concentration of free carboxyl groups.

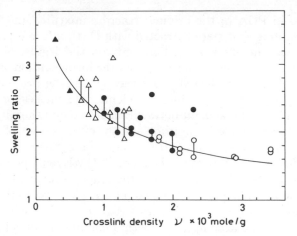

Fig. 2. Plot of swelling ratio vs crosslink density: (O) PGA-PEG300; (●) PGA-PEG600; (△) PGA-PEG900; (▲) PGA-PEG1800.

swelling ratio q, the crosslink density ν, and the concentration of the free carboxyl groups C. For d, g, and q are shown the upper and lower limit values that were obtained from the measurements made on many samples of the same compositions. The ν and C values were determined by the equations below under the assumption that the sol consisted only of PEG:

$$\nu = \frac{2(g-x)}{M \cdot g} \text{ mole/g}, \qquad C = \left\{ \frac{x}{129} - \frac{2(g-x)}{M} \right\} \times \frac{1}{100} \text{ mole/g}$$

where x is the weight percent of PGA and M is the molecular weight of PEG. As Figure 2 illustrates, q decreases gradually as ν increases. A smooth curve may be drawn, within the limits of experimental errors, for the heterogeneous network polymers composed of PEG of different molecular weights. The data points in Figure 2 that deviate extremely upward are those from polymers whose gel per cents were less than 90%; this is indicative of the formation of ineffective networks in such polymers. Excluding these, we may conclude that the heterogeneous networks were actually formed, for q depends chiefly on ν.

Figures 3 and 4 show the infrared spectra of PGA, PEG900 and PGA-PEG900 (70/30), respectively. PGA-PEG900 (70/30) has characteristic bands of an α-helix at 1640 cm^{-1} (amide I), 1540 cm^{-1} (amide II), 605 cm^{-1} (amide V) and 395 cm^{-1}. There are also weak characteristic bands of β-form at 1630 cm^{-1}, 700 cm^{-1}, and of random coil at 650 cm^{-1}. A strong band at around 1090 cm^{-1} arises from C—O—C stretching vibration of PEG. Figure 4 is very similar to Figure 1.

We conclude that most of PGA chains of heterogeneous network polymers exist in α-helix form and that the network is formed by esterification.

Dynamic Mechanical Properties

Effect of PGA Content

Figures 5, 6, and 7 show the dynamic mechanical properties of heterogeneous network polymers as a function of PGA content. As the PGA content increases

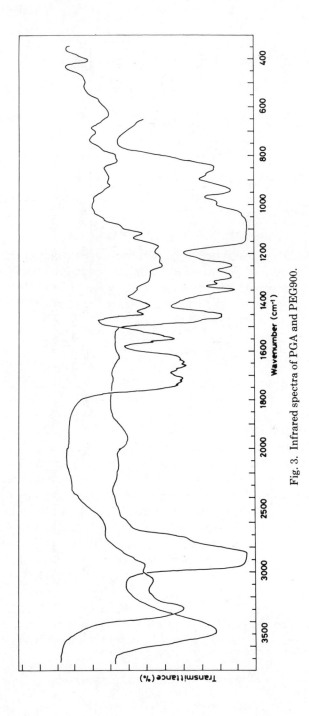

Fig. 3. Infrared spectra of PGA and PEG900.

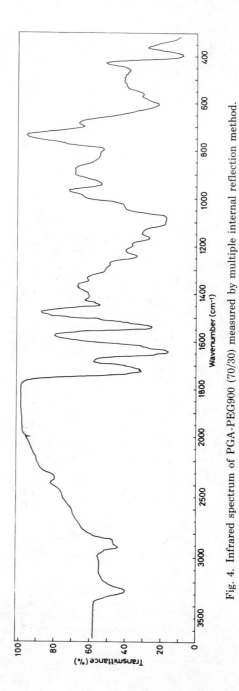

Fig. 4. Infrared spectrum of PGA-PEG900 (70/30) measured by multiple internal reflection method.

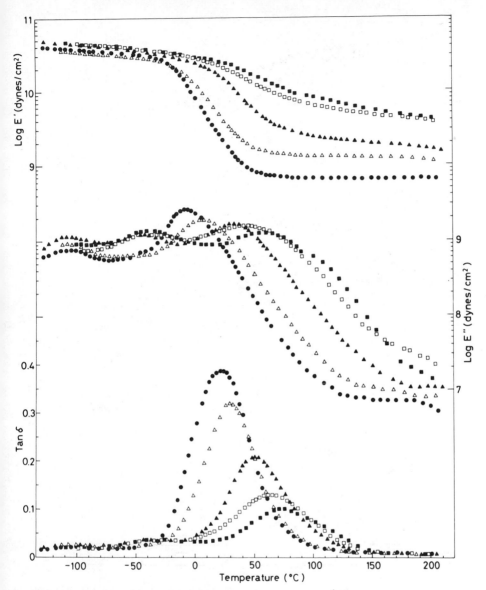

Fig. 5. Dependence of dynamic mechanical properties of PGA-PEG300 on PGA content; (●) PGA-PEG300 (40/60); (△) PGA-PEG300 (50/50); (▲) PGA-PEG300 (60/40); (□) PGA-PEG300 (65/35); (■) PGPEG300 (70/30).

from 30% to 70% while the molecular weight of PEG is kept constant, (1) the peak temperatures of tan δ and E'' shift to higher temperatures; (2) tan δ and E'' curves broaden and decrease in magnitude; (3) E' above the transition region increases. These crosslinked polymers have relatively high moduli; even the lowest E' in the series exhibited by PGA-PEG900 (30/70) had a value of 3×10^8 dynes/cm^2.

Figure 8 is a recapitulation of the above observation (1); a sharp break at around 60% PGA content is obvious. An interpretation of the above dynamic mechanical behavior follows. The increase in the content of PGA (hard com-

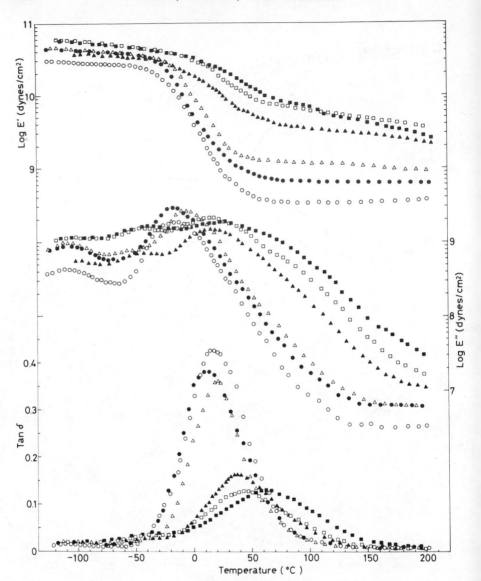

Fig. 6. Dependence of dynamic mechanical properties of PGA-PEG600 on PGA content; (O) PGA-PEG600 (30/70); (●) PGA-PEG600 (40/60); (△) PGA-PEG600 (50/50); (▲) PGA-PEG600 (60/40); (□) PGA-PEG600 (65/35); (■) PGA-PEG600 (70/30).

ponent) naturally raised the peak temperatures of tan δ and E'' owing to a copolymer effect. There remains one point to be mentioned, however. If we increase the PGA content while keeping the molecular weight of PEG constant, as we did in this work, we are simultaneously decreasing the concentration of crosslink points as evidenced in Table II. The decrease in crosslink density would cause a depression of the peak temperatures of tan δ and E''—the reverse of what was observed. In this respect, we previously demonstrated that the copolymer effect predominates over the crosslinking effect in our heterogeneous network polymer system.[8,9]

In general, the dynamic mechanical properties of a composite material depend

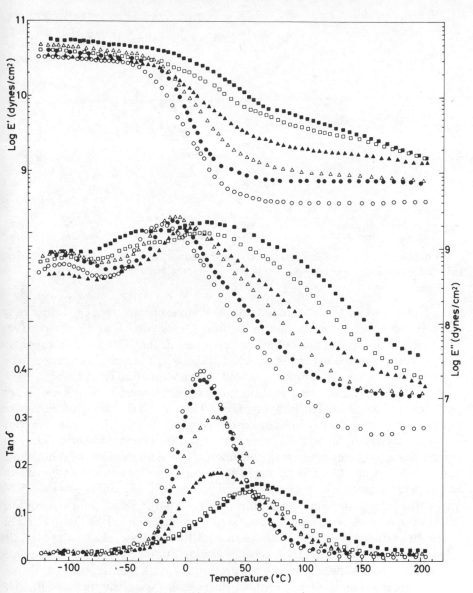

Fig. 7. Dependence of dynamic mechanical properties of PGA-PEG900 on PGA content; (○) PGA-PEG900 (30/70); (●) PGA-PEG900 (40/60); (△) PGA-PEG900 (50/50); (▲) PGA-PEG900 (60/40); (□) PGA-PEG900 (65/35); (■) PGA-PEG900 (70/30).

greatly on the nature of the continuous phase.[10] If a rigid component forms the continuous phase, an applied stress will be transmitted through the rigid continuous phase to a soft dispersed phase. If, on the other hand, the continuous phase is made of a soft omponent, the stress will not be effectively transmitted through the soft continuous phase to a rigid dispersed phase. This generalized picture appears to explain well the behavior of our particular network polymer systems, if we assume that a phase inversion takes place at around 60% PGA content. Moreover, our heterogeneous network polymer systems are very similar to segmented polyurethane block copolymers in the following respects: (1) they

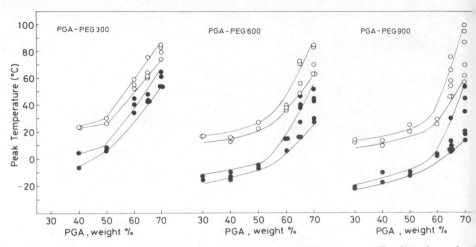

Fig. 8. Plot of peak temperature of tan δ (O) and E'' (●) vs PGA content. Two lines for each of tan δ and E'' indicate upper and lower limits of peak temperature.

consist of a hard and a soft component; (2) the hard component crystallizes and the soft component consists of a polyether; (3) the viscoelastic properties are attributed to the aggregation of the hard component; and (4) the hard-component domains are dispersed in the soft-component matrix, and a phase inversion takes place depending on the composition and the experimental conditions.

Huh et al.[11] studied the dynamic mechanical properties of polyester and polyether polyurethane block copolymers. They found that the glass transition temperatures were greatly influenced by the molecular weight of the soft component, the content of the hard component, and the thermal history. They assigned the relaxation process to the micro-Brownian motions of amorphous macroglycol segments. The effects of these influencing factors are very similar to our heterogeneous network systems when the PEG content is less than 50% and a similar explanation may be applicable. That is, when the PGA content is less than 50%, the continuous phase is presumably rich in PEG and the stress is almost exclusively carried by this soft continuous phase. Consequently, the relaxation has its origin in the micro-Brownian motions of the PEG segments, the tan δ curves are nearly symmetric around the peak temperatures, and their heights decrease as the PEG content decreases. With the increase in PGA content, the peak temperatures of tan δ and E'' shift to higher temperatures but slightly, because the increase in the content of PGA occurs almost exclusively in the dispersed phase. On the other hand, if the PGA content exceeds 60%, PGA, in turn, becomes the major constituent of the continuous phase. The relaxation arises not only from the micro-Brownian motions of the PGA segments in the disordered regions but also from the PEG segments. As a result, the tan δ curves become broad and unsymmetric. With the increase in the PGA content, the peak temperatures of tan δ and E'' shift to higher temperatures considerably because the increase in the PGA content occurs in the continuous phase.

A small peak is also recognized in E'' curves at $-35° \sim -45°C$; this is probably due to the micro-Brownian motions of the unconstrained PEG segments that are remote from the crosslink points. The high moduli ($E > 3 \times 10^8$ dynes/cm^2) that are observed above the transition region are probably due to the fact that

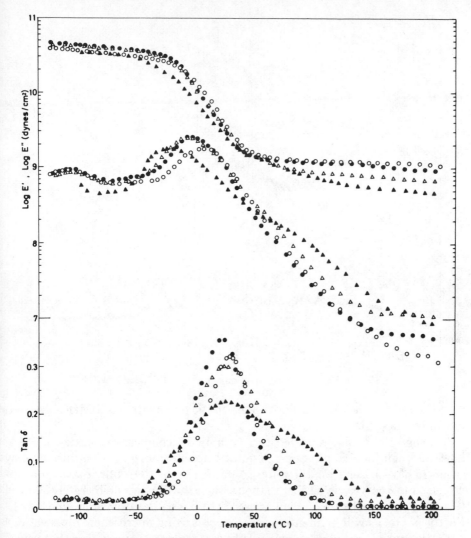

Fig. 9. Dependence of dynamic mechanical properties of PGA-PEG (50/50) on molecular weight of PEG; (○) PGA-PEG300 (50/50); (●) PGA-PEG600 (50/50); (△) PGA-PEG900 (50/50); (▲) PGA-PEG1800 (50/50).

the PGA component retains its rigid, rod-like α-helix conformation up to ca. 200°C.

At this point it may be worth reviewing some of the recent results reported for the viscoelastic behavior of polypeptide films.[12–25] In the studies on poly(γ-methyl D-glutamate) (PMDG), Kajiyama et al.[23,24] observed two kinds of crystalline relaxation processes in the temperature ranges of 150°–170°C (α_1 relaxation) and 180°–190°C (α_2 relaxation). They attributed the α_1 relaxation to shear deformation in the interhelix region of the crystals and the α_2 relaxation to tensile or bending deformations of the α-helix. They also assigned the β relaxation occurring at 100°–120°C to the micro-Brownian motions in the disordered region. Our previous study on a PGA film cast from N,N-dimethylformamide at 100°C showed the existence of a tan δ peak at ca. 135°C.[8] This

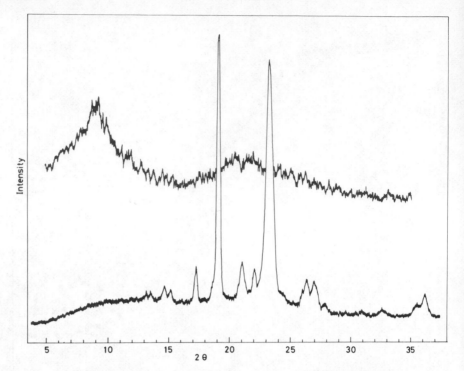

Fig. 10. Wide-angle x-ray diffraction patterns of PGA and PEG1800.

relaxation is now believed to correspond to the β relaxation of PMDG reported by Kajiyama et al.

Nguyen et al.[21] also reported the dynamic mechanical properties of PGA; however, their tan δ curve appeared quite different from ours. The discrepancy seems to have arisen from the water contained in the PGA film; for we, too, obtained a tan δ curve very similar to theirs when the film was deliberately allowed to absorb some moisture. In any event, PGA has a relaxation at around 135°C. Furthermore, as will be mentioned later, polarizing microscopic observations of heterogeneous network polymers at higher temperatures showed that bright regions existed up to 190° ± 10°C. This suggests that the ordered regions were not relaxed up to this temperature. Thus, we are inclined to believe that the observed relaxation of the heterogeneous network polymers with the PGA content larger than 60% is a superposition of the relaxations due to micro-Brownian motions of PEG segments (soft component) and those of PGA segments in the disordered regions.

Effects of Crosslink Density and Free Carboxyl Group Content

So far, we have been discussing the effect of PGA content while the molecular weight of PEG was kept constant. In this section, the situation is reversed; namely, we will discuss the effect of varying PEG molecular weight while the PGA content remains constant. An increase in the PEG molecular weight gives rise simultaneously to a decrease in crosslink density and an increase in the content of free carboxyl groups, as can be seen in Table II. According to Figures 8 and 9, an increase in the PEG molecular weight causes the following: (1) the peak

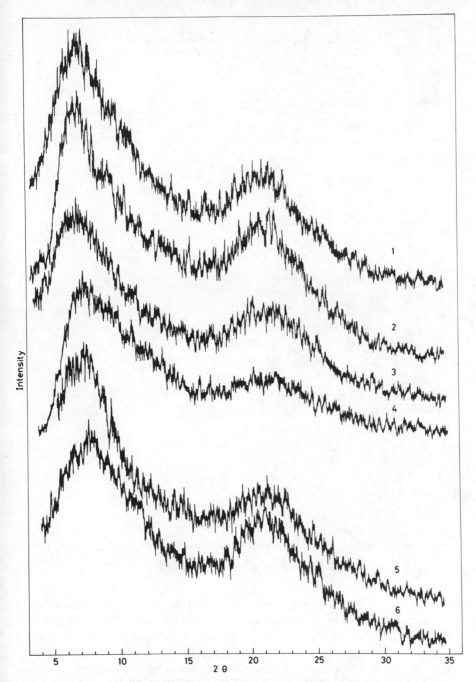

Fig. 11. Wide-angle x-ray diffraction patterns of (1) PGA-PEG600 (30/70), (2) PGA-PEG600 (40/60), (3) PGA-PEG600 (50/50), (4) PGA-PEG600 (60/40), (5) PGA-PEG600 (65/35), (6) PGA-PEG600 (70/30).

temperatures of tan δ and E'' shift to slightly lower temperatures; (2) the magnitude of E' above the transition regions decreases but slightly.

Ordinarily, crosslinking and hydrogen bonding influence very much the dynamic mechanical properties of a polymer above its transition temperature. In

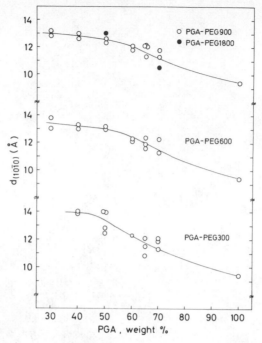

Fig. 12. Plot of $d_{10\bar{1}0}$ vs PGA content.

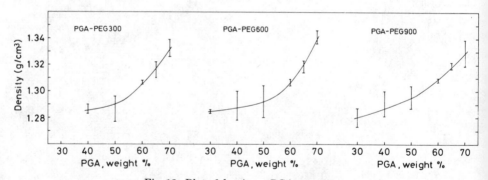

Fig. 13. Plot of density vs PGA content.

our heterogeneous network polymers, however, a decrease in crosslink density is always accompanied by an increase in hydrogen bonding due to the free carboxyl groups. Consequently, these two factors must cancel each other out to some extent. Observations (1) and (2) indicate that the effect of crosslink density is somewhat greater than that of the hydrogen bonding. In Figure 9, the existence of two tan δ peaks is recognized for PGA-PEG1800 (50/50). This suggests that when the PEG chain becomes very long, an extensive phase separation occurs.

X-Ray Diffraction

The state of aggregation affects very much the dynamic mechanical behavior of a composite system. In our PGA–PEG systems, the state of aggregation is

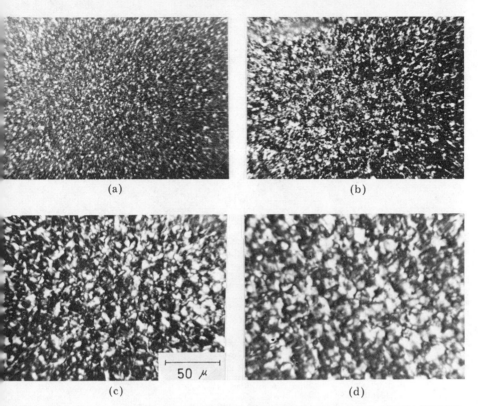

Fig. 14. Polarizing micrographs of PGA-PEG300: (a) PGA-PEG300 (40/60); (b) PGA-PEG300 (50/50); (c) PGA-PEG300 (60/40); (d) PGA-PEG300 (70/30).

governed by our choice of the composition, the relative amount of solvent used for sample preparation, and the rate of solvent evaporation, etc. To study the state of aggregation or the domain structures, we made use of wide-angle x-ray diffractions and polarizing microscopy. Figures 10 and 11 show x-ray diffraction patterns of PGA, PEG1800, and heterogeneous network polymers, respectively. PGA has a reflection at a Bragg angle of 2θ = ca. 9.3°, which is characteristic of the α-helix crystal structure.[26] PEG1800 has strong reflections at Bragg angles of 2θ = 17.0° (s), 18.8° (vs), 20.8° (s), and 23.1° (vs). We previously claimed, on the basis of wide-angle x-ray diffraction photographs, that PGA-PEG300 (60/40), 600 (60/40), 900 (60/40), and 1800 (60/40) were noncrystalline.[9] But the scintillation counting x-ray diffraction patterns given in Figure 11 indicate that every heterogeneous network polymer has a reflection at a Bragg angle of 2θ = 6°–9°, which probably corresponds to the $(10\bar{1}0)$ plane of the α-helix crystal form of PGA. Since the α-form crystal structure of PGA has not yet been determined, one might argue that the Bragg spacing could not necessarily be assigned to $(10\bar{1}0)$ spacing. Nevertheless, the α-helix crystal structure of poly(γ-methyl glutamate) is known.[27]

When PMDG is subject to partial hydrolysis, a linear relationship holds between the degree of hydrolysis and the α-helix spacing based on x-ray measurements.[28] By analogy, our assignment of the Bragg angle 2θ = 6°–9° to the $(10\bar{1}0)$ spacing seems reasonable. The lattice distance, $d_{10\bar{1}0}$, is plotted against the PGA content in Figure 12. A distinct break is recognized here again between

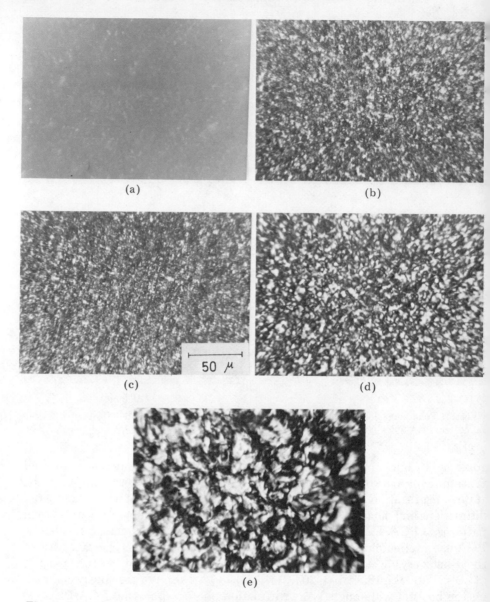

Fig. 15. Polarizing micrographs of PGA-PEG600: (a) PGA-PEG600 (30/70); (b) PGA-PEG600 (40/60); (c) PGA-PEG600 (50/50); (d) PGA-PEG600 (60/40); (e) PGA-PEG600 (70/30).

50% and 60% PGA. Since $(2/\sqrt{3}) \times d_{10\bar{1}0}$ corresponds to the distance between neighboring α-helices, the above observation means that the interhelix distance spreads gradually apart up until 40% PEG and suddenly becomes almost constant after a PEG content of ca. 50% is reached.

The density of heterogeneous network polymer is plotted against the PGA content in Figure 13. Also in this case, a break point is recognized between 50% and 60%.

It is well known that synthetic polypeptides form a cholesteric liquid crystal in various solvents,[29,30] and the cholesteric structure is retained also in the solid films prepared by evaporation of the solvents.[30-33] Friedman et al.[31] showed

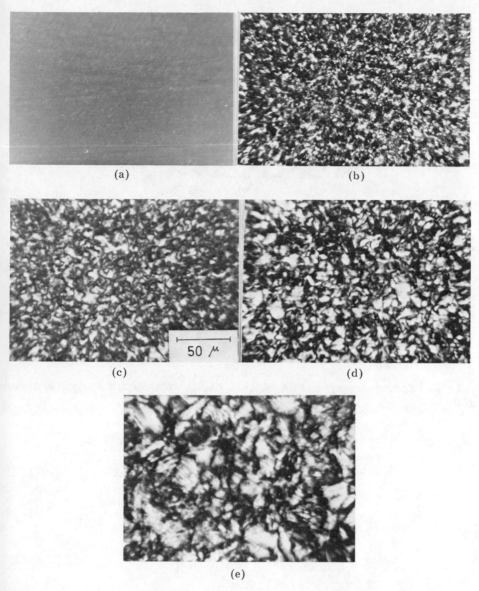

Fig. 16. Polarizing micrographs of PGA-PEG900: (a) PGA-PEG900 (30/70); (b) PGA-PEG900 (40/60); (c) PGA-PEG900 (50/50); (d) PGA-PEG900 (60/40); (e) PGA-PEG900 (70/30).

that solid PGA which was plasticized with 35% 3,3′-dimethylbiphenyl possessed a domain texture of parallel-packed chains. Moreover, Samulski et al.[33] showed that the cholesteric structure does exist in solid poly(γ-benzyl L-glutamate) (PBDG) plasticized with chlorinated polyphenyls; $d_{10\bar{1}0}$ spacing expands with an increase in the plasticizer content, but when the volume fraction of the plasticizer exceeds 0.5, $d_{1\bar{1}0}$ spacing stops expanding. In view of these properties of PGA and other polypeptides, we propose the following mechanism of microphase separation and the phase inversion in our heterogeneous network polymers which is consistent with the observed dynamic mechanical behavior, x-ray diffractions, and the densities.

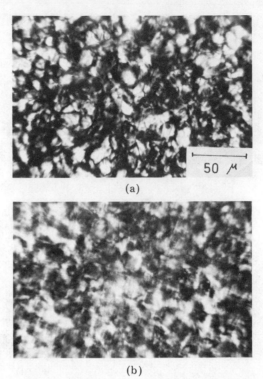

(a)

(b)

Fig. 17. Polarizing micrographs of PGA-PEG1800: (a) PGA-PEG1800 (50/50); (b) PGA-PEG1800 (70/30).

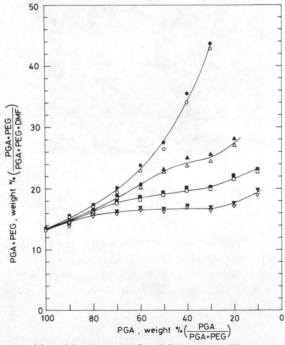

Fig. 18. Plot of composition of A point at 30°C vs PGA content. The concentration is expressed by PGA + PEG concentration. Filled and open marks indicate anisotropic and isotropic regions, respectively: (○) PGA-PEG300-DMF; (△) PGA-PEG900-DMF; (□) PGA-PEG1800-DMF; (▽) PGA-PEG4000-DMF.

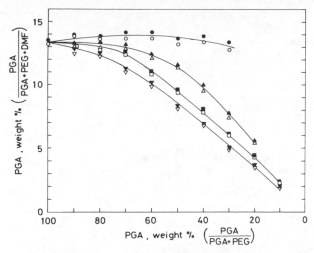

Fig. 19. Plot of composition of A point at 30°C vs PGA content. The concentration is expressed by PGA concentration. Filled and open marks indicate anisotropic and isotropic regions, respectively: (O) PGA-PEG300-DMF; (△) PGA-PEG900-DMF; (□) PGA-PEG1800-DMF; (▽) PGA-PEG4000-DMF.

Fig. 20. Polarizing micrographs of PGA-PEG900-DMF [PGA/PEG = 70/30, (PGA + PEG)/(PGA + PEG + DMF) × 100 = 18.5%].

Fig. 21. Polarizing micrographs of PGA-PEG900 (70/30).

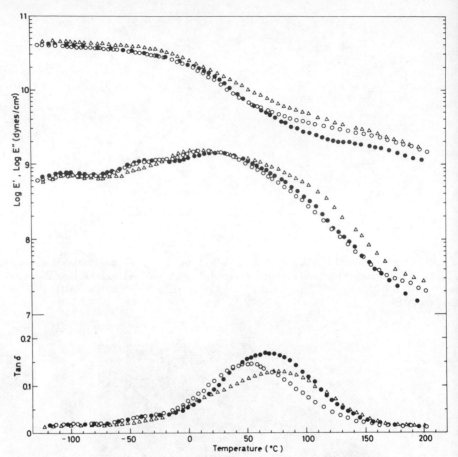

Fig. 22. Dynamic Mechanical Properties of PGA-PEG900 (65/35): (○) PGA-PEG900 (65/35); (●) PGA-PEG900 (65/35); (△) PGA-PEG900 (65/35).

The DMF solution of PGA and PEG is concentrated as the DMF evaporates, and the PGA α helix chains aggregate or form liquid crystals. The PEG chains, which are now chemically bound to PGA, are sandwiched by the PGA helices or curl around the PGA helices owing to hydrogen bonding between the carboxyl groups of PGA and the ether linkages of PEG. So far, as the PGA content is larger than 60%, most PEG chains can be accommodated within the interhelical regions of PGA. If the PGA becomes as lean as 50% or less, a considerable proportion of PEG cannot associate with PGA and forms a continuous phase; as a result, $d_{10\bar{1}0}$ no longer increases.

Polarizing Microscopy

The photographs of the heterogeneous network polymers taken under a polarizing microscope are shown in Figures 14–17. Optically anisotropic regions are present in every specimen except PGA-PEG600 (30/70) and 900 (30/70). The anisotropic regions exist up to 190° ± 10°C. The dimension and the concentration of the anisotropic regions decrease as the content of PGA decreases. When the PGA content is 70%, the size of bright spots is ca. 10–30 microns. If

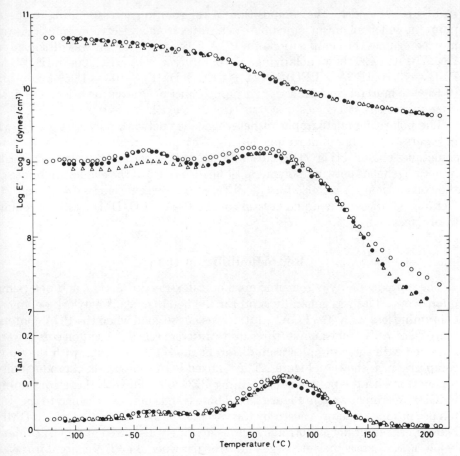

Fig. 23. Dynamic mechanical properties of PGA-PEG300 (70/30):   (○) PGA-PEG300 (70/30);
(●) PGA-PEG300 (70/30); (△) PGA-PEG300 (70/30).

the specimens are rotated, the bright and dark regions invert. This suggests that
most of the domains are oriented and that the direction of orientation of each
region varies.   On the other hand, when the PGA content is 40%, the size of bright
spots becomes smaller than a few microns and isotropic regions do exist; for some
regions that remain dark no matter how the specimens are rotated are observed.

The heterogeneous network polymer films consisting of 30% PGA and 70%
PEG are transparent and almost dark under a polarizing microscope. The results
of the polarizing microscopic observations provide more supporting evidence
for the inversion of phase separation in these systems. At 70% PGA content,
the rod-like α-helix chains of PGA aggregate, occluding most of the PEG chains
around them to form the optically anisotropic regions. At 40% PGA, part of the
PEG chains cannot be incorporated and they separately form the isotropic regions. At 30% PGA, the anisotropic regions due to PGA are so finely dispersed
that the film becomes optically isotropic and transparent.

In order to elucidate the mechanism of phase separation and phase structure,
it may be necessary to investigate the liquid crystals of the PGA–PEG–DMF
system. We found that the PGA–PEG–DMF system also formed a liquid crystal.

In Figures 18 and 19, the composition of the solution corresponding to the A point, at which an anisotropic phase separates from an isotropic solution, was plotted against the composition of a PGA–PEG mixture that was dissolved in DMF. Figure 20 shows polarizing micrographs of PGA-PEG900-DMF [PGA/PEG = 70/30, (PGA + PEG)/(PGA + PEG + DMF) × 100 = 18.5%] in a thin (0.15–0.18 mm) rectangular cell. The appearance of alternating bright and dark lines suggests that a cholesteric structure does exist.

The polarizing micrographs of heterogeneous network polymers are shown in Figures 14–17, but photographs having alternating bright and dark lines were sometimes obtained (Fig. 21). This indicates that a cholesteric structure persists in heterogeneous network polymers. The difference of the evaporation rate of the solvent may be a cause for the difference between Figures 14–17 and 21. Detailed studies of the liquid crystals of the PGA–PEG–DMF system are now in progress.

Reproducibility of Data

The reproducibility of dynamic mechanical, x-ray diffraction, and polarizing microscopic data was generally good for the heterogeneous network polymers containing less than 50% PGA. But, it was not so good when the PGA content was 65% or 70%. For example, three quite different sets of relaxation curves were obtained with three samples from different runs of preparation with the same composition, as shown in Figure 22. At a fixed PGA content, the reproducibility was better with the polymers containing PEG300 than with those containing PEG900, as can be seen in Figure 23. These trends may be ascribed to the difference in superstructure caused by the variation of the evaporation rate of DMF. Namely, the optically anisotropic regions are finely dispersed at a PGA content below 50%, whereas they are large and irregular when the PGA content was 65% or 70%, as shown in Figures 14–17. The superstructure in the latter case must be much more sensitive to minor fluctuations in the conditions of film preparations, e.g., rate of solvent evaporation, than in the former.

Despite the considerable scatter of the plots in Figures 8 and 12 due to the superstructure variations discussed above, there still is no doubt that there is a sudden change between 50% and 60% PGA content. Studies concerning the effect of the evaporation rate of DMF on the dynamic mechanical properties, x-ray diffraction patterns, and polarizing micrographs are in progress.

The authors express their thanks to Dr. R. Tanaka for his very helpful suggestions during the course of this study. PMDG used in this study was kindly supplied by Ajinomoto Co., Ltd. This study was supported in part by the Scientific Research Fund of the Ministry of Education of Japan.

References

1. L. Bohn, *Rubber Chem. Technol.*, **41**, 495 (1968).
2. B. Schneier, *J. Appl. Polym. Sci.*, **18**, 1999 (1974).
3. E. Hirata, T. Ijitsu, T. Soen, T. Hashimoto, and H. Kawai, *Polymer*, **16**, 249 (1975).
4. Y. J. Chang and G. L. Wilkes, *J. Polym. Sci., Polym. Phys. Ed.*, **13**, 455 (1975).
5. E. Pedemonte, G. Dondero, G. C. Alfonso, and F. Candia, *Polymer*, **16**, 531 (1975).
6. R. W. Seymour, J. R. Overton, and L. S. Corley, *Macromolecules*, **8**, 331 (1975).
7. T. Tanaka, T. Yokoyama, Y. Yamaguchi, M. Furukawa, and T. Mori, *J. Polym. Sci.*, **A-1, 9,** 2745 (1971).

8. T. Mori, Y. Kuchihara, R. Tanaka, and T. Tanaka, *J. Polym. Sci., Polym. Phys. Ed.,* **12,** 501 (1974).

9. T. Mori, R. Tanaka, and T. Tanaka, *J. Polym. Sci., Polym. Phys. Ed.,* **13,** 1633 (1975).

10. T. Miyamoto, K. Kodama, and K. Shibayama, *J. Polym. Sci. A-2,* **8,** 2095 (1970).

11. D. S. Huh and S. L. Cooper, *Polym. Eng. Sci.,* **11,** 369 (1971).

12. R. G. Saba, J. A. Sauer, and A. E. Woodward, *J. Polym. Sci. A-1,* **1,** 1483 (1963).

13. K. Hikichi, K. Saito, M. Kaneko, and J. Furuichi, *J. Phys. Soc. Jpn.,* **19,** 577 (1964).

14. J. V. Koleske and R. D. Lundberg, *Macromolecules,* **2,** 438 (1969).

15. M. Date, T. Takashita, and E. Fukada, *J. Polym. Sci. A-2,* **8,** 61 (1970).

16. A. Hiltner, J. M. Anderson, and E. Borkowski, *Macromolecules,* **5,** 446 (1972).

17. A. Tsutsumi, K. Hikichi, T. Takahashi, Y. Yamashita, N. Matsushima, M. Kanake, and M. Kaneko, *J. Macromol. Sci.-Phys.,* **B8,** 413 (1973).

18. M. Kuroishi, T. Kajiyama, and M. Takayanagi, *Chem. Lett.,* 659 (1973).

19. M. Ichikawa, R. Sakamoto, Y. Abe, and K. Makishima, *Kobunshi Kagaku,* **30,** 346 (1973).

20. T. Noda, Y. Abe, and R. Sakamoto, *Kobunshi Ronbunshu,* **31,** 203 (1974).

21. A. L. Nguyen, B. T. Vu, and G. L. Wilkes, *J. Macromol. Sci.-Phys.,* **B9,** 367 (1974).

22. T. Fukuzawa and I. Uematsu, *Polym. J.,* **6,** 431 (1974).

23. T. Kajiyama, M. Kuroishi, and M. Takayanagi, *J. Macromol. Sci.-Phys.,* **B11,** 121 (1975).

24. T. Kajiyama, M. Kuroishi, and M. Takayanagi, *J. Macromol. Sci.-Phys.,* **B11,** 195 (1975).

25. Y. Yamashita, A. Tsutsumi, K. Hikichi, and M. Kaneko, *Polym. J.,* **8,** 114 (1976).

26. K. Kondo, K. Shimizu, T. Hayakawa, and Y. Go, *Kobunshi Kagaku,* **28,** 510 (1971).

27. C. H. Bamford, A. Elliott, and W. E. Hanby, *Synthetic Polypeptides,* Academic Press, New York, 1956, p. 239.

28. T. Mori, T. Yamada, R. Tanaka, and T. Tanaka, to appear.

29. P. Salujian and V. Luzzati, *Poly-α-Amino Acids,* G. D. Fasman, Ed., Marcel Dekker, New York, 1967, p. 157.

30. E. T. Samulski and A. V. Tobolsky, in *Liquid Crystals and Plastic Crystals,* Vol. 1, G. W. Gray and P. A. Winsor, Eds., Ellis Horwood, Chichester, England, 1974, p. 175.

31. E. Friedman, C. Anderson, R. Roe, and A. V. Tobolsky, *J. Polym. Sci. B,* **10,** 839 (1972).

32. E. T. Samulski and A. V. Tobolsky, *Nature,* **216,** 997 (1967).

33. E. T. Samulski and A. V. Tobolsky, *Mol. Cryst. Liq. Cryst.,* **7,** 433 (1969).

Received August 24, 1976
Revised October 26, 1976

JOURNAL OF APPLIED POLYMER SCIENCE   VOL. 21, 3407-3415 (1977)

Graft Copolymerization Onto Starch.   II. Grafting of Acrylonitrile to Granular Native Potato Starch by Manganic Pyrophosphate Initiation.   Effect of Reaction Conditions on Grafting Parameters

RAKESH MEHROTRA and BENGT RÅNBY, *Department of Polymer Technology, The Royal Institute of Technology, S-100 44 Stockholm 70, Sweden*

Synopsis

The effect of reaction conditions on the composition of native potato starch–polyacrylonitrile graft copolymers initiated by manganic pyrophosphate onto starch slurries at 30°C has been examined. In general, when the Mn^{3+} ion concentration was increased from $0.15 \times 10^{-3}M$ to $3.0 \times 10^{-3}M$ (other conditions kept constant), an increase in conversion of monomer to polymer and % add-on was observed, whereas frequency of grafts (anhydroglucose units, AGU, per grafted chain) decreased. Also, the average molecular weights of grafts showed a decrease from 2.2×10^5 to 1.5×10^5. Increasing the concentration ratio of starch to monomer during polymerization by a factor of 3 produced an increase in the conversion of monomer to polymer, whereas an increase in frequency of grafts (AGU/chain) was obtained. Values of % add-on and average molecular weights of the grafts showed, however, a decreasing tendency. It was observed that grafting onto starch took place readily even at acid additions as low as $10 \times 10^{-3}M$ H_2SO_4 (pH $\simeq$ 1.8). Selective solvent extraction of homopolymer and extremely low conversions of monomer to polymer (0.1%–1.5%) in duplicate runs without addition of starch indicated that grafting efficiencies were high in all cases. An attempt has been made to interpret the results in terms of variations in factors such as initial ratio of $(Mn^{3+})/(AGU)$, termination rate of acrylonitrile chain radicals by oxidation by Mn^{3+} ions, oxidation rate of radicals formed on anhydroglucose units by Mn^{3+} ions, and physical factors such as diffusion rate of Mn^{3+} ions through the polyacrylonitrile-grafted starch granules for terminating the radicals.

INTRODUCTION

A recent communication in this series described the first successful attempt to graft copolymerize vinyl monomers onto starch and its derivatives using the pyrophosphate complex of Mn^{3+} as initiator.[1] Grafting efficiencies and polymer yields were found to be high when starch and starch derivatives were grafted with acrylonitrile and methyl methacrylate. With acrylamide as monomer, however, low grafting efficiencies were obtained. This was attributed to oxidation of the enol of β-hydroxypropionamide by Mn^{3+} ions, which is an expected side reaction.

For studies of grafting of acrylonitrile onto starch and starch derivatives in granular form using Ce^{4+} initiation, the reader is referred to an extensive review by Fanta[2] and other papers.[3–7] This paper on Mn^{3+} initiation reports the effects of the reaction conditions on grafting parameters, i.e., grafting efficiency, % add-on, frequency on grafts, and the average molecular weights of the grafted chains, in grafting of acrylonitrile onto granular native potato starch using manganic pyrophosphate initiation. The definitions of grafting parameters are the same as given previously:[1,2] Grafting efficiency = percentage of the total synthetic polymer formed that has been grafted to the starch. % Add-on = percent synthetic polymer in the graft copolymer. Frequency of grafts = average number of anhydroglucose units (AGU) separating the grafted branches.

EXPERIMENTAL

Materials

Most chemicals used were analytical-grade reagents from Merck, Darmstadt, Germany, except for anhydrous magnesium sulfate from Mallinckrodt, U.S.A., and sodium hydroxide from EKA, Sweden, both analytical grade. The granular native potato starch used in the grafting reactions was supplied by AB Stadex, Malmö, Sweden. The acrylonitrile (synthetic grade from Merck) contained monomethyl ether of hydroquinone as inhibitor which was removed using aqueous alkali. The monomer was then dried with anhydrous magnesium sulfate, distilled under reduced pressure of N_2, and stored in the dark at 4°C.

Preparation of the Initiator

Concentrations of $MnSO_4 \cdot H_2O$ and $KMnO_4$ in water were selected so that for each desired Mn^{3+} concentration in the reaction vessel, 25 ml $KMnO_4$ solution was required to oxidize 25 ml $MnSO_4$ solution. For a particular concentration of Mn^{3+} ions desired in the reaction vessel, 25 ml of a solution of Mn^{2+} ions prepared according to Table I was added to a solution of sodium pyrophosphate, prepared by dissolving 6.69 g $Na_4P_2O_7 \cdot 10H_2O$ in 250 ml distilled water. The

TABLE I
Quantities of $MnSO_4 \cdot H_2O$ and $KMnO_4$
for the Preparation of the Manganic Pyrophosphate Initiator

$MnSO_4 \cdot H_2O$ per 100 ml distilled water, g	0.1217	0.2434	0.4057	0.8113	1.623	2.0285	2.434
$KMnO_4$ per 100 ml distilled water, g	0.0285	0.0569	0.095	0.1897	0.379	0.4745	0.569
Resulting concentration of Mn^{3+} in reaction vessel, mmole/l.	0.15	0.3	0.5	1.0	2.0	2.5	3.0

TABLE II
Volumes of Distilled Water Acidified with
Concentrated H_2SO_4 (96 wt-%) to Obtain Different Concentrations of H_2SO_4

Concentration of H_2SO_4 in reaction vessel, mmole/l.	10	20	40	80
Distilled water for 5 ml 96 wt-% H_2SO_4, ml	7200	3600	1800	900

pH of the resulting solution was adjusted to 6 by adding concentrated H_2SO_4 and using a Beckman Expandomatic pH Meter. The pH values of the solution were checked against standard buffers supplied by Merck. The Mn^{2+} solutions were then oxidized to Mn^{3+} ions by titrating potentiometrically with an aqueous $KMnO_4$ solution (Mn^{7+} ions) by the method of Lingane and Karplus[8] using a Metrohm EA 201 platinum electrode. The weight of $KMnO_4$ dissolved in 100 ml distilled water corresponded to the desired concentration of Mn^{3+} ions in the reaction vessel in accordance with Table I.

About 25 ml of the permanganate solution was required for each 25-ml batch of $MnSO_4$ solution. A total of 300 ml initiator solution was prepared; 25 ml of this solution was used in grafting each batch. A glass electrode was used for all pH measurements with a saturated calomel electrode as reference.

Graft copolymerization

A known weight (7.5, 10, 15, or 20 g on a moisture-free basis) of native potato starch was slurried in 100 ml acidified distilled water of the desired concentration (prepared as indicated in Table II) in a reaction vessel which was immersed in a thermostatically controlled water bath maintained at 30°C. The reaction vessel was equipped with a stirrer, a condenser, a thermometer, and a dropping funnel. Twenty-five milliliters of the initiator solution (pH 6) of the total 300 ml prepared according to the procedure previously described and corresponding

TABLE III
Reproducibility of Grafting Reactions[a]

Expt. no.	Product yield, g	Conversion of monomer to polymer, g/batch (%)	Grafting efficiency, %	% Add-on	Average molecular weight of grafted chains ($\overline{M}_n$)	Frequency of grafts, AGU/chain
1	37.7	17.7 (88.5)	98.1	46.5	156,000	1100
2	37.5	17.5 (87.5)	97.7	46.1	141,000	1020

[a] Starch substrate: 20 g potato starch (dry basis); $(H_2SO_4) = 80 \times 10^{-3}M$; acrylonitrile: 25 ml = 20.25 g; $(Na_4P_2O_7) = 10 \times 10^{-3}M$; reaction time = 3 hr; temperature = 30°C; $(Mn^{3+}) = 2.0 \times 10^{-3}M$.

TABLE IV
Effect of Decreasing Acidity on Grafting with Manganic Pyrophosphate[a]

Expt. no.	H_2SO_4 concn., mmole/l.	Product yield, g	Conversion of monomer to polymer, g/batch (%)	Grafting efficiency, %	% Add-on	Average molecular weight of grafted chains ($\overline{M}_n$)	Frequency of grafts, AGU/chain
1	80	37.7	17.7 (88.5)	98.1	46.5	156,000	1100
2	40	37.6	17.6 (88.0)	96.6	45.9	192,000	1400
3	20	37.5	17.5 (87.5)	97.11	45.95	185,000	1340
4	10	37.45	17.45 (87.25)	97.1	45.9	184,000	1340

[a] Starch substrate: 20 g (dry basis); acrylonitrile: 25 ml = 20.25 g; $(Na_4P_2O_7) = 10 \times 10^{-3}M$; reaction time = 3 hr; temperature = 30°C; $(Mn^{3+}) = 2.0 \times 10^{-3}M$.

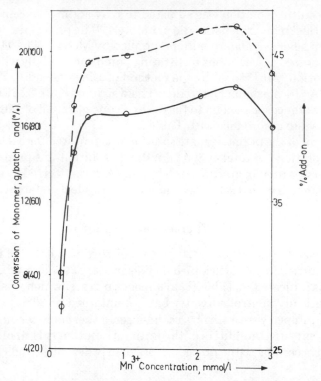

Fig. 1. Total conversion of monomer (——) and % add-on (– – – –) in grafting of AN onto starch. Reaction conditions: starch substrate = 20 g (dry basis); (H_2SO_4) = 80 mmole/l.; acrylonitrile = 25 ml = 20.25 g; ($Na_4P_2O_7$) = $10 \times 10^{-3}M$; reaction time = 3 hr; temperature = 30°C.

to the concentration of Mn^{3+} ions desired in the reaction vessel was placed in one chamber of the dropping funnel together with 25 ml purified acrylonitrile (AN).

A brisk stream of oxygen-free nitrogen (purified by passing through a bed of BASF R 3-11 regenerated catalyst pellets maintained at about 100°C) was bubbled for 30 min through the starch slurry in the reaction vessel and the initiator solution plus monomer in the dropping funnel. At 30°C, the content of the dropping funnel (i.e., initiator plus monomer) was emptied into the reaction vessel and the reaction allowed to proceed for 3 hr (all operations in an atmosphere of purified N_2). The temperature in the vessel was maintained between 30° and 32°C by cooling the water bath with ice. Without cooling, the temperature in the reaction vessel could increase to nearly 55°C owing to the heat of polymerization. After termination of the polymerization by letting air into the vessel, the reaction product was filtered, thoroughly washed with water, and dried overnight in a stream of dry air at 60°C.

The products of the grafting reactions were characterized as described previously.[1] In one case, the reaction products were extracted with hot N,N-dimethylformamide (DMF) by the procedure of Houtz.[9,10] Thus, a sample of approximately 2 g of the reaction product from experiment 1, Table III, was added to 100 ml DMF (being vigorously stirred) which had been previously cooled to 0°C in a flask. After a few minutes, the stirring was dicontinued and the slurry heated to 150°C for a period of nearly 45 min. The highly swollen mass was allowed to settle and the content of the flask cooled to room temperature. The

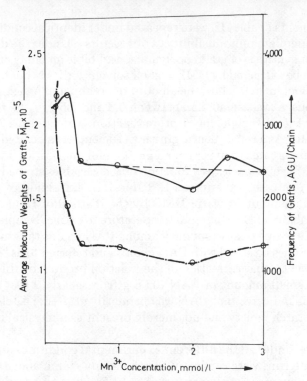

Fig. 2. Average molecular weight of grafts (——) and frequency of grafts (– · – · – · –) in grafting of AN onto starch. Reaction conditions: starch substrate = 20 g (dry basis); (H_2SO_4) = 80 mmole/l.; acrylonitrile = 25 ml = 20.25 g; $(Na_4P_2O_7)$ = 10 × 10 ^{-3}M; reaction time = 3 hr; temperature = 30°C.

clear extract, 20 ml, was added to an excess of distilled water to precipitate homopolymer (i.e., polyacrylonitrile). The precipitate was filtered, dried, and weighed on a porous glass filter to give the amount of homopolymer in 20 ml of the DMF extract.

RESULTS AND DISCUSSION

Based on studies of low molecular weight glycol compounds,[11] a reaction mechanism for initiation of graft copolymerization of vinyl monomers onto starch can be proposed. It should primarily involve the cleavage of glycol groups of the anhydroglucose units (AGU) in amylose and amylopectin as proposed in our previous paper.[1] The rate-determining step in the glycol-cleaving reaction of manganic pyrophosphate[11] appears to be the dissociation of the glycol–Mn^{3+} complex. The overall glycol-cleaving rate is governed by several factors,[12] such as Mn^{3+} concentration, "free" pyrophosphate concentration (taken as the difference between the total pyrophosphate concentration and thrice the Mn^{3+} concentration[12]), the acidity, and the glycol concentration.

We have kept the total pyrophosphate concentration constant at 10 × 10^{-3}M, while the initial Mn^{3+} concentration has been increased from 0.15 × 10^{-3} to 3.0 × 10^{-3}M. The concentration of anhydroglucose units was varied by increasing the amount of starch from 7.5 g to 20 g on a moisture-free basis. The acidity was varied by changing the H_2SO_4 concentration from 10 × 10^{-3}M to 80 × 10^{-3}M.

Two experiments (Table III) were repeated under identical conditions. They demonstrate adequate reproducibility of our results. Under the different conditions used for synthesis of graft copolymers, neglibible amounts of the reaction products could be extracted by DMF, a good solvent for PAN but a poor solvent for the graft copolymer.[2] Thus, the amount of homopolymer, estimated as described previously,[1] was small, i.e., between 0.3 and 0.5 g of the total product obtained after the graft copolymerization reaction, which means 2%–3% of the polymer formed. As a consequence, grafting efficiencies calculated as described previously[1] were greater than 96% in all graft copolymerization experiments.

Plots of grafting efficiencies as a function of the variables studied give no clear relations. In one case (experiment 1, Table III), extraction of the reaction product was carried out by warm DMF by the method of Houtz[9,10] to check whether the inability of DMF at room temperature to extract completely all PAN homopolymer was due to any tendency among PAN chains to associate (a phenomenon sometimes observed with PAN chains and referred to as "balling" [9,10]). We found, however, that extraction of the reaction product by this method removed only a small amount of PAN (0.08 g from nearly 2 g of the reaction product). This indicates that PAN was primarily grafted, i.e., chemically attached to the starch moiety and not merely present as a physical mixture with starch.

Furthermore, under all the different experimental conditions studied in this paper, duplicate runs were carried out without any starch added. Negligible conversion of monomer to polymer (i.e., 0.1%–1.5%) was observed as compared to conversions between 50% and 90% in the presence of starch substrate. These low conversions in the absence of starch substrate are presented as additional evidence for high grafting efficiencies obtained under all experimental conditions investigated in this paper. The results appear to be consistent with previous observations, indicating the high specificity of attack by manganic pyrophosphate on glycols, aldehydes, and ketones in spite of its inactivity toward acrylonitrile as reviewed by Waters.[11]

Since it is known that the glycol cleaving reaction of manganic pyrophosphate proceeds at a slower rate with decreasing acidity, it was of interest to observe whether or not any substantial grafting occurred at decreased acidity. The results obtained when the H_2SO_4 concentration was decreased from $80 \times 10^{-3}M$ to $10 \times 10^{-3}M$ are presented in Table IV. Normally, the H_2SO_4 concentration was kept at $80 \times 10^{-3}M$. We found that grafting occurred readily even at H_2SO_4 concentrations as low as $10 \times 10^{-3}M$. Grafting efficiencies were high, and both the products yields and the values of % add-on were high and showed only slight variations with acidity. When H_2SO_4 concentration was $80 \times 10^{-3}M$, the average molecular weight of grafted chains of PAN decreased by nearly 25%, and this fact is reflected in the more frequent grafts obtained. The reason for this variation is not clear, but one explanation may be the faster rate of termination at acidities as high as $80 \times 10^{-3}M$ by Mn^{3+} ions like most other oxidation reactions of this ion.[11]

The effect of the initiator concentration on various grafting parameters was studied by a 20-fold variation in Mn^{3+} concentration from 0.15×10^{-3} to $3.0 \times 10^{-3}M$. Figure 1 shows that conversion of monomer to polymer increased from 40.2% to 82% when Mn^{3+} concentration was increased from $0.15 \times 10^{-3}M$ to $0.5 \times 10^{-3}M$.

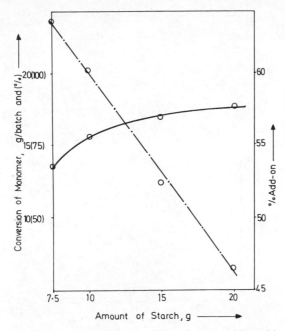

Fig. 3. Total conversion of monomer (———) and % add-on (– · – · – · –) in grafting of AN onto starch. Reaction conditions: $(Mn^{3+}) = 2.0 \times 10^{-3}M$; $(H_2SO_4) = 80 \times 10^{-3}M$; acrylonitrile $= 25$ ml $= 20.25$ g; $(Na_4P_2O_7) = 10 \times 10^{-3}M$; reaction time $= 3$ hr; temperature $= 30°C$.

Since a 20% decrease in average molecular weights of grafts was observed in this range (Fig. 2), the increased conversion was due to more frequent grafts (shown as a sharp decrease of AGU/chain in Fig. 2).   Increased Mn^{3+} concentration means also higher Mn^{3+}/AGU ratio.   A further increase in conversion of monomer to polymer from 82% to 88.5% was observed when Mn^{3+} concentration was increased from $0.5 \times 10^{-3}M$ to $2.0 \times 10^{-3}M$, and this is also attributable to an increasing number of grafts (Fig. 2) and a slight tendency for decreasing average molecular weights of grafts (Fig. 2).   Between Mn^{3+} concentrations $2.0 \times 10^{-3}M$ and $3.0 \times 10^{-3}M$, a slight maximum (i.e., at 91.5%) in conversion of monomer to polymer was observed at $Mn^{3+} = 2.5 \times 10^{-3}M$ and the value dropped to 80% at $Mn^{3+} = 3.0 \times 10^{-3}M$ (Fig. 1).   Since grafting efficiencies were high (greater than 95%) and almost constant, the curve for % add-on (Fig. 1) takes nearly the same shape as the curve of conversion of monomer to polymer (Fig. 1), and the same explanations hold in this case.   The average molecular weights of grafts were nearly 20% higher at 0.15 and $0.3 \times 10^{-3}M$ of Mn^{3+} than at all other concentrations of Mn^{3+}.   This may be attributed to a slower termination rate in the former case than in the latter by Mn^{3+} ions. Between Mn^{3+} concentrations of $0.5 \times 10^{-3}M$ and $3.0 \times 10^{-3}M$, the molecular weights of grafts showed only about 10% variation.

We studied the effects of the amount of starch used in the grafting reactions by varying it nearly threefold from 7.5 to 20 g.   Figure 3 shows that conversion of monomer to polymer increased from 68% to 88.5% as the amount of starch was increased from 7.5 to 20.0 g (on a dry basis).   The add-on (i.e., % synthetic polymer in graft copolymer[1,2]) decreased from 63.6% to 46.5% with increasing amounts of starch (Fig. 3).

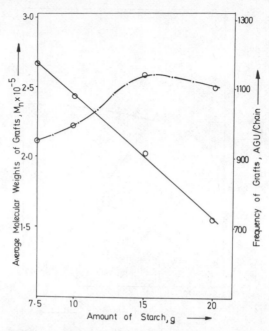

Fig. 4. Average molecular weight of grafts (——) and frequency of grafts (– · – · – · –) in grafting of AN onto starch. Reaction conditions: $(Mn^{3+}) = 2.0 \times 10^{-3}M$; $(H_2SO_4) = 80 \times 10^{-3}M$; acrylonitrile = 25 ml = 20.25 g; $(Na_4P_2O_7) = 10 \times 10^{-3}M$; reaction time = 3 hr; temperature = 30°C.

The slight increase in monomer conversion with increasing amount of starch charged may be attributed to the larger number of sites available for initiation of grafting. The % add-on decreases, however, because the amount of polymer formed increases more slowly than the amount of starch charged. A threefold increase in starch: Mn^{3+} ratio produced only a 20% variation in grafting frequency. The slight reduction in AGU/graft ratio observed at low starch concentration is due to the higher Mn^{3+}: starch ratio.

The increase in average molecular weights of the PAN chains as the amount of starch is decreased (Fig. 4) may be explained by considering that higher values of add-on of PAN at low amounts of starch may act as a stronger barrier to the diffusion of Mn^{3+} ions required for termination of the AN chain radicals by oxidation. It may also be due to higher propagation rates caused by higher ratios of monomer to the total number of radicals initiating grafting at lower amounts of starch. The total conversion of monomer to polymer (expressed as g/batch and % and depicted in Fig. 3) is dependent on the total number of radical sites capable of initiating graft copolymerization and the average molecular weights of the grafted chains so formed. Although the initial availability of Mn^{3+} ions per AGU decreases as the amount of starch charged in a grafting reaction increases, the total number of radicals formed which initiate grafting in the whole batch may be expected to increase with increasing amounts of starch. This increase in the total number of radicals leading to grafting becomes large enough to more than overcome the decrease in average molecular weights of PAN grafts with increasing amounts of starch. This would explain the increasing value of total conversion of monomer to polymer with increasing amount of starch as given in Figure 3.

It is known[2] that an increase in starch pretreatment temperature from 25° to 60° or 80°C increases the average molecular weights of grafts by a factor of 5–10 while grafting acrylonitrile onto starch by Ce^{4+} initiation. The effect of granule swelling on the graft copolymer composition is being studied and shall be reported in a forthcoming publication.

CONCLUSIONS

Based on the results presented in this paper, we conclude that manganic pyrophosphate is an efficient initiator for grafting of acrylonitrile onto starch under a wide range of experimental conditions. Little or no polyacrylonitrile is formed as homopolymer in physical mixture with the starch substrate.

Grafting parameters such as conversion of monomer to polymer, % add-on, and frequency of grafts can be varied within appreciable limits by varying the $(Mn^{3+})/(AGU)$ ratio, the substrate/monomer ratio, and, to some extent, the acidity. Changes in average molecular weights of grafts were substantial (from 2.6×10^5 to 1.5×10^5) when the substrate/monomer ratio was increased by a factor of 3.

The authors express their gratitude to AB Stadex, Malmö, Sweden, for generous financial support and The Swedish Institute, Stockholm, for a fellowship to R. M.

References

1. R. Mehrotra and B. Rånby, *J. Appl. Polym. Sci.*, **21**, 3407 (1977).

2. G. F. Fanta, in *Block and Graft Copolymerization,* Vol. 1, R. J. Ceresa, Ed., Wiley-Interscience, New York, 1973, p. 1.

3. G. F. Fanta, R. C. Burr, C. R. Russell, and C. E. Rist, *J. Appl. Polym. Sci.*, **13**, 133 (1969).

4. M. O. Weaver, L. A. Gugliemelli, W. M. Doane, and C. R. Russell, *J. Appl. Polym. Sci.*, **15**, 3015 (1971).

5. L. A. Gugliemelli, M. O. Weaver, C. R. Russell, and C. E. Rist, *J. Polym. Sci.*, **B9**, 151 (1971).

6. G. F. Fanta, R. C. Burr, W. M. Doane, and C. R. Russell, *J. Appl. Polym. Sci.*, **15**, 2651 (1971).

7. G. F. Fanta, F. L. Baker, R. C. Burr, W. M. Doane, and C. R. Russell, *Die Stärke,* **25** (5), 157 (1973).

8. J. J. Lingane and R. Karplus, *Ind. Eng. Chem., Anal. Ed.,* **18**, 191 (1946).

9. C. W. Davis and P. Shapiro, in *Encyclopedia of Polymer Science and Technology,* Vol. 1, H. F. Mark, N. G. Gaylord, and N. M. Bikales, Eds., Interscience, New York, 1964, p. 347.

10. R. C. Houtz (to E. I. du Pont de Nemours and Co., Inc.) U.S. Pat. 2,404,713 (1946).

11. W. A. Waters, *Q. Rev. (London),* **12**, 296 (1958).

12. A. Y. Drummond and W. A. Waters, *J. Chem. Soc.,* 3119 (1953).

Received September 23, 1976
Revised October 27, 1976

JOURNAL OF APPLIED POLYMER SCIENCE   VOL. 21, 3417–3426 (1977)

Effect of Slack Mercerization and Tension Mercerization on the Breaking Load Distribution of Cotton Fibers

T. H. SOMASHEKAR, A. K. KULSHRESHTHA, T. NARASIMHAM, and
N. E. DWELTZ, *Ahmedabad Textile Industry's Research Association,
Ahmedabad, India*

Synopsis

It has been shown that the breaking load histograms of raw, slack-mercerized, and mercerized-stretched cottons can be represented by β-distributions. The breaking load distribution is positively skewed for raw cotton. The influence of slack mercerization is to make the distributions symmetric and to reduce the variability of the breaking load by the elimination of weak links. The mode of the distribution shifts toward higher breaking load upon mercerization, and this shift increases with the extent of applied stretch. For various raw and mercerized cottons, the effect of increasing the gauge length is to reduce the mean, mode, and variability of the breaking load and to make the distributions less and less asymmetric. The application of stretch to swollen fibers influences the load distribution on the side of higher load and renders the distribution asymmetric.

INTRODUCTION

Cotton fibers can be considerably modified in terms of crystallinity, orientation of crystallites, as well as tensile and mechanical properties by subjecting them to swelling and stretching treatments[1-4] with selected reagents. The swelling treatment causes a decrystallization[3] of cotton at certain optimal concentrations of the reagent. The orientation of crystallites in cotton is slightly improved upon slack swelling[4] (when the fibers are allowed to shrink freely in the swelling agent). When stretch is applied to cotton fibers after slack swelling and these swollen-stretched fibers are subsequently washed in water and air dried, substantial improvements occur[5] in the degree of crystallite orientation, static Young's modulus, and average single fiber tenacity. These improvements may be attributed to the removal of structural imperfections or weak links in cotton during the combined swelling and stretching process.

The methodology for obtaining and analyzing the breaking load distribution of single cotton fibers has been described in detail in an earlier investigation.[6] It has been found that the rupture load in various raw cottons studied follows a β-distribution,[6] and the shape of this distribution is influenced by factors such as fiber maturity and the presence of weak links in the fibers.

The present paper attempts to examine the influence of fiber mercerization on the distribution of the breaking load. For this purpose, cotton fibers have

3417

been modified by controlled swelling and stretching in a 24% (w/w) aqueous sodium hydroxide solution. The breaking load data for various modified fibers were obtained at several gauge lengths and were utilized to study the influence of mercerization on fiber weak links. The effect of applied stretch on the variability of breaking load in mercerized fibers was also studied.

EXPERIMENTAL

Materials

Karnak cotton belonging to *G. barbadense* species was selected for the present work because of its long staple length, which is desirable as there is considerable shrinkage in the length of fibers upon swelling. Waxes and pectinous materials were removed by 5 hr of Soxhlet extraction in chloroform, followed by 1 hr in 1% sodium carbonate at the boil.

Fiber Treatment

A parallelized bundle of fibers was subjected to 1 hr of swelling in 24% (w/w) aqueous sodium hydroxide solution at 65% R.H. and 27°C. Different degrees of stretch could be applied to fibers in the swollen state by making use of a stainless steel frame[4] provided with a vernier scale and a movable stud, which could receive one pair of jaws. The length of the fibers could be measured on this stretching device before and after swelling. The stretch applied to the fiber bundle during swelling is expressed in terms of the original length of the fiber bundle. Three levels of stretch were used:

(a) *Slack.* The bundle, which had contracted freely in the swelling agent, was stretched on the Instron tensile tester so that a very small tension was developed. The percent difference between this length and the original bundle length was expressed as the stretch for slack swelling (a negative value).

(b) *0% Stretch.* The jaws holding the slack-swollen fibers were transferred to the stretching device, and the bundle of swollen fibers was restored to original length (before swelling) prior to washing.

(c) *5% Stretch.* The swollen fiber bundle was stretched to 5% beyond the original length prior to washing.

Table I gives the designation of various swollen and stretched samples and also lists some of their useful properties.

TABLE I
Properties of Swollen and Stretched Fibers

Series no.	Sample	Stretch,[a] %	Abbreviation used in the text	Density, g/cc	Tex
1	Karnak dewaxed	—	raw	1.564	0.14
2	Karnak swollen in NaOH (24%, 27°C, 1 hr)	−15.0	NaOH (slack)	1.544	0.17
3	Same as 2.	0.0	NaOH (0)	1.536	0.16
4	Same as 2.	5.0	NaOH (5)	1.533	0.15

[a] Applied after swelling and maintained during washing and drying of fibers.

Measurement of Rupture Properties of Swollen Cottons

Three hundred single-fiber tests were carried out at 27°C and 65% R.H. on an Instron tensile tester, using a rate of extension of 50%/min and a full-scale sensitivity of 10 g. Various fiber samples were tested at five test lengths, namely, 0.2, 0.4, 0.6, 0.8, and 1.0 cm. The cross-head speed had to be changed accordingly so as to maintain the rate of extension at 50%/min. Vibroscopy of single fibers was not carried out. Instead, the average linear density was obtained by cutting, counting, and weighing 1-cm lengths of fibers.

Analysis of Breaking Load Distribution of Single Fibers

The breaking load data obtained from single-fiber tests were classified into frequency arrays. Using the detailed procedure published earlier,[6] the observed breaking load histograms of raw and swollen cottons were fitted by a β-type probability density function:

$$y = K.x^{m-1}(a - x)^{n-1}$$

where y is the frequency of any breaking load x, K is a constant, a is the range of distribution, and m and n are parameters determining the shape of the distribution.

The curve fitting of β-functions to the observed breaking load histograms was carried out on an IBM-360 computer. The program output consisted of observed and calculated frequencies of breaking load, chi-square, m, n, and a values. The mean and mode of the breaking load could be determined in terms of m, n, and a:

TABLE II
Criterion for Determining the Type of the Frequency Curve

Cotton sample[a]	Test gauge length, mm	k Factor	Type of breaking-load frequency curve
Raw	2	−0.3905	β
	4	−0.0051	β
	6	−0.0167	β
	8	−0.1438	β
	10	−0.0290	β
NaOH (slack)	2	−0.0066	β
	4	−0.0107	β
	6	−0.0023	β
	8	−0.0004	β
	10	−0.0188	β
NaOH (0)	2	+0.1016	Pearson type IV
	4	−0.0843	β
	6	−0.0641	β
	8	−0.0121	β
	10	−0.0196	β
NaOH (5)	2	−0.0341	β
	4	−0.6657	Pearson type IV
	6	+0.5438	Pearson type IV
	8	−0.2326	β
	10	+0.0002	Pearson type IV

[a] Egyptian Karnak.

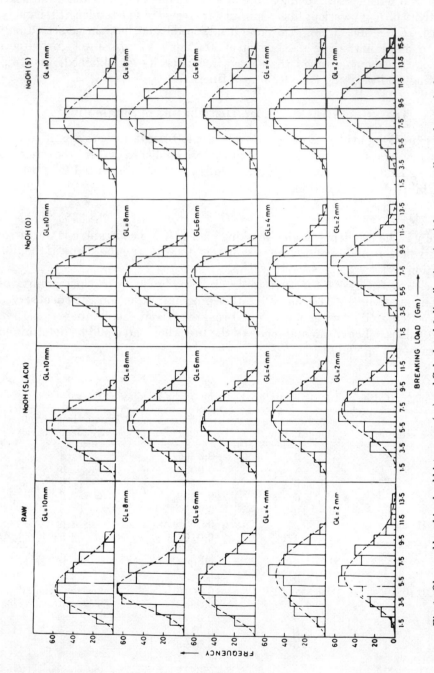

Fig. 1. Observed breaking load histograms (—) and Calculated β-distributions (- - -) for raw, swollen, and stretched cottons.

$$\text{mean} = \frac{m}{(m + n)} \cdot a$$

$$\text{mode} = \frac{(m - 1)}{(m + n - 2)} \cdot a$$

Prior to curve fitting, the information regarding the nature of the distribution was obtained using the k criterion of Pearson. The k factor was computed from the values of β_1 and β_2 determined[6] from the observed frequency data.

RESULTS

Table II lists the k criteria for raw, slack-swollen, and swollen-stretched samples at various test lengths. It turns out that 16 out of 20 breaking load histograms can be represented as β-distributions. In the remaining cases, all swollen-stretched samples NaOH (0) or NaOH (5), there is evidence regarding the existence of a Pearson type IV distribution. However, β-functions were fitted to all the histograms. The reasons for deviation of some of the histograms from a β-type frequency curve will be discussed later. The values of β_1 and β_2 listed in Table II also provide information regarding the asymmetry and breadth of the observed breaking load distributions. Since $\sqrt{\beta_1}$ is a measure of skewness, it would appear from the data presented in Table II that when the gauge length is increased, the distributions tend to become increasingly symmetric.

The observed breaking load histograms for raw, NaOH (slack), NaOH (0), and NaOH (5) cottons obtained at five different gauge lengths are shown in Figure 1. The fitted β-distributions are represented by the broken curves. It can be seen that the breaking load distribution becomes broader as the gauge length is decreased and also when the stretch applied subsequent to swelling is increased. Table III lists the values of the parameters m, n, a, χ^2, and the mean, mode, standard deviation, and coefficient of variation ($C.V.$) of the breaking load, obtained from the parameters of the fitted β-distributions. The chi-square values show that β-distributions give satisfactory fits to the observed histograms in most cases, with very few exceptions (marked "a" in Table III). The causes of unsatisfactory fits, particularly in the context of NaOH (5) cotton, will be discussed later.

The effect of increasing the gauge length is to reduce the constants m, n, and a, and the mean, mode, and standard deviation and to increase the $C.V.$ of the breaking load (Table III). The mode shifts to lower breaking loads as the gauge length is increased (Fig. 1). The decrease in breaking load with increase in gauge length is undoubtedly due to the "weak link effect." [7,8] Increase in $C.V.$ is merely a consequence of decreasing the mean breaking load. The variability of the breaking load decreases with increasing gauge length, as demonstrated by a reduction in the range a and the standard deviation (Table III).

Figure 2 shows a plot of the frequency constants m and n as a function of (a) applied stretch and (b) gauge length. The parameter n is more variant than m when the gauge length is changed. For raw cotton, n values are higher than m values at different gauge lengths, thus indicating a positively skewed distribution of the breaking load. For the slack-mercerized cotton, NaOH (slack), n, and m become nearly equal at all gauge lengths except the lowest, reflecting that the breaking load distributions have become symmetric or very nearly so. For NaOH

TABLE III

Variability of Breaking-Load in Raw Cotton and Various Swollen and Stretched Cottons

Series no.	Cotton sample[b]	Gauge length, mm	Parameters of fitted frequency curve			Goodness of fit χ^2	Measures of the Variability of Single Fiber Breaking Load				
			m	n	a		Mean, g	Mode, g	Standard deviation, g	C.V., %	Skewness
1	Raw	2	5.3	14.8	25.2	14	6.65	5.99	2.5	37.6	0.26
		4	2.8	2.6	11.2	11	5.81	5.93	2.4	41.3	-0.05
		6	2.9	3.5	11.5	8	5.21	4.97	2.1	40.3	0.11
		8	4.8	12.2	17.5	21[a]	4.94	4.43	2.0	40.5	0.26
		10	3.3	5.2	12.8	7	4.97	4.53	2.0	40.2	0.22
2	NaOH (slack)	2	6.4	12.1	21.5	18[a]	7.44	7.04	2.4	32.2	0.17
		4	4.1	4.5	13.7	4	6.53	6.43	2.3	35.2	0.04
		6	3.7	3.8	12.5	3	6.17	6.14	2.2	35.7	0.01
		8	3.6	4.0	12.6	9	5.97	5.85	2.3	38.5	0.05
		10	3.4	3.2	10.3	12	5.31	5.37	1.9	35.8	-0.03
3	NaOH (0)	2	8.7	13.8	21.0	11	8.12	8.29	2.3	28.3	-0.07
		4	8.1	16.0	23.1	14	7.76	7.42	2.2	28.4	0.15
		6	5.1	3.3	11.2	7	6.80	7.18	2.0	29.4	-0.19
		8	4.9	3.8	11.8	4	6.65	6.87	1.9	28.6	-0.12
		10	4.3	2.9	11.0	8	6.57	6.98	2.0	30.4	-0.20
4	NaOH (5)	2	8.6	18.8	30.3	26[a]	9.51	9.07	2.6	27.3	0.17
		4	8.9	21.9	30.5	10	8.81	8.37	2.6	29.5	0.17
		6	7.8	11.0	21.4	17	8.88	8.66	2.5	28.2	0.09
		8	8.3	12.2	20.5	14	8.30	8.09	2.5	30.1	0.08
		10	6.0	7.1	17.2	32[a]	7.88	7.75	2.5	31.7	0.05

[a] Empirical fits of β-distribution to the observed histograms are poor in these cases.
[b] Egyptian Karnak.

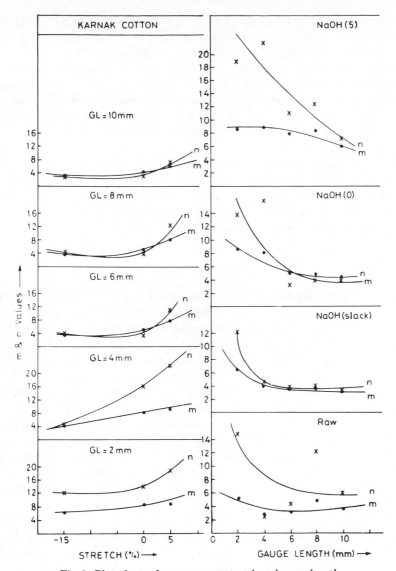

Fig. 2. Plot of m and n vs percent stretch and gauge length.

(0) and NaOH (5) cottons, n tends to be greater than m, particularly at lower gauge lengths. This difference between n and m is a function of applied stretch. The effect of increasing gauge length is to make the breaking load distributions less asymmetric. The increase in stretch makes the distributions more asymmetric, particularly at lower gauge lengths, where the difference between n and m is larger (Fig. 2).

On slack mercerization, the mode shifts to higher breaking loads at all gauge lengths (Fig. 1, Table III). The breaking load distributions become nearly symmetric. For NaOH (0) cotton, the mode shifts to still higher breaking load values, and, as a consequence, the breaking load distributions appear to be negatively skewed (Fig. 1, Table III). With further increase in applied stretch, i.e., for NaOH (5) cotton, the mode attains a maximum value. The breaking load distributions for NaOH (5) cotton become postively skewed again (Fig. 1) due to the strengthening of fibers on the higher load side of the distribution. The asymmetry, however, decreases with increasing gauge length.

The variability of breaking load, as inferred from standard deviation, is less for NaOH (slack) and NaOH (0) cottons than for raw cotton. NaOH (5), however, shows a greater variability of breaking load than raw cotton (Table III). This may also be inferred from values of the range a, which is not as reliable as standard deviation as a measure of variability. Mercerized cottons show a lower $C.V.$ than raw cotton.

When the gauge length is increased from 2 mm to 10 mm, the drop in average breaking load is 25%, 29%, 19%, and 17% for raw, NaOH (slack), NaOH (0), and NaOH (5), respectively. Stretching the cotton fibers subsequent to slack mercerization thus reduces the effect of weak-links and improves the uniformity of strength along the length of the fiber.

DISCUSSION

The x-ray orientation factors f_x for raw, NaOH (slack), NaOH (0), and NaOH (5) cottons are 0.70, 0.71, 0.84, and 0.88, respectively.[4] The improvement in breaking load in various slack and stretch-mercerized samples can largely be accounted for by an increase in the orientation of crystallites[9] in the fibers. The "weak links" in cotton fibers[10] can be places of low diameter, high internal strain (e.g., reversals), or nonglucosidic residues distributed randomly along the fiber length. Mercerization tends to strengthen each of these types of weak links. Wakeham and Spicer[11] showed that the tendency of cotton fibers to break preferentially at reversals is reduced by mercerization. Mercerization also improves the uniformity of the breaking load along the fiber length as is evident in the case of cottons NaOH (0) and NaOH (5) by the decreased effect of gauge length on the mean breaking load and also by the decreased $C.V.$ at a particular gauge length. The swelling and stretching treatments thus have an "annealing" effect on the fibers.

The distribution of single-fiber breaking load in raw cotton is due to the following: distortion of fiber shape, variation in fineness and intrinsic strength between fibers, and a variation in the breaking load along the length of fibers (i.e., the influence of weak links). Mercerization, which improves breaking load and the uniformity of fiber diameter, and removes some of the weak links, should, therefore, profoundly influence the distribution of the breaking load. In practice, however, the variation in breaking load between different fibers persists even after slack mercerization, hence the distribution is not greatly affected.

The breaking load distribution in raw cotton[6] is positively skewed. Upon slack mercerization, the distribution becomes nearly symmetric and shifts to a higher mode. This may be attributed to a relaxation of internal stresses and strains within fibers and also to the improved uniformity of fibers. For fibers which have been swollen and stretched to their original length, NaOH (0), the breaking load distribution shifts still further toward higher load values but becomes negatively skewed. The effect of stretch is not only to increase the crystallite orientation, but also to induce a reversion to a cellulose I lattice,[3,4] which is a more strained molecular configuration than cellulose II. The skewness may be due to this induced strain or may be produced by a strengthening of fibers on the higher load side of the mode. The breaking load distribution becomes positively skewed again and shifts to a still higher mode when the maximum stretch is applied to fibers after swelling [NaOH (5)]. This cotton has[4] as much as 17% cellulose I and a very high orientation factor of 0.88. The increase in crystallite orientation thus accounts for the development of very strong fibers, which contribute to the side of higher load in the distribution. The range (i.e., variability) of the distribution increases for NaOH (5); this may be partly explained in terms of recrystallized cellulose I.

It appears from Tables II and III that the distributions may not be conforming to the β-type for NaOH (5) cotton. This could be an artifact produced as a result of experimental difficulties in imparting uniformly the maximum stretch to alkali-swollen fibers. When fibers, with their ends gripped between jaws and wet with NaOH, are stretched, there may be some slippage of the fibers relative to each other, particularly at high levels of stretch. As a consequence, all the fibers may not be stretched to the same extent. This possibility, coupled with a reversion to cellulose I lattice,[4] induces a variability in the breaking load of NaOH (5) cotton and the standard deviation is consequently increased (Table III).

CONCLUSIONS

Mercerization influences the initial portion of the breaking load frequency curve (i.e., the portion of low breaking loads) by strengthening the weak fibers. As a result, the frequency curve becomes symmetric, the mode shifts to higher load values, and a higher mean and a lower $C.V.$ are obtained for breaking load. With increasing stretch applied after swelling, a progressive increase in the mean and a decrease in the $C.V.$ of the breaking load are obtained. However, the frequency curves for swollen-stretched cotton become skewed, presumably due to the development of stronger fibers which affect the tail on the high load side. With a few exceptions, the breaking load histograms of mercerized cottons can be satisfactorily represented by a β-distribution. The breaking load variability in cotton is reduced by slack mercerization as well as by increasing the gauge length.

The authors wish to thank the Director, ATIRA, for his kind permission to publish this work. They are grateful to Dr. V. S. Joshi for collecting the single-fiber data and to Shri N. R. Kothari for his assistance in computer processing of data. This research has been financed in part by a grant made by the United States Department of Agriculture, under PL-480.

References

1. Final Project Report on PL-480 Project FG-In-139, A Study of the Relation Between Fine Structure and Mechanical Properties of Cotton Fibers by Swelling and Stretching Treatments, as a Means of Improving the Properties and Thereby Increasing the Utilization of Cotton, ATIRA, Ahmedabad, India August 1967.

2. Modification of Cellulose and Other Polysachharides, ATIRA Silver Jubilee Monograph, ATIRA, Ahmedabad, India 1974.

3. N. B. Patil, N. E. Dweltz, and T. Radhakrishnan, Text. Res. J., 35, 517 (1965).

4. V. S. Joshi, B. R. Shelat, and T. Radhakrishnan, Text. Res. J., 37, 989 (1967).

5. V. S. Joshi, Ph.D., dissertation Gujarat University, 1968.

6. T. H. Somashekar, T. Narasimham, A. K. Kulshreshtha, and N. E. Dweltz, J. Appl. Polym. Sci., 21, 3417 (1977).

7. F. T. Peirce, *J. Text. Inst.*, **17,** T355 (1926).

8. L. J. Knox, Jr., and J. C. Whitwell, *Text. Res. J.*, **41,** 510 (1971).

9. R. S. Orr, A. W. Burgis, F. R. Andrews, and J. N. Grant, *Text. Res. J.*, **29,** 349 (1959).

10. J. O. Warwicker, R. Jeffries, R. L. Colbran, and R. N. Robinson, *A Review of the Literature on the Effect of Caustic Soda and Other Swelling Agents on the Fine Structure of Cotton,* Pamphlet No. 93, Shirley Institute, Manchester, England, December 1966.

11. H. Wakeham and N. Spicer, *Text. Res. J.*, **21,** 187 (1951).

Received August 31, 1976

JOURNAL OF APPLIED POLYMER SCIENCE   VOL. 21, 3427–3443 (1977)

Poly(carbamoyl Sulfonates) (Bisulfite Adducts of Polyisocyanates)

G. BRUCE GUISE, CSIRO, *Division of Textile Industry Belmont, Geelong, Victoria 3216, Australia*

Synopsis

In the reaction with aqueous sodium bisulfite of polyisocyanates derived from a poly(propylene oxide triol) (molecular weight 3000) and various diisocyanates, bisulfite adducts or poly(carbamoyl sulfonates) (PCS) are not formed unless a water-miscible lower alcohol or ether is used as solvent; and, with aromatic isocyanates, unless additional sulfite and/or a tertiary amine is added. The influence of reaction conditions on the yield of PCS has been examined in detail for the polyisocyanates derived from hexamethylene diisocyanate and 2,4-tolylene diisocyanate. PCS are water soluble, stable in acid solution, and hydrolyze in alkaline solution or on heating to insoluble polyureas. The chemistry of the reactions of PCS is reviewed and potential applications discussed.

INTRODUCTION

When Petersen[1] described in 1949 the formation and reactions of isocyanate bisulfite adducts (carbamoyl sulfonates),

Preparation:

$$RNCO + NaHSO_3 \rightarrow RNHCOSO_3^- \, Na^+ \qquad\qquad (i)$$

Side reactions:

$$RNCO + H_2O \rightarrow RNHCONHR$$

$$RNCO + R'OH \rightarrow RNHCOOR'$$

Reactions of carbamoyl sulfonates:

$$RNHCOSO_3^- \xrightarrow{\text{H}_2\text{O or OH}^-} RNHCONHR$$

$$RNHCOSO_3^- + R'NH_2 \rightarrow RNHCONHR'$$

he noted that they could be of use in textile finishing, particularly bifunctional products, as these would form high molecular weight condensation products on the fibers as a result of an initial aqueous treatment. Since then, only occasional reference[2,3] to carbamoyl sulfonates, mainly from low molecular weight mono- and diisocyanates, has been made. Even though polyisocyanates are widely used, the lack of methods to prepare PCS in high yields has prevented their exploitation. Work at CSIRO[4-8] has overcome this problem and resulted in the development of a new shrink-resist treatment for wool using PCS—the Sirolan BAP process.[8] Bayer AG· is now manufacturing a PCS for this application.

As part of the development of the Sirolan BAP process, the preparation and properties of PCS with various structures have been investigated in detail. This paper summarizes work on the bisulfite adducts (designated Ia ... etc.) of poly(ether polyisocyanates) I–XI prepared from a poly(propylene oxide triol) (molecular weight 3000, based on trimethylolpropane) and diisocyanates. Attention has been focused on the polyisocyanates I and II derived from hexamethylene diisocyanate and 2,4-tolylene diisocyanate, respectively, as these are typical aliphatic and aromatic diisocyanates and are similar to polyisocyanates used in surface coatings and cast elastomers. Shrink-resisting wool with PCS Ia–Xa has been reported briefly.[9] Work on other types of PCS will be reported later.

EXPERIMENTAL AND RESULTS

Commercial sodium metabisulfite of 95%–97% purity was used. These methods for the preparation of PCS are covered by CSIRO patent applications.

Preparation of Polyisocyanates

The polyisocyanates were prepared by heating dried Desmophen 3400 (Bayer), poly(propylene oxide triol), molecular weight 3000, and 5%–10% excess diisocyanate without solvent or catalysts for about 4 hr at the temperatures shown in Table I. The isocyanate content was determined by reaction with excess di-n-butylamine in dioxan and titration of the unreacted amine with hydrochloric acid.

TABLE I
Preparation of Polyisocyanates

Polyiso-cyanate[f]	Diisocyanate	Reaction temp., °C	Isocyanate content, %
I	Hexamethylene diisocyanate	110	3.5
II	2,4-Tolylene diisocyanate	60	4.1
III	Desmodur T65 (Bayer)[a]	60	4.2
IV	Desmodur T80 (Bayer)[a]	60	3.9
V	Isophorone diisocyanate (Veba)[b]	100	4.2
VI	Xylylene diisocyanate (Takeda)[c]	90	3.5
VII	Hylene W (du Pont)[d]	120	3.5
VIII	Trimethylhexamethylene diisocyanate (Veba)[e]	100	4.1
IX	2-Methoxycarbonylpentamethylene diisocyanate (Toray)	100	3.5
X	Bis(4-isocyanato-3-methylcyclohexyl)methane diisocyanate (BASF)	110	3.7
XI	4,4'-Diisocyanatodiphenylmethane	80	3.5

[a] 2,4- and 2,6-Tolylene diisocyanates, T65 = (65/35), T80 = (80/20).
[b] 3-Isocyanatomethyl-3,5,5-trimethylcyclohexylisocyanate.
[c] 70%-m and 30%-o.
[d] Bis(4-isocyanatocyclohexyl)methane.
[e] 2,2,4- and 2,4,4-Isomers.
[f] The corresponding PCS preparations have been numbered Ia ... etc.

Analysis of Carbamoyl Sulfonates

A PCS sample (5 g) was dissolved in a mixture of water (60 ml) and isopropanol (100 ml). Titration against 0.05M iodine solution containing potassium iodide to the iodine-color endpoint gives the free bisulfite content. Sodium hydroxide solution (10 ml of 300 g/l.) was then added to the titration solution and mixed thoroughly. After 2 min, this solution was acidified with sulfuric acid (25 ml of 200 g/l.) and immediately titrated against iodine. Sodium hydroxide quantitatively decomposes carbamoyl sulfonates to sulfite, which is estimated in the second titre. Control experiments established that aerial oxidation of sulfite was negligible under these conditions.

Reaction of Polyisocyanate I with Sodium Bisulfite

Influence of Solvent. To investigate this, a mixture of polyisocyanate I (4 g) and ethyl acetate (1 g) was dissolved in the solvent (45 ml), and a solution of sodium metabisulfite (0.35 g) in water (5 ml) was added with stirring.

After 24 hr, complete or partial gelation occurred with the following: water, acetone, methyl ethyl ketone, dimethylformamide, tetrahydrofuran, acetonitrile, formamide, sulfolane, butan-1,3-diol, diethylene glycol monomethyl ether, and diethylene glycol.

With the following solvents, gelation did not occur but dilution with water gave an insoluble precipitate: formic acid, acetic acid, dimethyl sulfoxide, hexamethylphosphoramide, 1,2-propylene glycol, 4-methylpentan-2-ol, N-methylpyrollidone, butan-1,4-diol, benzyl alcohol, diethylene glycol monoethyl, diethyl, and monobutyl ethers, ethylene glycol, furfuryl alcohol, ethylene glycol monobutyl ether.

In dioxan, 1,2-dimethoxyethane, and diethylene glycol dimethyl ether, about 80% conversion to carbamoyl sulfonate was obtained; but if more concentrated

TABLE II
Influence of Solvent in the Preparation of Ia

| | % Conversion of Isocyanates to Carbamoyl Sulfonates | | |
| | A[a] (dilute) | | B[a] (more concentrated) after 24 hr |
Solvent	After 10 min	After 24 hr	
Methanol	23	73	85
Ethanol	89	91	91
n-Propanol	20	78	54
Isopropanol	10	81	73
t-Butanol	3	56	32[b]
2-Methoxyethanol	gel		gel
2-Ethoxyethanol	16	86	86
Tetrahydrofurfuryl alcohol	25	85	gel
Dioxan	gel		gel
1,2-Dimethoxyethane	gel		gel
Diethyleneglycol dimethyl ether	gel		gel

[a] See experimental section.
[b] Water insoluble.

reaction mixtures were used, either I or sodium bisulfite separated and the yield dropped considerably.

The most effective solvents were investigated further, and the results are shown in Table II. In these experiments, a solution of polyisocyanate I (8 g) in ethyl acetate (2 g) was dissolved in the solvent with stirring, and without delay an aqueous solution containing sodium metabisulfite (0.7 g) was added. In set A, solvent (30 ml) and water (10 ml) were used, and, in set B, solvent (15 ml) and water (5 ml). Additional experiments in more concentrated solutions are shown in Table III, and the effect of bisulfite concentration is shown in Table IV.

Influence of the Concentrations of Ethanol and Water. As ethanol was the most practical solvent, it was investigated in some detail. Table V shows the results of experiments in which a solution of polyisocyanate I (40 g) in ethyl acetate (10 g) was reacted with a solution of sodium metabisulfite (4 g) in water and absolute alcohol with vigorous stirring. After 24 hr, water was added to redissolve any precipitated salts and the carbamoyl sulfonate content and functionality determined.

Large-Scale Preparation of Ia. The following method has been used on numerous occasions for the preparation of large batches of Ia. In a beaker, a solution of polyisocyanate I (1.6 kg) in ethyl acetate (400 g) was stirred mechanically with a wide-bladed paddle. Industrial methylated spirits (3.2 liter 95% ethanol containing 2% methanol) was added, and, as soon as the polyisocyanate had dissolved, a solution of sodium metabisulfite (160 g commercial food grade) dissolved in water (800 ml) was added. The reaction mixture was initially cloudy but cleared after 5–10 min. After half an hour, the mixture was diluted with water to give a product containing about 30% solids by weight. Such solutions can be concentrated *in vacuo,* but above 60% solids they were extremely viscous. This preparation can be acidified for improved shelf life by slowly stirring in a mixture of 30% hydrogen peroxide (20 ml) in water (40 ml).

Functionality of Ia. Ia prepared as above from I (40 g) in various ethanol–water mixtures was made up to a total volume of 250 ml so that the solvent contained 60% ethanol by volume. The functionalities were determined at a

TABLE III
Influence of Solvent and Concentration in Preparation of Ia[a]

Solvent, by volume	Total solids content, % by weight	% Conversion of Isocyanates to Carbamoyl Sulfonates[b]
75% Ethanol	25	87
	30	85
	35	82
	40	82
	45	76
	50	gel
75% Isopropanol	25	72
	30	70
	35	gel
85% 2-Ethoxyethanol	40	79
	50	gel

[a] Reaction of 80% solution of I in ethyl acetate with 10% excess sodium bisulfite.
[b] Determined after 24 hr.

constant volume to allow for intramolecular reactions which cause the apparent functionality to be concentration dependent, decreasing with dilution. The functionality was determined (for details see ref. 10) from the extent of reaction at the gel point in solutions to which excess triethylamine was added.

PCS IIa

To determine (see Table VI) the effect of coreactants, polyisocyanate II (10 g) was dissolved in dry dioxan (2.5 g) and stirred vigorously. Isopropanol (25 g) was added, immediately followed by an aqueous solution (18 g) of the coreactants. After 15 min, by which time formation of carbamoyl sulfonates was complete, a sample was removed and the carbamoyl sulfonate group content determined. The results of such experiments are shown in Table VI.

To determine the influence of solvent composition, the organic solvent was added to a well-stirred solution of the polyisocyanate (10 g) in dry dioxan (2.5 g), immediately followed by an aqueous solution containing the bisulfite and other reactants. The results are shown in Table VII.

Such preparations decomposed to water-insoluble material after two to three days unless stabilized by the addition of a mixture of concentrated hydrochloric acid and isopropanol (1:4 by volume) at the rate of 2–4 ml per 100 g PCS solution.

PCS IIIa–Xa

The polyisocyanates were handled as 80% (by weight) solutions in dry ethyl acetate or dioxan, as these solutions were much less viscous and gave better yields in PCS preparations due to more even mixing. These solutions were dissolved

TABLE IV
Influence of Bisulfite Concentration in the Preparation of Ia[a]

No. of equivalents of bisulfite per isocyanate group	% Conversion of isocyanates to carbamoyl sulfonates	Effect of dilution of reaction mixture with water[b]	Appearance of product
0.2	20	precipitate	gels after 24 hr
0.4	39	precipitate	gels after 24 hr
0.5	49	precipitate	gels after 24 hr
0.6	58	milky solution	gels after 24 hr
0.7	67	faintly cloudy solution	viscous gels after 3 months
0.8	76	clear solution	gels after 6 months
0.9	85	clear solution	stable
1.0	92	clear solution	stable
1.1	91	clear solution	stable
1.2	91	clear solution	stable
1.4	89	clear solution	stable
1.6	85	clear solution	stable
1.8	82	clear solution	stable

[a] Reaction of polyisocyanate I (40 g) in ethyl acetate (10 g) with a solution of the bisulfite in water (50 ml) in ethanol (150 ml).

[b] After 2 hr.

TABLE V
Preparation of Ia in Various Ethanol–Water Mixtures

Expt. no.	Volume[a] of ethanol and water	% Ethanol by volume	Initial appearance of reaction mixture	Time for reaction mixture to become homogeneous	Reaction time[b]	% Conversion to carbamoyl sulfonates	Apparent functionality
1	100 ml	50	2 phases	gels	3 hr	67	
2		55	2 phases	2 hr	2 hr	89	2.8
3		60	2 phases	45 min	50 min	90	
4		65	2 phases	10 min	13 min	93	2.8
5		70	2 phases	5 min	6 min	90	
6		75	homogeneous	—	3	91	2.8
7		80	homogeneous	—	4	76	
8		85	two phases	15	16	62	2.8
9		90	two phases	never	2 hr	89	
10	150 ml	60	two phases	14 min	15 min	93	2.9
11		70	two phases	4 min	5 min	91	2.9
12		80	homogeneous	—	2 min	67	2.9
13		90	two phases	never	90 min	—	2.8
14	200 ml	50	two phases	gels	—	81	
15		55	two phases	50 min	60 min	94	
16		60	two phases	13	13	93	2.8
17		65	two phases	4	5	94	
18		70	two phases	2	5	90	2.8
19		75	homogeneous	—	2	91	
20		80	homogeneous	—	2	78	2.9
21		85	homogeneous	—	2	44	
22		90	two phases	never	partially water soluble		

[a] Reaction with polyisocyanate I (40 g) in ethyl acetate (10 g).
[b] To give a clear solution when a sample is diluted with 10 parts water.

in the alcohol by vigorous mechanical stirring and without delay a solution of sodium metabisulfite (10%–20% excess of 95%) in water was added. To obtain maximum yields, efficient stirring was essential and it was necessary to experiment with various solids contents and alcohol–water proportions.

The reaction mixture should not be heated, although the heat of mixing of alcohol and water may cause a slight rise in temperature. The reaction mixture may not be clear initially, and once it has clarified it may become cloudy again due to separation of inorganic salts. This can be prevented by adding a little water when the reaction is complete.

To improve the shelf life of the preparations, sufficient 20% sulfuric acid, 10% hydrochloric, and/or 10% hydrogen peroxide were added to give an apparent pH of about 2–3. With hydrogen peroxide, this usually corresponds to the point at which the slight greenish coloration (due to dissolved sulfur dioxide) disappears. The addition of acid may cause some salts to separate, but this can be prevented by dilution with a little water.

TABLE VI
Influence of Reaction Condition on the Preparation of PCS—IIa

Expt. no.	No. of moles of reactant per mole of isocyanate groups	% Conversion of isocyanate groups to carbamoyl sulfonates
1	1.2 NaHSO$_3$	14
2	1.5 NaHSO$_3$	17
3	1.2 KHSO$_3$	13
4	1.2 NaHSO$_3$ + 0.1 triethylamine	68
5	1.2 NaHSO$_3$ + 0.2 triethylamine	74
6	1.2 NaHSO$_3$ + 0.4 triethylamine	75
7	1.2 NlaHSO$_3$ + 0.6 triethylamine	73
8	1.4 NaHSO$_3$ + 0.1 triethylamine	66
9	1.4 NaHSO$_3$ + 0.2 triethylamine	73
10	1.4 NaHSO$_3$ + 0.4 triethylamine	80
11	1.0 NaHSO$_3$ + 0.2 triethylamine	72
12	1.0 NaHSO$_3$ + 0.1 Na$_2$SO$_3$ + 0.1 triethylamine	74
13	1.2 NaHSO$_3$ + 0.1 Na$_2$SO$_3$ + 0.1 triethylamine	71
14	1.2 KHSO$_3$ + 0.2 triethylamine	72
15	1.2 NaHSO$_3$ + 0.2 pyridine	17
16	1.2 NaHSO$_2$ + 0.2 2-methylpyridine	33
17	1.2 NaHSO$_3$ + 0.2 2,4,6-trimethylpyridine	64
18	1.2 NaHSO$_3$ + 0.2 N,N-dimethylaniline	10
19	1.2 NaHSO$_3$ + 0.2 tri-n-butylamine	75
20	1.2 NaHSO$_3$ + 0.2 triethanolamine	73
21	1.2 NaHSO$_3$ + 0.1 1,4-diazabicyclo-2,2,2-octane	73
22	1.2 NaHSO$_3$ + 0.5 dibutyltin dilaurate	17
23	1.0 NaHSO$_3$ + 0.2 Na$_2$SO$_3$	72
24	1.0 NaHSO$_3$ + 0.4 Na$_2$SO$_3$	74
25	1.0 NaHSO$_3$ + 0.6 Na$_2$SO$_3$	73
26	0.8 NaHSO$_3$ + 0.4 Na$_2$SO$_3$	82
27	0.6 NaHSO$_3$ + 0.6 Na$_2$SO$_3$	60
28	1.2 NH$_4$HSO$_3$	21
29	1.2 NH$_4$HSO$_3$ + 0.2 triethylamine	36
30	1.2 NH$_4$HSO$_3$ + 0.2 Na$_2$SO$_3$	49
31	0.6 NaHSO$_4$ + 0.6 (NH$_4$)$_2$SO$_3$	40

DISCUSSION

Preparation of the Bisulfite Adduct of Polyisocyanate I

Low molecular weight isocyanates form carbamoyl sulfonates in reasonable yield with aqueous bisulfite solutions,[1,6] but under these conditions the water-insoluble I hydrolyzes to useless polyurea. Stirring or emulsification only increases the rate of formation of polyurea, but if the reactants are brought together in the same phase by adding water-miscible organic solvents,[6-8] Ia may form. Homogeneous reaction mixtures containing I and sodium bisulfite were obtained

TABLE VII

Influence of Solvent Composition and Solids Content on the Preparation of PCS IIa

Expt. no.	Solvent, % composition by weight	Solids content, %	% Conversion of isocyanates to carbamoyl sulfonates	
			A. 1.2 NaHSO$_3$ + 0.2 triethylamine	B. 1.0 NaHSO$_3$ + 0.2 Na$_2$SO$_3$
1	60% Isopropanol	5	72	75
2		10	78	75
3		15	79	74
4		20	74	72
5		30	55	56
6		35	42	
7	40% Isopropanol	25	24	
8	50% Isopropanol	25	61	53
9	55% Isopropanol	25	66	64
10	60% Isopropanol	25	69	66
11	65% Isopropanol	25	62	56
12	70% Isopropanol	25	46	33
13	80% Isopropanol	25	36	
14	50% Ethanol[a]	25	36	
15	60%	25	69	
16	70%	25	52	
17	80%	25	18	
18	60% Ethanol[a]	15	70	
19	60% Ethanol[a]	20	69	
20	60% Ethanol[a]	30	65	
21	60% Methylated spirits[b]	25	55	
22	60% Methanol	25	23	
23	60% n-Propanol	25	66	
24	60% sec-Butanol	25	18	
25	60% t-Butanol	25	49	
26	60% 2-Methoxyethanol	25	17	
27	60% 2-Ethoxyethanol	25	15	
28	60% Dioxan	25	24	
29	60% Dimethylformamide	25	9	
30	60% 1,2-Dimethoxyethan	25	17	
31	Tetrahydrofurfuryl alcohol	25	15	
32	Diethylene glycol diethyl ether	25	15	

[a] Absolute.

[b] 95% Ethanol, 5% methanol, may contain acidic impurities.

with a number of solvents, but Ia was only formed to any extent in certain ethers (but only in dilute solutions) or lower alcohols. Concentrated solutions of Ia could be prepared directly in alcohols, particularly ethanol (see Tables III and IV). The effectiveness of alcohols was surprising in view of the ease with which alcohols and isocyanates react,[12] but the relative rates of reaction of butyl isocyanate with water, ethanol, and bisulfite were found[6] to be approximately 1:1.5:500,000. Amines react[12] much faster with isocyanates than alcohols, and alcohols have been used as solvent for amine–isocyanate reactions.[13,14]

The direct preparation of concentrated solutions of Ia using alcohols is, no doubt, aided by the formation of supersaturated solutions when alcohols are added to aqueous sodium bisulfite. This was most pronounced with ethanol and 2-ethoxyethanol, and it often took many hours for the sodium bisulfite to precipitate completely. Supersaturation did not occur with other water-miscible solvents or with potassium or ammonium bisulfites, or with other sodium salts, e.g., sulfite, sulfate, bisulfate, thiosulfate, or chloride. Potassium or ammonium bisulfite react with I, but it was not possible to prepare very concentrated PCS solutions with these reagents.[11]

In the preparation of Ia in different alcohols (Table II and III), there was wide variations in both the rate of reaction and the extent of formation of carbamoyl sulfonates. Ethanol was the most practical, giving the fastest reaction and highest yields, particularly in concentrated reaction mixtures. The reaction was much slower in isopropanol, and the yield was lower even though side reactions should be less, as secondary alcohols are less reactive toward isocyanates.[12] It was not necessary to use purified ethanol; and in large-scale preparations, industrial methylated spirits was satisfactory.[11]

There was an optimum range of ethanol–water proportions for maximum conversion of isocyanates to carbamoyl sulfonates. As the solids content increased, the range of optimum solvent compositions became smaller and the extent of conversion to carbamoyl sulfonates fell (see Tables II, III, and V). Even though the proportion of ethanol influenced the reaction time considerably, the effect on the final yield was much less marked.

The addition of tertiary amines or organometallic catalysts did not improve the yield of Ia; instead, side reactions of the isocyanates with water or alcohol were promoted. These side reactions, which inevitably occurred to a small extent with the trifunctional I, will affect the functionality of Ia; reaction with water

TABLE VIII
Shelf Life of Ia at Elevated Temperatures

Preparation	Shelf life,[c] days	
	60°C	70°C
30% Ia[a]	15 (30[d])	6 (10[d])
30% Ia + 0.2% H$_2$SO$_4$	~70 (80[d])	30 (40[d])
30% Ia + 0.4% H$_2$SO$_4$	~100	50
30% Ia + hydrogen peroxide[b]	~80	30

[a] Large-scale preparation, experimental section.
[b] See experimental section.
[c] Gel time or time to become water insoluble.
[d] Diluted with water 1:1.

TABLE IX
Preparation of PCS IIIa–Xa

No.	Coreactants[a]	Diluent[b]	Solvent, by volume	Solids content	% Conversion of isocyanates to carbamoyl sulfonates		
					After 10 min	After 20 min	After 24 hr
IIIa	1.2 NaHSO₃ + 0.2 Et₃N	dioxan	70% isopropanol	20	77	76	51 (75)[c]
IVa	1.2 NaHSO₃ + 0.2 Et₃N	dioxan	70% isopropanol	20	75	74	55 (74)[c]
Va	1.1 NaHSO₃	ethyl acetate	75% ethanol	20	64	82	90
VIa	1.1 NaHSO₃	ethyl acetate	75% ethanol	20	94	94	88
VIIa	1.2 NaHSO₃	ethyl acetate	80% ethanol	15	5	8	80
VIIIa	1.1 NaHSO₃	ethyl acetate	75% ethanol	20	87	92	95
IXa	1.1 NaHSO₃	ethyl acetate	75% ethanol	20	88	88	86
Xa	1.1 NaHSO₃	ethyl acetate	75% ethanol	20	10	19	95

[a] Number of equivalents per isocyanate.
[b] 25 g per 100 g Poly.
[c] Acid stabilized after 20 min.

increases the functionality of the product, whereas reaction with ethanol should cause a decrease. A detailed study[10] of the functionality of the PCS prepared from I under one set of reaction conditions showed a small increase in functionality (to 3.8 with a polyisocyanate I of functionality 3.2). However, in experiments (Table V) at different ethanol–water proportions, there were no significant differences in the apparent functionality.

Reaction of I with less than one equivalent of bisulfite per isocyanate group (see Table IV) resulted in rapid gelation below about 0.5 equivalent; and below about 0.8 equivalent, the products were viscous and gelled after several months. With a large excess of sodium bisulfite, the carbamoyl sulfonate formation dropped; this may be due to a reduction in the free sulfite concentration, the species which actually reacts with the isocyanates.[6]

Stability of PCS Ia

Thirty percent solutions of Ia after two years of storage at 20°C still contained 85% or more of the carbamoyl sulfonate originally present, but preparations containing more than 40% solids or those in which there had been less than 85% initial conversion of isocyanates to carbamoyl sulfonates had poorer shelf life.[11] The shelf life of PCS could be improved (see Table VIII) by adding hydrochloric or sulfuric acid but not acetic or formic acid,[11,15] by adding hydrogen peroxide (which forms sulfuric acid by oxidizing the residual bisulfite),[15] by adding organic sulfonic acids[16] or, to a lesser extent, by dilution.[11]

This "acid stabilization" is due to the rate of hydrolysis of carbamoyl sulfonate falling as the pH decreases.[6] PCS preparations are probably to some extent self-stabilizing as aerial oxidation of residual bisulfite or any bisulfite released on hydrolysis caused the preparations to become more acidic. For an explanation for the dependence of the shelf life on concentration and the initial yield of carbamoyl sulfonates, consider the extent of reaction, p, at the gel point of a PCS of functionality f which is given by eq. (ii):[10]

$$p = (f - 1)^{-1} \qquad \text{(ii)}$$

Therefore, increasing the apparent functionality decreases p and reduces the gel time, which will be reflected in reduced shelf life. In gel point experiments, the apparent functionality obtained increases with concentration as intramolecular reactions become less favorable.[10] Preparations of Ia with low conversions to carbamoyl sulfonates were more viscous, suggesting increased molecular weight from side reactions of isocyanates with water; and as it is polyfunctional, the functionality should have been increased.

Bisulfite Adduct of Polyisocyanate II

The optimum methods to convert I into Ia gave low conversions with II, forming useless products;[8] but reasonable yields of IIa could be obtained by adding sodium sulfite and/or tertiary amines[17] to the reaction mixture (see Table VI); however, the maximum extent of conversion to IIa was still less than with Ia. The optimum ethanol concentration to prepare IIa was lower and the range of usable compositions narrower, and the yield dropped more rapidly with increasing solids content, when compared with the preparation of Ia (see Table

VII). In contrast to Ia slightly higher yields of IIa were obtained in isopropanol than ethanol.

Tertiary amines catalyze reactions of isocyanates with alcohols,[12] although in this case they probably only increase the sulfite concentration by neutralizing bisulfite. The yield of IIa increases with the tertiary amine base strength, and pyridine which catalyzes some isocyanate reactions[12] was not effective. The effect of adding sulfite or tertiary amine can, therefore, be accounted for by the mechanism proposed[6] for the butyl isocyanate–bisulfite reaction where it was demonstrated that the species which actually reacts with the isocyanate is sulfite, not bisulfite. A similar mechanism has been advanced for the addition of bisulfite to aldehydes and ketones.[18]

Even though aromatic isocyanates are more reactive than aliphatic ones—I and II gel in 60% ethanol in 3 hr and 15 min, respectively, at 20°C[11]—the reaction with sulfite should also be faster, which suggests a smaller rate difference between the reaction of aromatic isocyanates with bisulfite and water or alcohol compared with aliphatic isocyanates.

PCS IIa hydrolyzed much faster than Ia and, unless acidified immediately after the reaction, decomposed to useless material within several days. In acid solutions, IIa was stable and had a shelf life of over a year.[11]

Bisulfite Adducts of Polyisocyanates III–XI

Experiments on the formation of PCS from polyisocyanates III–XI are summarized in Table IX. Gelation occurred with the polyisocyanate XI; and with the slow-reacting VII, lower conversion was obtained presumably due to separation of bisulfite from the supersaturated reaction mixture.

PCS preparations have also been prepared[11] from other polyisocyanates derived from poly(propylene oxide) polyols with lower molecular weights and functionalities and a number of commercial poly(ether polyisocyanates) of undisclosed structures. Polyisocyanates used for surface coatings often contain solvents which should be removed in order to obtain good conversions to carbamoyl sulfonates. In general, as the isocyanate content of the polyisocyanate increased, the conversion to carbamoyl sulfonates decreased, probably because of the problem of keeping increasing amounts of bisulfite in solution.

Properties and Reactions of PCS

The PCS Ia–Xa are readily soluble in water giving solutions with low surface tensions. The carbamoyl sulfonate group is an effective solubilizing group for the poly(propylene oxide) backbone, although the polar nature of such polyethers no doubt assists. Poly(propylene oxide) PCS preparations of this type with equivalent weights 1500–2000 are readily water soluble, whereas the parent polyols are not.[11]

Carbamoyl sulfonates have different reactivity from the parent isocyanates, which has useful technical consequences. The preparation and storage of PCS in aqueous media depends on the rate of hydrolysis at room temperature of carbamoyl sulfonates being less than isocyanates, otherwise conversion of a polyisocyanate into a water-soluble form would only serve to facilitate hydrolysis.

At higher temperatures, the rate difference in hydrolysis of PCS and polyisocyanates appears to be smaller; for example, Ia and I cure on wool at similar rates at 100°C, but at 20°C, Ia cures very much more slower.[9] This is probably a reflection of the differences in the activation energies, 87 ± 5 and 62.3 kJ/mole, reported for the hydrolyses of butyl carbamoyl sulfonate[6] and butyl isocyanate,[19] respectively.

A further consequence of the reduced reactivity of carbamoyl sulfonates is that, apart from hydrolysis to symmetric ureas, the only other reactions reported[1,6] are with primary and secondary amines to form unsymmetric ureas, reactions (i). Reactions of carbamoyl sulfonates with weaker nucleophiles are not observed, presumably because hydrolysis by the water inevitably present forms more reactive amines.

Mechanism of Carbamoyl Sulfonate Hydrolysis

The hydrolysis of PCS to polyurea will be considered in detail as this reaction is the basis of PCS shrink-resist treatments.[4-8] In many discussions of isocyanate chemistry, carbamoyl sulfonates have been classified as "blocked isocyanates" which decompose thermally to reform free isocyanate, reaction (iii):[12,20]

Mechanisms of Carbamoyl Sulfonate Reactions

Blocked Isocyanates
Unblocking:

$$RNHCOX \rightleftharpoons RNCO + HX \quad (X = -OPh, etc.) \qquad (iii)$$
$$\downarrow YH$$
$$RNHCOY$$

Direct substitution:

$$YH + RNHCOX \longrightarrow RNHCOY + HX \qquad (iv)$$

"Unblocking" or S_n1 Mechanism

$$RNHCOSO_3^- \overset{\Delta}{\rightleftharpoons} RNCO + HSO_3^- \qquad (v)$$

S_n2 ($B_{ac}2$) Mechanism

$$\underset{\underset{OH}{|}}{RNHC} - SO_3$$

$$RNHCOSO_3^- + OH^- \rightleftharpoons RNH\overset{O^-}{\underset{OH}{\overset{|}{C}}} - SO_3 \longrightarrow RNHCO_2H + 2SO_3^{2-} \qquad (vi)$$
$$\downarrow$$
$$RNH_2$$
$$\downarrow RNHCSO_3^-$$
$$RNHCONHR \qquad (vii)$$

$E_{1c}B$ Mechanism

$$RNHCOSO_3 + OH^- \overset{fast}{\longrightarrow} RNCOSO_3^- + H_2O \qquad (viii)$$
$$XII$$
$$slow \downarrow$$
$$RNCO + SO_3^{2-}$$

Mechanism of Carbamoyl Sulfonate Formation

$$RNCO + SO_3^{2-} \overset{slow}{\longrightarrow} RNCOSO_3^- \overset{fast}{\longrightarrow} RNHCOSO_3^- \qquad (ix)$$
$$XII$$

This type of thermal equilibrium, reaction (v), has been considered[6,21] for PCS. However, it is generally[20] appreciated that other reaction pathways, e.g., the direct substitution, reaction (iv), are significant with blocked isocyanates, and this also seems to be the case with PCS.

The strongest evidence against the equilibrium (v) is that PCS preparations are stable in neutral and acid aqueous solutions at room temperature,[6,11] whereas the corresponding isocyanates rapidly hydrolyze and the rate of hydrolysis is higher in acid solution than in neutral solution.[22] For example, I in aqueous dioxan gels in a few hours at 20°C and hydrolyzes very rapidly if acid is added, whereas in acid solution Ia is stable for at least four years. Also, PCS are stable in the presence of oxidizing agents or barium salts which would be expected to remove bisulfite and shift the equilibrium to the right.[6,11] Thus, if there is an equilibrium, the equilibrium constant must be extremely small at 20°C, and it is difficult to see why this should change significantly at 100°C as required by the S_n1 mechanism, reaction (v).

The thermal decomposition of the potassium bisulfite adduct of butyl isocyanate[6] was investigated (Table X) by heating under a vacuum of 0.5 mm/Hg. Butyl isocyanate (boiling point 115°/760 mm), if formed, should be removed; however, there was only slight loss in carbamoyl sulfonate content after several hours at 100°C. In contrast, Ia cures on wool in a few minutes at 100° in steam;[9] therefore, hydrolytic reactions must be involved rather than the thermal equilibrium (v). This would explain the observation[7] that for the development of shrink resistance with a PCS, it was necessary to have water present as well as heat.

The rate of hydrolysis of n-butylcarbamoyl sulfonate increased continually as the solution became more alkaline, and there was no apparent leveling off or increase in rate in acid.[6,11] In the pH range of 2–7, plots of $\log K$ (at 60°–80°C) against pH gave[6] straight lines with slopes of about $1/2$, and studies[11] in the range of 7–11 (at 20°) have found a similar linear relationship. Above pH 11, the rate was extremely fast. The observed pH dependence suggests base catalysis or direct reaction with hydroxide ion and is not consistent with an S_n1 mechanism, such as the forward reaction of the equilibrium (v) which should be independent of pH, although the reverse and subsequent reactions may not be. The most likely mechanism is the S_n2 or $B_{ac}2$ reaction (vi), but it is also necessary to consider the base-catalyzed $E1_cB$ reaction (viii) to account for the detection[6]

TABLE X
Thermal Decomposition of Potassium Butylcarbamoyl Sulfonate[a]

Heating conditions	Carbamoyl sulfonate groups remaining,[b] %
1.0 hr 100°C	97
2.0 hr 100°C	96
0.5 hr 120°C	95
1.0 hr 120°C	81
2.0 hr 120°C	67
1.0 hr 140°C	8

[a] Heating in glass under 0.5 mm Hg.
[b] Determined iodometrically.

y infrared spectroscopy of some isocyanate intermediate in the hydrolysis of -butylcarbamoyl sulfonate at pH 6 and 80°C. In the $E1_cB$ mechanism, the oss of a proton to form the dianion XII should be rapid and thus not rate determining; however, as the amide-like NH proton will only be weakly acidic, the oncentration of XII should depend on the pH. Thus, the rate of the $E1_cB$ reaction would be expected to increase with pH until, in very strong alkali, it levels ff to a constant value.

Support for the $E1_cB$ mechanism comes from the hydrolysis of carbamate esters ($RNHCO_2R'$) where this type of mechanism with isocyanate intermediates as been established[24,25] and with carbamoyl phosphates ($RNHCOPO_4^{2-}$) where t is also considered to occur.[24] With carbamate esters, the $E1_cB$ mechanism, f possible, is much more favorable than the $B_{ac}2$ reaction, as some disubstituted esters (R_2NCO_2R') hydrolyze up to 10^6 times slower than monosubstituted analogues ($RNHCO_2R'$).[24,25] The $E1_cB$ reaction (viii) is, in effect, the reverse of he mechanism, equation (ix), established[6] for the formation of carbamoyl sulfonates, i.e., a rate-determining addition of sulfite (not bisulfite) to the isocyanate, ollowed by rapid protonation. Aldehyde and ketone bisulfite adducts hydrolyze oy an $E1_cB$ mechanism, also the reverse of the mechanism of their formation.[18]

Williams[24] has discussed the use of entropy of activation to distinguish between $E1_cB$ and $B_{ac}2$ mechanisms in carbamate hydrolysis, but it is not unequivocable; $B_{ac}2$ mechanisms usually give larger negative values than $E1_cB$ mechanisms. An S_n1 mechanism, reaction (v), would be expected to show a positive entropy of activation (e.g., as found[25] for the hydrolysis of diphenyl carbamoyl chloride). Calculations[11] from the limited amount of kinetic data[6] at different temperatures or the hydrolysis of butyl carbamoyl sulfonate suggest a large negative value approx. -20 eu) for the entropy of activation.

With the $E1_cB$ mechanism, even if it was the major reaction pathway, there vill only be a very small steady-state concentration of free isocyanates as their subsequent reactions with water or amines are faster. Furthermore, if the $E1_cB$ mechanism was the sole pathway, not every carbamoyl sulfonate would be converted to an isocyanate, as many will react in an S_n2 reaction with the amines ormed, reaction (vii). In PCS containing several carbamoyl sulfonate groups which react independently, as in Ia, the amount of the free parent polyisocyanate eformed throughout hydrolysis must be quite small. Thus, in understanding he textile applications of PCS, it would appear incorrect to consider that the PCS is converted back to the parent isocyanates which then behaves in the same vay as if it were applied from a solvent.

Urea Formation in Carbamoyl Sulfonate Hydrolysis

The extent, as well as the rate, of urea formation from PCS hydrolysis is important as the ureas crosslink the cured polymer. Thus, factors such as pH, temperature, and solvent will influence properties of the cured polymer. For example, in polyisocyanate shrink-resist treatments for wool, the extent of urea crosslinking was found to influence the shrink-resist effectiveness,[28] and similar effects would be expected with PCS.

The conversion of carbamoyl sulfonate to symmetric urea will be prevented n strong acid or alkali. In acid solutions, the intermediate amine will be pro-

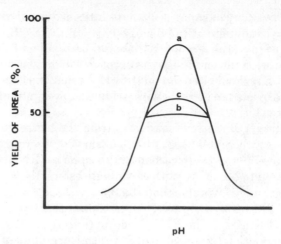

Fig. 1. Influence of pH on extent of urea formation in carbamoyl sulfonate hydrolysis: (a) hydrolysis of a monocarbamoyl sulfonate; (b) hydrolysis of a PCS at the gel point; (c) hydrolysis of a PCS at complete reaction.

tonated, which prevents subsequent reaction with either isocyanates or carbamoyl sulfonate to form ureas. In strong alkali, the intermediate carbamic acid salt accumulates, as the rate of hydrolysis of carbamate to amine shows the reverse pH dependence to carbamoyl sulfonate hydrolysis, i.e., decreased with increasing pH.[27] Thus, urea formation from a mono- or dicarbamoyl sulfonate would be expected to show a pH dependence, with the maximum yield of urea (which must be less than 100%) occurring in a narrow, slightly alkaline pH region as shown in Figure 1.

In the hydrolysis of a polyfunctional carbamoyl sulfonate, urea formation gives a product of increased molecular weight. If the functionality is greater than 2, a gel of infinite molecular weight forms, provided urea formation is not rate limiting, such as in strong acid or alkali. As discussed above, eq. (ii) gives the extent of reaction at the gel point which must be less than 1. Some additional ureas will form after the gel point, but this will be hindered by the restricted mobility of reacting groups in a gel and their wide separation in structures such as Ia. The overall effect of gelation in PCS hydrolysis (summarized in Fig. 1) is to make the extent of urea formation less pH dependent than with monocarbamoyl sulfonates.

Applications of PCS

PCS I–Xa can be used to shrink-resist wool.[4,9] This application utilizes the water solubility of PCS, the ready hydrolysis to an insoluble polyurea at 100°C together with stability of PCS in neutral or acid solutions at room temperature. This combination of properties may find other applications. Also, conversion to a water-soluble form overcomes two of the problems associated with handling polyisocyanates, namely, their sensitivity to reaction with moisture and the toxicity of any residual diisocyanate. A water-soluble product facilitates industrial application of textiles from established equipment designed for aqueous processing and avoids problems associated with organic solvents.

Such considerations suggest that PCS may also be useful for coating various substrates in particular leather or paper.   In considering potential applications, the following points should be noted:

(1) The curing of a PCS releases an inorganic salt.

(2) The bisulfite released during curing acidifies the reaction mixture which is increased by subsequent aerial oxidation of bisulfite.   This acidification reduces the rate of hydrolysis of carbamoyl sulfonate and may inactivate polyamine crosslinking agents, if present, by protonation.

(3) The different reactivity of PCS to polyisocyanates influences the choice of crosslinking agents.   Crosslinking with polyols is feasible only under anhydrous conditions.   Polyamines that gel immediately on mixing with polyisocyanates may react at a more controllable rate with PCS.

The assistance of Dr. M. B. Jackson in some of the preliminary experiments, technical assistance by C. G. Zoch and G. N. Freeland, and preparation of some polyisocyanate samples by Dr. F. W. Jones and M. A. Rushforth is gratefully acknowledged.   Intermediates for the preparation of the polyisocyanates were kindly provided by Bayer A. G.

References

1. S. Petersen, *Liebigs Ann.,* **562,** 205 (1949).
2. Bradford Dyers Assn., U.S. Pat. 2,786,734 (1957).
3. Farbenfabriken Bayer A. G., Ger. Pat. 922,711 (1955).
4. CSIRO, U.S. Pat. 3,898,197 (1975).
5. CSIRO, Ger. Pat. 2,418,384 (1974).
6. G. B. Guise, M. B. Jackson, and J. A. Maclaren, *Aust. J. Chem.,* **25,** 2583 (1972).
7. G. B. Guise and M. B. Jackson, *J. Text. Inst.,* **64,** 655, (1973).
8. K. W. Fincher and M. A. White, *Knitting Times,* **45** (No. 13), 49 (1976).
9. G. B. Guise and M. A. Rushforth, *J. Soc. Dyers Colour.,* **92,** 265 (1976).
10. G. B. Guise and C. G. Zoch, *J. Polym. Sci., Polym. Symp.,* in press.
11. G. B. Guise, unpublished results.
12. J. H. Saunders and K. C. Frisch, *Polyurethanes: Chemistry and Technology,* Vols. I and II, Interscience, New York, 1962.
13. BASF-Wyandotte, U.S. Pat. 3,719,621 (1973).
14. USM Corp., U.S. Pat. 3,752,786 (1973).
15. CSIRO, U.S. Pat. 3,989,458 (1976).
16. Bayer A. G., Ger. Pat. 2,414,470 (1975).
17. CSIRO, Austral. Pat. Applic. PC4203 (1976).
18. T. D. Stewart and L. H. Donally, *J. Am. Chem. Soc.,* **54,** 3559 (1932).
19. M. B. Jackson and D. H. Solomon, *J. Macromol. Sci. (A),* **6,** 471 (1972).
20. Z. W. Wicks, *Progr. Organ. Coat.,* **3,** 73 (1975).
21. D. J. Kilpatrick, J. A. Rippon, M. A. Rushforth, and T. Shaw, *J. Appl. Polym. Sci.,* to appear.
22. A. Williams and W. P. Jencks, *J. Chem. Soc.,* Perkin II, 1753 (1974).
23. A. F. Hegarty and L. N. Frost, *J. Chem. Soc.,* Perkin II, 1719 (1973).
24. A. Williams and K. T. Douglas, *Chem. Rev.,* **75,** 627 (1975).
25. A. Williams, *J. Chem. Soc.,* Perkin II, 808 (1972).
26. S. L. Johnson and H. M. Giron, *J. Org. Chem.,* **37,** 1383 (1972).
27. M. Caplow, *J. Amer. Chem. Soc.,* **90,** 6795 (1968).
28. G. B. Guise and M. A. Rushforth, *J. Soc. Dyers Colour.,* **91,** 389 (1975).

Received September 14, 1976
Revised October 25, 1976

JOURNAL OF APPLIED POLYMER SCIENCE   VOL. 21, 3445–3456 (1977)

Infrared Spectra of Poly(ethylene 2,6-Naphthalate) and Some Related Polyesters

ISUKE OUCHI, MASAHIRO HOSOI, and SAKAE SHIMOTSUMA,*

Plastics Research Institute, Teijin Limited, Sagamihara, Japan

Synopsis

Infrared spectra of some poly(methylene terephthalates) and some poly(methylene 2,6-naphthalates) were compared. To interpret the spectral changes during drawing and heat treatment, the concept of rotational isomerism of the $-O-(CH_2)_m-O-$ part, which was fairly successful in poly(ethylene terephthalate) (C_2T), was tried to apply to the polyesters other than C_2T. Also, the bands originated from a benzene ring and from a naphthalene ring were distinguished. Poly(ethylene 2,6-naphthalate) (C_2N) has some bands behaving differently from those of other polyesters. This would be due to the existence of certain intermolecular interactions arised from tight packing of the molecules in the crystal of C_2N.

INTRODUCTION

Poly(ethylene 2,6-naphthalate) (C_2N) is relatively well known among poly(methylene 2,6-naphthalates) with different numbers of methylene groups:

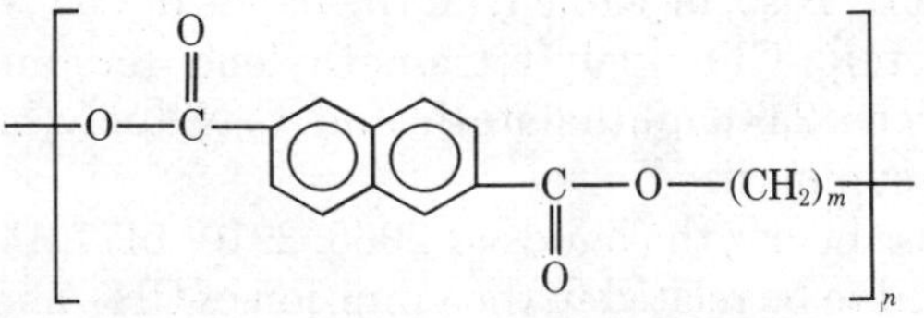

The properties and the crystal structure of C_2N have been discussed by several authors,[1–5] but its infrared spectrum has not been reported yet. On the other hand, the infrared spectrum of poly(ethylene terephthalate) (C_2T) whose repeat unit has a benzene ring instead of a naphthalene ring in the main chain has been the subject of extensive studies since the late fifties.[6–10] Most spectral changes during drawing and heat treatment of C_2T were explained by a number of workers, except Liang and Krimm,[8] in terms of rotational isomerism of ethylene glycol residue. It would be of interest to compare the spectra of various poly(methylene terephthalates) and poly(methylene 2,6-naphthalates) and to see if the spectral changes due to drawing or heat treatment in these polymers, particularly in C_2N, conform to the above interpretation in C_2T. The comparison of the spectra would also provide knowledge on the difference between the bands originating from a benzene ring and from a naphthalene ring.

* Present address: Teijin-Konishiroku Film Co., Sagamihara, Japan.

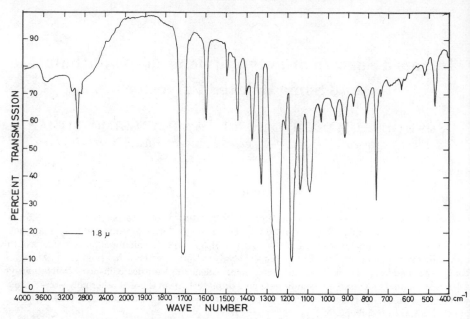

Fig. 1. Infrared spectrum of C_2N.

BANDS ASSOCIATED WITH —O-$(CH_2)_m$-O—

Infrared spectra in the range between 4000 and 400 cm^{-1} were taken by means of a Japan Spectroscopic Co., Type IRA-2 spectrometer. The spectrum of C_2N is shown in Figure 1. Also, in Table I, all the bands of C_2T, C_3T [poly(trimethylene terephthalate)], C_4T [poly(tetramethylene terephthalate)], $C_2N_1C_4N$ [poly(tetramethylene 2,6-naphthalate)], and C_6N [poly(hexamethylene 2,6-naphthalate)] are summarized.

As we will discuss below, the bands at 2965, 2910, 1477, 1453, 1370, and 1330 cm^{-1} are considered to be related to the vibration of CH_2, and the bands at 1090 and 1044 cm^{-1} may be associated with the vibration of C—O in ethylene glycol residue in C_2N.

The bands at 2965 and 2910 cm^{-1} of C_2N correspond to the bands at 2950 and 2900 cm^{-1} of C_2T and should be the antisymmetric and symmetric vibration of CH_2, respectively. By heat treatment, structures appear at 2990 and 2890 cm^{-1} as shown in Figure 2. The spectra of C_3T, C_4T, C_4N, and C_6N have corresponding bands but do not show distinct structures as in C_2N upon heating. A spectrometer of high dispersion may be necessary to investigate these points further.

The bands around at 1470 and 1450 cm^{-1} exist in all the polyesters concerned here. In C_2N, the σ band at 1477 cm^{-1} intensifies and the π band at 1433 cm^{-1} weakens by drawing or heat treatment, as shown in Figure 3. These bands may be assigned as CH_2 bending vibrations of trans and gauche configurations, respectively, as in C_2T. This assignment may be supported by the fact that there are two absorption bands between 1440 and 1470 cm^{-1} in bis(β-hydroxyethyl) 2,6-naphthalate and diethyl 2,6-naphthalate, but that there are no absorption in this range in naphthalene and 2,6-naphthalic acid, which have no CH_2 group in the molecules. The 1477 cm^{-1} band of C_2N shows much sharper σ polarization

TABLE I
Infrared Spectra of Various Polyesters

C'2T Freq cm⁻¹	C'2T Int. pol. spectral change	C3T Freq cm⁻¹	C3T Int. pol. spectral change	C4T Freq cm⁻¹	C4T Int. pol. spectral change	C2N Freq cm⁻¹	C2N Int. pol. spectral change	C4N Freq cm⁻¹	C4N Int. pol. spectral change	C6N Freq cm⁻¹	C6N Int. pol. spectral change	Assignment
3650	vw	3650	vw	3630	vw	3650	vw	3610	vw	3610	vw	ν(OH)
3560	vw	3550	vw	3550	vw	3550	vw	3550	vw	3540	vw	overtone ν(C=O)
3440	w ⊥	3430	w ⊥	3420	w ⊥	3430	w ⊥	3400	w ⊥	3400	w ⊥	ν(arom. CH)
3055	w ‖	3050	w	3050	w	3060	w ⊥	3050	w	3050	w	ν(arom. CH) crys.
						3050	sh crys.			3030	sh	
						2990	mw ‖ crys.					νa(CH₂) crys.
2950	m ‖	2970	m ‖	2950	m ‖	2965	m	2940	m ‖	2930	m ‖	νa(CH₂) amorph.
2900	mw ‖	2900	mw ‖	2880	mw ‖	2910	w ⊥	2880	mw ‖	2850	m ‖	νs(CH₂) amorph.
						2890	sh crys.					νs(CH₂) crys.
1957	w	1950	w	1950	w	1950	w	1950	w	1950	w	
1830	vw					1820	vw					
1715	vs ⊥	1715	vs ⊥	1715	vs	1715	vs ⊥	1715	vs ⊥	1715	vs ⊥	ν(C=O)
1615	w	1610	w	1610	w	1600	s ‖	1600	s ‖	1600	s ‖	arom. ring vibration
1575	m ‖	1575	mw ‖	1575	mw ‖	1570	vw ⊥	1570	vw ⊥ ‖			arom. ring vibration
1508	m ‖	1500	m ‖	1500	m ‖	1500	m ⊥	1500	m	1500	m ‖	arom. ring vibration
1475	w ⊥ +	1470	mw ⊥ +	1470	m sh	1477	m ⊥ +	1460	m	1470	m ⊥	δ(CH₂) trans
				1460	sh	1455	sh					
1450	m ‖	1450	m ‖	1450	m sh	1450	m −	1445	m	1450	sh ‖	δ(CH₂) gauche
				1440	sh ⊥	1440	sh					
1400	s ‖	1400	s ‖	1400	s ‖	1400	m ‖	1400	m ‖	1400	m ‖	arom. ring vibration
1380	mw ‖ crys.	1380	mw ‖ crys.	1380	ms ‖	1370	ms −	1380	m ‖	1365	ms ‖	γw(CH₂) gauche
1365	mw ‖ −	1365	mw ‖	1350	mw ‖	1337	s +	1340	ms ‖	1340	s ‖	γw(CH₂) trans
1337	s ‖ +	1340	s +	1320	ms ‖	1332	sh ‖ crys.	1320	mw· ‖			γw(CH₂) trans

TABLE I (continued)

	C2T		C3T		C4T		C2N		C4N		C6N	
Assignment	Frequency cm⁻¹	Intensity polarization spectral change	Frequency cm⁻¹	Intensity polarization spectral change	Frequency cm⁻¹	Intensity polarization spectral change	Frequency cm⁻¹	Intensity polarization spectral change	Frequency cm⁻¹	Intensity polarization spectral change	Frequency cm⁻¹	Intensity polarization spectral change
$\nu(=C-O)$ + arom.	1280		1280				1270	vs =	1270	vs =	1270	vs ‖
$\nu(=C-O)$ + arom.	1250	vs =	1260	vs =	1260	vs =	1250	vs =	1250	vs =	1250	vs =
arom. ring vibration	1240	=	1240		1240	w	1210	m —	1210	m =	1220	m ‖
naphthalene ring vibration					1200	w	1180	vs —	1180	vs =	1180	vs =
$\gamma_t(CH_2)$ gauche	1172	w	1170	w	1170	w						
naphthalene ring vibration							1135	s ‖—	1135	s =	1135	s ‖
benzene ring vibration	1120	s =	1120	s =	1120	s =						
$\nu_s(O-C)$ gauche	1100	vs =	1100	vs =	1100	vs =	1090	s ‖—	1090	s ‖	1090	s ‖
$\nu_a(O-C)$ gauche	1042	w =	1040	w =			1044	w —	1040	mw ‖		
	1022	s =	1020	s =	1020	s =	1005	m crys.				
					980	sh =			980	m =	980	ms ‖
	988	vw +			950	sh =	984	m ‖+	960	s =		
δ(arom. CH in-plane)	973	m ‖+	970	m ‖+	930	ms ‖=	968	m ‖—	940	s =	970	m ‖
					920	m +						

S1	S2	S3	S4	S5	S6	Assignment
930 vw −	930 w +		930 m ⊥ +			
				920 s ⊥	920 m ⊥	γr(CH₂) gauche; δ(arom. CH out-of-plane)
			919 m ⊥ − crys.			
			905 sh ⊥ =			
	900 sh = −					
895 sh =						
			880 w −			
	875 ms ⊥			875 vw		
873 ms ⊥						
		870 ms =				
848 m +						
	840 m ∥ +	840 w =				
			835 m ⊥ crys.			
			822 m −			
				820 m ⊥	820 m ⊥	γr(CH₂) trans
		810 w +	810 m ∥ crys.			
794 w						
	790 w	790 w ⊥		790 mw ∥	790 mw ∥	γr(C=O) + δ(CCO)
			765 s ⊥	765 s ⊥	765 s ⊥	δ(arom. CH out-of-plane)
		740 w +	740 w −	740 w ⊥		
730 s ⊥					730 w	
	725 s ⊥	725 s ⊥				
710 sh						
		700 w ⊥	700 vw			
				690 vw		
680 sh	680 vw	680 vw	680 vw			
				650 vw		
			640 mw	640 m	640 m	δ(COC) + arom. ?
630 vw	630 vw	630 vw =				
			620 w	620 w		
			580 w	580 w		
575 sh =						
				555 sh ⊥		
			550 sh =		550 w	
				530 mw		
			525 mw ⊥ +			
520 sh =	520 w ∥				520 w	
500 mw ∥	500 mw ∥	500 m				
480 w			480 ms ⊥ crys.			
			470 ms ∥ −	470 ms ⊥	470 ms ⊥	δ(arom. CH out-of-plane)
				440 sh		
430 mw ∥ crys.	430 mw ∥					
420 mw ∥				420 w		

ν = stretching; δ = bending; γ𝓌 = wagging; γr = rocking; crys. = bands which exist only in crystalline state; + = bands which increase in intensity upon crystallization; − = bands which decrease in intensity upon crystallization.

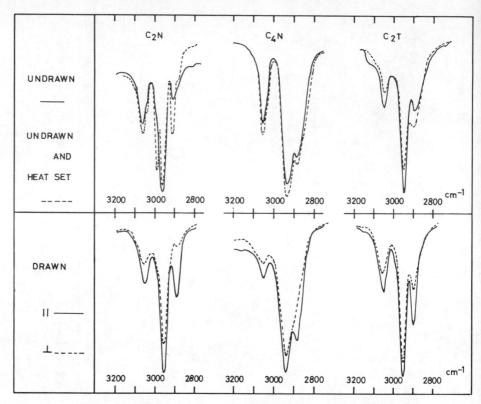

Fig. 2. Infrared spectra of some polyesters between 2800 and 3400 cm^{-1}.

than those of C_2T and other polymers, indicating that C_2N would take the trans configuration more easily. For C_4T, the 1470 cm^{-1} band is not distinct and does not increase in intensity by crystallization. According to Menčik,[11] C_4T crystals have methylene linkages arranged as GTT so that the polarization of the bands associated with methylene vibration in the crystals should be different from those of C_2T and C_2N. For C_4N, Watanabe,[12] in our laboratory, found the existence of two crystal forms: fully extended and contracted. So far, we have not succeeded in finding the difference in the infrared spectra of these two forms.

The CH_2 wagging vibrations of C_2N are assigned to the bands at 1370 cm^{-1} (gauche) and 1337 cm^{-1} (trans) as in C_2T. By heat treatment, the 1337 cm^{-1} band gives rise to a shoulder at 1332 cm^{-1}. The intensity change during crystallization is not as prominent for these bands as for CH_2 bending vibrations. For C_2T and C_3T, drawn and heat-treated samples show a relatively weak band at 1380 cm^{-1}. For C_4T and C_4N, three distinct bands always exist in this region: at 1380, 1350, and 1320 cm^{-1} for C_4T and at 1365, 1340, and 1320 cm^{-1} for C_4N. Thus, there are some variations in the spectra concerning the CH_2 wagging modes of different lengths of methylene groups.

The CH_2 rocking vibrations of C_2T were assigned to 848 cm^{-1} (trans) and 895 cm^{-1} (gauche) by Miyake.[9] We tried arbitrarily to assign the band at 822 cm^{-1} of C_2N to CH_2 rocking vibration. But the behavior of this band is rather complicated, as shown in Figure 4. Namely, on drawing, the 822 cm^{-1} band shows sharp σ polarization and a band appears at 810 cm^{-1} with π polarization. On

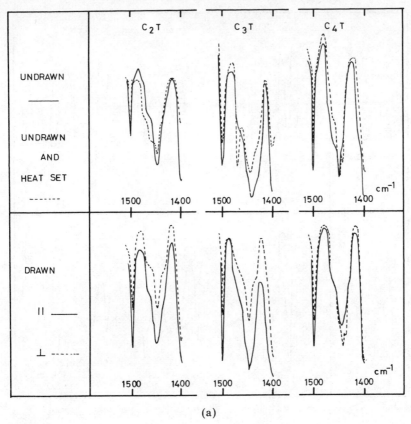

(a)

Fig. 3. Infrared spectra of some polyesters between 1400 and 1500 cm^{-1}.

heating either undrawn or drawn films, the 822 cm^{-1} band decreases in intensity and, instead, bands grow at 835 and 810 cm^{-1}. The 835 cm^{-1} band is of σ character. A band at 820 cm^{-1} exists in C$_4$N and C$_6$N, too, but it is a simple σ band and does not bring about 810 or 835 cm^{-1} bands upon crystallization. Thus, the bands that appeared at 810 and 835 cm^{-1} are characteristic of C$_2$N and probably originate from certain intermolecular interactions existing in oriented or crystalline states of C$_2$N, as discussed later.

The strong bands at 1090 cm^{-1} in C$_2$N, C$_4$N, and C$_6$N would correspond to the bands at 1100 cm^{-1} in C$_2$T, C$_3$T, and C$_4$T. They are of π polarization and decrease in intensity by heat treatment and may be assigned to the C—O symmetric stretching vibration of the gauche form. This assignment in case of C$_2$T was made by Miyake[9] and others and differs from the views of Grime and Ward[7] and some others; but it may be supported for C$_2$N by the fact that there is no intense absorption in the vicinity of 1100 cm^{-1} in the spectra of naphthalene and 2,6-naphthalic acid, which have no ethylene glycol residue, and that there is such an absorption in diethyl 2,6-naphthalate, bis(β-hydroxyethyl) 2,6-naphthalate, etc.

Although there are disagreements, Miyake[9] assigned the band at 1042 cm^{-1} of C$_2$T to antisymmetric C—O stretching vibration of the gauche form. The weak band at 1044 cm^{-1} in C$_2$N would correspond to the above vibration of C$_2$T. Corresponding bands exist in C$_3$T and C$_4$N but are too weak to be seen in C$_4$T

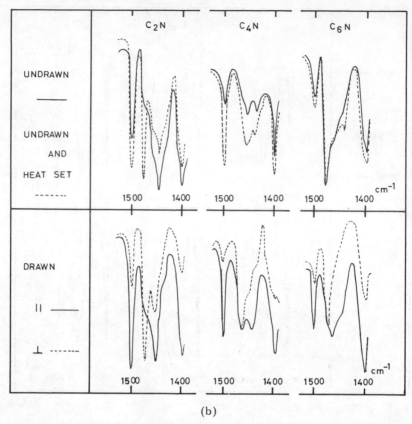

(b)

Fig. 3. (*continued from previous page*)

and C_6N. Making a couple with the 1040 cm^{-1} band, the parallel band at 973
cm^{-1} of C_2T was assigned to antisymmetric C—O stretching vibration of trans
form by Miyake,[9] although Liang and Krimm[8] assigned it to a benzene ring vibration. The 973 cm^{-1} band exist in C_3T, but in C_4T it has a peak at 930 cm^{-1}
with shoulders at 950, 980, and 920 cm^{-1}, which would throw some doubts on
the assignment as C—O vibration. There are corresponding bands in C_2N, C_4N,
and C_6N, but the spectral change of the 968 cm^{-1} band of C_2N is rather complex,
as shown in Figure 4. On drawing, the shoulder at 984 cm^{-1} grows and both
bands at 968 and 984 cm^{-1} show parallel dichroism. On heating, the original
band decreases in intensity and a new band appears at 1005 cm^{-1}. The latter
forms a distinct band for undrawn films, but is hidden behind the 984 cm^{-1} band
for drawn films and has no perpendicular component. This behavior again must
be related to some effects of intermolecular interactions under crystalline field
characteristics to C_2N.

The origin of the intermolecular interactions which give birth to the new bands
at 810, 835, and 1005 cm^{-1} is considered to be the close packing of molecules in
the unit cells of C_2N. According to Menčik,[1] the unit cell of C_2N has dimension
$a = 6.51$ Å, $b = 5.75$ Å, $c = 13.2$ Å, $\alpha = 81°21'$, $\beta = 144°00'$, and $\gamma = 100°00'$. The
projection of the molecules along the c axis is shown in Figure 5(a), and the
projection normal to the plane of the molecule is shown in Figure 5(b). In contrast to the configuration of C_2T and C_4T, all the atoms of the polymer chain
including O=C—O (except the hydrogens of CH$_2$) are coplanar in C_2N. This

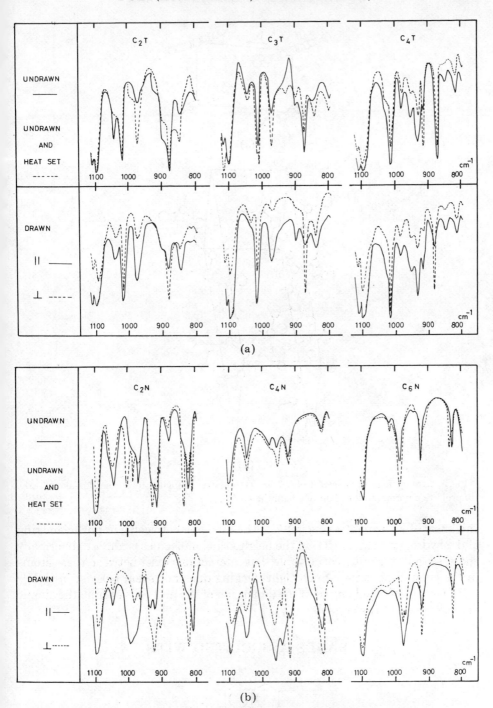

Fig. 4. Infrared spectra of some polyesters between 800 and 1100 cm⁻¹.

plane is approximately ($\bar{4}$30) whose lattice distance is 0.88 Å. Therefore, the distance between the neighboring molecular planes perpendicular to the naphthalene ring is 3.54 Å. On the other hand, since the angle β is large, one of the C atoms of —CH₂—CH₂— is just above a naphthalene ring, as seen from Figure 5(b). Considering that the van der Waals radius of a CH₂ is 2 Å and a half-

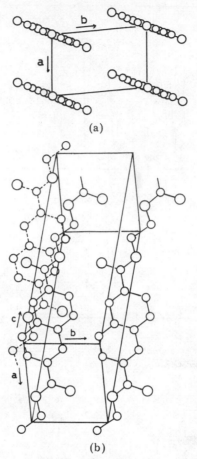

(a)

(b)

Fig. 5. Arrangement of molecules of C_2N in crystal (after Menčik): (a) projection along c axis. (b) projection normal to the plane of a naphthalene ring.

thickness of an aromatic ring is 1.7 Å, the distance between a naphthalene ring and a hydrogen atom of CH_2 in the neighboring molecules is almost abnormally short, so that it is quite conceivable that interactions exist between these atoms in the crystalline state. Such tight packing does not seem to exist in C_2T,[13] C_4T,[11] and C_4N,[12] judging from the dimension of the unit cells or from the atomic arrangements in the crystal.

BANDS ASSOCIATED WITH

The σ band at 3060 cm^{-1} with a shoulder at 3050 cm^{-1} of C_2N may be safely assigned to ν (aromatic CH), although it is of parallel polarization in C_2T. The other C_mT and C_mN have this band at this region. Corresponding with the 875 cm^{-1} band of C_2T, C_3T, and C_4T, the band at 919 cm^{-1} in C_2N, C_4N, and C_6N

might be associated with an aromatic CH out-of-plane vibration. However, since the nearest band in the spectrum of naphthalene is at 955 cm^{-1} and compounds such as 2,6-naphthalic acid contain a band in this region, it may be better to consider the band due to O=C—O out-of-plane bending vibration. This band in C$_2$N is weakened on heating, and, instead, bands grow at 933 and at 905 cm^{-1} with σ polarization.

The bands at 765 cm^{-1} of C$_2$N, C$_4$N, and C$_6$N are very intense and of of σ polarization and correspond to the 730 cm^{-1} band of C$_2$T, C$_3$T, and C$_4$T. The latter was a controversial one for a long time. First, Miller and Willis[6] assigned it to a C—O—C bending vibration, but this was refuted by Grime and Ward[7] since this band exists in terephthalic acid and other compounds containing no C—O—C linkage. Then, Miyake[9] assigned it to the O=C—O out-of-plane bending vibration based on a number of spectra of the related compounds. However, in the spectrum of poly(ethylene terephthalate-D$_4$), the 730 cm^{-1} band shifts to 640 cm^{-1} so that the former does not seem to be associated, at least exclusively, with O=C—O bending. Thus, Grime and Ward[7] and Liang and Krimm[8] assigned the 730 cm^{-1} band to an aromatic CH out-of-plane vibration. Since naphthalene has a strong band at 780 cm^{-1}, we favor the assignment of the 765 cm^{-1} band of C$_2$N, C$_4$N, and C$_6$N to aromatic CH out-of-plane vibration.

The band at 470 cm^{-1} in C$_2$N, C$_4$N, and C$_6$N would correspond to the band at 430 cm^{-1} of C$_2$T which was assigned to aromatic CH out-of-plane bending by Liang and Krimm.[8] This may be supported by the intense bands of naphthalene at 480 and 470 cm^{-1}. In C$_2$N, the behavior of the 470 cm^{-1} band is a little different from the others: upon heating, a band appears at 480 cm^{-1}. The 470 cm^{-1} band is of σ polarization, and the 480 cm^{-1} band is of π polarization.

Besides the bands described above, there are more bands related to aromatic ring vibrations at 1600, 1570, 1500, and 1400 cm^{-1}. The strong σ bands at 1180 and 1135 cm^{-1} do not exist in terephthalate polymers and are characteristic for the compounds having a naphthalene ring.

The intense band at 1715 cm^{-1} is, of course, due to C=O stretching vibration. Its overtone appears around 3400 cm^{-1}.

The stretching vibration of =C—O can be assigned to the doublet at 1250 and 1270 cm^{-1}, which is the most intense in the spectrum. Since there is a strong absorption at 1265 cm^{-1} in naphthalene, the doublet may be partially associated with aromatic ring vibrations in addition to the =C—O stretching vibration.

In summary, among the poly(methylene 2,6-naphthalates), C$_2$N, C$_4$N, and C$_6$N have much in common in the infrared spectra, which also correspond fairly well to the spectra of C$_2$T, C$_3$T, and C$_4$T. However, at some frequencies, the spectral changes of C$_2$N show unique behavior owing to the existence of a characteristic crystalline field arising from the tight packing of the molecules in the crystal.

The authors wish to thank Messrs. S. Kawase and T. Kuratsuji, Products Development Institute, for making various polyesters for us. They are also thankful for the help from their colleagues at Plastics Research Institute.

References

1. Z. Menčik, *Chem. Průmysl*, **17**, 78 (1967).
2. R. S. Rogowski and G. F. Pezdirts, *J. Polym. Sci. A-2*, **9**, 2111 (1971).

3. R. R. Richards and R. S. Rogowski, *J. Polym. Sci. Phys.*, **12**, 89 (1974).

4. I. Ouchi, H. Aoki, S. Shimotsuma, T. Asai, and M. Hosoi, in *Proc. 17th Japan Congr. Materials Research,* 1974, p. 217.

5. I. Ouchi, M. Hosoi, and F. Matsumoto, *J. Appl. Polym. Sci.,* **20**, 1983 (1976).

6. R. G. J. Miller and H. A. Willis, *J. Polym. Sci.,* **19**, 485 (1956).

7. D. Grime and I. M. Ward, *Trans. Faraday Soc.,* **54**, 959 (1958).

8. C. Y. Liang and S. Krimm, *J. Mol. Spectrosc.,* **3**, 554 (1959).

9. A. Miyake, *J. Polym. Sci.,* **38**, 479 (1959); *ibid.,* **38**, 496 (1959).

10. S. K. Bahl, D. D. Cornell, F. J. Boerio, and G. E. McGraw, *J. Polym. Sci., Polym. Lett.,* **12**, 13 (1974).

11. Z. Menčik, *J. Polym. Sci. Phys.,* **13**, 2173 (1975).

12. H. Watanabe, *Kobunshi Ronbunshu,* **33**, 229 (1976) (in Japanese).

13. R. de P. Daubeny and C. W. Bunn, *Proc. R. Soc.,* **A226**, 531 (1954).

Received July 20, 1976
Revised November 4, 1976

JOURNAL OF APPLIED POLYMER SCIENCE   VOL. 21, 3457–3463 (1977)

Diffusion of Stabilizers in Polymers. IV. 2,4-Dihydroxybenzophenone in Plasticized Poly(vinyl Chloride)

M. JOHNSON and R. G. HAUSERMAN, *Department of Chemistry, University of Lancaster, Bailrigg, Lancaster, England LA1 4YA*

Synopsis

The diffusion of the radioactively labeled ultraviolet stabilizer 2,4-dihydroxybenzophenone in compression-molded sheets of plasticized poly(vinyl chloride) was studied over the temperature range of 30°–75°C. No detectable diffusion occurred in the 0% and 10% plasticized poly(vinyl chloride) when the diffusion temperature was below the glass transition temperatures of the polymers. Diffusion coefficients have been measured for plasticizer concentrations of 20, 30, 40, and 50 wt %. In each case, the variation of the diffusion coefficient D with temperature T can be represented by an Arrhenius expression $D = D_0 \exp(-E/RT)$. The linear relation $\log D_0 = -7.1 + 0.20E/T$ was obtained as an empirical expression of the results.

INTRODUCTION

Previous papers in this series reported on the diffusion of hydroxybenzophenones in polyolefins[1,2] and polyurethanes.[3] The experiments were performed at temperatures within the range of 36°–75°C, which were well above the glass transition temperatures (T_g) of the polymers.

The glass transition temperature of poly(vinyl chloride) can be readily altered from around 80°C down to −50°C by the incorporation of a suitable concentration of a plasticizer.[4] These changes in glass transition temperature will influence the rate at which other additives (e.g., UV stabilizers, antioxidants, HCl absorbers) diffuse within the polymer. Diffusion can be important in controlling the retention of additives in polymers[5,6] and also in determining the ability of a stabilizer molecule to diffuse to reactive sites, which are, for example, in the surface layers of polymers,[7] so that the incorporation of a plasticizer into PVC may affect the efficiency with which additives stabilize the polymer.

The present paper reports the results obtained for the diffusion of 2,4-dihydroxybenzophenone, a UV stabilizer, in PVC plasticized with various concentrations of a phthalate ester. The experiments were carried out within the range of 30°–75°C, which meant that in most cases the experimental temperature was above the T_g of the polymer, but in some cases it was below the T_g of the polymer.

EXPERIMENTAL

Materials

Ultraviolet Stabilizer. The preparation and purification of the ^{14}C-labeled sample of 2,4-dihydroxybenzophenone have been reported previously.[1]

Plasticizer. The plasticizer used was a commercial sample (Shell Chemicals (UK) Limited) of the phthalate of Linevol 79. Linevol 79 is a blend of predominantly (>80%) linear C_7, C_8, and C_9 alcohols.

Polymer. An atactic, commercial-grade PVC resin (Breon S.125/12, BP Chemicals Limited) in the form of a white powder was used throughout this work.

Formation of Polymer Sheets

Sheets of PVC were prepared with plasticizer at concentrations of 0, 10, 20, 30, 40, and 50 wt %.

The various compositions of plasticizer and PVC powder were made up together with 2% of a barium/cadmium/zinc stabilizer system and 0.5% stearic acid as a lubricant, initially mixed by hand and then thoroughly mixed for 4 min at a temperature of 155°C on a two-roll mill (D. Bridge and Co. Limited) before being calendered to sheets with thicknesses of ∼0.14 cm.

Disks (3.5 cm in diameter) of the polymer were cut from sheets prepared by pressing 7 cm × 7 cm square pieces (one or more depending on the thickness required) of the calendered sheets between two sheets of mold release paper using a compression molding machine. This technique has already been described in detail.[3] The molding conditions used varied somewhat with the plasticizer concentration, and these conditions are shown in Table I. The sheets were cooled (∼25°C/min) to room temperature while under pressure by passing water through the platens.

Glass Transition Temperature and Density Measurements

The glass transition temperatures of the PVC samples were measured to an accuracy of ±5°C using a differential scanning calorimeter (Perkin–Elmer

TABLE I
Compression Molding Conditions

Plasticizer, wt %	Thickness of sheet, cm	Mold temperature, °C	Mold pressure, tons on 4-in.-diam. ram	Preheat time, min	Compression time, min
0	0.02–0.03	175	12	5	3
10	0.02–0.03	170	12	5	3
20	0.06–0.10	167.5	15	5	3
30	0.14–0.20	162.5	15	5	3
40	0.16–0.22	157.5	15	6	3
50	0.20–0.22	150	15	6	3

TABLE II
Polymer Properties

Plasticizer, wt %	Glass transition temp., °C	Density, g/cm³
0	76	1.41
10	57	1.36
20	43	1.31
30	27	1.27
40	10	1.21
50	−15	1.17

DSC-1B, Norwalk, Connecticut, U.S.A.). These results are shown in Table II together with the value of the densities of the polymers which were obtained by weighing several disks of each of the polymers in air and water.

Determination of Diffusion Coefficients

The apparatus and procedure have been described elsewhere.[1] The experiments were carried out in the temperature range of 30°–75°C with disks of the polymers whose thicknesses were such that the equilibrium counting rates were reached after between 40 and 1500 hr. The 2,4-dihydroxybenzophenone was as usual applied to the polymer disks as a standard solution in acetone. Amounts were used which gave final equilibrium counting rates of between 100 and 250 counts/min. These amounts were very similar to those used for the experiments

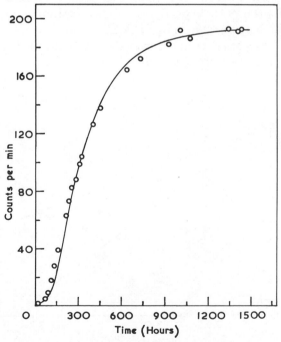

Fig. 1. Variation in surface counting rate for diffusion in 30% plasticized PVC: temperature, 40°C; disk thickness, 0.142 cm; (O O O O O) experimental points; (———) theoretical curve for $D = 2.54 \times 10^{-9}$ cm²/sec.

TABLE III
Arrhenius Parameters for Diffusion

Plasticizer, wt %	D_0, cm²/sec	Activation energy, kcal/mole
20	5.9×10^9	27.9
30	3.5	13.1
40	3.3×10^{-2}	9.1
50	1.7×10^{-3}	6.9

with polyurethanes[3] for polymer disks of equivalent thicknesses. It was shown[3] that the polyurethanes were not saturated with the stabilizer at concentrations corresponding to these counting rates. It, is, therefore, unlikely that the PVC samples were saturated at these concentrations of the stabilizer. This was confirmed by doubling the amounts of stabilizer applied to disks with the various plasticizer concentrations and following the diffusion at the lowest temperature studied. The equilibrium counting rates in all these cases were double those previously recorded, which confirmed that saturation of the polymer disks did not occur. The diffusion equation which corresponded to nonsaturation conditions[1] was, therefore, used to evaluate the diffusion coefficients throughout the present work.

RESULTS AND DISCUSSION

The theoretical diffusion equation requires a value of the absorption coefficient of the polymer for the ¹⁴C beta particles. This was obtained[1] from the value of the density of the polymer shown in Table II.

Diffusion studies were conducted over the temperature range of 30°–75°C. For thin disks (thickness 0.02 cm) of rigid PVC (0% plasticizer), no measurable

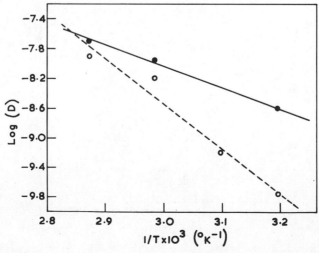

Fig. 2. Arrhenius plot of log D vs $1/T$ for diffusion in 20% plasticized PVC (○----) and 30% plasticized PVC (●——).

TABLE IV
Values of Diffusion Coefficients for 2,4-Dihydroxybenzophenone in Various Polymers at 25°C

Polymer	D, cm²/sec	Reference
Isotactic polypropylene	5.4×10^{-13}	1
High-density polyethylene B	3.2×10^{-11}	1
High-density polyethylene A	5.4×10^{-11}	1
Low-density polyethylene	4.6×10^{-10}	1
Polyurethane E.1	1.6×10^{-10}	3
Polyurethane E.2	2.7×10^{-9}	3
20% Plasticized PVC	2.0×10^{-11}	This paper
30% Plasticized PVC	8.6×10^{-10}	This paper
40% Plasticized PVC	7.0×10^{-9}	This paper
50% Plasticized PVC	1.5×10^{-8}	This paper

diffusion had occurred even after 700 hr at 75°C. In the case of the 10% plasticized PVC, no diffusion was detected below 50°C; but it was just detectable at higher temperatures after very long times: after 700 hr at 62°C and 400 hr at 75°C. So that when the temperature is below the T_g of the polymer (Table II), diffusion of the 2,4-dihydroxybenzophenone must be extremely slow and remains undetected by the present technique.

Diffusion coefficients were obtained for plasticizer concentrations of 20%, 30%, 40%, and 50%. At each plasticizer concentration, measurements were carried out for at least three temperatures. Typical results are shown in Figure 1 for the diffusion of the stabilizer in 30% plasticized PVC at 40°C. The open circles represent the experimental data, the solid curve being the theoretical curve corresponding to a value of 2.54×10^{-9} cm²/sec for the diffusion coefficient. The accuracy and reproducibility of the values of the diffusion coefficients were the same as in previous work.[3]

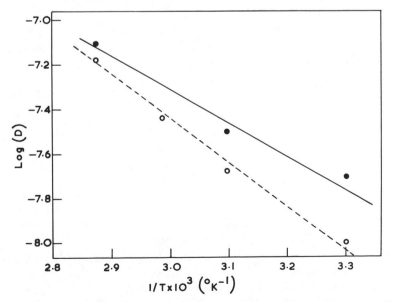

Fig. 3. Arrhenius plot of log D vs $1/T$ for diffusion in 40% plasticized PVC (o----) and 50% plasticized PVC (●——).

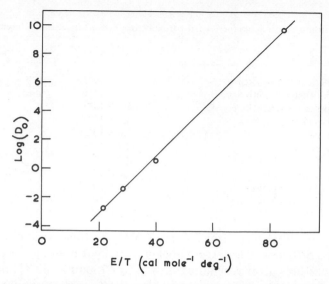

Fig. 4. Relationship between $\log D_0$ and E/T for diffusion in plasticized PVC.

Plots of $\log D$ versus $1/T$, for the various plasticizer concentrations are presented in Figures 2 and 3. The values of D_0 and E, in the Arrhenius expression $D = D_0 \exp(-E/RT)$, obtained from these graphs are given in Table III.

As the plasticizer concentration increases, the polymer becomes more flexible (T_g decreases), which produces a decrease in the activation energy for diffusion. The decrease in the activation energy is accompanied by a decrease in the corresponding value of D_0, a phenomenon which has been noted previously for diffusion in a number of polymer systems.[8-11] Thus, the decrease in activation energy is compensated somewhat by a decrease in the entropy of activation as the polymer becomes more flexible.

An empirical linear relation between $\log D_0$ and E/T has already been established for a number of systems,[8-11] and a similar situation exists in the present work as shown in Figure 4 (T is the mean value of the temperature range over which D_0 and E were obtained). The correlation

$$\log D_0 = -7.1 + 0.20 E/T$$

is obtained from this figure which, together with the Arrhenius expression $D = D_0 \exp(-E/RT)$, leads to the equation

$$\log D = -7.1 - 0.019 E/T$$

This is similar to the corresponding equations for the diffusion of gases in rubbers[8,9] and for organic compounds in polyolefins.[11] A possible use of such an equation may be to estimate a value of the activation energy for diffusion from the measurement of D at one temperature only.

In Table IV, the diffusion coefficients that we have obtained for the diffusion of 2,4-dihydroxybenzophenone in various polymers at 25°C are listed; the values were calculated at this temperature from the appropriate Arrhenius equations. There is a very wide range of values for the diffusion coefficients in the different polymers ranging from 5.4×10^{-13} cm²/sec in isotactic polypropylene up to 1.5

$\times 10^{-8}$ cm^2/sec in the 50% plasticized PVC. Correlations of the changes in the values of the diffusion coefficients with changes in the structure of the polymers have been pointed out previously[1,3] as well as in the present paper. The data in Table IV will be reliable for predicting the diffusion behavior of the stabilizer in the polymers at room temperature since the extrapolation of the results using the Arrhenius equation will be fairly accurate, 25°C being only just outside the experimental temperature range.

References

1. J. F. Westlake and M. Johnson, *J. Appl. Polym. Sci.*, **19**, 319 (1975).
2. M. Johnson and J. F. Westlake, *J. Appl. Polym. Sci.*, **19**, 1745 (1975).
3. R. G. Hauserman and M. Johnson, *J. Appl. Polym. Sci.*, **20**, 2533 (1976).
4. K. Wolf, *Kunstoffe*, **41**, 89 (1951).
5. R. V. Albarino and H. Schonhorn, *J. Appl. Polym. Sci.*, **17**, 3323 (1973).
6. J. Durmis, M. Karvas, P. Caucik, and J. Holcik, *Europ. Polym. J.*, **11**, 219 (1975).
7. D. J. Carlsson, T. Suprunchuk, and D. M. Wiles, *J. Appl. Polym. Sci.*, **16**, 615 (1972).
8. G. J. van Amerongen, *Rubber Chem. Technol.*, **37**, 1065 (1964).
9. R. M. Barrer and H. T. Chio, *J. Polym. Sci. C*, **10**, 111 (1965).
10. M. Dubini, O. Cicchetti, G. P. Vicario, and E. Bua, *Europ. Polym. J.*, **3**, 473 (1967).
11. O. Cicchetti, M. Dubini, P. Parrini, G. P. Vicario, and E. Bua, *Europ. Polym. J.*, **4**, 419 (1968).

Received September 22, 1976
Revised October 28, 1976

JOURNAL OF APPLIED POLYMER SCIENCE   VOL. 21, 3465–3471 (1977)

Characterization of the Chromium(III)-Crosslinked Collagen–Poly(Butyl Acrylate) Graft Copolymer

H. A. GRUBER, E. H. HARRIS, Jr., and S. H. FEAIRHELLER, *Eastern Regional Research Center, Agricultural Research Service, U.S. Department of Agriculture, Philadelphia, Pennsylvania 19118*

Synopsis

The redox, free radical-initiated graft polymerization of butyl acrylate onto chromium(III)-crosslinked collagen has been investigated previously. In the experiments reported here we set out to determine whether true grafting had occurred and, if so, the molecular weight of the synthetic polymer that was grafted to the collagen. The butyl acrylate grafted product was successively extracted with acetone and ethyl acetate to remove homopolymers. The solvent-extracted product was then subjected to enzymatic degradation, followed by chloroform fractionation, and finally gel permeation chromatography of the chloroform-soluble fraction. Viscosity studies of the final fractionated product indicated that the molecular weight was about 1 million. Viscosity studies of the two homopolymers extracted with acetone and ethyl acetate show that the molecular weights of these homopolymers were somewhat less than that of the isolated polymer–peptide fragment. The fractionated polymer–peptide unit contained 2.83% amino acids, indicating that there are about 288 amino acids in the peptide attached to the polymer molecule. This polymer is composed of approximately 8100 monomer units. The IR spectra confirmed that this fraction is principally poly(butyl acrylate) with amide, OH, and NH absorption bands contributed by the peptide. The isolation and characterization of the polymer–peptide fragment provided proof of graft polymerization onto the collagen molecule.

INTRODUCTION

Recently, Korn et al.[1,2] and Harris et al.[3] have shown that it is possible to graft polymerize vinyl monomers onto collagen using a redox initiation system in the absence of air. In these studies, chromium(III)-crosslinked sheepskin collagen was used as the substrate, and the graft polymerization was found to enhance the properties of the leather made from these skins. Since butyl acrylate appeared to be one of the monomers of choice in producing the best overall leather, the collagen substrate in this study was grafted with butyl acrylate. It has been determined that this gives a leather product containing about 18% of the graft copolymer which is irreversibly bound and unextractable with organic solvents. In the present work, we have enzymatically degraded and solvent fractionated the graft copolymer, thereby obtaining a polymeric product which was mainly poly(butyl acrylate) with a relatively small peptide attached. Viscosity determinations, amino acid analyses, and the IR spectra enabled us to prove that true grafting had occurred, and to determine the approximate molecular weight of the grafted synthetic polymer.

3465

EXPERIMENTAL

Materials

Commercially chrominum(III)-tanned Nigerian sheepskins were graft polymerized with butyl acrylate obtained from Rohm and Haas Company. The butyl acrylate contained 5 ppm of the monomethyl ether of hydroquinone (MEHQ) as an inhibitor and was used as received. Other chemicals were obtained from a number of sources and used as received: (1) Poly(butyl acrylate), secondary standard, Aldrich Chemical Co. (2) Triton X-100 (alkylphenoxy polyethoxy ethanol), Rohm & Haas Co. (3) Potassium persulfate, Fisher Scientific Co. (4) Sodium bisulfite, practical, Eastman Kodak Co. (5) Ethyl acetate, Eastman Kodak Co. (6) (Ethylenedinitrilo)tetraacetic acid disodium salt (EDTA), Eastman Kodak Co. (7) Acetone, nanograde, Mallinckrodt Chemical Works. (8) Chloroform, reagent grade, J. T. Baker Chemical Co. (9) Sephadex LH-20, Pharmacia Fine Chemicals. (10) Pepsin, hog stomach mucosa, 3X cryst., Nutritional Biochemicals Co. (11) Pronase, B grade, 45,000 P.U.K./g, Calbiochem.

Graft Polymerization

Approximately 200-g samples (45 g on a dry weight basis) of the substrate were used. These were placed in ½-gallon Mason jars with 400 ml deionized water, 1.8 g of the emulsifer Triton X-100, and, as the redox initiator system, 1.8 g potassium persulfate and 0.9 g sodium bisulfite (to avoid the release of SO_2, do not contact sodium bisulfite with acids). Sufficient Dry Ice was used to displace all the air, and ambient temperature was used throughout. After the Dry Ice had sublimed, the jars were sealed and then tumbled end-over-end for 30 min. At this point, 45 g n-butyl acrylate and additional Dry Ice to ensure a continued oxygen-free atmosphere were added, and the jars capped after allowing the dry ice to sublime. Tumbling was continued for 24 hr, at which time all of the monomer had been consumed as determined by gas-chromatographic analysis of a portion of the aqueous phase. The samples were then removed, washed thoroughly in cold running tap water, and allowed to dry at room temperature. Appropriate care must be taken in handling all monomers because of possible flammability and toxic nature of these chemicals.

Isolation of the Synthetic Graft

As outlined in Figure 1, a preliminary Soxhlet extraction with acetone for 6 hr was performed prior to grinding the grafted leather in a Wiley mill. The ground butyl acrylate-grafted product was additionally extracted for 24-hr periods with 150 ml acetone and with two 150-ml portions of ethyl acetate by refluxing using a Soxhlet extractor under atmospheric conditions.

As shown in Figure 2, 5.00 g of the air-dried solvent-extracted sample and 0.5 g EDTA in 400 ml water were autoclaved at 15 psi for 1 hr to degrade the chrome-tanned collagen. The solution was cooled and the pH adjusted to 2.0 with dilute hydrochloric acid. Pepsin, 0.5 g, was added and the sample was agitated intermittently for 72 hr. The pH was adjusted periodically when necessary. The sample was centrifuged, then filtered through sintered glass, and

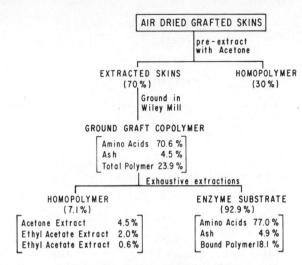

Fig. 1. Properties of initial product.

washed with 0.1N HCl, water, 0.1N NaOH, and finally water until the filtrate was neutral.   The air-dry weight of the residue was 2.3 g.   This residue and 0.23 g EDTA in 400 ml water were autoclaved at 15 psi for 1 hr.   The solution was cooled to room temperature and the pH adjusted to 8.0 with dilute sodium hydroxide.   Pronase, 0.23 g, was added and the enzymatic degradation continued as before for 72 hr.   At the end of this period, the residue was filtered and washed with acid, alkali, and water as before.   The weight was now 1.02 g.

Gel Permeation Chromatography

As shown in Figure 3, a portion of this residue was solvent fractionated in 50 ml chloroform by stirring intermittently for 72 hr.   The sample was centrifuged, and the soluble portion was fractionated on a 2.5 × 75 cm Sephadex LH-20 column using chloroform as the eluant.   A reverse flow was used and 8.4-ml fractions were collected in test tubes at the approximate rate of 1 ml/min.   The fractions were transferred to 50-ml round-bottom flasks and the chloroform

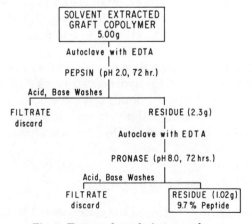

Fig. 2. Enzyme degradation procedure.

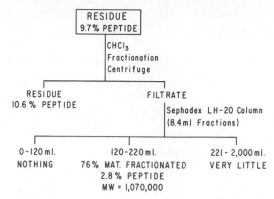

Fig. 3. Fractionation of enzyme-degraded residue.

removed by evaporation under reduced pressure and ambient temperature to obtain any polymer present. Only one component was present, and this material was combined as one fraction.

Viscosity Determinations for Molecular Weight Calculations

The samples were dissolved in acetone and several dilutions made. The specific viscosities were determined at 25°C using a Cannon-Manning semimicro viscometer. The data for the specific viscosities at various concentrations were extrapolated to zero concentration to obtain the intrinsic viscosity. The intrinsic viscosities thus obtained were used in the equation $[\eta] = KM^a$ to determine the molecular weights using literature values[4] for K and a.

Amino Acid Analyses

The samples were prepared for amino acid analysis by hydrolyzing in $6N$ hydrochloric acid solution for 24 hr under an atmosphere of nitrogen. The polymer residue was filtered off, and the excess hydrogen chloride was removed by repeated evaporations under reduced pressure with the intermittent addition of deionized water. The final residues were then diluted to a known volume with $0.1N$ hydrochloric acid solution. The analyses were run on a Piez–Morris[5]-type ion exchange column with a continuous-gradient elution buffer. The results were calculated and tabulated on an IBM 1130 computer using programs developed at our laboratory.

Due to the small amount of sample remaining after the molecular weight studies, another method was used for hydrolyzing this sample. An aliquot was transferred to a test tube; and after evaporating the acetone, 2 ml $6N$ hydrochloric acid was added and the tube sealed under vacuum. It was hydrolyzed in an oven at 100°C for 24 hr and then prepared for the amino acid analyzer as previously described.

IR SPECTRA

The secondary standard, poly(butyl acrylate), and the unknown polymer fractions in acetone were applied dropwise to separate sodium chloride crystals.

Several applications were made to form a film, and the crystals were dried with an infrared lamp between applications. A Perkin–Elmer 137 spectrophotometer was used for the studies.

Nitrogen Analyses

The percent nitrogen was determined by the semimicro Kjeldahl method.

RESULTS AND DISCUSSION

Although some research has been done recently on the graft polymerization of vinyl monomers onto hides and skins, little is known of the actual grafting site on the collagen molecule or the size of the polymer formed. Rao et al.[6,7] have enzymatically hydrolyzed collagen–vinyl graft copolymers and isolated the grafted vinyl polymer side chains. They determined proof of grafting through the detection of amino acid endgroups by using a ninhydrin solution on the isolated grafts. It appeared to us that this product might have contained entrapped proteinaceous material as a result of the isolation methods used, although in all probability it was a true graft copolymer. Subjecting the residue from enzymatic digestions to acid and base washes, dissolution in organic solvents and chromatographic fractionation procedures should eliminate this possibility.

As shown in Figure 1, the collagen–poly(butyl acrylate) graft copolymer was acetone preextracted to remove most of the homopolymer prior to grinding in the Wiley mill, since the presence of homopolymer made the grinding difficult or even impossible and made the Wiley mill overheat. This extraction removed 30% of the original material as homopolymer. Analysis of the ground graft copolymer showed that amino acids accounted for 70.6% of the material (calculated on a molecular weight basis), and the ash content was 4.5%. In addition to the homopolymer extracted prior to grinding the sample, three 24-hr periods of Soxhlet extraction removed only 7.1% homopolymer. The first 24-hr extraction using acetone yielded 4.5% homopolymer with a molecular weight of about 500,000. The second 24-hr extraction with ethyl acetate gave 2.0% homopolymer with a molecular weight of about 800,000. The final extraction with ethyl acetate gave only 0.6% homopolymer, which was insufficient material for a molecular weight determination. These exhaustive extractions were done to avoid contaminating the isolated graft fraction with homopolymer fractions. The extracted graft copolymer containing 18.1% bound polymer was enzyme degraded and then solvent fractionated to obtain the isolated graft fraction. The percent bound polymer was calculated from Kjeldahl nitrogen determinations before and after treatment with butyl acrylate. If we add the amino acids, the ash content, and the total polymer, 99.0% of the starting material is accounted for in the ground graft copolymer. This sample was used for all of the analytical work; however, analysis of the enzyme substrate was obtained by calculation and is shown in Figure 1.

To assure eliminating as much proteinaceous material as possible, several experiments were performed to study the enzyme degradation procedure using conditions other than those reported here. EDTA was found to be helpful in complexing the chromium(III) and preventing its reaction with the enzymes. In one experiment, the solution was discarded after autoclaving with EDTA, and

M.W. OF POLYMER-PEPTIDE UNIT   = 1,070,000

1,070,000 X 2.83% AMINO ACIDS   = 30,281 M.W. FOR AMINO ACIDS

$$\frac{30,281}{105.67 \text{ (AVG. R.M.W. FOR AMINO ACIDS)}} = 287 \text{ AA PEPTIDE} + 1 \text{ ON POLYMER}$$

1,070,000 - 30,281   = 1,039,719 M.W. FOR POLYMER

$$\frac{1,039,719}{128.17 \text{ (M.W. OF BUTYL ACRYLATE)}} = 8,112 \text{ MONOMER UNITS}$$

Fig. 4. Composition of graft copolymer.

the same amount of deionized water was added to the residue prior to adding the enzymes. It appeared, however, that more protein was digested in the experiments where the EDTA was present with the enzymes. This is probably due to continued protection of the enzyme from being poisoned by chromium released during protein cleavage. Increasing the temperature to 37°C during the enzyme digestions was not beneficial. However, the dilute acid and dilute alkali washes of the digested residues were necessary for removing some of the entrapped material. The residues were washed exhaustively until a negative ninhydrin test was obtained on the solutions.

After the enzyme digestions, air drying was used to avoid possible problems in subsequent rehydration of a small peptide group attached to a large hydrophobic polymer which might then interfere with the enzyme attack. The air-dried product remaining after the enzyme digestions amounted to 1.02 g, or about 20% of the starting material. Amino acid analysis of the residue after enzyme digestion showed that there was a peptide still bound to the graft, amounting to 9.7% of its weight.

As shown in Figure 3, a portion of the residue was solvent fractionated in chloroform. The insoluble part of the residue (85%) was found to contain 10.6% amino acids on a weight basis as a peptide. This peptide was low in hydroxyproline, proline, glycine, and alanine when compared to the collagen substrate.

In order to carry out fractionation on the Sephadex LH-20 column, it was necessary to apply the sample to the column in a single 50-ml portion of chloroform. Some peak broadening would be expected. The bulk of the sample eluted between 120 and 220 ml; this was combined as one fraction. Although an additional 1780 ml chloroform was run through the column, very little further material eluted. Seventy-six percent of the sample applied to the column was recovered in the one fraction. The molecular weight of this copolymer as determined by viscosity measurements was 1,070,000. This solvent-fractionated product contained 2.83% amino acids on a weight basis as a peptide which was low in hydroxyproline, proline, glycine, alanine, and arginine when compared with collagen.

While we were not able to determine the molecular weight of the chloroform-insoluble enzyme-degraded copolymer fraction, the following considerations lead us to postulate that the poly(butyl acrylate) portion has about the same molecular weight as that of the chloroform-soluble fraction, or about 1,000,000: (1) Poly(butyl acrylate) homopolymers are soluble in chloroform; therefore, the degree of solubility of the copolymers is determined by the size of the polypeptide portion. (2) The enzyme attack should be random; therefore, the molecular weight distribution of the poly(butyl acrylate) in the soluble and insoluble copolymer fractions should be the same.

If the molecular weight of the polymer–peptide fragment is 1,070,000, then the amino acid portion of this would amount to 30,281 molecular weight units, as shown in Figure 4. On the basis of the amino acids found and the relative amounts of each, the average residue molecular weight was calculated as 105.67. This would indicate that there are 287 amino acids on the peptide chain plus one amino acid that is probably impervious to acid hydrolysis and remains attached to the polymer molecule. Dividing the molecular weight of the polymer by the molecular weight of the monomer indicates that there are about 8112 monomer units in this polymer–peptide fragment.

The IR spectra of the polymer–peptide fragment confirms that it is principally poly(butyl acrylate) when compared with the standard. Amide absorption bands around 1650 cm^{-1} and NH and OH absorption bands around 3200–3500 cm^{-1} are contributed by peptide fragment.

It was also important to determine whether the autoclaving of the grafted collagen alters the homopolymer or graft copolymer in any way that would affect the molecular weight. In another experiment, the preextracted ground graft copolymer was autoclaved and the homopolymer then extracted with acetone. Viscosity determinations showed only a 10% increase in the molecular weight of the homopolymer, indicating that autoclaving has only a negligible effect on the molecular weight. Also, gas-chromatographic analysis of the autoclave liquor indicated there was no hydrolysis of the ester groups of the polymer to butyl alcohol.

In conclusion, these experiments provide evidence for the true graft polymerization of collagen in hides. The sequential enzyme digestions, chloroform solubility, LH-20 chromatography, and IR spectra, taken together, prove that grafting to the collagen molecule has taken place.

It is anticipated that methyl methacrylate graft copolymers will be studied in future experiments, since preliminary experiments show that acid hydrolysis does not appear to attack the ester linkages as it does with the butyl acrylate graft copolymers. These results could then be compared with those obtained using the enzyme degradation procedure. Reference to brand or firm name does not constitute endorsement by the U.S. Department of Agriculture over others of a similar nature not mentioned.

References

1. A. H. Korn, S. H. Feairheller, and E. M. Filachione, *J. Am. Leather Chem. Assoc.*, **67**, 111 (1972).

2. A. H. Korn, M. M. Taylor, and S. H. Feairheller, *J. Am. Leather Chem. Assoc.*, **68**, 224 (1973).

3. E. H. Harris, M. M. Taylor, and S. H. Feairheller, *J. Am. Leather Chem. Assoc.*, **69**, 182 (1974).

4. J. Brandrup and E. H. Immergut, Eds., *Polymer Handbook*, Wiley-Interscience, New York, 1973, p. IV-21.

5. K. A. Piez and L. Morris, *Anal. Biochem.*, **1**, 187 (1960).

6. K. P. Rao, K. T. Joseph, and Y. Nayudamma, *J. Polym. Sci. A-1*, **9**, 3199 (1971).

7. K. P. Rao, K. T. Joseph, and Y. Nayudamma, *J. Appl. Polym. Sci.*, **16**, 975 (1972).

Received July 20, 1976

ERRATUM

Preparation of Macroreticular Anion Exchange Membrane and its Behavior Relating to Organic Fouling

KOSHI KUSUMOTO, HIROFUMI IHARA, and YUKIO MIZUTANI

Tokuyama Soda Co., Ltd., Tokuyama-City, 745, Japan

[article in *J. Appl. Polym. Sci.* **20,** 3207–3213 (1976)]

Please note the following corrections to the above article:

On p. 3211, the copy "brane no. 4 was more than that in" should be deleted from the first line.   On the sixth line "Na-Dbs" should read "Na-DBS."

Also, Table was omitted from the experimental section and is presented here.

TABLE I
The Recipe by Weight Ratio

No.	St + DVB	DVB/ (St + DVB)	PB[a]	t-AmOH[b]/ (St + DVB)
1	1	0.3	0.1	0.4
2	1	0.3	0.1	0.5
3	1	0.3	0.1	0.8
4	1	0.3	0.1	1.0

[a] Polybutadiene.
[b] Tertiary amylalcohol.

AUTHOR INDEX TO VOLUME 21

Fellers, J. F.: see Lenk, R. S.

Ferrillo, R. G.: see Granzow, A.

Ferry, J. D.: see Rhee, C.-K.

Fetters, L. J.: see Ambler, M. R.

——: see Rhee, C.-K.

Francis, M. A.: see Vaughan, M. F.

Frank, A. W. and Drake, G. L., Jr.: Uses of Aldehydes Other Than Formaldehyde in THPOH/Ammonia Flame Retardant Finishes for Cotton, 3087

Frank, P. P.: see Meier, J. F.

Freedman, B.: see Windle, J. J.

Fricke, A. L.: see Pusatcioglu, S. Y.

Frisch, H. L.: see Kim, S. C.

Frisch, K. C.: see Kim, S. C.

Froehling, P. E., Koenhen, D. M., Smolders, C. A., and Bantjes, A.: Uptake of Tridodecylmethylammonium Chloride by PVC, 2855

Fujii, M.: see Koros, W. J.

Fujiyama, M. and Kimura, S.: Effect of Some Molecular Parameters on the Flexural Properties of Injection-Molded Polypropylene, 2283

——, M., Awaya, H., and Kimura, S.: Mechanical Anisotropy in Injection-Molded Polypropylene, 3291

Fukuda, M.: see Kato, Y.

Fukutomi, M.: see Kato, Y.

Furukawa, J., Kobayashi, E., and Kawagoe, T.: Acetylene–Butadiene Copolymer for Polymer Coatings, 597

Gaesser, G. J.: see Slagowski, E. L.

Gajewski, M.: see Brzozowski, Z.

Gallot, Z.: see Guenet, J. M.

——: see Marais, L.

Gan, L. M., Soh, G. B., and Ong, K. L.: Vulcanization of Butyl Rubber by p-Quinone Dioxime, 1771

Garrett, T. B. and Goldfarb, L.: Annealing of Plasticized PVC. Dilatometric and DSC Observations, 1395

Garton, A.: see Carlsson, D. J.

Gazicki, M., Wróbel, A. M., and Kryszewski, M.: Studies on Soluble Fraction of Glowing Discharge Polysilazane Formed from Hexamethylcyclotrisilazane, 2013

Gebauer, R. C.: see Slagowski, E. L.

Geil, P. H.: see Singleton, C. J.

Gent, A. N. and Hamed, G. R.: Peel Mechanics for an Elastic-Plastic Adherend, 2817

George, G. A., Sacher, R. E., and Sprouse, J. F.: Photooxidation and Photoprotection of the Surface Resin of a Glass Fiber–Epoxy Composite, 2241

Gettings, M., Baker, F. S., and Kinloch, A. J.: Use of Auger and X-ray Photoelectron Spectroscopy to Study the Locus of Failure of Structural Adhesive Joints, 2375

Ghafoor, A. and Still, R. H.: Thermal Degradation of Polymers. XVII. Thermal Analysis of Polyquinazolones and Related Systems, 2905

Gilbert, A. S., Pethrick, R. A., and Phillips, D. W.: Acoustic Relaxation and Infrared Spectroscopic Measurements of the Plasticization of Poly(methyl Methacrylate) by Water, 319

Gillen, K. T.: see Salazar, E. A.

Gillham, J. K., Stadnicki, S. J., and Hazony,

Y.: Low-Frequency Thermomechanical Spectrometry of Polymeric Materials: Tactic Poly(methyl Methacrylates), 401

——: see Kiran, E.

Gipstein, E., Moreau, W., Chiu, G., and Need, O. U., III: The Synthesis and Evaluation of Cyclic Olefin Sulfone Copolymers and Terpolymers as Electron Beam Resists, 677

——: see Chu, W. H.

——: see Kiran, E.

Goldfarb, L.: see Garrett, T. B.

Gordon, R. J.: see Chiou, C. S.

——: see Everage, A. E., Jr.

Goswami, D. N. and Bhattacharya, P. R.: The Dialectric Behavior of the Natural Resin Manila Copal, 2465

Gotō, K.: see Iida, T.

Graessley, W. W.: see Chatterjee, A.

Graham, S. G.: see Warwicker, J. O.

Grandt, A. F., Jr.: see Banasiak, D. H.

Granzow, A., Ferrillo, R. G., and Wilson, A.: The Effect of Elemental Red Phosphorus on the Thermal Degradation of Poly(ethylene Terephthalate), 1687

Griffin, C. F.: see Von Meerwall, E.

Gruber, H. A., Harris, E. H., Jr., and Feairheller, S. H.: Characterization of the Chromium (III)-Crosslinked Collagen–Poly(Butyl Acrylate) Graft Copolymer, 3465

Grzywna, Z.: see Izydorczyk, J.

Guenet, J. M., Gallot, Z., Picot, C., and Benoit, H.: Isotactic Polystyrene Characterization by Gel Permeation Chromatography in Tetrahydrofuran, 2181

Guise, G. B.: Poly(carbamoyl Sulfonates) (Bisulfite Adducts of Polyisocyanates), 3427

Gumbs, R. W.: see Paul, D. F.

Gupta, R. N., Jain, P. C., and Nanda, V. S.: Effect of Pressure on Melting Temperature and Other Associated Thermodynamic Functions of Polyethylene, 2621

Hebeish, A.: see Abdel-Fattah, S. H.

Hakim, I. K., Bishal, A. M. and Hanna, F. F.: Effect of Natural Aging on the Dielectric Properties of Natural Rubber Mixed with Some White Fillers, 1155

Hamazaki, T., Kanchiku, Y., Handa, R., and Izumi, M.: Electron-Microscopic Procedure for Acrylic Rubber, 1569

Hamed, G. R.: see Gent, A. N.

Hamielec, A.: see Shinozaki, D. M.

Hammon, H. G., Ernst, K., and Newton, J. C.: Noble Gas Permeability of Polymer Films and Coatings, 1989

Han, C. D., Villamizar, C. A., Kim, Y. W., and Chen, S. J.: Morphology and Mechanical Properties of Injection-Molded Specimens of Two-Phase Polymer Blends, 353

——: see Kim, Y. W.

Hancock, T. A., Spruiell, J. E., and White, J. L.: Wet Spinning of Aliphatic and Aromatic Polyamides, 1227

Handa, R.: see Hamazaki, T.

Hanna, A. A.: see Shinouda, H. G.

Hanna, F. F.: see Hakim, I. K.

Harel, H.: see Marom, G.

Harris, E. H., Jr.: see Gruber, H. A.

Hartstein, A. M.: see Kratzer, R. H.

Hartz, R. E. and Adams, H. T.: Effects of Atmospheric Pollutants at High Temperatures on the Adhesion of RFL-Coated Tire Cords to Rubber, 525

Mantovani, E., Mazzei, M., Robertiello, A., and Zanobi, A.: Photosensitized Degradation of Polyolefins. II., 589

Marais, L., Gallot, Z., and Benoît, H.: A New Method for Correcting Axial Dispersion in GPC, 1955

Marom, G., Harel, H., and Rosner, J.: Fracture Energies of Composite Propellants, 1629

——: see Konieczny, N.

Matsunga, T.: Surface Free Energy Analysis of Polymers and Its Relation to Polymer Constitution, 2847

Matsuura, T.: see Kutowy, O.

Matsuzaki, K.: see Nakamura, S.

Mazzei, M.: see Mantovani, E.

McCrackin, F. L.: Calibration of Gel Permeation Chromatography Columns Using Polydisperse Polymer Standards, 191

——: see Wagner, H. L.

McDonnell, M. E. and Jamieson, A. M.: The Molecular Weight Average Obtained by Combining Quasielastic Light-Scattering and Intrinsic Viscosity Measurements, 3261

McGee, H. A., Jr.: see Pusatcioglu, S. Y.

McIntyre, D.: see Ambler, M. R.

McIver, W.: see Snyder, C.

McKellar, J. F.: see Allen, N. S.

McPeters, A. L.: see Paul, D. R.

Mehrotra, R. and Rånby, B.: Graft Copolymerization Onto Starch. I. Complexes of Mn^{3+} as Initiators, 1647

—— and ——: Graft Copolymerization Onto Starch. II. Grafting of Acrylonitrile to Granular Native Potato Starch by Manganic Pyrophosphate Initiation. Effect of Reaction Conditions of Graft in Parameters, 3407

Mehta, B. S., DiBenedetto, A. T., and Kardos, J. L.: Sorption and Diffusion of Water in Glass Ribbon-Reinforced Composites, 3111

Meier, J. F., Bellott, E. M., Jr., and Frank, P. P.: Preparation and Properties of Phenolic Resin Laminates. I. Laboratory Evaluation, 1383

Meluch, W. C.: see Campbell, G. A.

Merrill, E. W.: see Peppas, N. A.

Merrill, R. G. and Roberts, C. W.: Photophysical Processes and Interactions Between Poly(ethylene Terephthalate) and 1-Amino-2-(2-methoxyethoxl)-4-hydroxy-9,10-Anthoquinone, 2745

Miltz, J.: see Narkis, M.

Minoura, Y.: see Nakano, A.

——: see Ono, K.

Mitcham, D.: see Jung, H. Z.

Miyano, Y.: see Suzuki, K.

Mizutani, Y.: see Kusomoto, K.

Montague, P. E.: see Ray, P. K.

Montulli, L. T.: see Banasiak, D. H.

Moreau, W.: see Gipstein, E.

Mori, S.: High-Speed Gel Permeation Chromatography. A Study of Operational Variables, 1921

Mori, T., Ogawa, K., and Tanaka, T.: Heterogeneous Network Polymers. IV. Dynamic Mechanical Properties—Composition—Phase Structure Relationships, 3381

Morishita, N.: see Ishigaki, I.

Morita, Y., Ishigaki, I., Watanabe, Y., Okubo, H., and Ito, A.: Iodine-Initiated, Solid-State Copolymerization of Tetraoxane with 1,3-Dioxolane in the Presence of Methylal. II. Properties of Copolymer Obtained by Beaker-Scale Copolymerization, 723

——: see Ishigaki, I.

——: see Motomura, H.

Morosoff, N.: see Liepins, R.

Morris, C. E. M.: Aspects of Vapor Pressure Osmometry, 435

Motomura, H. and Morita, Z.: Diffusion with Simultaneous Reaction of Reactive Dyes in Cellulose, 487

Moursi, A. Z.: see Hebeish, A.

Moustafa, A. B. and Abd-El-Hakim, A. A.: Sodium Bisulfite-Initiated Polymerization of Methyl Methacrylate in Aqueous Medium in the Presence of the Metal Oxides CuO and MnO_2, 905

Mulder, M. H. V.: see Koenhen, D. M.

Munari, S.: see Vigo, F.

Murakami, K. and Takasugi, S.: Chemorheological Studies on Polymer Degradation, 55

Nadella, H. P., Henson, H. M., Spruiell, J. E., and White, J. L.: Melt Spinning of Isotactic Polypropylene: Structure Development and Relationship to Mechanical Properties, 3003

Nagashiro, W. and Tsunoda, T.: Degradation of Polyacrylamide Molecules in Aqueous Solutions by High-Speed Stirring, 1149

Nakagawa, H.: see Suzuki, J.

Nakagawa, T.: see Uegaki, Y.

Nakahara, J. H.: see Kratzer, R. H.

Nakajima, A. and Shinoda, K.: Permeation Properties of Glycol Chitosan–Mucopolysaccharide Complex Membranes, 1249

Nakajima, N., Bowerman, H. H., Collins, E. A.: Nonlinear Viscoelastic Behavior of Butadiene–Acrylonitrile Copolymers Filled with Carbon Black, 3063

Nakamura, S., Sato, H., and Matsuzaki, K.: Graft Copolymerization of Styrene onto Poly(vinyl p-Nitrobenzoate) by Chain Transfer Reaction (Erratum), 585

——: see Magoshi, J.

Nakano, A. and Minoura, Y.: Degradation of Aqueous Poly(vinylpyrrolidone) Solution by High-Speed Stirring, 2877

Nanda, V. S.: see Gupta, R. N.

Narasimham, T.: see Somashekar, T. H.

Narkis, M. and Miltz, J.: Peroxide Crosslinking of Ethylene–Vinyl Acetate Copolymer, 703

——, Siegmann, A., Dagan, A. and Di Benedetto, A. T.: Precipitation from Glassy Polymer Solutions, 989

——: see Siegmann, A.

Need, O. U., III: see Gipstein, E.

Negishi, Y.: see Ohya, H.

Nelson, R. A.: The Determination of Moisture Transitions in Cellulosic Materials Using Differential Scanning Calorimetry, 645

Neuse, E. W. and Van Schalkwyk, J. D.: Cardanol Derivatives as PVC Plasticizers. II. Plasticizer Evaluation, 3023

Newton, J. C.: see Hammon, H. G.

Nielsen, L. E.: Polymeric Composite Systems with Two Continuous Phases, 1579

Niki, E.: see Shiono, T.

Nishimura, K.: see Ishigaki, I.

Nishimura, T.: see Ono, K.
North, A. M.: see Phillips, D. W.
Nozawa, Y.: see Omata, K.

O'Driscoll, K. F. O.: see Mahabadi, H. K.
Ogawa, T. and Inaba, T.: Gel Permeation Chromatography of Ethylene-Propylene Copolymerization Products, 2979
Ogawa, K.: see Mori, T.
Ohara, K.: Load and Temperature Dependence of Frictional Force and Frictional Electrification in Friction Between Polymer Films Obtained by Simultaneous Measurements, 1409
Ohshima, T.: see Kishimoto, Y.
Ohtani, N.: see Kobayashi, A.
Ohya, H., Konuma, H., and Negishi, Y.: Post-treatment Effects on Pore Size Distribution of Loeb-Sourirajan-Type Modified Cellulose Acetate Ultrathin Membranes, 2515
Okada, T.: see Takezaki, J.
Okamoto, H.: see Ono, K.
Okaya, T.: see Sakota, K.
——: see Sato, T.
Okubo, H.: see Morita, Y.
Olabisi, O. and Simha, R.: A Semiempirical Equation of State for Polymer Melts, 149
Olf, H. G.: see Yasuda, H.
Omata, K., Nozawa, Y., and Higashide, F.: Drug Release from Cellulose Acetate Phthalate Gel, 2009
Ong, K. L.: see Gan, L. M.
Onishi, H.: see Inagaki, N.
Ono, K., Shimada, H., Nishimura, T., Yamashita, S., Okamoto, H., and Minoura, Y.: Effects of Number-Average Molecular Weight of Liquid Hydroxyl-Terminated Polybutadiene on Physical Properties of the Elastomer, 3223
Oono, R.: Distribution of Carbon Black in SBR, 1743
Otterstedt, J.-E. A.: Water Vapor Permeability in Layered Polymer Films, 573
——: Flex-Resistant Permeable PVC & Films, 1971
Ouano, A. C.: see Chu, W. H.
Ouchi, I., Hosoi, M., and Shimotsuma, S.: Infrared Spectra of Poly(ethylene, 2,6-Naphthalate) and Some Related Polyesters, 3445
Ozari, Y., Tanny, G., and Jagur-Grodzinski, J.: Dynamic Deposition of Polyacids on Porous Membrane Supports, 555

Paciorek, K. L.: see Kratzer, R. H.
Padhye, R.: see Venkatraman, A.
Padhye, M. R.: see Lockhande, H. T.
Paipetis, S. A.: see Paranicolaou, G. C.
Papanicolaou, G. C., Paipetis, S. A., and Theocaris, P. S.: Thermal Properties of Metal-Filled Epoxies, 689
Pappalardo, L. T.: DSC Evaluation of Epoxy and Polyimide-Impregnated Laminates (Prepregs), 809
Paralikar, K. M. and Betrabet, S. M.: Electron Diffraction Technique for the Determination of Cellulose Crystallinity, 899
Parker, J. P. and Lindenmeyer, P. H.: On the Crystal Structure of Nylon 6, 821
Paul, D. F. and Gumbs, R. W.: Solar Energy Collector Coatings from Cyclopolymers of Butadiene and Acrylonitrile, 959
Paul, D. R. and McPeters, A. L.: Effect of Spin Orientation on Drawing of Wet-Spun Fibers, 1699
——: see Koros, W. J.
Pavlov, P., Dimov, K., and Simeonov, N.: Grafting of Cellulose Copolymers with Water-Insoluble Monomers with Redox System Cellulose Xanthogenate–Hydrogen Peroxide, 291
Pearson, D. S.: see Böhm, G. G. A.
Peppas, N. A. and Merrill, E. W.: Crosslinked Poly(vinyl Alcohol) Hydrogels as Swollen Elastic Networks, 1763
Peric, D., Bell, A. T., and Shen, M.: Reverse Osmosis Characteristics of Composite Membranes Prepared by Plasma Polymerization of Allylamine. Effects of Deposition Conditions, 2661
Perrault, G. and Duchesne, G.: Evaluation of Surface-Active Agents by Mechanical Properties of Highly Filled Composites, 3153
Pethrick, R. A.: see Gilbert, A. S.
——: see Phillips, D. W.
Petit, M. A. and Jozefonvicz, J.: Synthesis of Copper (II) Complexes of Asymmetric Resins Prepared by Attachment of α-Amino Acids to Crosslinked Polystyrene, 2589
Peyser, P. and Bascom, W. D.: Kinetics of Epoxy Resin Polymerization Using Differential Scanning Calorimetry, 2359
Phillips, D. W., North, A. M., and Pethrick, R. A.: Ultrasonic Studies of Polycarbonate, Polysulfone, and Polyether Sulfone, 1859
——: see Gilbert, A. S.
Piatrik, M.: see Williams, J. L.
Picot, C.: see Guenet, J. M.
Plåcek, J.: see Szöcs, F.
Plazek, D. J.: see Agarwal, P. K.
Podkówka, J.: see Izydorczyk, J.
Poindexter, E. H.: see Helbert, J. N.
Prausnitz, J. M.: see Renuncio, J. A. R.
Prochaska, K. and Wypych, J.: Basic Principals of Thermal Degradation and Thermal Stabilization of Poly(vinyl Chloride). Mathematical Model of the Action of PVC Thermal Stabilizers, 2113
Prud'Homme, R. E.: Mechanical Properties of Polymer–Paper Laminates, 947
Pulido, J.: see Yenwo, G. M.
Pusatcioglu, S. Y., McGee, H. A., Jr., Fricke, A. L., and Hassler, J. C.: Thermal Stability and Molecular Weight of Two New Boron–Nitrogen Polymers, 1561

Rabek, J. F., Canbäck, G., and Rånby, B.: Studies on the Photo-oxidation Mechanisms of Polymers. VI. The Role of Commercial Thrmostabilizers in the Photostability of Poly(vinyl Chloride), 2211
Rånby, B.: see Mehrotra, R.
——: see Rabek, J. F.
——: see Svanson, S. E.
Ranganath, R.: see Barlow, A.
——: see Wild, L.
Ravey, M.: The Mechanism of Scale Formation in PVC Reactors, 839
——: see Waterman, J. A.
Ray, P. K. and Montague, P. E.: Crystallinity in Jute Fiber as Revealed by Multipeak Resolution, 1267

SUBJECT INDEX TO VOLUME 21